2023/24

THE GUIDE TO MAJOR TRUSTS

17th edition

Abigail O'Loughlin

dsc
directory of social change

Published by the Directory of Social Change (Registered Charity no. 800517 in England and Wales)

Office: Suite 103, 1 Old Hall Street, Liverpool L3 9HG

Tel: 020 4526 5995

Visit www.dsc.org.uk to find out more about our books, subscription funding website and training events. You can also sign up for e-newsletters so that you're always the first to hear about what's new.

The publisher welcomes suggestions and comments that will help to inform and improve future versions of this and all of our titles. Please give us your feedback by emailing publications@dsc.org.uk.

First published 1986
Second edition 1989
Third edition 1991
Fourth edition 1993
Fifth edition 1995
Sixth edition 1997
Seventh edition 1999
Eighth edition 2001
Ninth edition 2003
Tenth edition 2005
Eleventh edition 2007
Twelfth edition 2010
Thirteenth edition 2012
Fourteenth edition 2014
Fifteenth edition 2016
Sixteenth edition 2018
Seventeenth edition 2022

ISBN 978 1 78482 070 1

British Library Cataloguing in Publication Data
A catalogue record for this book is available from the British Library

Cover and text design by Kate Griffith
Typeset by Marlinzo Services, Frome
Printed and bound in Great Britain by CPI Group, Croydon

Contents

Foreword

Since Luke Fitzherbert produced the first ever edition of this guide to major grant-makers in 1986, the world of fundraising has changed dramatically, but this resource remains required reading as much today as it ever was.

As fundraisers, we know how important access to reliable and accurate information is to the success of our work. What *The Guide to Major Trusts* offers is all of this and more, enabling trust fundraisers to take their work to the next level – engaging high-value grant-making charities in a genuine and meaningful way which truly resonates with them. Now, more than ever, the most successful fundraising teams are engaging high-value supporters with a vision and inspiring them to be a partner, not just a donor, in delivering this change.

In 2019/20 we saw a marked increase in grant-making of 7.8%, leading to combined giving of £3.48 billion.[1] A huge amount! While the COVID-19 pandemic certainly disrupted charitable giving in many ways, we saw the funders of all sizes step in to address the funding crisis facing the sector. Grant-making during the pandemic was done at record speed, with fewer hoops to jump through and in greater collaboration with others. I am confident that this experience during a time of great need will accelerate the transition towards funders and recipients working in partnership to deliver the greatest impact.

Partnership-building chimes with everything I believe in as a fundraiser. While creating well-written proposals remains a vital tool, we must all become relationship fundraisers – engaging funders, listening to them and crafting partnerships that deliver a far greater return to both the funder and recipient charity. Most importantly, fundraisers act as a conduit between those who seek to make a difference and donors who need support to fulfil their ambitions to change the world. If we can get these elements right, then we can ensure maximum impact for beneficiaries and drive the movement in fundraising away from being transactional towards becoming transformational.

This movement towards partnership is aided by the research and insight offered within this, now 17th, edition of *The Guide to Major Trusts* which is a key implement in your fundraising toolkit. Society faces some truly enormous challenges, and it has never been more important to bring funders and fundraisers together to create solutions to the problems we are all trying to address. I wish you every success on your journey.

Chris Jarrett
Director of Fundraising, RNIB

[1] Catherine Walker and Cathy Pharoah, *Foundation Giving Trends 2021. Top 300 foundation grant-makers* [PDF], The Association of Charitable Foundations, 2021, https://pearsfoundation.org.uk/wp-content/uploads/ACF179-Foundation-Giving-Trends-2021_Design_DigitalVersion_v3.pdf.

About DSC

At the Directory of Social Change (DSC), we believe that the world is made better by people coming together to serve their communities and each other. For us, an independent voluntary sector is at the heart of that social change and we exist to support charities, voluntary organisations and community groups in the work they do. Our role is to:

- **Provide practical information** on a range of topics from fundraising to project management in both our printed publications and our e-books
- **Offer training** through public courses, events and in-house services
- **Research funders** and maintain a subscription database, *Funds Online*, with details on funding from grant-making charities, companies and government sources
- **Offer bespoke research** to voluntary sector organisations in order to evaluate projects, identify new opportunities and help make sense of existing data
- **Stimulate debate and campaign** on key issues that affect the voluntary sector, particularly to champion the concerns of smaller charities

We are a registered charity ourselves but we self-fund most of our work. We charge for services, but cross-subsidise those which charities particularly need and cannot easily afford.

Visit our website **www.dsc.org.uk** to see how we can help you to help others and have a look at **www.fundsonline.org.uk** to see how DSC could improve your fundraising. Alternatively, call our friendly team at **020 4526 5995** to chat about your needs or drop us a line at **cs@dsc.org.uk**.

Introduction

Welcome to the 17th edition of *The Guide to Major Trusts*. The purpose of the guide is to provide a comprehensive and practical funding resource that enables charity professionals, including trustees, chief executives, fundraisers and volunteers, to access the billions of pounds awarded in the UK by grant-makers each year. We are delighted to return with this 17th edition after our research was interrupted by the COVID-19 pandemic in 2020/21.

Data collection

This guide contains over 1,000 of the UK's largest grant-makers taken from DSC's database, which contains details of over 8,000 charitable funders.

Over the course of our research, we looked at charity regulators' records, annual reports and accounts, websites and social media platforms. In this edition, the majority of the accounts we used were from 2020/21 (59.3%) and 2020 (26.1%). However, some charities' accounts were not available to view on the relevant charity regulator's website due to them having an income of less than £25,000. In these circumstances, grant totals were estimated based on the charity's total expenditure and previous patterns of giving. Where up-to-date accounts had not been submitted, the latest available accounts were used. This edition also includes a small number of charities that give in the UK but are not UK registered. In these cases, full financial information is often unavailable, and so we have relied on, for example, the charity's website or annual review to estimate its giving.

Criteria for inclusion

To be included in the guide, grant-makers must have the potential to award at least £250,000 in grants in the UK per year. Those in the guide with grant total under this threshold may have given over this amount in previous years or are likely to have the potential to exceed this amount in the near future. Some grant-makers' levels of giving may have been negatively impacted by the COVID-19 pandemic, and we have included such funders if they typically award over £250,000 per year. In order to make the guide as useful as possible to fundraisers, certain grant-makers have been excluded. These are mainly grant-makers that:

- Predominantly give overseas
- Give to a small number of beneficiaries each year
- Give to the same beneficiaries each year
- Give only to individuals

We have also excluded grant-makers that have ceased to exist or are being wound up with any remaining funds fully committed. Some grant-makers that are in the process of winding up or have wound up since the previous edition of this guide include Debenhams Foundation, The British Council for Prevention of Blindness, The Hillingdon Community Trust and The Vail Foundation.

In this edition, we have included over 160 grant-makers that have not been included in any previous editions of the guide. These are a mixture of grant-makers that have increased their grant-making capacity, newly registered charities and funders not previously known to us.

Findings

The 1,015 grant-makers included in this guide awarded a combined total of £7.33 billion in grants. A further £199.81 million was distributed by the 47 UK community foundations listed in the table on page 447. The amount distributed by the community foundations annually is typically around £100 million, but this increased in 2020/21 due to funding related to COVID-19.

Although the vast majority of funders featured in this guide are registered grant-making charities, there are also a number which are not. Some of the largest funders, such as The National Lottery Community Fund (giving £509.15 million in grants during 2020/21), The National Lottery Heritage Fund (£315.42 million in 2020/21), Arts Council England (£1.64 billion in 2020/21), Arts Council of Wales (£50.3 million in 2020/21), Arts Council of Northern Ireland (£11.65 million in 2019/20) and Creative Scotland (£139.52 million in 2020/21) are non-departmental public bodies. Excluding the funding given by these bodies, funding from grant-making charities amounted to £4.67 billion. If we look at the 769 grant-makers which appear in both this edition and the previous edition, there has been an overall increase in giving of around £1.36 billion, or 26.3%.

This guide includes a diverse range of grant-makers: from those supporting general charitable purposes (34.5% of the funders in this guide) and charities working in areas such

Top 25 grant-makers

(excluding public bodies, i.e. – The National Lottery Community Fund, arts councils and The National Lottery Heritage Fund)

		Areas of work	Total grants
1 (1)	The Wellcome Trust	Medical research, including research into mental health, infectious disease and the effects of climate change on health.	£759.5 million
2 (-)	Cancer Research UK	Cancer research.	£273.7 million
3 (-)	Hospice UK	Hospice and palliative care, and professional development for hospice staff.	£258.5 million
4 (-)	Arcadia Fund	Preserving endangered culture; protecting endangered nature; promoting open access to information.	£113.65 million
5 (7)	The Garfield Weston Foundation	Social welfare; young people; community; the arts; faith; the environment; education; health; museums and heritage.	£98.3 million
6 (3)	The Leverhulme Trust	Academic research.	£96.05 million
7 (-)	The Football Foundation	Grassroots and community football.	£69.9 million
8 (4)	Comic Relief	Tackling poverty and social injustice; children and young people; women and girls; community development; mental health.	£65.8 million
9 (-)	International Bible Students Association	Jehovah's Witnesses; overseas aid.	£60.29 million
10 (-)	The City Bridge Trust (Bridge House Estates)	Social welfare; the environment; mental health; homelessness; older people; children and young people; food poverty.	£57.4 million
11 (-)	Corra Foundation	Social welfare; children and young people; homelessness; families affected by substance abuse; international development (Zambia, Rwanda, Malawi and Pakistan).	£56.09 million
12 (15)	The British Academy for the Promotion of Historical Philosophical and Philological Studies (The British Academy)	Humanities and social sciences.	£54.4 million
13 (-)	Quadrature Climate Foundation	Climate change.	£54.06 million
14 (23)	Versus Arthritis	Research into all types of arthritis and musculoskeletal conditions.	£53.98 million
15 (8)	Esmée Fairbairn Foundation	Preservation of species and habitat; freshwater; sustainable and ethical food; injustice and structural inequality; young leaders and artists; community development; local economies; art and culture.	£53.53 million
16 (2)	British Heart Foundation (BHF)	Clinical and non-clinical cardiovascular research.	£51.9 million
17 (9)	The Gatsby Charitable Foundation	Plant science; neuroscience; STEM education; causes in Africa; public policy; the arts.	£50.47 million
18 (6)	BBC Children in Need	Disadvantaged children and young people (aged 18 and under).	£49.85 million
19 (-)	The Master Charitable Trust	General charitable purposes.	£43.53 million
20 (22)	Paul Hamlyn Foundation	Arts; education; young people; social justice.	£40.27 million
21 (16)	The Henry Smith Charity	Social welfare; community services and development; Christian projects; holiday grants for children.	£38.38 million
22 (-)	Reuben Foundation	Healthcare; education; community; culture.	£35.88 million
23 (14)	The Wolfson Foundation	Education; medicine and science; the arts; humanities; health; disability.	£35.72 million
24 (-)	The Wood Foundation	Education and economic development.	£35.5 million
25 (17)	Achisomoch Aid Company Limited	Orthodox Jewish causes and general charitable purposes.	£35.19 million
		Total	**£2.54 billion**

as social welfare (59.8%), health (53.6%) or education (56%); to those specifically concentrating on so-called less popular causes, such as providing support for people with substance abuse (2.4%), violence/abuse survivors (3.9%) and LGBTQ+ (0.5%) groups.

The top 25 funders by total grants awarded gave a combined £2.54 billion, accounting for 35.3% of this edition's grant total. In the previous edition, the contributions made by the top 25 amounted to £1.86 billion. Just like in the previous edition, The Wellcome Trust remains the largest grant-maker in the guide (giving just over £759 million in 2020/21), and its annual giving can often have a significant effect on the overall grant total for our guides. For this edition, the cut-off figure for inclusion in the top 25 is an annual grant total of £35.2 million, compared with £18.75 million in the previous edition. As is our usual practice, we have not included public bodies – The National Lottery Community Fund, The National Lottery Heritage Fund, the arts councils or Creative Scotland – in this table, as it is an opportunity to celebrate the work of those grant-makers that are registered charities.

There are 11 new entries in the top 25 grant-makers table this edition, most of which are financially large, established grant-makers. These new entries among the top 25 include:

- Hospice UK, which is a national charity that makes grants towards the provision of hospice and palliative care. Since the previous edition, Hospice UK's grant

total has increased by over £257 million, with it giving £258.5 million in 2020/21 compared to £830,000 in 2016/17. This was due to funding it received from the government to support hospices in response to the COVID-19 pandemic.
- The Football Foundation, which receives its funding from The Football Association (The FA), the Premier League and the Department for Digital, Culture, Media and Sport. The foundation helps to deliver a programme of new and improved community sports facilities in towns and cities across England. In recent years, the foundation has increased its grant-making, awarding £69.9 million 2020/21 compared to £10.5 million in 2016/17.
- Quadrature Climate Foundation, which was established by Quadrature Capital Ltd in 2019. The foundation's work focuses on decreasing global emissions of greenhouse gases. In 2020/21 it awarded grants totalling around £54 million to environmental organisations, which was an increase from the previous year (2019/20), during which it awarded £21.4 million to the same causes.

COVID-19 impact and response

In the wake of the COVID-19 pandemic, many grant-makers have had to adapt and respond to challenges facing the charity sector. During our research, we found many funders noted a change, often negative, in income levels as a result of the pandemic. This was caused by several factors including:

- Cancelled fundraising events
- Lockdowns and restrictions resulting in less income from retail stores/property companies (for charities that rely on funding from such sources)
- Lower investment income

For example, Kidney Research UK noted a significant impact on income due to cancelled events and supporters donating less. As a result, the charity had to furlough employees and temporarily pause the funding of new research, focusing on a small number of COVID-19-related projects instead. Similarly, The LankellyChase Foundation saw a decline in investment income during 2020/21. The foundation noted this was primarily due to the fact that many companies in its portfolio significantly reduced or even cancelled their dividends during the 2021 financial year, in response to the pandemic.

On the other hand, some charities saw no impact or even an increase in their income and expenditure during the pandemic. This was largely due to higher private donations or government funding. For example, Bridgepoint Charitable Trust launched a £3.3 million COVID-19 Relief Fund that was funded by board member salary contributions, meaning its income was not affected. The Corra Foundation received £34 million from the Scottish Government's COVID-19 emergency funding, which meant that its income increased.

The overall grant total in this edition was £1.86 billion higher than in the previous edition, which was due to the arts councils, Hospice UK and other organisations receiving government funding to distribute during the COVID-19 pandemic.

Impact on applications

As well as changes to income, some charities also noticed a reduction in the number of applications received compared to previous years. For example, William Harding's Charity reported it received fewer applications than usual due to the closure of schools and educational organisations. This, in turn, resulted in lower expenditure on grants.

Grant-makers' response

In some cases, to help with the impact of the COVID-19 pandemic, charities launched emergency grant programmes to support communities and organisations in need. For example, The Theatres Trust Charitable Fund launched a COVID-19 Support Fund to help theatres manage during the lockdowns. It also established the Theatre Reopening Fund, through which it awarded funds to theatres to enable them to open safely when restrictions eased. Other charities adapted their existing grant programmes to focus on COVID-19 support or provided greater flexibility to existing grantees. According to our research, 344 (33.9%) of the charities in this guide awarded grants specifically for COVID-19-related needs. In contrast, some charities were forced to temporarily postpone their programmes or reduce the level of support they could provide.

Social media

Over the past two decades or so, organisations within the charity sector have become increasingly adept at exploiting the opportunities offered by digital technologies and the web. Of the grant-makers listed in this edition of the guide, 64.2% have their own website (compared to 59.5% in the previous edition). Many of these websites are used to accept and process applications, as well as provide essential information about grant programmes, including deadlines, eligibility criteria and application procedures.

Apart from providing a simpler, quicker and less costly means by which funding applications can be submitted, digital technologies also offer the possibility for grant-makers to advertise their grant programmes and promote the impact of their funding to a much wider audience than would otherwise be possible. While many grant-makers choose to do this using their own website, a growing number of funders are also utilising social media platforms such as Facebook, Instagram and Twitter. Of the funders listed in this edition of the guide, 22.8% have a Twitter profile (compared to 15% in the previous edition), over 17% (11% in the previous edition) have a Facebook page, and nearly 10% (3.6% in the previous edition) have an Instagram account. Often these social media accounts are used to promote and celebrate the important work of the funder's beneficiaries but are also, on occasion, used to share information about funding opportunities. As such, following grant-makers' social media activities can provide fundraisers with a simple and convenient means of keeping up to date with the latest news and updates from multiple funders at once.

Given the growing use of social media by grant-makers, we included details of grant-maker's Twitter, Facebook and Instagram accounts for the first time in the 16th edition of *The Guide to Major Trusts*. This information continues to be featured in this edition at the top of each record alongside the grant-maker's contact details and web address.

Applying for grants

Writing and assessing grant applications can be an incredibly time-consuming process, with every unsuccessful application representing a significant waste of resources for both the charity and funder alike. Despite this, each year thousands of hours continue to be spent by applicants and grant-makers completing and processing applications that stand little or no chance of being successful. Given the limited resources available to both, making the grant-making process as efficient as possible – by reducing the number of ineligible applications submitted to funders – should be in the interests of everyone.

On the one hand, of course, it is the responsibility of the charities themselves to ensure that the time they dedicate to fundraising is used as efficiently and effectively as possible. Publications such as this one, as well as online resources such as DSC's funding website, can help charities to identify grant-makers that may be relevant to their causes. However, it is also important that charities carefully tailor their applications for each funder and only submit applications which they genuinely believe to have a good chance of success.

On the other hand, DSC has long argued that it is also the responsibility of the grant-makers to help to minimise the administrative burden of the grant-making process, by providing clear guidance on the types of project that they would be willing to fund and making their application processes as simple and proportionate as possible. This can be especially important in situations where grant programmes are likely to be competitive or likely to receive a high number of applications, which is frequently the case with major grant-makers featured in this guide.

From a practical perspective, there are a number of things that grant-makers can do to help reduce the number of ineligible applications they receive. Firstly, and most simply, grant-makers may choose to provide applicants with a simple list of eligibility criteria, outlining their geographical area of benefit and focus, as well as details about the types of organisation or activities that they will or will not fund. By being open and honest about their funding preferences, grant-makers can help prospective applicants to make a more informed judgement about their chances of success and determine whether completing an application would be a worthwhile use of their time.

Technically savvy grant-makers may choose to take this concept one stage further and provide applicants with the option of testing their eligibility using an interactive 'eligibility checker'. Usually presented in the form of an online questionnaire, this option enables applicants to determine their suitability to apply for funding in just a few clicks. In some cases, eligibility checkers may also be used to restrict access to application forms to only those organisations that have met the grant-maker's criteria.

Next, a less technical (but no less effective) alternative adopted by many grant-makers is to invite prospective applicants to contact them by phone or email prior to completing a full application. Often a short email exchange or brief telephone conversation is enough for applicants to determine whether their project fits within the priorities of the funder, which can help them avoid wasting time writing applications that are unlikely to be accepted.

Finally, some grant-makers may choose to use a two-stage application process, whereby applicants are initially required to submit a much shorter version of the application form before completing a full application if invited to do so. By using the much simpler first stage of the application process to create a shortlist, grant-makers can help to minimise the time wasted by unsuccessful applicants. This option is particularly useful for grant-makers that require applicants to complete lengthy or detailed applications, such as those that fund medical or scientific research.

During the process of researching this edition of *The Guide to Major Trusts*, DSC collected data about the information that grant-makers provide to applicants as well as the nature of their application processes. Analysis of the data collected reveals that, of the funders accepting unsolicited applications, around 24.7% had an online application form, 13% welcomed contact from applicants prior to the submission of a formal application form, around 6.6% of funders used a multi-stage application process, and 4.6% offered applicants the option to check their eligibility using an online eligibility checker.

It is worth noting that many grant-makers openly invite applications from a wide range of charities and often choose to place no restrictions on the types of project that they would be willing to fund. This means they don't require such a rigorous application process to sift out unsuitable applications. Furthermore, it should also be acknowledged that some of these solutions may only be appropriate for larger grant-makers with the staff, resources and technical expertise required to respond to enquiries, administer two-stage application processes or create online questionnaires. Conversely, many smaller grant-makers often rely on volunteers and part-time staff and so may not have the resources needed to undertake these initiatives.

While it is not possible to draw any general conclusions or make recommendations for how UK grant-making practice may be improved without additional research, these figures provide an interesting insight into the current approach of major UK grant-makers to the processing of applications.

DSC's policy and campaigning

DSC's policy and campaigning activities aim to make the UK a better environment for charities to thrive and help their beneficiaries. In these activities, we act independently in the role of a concerned citizen to champion the needs of the voluntary sector. We ask critical questions, challenge the prevailing view and try to promote debate on issues we consider to be important.

Grants for Good campaign

Grant-funding from government is essential for the work of many charities and voluntary groups. Grants can empower organisations to identify and solve problems, as well as addressing needs in a way that is centred on beneficiaries.

Grants for Good is a campaign that aims to tackle the decline in grant-funding from the public sector, which has taken place over many years. The campaign is currently trying to establish the level of grant-making from local authorities and to produce guidance for local commissioners, aiming to demystify grants and encourage their use.

Grants have many advantages over restrictive and inflexible contracts, particularly for supporting smaller voluntary organisations, and can deliver better outcomes for beneficiaries. Grants are effective for:

- Adapting to change
- Empowering people
- Investing locally
- Nurturing innovation
- Saving time, effort and resources
- Supporting community
- Sustaining services

Many of the grant-making charities in this guide will also have been affected by the decline in government grants and the shift towards contracts.

Despite attempts to reform commissioning and procurement, smaller charities are often unable to compete for larger government contracts or to find relevant funds to support their area of work – this, in turn, increases the pressure upon charitable grant-makers. With fewer and fewer grants available from both local and national government, charities that previously relied on this source of funding, or charities working in areas that have experienced large cuts in government expenditure (such as the arts), will have to turn to other sources for support, such as the grant-makers in this guide.

The Grants for Good campaign needs the support of charities and voluntary organisations so that we can influence commissioners and politicians, and champion the benefits of grants. There are a number of ways in which you can get involved: visit www.dsc.org.uk/grantsforgood for more information.

DSC's Big Lottery Refund campaign

The National Lottery occupies a unique place in the grant-making world. While the various distributors of National Lottery funds are statutory bodies which distribute public money (technically speaking), their activities, aims and beneficiaries have much in common with grant-making charities. Many of the readers of this guide will be familiar with the Big Lottery Fund, now known as The National Lottery Community Fund, which distributes funding for projects that benefit communities across the UK. The fund's grants, many of which are for less than £10,000, support charities and voluntary organisations often with local, grassroots projects.

The Big Lottery Refund campaign was created in 2007, in response to a government decision to divert a huge amount of the Big Lottery Fund money (£675 million in total) to put towards the infrastructure for the London 2012 Olympic Games. In total, £425 million of this, which should have been used to support charities and communities, is still owed to the Big Lottery Fund (now The National Lottery Community Fund). An agreement was made between the government and the London Legacy Development Corporation to pay this money back following the sales of the Olympic assets. However, both the current and previous governments have stated that this now will not happen until the 2020s or even 2030s.

We think that this situation is unacceptable. Our campaign aims to get the government to pay the money back immediately. Giving back this money now would make a huge difference to organisations and the individuals they serve, at a time when so many people are in need of support. Find out more and sign up at www.dsc.org.uk/big-lottery-refund or follow us on twitter @BigLotteryRfnd for updates.

Acknowledgements

The research for this book has been conducted as carefully as possible. Many thanks to those who have made this easier, especially the funders themselves through their websites, their staff who provided additional information and the trustees and others who have helped us. Further thanks go to the Charity Commission for England and Wales, the Office of the Scottish Charity Regulator and the Charity Commission for Northern Ireland for making the annual reports and accounts available online.

We would also like to thank Chris Jarrett, Director of Fundraising at RNIB, for contributing the foreword to this edition.

Disclaimer

We are aware that some of this information may be incomplete or will become out of date. We are equally sure we will have missed some relevant charities. If you come across any omissions or mistakes, or if you have any suggestions for future editions of this book, do let us know. We can be contacted by either phone on 020 4526 5995 or email at cs@dsc.org.uk.

How to use this guide

The funders in this guide are listed alphabetically and the indexes are at the back of the book. There are subject and geographical indexes, which will help you to identify the funders working in your field and area.

Read each funder's entry carefully before deciding to apply. Sometimes, a funder's interest in your field will be very specific or it may have strict guidelines for how to make an application. When you have drawn up a shortlist of funders which your organisation may be eligible to apply to, we recommend that you prioritise them in order of the amount of information they have available. We think it's better to apply to a smaller number of grant-makers for which more information is available, as this means you can properly tailor your application and have a better chance of success.

It is particularly important to show awareness of all the information available from the funder, to acquire up-to-date guidelines where possible and to target your applications with respect to each funder's published wishes where such information exists. Fortunately, there are more funders with an online presence than ever before, so it's becoming increasingly easy for them to communicate their priorities and policies.

Remember that when funders maintain specific guidelines or state that they do not accept unsolicited applications, they are not just being fussy – they are trying to save themselves and applicants precious time and resources. Inappropriate and ill-considered approaches, especially those that show you have not read the published guidelines, can annoy funders and even result in damaging your organisation's reputation. Of course, many funders continue to publish little or no additional material and the only information we have to rely on is that which is available from the relevant charity regulator. Unfortunately, this may result in a waste of your time and the funder's if they reject an application that they deem to be ineligible.

Notes on the entries

These notes complement 'A typical entry' on page xvi and explain how the entries are put together.

The main areas of funding

These categories have been chosen by DSC researchers from an analysis of the areas of work supported by the funder. They are indicative rather than definitive and are useful in a preliminary trawl through the guide. They are no substitute for a close reading of each entry.

Beneficial area

This is the area or areas within which the funder operates, either legally or as a matter of policy or practice. When a funder with a UK-wide remit shows an interest in a particular locality, this is noted. While the information usually comes from the funder itself, it may also arise from a pattern of grant-making identified by DSC researchers.

Grant total and financial year

The most up-to-date financial information available is given here. For the majority of funders in this guide, we were able to obtain financial information from the 2020 financial year onwards. For a small number of entries, we had to use financial information from an earlier year, as this was the latest available at the time of writing. In the majority of cases, this was because the grant-maker's annual report and accounts were not yet due at the relevant charity regulator.

The correspondent

This is the lead contact. Sometimes this is a solicitor or an accountant handling the affairs of a grant-making charity solely on a 'post box' basis, and in other cases it is the relevant department at an organisation. Other useful administrative contacts may also be given in the 'Applications' section or within the main body of text.

The main body of the entry

A summary of the funder's grant-making activities and eligibility criteria. Policy notes and guidelines for applicants, where available, are normally listed in detail, as given by the funder. However, there are cases in which these are so lengthy or subject to change that some abridgement has had to be undertaken and, where appropriate, we direct readers to the funder's website, where extensive or up-to-date information is available. More grant-makers now analyse the distribution of their funding in their annual reports and, where available, this material will also usually be quoted in full. Some analysis has also been carried out by the authors based on grants lists accompanying the accounts.

Exclusions

Where information on exclusions is available, this section notes things that the funder will not or cannot support. In most cases, this has been gathered from the information on websites or in annual reports, although, occasionally, the detail has been communicated directly to DSC by the funders themselves.

Applications

In this section we explain how to make an application to the funder. You will notice that there are some grant-makers that do not accept unsolicited applications – we include these funders to both promote transparency in grant-giving and help save the time and resources of organisations that may otherwise apply in vain for funding.

Sources of information

This section notes the sources of information we have used for the entries. If there is a website, this is usually the best starting point for information, but we also use the charity regulators' (the Charity Commission for England and Wales, the Office of the Scottish Charity Regulator and the Charity Commission for Northern Ireland) registers of charities extensively.

How to apply to a funder

If you are looking for some detailed help in this area, DSC offers training for new and established fundraisers (see www.dsc.org.uk/training) and publishes books that can help, including *Grants Fundraising* and *The Complete Fundraising Handbook.* However, there is no need to be daunted by the challenge of making effective applications. If your charity's work is in demand – and of a kind supported by the funder in question – a very simple letter (of one uncrowded A4 page or less, backed by a clear annual report and set of accounts) will probably do 90% of everything that can be done.

If there is an application form and/or detailed application requirements, simply follow them.

1) Select the right grant-makers to approach

If they fund organisations or work like yours, and you genuinely fit within any guidelines they publish, put them on your list.

2) Call them

If the entry makes this sound sensible, ring the grant-maker to check that the guidelines in this guide still apply and that the kind of application you are considering is appropriate.

3) Send in an application

Unless the grant-maker has an application form, we suggest that the main part of this should be a letter that fits easily on one side of an A4 sheet of paper (back-up materials such as a formal proposal may be necessary for a big or complex project but are usually, in our view, secondary). We suggest that the letter contains the following points:

- **A summary sentence such as:** 'We would like to reward our hard-working and valued volunteers with a training programme to develop their skills, and I am writing to you requesting a contribution of £5,000.'
- **The problem the work will address:** This should normally be the beneficiaries' problem, not your charity's problem: 'Mothers of children with learning disabilities in our area get very little help from the statutory services in coping with their children's day-to-day needs. We are aware of the very helpful support you have given to similar projects and feel that the purpose of the project complements your charity's ethos and aims.'
- **What you are going to do about this:** 'Our volunteers (who have been in the same situations themselves) support and help our beneficiaries but need and want better training, especially on home safety. Our beneficiaries, as you'll be aware, often struggle with meeting the needs of their children. This award would develop our volunteers' skills and, as a result, their experience and knowledge. This will then help us provide significantly better, more qualified support to help our beneficiaries more effectively.'
- **Details of the work:** 'We want to commission an expert from our sister charity Dean Cambridge Foundation to develop and test suitable training materials that we will be able to use.'
- **Information about your charity:** 'We attach one of our general leaflets explaining what we do, a copy of our latest annual report and accounts, and a copy of the quote received from the Dean Cambridge Foundation to supply the initial training which we can then develop (with funding we hope to be awarded from Awards for All).'
- **Repeat the request:** 'We are all very keen to see this project happen and hope that you will be able to help us.'

And that is all. Keep the style simple and informal. If posting your letter rather than sending it via email, handwrite the date, salutation and signature. A charity is not a business and is usually not impressed by applicants trying to sound like one. The best letter comes from someone who understands the project and is going to be involved with it. In this way, they can speak authoritatively and with enthusiasm should someone from the funder call for more information. Making the letter longer will often reduce rather than increase its impact, but attaching compelling material is fine.

A letter of endorsement might also be nice – your local GP practice saying your work is wonderful, for example.

Appearance matters. It is a great help if you have a good-quality letterhead on something better than photocopy paper if you are posting your request, and if your report and accounts and literature are of appropriately high quality for your kind of organisation. However, you don't want to give the impression that your charity spends unnecessary money on expensive materials rather than on carrying out its work.

Good luck!

A typical entry

The Fictitious Charity

 Social welfare; education; health

 UK, with come preference for New Town

£ £1.3 million (2020/21)

CC number: 123456

Correspondent: Ann Freeman, Appeals Secretary, The Old Barn, New Town ZC48 2QQ

Trustees: Eva Appiah; Rita Khan; Lorraine Murphy.

 www.fictitious.org.uk

 facebook.com/fictitious

 @fictitious

 @fictitious

General information

This charity makes grants to organisations working in the areas of social welfare (particularly homelessness), education and health. The trustees will support both capital and revenue projects; the annual report for 2020/21 stated that 'specific projects are preferred to general running costs'.

Financial information

Year end	31/03/2021
Income	£1,500,000
Assets	£20,300,000
Grants to organisations	£1,300,000
No. of grants	127

Further financial information

In 2020/21, grants awarded to organisations were broken down as follows: social welfare (£900,000); health (£300,000); education (£100,000).

Beneficiaries included: Homeless UK (£200,000); Shelter (£150,000); Charity Workers' Benevolent Society (£80,000); Learning Foundation (£50,000); New Town Citizens Advice (£10,000); Getwell Hospice UK (£5,000).

Exclusions

No grants are made to non-registered charities, individuals or religious organisations.

Applications

Apply in writing to the correspondent. The trustees meet in March and September each year. Applications should be received by the end of January and the end of July respectively.

Sources of information

Accounts; annual report; Charity Commission record; funder's website.

- **Name of the charity**
- **Main focus areas:** what the charity funds in practice.
- **Geographical area of grant-making:** including where the funder can legally give and where it gives in practice.
- **Grant total:** total amount given to organisations in the most recent financial year available.
- **Registered charity number**
- **Correspondent and contact details:** including telephone, email, website and social media details if available.
- **Trustees**
- **General information:** a summary of the funder's policies.
- **Financial information:** the charity's financial year end, annual income, assets, and the total amount and number of grants awarded to organisations, where available.
- **Further financial information:** additional information, such as the breakdown of grants.
- **Beneficiaries included:** a list of typical beneficiaries supported by the charity. This is often the clearest indication of what a funder is prepared to fund.
- **Exclusions:** a list of any areas, subjects or types of grant the funder will not consider supporting.
- **Applications:** this includes how to apply and, where available, when to submit an application.
- **Sources of information:** where we have obtained the information in the entry from.

Grant-makers in alphabetical order

The 1989 Willan Charitable Trust

General charitable purposes; community development; social welfare

Tyne and Wear, Northumberland, County Durham and Teesside

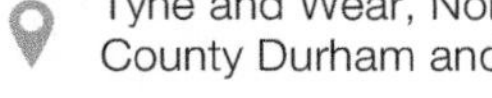

£504,300 (2019/20)

CC number: 802749

Correspondent: Nils Stronach, Head of Grant Practice and Programmes, c/o Community Foundation, Philanthropy House, Woodbine Road, Gosforth, Newcastle upon Tyne, Tyne and Wear NE3 1DD (tel: 0191 222 0945; email: ns@communityfoundation.org.uk)

Trustees: Francis Chapman; Alex Ohlsson; Willan Trustee Ltd.

www.communityfoundation.org.uk/group_grant/the-1989-willan-charitable-trust

General information

The trust was established in 1989 by the Willan family out of funds derived from a shipping business in the north-east of England. The trust supports general charitable purposes by making grants to registered charities, exempted and excepted organisations whose activities benefit residents of Tyne and Wear, Northumberland, County Durham and Teesside. Preference is given to local registered charities with expenditure of less than £1 million. Applications from national charities are welcomed, but only for projects that solely benefit the North East.

The trust's 2019/20 annual report notes the following:

> In recognition of the origins of the trust fund and the economic impact that the decline of shipbuilding has had on the region, the trustees tend to concentrate their support towards causes that are active in Tyne and Wear and its immediate surroundings. The trustees favour causes which aim to ease social deprivation and/or enrich the fabric of the local community and the quality of life of individuals within that community. They may also support education where that is aimed at improving the economy in areas of deprivation.
>
> In considering which local causes to support and the level of support given, the trustees will also have regard to an applicant's ability to raise funds elsewhere. Consequently, the trustees tend to weigh their support towards local charitable institutions rather than national or international ones [...]
>
> In cases of great need such as major natural disasters, conflicts, or accidents, causes may be supported outside the trustees' normal parameters stated above.

Grants are given for core costs or project costs, and awards typically range from £750 to £10,000, although there is no maximum or minimum grant. Projects where the grant will represent a significant contribution to the overall cost are prioritised. Grants are usually for a maximum of one year. The trust can also provide in-kind support, in the form of premises for charitable organisations.

Some examples of projects the trust will support include:

- Projects that meet the needs of communities experiencing high levels of deprivation
- Services for young people that address educational needs or offer diversion from crime and anti-social behaviour
- Self-help initiatives
- Art projects that help tackle deprivation
- The work of youth organisations, in particular, the Sea Cadets, Scouts, Guides and other uniformed groups (grants of up to £1,500)
- Projects that draw on the region's rich maritime tradition
- Gap year voluntary work through the Project Trust (grants of up to £500 for expenses)

The Community Foundation for Tyne and Wear and Northumberland (Charity Commission no. 700510) provides administrative support to the trust's grant-making in the North East region, receiving and vetting applications for the trustees. A list of examples of projects the trust might fund is available on the community foundation's website.

Financial information

Year end	30/09/2020
Income	£505,000
Assets	£21,170,000
Grants to organisations	£504,300
No. of grants	75

Further financial information

Grants were broken down as follows:

Improving health	29	£200,900
Participation in community life	21	£159,400
Building children's future	21	£130,600
Enjoying later life	4	£13,500

£10,001 and above	1	£25,000
£5,001–£10,000	36	£334,800
£1,000–£5,000	38	£144,500

Beneficiaries included: A full list of grants awarded is available on request from the Community Foundation for Tyne and Wear and Northumberland.

Exclusions

According to the community foundation's website, the trust will not provide funding for the following, unless the project primarily addresses local deprivation:

- Trips abroad
- Individuals, except Project Trust (gap year voluntary work) applications from residents of the beneficial area
- Projects focused on heritage and the environment, scientific and/or medical research

Applicants that do not provide feedback on previous awards will not generally be considered for further funding. The community foundation's website also notes: 'Applicants with more than six months' running costs in reserve will not usually be considered for a grant, unless the application demonstrates that funding the project from reserves will reduce them to an imprudent level.'

Applications

Applications can be made online via the Community Foundation for Tyne and Wear and Northumberland's website. Refer to the website for full details before making an application. The fund panel meets in March, June, September and December. Applications will generally be considered at the next scheduled trustee meeting, provided they are received by the 15th of the preceding month. However, applicants are encouraged to submit their applications as early as possible to ensure they are considered at the next available trustees' meeting.

Sources of information

Accounts; annual report; Charity Commission record; Community Foundation for Tyne and Wear and Northumberland (website).

The 29th May 1961 Charitable Trust

Arts and museums; conservation and protection; employment, education and training; homelessness and housing; leisure, recreation and young people; medical causes; people who have offended; social welfare

UK, with a preference for the Warwickshire and Coventry areas

£4.69 million (2020/21)

CC number: 200198

Correspondent: The Trustees, One Eastwood, Binley Business Park, Coventry CV3 2UB (tel: 020 7024 9034; email: enquiries@29may1961charity.org.uk)

Trustees: Paul Varney; Andrew Jones; Elizabeth Rantzen; Geoffrey Cox; Charles Martin.

General information

The trust takes its name from the date on which it was established by the settlor, the late Helen M. Martin. The settlor inherited her wealth from Smirnoff, now owned by Diageo, and was keen to support the newly founded University of Warwick, which continues to receive funding.

The trustees give the following description of its grant-making policy, aims and objectives in their annual report for 2020/21:

> The 29th May 1961 Charitable Trust is a general grant making trust. The policy of the trustees is to support a wide range of charitable organisations across a broad spectrum. Although for disclosure purposes grants are analysed into separate categories, the trustees are interested in funding initiatives which meet their selection criteria regardless of the charitable area into which the grant falls. Grants are made for both capital and revenue purposes. Some grants are one-off, some recurring and others spread over two or three years. The majority of grants are made to organisations within the United Kingdom and preference is given, where possible, to charities operating in the West Midlands and in particular the Coventry and Warwickshire area. The trustees do not typically fund projects outside the UK.

Financial information

Year end	05/04/2021
Assets	£127,780,000
Grants to organisations	£4,690,000

Further financial information

Grants were awarded to 437 organisations during the year. Grants were broken down as follows:

Social welfare	186	£1.69 million
Medical	36	£617,000
Leisure, recreation and youth	78	£615,500
Art and museums	32	£614,800
Homelessness and housing	40	£505,500
Employment, education and training	39	£438,000
People who have offended	13	£153,000
Conservation and protection	13	£49,500

Beneficiaries included: University of Warwick (£290,000); Moorfields Eye Hospital (£200,000); City Gateway (£60,000); Crisis (£50,000); Coventry University (£45,000); NACRO (£30,000); Child Brain Injury Trust (£22,500); Alzheimer's Society (£10,000); St Paul's Community Development Trust (£5,000).

Exclusions

The trust does not make grants to individuals or unregistered charities.

Applications

Apply in writing to the correspondent, enclosing the most recent annual report and accounts. Follow-up visits to charities may be requested to better understand applicants' requirements. The trustees typically meet in February, May, August and November. Due to the large number of applications received, applications are not acknowledged and unsuccessful applicants are not notified.

Sources of information

Accounts; annual report; Charity Commission record.

The 3Ts Charitable Trust

General charitable purposes

UK and overseas

£1.54 million (2020/21)

CC number: 1109733

Correspondent: The Trustees, PO Box 68, Knebworth, Hertfordshire SG3 6UZ (tel: 01892 701743; email: info@3tscharitabletrust.com)

Trustees: William Medlicott; Charles Sherwood; Tim Sherwood; Tabitha Sherwood; Tatiana Sherwood; Rosemary Sherwood.

General information

The 3Ts Charitable Trust was established in 2005. It makes grants, mainly to registered charities, for general charitable purposes throughout the UK and overseas.

Financial information

Year end	31/03/2021
Income	£1,550,000
Assets	£13,000,000
Grants to organisations	£1,540,000
No. of grants	35

Beneficiaries included: Imperial College London (£140,000); Marie Curie Cancer Care (£125,000); St Mungo's (£75,000); Big Issue Foundation (£50,000); Tottenham FC (£45,000); Médecins Sans Frontières (£25,000); Hardman Trust (£10,000); Isabel Hospice (£6,500); Cerebral Palsy Alliance Research (£550).

Applications

The trust's Charity Commission record states:

> The trustees are proactive in seeking charities to support and it is unusual for them to make grants in response to unsolicited applications.

Sources of information

Accounts; annual report; Charity Commission record.

4 Charity Foundation

General charitable purposes; social welfare; education; health; Jewish causes

UK and Israel

£724,600 (2020/21)

CC number: 1077143

Correspondent: Jacob Schimmel, Trustee, 121 Princes Park Avenue, London NW11 0JS (tel: 020 8455 0100; email: four4charities@gmail.com)

Trustees: Jacob Schimmel; Verette Schimmel; Johnathan Schimmel.

General information

The foundation was set up in 1999 to make grants to Jewish charitable organisations for religious, educational, welfare and general charitable purposes.

Financial information

Year end	31/03/2021
Income	£157,700
Assets	£4,390,000
Grants to organisations	£724,600

Further financial information

Grants awarded in 2020/21 were broken down as follows:

Education	£424,000
Health and saving lives	£135,400
The relief of poverty	£115,300
Other	£50,000

Only beneficiaries of grants of £10,000 and above were listed in the foundation's 2020/21 accounts. Grants of under £10,000 totalled £17,600.

Beneficiaries included: JNF Charitable Trust (£214,200); Asser Bishvil Foundation (£137,800); Girl Effect (£54,900); The Marque Foundation (£50,000); Ahavat Yisroel UK (£38,000); Hasmonean High School Charitable Trust (£18,000).

Applications

The foundation does not accept unsolicited applications.

Sources of information

Accounts; annual report; Charity Commission record.

The A. and J. Charitable Trust

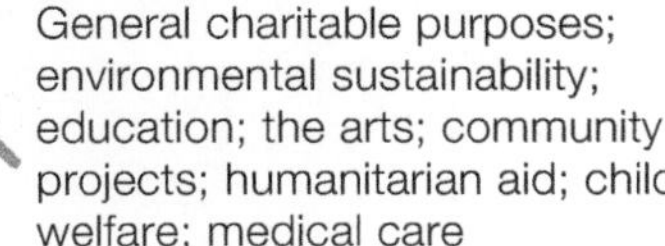

General charitable purposes; environmental sustainability; education; the arts; community projects; humanitarian aid; child welfare; medical care

UK

£300,000 (2020/21)

CC number: 1058058

Correspondent: Suzanne Rose, c/o Dixon Wilson, 22 Chancery Lane, London WC2A 1LS (tel: 020 7680 8100; email: suzannerose@dixonwilson.co.uk)

Trustees: Lady Jane Parker; Sir Alan Parker; Graham Chambers.

General information

The A. and J. Charitable Trust, formerly known as KPR Charitable Trust, was established in 1996. It makes grants to charitable organisations for general charitable purposes including:

- Education and the arts
- Environmental sustainability
- Community projects
- Humanitarian aid and the welfare of children
- Medical care

Financial information

Year end	05/04/2021
Income	£650,100
Assets	£348,100
Grants to organisations	£300,000
No. of grants	18

Further financial information

During 2020/21, grants were distributed as follows:

Environmental sustainability	£160,000
Education and the arts	£68,000
Community projects	£42,300
Humanitarian aid and child welfare	£19,700
Medical care	£10,000

Beneficiaries included: Leaders Quest Foundation (£100,000); Sustainable Food Trust (£50,000); Dragon School Trust (£30,000); Chelsea Physic Garden (£10,000); Cotswold Friends (£4,000); Upper Slaughter Village Hall (£2,000); Re-form Heritage (£1,000).

Applications

Apply in writing to the correspondent.

Sources of information

Accounts; annual report; Charity Commission record.

The A. B. Charitable Trust

Migrants, refugees and asylum seekers; criminal justice and penal reform; human rights; access to justice

UK

£3.87 million (2020/21)

CC number: 1000147

Correspondent: Havva Hassan, Grants Administrator, c/o Woodsford, 3rd Floor, 8 Bloomsbury Street, London WC1B 3SR (tel: 020 7313 8070; email: mail@abcharitabletrust.org.uk)

Trustee: ABCT Trustee Ltd.

www.abcharitabletrust.org.uk

General information

The A. B. Charitable Trust was established in 1990 by the businessman and author Yves Bonavero and his wife Anne and is funded annually by the Bonavero family. The trust awards grants to small and medium-sized charities that work to promote human dignity and defend the human rights of marginalised and excluded people. The trust's three priority areas are:

- Migrants and refugees
- Criminal justice and penal reform
- Human rights, particularly access to justice

The trust operates three funding programmes:

- The Open Programme: aimed at single-focus organisations working within the trust's priority areas. Grants are typically available for core costs and are usually between £10,000 and £20,000. Project funding is also available
- Special Initiatives: grants made under this scheme are by invitation only and are typically larger than those awarded through the Open Programme, often working with partner grantees and other funders
- The Anchor Programme: grants made under this scheme are by invitation only and are aimed at key organisations with their respective sectors. They are intended as a long-term form of support

To be eligible for the Open Programme, organisations must: be a UK charity working in one of the trust's priority areas; have an annual income between £150,000 and £1.5 million; have been operating for at least one year; and be able to provide a full year's audited or independently examined accounts.

Financial information

Year end	30/04/2021
Income	£4,730,000
Assets	£1,040,000
Grants to organisations	£3,870,000
No. of grants	163

Further financial information

Overall, 163 grants were awarded to 154 charities. Grants were awarded in the three priority areas: migrants and refugees (£1.73 million); access to justice (£1.44 million); criminal justice (£705,000).

During the year, 63 grants totalling £985,000 were distributed through the Open Programme. The charity received 136 applications to the Open Programme, of which 108 were eligible. The average grant amount was £15,600.

Beneficiaries included: Refugee Action (two grants totalling £300,000); The Bonavero Institute of Human Rights (£100,000); Clinks (£50,000); Prison Reform Trust (£40,000); Welsh Refugee Council (£20,000); Migration Museum Project (£10,000).

Exclusions

The trust does not make grants to/for:

- Individuals
- The promotion of religion
- Capital appeals
- Academic research

The trust does not usually award charities with large national links and prefers to fund smaller to medium-sized charities.

Applications

Applications can be completed online via the trust's website. Beforehand, a four-step eligibility checker can be completed on the website. The grants committee meets four times a year to assess and decided on applications. Application deadlines are typically in January, April, July and October, but check the website for up-to-date deadlines. Full guidelines and answers to frequently asked questions are available on the trust's website.

Sources of information

Accounts; annual report; Charity Commission record; funder's website.

The A Team Foundation Ltd

Food and land projects that are ecologically, economically and socially conscious

UK

£840,900 (2020/21)

CC number: 1077094

Correspondent: The Trustees, 61 Grosvenor Street, London W1K 3JE (tel: 020 3011 1100; email: info@ateamfoundation.org)

Trustees: Benjamin Arbib; Tamara Arbib; Paul Reynolds.

 www.ateamfoundation.org

 facebook.com/ateamfoundation

 @ateamfoundation

General information

The A Team Foundation was registered with the Charity Commission in 1999. According to the foundation's website, its main objectives are:

> The promotion of a greater understanding of the links between the consumption and production of foods and their effects on human health, social wellbeing and the environment.

Financial information

Year end	05/04/2021
Income	£4,040,000
Assets	£17,550,000
Grants to organisations	£840,900

Beneficiaries included: The Landworkers' Alliance (£97,000); Sustain (£68,600); Organic Leaf (£54,200); Pesticide Action Network UK (£40,500); Farming the Future (£30,000); Farming and Wildlife Advisory Group (£20,000); Beyond GM (£10,000); GM Freeze (£6,300); The Kindling Trust (£4,500).

Applications

The foundation does not accept unsolicited applications.

Sources of information

Accounts; annual report; Charity Commission record; funder's website.

A. W. Charitable Trust

Social welfare and Orthodox Jewish causes

London, Gateshead, Manchester and Salford; Israel

£5.43 million (2019/20)

CC number: 283322

Correspondent: The Trustees, 66 Waterpark Road, Manchester M7 4JL (tel: 0161 740 0116)

Trustees: Rabbi Aubrey Weis; Rachel Weis; Sir Weis.

General information

This trust was established in 1981 for general charitable purposes. It is the charitable trust of Aubrey Weis, director of Aberdeen Estate Company, the owner of land and property throughout the North West. All the trustees are also trustees of The Helping Foundation which shares similar objectives to this trust.

The trust aims to support Orthodox Jewish causes and it meets this object by making grants to Jewish education and religious organisations both in the UK and abroad. Its grant-making policy is outlined in the 2019/20 annual report as follows

> The policy is to assist in the furtherance of Jewish education and religion, relieve poverty, assist with those in need of medical help and to alleviate hardship wherever possible.

Financial information

Year end	30/06/2020
Income	£17,080,000
Assets	£255,610,000
Grants to organisations	£5,430,000

Beneficiaries included: A list of beneficiaries was not available. Previous beneficiaries include: Asser Bishvil Foundation; Beenstock Home; British Friends of Kupat Hair; Chevras Oneg Shabbos-Yomtov; Friends of Mir; Purim Fund; Toimchei Shabbos Manchester; Zoreya Tzedokos.

Applications

Contact the correspondent for further information.

Sources of information

Accounts; annual report; Charity Commission record.

The A. H. Trust

Advancement of the Jewish religion; social welfare; education

England and Wales

£391,000 (2020/21)

CC number: 1101843

Correspondent: Ivor Smith, Trustee, New Burlington House, 1075 Finchley Road, London NW11 0PU (tel: 020 8203 9991; email: mail@cohenarnold.com)

Trustees: Elisabeth Smith; Arye Grossnass; Sarah Smith.

General information

The A. H. Trust was registered with the Charity Commission in 2004. According to its 2020/21 annual report, the objectives of the trust are as follows:

- the advancement and promotion of the Jewish religion including the provision of instruction or edification of the public in all its aspects and in any part of the world.
- the relief of aged, vulnerable and impoverished persons of all ages in any part of the world.
- the advancement of education and learning and/or establishment and/or support of schools and other institutions of Jewish learning including the establishment and support of colleges and educational establishments in all parts of the world.

Financial information

Year end	31/03/2021
Income	£426,400
Assets	£1,240,000
Grants to organisations	£391,000

Beneficiaries included: LTC Trust Co. (£149,400); Beis Hillel Trust (£69,500); North London Welfare and Educational Foundation (£60,000).

Applications

Apply in writing to the correspondent.

Sources of information

Accounts; annual report; Charity Commission record.

The Abbeyfield Research Foundation

Research relating to older people

UK

£277,300 (2020/21)

CC number: 1167685

Correspondent: The Trustees, St Peter's House, 2 Bricket Road, St Albans, Hertfordshire AL1 3JW (tel: 01727 734067; email: research@abbeyfield.com)

Trustees: Prof. Brian Williams; Kenneth Staveley; Robin Means.

 www.abbeyfieldresearch foundation.org

General information

The foundation was registered with the Charity Commission in June 2016 and is a subsidiary charity of The Abbeyfield Society – a nationwide charity that provides housing, support and care for older people.

The foundation's website states:

> The strategic aim of the Abbeyfield Research Foundation's is to drive forward the pursuit of robust peer-reviewed evidence to underpin progress and sustainable high standards in the promotion of quality of life and provision of care for older people, both within the scope of its founding parent charity and across the wider sector.

The foundation aims to achieve this through funding research with the following priorities:

- Well-being
- Equality of access to, and integration of, health and social support services
- Reducing social isolation, loneliness and supporting community integration
- The prevention of disability and its progression, including falls and fractures
- Nutrition
- The practical benefits of consideration of the 'whole' person
- The built environment
- Quality of life and living
- Digital innovation and older people

The trust funds research through three types of grant:

- PhD studentships of around £20,000 to £30,000 per year (over three years) to provide a stipend, cover fees and project costs;
- Small project grants of up to £50,000 per year (over two years) to cover salaries, running costs and equipment;
- Pump-priming grants of up to £20,000 (over one year) to cover preliminary evaluation of an innovative project

Financial information

Year end	31/03/2021
Income	£302,000
Assets	£63,800
Grants to organisations	£277,300

Beneficiaries included: Sheffield Hospitals NHS Trust (£86,800); Brunel University (£73,200); Cambridge/ University of East Anglia (£56,000); Glasgow Caledonia University (£46,300); Sheffield Hospitals NHS Trust (£15,000).

Exclusions

The foundation does not currently fund research using animals.

Applications

The foundation invites applications annually, typically in October. Application forms can be downloaded from the foundation's website and returned via email. Successful applicants at stage one are invited to complete a second stage.

Sources of information

Accounts; annual report; Charity Commission record; funder's website.

The Aberdeen Foundation

Jewish causes; education and training; health; social welfare; general charitable purposes

UK and overseas

£8.14 million (2020/21)

CC number: 1151506

Correspondent: The Trustees, 2nd Floor, 7 Hartom Street, Har Hotzvim, Jerusalem (email: aberdeenfoundation@ gmail.com)

Trustees: Albert Friedberg; Nancy Friedberg; Chaya Spitz; Paul Staszewski; Shraga Zaltzman; Michael Shumacher.

General information

The Aberdeen Foundation was registered with the Charity Commission in April 2013. The foundation's 2020/21 annual report indicates three key areas of grant-making: education, health and the relief of poverty (social welfare). The foundation makes grants worldwide and may have a preference for Jewish causes.

Financial information

Year end	31/03/2021
Income	£567,800
Assets	£24,270,000
Grants to organisations	£8,140,000

Further financial information

Grants were broken down as follows:

Advancement of education	£4.95 million
Advancement of health	£2.34 million
Relief of poverty	£845,100

The financial information has been converted from US dollars using the exchange rate at the time of writing (May 2022).

Beneficiaries included: Yedidut Toronto (£5.23 million); Career 21 (£1.1 million); Freiburg Economic Institute (£220,000); Vehechezakta (£96,900).

Applications

Unsolicited applications are not accepted. The foundation's 2020/21 annual report and accounts state that:

> The trustees are proactive in seeking out charities that match their strategic interests. They form strong relationships with these charities and do not have an open grant application process.

Sources of information

Accounts; annual report; Charity Commission record.

ABF The Soldiers' Charity

Support for British Army soldiers, veterans and their immediate families

UK and overseas

£3.54 million (2020/21)

CC number: 1146420

Correspondent: The Trustees, Mountbarrow House, 6–20 Elizabeth Street, London SW1W 9RB (tel: 020 7901 8900; email: externalgrants@ soldierscharity.org)

Trustees: Paul Hearn; Simon Martin; Maj. Gen. Malcolm Wood; Mary Fagan; James Rous; Amanda Metcalfe; Lisa Worley; Lt Gen. Philip Jones; Anthony Scott; Rowena Fell; Simon Heale; Rachel Booth; David London; Maj. General Griffiths.

 www.soldierscharity.org

 facebook.com/soldierscharity

 @soldierscharity

General information

Since 1944 this charity has supported soldiers, former soldiers and their immediate families. The charity's vision, as stated on its website, is: 'That all serving and former soldiers and their dependants should have the opportunity to avoid hardship and enjoy independence and dignity.'

The current policy set by the trustees is to support individuals through regimental and corps benevolence funds, and to support other specialist charities which look after the needs of the serving and retired army community.

Grants to organisations

The charity has established guidelines for organisations, available on its website, which explain that the charity supports:

> All registered charities and other organisations which support the Army community, which includes veterans, serving soldiers, their families and immediate dependants, may apply.
>
> We support in the first instance a broad range of charities, with a preference to members of COBSEO (Confederation of Service Charities)/Veterans Scotland. That said, when appropriate we will consider applications on a case by case basis from:
>
> - Not-for-profit organisations and Community Interest Companies (CICs)

- Community projects
- Housing associations

The charity typically funds up to 100 organisations each year.

Financial information

Year end	31/03/2021
Income	£11,850,000
Assets	£93,850,000
Grants to organisations	£3,540,000
No. of grants	43

Further financial information

Grants to organisations were awarded in the following categories during the year:

Well-being	£1.16 million
Family	£986,400
Older people	£604,000
Employment and training	£403,400
Housing	£393,600

Beneficiaries included: Defence Medical Welfare Service (£593,700); Queen Victoria Seamen's Rest (£226,000); Combat Stress (£126,000); SSAFA Central Office (£70,000); Royal Hospital Chelsea (£40,000); Army Families Federation (£30,000); Resume Foundation (£15,000); Phyllis Tuckwell Hospice (£5,000); Thistle Health and Well-being (£2,500).

Exclusions

The charity's website states:

- We are not able to accept applications from those organisations that do not support serving soldiers, veterans and their immediate families, and/or the wider Army community.
- We will not normally consider any funding request made within 12 months of the outcome of a previous application, whether a grant was received or not.
- Whilst we do support some educational and training activities, this does not include gap years, study trips, fundraising expeditions or sponsorship. Sponsorship referrals should be passed to the Charity's communications department.
- The Charity does not normally fund specific (i.e. named) posts and salaries. Trustees will consider contributing to an organisation's core operating costs of which we recognise general salary costs will be a part of this. This is primarily because grants are single-year commitments.
- The Charity will not fund the full cost recovery of any project, but may consider a request to contribute towards this.
- Typically grants are made for a single year; however, the Charity's Trustees may consider making a grant spread over a number of years at their discretion if they feel this would be appropriate.
- The Charity tends not to support umbrella organisations, preferring to support those organisations working directly with beneficiaries at a grassroots level.

Applications

Application forms are made available on the charity's website when funding rounds open and should be returned to externalgrants@soldierscharity.org. Application deadlines and full guidelines are also available from the charity's website.

Sources of information

Accounts; annual report; Charity Commission record; guidelines for applicants; funder's website.

abrdn Charitable Foundation

Financial and digital education and inclusion; habitat and wildlife restoration; equality; community

UK and overseas where the company has a presence

£778,700 (2020)

OSCR number: SC042597

Correspondent: The Trustees, 1 George Street, Edinburgh EH2 2LL (email: charitablefoundation@abrdn.com)

Trustees: Tamsin Balfour; Paul Aggett; Sarah Anderson; Bev Hendry; Michael Tumilty; Sam Walker; Amanda Young; D. Gorman.

www.abrdn.com/corporate/corporate-sustainability/charitable-giving

General information

Registered in 2011, this is the charitable foundation of abrdn plc (formerly known as Standard Life Aberdeen plc), a global investment management group. The foundation's name was changed from Standard Life Aberdeen Charitable Foundation in October 2021.

The foundation provides funding to charities and projects that are local to the areas in which the group operates. The foundation supports local projects under the following themes:

- **Connecting people:** overcoming barriers, promoting sustainable development for communities that face social isolation or disadvantage. The foundation's website states that projects supported in these areas are 'primarily focused on financial or digital education and inclusion, or promoting the development of fair and inclusive employment, particularly for socio-economically disadvantaged groups.'
- **Connecting planet:** protecting nature or supporting habitat and wildlife restoration

Criteria for funding

The following information has been taken from the foundation's website:

- Donations are granted to established organisations such as registered charities and community groups
- Requests must be aligned with the foundation's focus on 'building connection'
- UN Sustainable Development Goals – the project must support at least one of these.
- Donations should fully fund a project which has specific, meaningful and measurable objectives. The foundation does not contribute towards projects that include capital build costs. The foundation prefers to fund projects that give the group's employees the opportunity to be involved.
- The activity, and beneficiaries of any donation, should be located in a community local to one of the group's offices
- [Funding] should be spent within six months of being granted but exceptions are made for multi-year funding

Emerging markets partnerships

In addition to its local grant-making, the foundation establishes partnerships with charities that are working to improve the needs of disadvantaged children in emerging market countries. A new partnership is chosen annually and lasts for a three-year period. In 2020, the foundation concluded its latest partnership with Able Child Africa.

Financial information

Year end	31/12/2020
Income	£1,050,000
Assets	£412,100
Grants to organisations	£778,700

Further financial information

Grants were broken down as follows in 2020: local community support (£644,400) and emerging markets projects (£134,300). Included in the grant total for local community support were grants for COVID-19 support and grants to charities that work with ethnic minority communities.

Beneficiaries included: A list of beneficiaries was not available.

Exclusions

The foundation's local community funding does not support:

- Projects that promote religious or political views or discriminate against sexual orientation, gender, etc.
- Crowdfunding initiatives
- Individuals
- Capital build costs
- Projects that do not support at least one of the UN Sustainable Development Goals
- Activities located outside a community local to an abrdn plc office

Applications

An application form can be downloaded from the foundation's website. This should be returned to charitablefoundation@abrdn.com, along with a PDF copy of your latest audited accounts. Successful applicants will be notified within a three-month period following submission of the application form.

Sources of information

Accounts; annual report; funder's website; OSCR record.

abrdn Financial Fairness Trust

Financial well-being; research, campaigning and policy work

UK, with a preference for Scotland

£548,500 (2020)

OSCR number: SC040877

Correspondent: The Trustees, Level 5, 6 St Andrew Square, Edinburgh EH2 2AH (tel: 0131 528 4243; email: enquiries@financialfairness.org.uk)

Trustees: Alistair Darling; James Daunt; Naomi Eisenstadt; Prof. David Hall; Prof. Wendy Loretto; Graeme McEwan; Keith Skeoch; Euan Stirling; Lucy Heller; Ella Hugh.

www.financialfairness.org.uk/en

@finan_fairness

General information

This is one of the corporate charities of abrdn plc (formerly Standard Life Aberdeen plc). The trust's website explains its history as follows:

> We were established in 2009 and became Standard Life Foundation in 2017 upon receiving a substantial donation from the unclaimed assets following Standard Life's demutualisation. At this time, our constitution, governance structure and name were all revised to align with this change.
>
> Standard Life plc merged in 2017 to become Standard Life Aberdeen, and in 2021 became abrdn plc. We took this opportunity to choose a new, more descriptive, name for the organisation. From December 2021 we became abrdn Financial Fairness Trust.
>
> Our new, mission-led name, also recognises the help and support provided by the company, from which we receive in-kind donations of office space and professional support.

The trust's mission is to improve financial well-being in the UK. It achieves this by funding research, campaigning and policy work (it intends to award around £3 million per year).

More specifically, the work it supports examines and promotes measures to:

- Increase incomes for those on low-to-middle incomes.
- Ensure people have an adequate safety net, building savings and assets.
- Reduce the cost of living, making sure those on lower incomes are not paying more.
- Address issues related to spending and borrowing, particularly where it becomes problematic.

The trust's funding programmes are focused on three areas that influence financial well-being:

- **Income:** wages, social security, pensions and taxation
- **Spending:** cost of living, consumer spending, problem gambling, borrowing and payment problems
- **Assets:** general saving, retirement saving, housing and taxation

Applications are invited from any charitable organisation including voluntary organisations, think tanks, campaigning groups, research bodies and universities. The trust supports UK-wide organisations but is keen to support work within Scotland, or UK-wide work with a Scottish focus.

Grants are typically made for between one and three years, with grant sizes ranging from £10,00 to £200,000. Funding is given for specific projects or for ongoing costs, including staff salaries and overheads. Organisations are encouraged to include a reasonable amount of core costs to cover their overheads when applying for funding.

Financial information

Year end	31/12/2020
Income	£2,180,000
Assets	£93,360,000
Grants to organisations	£548,500
No. of grants	17

Further financial information

During the year, nine grants were awarded through the trust's open grant programmes, and eight grants were awarded through an emergency fast-track COVID-19 funding round. Grants ranged from £12,500 to £159,000, and the average grant size was £77,200. Grants were awarded via the trust's three programmes: Income (£356,000); Spending (£125,500); Assets (£67,000).

Beneficiaries included: University of Edinburgh (£159,000); University of Bristol – Personal Finance Research Centre (£125,000); Women's Budget Group (£159,000); YouGov plc (£86,200); Bevan Foundation (£68,000); Gingerbread (£48,600); Resolution Foundation (£21,000); Demos (£12,500).

Exclusions

The trust's funding guidelines state that it will not support applications:

- For the direct delivery of services, unless this is testing a new approach which has good potential to lead to wider change and be of significant benefit.
- For work that does not address those on low-to-middle incomes living in the UK.
- For work that is not charitable.
- From individuals.
- For work that is primarily the responsibility of statutory authorities.
- From organisations which have fewer than three non-executive people on their governing body (trustees/directors). You must have at least three who are not employees of the organisation or affiliated to it in any other way.
- For work that has already taken place.
- For general appeals.
- From organisations seeking to distribute grants on our behalf.
- For the promotion of religion.
- From organisations who have been rejected by us in the last 12 months. We may accept a further application within a 12-month period from universities if the application is from a different department and addresses different subject matter.
- From organisations whose accounts are in serious financial deficit.
- Where organisations have significant unrestricted reserves (including those that are designated). Generally up to nine months' expenditure is normally acceptable. We will make exceptions for some institutions which need to holder larger reserves such as universities and housing associations.

Applications

Applications should be sent to applications@financialfairness.org.uk. The trust has two annual deadlines (in February and June). See the trust's website for a complete overview of the information that must be included in an application or to download a template form.

The trust's website states the following:

> Please read our Funding Guidelines first. If you think your project would be a good fit we'd be happy to talk to you about your idea. In the first instance contact us on 0131 528 4243.

Sources of information

Accounts; annual report; funder's website; guidelines for applicants; OSCR record.

Access Sport CIO

Improving access to sport for young people in disadvantaged communities

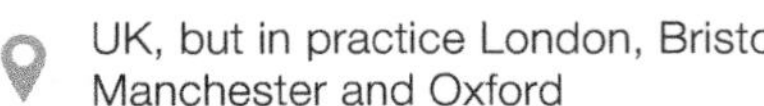
UK, but in practice London, Bristol, Manchester and Oxford

£108,800 (2020/21)

CC number: 1156819

Correspondent: The Trustees, 3 Durham Yard, Teesdale Street, London E2 6QF (tel: 020 7993 9883; email: info@accesssport.co.uk)

Trustees: Martin McPhee; David Ascott; Christine Gibbons; Mandans Pour; John Baker; Nichola Janvier; Mark Burgess; Paul Lee.

 www.accesssport.org.uk

 facebook.com/AccessSport

 @AccessSport

General information

This charity was founded in 2004 and became a CIO in April 2014. The aim of the charity is to improve the health and well-being of children and young people in deprived communities. There is a strong emphasis on supporting projects that help young people with disabilities.

Its website details its aims and activities:

> We believe every child should have access to the developmental and health benefits of sport and every community should have a thriving, inclusive and sustainable sporting offer.
>
> To achieve this:
>
> **We develop community sports clubs**, equipping local people to provide transformational development opportunities for children and young people, irrespective of their background or ability.
>
> **We build, equip and up-skill local sports clubs** and turn them into thriving local facilities, connected into other local partners such as schools, disabled people's organisations and other local charities – all working together to deliver real change and opportunity for local young people.
>
> **We train and support volunteer sports coaches and club leaders** in a range of vital skills such as establishing new sessions to attract more deprived and disabled young people, building personal development pathways for participants towards education or employment and building the financial sustainability of the club so it can grow and serve more local young people for years to come.

Programmes

Support is given through three core programmes: Making Trax Cycling Inclusion Programme (formerly known as BMX Legacy Programme); Social Inclusion Programme; and Ignite Programme. For more information, including contact details for each programme, see the charity's website.

Financial information

Year end	31/03/2021
Income	£1,250,000
Assets	£596,300
Grants to organisations	£108,800

Further financial information

The charity awarded grants totalling £108,800 during the year; however, in previous years it has given over £300,000.

Beneficiaries included: A list of beneficiaries was not available.

Applications

Contact details for each of the projects can be found on the charity's website. General enquiries should be directed to the correspondent.

Sources of information

Accounts; annual report; Charity Commission record; funder's website.

The Access to Justice Foundation

 The provision of legal assistance to people in need

UK

£10.47 million (2020)

CC number: 1126147

Correspondent: The Trustees, PO Box 64162, London WC2A 9AN (tel: 020 7092 3973; email: enquiries@atjf.org.uk)

Trustees: Laurence Harris; Nicola Sawford; Joe Snape; Natalia Rymaszewska; Rebecca Samaras; Andrew Seager; Sarah Stephens; Audrey Haaxman; Maura McGowan; Gavin Mansfield; Simon Davis; Maxcine Akinsowon.

 https://atjf.org.uk

 facebook.com/Access2JusticeF

 @Access2JusticeF

 @accesstojusticefoundation

General information

Established in 2008, the foundation makes grants to support the provision of pro bono legal assistance to people in need.

Grants

In response to the COVID-19 pandemic the foundation established the Community Justice Fund, a joint initiative that gives financial and other support to specialist social welfare legal advice organisations to help them 'cope with the immediate impact of the COVID-19 pandemic and lay the foundations for longer-term renewal', as stated on the foundation's website. Since 2020 the foundation has been making the majority of its grants through this fund.

Financial information

Year end	31/12/2020
Income	£11,600,000
Assets	£979,600
Grants to organisations	£10,470,000
No. of grants	173+

Further financial information

The foundation's income and grant total was higher than usual during the year due to the funds it received/expended to deliver the Community Justice Fund. Included in the grant total is £8.6 million of COVID-19 emergency grants awarded to 173 not-for-profit legal advice organisations.

Beneficiaries included: Shelter (£296,400); Rights of Women (£124,200); Norfolk Community Law Service (£75,000); Civil Liberties Trust (£50,000); Citizens Advice Middlesbrough (£35,000); Wanstead and Woodford Migrant Support (£17,500); Bristol Law Centre (£5,400); Isle of Wight Law Centre (£1,800).

Applications

Visit the foundation's website for the latest information on funding opportunities.

Sources of information

Accounts; annual report; Charity Commission record; funder's website.

Achisomoch Aid Company Ltd

 Orthodox Jewish causes and general charitable purposes

UK and overseas

£35.19 million (2020/21)

CC number: 278387

Correspondent: The Trustees, Enterprise House, 2 The Crest, London NW4 2HN (tel: 020 8731 8988; email: admin@achisomoch.org)

Trustees: Jack Emanuel; Isaac Katz; Michael Hackenbroch; Richard Denton; Anthony Katz.

 www.achisomoch.org

General information

This charity was established in 1979 to advance religion in accordance with the Orthodox Jewish faith and to support general charitable purposes. The charity's 2020/21 annual report states that it provides support to a range of charities that provide benefits such as:

- Provision of basic necessities and financial support to the poor
- Relief of suffering in regard to illness and disabilities
- Jewish education and places of worship for the Jewish community

Financial information

Year end	31/03/2021
Income	£36,100,000
Assets	£11,970,000
Grants to organisations	£35,190,000

Further financial information

During 2020/21, grants were distributed as follows:

Education	£19.9 million
Prevention and relief of poverty	£6.3 million
Advancement of the Jewish religion	£4.24 million
Advancement of health and saving of lives	£2.8 million
Relief of those in need, by reason of youth, age, ill health, disability, financial hardship or other disadvantage	£2.1 million
Other	£376,300
Advancement of amateur sport	£118,900
Community development	£103,800
Arts, culture, heritage or science	£50,000

Only beneficiaries receiving grants of over £100,000 were listed in the accounts. Grants of less than £100,000 totalled £18.5 million.

Beneficiaries included: Hasmonean High School Charitable Trust (£1.2 million); Amud Hatzdokoh Tru (£612,500); Camp Simcha (£328,800); Give It Forward Today (£282,600); London Academy of Jewish Studies (£186,400); Aish Hatorah UK Ltd (£113,700); Nachlat Tzvi Shendor (£102,500).

Applications

Apply in writing to the correspondent.

Sources of information

Accounts; annual report; Charity Commission record; funder's website.

Action Medical Research

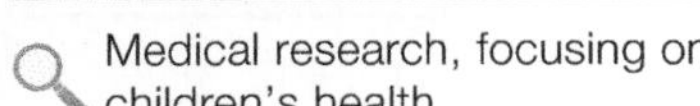
Medical research, focusing on children's health

UK

£1.56 million (2020)

CC number: 208701

Correspondent: The Trustees, Vincent House, 31 North Parade, Horsham, West Sussex RH12 2DP (tel: 01403 210406; email: info@action.org.uk)

Trustees: Esther Alderson; Luke Bordewich; Prof. David Edwards; Richard Wild; Kathy Harvey; Prof. David Rowitch; Richard Stoneham-Buck; Karen Last.

www.action.org.uk

facebook.com/actionmedres

@actionmedres

@actionmedres

General information

The charity was founded in 1952 by Duncan Guthrie, a disability rights campaigner, to fund research into poliomyelitis. Early research funded by the charity helped to develop the first oral polio vaccine which, at the time, eradicated new cases of the disease in the UK.

Research grants

The charity's website states: 'we fund research most likely to make a difference to the lives of sick babies, children and young people.'

Under the umbrella of child health, the charity supports a broad spectrum of research with the objective of preventing disease and disability and alleviating physical disability. Current and former projects funded by the charity include research into premature birth, childhood infections, juvenile arthritis and other rare conditions, cerebral palsy and leukaemia. Note that the charity's emphasis is on clinical research or research at the interface between clinical and basic science. The charity also encourages research into medical engineering i.e. the development of equipment and techniques to improve diagnosis.

Grants are typically for up to £200,000, but joint calls may have a different upper limit. Grants cover project costs such as salaries, consumables and items of dedicated equipment.

The charity also supports individuals by funding research training fellowships.

Financial information

Year end	31/12/2020
Income	£3,600,000
Assets	£6,640,000
Grants to organisations	£1,560,000

Further financial information

In 2020, the charity made grants for medical research totalling £1.56 million, compared to £2.6 million in 2019.

Beneficiaries included: University of Oxford (£250,000); Imperial College London (£222,300); St George's University of London and University College London (£200,000 each); UCL Great Ormond Street Institute of Child Health (£113,800).

Exclusions

According to the charity's website it does not provide:

- Grants towards service provision and audit studies
- Grants purely for higher education (although Research Training Fellows are strongly encouraged to independently register for a PhD)
- Course fees for degrees or subsistence costs
- Grants for medical or dental electives
- Grants for work undertaken outside the UK
- [Grants for indirect] costs such as administrative or other overheads imposed by the university or other institution
- Costs associated with advertising and recruitment of staff
- 'Top up' funding for work supported by other funding bodies
- Costs to attend conferences (current Action Medical Research grant holders may apply separately as the need arises during the grant)
- [Requests for general] appeals from other charities. Applications would normally come directly from research teams and projects need to be passed through our scientific peer review system
- Grants for research into complementary/alternative medicine
- Grants on how best to train clinical staff
- Grants on social research, family relationships or socioeconomic research
- Grants for very basic research with little likelihood of clinical impact within the short to medium term

Applicants based in core funded units can apply but need to demonstrate added value.

Applications

Details of open grant programmes, closing dates and application processes can be found on the website. Typically, applicants are expected to complete an outline proposal which will be reviewed before a full application can be made.

Sources of information

Accounts; annual report; Charity Commission record; funder's website.

The Adint Charitable Trust

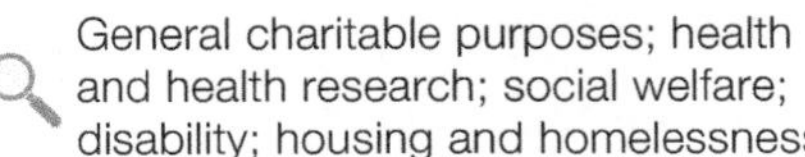
General charitable purposes; health and health research; social welfare; disability; housing and homelessness

UK

£510,000 (2020/21)

CC number: 265290

Correspondent: The Trustees, c/o Hazlewoods, Windsor House, Bayshill Road, Cheltenham GL50 3AT (email: adintct@btinternet.com)

Trustees: Anthony Edwards; Douglas Oram; Brian Pate; Claire Edwards.

General information

This trust was established in 1973 and makes grants to UK-registered charities for general charitable purposes. Grants typically range from £5,000 to £10,000 and are given to a range charities working in the fields of health, social welfare and disability.

Financial information

Year end	05/04/2021
Income	£142,600
Assets	£9,810,000
Grants to organisations	£510,000

Beneficiaries included: Salvation Army and St Giles Trust (£15,000 each); Blind in Business and Crisis UK (£10,000 each); Bag Books and Dementia UK (£5,000 each); Green Fold School – Bolton (£2,500).

Exclusions

The trust can only support UK-registered charities.

Applications

Apply in writing to the correspondent including full details of the charity for which the funding is requested. No acknowledgements are made to unsuccessful applicants.

Sources of information

Accounts; annual report; Charity Commission record.

The AIM Foundation

Nutrition for health and well-being; children and young people; the environment

UK

£773,300 (2019/20)

CC number: 263294

Correspondent: The Trustees, c/o Albert Goodman LLP, Goodwood House, Blackbrook Park Avenue, Taunton, Somerset TA1 2PX (tel: 01823 286096; email: collaborate@theaimfoundation.org.uk)

Trustees: Philippa Bailey; Caroline Marks; Nicholas Marks; Angela Marks; Joanna Precious.

https://theaimfoundation.org.uk

General information

Set up in 1971 as the Ian Roy Marks Charitable Trust, this charity changed its name to the AIM Foundation in 1993. The foundation stresses that its grant-making policy is highly proactive in seeking out potential partners.

Areas of work

The following information has been taken from the foundation's 2019/20 annual report:

> Our overall aim is to support work to promote wellbeing by funding charitable organisations working to address today's needs and to prevent problems arising. In order to achieve this overall goal, AIM has a strategy to identify and fund three strands of work (Research and Policy, Prevention and Direct Delivery of Support) across our current three strategic areas:
>
> **Nutrition for Health and Wellbeing** – to increase the understanding of the importance of nutrition and life-style for health and wellbeing.
>
> **Young People** – to improve the life chances of young people, especially around the transition from school to employment, and their emotional and mental wellbeing.
>
> **Early Years** – to improve the emotional and social development of young children from vulnerable families by giving them the best start, through developing attuned parent infant relationships
>
> During the year the Trustees, together with the wider members of the Family, began planning towards adding a further strategic area:
>
> **Environment** – Due to the decision to respond to the Covid 19 pandemic, and the challenges it presented to our grantee organisations, by awarding them extra grants, our first grant commitments were postponed until 2021.

Financial information

Year end	31/08/2020
Income	£8,470,000
Assets	£11,310,000
Grants to organisations	£773,300
No. of grants	34

Beneficiaries included: Impetus-PEF (£50,000); Institute of Health Visiting (£40,000); Nutritank (£35,000); The Wave Trust (£25,000); College of Medicine (£10,000); Chelmsford Chess (£5,000); Breast Cancer Care and British Red Cross (£1,000 each).

Applications

The foundation proactively seeks out potential partners and does not accept unsolicited applications.

Sources of information

Accounts; annual report; Charity Commission record; funder's website.

The Aimwell Charitable Trust

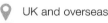

Education; care of young people, older people or those who have a disability or illness; community development and services; Jewish causes

UK and overseas

£975,000 (2020/21)

CC number: 1039415

Correspondent: Geoffrey Jayson, Trustee, c/o Baystone Associates, 3rd Floor, 52 Conduit Street, London W1S 2YX (tel: 020 7317 8980; email: geoffrey@jaysonconsulting.co.uk)

Trustees: Isaac Kaye; Steven Kaye; Geoffrey Jayson; Warren Roiter; Craig Cowan.

General information

The Aimwell Charitable Trust was set up by Isaac and Myrna Kaye to benefit a variety of organisations and projects. The trust's 2020/21 annual report states it makes grants for the following:

- The furtherance of education
- The care of the young, sick, disabled and elderly
- The furtherance of understanding amongst communities
- Providing community protection and other services

The charity achieves these aims by:

> contributing to educational establishments which provide education to young people and research opportunities; and making grants to various charitable organisations which deliver the care and other objectives listed above.

Financial information

Year end	31/03/2021
Income	£115,200
Assets	£14,970,000
Grants to organisations	£975,000

Further financial information

Only grants of over £50,000 are included in the list of beneficiaries.

Beneficiaries included: British Friends of the Hebrew University (£229,400); Portland Trust (£157,000); Jewish Care (£50,000).

Applications

Apply in writing to the correspondent.

Sources of information

Accounts; annual report; Charity Commission record.

AKO Foundation

Education; the arts; the environment

UK and overseas, including Germany, Denmark, Norway, Sri Lanka, USA and Africa

£23.29 million (2020)

CC number: 1151815

Correspondent: The Trustees, c/o Ako Capital LLP, 61 Conduit Street, London W1S 2GB (tel: 020 7070 2400; email: enquiries@akofoundation.org)

Trustees: David Woodburn; Henrik Syse; Sally Procopis.

www.akofoundation.org

General information

The foundation was established in 2013 by Nicolai Tangen, CEO and founder of AKO Capital LLP. The foundation receives donations from the founder and a share of profit from the company.

The foundation awards grants to charities for the following causes:

- Education
- The arts
- Climate change

Financial information

Year end	31/12/2020
Income	£439,770,000
Assets	£650,640,000
Grants to organisations	£23,290,000

Beneficiaries included: AKO Kunststiftelse (£5.9 million); Client Earth and University of the Arts (£1.5 million each); PeopleUKnow (£40,000); Little Sun Foundation (£30,000); The Courtauld Institute (£3,000).

Applications

Unsolicited applications are not accepted. The foundation's website states:

> The Foundation adopts a proactive approach to grant-making; accordingly, it does not seek applications for grants, and does not make grants in response to unsolicited applications.

Sources of information

Accounts; annual report; Charity Commission record; funder's website.

The Alborada Trust

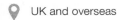

Medical and veterinary causes; medical research; education; animal welfare; disaster relief; refugees; conservation

UK and overseas

£4.77 million (2020)

CC number: 1091660

Correspondent: The Trustees, Lanwades Stud, Moulton, Newmarket, Suffolk CB8 8QS

Trustees: Roland Lerner; Capt. James Nicholson; Eva Rausing; Robert Goff; Larry Pillard.

 www.alboradatrust.com

General information

The Alborada Trust was established in October 2001 and is named after the racehorse Alborada.

The trust's website states:

> The trustees' primary aims are the funding of medical and veterinary research and education, welfare of animals and help with refugees and in providing relief to disaster areas worldwide. We work on these aims primarily as partners with leading national and international charities such as ActionAid, Alzheimer's Research UK, The Brooke and Médecins Sans Frontières. Substantial grants are made for education through Cambridge University and for veterinary research through various veterinary colleges.
>
> So, you must bear in mind the trustees priorities which, in more detail and in order of importance, are:
>
> In veterinary research, One Health and Zoonosis, Virology and the thoroughbred racehorse and its breeding. Education, with emphasis on medical/veterinary matters and in the relief of poverty. Medical research with particular emphasis on dementia and cancer. Horse welfare particularly in relation to working equines. Refugee aid and disaster relief. Conservation and wildlife.

The trust prefers to support revenue rather than capital projects.

Financial information

Year end	31/12/2020
Income	£6,330,000
Assets	£1,390,000
Grants to organisations	£4,770,000

Further financial information

According to the trust's website, grants were broken down as follows:

Medical research	32%
Education	20%
COVID-19	11%
Disaster relief	10%
Animal health	6%
Refugee aid	6%
Human health	5%
Horse racing charities	4%
Veterinary research	4%
Conservation	2%

Beneficiaries included: University of Cambridge (£378,600); Addenbrookes Charitable Trust (£200,000); Médecins Sans Frontières (£165,100); Anne Robson Trust (£30,000); World Horse Welfare (£25,000); Brooke Hospital for Animals (£1,800).

Exclusions

According to its website, the trust does not normally support charities that receive substantial government aid, those involved in pet welfare, the arts and culture, marriage guidance, children's welfare charities (in the UK), zoos and charities involved in political or media lobbying.

Applications

Application forms can be downloaded from the trust's website.

Sources of information

Accounts; annual report; Charity Commission record; funder's website.

The Alchemy Foundation

The Alchemist Scheme (funding the costs of fundraisers assigned to other charities to assist with their fundraising efforts); water projects in financially developing countries; disability; social welfare; families; homelessness; personal reform; penal reform; medical research and aid; individual enterprise; respite for carers

UK and overseas

£622,800 (2020/21)

CC number: 292500

Correspondent: The Trustees, Trevereux Manor, Trevereux Hill, Limpsfield Chart, Oxted, Surrey RH8 0TL

Trustees: Alexander Armitage; Antoun Elias; Andrew Murison; Sir Richard Stilgoe; Dr Jemima Stilgoe; Lady Annabel Stilgoe; Jack Stilgoe; Holly Stilgoe; Joseph Stilgoe; Rufus Stilgoe; Caroline Pedley.

General information

The charity was established as The Starlight Foundation on 14 August 1985 and is funded from the British songwriter and musician Sir Richard Stilgoe's royalties from American productions of *Starlight Express* and *The Phantom of the Opera*. The name was changed to The Alchemy Foundation in 1987. The foundation is connected to and shares trustees with The Orpheus Centre Trust, with which it co-operates in pursuit of its charitable objectives.

The 2020/21 annual report states that the foundation's work focuses on:

- The Alchemist Scheme (funding the costs of fundraisers assigned to other charities to assist with their fundraising efforts)
- Water projects in the financially developing countries
- Disability (particularly mobility, access, helplines and communications)
- Social welfare (inner city community projects, disaffected youth, family mediation, homelessness)
- Personal reform
- Penal reform (work with prisoners, especially young prisoners and their families)
- Medical research and aid (especially in the areas of blindness and disfigurement)
- Individual enterprise (by helping Raleigh International, Project Trust and similar organisations to give opportunities to young people according to need)
- Respite for carers

Financial information

Year end	05/04/2021
Income	£47,700
Assets	£1,180,000
Grants to organisations	£622,800

Further financial information

Grants were awarded in the following categories:

Social welfare	£92,600
Disability	£73,400
Other	£51,800
The Alchemist Scheme	£47,300
Penal reform	£32,500
Respite for carers	£5,500
Individuals on behalf of registered charities	£4,800

The foundation's annual report states: 'Over the years, the charity accumulated a larger amount of unrestricted funds than has been required for its average annual spend. The trustees therefore decided to make a substantial one off spenddown of a part of these funds.' The 'spenddown' amounted to £315,000 and is included in the grant total.

Beneficiaries included: A list of beneficiaries was not available.

Applications

Apply in writing to the correspondent.

Sources of information

Accounts; annual report; Charity Commission record.

The Aldama Foundation

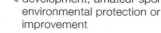

Arts, culture, heritage or science; social welfare; education; health; citizenship and community development; amateur sport; environmental protection or improvement

UK and overseas

£852,100 (2020/21)

CC number: 1126791

Correspondent: The Trustees, 4th Floor, 10 Bruton Street, London W1J 6PX (tel: 020 7907 2100; email: charity@mfs.co.uk)

Trustee: The Dickinson Trust Ltd.

General information

The foundation was established by James and Clare Kirkman in 2008. Grants are made for a range of charitable purposes in the UK and overseas.

Financial information

Year end	05/04/2021
Income	£54,700
Assets	£5,530,000
Grants to organisations	£852,100

Further financial information

Grants were broken down as follows:

Health and saving lives	£415,000
Relief in need	£236,600
Arts, culture, heritage and science	£136,100
Prevention or relief of poverty	£44,000
Citizenship and community development	£20,000
Other charitable purposes	£250
Education	£120

Beneficiaries included: FareShare (£80,000); National Gallery (£25,000); World Monuments Fund (£10,000); AIDS Ark (£5,000); Garden Museum (£700).

Applications

Apply in writing to the correspondent.

Sources of information

Accounts; annual report; Charity Commission record.

Beryl Alexander Charity

Mental heath

England

£380,900 (2020)

CC number: 1179895

Correspondent: The Trustees, 4 London Road, Stanmore, HA7 4NZ (tel: 020 8958 8970)

Trustees: Joshua Alton; Jeremy Alton; Ruby Alton; Dr Laurence Lions.

General information

The charity was registered in 2018 and supports organisations helping people with mental health problems.

Grant-making policy

The charity's 2020 annual accounts state:

> The criteria used for awarding grants are:
> - The applicant charity's area of benefit will be in the UK and may be but need not be UK wide
> - The applicant charity will be registered with the Charity Commission of England and Wales
> - The applicant charity will be well established, with a strong reputation in its field, and a proven track record on delivering projects
> - The proposed project will be innovative and have been running for less than 5 years

Financial information

Year end	31/12/2020
Income	£34,100
Assets	£2,390,000
Grants to organisations	£380,900

Beneficiaries included: Great Ormond Street Hospital Charity (£263,000); University of Cambridge (£102,800); Refugee Rights Europe (£15,000).

Applications

Apply in writing to the correspondent.

Sources of information

Accounts; annual report; Charity Commission record.

The Allen & Overy Foundation

Disaster relief; access to justice; access to education, employment and training

London; UK; Worldwide

£1.49 million (2020/21)

CC number: 1153738

Correspondent: The Trustees, One Bishops Square, London E1 6AD (tel: 020 3088 0000; email: allenoveryfoundation@allenovery.com)

Trustees: Mark Mansell; Andrew Wedderburn-Day; Philip Mansfield; Brendan Hannigan; Angela Clist; Joanna Page; Hilde van der Bann; Mary Johnston; Franz Ranero.

www.allenovery.com/en-gb/global/about_us/corporate_responsibility/charitable_giving

General information

Allen & Overy is a large international law firm with its headquarters in London. Its corporate foundation is funded by contributions from all Allen & Overy partners around the world. The core themes are:

- Access to justice
- Access to employment, education and training

Grant programmes

The following information about the two grant programmes has been taken from the foundation's website:

Local Charitable Giving

> One example of our local charitable funds is the Allen & Overy Foundation's work in London. The Foundation, administered by the London Grants Committee, makes donations to charities that meet one or more of the following criteria:
> - Charities which work to promote access to justice in the UK.
> - Charities which support and develop projects focusing on issues of education, employment and training, based in or benefiting those in Tower Hamlets or Hackney.
> - Charities to which AandO volunteers have made a significant contribution, by participating in their activities or providing pro bono and volunteering support.

The typical grant size is between £5,000 and £10,000.

Global Grants Programme

> The Foundation is funded by contributions from AandO partners worldwide and, through the Global Grants Programme, supports:
> - Our global charity partnership
> - Disaster relief efforts
> - Charities that address our core themes of access to justice, education and employment

Three charities are awarded grants of approximately £50,000 for one, two, or three years. Charities may use 20% of the grant for core funding.

The staff at Allen and Ovary also select a global charity partner, which they fundraise for over a period of two years.

Financial information

Year end	30/04/2021
Income	£1,620,000
Assets	£813,700
Grants to organisations	£1,490,000

Beneficiaries included: Hope and Homes for Children (£373,800); Charities Aid Foundation (£125,700); UN High Commissioner for Refugees (£75,000); The Redress Trust (£50,000); Law Centres Network (£25,000); Protect (£10,000); Prisoners' Advice Service (£5,000).

Applications

Application guidelines and up-to-date information on application submission dates for each grants programme are available on the foundation's website.

Sources of information

Accounts; annual report; Charity Commission record; funder's website.

D. C. R. Allen Charitable Trust

General charitable purposes, especially disadvantaged young people

UK

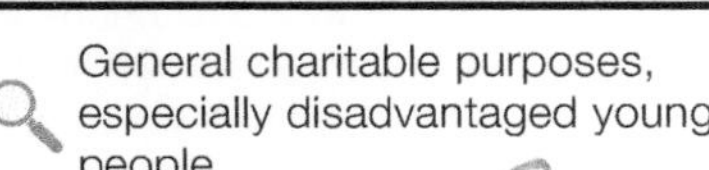

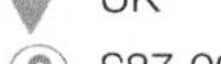

£87,000 (2020/21)

CC number: 277293

Correspondent: Julie Frusher, Trustee, Edgcote House, Edgcote, Banbury, Oxfordshire OX17 1AG (tel: 01295 660077; email: julie.frusher@edgecote.com)

Trustees: Julie Frusher; Tristram Allen; Colin Allen.

General information

This trust awards grants to a wide range of charitable organisations and purposes but is particularly interested in supporting charities, organisations or projects which help disadvantaged young people. Projects aiming to help young people progress towards a more fulfiling lifestyle are of special interest.

Grant-making policy

Grants can be made to fund capital expenditure as well as operational expenses. Small and medium-sized charities are favoured and well-established nationally known charities are less likely to be considered. Grants are typically £1,000 to £5,000, but larger grants may be considered, particularly in respect of specific or innovative capital projects. A high proportion of grants are made to new applicants and such applications continue to be encouraged.

Financial information

Year end	05/04/2021
Income	£121,500
Assets	£5,900,000
Grants to organisations	£87,000
No. of grants	12

Further financial information

During 2020/21, grants totalled £87,000; however, in previous years the trust has awarded grants totalling over £250,000. Grants were distributed as follows in 2020/21: youth projects (£32,000); disability (£30,000); education (£25,000).

Beneficiaries included: A list of beneficiaries was not available. Previous beneficiaries include: Centrepoint and NORPIP (£25,000 each); Designability (£20,000); Greenham Community Trust and Operation New World (£10,000 each); Bright Ideas Trust (£5,000); Young Asian Voices (£2,000); Great Ormond Street Hospital Charity (£1,000); St Leonard's Church – Aston-le-Walls (£500).

Exclusions

Our previous research suggests that the trust does not make grants for the following: individuals, funding of services usually provided by statutory sources, causes outside the UK, evangelical or worship activities, animal welfare, medical research, heritage conservation/preservation, the arts or collections and performing arts.

Applications

Applications should be made by email. According to our previous research, applications should include a statement of accounts, any supporting information and an official charity number. The trustees meet regularly throughout the year to consider applications.

It is not possible for the trustees to respond to unsuccessful applicants, so if no response has been received within eight weeks of the application date, then applicants may assume that they have not been successful.

Sources of information

Accounts; annual report; Charity Commission record; information previously provided by the funder.

Alzheimer's Research UK

Research into cause, diagnosis/detection, prevention and treatment of Alzheimer's disease and other dementias

UK

£17.3 million (2020/21)

CC number: 1077089

Correspondent: The Trustees, 3 Riverside, Granta Park, Cambridge CB21 6AD (tel: 0300 111 5333; email: enquiries@alzheimersresearchuk.org)

Trustees: Shirley Cramer; Rupert Evenett; Prof. Rob Howard; David Mayhew; Michael Cooper; Nicholas Antill; Christopher Carter; Caroline van den Brul; Giles Dennison; Dr Ruth McKernan.

 www.alzheimersresearchuk.org

 facebook.com/AlzheimersResearchUK

 @ARUKnews

 @alzheimersresearchuk

General information

Alzheimer's Research UK funds biomedical research in order to understand the causes of dementia and to improve diagnosis, prevention and treatment.

The charity's mission is to support research that will improve the lives of people living with dementia now and in years to come. According to its website, the charity aims to achieve this objective by focusing on the following four goals:

- Understand the diseases that cause dementia
- Diagnose people earlier and more accurately
- Reduce risk, backed by the latest evidence
- Treat dementia effectively

Inspire Fund

The Inspire Fund is open to individuals, organisations and communities with the ideas, passion and ability to realise innovative public engagement projects on the topic of dementia.

The charity is offering grants of up to £25,000 to support public engagement projects that meet one or more of the following criteria:

- Engage with under-served audiences on the topic of dementia, including minority ethnic communities, marginalised or socioeconomically disadvantaged people
- Build knowledge and engage the public with the topic of brain health

- Engage and create a dialogue with people about the progress being made in dementia research

It has three funding tiers:

- Bronze (up to £5,000)
- Silver (up to £15,000)
- Gold (up to £25,000)

Financial information

Year end	31/03/2021
Income	£39,240,000
Assets	£22,290,000
Grants to organisations	£17,330,000

Beneficiaries included: University of Oxford (£3.4 million); University of Cambridge (£2.2 million); UK Dementia Research Institute Ltd (£2 million); Newcastle University (£721,500); The Alan Turing Institute (£495,000); Imperial College London (£153,000); The Florey Institute of Neuroscience and Mental Health (£4,900).

Exclusions

The charity does not accept applications from individuals.

Applications

Full details of all available grant schemes including deadlines, eligibility criteria and application procedures are available on the charity's website.

Sources of information

Accounts; annual report; Charity Commission record; funder's website.

Alzheimer's Society

Research into dementia

UK

£5.42 million (2020/21)

CC number: 296645

Correspondent: Research Team, 43–44 Crutched Friars, London EC3N 2AE (tel: 020 7423 5136; email: grantenquiries@alzheimers.org.uk)

Trustees: Caroline Fawcett; Alison Harrison; Manish Shah; Andrew Lynch; Stephen Hill; Sarah Weir; Prof. McKenna; Duncan Jones.

 www.alzheimer's.org.uk

 facebook.com/alzheimerssocietyuk

 @alzheimerssoc

 @alzheimerssoc

General information

The Alzheimer's Society supports people in England, Wales and Northern Ireland affected by any form of dementia, as well as investing in research into dementia and campaigning to improve understanding and influence policy.

Research funding

The charity funds research across all areas of dementia. Its website states:

> Alzheimer's Society will be prioritising research with a high relevance to dementia in people, and clear routes to potential benefit for people affected by the condition.
>
> We fund research in to all forms of dementia, including studies that address pre-symptomatic or 'at risk' stages of the disease.
>
> Researchers applying to our biomedical funding stream using model systems should be able to demonstrate the relevance of these systems to human disease.
>
> The scope of research to be considered under this funding stream includes:
>
> - **Preclinical, translational and clinical research** into the causes of any form of dementia and associated symptoms.
> - Research on **post-mortem brain tissue**, including those that have been collected from the Brains for Research programme.
> - Discovery and validation of **biomarkers** (including fluid, neuroimaging, cognitive and other less established modalities) in research and clinic settings to be utilised in diagnosis or monitoring of disease progression.
> - **Neuropsychology**
> - Medical approaches to **symptom management**
> - **Clinical observational and interventional studies**, including clinical trials.

The charity also provides career development grants which include studentships, fellowships, bursaries and partnerships.

Financial information

Year end	31/03/2021
Income	£111,120,000
Assets	£66,710,000
Grants to organisations	£5,420,000

Beneficiaries included: University College London (£1.19 million); Dementia Research Institute (£1 million); University of Edinburgh (£523,000); University of the West of Scotland (£257,000); University of Stirling (£85,000); Brighton and Sussex Medical School (£75,000); University of Portsmouth (£5,000).

Exclusions

Refer to the website for exclusions from individual funding schemes.

Applications

For information on how to apply to one of Alzheimer's Society's current grant schemes, refer to the website. Funding calls are advertised on the website and applications should be submitted online.

Sources of information

Accounts; annual report; Charity Commission record; funder's website.

Amabrill Ltd

Orthodox Jewish religion, education and social welfare

 UK and overseas

£3.35 million (2020/21)

CC number: 1078968

Correspondent: The Trustees, 1 Golders Manor Drive, London NW11 9HU (tel: 020 8455 6785; email: mail@venittandgreaves.com)

Trustees: Israel Grossnass; Frances Lerner; Mr C. Lerner; Irving Lerner

General information

The principal activity of this charity is the advancement of education and religious practice in accordance with the teachings of the Orthodox Jewish faith. The charity also supports the relief of poverty among people of the Jewish faith.

The charity's annual report for 2020/21 explains that:

> Grants are made both for capital purposes, – which can include buildings, equipment and educational material – and towards the general running costs of the grantee institution. Other grants are made for the relief of poverty and these are only made after appropriate certification has been seen. (An independent organisation has been set up in North West London to verify the identity and means of Orthodox Jewish persons for this purpose).

Financial information

Year end	28/02/2021
Income	£3,300,000
Assets	£26,300,000
Grants to organisations	£3,350,000

Further financial information

Grants awarded in 2020/21 were broken down as follows: education (£1.43 million); relief of poverty (£1.31 million); the advancement of the Jewish faith (£613,900). Only beneficiaries of grants of £50,000 and above were listed in the accounts. Grants of under £50,000 totalled £1.49 million.

Beneficiaries included: Amud Hatzdokoh Trust (£434,700); Kahal Chasidim Bobov (£231,200); Achisomoch Aid Company Ltd (£225,400); Beis Hillel Trust (£116,000); The Ruzin Sadagora Trust (£101,000); Friends of Yeshivas Torah Ohr (£60,000).

Applications

Apply in writing to the correspondent. The charity's 2020/21 annual report explains: 'Appeal letters are received from, and personal visits made by representatives of Jewish charitable, religious and educational institutions. These requests are then considered by the trustees and grants are made in accordance with the trustees decisions.'

Sources of information

Accounts; annual report; Charity Commission record.

Viscount Amory's Charitable Trust

Education; religion; general charitable purposes

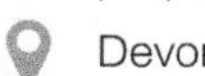
Devon

£350,800 (2020/21)

CC number: 204958

Correspondent: Mrs S. Curtis, The Island, Lowman Green, Tiverton, Devon EX16 4LA (tel: 01884 242200; email: office@vact.org.uk)

Trustees: Sir Ian Amory; Catherine Cavender.

www.vact.org.uk

General information

The trust was established in 1962 with the aim of supporting people in Devon in the areas of education, religion and general charitable purposes. Applicants and activities must be based in Devon.

Financial information

Year end	05/04/2021
Income	£381,400
Assets	£14,040,000
Grants to organisations	£350,800
No. of grants	171

Further financial information

Grants were distributed as follows:

Education	85	£171,200
Social and environmental	44	£149,600
Religion	18	£14,800
Health	14	£8,900
Relief of poverty	10	£6,300

Beneficiaries included: Rona Sailing Project (£92,000); Exeter Cathedral School (£41,000); Tiverton Museum of Mid Devon Life (£27,000); Cheltenham College (£7,800).

Exclusions

The website states that the trust will not support the following:

- Applications from individuals for grants for the relief of poverty.
- Applications for grants or short term loans for individuals' immediate needs or wants.

Applications

The trust has no formal application form, the website states that applications should be made by letter and must include the following information:

- Your address
- Your e-mail address, if available. (We may reply by e-mail)
- General background information about your appeal
- The nature of the sponsoring or associated organisation
- The total amount you are looking to raise
- How much has been raised to date
- How you propose raising any shortfall
- Any further information you feel would be relevant for the attention of the Trustees

Applications should be sent by post, not email, to the correspondent's address. The trustees aim to meet each month to consider applications.

Sources of information

Accounts; annual report; Charity Commission record; funder's website.

The Ampersand Foundation

Visual arts projects including exhibitions, acquisitions and artists' commissions

UK

£371,300 (2020/21)

CC number: 1167018

Correspondent: The Trustees, Third floor, 21 Conduit Street, London W1S 2XP (tel: 01429 234414; email: info@theampersandfoundation.com)

Trustees: John Kirkland; Simon Conway; Thiago Carvalho; Alastair Sooke; Victoria Siddall.

www.theampersand foundation.com

General information

The foundation was established in 2011 by businessman, collector and philanthropist Jack Kirkland to support visual art projects in the UK, including grants to cover exhibition and acquistion costs, and artists' commissions.

Financial information

Year end	31/03/2021
Income	£431,700
Assets	£4,610,000
Grants to organisations	£371,300
No. of grants	15

Beneficiaries included: Graves Gallery (£99,000); Manchester Art Gallery (£37,000); Nottingham Contemporary (£25,000); Smart History (£20,900); Liverpool Biennial (£15,000); Wicksworth Art Festival (£5,000); University of Oxford (£2,000).

Applications

Apply in writing to the correspondent. Applications should include:

- A brief description of the organisation's purpose and objectives
- The organisation's charity number if applicable
- The details of the project
- The amount being requested
- How the organisation or project and the public would benefit from the foundation's support

See the foundation's website for up-to-date application deadlines.

Sources of information

Accounts; annual report; Charity Commission record; funder's website.

Andrews Charitable Trust

Housing; welfare; Christian community projects

Bristol; South Gloucester; Bath and North East Somerset; Gloucestershire; Oxfordshire; London; Surrey; West Sussex; Essex; Buckinghamshire; Hertfordshire; East Sussex

£296,900 (2020)

CC number: 1174706

Correspondent: The Trustees, The Clockhouse, Bath Hill, Keynsham, Bristol BS31 1HL (tel: 0117 946 1834; email: info@andrewscharitabletrust.org.uk)

Trustees: Alastair Page; Alison Kelly; Ami Davis; David Westgate; Elizabeth Hughes; Nicholas Wright; Paul Heal; Ruth Knagg; Helen Battrick; Alexandra McDonald; Paul Bumford; Carl Tomlin; Nathan Moore; Brett Ford.

www.andrewscharitabletrust.org.uk

General information

Established in 1965, the trust is funded by dividends from Andrews and Partners, a group of companies with activities including estate agents, letting agents, property management and financial services.

According to the trust's 2020 annual report, the objects of the charity are:

- the advancement of the Christian religion including the declaration of eternal life; and
- the relief of sickness, poverty and distress in any part of the world as an expression of Christian love.

Funding

The trust has three funding programmes, details of which have been taken from the trust's website.

Christian Community grants

Grants of £2,000 are given to innovative community projects which offer practical help to others as an expression of Christian compassion beyond the Church. Projects must support disadvantaged or marginalised people (of all faiths and none) in the community.

Grants of up to £800 are given for the purchase of Christian books at times of need. Grants are given to libraries, schools, prisons, churches or anywhere a book can be borrowed.

Establish programme

The trust's website states that '[Establish] combines the resources and charity support skills of ACT with the professional expertise of Andrews Property Group in a unique collaboration to support young people who have been through the care system.' Launched in 2016, the aim of the programme is to purchase one house a year for the next 50 years across the area covered by the Andrews branch network. By partnering with local youth housing organisations, the trust makes good quality accommodation and continued personal support available to young people.

Housing-related poverty

The trust focuses on tackling housing-related poverty by funding early-stage ventures that increase the supply of safe, affordable housing and respond to the needs of people in housing poverty. It also supports ideas that bridge the gap between emergency shelter and permanent housing for communities after emergencies.

Financial information

Year end	31/12/2020
Income	£22,980,000
Assets	£17,520,000
Grants to organisations	£296,900

Further financial information

Grants were broken down as follows:

Relief of poverty	£142,600
Christian projects	£72,000
Carers	£45,300
Establish – young people	£37,000

Beneficiaries included: Lighthouse (£92,000); Cinnamon Network (£70,000); Carers Worldwide (£45,300); The Archbishop of Canterbury's Council (£20,500); 1625 Independent People (£17,000); Christian Funders Forum (£2,000).

Applications

The trust only accepts applications for its Christian Community Grants programme via The Cinnamon Network (for innovative community projects) and Speaking Volumes (for the purchase of books). Applications can be made via these organisations' websites. Although applications are not accepted for the trust's other programmes, the trust does welcome recommendations for partnerships from those who work in the sector.

Sources of information

Accounts; annual report; Charity Commission record; funder's website.

Anglo American Foundation

Accountability and policy advocacy; health and well-being; education; livelihoods; the environment and biodiversity

UK; Australia; Botswana; Brazil; Canada; Chile; Colombia; Ecuador; Ireland; Namibia; Peru; Sierra Leone; Singapore; South Africa; Zimbabwe

£4.36 million (2020)

CC number: 1111719

Correspondent: The Trustees, 17 Charterhouse Street, London EC1N 6RA (tel: 020 7968 8888; email: aagf@angloamerican.com)

Trustees: Jonathan Samuel; Duncan Wanblad; Anik Michaud-Ahmed; Norman Mbazima; Yvonne Mfolo.

www.angloamericangroup foundation.org

General information

The foundation was established in 2005 by Anglo American plc, a multinational mining company. The foundation's website states that:

> The Foundation supports programmes aligned with the Group's Sustainable Mining Plan, focusing on the areas of accountability and policy advocacy, health and well-being, education, livelihoods and biodiversity. Our priorities are informed by the UN's Sustainable Development Goals and we aim to make progress against them in the countries we operate in.

The foundation receives donations from Anglo American and supports development initiatives in the areas where the company has operations, projects or representative offices, these include: UK, Australia, Botswana, Brazil, Canada, Chile, China, Colombia, Peru and Zimbabwe. In 2020 grants were also awarded in Ecuador, Germany, Ireland, Namibia, Singapore and Sierra Leone.

The foundation's 2020 accounts provides the following information on its giving structure:

> The Foundation seeks to develop continuing relationships with a select number of charitable organisations which contribute to its identified funding priorities and therefore mostly does not accept unsolicited funding applications. Through internal and external engagement, the Foundation identifies funding opportunities and develops joint solutions to foster sustainable socio-economic development (SED) in host communities. Resources are also allocated by way of matching funds raised for charities by employees who work in the Anglo American London office and through the employee volunteering programme Ambassadors for Good.

Financial information

Year end	31/12/2020
Income	£4,420,000
Assets	£417,500
Grants to organisations	£4,360,000

Further financial information

Grants were broken down as follows:

Education and training	£1.67 million
Community development	£1.64 million
Health and welfare	£557,400
Employee matched funding	£486,200
Other social investments	£10,100

We were unable to determine the portion of grants awarded in the UK. Only a selection of larger grants were available to view in the 2020 accounts.

Beneficiaries included: Engineers Without Borders UK (£700,000); Pyxera Global (£534,700); Institute for Human Rights and Business (£450,000); CARE International (£101,100);

Applications

The foundation does not accept unsolicited applications.

Sources of information

Accounts; annual report; Charity Commission record; funder's website.

Anguish's Educational Foundation

The education of children and young people (under 25 years old)

Norwich and the parishes of Costessey, Hellesdon, Catton, Sprowston, Thorpe-next-Norwich and Corpusty

£554,400 (2020/21)

CC number: 311288

Correspondent: David Hynes, c/o Norwich Charitable Trusts, 1 Woolgate Court, St Benedicts Street, Norwich, Norfolk NR2 4AP (tel: 01603 621023; email: david.hynes@norwichcharitabletrusts.org.uk)

Trustees: David Fullman; Jeanne Southgate; Michael Flynn; Cllr Karen Davis; Boyd Taylor; Philip Davies; John Garside; Prof. Eneida Mioshi; Jacqueline Hanlon; Laura McCartney-Gray; Adam Giles; Sally Button; Vivien Thomas; Ashley Ford-McAllister.

www.anguishseducational foundation.org.uk

General information

The foundation is named after Thomas Anguish, who lived between 1536 and 1617 and was a merchant of the City of Norwich and its Mayor. He left money in his will to set up the foundation in 1611. The foundation is now administered alongside Norwich Consolidated Charities, the Norwich

Town Close Estate Charity and the Marion Road Centre Trust. Collectively, they are known as the Norwich Charitable Trusts.

Grants are predominantly available for individuals in the beneficial area, to cover the costs of school uniforms, trips, extra curricular activities and school or university fees. Grants are also available for local organisations working with disadvantaged children in order to improve their educational attainment.

The 2020/21 annual report states that during the year, grants were awarded for or to the following:

- The provision of, and enablement of access to, drama, music, and circus opportunities (creative, participatory and as audience members) for children and young people
- The provision of musical instrument tuition and ensemble/orchestral participation for young people, including for those with additional needs
- Support for children and young people who are refugees, asylum seekers and isolated migrants
- Enabling volunteers to provide support to young carers
- A support hub at a primary school providing support for the most disadvantaged pupils and their parents and families
- Online creative activities for young children with their parents/carers
- School-based therapeutic work, staff training and equipment to support pupils' post-lockdown return to school
- Advice, support and networking to prevent destitution/unemployment and to enable secure and satisfying lives for young people
- The attendance at Forest School of 12, 14-year-old boys facing challenging life situations and the provision of specialist in-school equipment
- The pilot project of a resilience-building online game and board game
- Laptop/tablet computers for school pupils (for home learning during lockdown)
- An education programme for small groups of school and college pupils supporting them with the impact of COVID-19
- The development and provision of one-to-one and group sessions for young people struggling with substance/drug/ alcohol abuse and/or mental health issues

Financial information

Year end	31/03/2021
Income	£945,200
Assets	£25,940,000
Grants to organisations	£554,400
No. of grants	24

Beneficiaries included: Mancroft Advice Project (£121,100); Norca 8 Sistema Norwich (£50,000); The Garage Trust (£30,000); GRB AS UR (£15,000); Norwich International Youth Project (£12,500); Musical Keys (£7,100); And Action Projects (£2,900).

Applications

Apply in writing to the correspondent. There is no formal application form.

Sources of information

Accounts; annual report; Charity Commission record; funder's website.

The Annandale Charitable Trust

General charitable purposes

UK

£0 (2020/21)

CC number: 1049193

Correspondent: The Trustees, HSBC Trust Company (UK) Ltd, Forum 1, 2nd Floor, Parkway, Whiteley, Fareham, Hampshire PO15 7PA (tel: 023 8199 9231)

Trustee: HSBC Trust Company (UK) Ltd.

General information

This trust has general charitable purposes and supports a range of UK charities.

Financial information

Year end	05/04/2021
Income	£352,000
Assets	£15,120,000
Grants to organisations	£0

Further financial information

During 2020/21 no grants were awarded; however, in previous years, grants have totalled more than £300,000. The 2020/21 annual report states that the trust aims to continue to provide grants in a similar way to the 'recent past'.

Beneficiaries included: A list of beneficiaries was not available. Previous beneficiaries include: Cornwall Air Ambulance Trust (£10,000); Chestnut Tree House Hospice (£6,700); Abby's Heroes and Activity Club for Children (£3,000 each); Forget Me Not Children's Hospice and Ruby's Fund (£1,600 each).

Applications

Apply in writing to the correspondent.

Sources of information

Accounts; annual report; Charity Commission record.

The Anson Charitable Trust

Arts and culture; medical research and the sciences; social organisations; the environment and ecology

UK, with a preference for Buckinghamshire

£319,700 (2020/21)

CC number: 1111010

Correspondent: The Trustees, The Lilies, High Street, Weedon, Aylesbury, Buckinghamshire HP22 4NS (tel: 01296 640331; email: mail@ ansoncharitabletrust.org.uk)

Trustees: George Anson; Kirsty Anson.

 www.ansoncharitabletrust.org.uk

General information

The trust was established in May 2005 by the Anson Family to support and fund not-for-profit and charitable organisations. The trust is entirely funded by the Anson family. According to its website, the trust's main areas of interest include:

- Arts and culture
- Medical research and science
- Social organisations
- The environment and ecology
- Charities and organisations based in Buckinghamshire

Financial information

Year end	05/04/2021
Income	£405,000
Assets	£169,700
Grants to organisations	£319,700

Beneficiaries included: The Pace Centre (£12,100 in 13 grants); Tate Gallery (£5,000); Royal Hospital for Neuro-disability (£3,000); Thames Valley Air Ambulance (£2,000); Royal Shakespeare Company (£1,500); The Almshouse Association (£1,000); The College of St Barnabas (£50).

Exclusions

Grants will not be awarded to individuals or towards studies.

Applications

Application forms can be downloaded from the trust's website.

Sources of information

Accounts; annual report; Charity Commission record; funder's website.

The Apax Foundation

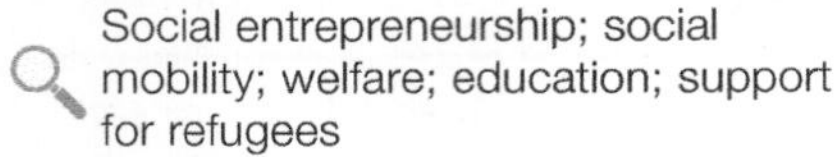

Social entrepreneurship; social mobility; welfare; education; support for refugees

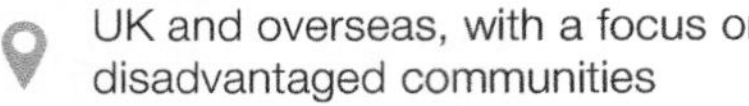

UK and overseas, with a focus on disadvantaged communities

£5.9 million (2020)

CC number: 1112845

Correspondent: Kate Albert, Foundation Manager, 33 Jermyn Street, London SW1Y 6DN (tel: 020 7872 6300; email: foundation@apax.com)

Trustees: Sir Ronald Cohen; Dr Peter Englander; David Marks; Simon Cresswell; Mitch Truwit; Shashank Singh; Rohan Haldea; Jason Wright.

www.apax.com/responsibility/apax-foundation

General information

The Apax Foundation is the corporate charity of Apax Partners LLP and receives a percentage of the firm's profits to distribute to good causes. The foundation focuses its grant-making on charitable organisations and social enterprises which work with under-served communities to support:

- Relief of financial hardship
- Social mobility
- Entrepreneurship
- Education
- Helping refugees into work or entrepreneurship

As well as making grants, the foundation also runs a matched-giving scheme for Apax employees.

Financial information

Year end	31/12/2020
Income	£4,080,000
Assets	£65,080,000
Grants to organisations	£5,900,000

Further financial information

Grants were broken down as follows:

COVID-19 grants	£4.94 million
Education	£272,600
Social enterprise and relief of financial hardship	£270,400
Other charitable purposes	£412,400

A sample of large grants was listed in the 2020 accounts.

Beneficiaries included: Stamford Hospital Foundation (£421,000); The Private Equity Foundation (£255,000); Robin Hood Foundation (£208,900); British Red Cross (£121,500); Street Child (£107,800); Northwestern Memorial Foundation (£90,000).

Applications

Apply in writing to the correspondent.

Sources of information

Accounts; annual report; Charity Commission record; funder's website.

The John Apthorp Charity

Children and young people; older people; social welfare; health; education

Hertfordshire; Bedfordshire; Cambridgeshire

£287,000 (2020)

CC number: 1102472

Correspondent: The Trustees, 29 Newlands Avenue, Radlett, Hertfordshire WD7 8 EJ (email: johnapthorpcharity@hotmail.com)

Trustees: Duncan Apthorp; John Apthorp; Kate Arnold; Dr Christina Apthorp.

www.johnapthorpcharity.org

facebook.com/JohnApthorpCharity

General information

This is the charity of John Apthorp CBE, who founded the frozen food chain Bejam, which he later sold to Iceland, and co-founded Wizard Wine, which became Majestic Wine. The charity was established in 2003 and its objects, as stated on its Charity Commission record, are 'helping the young, the old, the disabled and the general community in Hertfordshire, Bedfordshire and Cambridgeshire'.

Financial information

Year end	31/12/2020
Income	£360,900
Assets	£11,010,000
Grants to organisations	£287,000
No. of grants	23

Beneficiaries included: Kids in Action (£50,000); Dallow Development Trust (£10,000); Aspire (£6,300); Amersham Band (£3,000); Amersham Band (£2,000); Music 24 (£950).

Exclusions

The following will not be considered:

- Projects outside the geographic catchment area
- Charities that have large unrestricted reserves
- Core funding
- Retrospective funding
- Any institution which is not a registered charity
- Any institution which has recently received funding from the charity

Applications

Apply in writing via email. Full details of what should be included in an application can be found on the charity's website.

Sources of information

Accounts; annual report; Charity Commission record, funder's website.

The Annabel Arbib Foundation

General charitable purposes; education; medical causes; health

UK

£455,300 (2020/21)

CC number: 296358

Correspondent: Paula Doraisamy, 61 Grosvenor Street, London W1K 3JE (tel: 020 3011 1100; email: admin@61grosvenorstreet.com)

Trustees: Annabel Nicoll; Paddy Nicoll; Rory Nicoll; Phoebe Nicoll; Sam Nicoll.

General information

The Annabel Arbib Foundation was registered with the Charity Commission in 1987.

The foundation's grant-making is described in the 2020/21 annual report as follows:

> Potential recipients of grants are identified by the trustees individually, in areas where it is perceived that public benefit will be achieved. The opportunity to benefit is not restricted in any way except that grants are principally made to charitable organisations within the UK, not least to facilitate the trustees being able to follow up on efficacy of the grants made.

The foundation also makes regular grants to The Arbib Education Trust.

Financial information

Year end	05/04/2021
Income	£345,100
Assets	£14,790,000
Grants to organisations	£455,300

Beneficiaries included: Arbib Educational Trust (£284,300); River and Rowing Museum Foundation (£24,000); Rainbow Trust Children's Charity (£10,000); Henley Festival Trust (£5,000); Rotary Club of Henley (£250).

Exclusions

No grants to individuals.

Applications

Apply in writing to the correspondent. Note that grants are typically made to organisations that are connected to the trustees; therefore, unsolicited applications are unlikely to be successful.

Sources of information

Accounts; annual report; Charity Commission record.

Arcadia Fund

Preserving endangered culture; protecting endangered nature; promoting open access to information

Worldwide

£113.65 million (2021)

Correspondent: Grants Team, Sixth floor, 40 Villiers Street, London WC2N 6NJ (email: info@arcadiafund.org.uk)

Trustee: Talvik Trust Services AG.

 www.arcadiafund.org.uk

 @ArcadiaFund

General information

Formerly the Lisbet Rausing Charitable Fund, Arcadia was set up in 2001 and appears to have operated in parallel with the Lisbet Rausing Charitable Fund until that fund was officially dissolved at the end of 2008. The charity is not registered in the UK and therefore does not have a Charity Commission record. It is, however, managed by a London-based team.

Funding themes

Arcadia currently provides funding under three themes, which are stated on the website as follows:

> **Preserving endangered culture** – Our aim is to ensure knowledge of the world's cultural diversity is not lost. Our grants support the documentation of endangered cultural heritage, ensuring it is available to future generations. Focus areas:
>
> - Archives and manuscripts
> - Intangible culture
> - Heritage sites
>
> **Protecting Endangered Nature** – Our goal is to protect the natural diversity of the world, now and in the future. Our grants help to safeguard and restore unique and biodiverse areas of land and sea. Focus areas:
>
> - On-site interventions
> - Governance
> - Leadership
>
> **Promoting Open Access** – Our aim is to improve access to human knowledge. Our grants help make information free for anyone, anywhere to access and use, now and in the future. Focus areas:
>
> - Copyright and intellectual property issues
> - Longform scholarship
> - Discoverability

Grant types

Arcadia's website states:

> We make few, multi-year grants. We fund operational costs, existing projects or develop partnerships to create new schemes. We build long-term relationships with our grant recipients: we replicate and expand successful projects and award repeat grants to continue outstanding work.

Financial information

Year end	31/12/2021
Grants to organisations	£113,650,000
No. of grants	37

Further financial information

According to its 2021 annual report (available on its website), Arcadia awarded £113.65 million to organisations worldwide. Grants were distributed as follows:

The environment	£65.82 million
Culture	£32.30 million
Open access	£15.22 million
Discretionary grants	£504,700

Note: the financial figures were converted from US dollars using the exchange rate at the time of writing (May 2022).

Beneficiaries included: Stitching Open Rivers (£40.92 million); Fauna and Flora International (£1.6 million); theguardian.org (£725,100); University of London (£222,400); University of Cambridge (£111,200); Pesticide Action Network UK (£89,000); Heritage and Beyond (£64,200).

Applications

Unsolicited applications are not accepted. The charity's website states:

> Our giving is led by our founders and their vision. They make decisions on our strategy and grant-making.
>
> We do not accept applications for funding. We rely on our own research and networks and seek out those that most align with our vision and approach.
>
> Because we are a small team, we are not able to respond to all enquiries and requests for meetings.
>
> We outsource some of our grant-making so that we can effectively identify and respond to on-the-ground needs. Organizations and individuals can apply for funding through our regranting programmes: the Endangered Languages Documentation Programme, Endangered Archives Programme, The Endangered Modern Archives Program, The Endangered Material Knowledge Programme and the Endangered Landscapes Programme.

Sources of information

Annual report; funder's website.

The Architectural Heritage Fund

Heritage and conservation

 UK

£6.74 million (2020/21)

CC number: 266780

Correspondent: The Trustees, 3 Spital Yard, Spitalfields, London E1 6AQ (tel: 020 7925 0199; email: ahf@ahfund.org.uk)

Trustees: Myra Barnes; Elizabeth Peace; David Hunter; Suzanne Snowden; Adebayo Alao; Karen Latimer; Eleanor McAllister; Roy Hodson; Graham Fisher; James Bowdidge; Carole-Anne Davies; Gregory Pickup; Dr Neal Sashore.

 www.ahfund.org.uk

 facebook.com/archhfund

 @ArchHFund

 @archhfund

General information

The Architectural Heritage Fund was established in 1976 to promote the conservation and sustainable re-use of historic buildings for the benefit of communities across the UK, particularly in economically disadvantaged areas. According to its website, the charity helps communities 'find enterprising new ways to revitalise the old buildings they love' by providing advice, grants and loans.

Charitable activities

The charity offers a unique range of support, designed to cover the life-cycle of a given project. This includes start-up advice, grants and loans.

Grant programmes

'Not-for-private-profit organisations' and the lowest tiers of local government can apply for funding. See the detailed list of eligible organisations featured on the charity's website to confirm your eligibility.

In Northern Ireland, Scotland and Wales, applications for projects located anywhere (i.e. in cities, towns or rural areas) are welcomed.

In England, applications for funding can be made **only** if:

- The project involves a heritage building (listed or in a conservation area) located in a high street or town centre in England **and**
- This location is the focus of a wider strategy or initiative which aims to revitalise the high street or town centre **and**
- You are a not-for-private-profit organisation, **and**
- Your organisation has, or is intending to acquire, the freehold or a long lease on the building

There are several different grant schemes available – see the charity's website for more information.

Loans

Loans are awarded to charities and other non-profit organisations for buildings of historic or architectural importance. This means that the building may be listed, in a conservation area, or may be of special significance to the community.

Loans are made to cover the acquisition of a building, to provide working capital throughout a restoration project, to bridge further funding or to kick start enterprising activities to secure the future sustainability of the organisation and the building.

Financial information

Year end	31/03/2021
Income	£9,820,000
Assets	£17,300,000
Grants to organisations	£6,740,000
No. of grants	287

Further financial information

In 2020/21, 287 grants were awarded through a variety of grant programmes. The following breakdown was provided in the accounts:

Project viability	112
Project development	93
Transformational project and capital grants	44
Recovery grants	23
Emergency support grants	8
Other	7

Beneficiaries included: Refugee Support Network (£200,000); White Rock Neighbourhood Ventures Ltd (£78,600); Grimsby Youth Zone (£50,000); Middleton Hall Trust (£22,700); Levenshulme Old Library CIO (£11,500); East Suffolk Building Preservation Trust (£5,000); Sinai Park House Trust (£2,200).

Exclusions

According to the charity's website, grants are not awarded to:

- Private individuals
- Local authorities and other public sector bodies (except parish and town councils and unless applying on behalf of an organisation still in formation)
- Universities, colleges and other mainstream educational institutions
- For-profit companies (unless in a partnership led by a non-profit organisation)
- Unincorporated organisations
- Organisations with fewer than three trustees or directors (if there are only three trustees/directors, none of these should be related to one another)
- Limited liability partnerships
- Churches or other places of worship, where the building will remain in use primarily as a place of religious worship – defined as hosting regular religious services or religion-based activities

Applications

Online application forms can be found on the charity's website. Applicants are advised to speak with their local support officer, whose details can be found on the website. Application deadlines can be found on the charity's website along with full guidelines.

Sources of information

Accounts; annual report; Charity Commission record; funder's website.

Ardbarron Trust Ltd

Awareness and understanding of the Christian gospel; social welfare; health care; literacy

Possible

UK and overseas

£4.42 million (2020)

CCNI number: NIC101111

Correspondent: The Trustees, 9 Hightown Avenue, Newtownabbey, County Antrim BT36 4RT (tel: 028 9034 2733)

Trustees: Martin Agnew; Geoffrey Agnew; John Agnew; Malcolm Johnston.

General information

Ardbarron Trust Ltd is funded by donations from John Henderson (Holdings) Ltd.

The trust makes grants to UK-registered charities as well as charities operating in financially developing countries. It also supports worldwide relief organisations and responds to emergency appeals where practical and medical aid is needed.

The trust's 2020 accounts state:

> The Trust exists to promote the Christian Gospel in Word and Deed, to help the prevention and relief of poverty, the provision of healthcare and literacy, and the relief of those in need by reason of youth, age, ill-health, disability, financial hardship or other disadvantage.

Financial information

Year end	31/12/2020
Income	£5,050,000
Assets	£188,280,000
Grants to organisations	£4,420,000
No. of grants	276

Beneficiaries included: Christian Missions Charitable Trust; Echoes of Service; Operation Mobilisation; Strategic Resource Group; Tear Fund; Youth for Christ.

Applications

Apply in writing to the correspondent.

Sources of information

Accounts; annual report; CCNI record.

The Ardeola Charitable Trust

General charitable purposes; arts and culture; health

UK

£1.18 million (2019/20)

CC number: 1124380

Correspondent: The Trustees, Zedra UK Trusts, Booths Hall, Booths Park, Chelford Road, Knutsford, Cheshire WA16 8GS (tel: 01565 748829)

Trustees: Graham Barker; Joanna Barker; William Hiscocks; Prof. John Cornwall; Zedra Trust Company (UK) Ltd.

General information

This trust was established in 2008 and makes grants for general charitable purposes.

Financial information

Year end	31/05/2020
Income	£152,100
Assets	£6,730,000
Grants to organisations	£1,180,000

Beneficiaries included: British Museum (£530,300); Durham Cathedral (£35,000); Ashmolean Museum (£10,000); The Art Fund (£2,100).

Applications

Unsolicited applications are not accepted.

Sources of information

Accounts; annual report; Charity Commission record.

The Armed Forces Covenant Fund Trust

The armed forces community

UK

£25 million (2020/21)

CC number: 1177627

Correspondent: Carol Stone, Director of Grants, 7 Hatherley Street, London SW1P 2QN (tel: 020 7154 1725; email: admin@covenantfund.org.uk)

Trustees: Helen Helliwell; Wendy Cartwright; Commodore Rex Cox; General Sir John McColl; Gerald Oppenheim; John Pitt Brooke; Prof. David Rose; Anna Wright; Maj. General David Eastman; Cerys Gage; Lesley O'Rourke; John Mooney.

www.covenantfund.org.uk

facebook.com/CovenantTrust

@CovenantTrust

General information

The trust was established to continue the work of the Covenant Fund team, which began operating within the Service Personnel Support department of the Ministry of Defence (MOD) in 2015. This team managed the first three years' grant-making activity of the Covenant Fund, which has an annual commitment from HM Treasury of £10 million. After this period, the governance and management arrangements of the in-house MOD team were reviewed and The Armed Forces Covenant Fund Trust was set up to continue the same activities as an independent trust.

The trust's main purpose is to provide charitable assistance and support to those who serve in the armed forces, whether regular or reserve, those who have served in the past, and their families and carers. The wider community around a base or in an area with an armed forces population can also benefit from some funding programmes, as the trust has supported projects that will help to encourage good relations between armed forces and civilian communities.

The trust aims to meet these purposes by developing and delivering grant programmes, making awards to organisations in the voluntary and public sectors.

The trust's website states that it has four broad funding themes:

- Removing barriers to family life.
- Extra support in and after Service for those that need help.
- Measures to integrate military and civilian communities and allow the armed forces community to participate as citizens.
- Non-core healthcare services for veterans.

Financial information

Year end	31/03/2021
Income	£26,750,000
Assets	£1,330,000
Grants to organisations	£25,030,000

Beneficiaries included: A full list of beneficiaries can be found on the website.

Exclusions

Applications from individuals will not be accepted.

Applications

Check the trust's website for current programmes and apply via the website.

Sources of information

Accounts; annual report; Charity Commission record; funder's website.

The John Armitage Charitable Trust

General charitable purposes; medical causes; arts and culture; social welfare; education; young and older people; religion

England and Wales

£3.96 million (2020/21)

CC number: 1079688

Correspondent: The Trustees, c/o Sampson West, Forum House, 1st Floor, 15–18 Lime Street, London EC3M 7AN (tel: 020 7404 5040)

Trustees: John Armitage; Catherine Armitage; William Francklin; Celina Francklin; Robert MacInnes.

General information

Established in 2000, this is the trust of John Armitage, co-founder of Egerton Capital, the City-based hedge fund. The 2020/21 annual report states that the current priorities for the trust are the following: disadvantaged children and youth support (including parenting support), education, medical care, arts and culture, people who have offended (including young individuals) and religious organisations.

Grants are normally made to organisations for a three-year period, with the majority being for between £30,000 and £40,000 per year.

Financial information

Year end	05/04/2021
Income	£12,090,000
Assets	£150,100,000
Grants to organisations	£3,960,000

Beneficiaries included: Harris Federation (£330,000); Hartlepool Hospice (£130,000); Magic Breakfast (£125,000); Teacher Development Trust (£123,200); The Forward Trust and Mind (£100,000 each).

Applications

The trust does not consider unsolicited requests for funding.

Sources of information

Accounts; annual report; Charity Commission record.

The Armourers' and Brasiers' Gauntlet Trust

Materials science; community projects; armed forces; children and young people; education; health and medical causes; the arts

UK, with some preference for London

£1.16 million (2020/21)

CC number: 279204

Correspondent: Anne-Marie Clift, Trust Chief Executive, Armourers' Hall, 81 Coleman Street, London EC2R 5BJ (tel: 020 7374 4000; email: charities@armourershall.co.uk)

Trustees: Prof. William Bonfield; Edward Pitt; Nicola Davies; Jonathan Hale; Prof. Emma Ream; Dr Roger Bowdler.

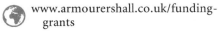

www.armourershall.co.uk/funding-grants

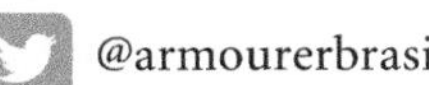

@armourerbrasier

General information

The trust is the charitable arm for the Worshipful Company of Armourers and Brasiers and was set up in 1979. The trust has three main grant programmes outlined below.

Science education in schools

The website states that grants are awarded towards the costs of equipment 'to run science enrichment projects in schools, or to enable students to participate in science events and competitions'. Primary schools are awarded £600 and secondary schools £1,000.

Small charities programme

Multi-year grants are available to small charities working the following areas:

- Community development and the armed forces
- Children, young people and general education
- Health and medical charities
- The arts, particularly those related to the craft or history of arms or armour

The website states that the trustees are looking to build long-term relationships with the small charities they support. Grants are typically for £3,000 per year for three years (i.e. £9,000 in total). Funding is for core costs or specific project costs. The impact of the grant should be measurable.

The website states that applicants should:

- be charities registered in the UK (with the Charity Commission of England Wales, the Scottish Charity Regulator or the Charity Commission for Northern Ireland)
- be operating either nationally throughout the UK or in London (defined as within the M25).
- have had income below £500,000 in the last financial year for which full accounts are available

Research in Materials Science

Around £250,000 is awarded in grants each year in support of university level Materials Science education and research, specially projects that closely align with the ancient craft of working with metals and materials. The trust works in partnership with leading UK companies to deliver this funding. Travel grants and industrial placement grants are available.

Financial information

Year end	31/03/2021
Income	£366,700
Assets	£9,410,000
Grants to organisations	£1,160,000
No. of grants	32

Further financial information

Grants totalling £1.16 million were made to 32 organisations during the year. Five grants totalling £19,800 were made to small charities and a COVID-19 grant of

£30,000 was awarded to The City Bridge Trust. To celebrate the company's 700th anniversary, a donation of £1 million was made to Imperial College London during the year towards the creation of The Armourers and Brasiers Chair in Materials Science.

Beneficiaries included: Imperial College London (£1 million); The City Bridge Trust (£30,000); University of Sheffield Industrial Training Project (£7,500); The Richard House Hospice and The Ulysses Trust (£2,000 each); Guildhall School of Music and Drama (£1,000); Royal Army Chaplains Department (£250).

Exclusions

According to the exclusions listed on the website, applicants to the small charities programme should not:

- be applying for general maintenance, repair or restoration of buildings
- be applying for sponsorship as individuals
- be applying for the benefit of an individual
- be applying for charities or projects outside the UK

Applications

The trust's three grant programmes have separate applications processes. Online application forms are available on the website, alongside guidelines and deadlines. Applicants who are shortlisted for the small charities programme will be interviewed, and the trust may request to visit your charity before the interview.

Sources of information

Accounts; annual report; Charity Commission record; funder's website.

The Arsenal Foundation

Education; sport; health and medical causes; disability; social welfare

North London

£222,700 (2020/21)

CC number: 1145668

Correspondent: Samir Singh, Highbury House, 75 Drayton Park, London N5 1BU (tel: 020 7704 4406; email: ssingh@arsenal.co.uk)

Trustees: Svenja Geissmar; Kenneth Friar; Alan Sefton; Andrew Jolly; Vinaichandra Venkatesham; Frederick Hudson.

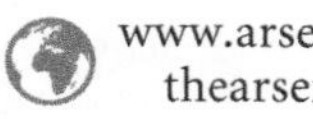
www.arsenal.com/thearsenalfoundation

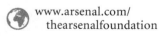

facebook.com/TheArsenalFoundation

@AFC_Foundation

@arsenal_foundation

General information

The Arsenal Foundation was established in 2012 as the corporate charity for Arsenal FC. The foundation aims to help young people in North London and around the world fulfil their potential.

The Gunners Fund

The aim of The Gunners Fund is to support charities in the boroughs of Islington, Camden and Hackney by offering grants of up to £2,500 for community projects.

The following information is taken from the fund's grant-making guidelines:

> In line with the overall objectives of The Foundation, priority will be given to the following areas of need:
>
> Education (including academic, social, physical education, skills training and community engagement); Sports capable of improving health; Medical; Sickness and the relief of suffering; Disability; Poverty; and Individual misfortune.
>
> The following is a non-exhaustive list of potential beneficiaries or groups of beneficiaries:
>
> Organisations connected to Arsenal FC; Charity or community projects connected to Arsenal FC; Community groups, societies or projects; Projects that have been developed by Arsenal FC's community team; Staff-initiated projects; Supporter-initiated projects; Projects where The Foundation's donation, even though relatively small, will make a difference; Projects where the gesture of support from a charity associated with Arsenal FC can have a greater effect than the money itself; Football-linked campaigns or public bodies; Projects where the person requesting a donation is doing something active to raise money for the cause; Projects where the person is playing a significant and voluntary role in raising money for the charity; and Awards to reward success or achievement in areas of endeavour that fall within the objectives of The Foundation

The foundation has also partnered with Islington Giving to make grants to voluntary organisations.

Financial information

Year end	31/05/2021
Income	£266,900
Assets	£1,040,000
Grants to organisations	£222,700

Further financial information

In previous years grants have totalled around £1 million.

Beneficiaries included: Save the Children (£192,000).

Applications

Application forms for the Gunners Fund are available to download from the foundation's website, along with grant-making guidelines. The foundation states that it is unable to respond to all of the applications it receives, due to the high volume, so if you do not receive a response within two months, you should assume that you have been unsuccessful.

Sources of information

Accounts; annual report; Charity Commission record; funder's website.

The Art Fund

Museums and galleries, including the acquisition of works of art

UK

£3.64 million (2020)

CC number: 209174

Correspondent: Museum Services, 2 Granary Square, King's Cross, London N1C 4BH (tel: 020 7225 4800; email: info@artfund.org)

Trustees: Dame Liz Forgan; Alastair Laing; Chris Smith; Jeremy Palmer; Richard Ra; Axel Ruger; Prof. Marcia Pointon; Isaac Ra; Monisha Shah; Tessa Jackson; Katrina Brown; Anupam Ganguli; Madeleine Kennedy; Susan Rees.

www.artfund.org

@artfund

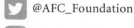

@artfund

General information

This fundraising and membership charity believes that everyone should have the opportunity to experience great art at first hand. According to the fund's website, it works to achieve this by:

- Giving grants to museums to buy works of art and develop new collections;
- Supporting the showing of art through tours and exhibitions;
- Seeking to influence government policy and stimulating debate; and
- Offering funding to museum professionals to help them develop their skills

Grant programmes

The charity advertises open funding rounds on its website. Some longer standing programmes include:

Acquisition grants – grants to help UK museums and galleries acquire objects and works of art for their collections. Around £4 million is awarded through this programme each year.

Jonathan Ruffer curatorial grants – funding for curators towards travel and other costs, to enable collections and exhibition research projects in the UK or abroad.

Small projects grants – funding to help museums, galleries and other visual arts organisations realise adventurous projects, up to £10,000, across a range of activities to benefit their audiences.

Eligibility

While each funding programme has some specific criteria, generally the following points apply:

- Applications are welcomed from organisations whose primary purpose relates to object-based collections and works of art
- Grants are available to charities, CIOs, CICs and charitable community benefit societies
- Museums or galleries that are associated with universities, or which receive funding from government or local authorities are also eligible to apply

Financial information

Year end	31/12/2020
Income	£14,470,000
Assets	£56,260,000
Grants to organisations	£3,640,000
No. of grants	317

Further financial information

The grant total includes £2.25 million worth of grants distributed through the fund's Respond and Reimagine COVID-19 emergency programme.

Beneficiaries included: The National Gallery (£1 million); Norwich Castle Museum and Art Gallery (£223,800); Tate Britain (£100,000); British Library (£50,000); Create London (£23,600); Gallery of Modern Art – Glasgow (£9,700); Jane Austen's House Museum (£3,000); National Portrait Gallery (£150).

Exclusions

Programme-specific exclusions can be found on the charity's helpful website. In general, the following are not funded:

- Organisations that exist to make profit (e.g. private limited companies, public limited companies, unlimited companies or sole traders)
- General partnerships, limited partnerships, or limited liability partnerships
- Commercial organisations
- Artists' groups
- Hospitals and healthcare settings
- Places of worship
- Organisations with a focus on art forms outside the visual arts (e.g. music, drama, dance)
- Organisations based outside the UK

Applications

Applications can be made via the fund's online portal.

Sources of information

Accounts; annual report; Charity Commission record; funder's website.

The Artemis Charitable Foundation

Health; poverty; education; the environment; disaster appeals

UK and overseas

£963,100 (2020)

OSCR number: SC037857

Correspondent: Marisa Charosky, Foundation Co-ordinator, 6th Floor, Exchange Plaza, 50 Lothian Road, Edinburgh EH3 9BY (email: charitablefoundation@artemisfunds.com)

www.artemisfunds.com/en/about-artemis/artemis-charitable-foundation

General information

The Artemis Charitable Foundation was founded in 2007 as the corporate charity of Artemis Investment Management LLP. According to its website, the foundation awards grants to 'core' charities in the UK and internationally in the following key areas:

- Health
- Poverty
- Education
- The environment

The foundation also makes donations to global disasters and emergencies when they occur.

According to the 2020 accounts, the trustees' policy is to award one-off grants; however, multi-year grants are awarded on a small number of occasions. The foundation's website states that initial grants are generally between £1,000 and £10,000, but amounts can increase if a partnership develops into a multi-year relationship.

The foundation will consider providing unrestricted funding.

Eligibility

Charities must be registered in the UK but can operate in the UK or internationally. Preference is given to small and medium-sized charities (those with an income of less than £2 million per year). Innovative and sustainable projects that can be scaled up/replicated are preferred.

Charity of the Year

In addition to its annual core charity partners, Artemis employees vote for a Charity of the Year to fundraise for. In 2020, employees chose to support Challenge Partners, an education charity, and in 2021 employees chose Children's Hospices Across Scotland.

Financial information

Year end	31/12/2020
Income	£904,200
Assets	£568,500
Grants to organisations	£963,100

Further financial information

Grants were broken down as follows in the foundation's 2020 annual report:

Other donations under £10,000	£465,900
Grants to 'core' charities	£442,200
Disaster relief	£30,000
Charity of the Year	£25,000

Beneficiaries included: Shivia Microfinance (£68,000); The Trussell Trust (£58,000); Client Earth (£50,000); Challenge Partners and Crisis (£25,000 each); City Harvest (£17,800); Cool Earth (£10,000); Jamie's Farm (£5,000); Mercy Corps (£280).

Applications

Apply in writing via email with a covering letter, a brief proposal (ideally no more than two or three pages) containing an overview of your organisation's work and funding priorities, and details of your organisation's basic financial information, including income and expenditure activity from your latest accounts.

The trustees meet at the end of every month to consider applications.

Sources of information

Accounts; annual report; funder's website; OSCR record.

Arts Council England

Arts and culture

England

£1.64 billion (2020/21)

CC number: 1036733

Correspondent: Customer services, Bloomsbury Street, Bloomsbury, London WC1B 3HF (tel: 0161 934 4317)

www.artscouncil.org.uk

facebook.com/artscouncilofengland

@ace_national

@aceagrams

General information

Arts Council England invests public money from the government and National Lottery to support activities across the arts, museums and libraries in England. The Arts Council's website describes its work as follows: 'We champion, develop and invest in artistic and cultural experiences that enrich people's lives. We support activities across the arts, museums and libraries – from theatre to digital art, reading to dance, music to literature, and crafts to collections.'

At the start of 2020 the Arts Council published its new ten year strategy, Let's Create. According to the Arts Council's website the strategy has three main outcomes:

- **Creative People** – ensuring that everyone has the chance to develop and express their own creativity
- **Cultural Communities** – making sure that people in villages, towns and cities across the country have access to the highest quality cultural experiences
- **A Creative and Cultural Country** – enabling England's cultural sector to be innovative and collaborative, and able to support the country's creative industries, national economy and place on the world stage

Grant programmes

The Arts Council has various grant programmes which open and close during the year. Check the Arts Council's website for the latest information on these programmes.

Financial information

Year end	31/03/2021
Income	£1,505,930,000
Assets	£250,372,000
Grants to organisations	£1,642,000,000

Beneficiaries included: See the case studies on the funder's website to explore the projects it has invested in.

Exclusions

Exclusions may vary depending upon the specific grants programme.

Applications

There is a helpful funding finder facility on the Arts Council's website which allows users to browse its funding programmes. Applications can made via the Grantium grants portal.

Sources of information

Accounts; annual report; Charity Commission record; funder's website.

Arts Council of Northern Ireland

Arts development

Northern Ireland

£11.65 million (2019/20)

Correspondent: The Arts Development Department, Linen Hill House, 23 Linenhall Street, Lisburn, County Antrim BT28 1FJ (tel: 028 9262 3555; email: info@artscouncil-ni.org)

 www.artscouncil-ni.org

 facebook.com/ArtsCouncilNI

 @ArtsCouncilNI

 @artscouncilni

General information

The Arts Council's website provides the following information:

> The Arts Council of Northern Ireland is the development and funding agency for the Arts in Northern Ireland.
>
> We distribute public money and National Lottery funds to develop and deliver a wide variety of arts projects, events and initiatives across Northern Ireland.
>
> From theatre and literature to art in the community, we work in partnership with hundreds of artists, arts organisations and venues. Art has the ability to reach across boundaries, inspiring, teaching and bringing people together.
>
> That's why we believe in placing "Art at the Heart" because we know that art makes a difference.

Details of all funding programmes and grants awarded can be found on the council's website.

Financial information

Year end	31/03/2020
Income	£1,660,000
Assets	£2,420,000
Grants to organisations	£11,650,000

Further financial information

Expenditure on the arts in 2019/20 was broken down as follows in the 2019/20 annual report and accounts (we have used the sum of this expenditure as the grant total – note that the grant total may include grants to individuals):

Purpose	Amount
Annual funding programme	£8.52 million
Capital programme	£1.61 million
In-year project funding	£976,900
Support for individual artists programme	£262,400
Arts Development Fund	£213,900
Strategy	£33,000
The arts and older people	£14,100
Young people and well-being	£14,100

Beneficiaries included: Examples of projects supported by the council can be found on its website.

Applications

Information on what funding is currently available, guidelines and full details of how to apply can be found at the Arts Council's website.

Sources of information

Accounts; annual report; Charity Commission record; funder's website.

Arts Council of Wales (also known as Cyngor Celfyddydau Cymru)

Arts and culture

Wales

£50.3 million (2020/21)

CC number: 1034245

Correspondent: Grants and Information Department, Bute Place, Cardiff CF10 5AL (tel: 0330 124 2733; email: a contact form is available on the charity's website)

 www.arts.wales

 facebook.com/celfyddydau

 @Arts_Wales_

 @celfcymruarts

General information

Arts Council of Wales, which was established by Royal Charter in 1994, is the official body that funds and develops the arts in Wales. The majority of the council's income comes from the Welsh Government and it also distributes money on behalf of the National Lottery. Where possible, the council raises money from a range of other sources across the public and private sectors.

Strategy

The following information on the council's strategy has been taken from its website:

> Our strategy can be summed up in three words: **make, reach, sustain.**
>
> **Make**
>
> To make art, in all its forms, is what we aim to enable. We want to foster an environment for the best artists and organisations in Wales to create their best work. When excellent work is created, it strikes a chord with people. This is when people truly experience art, and once that connection is made, it is valued.
>
> **Reach**
>
> The ability to reach people goes hand in hand with making extraordinary art. The more people experience and embrace art in communities, theatre, schools or galleries the further we reach.

Sustain

For economic sustainability, the arts must remain relevant to people. We want to help valued organisations to find and develop new business models that encourage resilience and longevity.

Funding

The charity offers a range of funding types, these are:

- Individual
- Organisation
- Creative learning
- International
- National Lottery funding

Extensive details of all funding programmes and grants awarded can be found on the council's website.

Financial information

Year end	31/03/2021
Income	£55,280,000
Assets	£2,470,000
Grants to organisations	£50,330,000

Further financial information

During 2020/21, £50.3 million was awarded in grants to organisations, £20 million of which was awarded as COVID-19 support. Grants for organisations and individuals were distributed as follows:

Strategic awards	£23.34 million
Theatres and arts centres	£7.1 million
Theatre production and presentation	£6.73 million
Opera	£4.91 million
Visual and applied arts	£1.79 million
Dance	£1.74 million
Music	£1.45 million
Arts and young people	£1.17 million
Community arts	£1.1 million
Creative learning through the arts	£992,000
Literature	£750,400
Circus and carnivals	£196,700
Disability arts	£167,200

Beneficiaries included: Welsh National Opera (£4.6 million); Torch Theatre Company Ltd (£350,000); Disability Arts Cymru (£167,200); Live Music Now Wales (£30,000); Cardiff Pottery Workshops Foundation (£23,900); St Mary's RC Primary Newport (£10,000); The North Wales Development Trust Ltd (£1,800).

Applications

Details of the application process and application deadlines for each programme can be found on the council's website.

Sources of information

Accounts; annual report; Charity Commission record; funder's website.

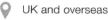

Ove Arup Partnership Charitable Trust

Education; social care; health and welfare; disaster relief and poverty alleviation; local community development; the environment

UK and overseas

£589,400 (2020/21)

CC number: 1038737

Correspondent: Stephanie Wilde, Ove Arup and Partners Ltd, 8 Fitzroy Street, London W1T 4BJ (tel: 020 7636 1531; email: stephanie.wilde@arup.com)

Trustee: Ove Arup Partnership Trust Corporation Ltd.

General information

The Ove Arup Partnership Charitable Trust was established in January 1978. The annual report for 2020/21 explains that the trust 'is not in receipt of a regular income and relies on gifts from Arup Group Ltd', a company affiliated with the trust.

Income from the company is used to make donations to charities. With respect to the trust's grant-making policy, the trust's 2020/21 annual report and accounts state that:

> The Trustee considers causes and charities that operate in areas related to Arup's skills and business activities where these are aligned with Arup's values, as expressed in Ove Arup's 'Key Speech', of doing socially useful work and of being engaged in activities for the benefit of society at large.
>
> In deciding on specific recipients, the Trustee has regard to the size and structure of the recipient organisation in relation to the size of donation in order to maximise the impact and effectiveness of that donation.

Grants have previously been made for a wide range of purposes including education, social care, health, welfare, disaster relief, poverty alleviation, local community development and the environment.

Financial information

Year end	31/03/2021
Income	£616,200
Assets	£41,800
Grants to organisations	£589,400

Beneficiaries included: The Ove Arup Foundation (£400,000); Drukpa Trust (£80,000); Bridges to Prosperity (£22,600); Mission Remission and Marmalade Trust (£1,000 each).

Applications

Apply in writing to the correspondent.

Sources of information

Accounts; annual report; Charity Commission record.

The Asda Foundation

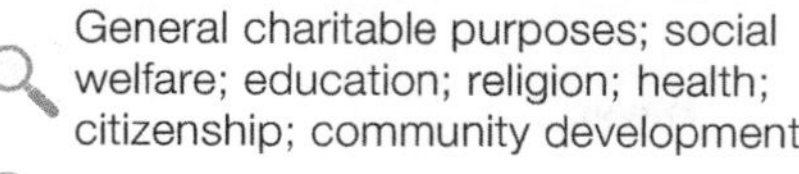

General charitable purposes; social welfare; education; religion; health; citizenship; community development

England and Wales

£4.42 million (2020)

CC number: 1124268

Correspondent: Grants Team, Asda House, Great Wilson Street, Leeds, West Yorkshire LS11 5AD (email: asdafoundation@asda.co.uk)

Trustees: John Cookman; Jane Earnshaw; Jason Martin; Andrew Murray; Jodie Tate; Rukia Hussain; Simon Lewis; Patricia Mitchell; Susan Hennessey.

 www.asdafoundation.org

 @asdafoundation

General information

The Asda Foundation is the corporate charity of the supermarket, Asda. The foundation supports small, grassroots organisations with the aim of transforming communities and improving lives.

Open grant programmes are advertised on the foundation's website. At the time of writing (February 2022) the following programmes were being delivered:

Empowering Local Communities Grant

This programme supports a broad range of community activities under four themes:

- **Building resilient communities** – supporting community groups with the equipment, essentials and facilities to enable activity to take place
- **Active lives** – supporting participation in group physical activities
- **Seasonal celebrations and festivals**
- **Leading healthier lives** – supporting health in mind, body and soul

Groups can apply for one grant per year from £500 to £1,500.

Under 18 Better Starts Grant

In response to the COVID-19 pandemic, the foundation invested £500,000 into its U18 Better Starts Grants programme to help give young people under the age of 18 a better start in life. The programme supports activities under four themes:

- **Supporting essentials** – supporting the provision of food, hygiene and health-related supplies
- **Being active** – funding physical activities that are inclusive for all children
- **Improving well-being** – supporting mental health and creativity

- **Celebrating and bringing children together** – grants enabling under 18's to celebrate what matters to them

Groups can apply for one grant per year from £500 to £1,500.

Green Token Giving

Asda customers can nominate a small, local grassroots charity or good cause to be put forward for a quarterly customer vote. Winners of the vote receive £500 and runners-up receive £200. Since 2021 the programme has been delivered online, rather than in-store.

Emergency funding

The foundation can provide assistance during times of emergency. This includes emergencies on a personal level, such as a house fire, or a community-wide disaster, such as floods.

Other

The foundation matches Asda employees' fundraising efforts up to £300 per year. It also works in partnership with other charitable organisations.

Financial information

Year end	31/12/2020
Income	£3,660,000
Assets	£5,090,000
Grants to organisations	£4,420,000

Further financial information

Grants to organisations were broken down as follows:

Green token giving	£1.84 million
Other	£1.53 million
Local impact	£778,100
Community projects	£274,300
Matched funding	£1,100

In addition, hardship grants totalling £59,400 were awarded to Asda colleagues.

Only beneficiaries of grants over £10,000 were listed in the foundation's accounts.

Beneficiaries included: Royal Voluntary Service (£460,200); Crisis UK (£287,100); University of Leeds (£180,000); Tattyreagh Gaelic Athletic Club (£30,000); Parkhead Housing Association (£14,600); Village Hall Ropsley (£11,600); Perth and Kinross Association of Voluntary Service (£10,600).

Exclusions

Each programme has specific exclusions – see the relevant guidance on the foundation's website.

Applications

Further information on eligibility and how to apply for grants can be found on the foundation's website. In most cases, applicants are encouraged to contact their local Asda Community Champion to discuss eligibility and to receive an application form. For emergency grants, contact your local Asda store.

Sources of information

Accounts; annual report; Charity Commission record; funder's website; guidelines for applicants.

The Asfari Foundation

Youth empowerment; civil society development; humanitarian relief

UK; Syria; Lebanon; Palestine; Jordan

£2.77 million (2020)

CC number: 1116751

Correspondent: Programmes Team, Unit A, 1–3 Canfield Place, London NW6 3BT (tel: 020 7372 3889; email: info@asfarifoundation.org.uk or programmes@asfarifoundation.org.uk)

Trustees: Adeeb Asfari; Ayman Asfari; Sawsan Asfari; John Ferguson; Dr Marwan Muasher; Rasha Elmasry; Kareem Asfari.

www.asfarifoundation.org.uk

facebook.com/theasfarifoundation

@asfari_found

@asfarifoundation

General information

The foundation's mission is to help young people make a valuable contribution to society by empowering them through education, research and the power of free thinking. The foundation also encourages the development of civil society, as well as providing humanitarian relief in emergencies in its target countries (mainly Syria, Lebanon, Palestine and UK). The foundation does all its work through partnerships with other organisations. The foundation achieves this through its three programmes:

- Youth learning, entrepreneurship and innovation programme
- Civil society programme
- Relief programme

Further information about each of the foundation's programmes is given on its website.

Work in the UK

The foundation's website states:

> The Foundation supports organisations working with disadvantaged young people in the UK, partners with British organisations to host scholars from its Middle Eastern target countries, partners with think tanks and research organisations, and supports British INGOs working with young Palestinians, Syrians and Lebanese people in the Arab region.

Financial information

Year end	31/12/2020
Income	£3,700,000
Assets	£15,240,000
Grants to organisations	£2,770,000

Further financial information

Grants were broken down as follows:

Civil society	£1.35 million
Youth empowerment	£1.06 million
Strategic learning and engagement	£196,900
Relief	£165,800

Grants to UK-based organisations totalled approximately £420,000.

Beneficiaries included: Hands Up Foundation (two grants totalling £82,000); Galilee Foundation and Year Here (£75,000 each); Humanitarian Leadership Academy (£35,300); Good Chance Theatre (£20,000); Technovatio (£18,000).

Applications

The foundation invites applications for funding once a year through an open call, usually in January. Eligibility and application criteria vary from year to year – check the foundation's website for updated information.

Sources of information

Accounts; annual report; Charity Commission record; funder's website.

The Ashley Family Foundation

The arts; community projects; rural communities

England and Wales, with preference for Wales

£563,500 (2019/20)

CC number: 288099

Correspondent: The Administrator, 6 Trull Farm Buildings, Trull, Tetbury, Gloucestershire GL8 8SQ (tel: 0303 040 1005; email: info@ashleyfamilyfoundation.org.uk)

Trustees: Laura Ashley; Prof. Oriana Baddeley; Emma Shuckburgh; Jeremy McIlroy; Alexis Korner; Julian Ashley; Anita George.

www.ashleyfamilyfoundation.org.uk

General information

In 1986, a year after the death of the Welsh fashion designer and businesswoman Laura Ashley, her family officially established The Laura Ashley Foundation. The trustees changed the name to The Ashley Foundation in 2011.

Focus

The foundation has five focus areas, as stated on its website:

- **Wales** – Half our funding goes to projects in Wales and we continue to maintain strong links with communities in mid Wales.
- **Rural** – We are especially interested in projects that open up opportunity in areas where it might not otherwise exist and that help alleviate the isolation and other hardships that can affect rural communities.
- **Arts** – We want to help bring art to those people that it can help, and help those who will go on to bring art to the people. As a result we support organisations that provide a wide range of educational and creative activities, including applied arts and crafts, music, drama, and textiles. We also fund arts education with a focus on helping promising young Welsh talent.
- **Community** – We are attracted to projects that bring people together, to help each other out and make their community a better, more joyful place. We support a range of community projects, including those focused on helping people who suffer from isolation and/or social disadvantage.
- **Small Charities** – The Foundation has an affinity with small charities, the ones set up by people who are driven by love and kindness to help better the lives of those around them.

Grants

There is no minimum or maximum grant amount, but requests under £10,000 are preferred. The foundation prefers to fund revenue, project and capital costs. Most grants are for one-off projects, but multi-year grants will be considered.

Eligibility

The foundation's website states:

> Grants are made primarily for project costs to organisations registered with the Charity Commission for England and Wales and to unregistered organisations providing arts and/or community and social welfare projects when supported by a registered charity.
>
> We are keen to fund good small scale arts and community projects in England and Wales and welcome proposals from community museums, organisations, farms and gardens for funding for arts subjects.

Financial information

Year end	30/09/2020
Income	£301,900
Assets	£12,710,000
Grants to organisations	£563,500
No. of grants	50+

Beneficiaries included: Cygnor Powys Citizens Advice (£23,900); Wales Covid Resilience Fund (£20,000); Create Play Community Company and Small World Theatre (£10,000 each); Colchester Gateway Clubs (£5,000); Whitchurch Silk Mill Trust (£3,000); Portobello Radio CIC (£1,500); Skate Cardiff Spit and Sawdust (£430).

Exclusions

The foundation does not give grants for:

- Individuals
- Business ventures
- Overseas projects
- Religious projects
- Schools directly
- Retrospective costs

The foundation is also unlikely to fund:

- Sports-focused projects
- Well-supported causes (such as cancer and animal welfare)

Applications

Applications can be made online through the foundation's website where application deadlines can also be found. Applicants are encouraged to read the grants criteria on the website and speak to the foundation's staff before applying.

To discuss an application in Welsh, contact Ffion Roberts at the Community Foundation in Wales, on 029 2037 9580.

Sources of information

Accounts; annual report; Charity Commission record; funder's website.

Asthma and Lung UK

Research into lung diseases

UK

£2.92 million (2020/21)

CC number: 326730

Correspondent: Research Team, 18 Mansell Street, London E1 8AA (tel: 0300 222 5800; email: info@asthmaandlung.org.uk)

Trustees: John Graham; Isabel Divanna; Emily Bushby; Baroness Tessa Blackstone; Prof. Edwin Chilvers; James Bowes; Prof. Ian Hall; Prof. Ian Sabroe; Katherine Morgan; Niren Patel; Michael O'Connor; Caroline Karlsen.

 www.asthmaandlung.org.uk

 facebook.com/asthmalunguk

 @asthmalunguk

 @asthmaandlunguk

General information

On 1 January 2020, the British Lung Foundation and Asthma UK and merged to become a new charity – the Asthma UK and British Lung Foundation Partnership (Asthma and Lung UK).

According to Asthma and Lung UK's website, the partnership builds on earlier joint working and its mission is to reduce deaths and ill health caused by lung conditions by 20% by 2027. To achieve this, the partnership aims to:

- **Prevent lung disease** – fighting for clean air and against smoking
- **Diagnose lung disease earlier and more accurately** – improving public awareness of the symptoms of lung disease and developing diagnosis
- **Enable everyone to live well with a lung condition** – providing support and information
- **Drive life-changing research and innovation** – increasing public funding to find better treatment and cures

The partnership funds research into the prevention, treatment, alleviation and cure of chest and lung diseases. It funds research projects, senior research fellowships and research centres for periods of up to five years. Open calls are advertised on its website as they arise.

Financial information

Year end	30/06/2021
Income	£15,110,000
Assets	£15,410,000
Grants to organisations	£2,920,000

Beneficiaries included: Papworth Hospital (£532,000); University of Glasgow (£305,000); Innovate UK (£280,000 in two grants); University of Birmingham (£98,000); University of Nottingham (£40,000).

Exclusions

Exclusion criteria may vary according to the programme being applied to. See the partnership's website for further information.

Applications

The following information is taken from the 2018/19 accounts:

> We invite applications for lung research projects through a variety of methods such as advertising on our website, through publicity at conferences and via news bulletins issued by related organisations and professional societies. Applicants submit their proposals and these are reviewed by our research committee and external peer reviewers. The research committee is made up of 14 respiratory researchers and two lay members. The committee then ranks the applications in order of scientific merit and benefit to people with lung disease and makes recommendations to our trustees. Funding is granted to the top-ranking grants, taking into account our priority areas and the funding available.

Sources of information

Accounts; annual report; Charity Commission record; funder's website; guidelines for applicants.

Atkin Charitable Foundation

General charitable purposes and Jewish causes

UK and Israel

£680,100 (2020/21)

CC number: 1112925

Correspondent: Raymond Harris, Trustee, 16 Rosemont Road, London NW3 6NE (tel: 07932 279494; email: info@atkinfoundation.org)

Trustees: Barry Gold; Ross Atkin; Celia Atkin; Edward Atkin; Lara Atkin.

General information

The Atkin Charitable Foundation is a grant-making charity established in January 2006 and funded by private donations from the Atkin family. Its objects are the relief of poverty, distress and sickness, the advancement of education, the protection of health and other charitable purposes.

Financial information

Year end	05/04/2021
Income	£1,400
Grants to organisations	£680,100

Further financial information

Full accounts were not available to view on the Charity Commission's website due to the foundation's low income. We have therefore estimated the foundation's grant total based on its total expenditure.

Beneficiaries included: Roundhouse Trust (£85,000); JAMI (£50,000); Jewish Care (£35,000); Great Ormond Street Hospital Charity (£20,000); Design Museum and National Holocaust Centre and Museum (£10,000 each); Royal Academy of Art (£8,400).

Applications

Apply in writing to the correspondent.

Sources of information

Accounts; annual report; Charity Commission record.

Atlas Memorial Ltd

Jewish religion and religious education; relief of poverty for Jewish communities; maintenance of buildings used for religious practice

Worldwide

£1.45 million (2020/21)

CCNI number: NIC101043

Correspondent: Michael Salomon, 86 Filey Avenue, London N16 6JJ (tel: 020 8806 0088)

Trustees: Joel Gross; Abraham Gross; Israel Gross; Berish Gross.

General information

Atlas Memorial Ltd was established in 2015, with the aims of furthering the Orthodox Jewish religion and religious education through the funding of religious organisations and places of worship, as well as the relief of poverty for the Jewish community.

According to the charity's 2020/21 accounts:

> This charity was set up to support the activities of religious Jewish organisations especially in the field of education. The trustees identify institutions and organisations which meet its criteria and regularly support a number of these institutions and organisations, which themselves are growing worldwide. The charity is also supportive of organisations which are solely committed to the relief of poverty. Such organisations assist needy Jewish families financially and also through distribution of basic needs.

Financial information

Year end	31/01/2021
Income	£850,000
Assets	£3,460,000
Grants to organisations	£1,450,000

Further financial information

Only beneficiaries of grants over £70,000 were listed in the accounts. Grants under £70,000 totalled £508,300.

Beneficiaries included: Asser Bishvil Foundation (£322,000); United Talmudical Association (£295,000); Notzar Chesed (£236,000); Friends of Beis Chinuch Lebonos (£88,000).

Applications

The accounts suggest that the trustees both accept applications from charities and actively seek potential applicants. Contact the correspondent for further information.

Sources of information

Accounts; annual report; Charity Commission for Northern Ireland record.

Lawrence Atwell's Charity (Skinners' Company)

Support for young people to move into employment

England and Wales, with priority given to London and Kent

£332,800 (2019/20)

CC number: 210773

Correspondent: Grants Officer, Skinners' Hall, 8 Dowgate Hill, London EC4R 2SP (tel: 020 7213 0561; email: atwell@skinners.org.uk)

Trustee: The Worshipful Company of Skinners.

 www.skinners.org.uk/grants-and-trusts/atwell

General information

Lawrence Atwell's Charity dates back to 1588 when it was established to support young people from low-income backgrounds, to help them move into work, develop vocational qualifications and improve their life chances. The charity does this through two main programmes of funding.

Charities programme: funds programmes of work principally based in London and Kent, which support young people who are not in employment, education or training to help them move into work. Grants of up to £10,000 per annum are available, with awards for three years open to consideration.

Individuals programme: Grants are available for young people living in England and Wales from low-income backgrounds, to help them gain vocational, accredited qualifications. Grants are offered up to £1,500 for people aged 16 to 26, to take courses (up to level 3) that will help them move into employment.

Financial information

Year end	30/06/2021
Income	£387,600
Assets	£19,140,000
Grants to organisations	£332,800

Beneficiaries included: Circle Community (£10,000); Young Lives Foundation (£9,900); The Gifted Organisation Ltd (£9,300); Pathways for All People (£6,000).

Exclusions

According to its website, the charity will not fund:

- Work that does not support young people into employment or to become employment ready
- Projects that have no community or charitable element
- Retrospective funding, deficits or loans
- Organisations which are not a registered not-for-profit organisation
- Organisations with an annual turnover above £1,000,000
- Organisations with reserves of more than 12 months' expenditure
- Organisations that do not provide direct services to clients
- Organisations which applied to us unsuccessfully within the previous 18 months
- Capital Costs
- Services which are a statutory responsibility
- Projects that are purely for the advancement of religion or politics (this does not exclude faith based charities, however we may ask for a copy of your non-proselytizing policy)
- Overseas work

Applications

For the Charities programme, the trustees ask applicants to contact them by email with a short outline of the project. If you are eligible, the charity will be in touch with full details of how to apply. Further information, including application deadlines, can be found on the charity's website.

Sources of information

Accounts; Charity Commission record; funder's website; advice from funder.

The Aurora Trust (The Ashden Trust)

Sustainable farming; deforestation; climate change; homelessness (particularly among young people and women); connecting people and nature

UK and overseas

£1.26 million (2020/21)

CC number: 802623

Correspondent: The Trustees, The Peak, 5 Wilton Road, London SW1V 1AP (tel: 020 7410 0330; email: info@sfct.org.uk or ashdentrust@sfct.org.uk)

Trustees: Sarah Butler-Sloss; Claire Birch; Grace Yu.

www.ashdentrust.org.uk

General information

This is one of the Sainsbury Family Charitable Trusts, which share a joint administration but work autonomously as independent legal entities. They have a common approach to grant-making and generally discourage applications from organisations not already in contact with the trust concerned, but some are open to unsolicited approaches.

The Aurora Trust, formerly known as the Ashden Trust was established in 1989 and its primary purpose is to tackle climate change through its four programme areas:

- Sustainable farming
- Connecting people and nature
- Stopping deforestation
- People at risk of homelessness

Financial information

Year end	05/04/2021
Income	£2,040,000
Assets	£42,090,000
Grants to organisations	£1,260,000
No. of grants	47

Further financial information

During 2020/21, grants were distributed as follows:

Climate change collaboration and divest invest	£344,800
Ashden – climate solutions in action	£320,000
Connecting people with nature	£187,000
Stopping deforestation	£185,200
Sustainable farming	£145,000
General	£53,500
Payments made in former grant-making categories	£21,300

Beneficiaries included: Wild in the City (£68,800); Citizens UK (£55,000); Gecko project (£50,000); Students Organising for Sustainability (£15,000); People's Kitchen Belfast (£5,000); The Commitment (£3,300); Resurgence Trust (£2,000).

Exclusions

The trust does not make grants to individuals.

Applications

The trust does not generally accept unsolicited applications. However, the trust's website states: 'We may put out a 'Call for Proposals' to expand one of our programme areas – this will set out what activities and type and size of organisation we are looking to fund.'

Sources of information

Accounts; annual report; Charity Commission record; funder's website.

The Avon and Somerset Police Community Trust

Community safety/quality of life and crime reduction and prevention

The Avon and Somerset Constabulary area

£414,600 (2020/21)

CC number: 1076770

Correspondent: Rachael Callow, Trust Officer, PO Box 37, Valley Road, Portishead, Bristol BS20 8QJ (tel: 01278 646650; email: policecommunitytrust@avonandsomerset.police.uk)

Trustees: Paul Hooper; Patricia Hunt; Sue Mountstevens; Andy Marsh; James Makepeace; David Wood; Roger Opie; Robert Bernays.

www.avonandsomerset.police.uk/apply/police-community-trust

General information

The Avon and Somerset Police Community Trust was formed in July 1999 to provide an opportunity to invest in projects that improve the safety and quality of life within the Avon and Somerset Constabulary area, with particular emphasis on helping young people, people who are vulnerable and older people.

According to the trust's 2020/21 annual report and accounts, the trust aims to:

- Protect local people and property from crime
- Reduce anti-social behaviour
- Educate young people on the dangers of drug, alcohol and solvent abuse
- Increase community safety for all, but especially young people, people who are vulnerable and older people
- Divert young people away from crime and anti-social behaviour, encouraging their growth into responsible young adults
- Build good community relations

The trust makes grants through several funds, in particular:

- **Road Safety Fund:** grants of up to £5,000 for road safety projects aiming to reduce accidents and casualties, educate the community, and reduce economic and personal costs
- **General Fund:** grants, typically of up to £1,000, to support the trust's aims
- **Commissioner's Community Action Fund:** grants of up to £5,000 for community projects supporting the priorities of the Police Crime Plan. Note: at the time of writing (April 2022), this fund was closed to applications – see the trust's website for updates

Further information about each fund can be accessed on the trust's website.

Financial information

Year end	31/03/2021
Income	£329,800
Grants to organisations	£414,600

Further financial information

In 2020/21, grants of £5,000 or less totalled £330,500, and grants of over £5,000 totalled £84,200. A full list of beneficiaries was not provided in the trust's 2020/21 accounts. The trust's net assets for the year were illegible in the accounts.

Beneficiaries included: LifeSkills and The Wheels Project (£30,000 each); Bobby Vans (£14,200).

Exclusions

See the trust's website for fund specific exclusions.

Applications

See each fund's page on the trust's website for criteria, guidance and a relevant online application form. Deadlines for the Commissioner's Community Action Fund are as follows:

- 31 July – decision to be made in September
- 30 September – decision to be made in November
- 30 November – decision to be made in January

Deadlines for the Road Safety Fund and General Fund are as follows:

- 1 March – decision date end of April
- 1 June – decision date end of July

- 1 September – decision date end of October
- 1 December – decision date end of January

Sources of information

Accounts; annual report; Charity Commission record; funder's website.

B&Q Foundation

Community spaces; homelessness

UK and the Republic of Ireland

£688,800 (2020/21)

CC number: 1183275

Correspondent: The Trustees, B&Q House, Chestnut Avenue, Chandler's Ford, Eastleigh SO53 3LE (email: B&QFoundation@b-and-q.co.uk)

Trustees: Catherine Burge; Simon Hewett-Avison; Anna Peters; Aleah Truscott; Vicki Carroll; Antony Purnell; Andrew Moat; Paul Crisp.

 www.diy.com/corporate/bandq-foundation

General information

This foundation registered with the Charity Commission in May 2019. It is the corporate charity of B&Q, a British DIY and home improvement retailing company. It is supported by the fundraising efforts and volunteering of the company's employees.

The foundation aims to makes grants to registered charities that work to improve housing and community spaces and support people who are experiencing poor quality housing and homelessness. Charities must be based in the UK or Ireland.

Grants will typically be one-off and up to the value of £5,000. Occasionally, higher-value grants may be awarded.

Financial information

Year end	31/01/2021
Income	£926,100
Assets	£278,600
Grants to organisations	£688,800

Beneficiaries included: A list of beneficiaries was not available.

Applications

The foundation's website has a link to the Neighbourly website, where applicants can register their interest for the next round of funding.

Sources of information

Accounts; annual report; Charity Commission record; funder's website.

Backstage Trust

The performing arts

UK

£4.73 million (2020/21)

CC number: 1145887

Correspondent: The Trustees, North House, 27 Great Peter Street, London SW1P 3LN (tel: 020 7072 4498; email: info@backstagetrust.org.uk)

Trustees: Lady Susie Sainsbury; David Wood; Dominic Flynn.

General information

The trust was established in February 2012 by Lady Susan Sainsbury for general charitable purposes. In practice, the trust's priorities are focused on the arts, particularly theatre and the performing arts. Lady Sainsbury is the Deputy Chair of both the Royal Shakespeare Company and the Royal Academy of Music, and she and her husband, Lord David Sainsbury of Turville, are high-profile patrons of the arts.

The trustees' report for 2020/21 provides the following information:

> Backstage can only offer assistance to registered charities or to activities which have clear charitable aims; the trust cannot fund individuals directly. The majority of grants awarded since the Trust was established come under one of the following headings:
>
> - Providing advice and mentoring to help professional development of small and medium scale arts organisations, helping to encourage diversity and remove barriers
> - Providing advice on fundraising, helping devise fundraising strategy and preparing a case for support
> - Assisting with feasibility studies for capital projects and advice on project management
> - Funding elements (particularly the less appealing items) of capital projects
> - Encouraging new writing
> - Providing support to the arts' freelance community
> - Assisting live arts projects (not all in the UK) which encourage community participation and equal opportunities
> - Encouraging the involvement of young people in the performing arts

Financial information

Year end	05/04/2021
Income	£4,470,000
Assets	£2,420,000
Grants to organisations	£4,730,000

Beneficiaries included: The Old Vic Theatre (£550,000); Roundhouse (£250,000); Riverside Studios (£100,000); The Davey Consort (£45,000); English Touring Opera (£32,500).

Applications

Apply in writing to the correspondent. The following is taken from the trust's 2020/21 annual report:

> Applicants need to demonstrate clearly the potential viability of their project, and show that the organisation, through good governance and management, has the capacity to use charitable funding in the most effective way. Trustees will want to see evidence of realistic fundraising plans, and an understanding that while Backstage might act as a catalyst to encourage other grant-giving bodies, it should not be regarded as sole funder. A critical need for most arts organisations – in addition to enthusiasm, energy and a determination to make a difference – is professional advice providing support in areas where they, understandably, are unable to gain access to or afford appropriate guidance. Backstage can sometimes provide, or cover the costs of such advice, allowing a small organisation to benefit from help which would be beyond their means.

Sources of information

Accounts; annual report; Charity Commission record.

The Bagri Foundation

Asian culture; the arts and culture; education; health

Mainly UK and India

£512,000 (2019/20)

CC number: 1000219

Correspondent: The Trustees, c/o Ferguson Maidment and Co., 167 Fleet street, London EC4A 2EA (tel: 020 7280 0000; email: enquiries@bagrifoundation.org)

Trustees: Lady Bagri; Hon. Mr A. Bagri; Hon. Mrs A. Bagri; Amisha Bagri; Aditi Malhotra.

http://bagrifoundation.org

facebook.com/bagrifoundation

@BagriFoundation

@bagrifoundation

General information

The Bagri Foundation's principal activities relate to the promotion of Asian cultural heritage, particularly through artistic, cultural and educational projects in the UK and Indian sub-continent.

The aims of the foundation, as stated on its website, are to:

- Contribute to global discourse by encouraging artistic dialogue between cultures and disciplines
- Support new artistic work by extraordinary talent

- Share knowledge and expertise from, about or inspired by cultures across Asia
- Support ground-breaking artistic interpretations and new ideas that creatively engage both the traditional and the contemporary

The foundation's website states that its areas of interest are:

- Promotion of arts and culture of all Asia and the diasporas
- Supporting established and mid-career level artists
- Partnerships that explore global topics in creative ways
- Courses, lectures, research projects, exhibitions and symposiums that cover a wide range of topics from Asia.

It also notes that 'London is [the foundation's] prime city for showcasing talent. International projects and those in other parts of the UK are considered occasionally.'

According to the foundation's annual report, it also makes grants to medical institutes for the advancement of health. Grants range from £5,000 to £150,000 and are awarded in two rounds per year.

Financial information

Year end	31/08/2020
Income	£2,470,000
Assets	£13,210,000
Grants to organisations	£512,000

Beneficiaries included: A list of beneficiaries was not available.

Applications

See the foundation's website for details of how to apply. The foundation's Charity Commission record states that applications for support from the UK and overseas will be considered. According to its website, the trustees meet twice a year to consider applications:

- Round 1: 1 December to 31 May (close at midnight GMT) – decision by June
- Round 2: 1 June to 30 November (close at midnight GMT) – decision by December

Sources of information

Accounts; annual report; Charity Commission record; funder's website.

The Baily Thomas Charitable Fund

Supporting people with learning disabilities and research into learning disabilities

UK

£2.48 million (2019/20)

CC number: 262334

Correspondent: Ann Cooper, Secretary to the Trustees, c/o TMF Global Services (UK) Ltd, 960 Capability Green, Luton, Bedfordshire LU1 3PE (tel: 01582 439225; email: info@bailythomas.org.uk)

Trustees: Prof. Anne Farmer; Suzanne Marriott; Kenneth Young; Prof. Sally-Ann Cooper; Jonathan Snow.

www.bailythomas.org.uk

General information

The Baily Thomas Charitable Fund was established in 1971, and since 2001 the fund's sole priority for funding has been learning disabilities. The fund awards grants to registered or exempt charities to aid research into learning disabilities and to aid the care and relief of people affected by learning disabilities. The fund's website states:

> Learning disabilities (intellectual disabilities), and autism are our priorities for funding. We consider projects for children or adults. We do not give grants for research into or care of people with mental illness, dyslexia, dyspraxia nor ADHD, if they do not also have learning disabilities (intellectual disabilities).

General grants programme

General grants, of over £250, are considered for capital and revenue costs and for both specific projects and general running/core costs. Grants are usually awarded on a one-off basis but occasionally new projects are funded for two or three years. Full guidelines are available on the fund's website.

Applications for grants of between £250 and £10,000 are considered 'small grants'.

Research grants programme

Research grants are usually directed towards the initiation of research, so it can progress to a point where there is sufficient data to support an application to a major funding body. The fund's website states that funding is for the 'directly incurred costs of research', including salary costs of researchers employed on the project.

In addition, up to two fellowships are awarded each year to support promising researchers to complete a PhD on a relevant topic. Full guidelines are available on the charity's website.

Financial information

Year end	30/09/2020
Income	£2,270,000
Assets	£83,840,000
Grants to organisations	£2,480,000

Further financial information

During the year, the fund committed 255 grants totalling £3 million. Grants paid during the year totalled £2.48 million.

Only beneficiaries of grants over £20,000 were listed in the 2019/20 accounts. Grants under £20,000 totalled £728,400.

Beneficiaries included: King's College London (£111,900); Rix-Thompson-Rothenberg Foundation (£100,000); University of Cambridge (£51,900); University of Sheffield (£40,200); Linkage Community Trust (£23,100); Where Next Association (£20,000).

Exclusions

Grants are not normally awarded to individuals or CICs. The fund's website states that the following conditions alone, without additional learning disabilities (intellectual disabilities) are unlikely to receive funding:

- Autism/autism spectrum disorders/ Asperger syndrome
- Specific learning disabilities (as this is an overarching term for conditions like dyslexia, dyscalculia)
- Dyslexia
- Dyscalculia
- Specific language disorders
- Dyspraxia
- Attention deficit hyperactivity disorder
- Blind
- Deaf
- Epilepsy
- Specific motor disorders
- Head injury in adulthood
- Stroke in adulthood
- Alzheimer disease or other dementias in adulthood
- Learning difficulties (as this is a broad term that includes other conditions as well as or instead of intellectual disabilities)
- Developmental disorders (as this is a broad term that includes other conditions as well as or instead of intellectual disabilities)
- Additional support needs (as this is a broad term that includes other conditions as well as or instead of intellectual disabilities)
- Special educational needs (as this is a broad term that includes other conditions as well as or instead of intellectual disabilities)

Applications for research grants will only be considered from university departments. The charity does not accept applications from CICs.

Applications

Applications should be made using the fund's online application portal. There are no submission deadlines for applicants seeking funding up to £10,000 and grants under £5,000 are considered solely by the chair of trustees. All other grants are considered at main grant board meetings, details of which can be found on the fund's website along with comprehensive guidelines.

For research grants, the website states: 'Before submitting a full application, it is recommended that researchers submit a one page summary of the proposed study so that the Trustees may indicate whether they are prepared to consider a full application.'

Applications to the Baily Thomas Doctoral Fellowship should be sent by email to the correspondent. Guidelines are available on the fund's website.

Sources of information

Accounts; annual report; Charity Commission record; funder's website.

The Baird Trust

Maintenance and repair of churches; social welfare; community development

Scotland

£237,100 (2020)

OSCR number: SC016549

Correspondent: Iain Mowat, Secretary, 182 Bath Street, Glasgow G2 4HG (tel: 0141 332 0476; email: info@bairdtrust.org.uk)

 www.bairdtrust.org.uk

General information

The Baird Trust was founded by the Scottish industrialist James Baird in 1873. According to its Charity Commission record, it makes grants for the following objectives:

(a) the advancement of religion

(b) the advancement of citizenship or community development

(c) the relief of those in need by reason of age, ill-health, disability, financial hardship or other disadvantage

(d) the advancement of heritage and culture and

(e) the advancement of education.

There are two categories of grants for organisations: general grants, awarded for project costs; and grants awarded for repairs, renovations or new buildings of churches or church halls.

With respect to capital costs, the trust prioritises as follows:

1 Work to maintain buildings
2 Work to comply with statutory obligations, for example toilets for people with disability and disability access
3 All other work

The trust also supports active and retired ministers and their families.

Financial information

Year end	31/12/2020
Income	£386,500
Assets	£12,130,000
Grants to organisations	£237,100

Further financial information

During the year, the trust's grant total was lower than usual as the closure of churches during the COVID-19 pandemic led to fewer grant applications. The trust typically makes grants totalling over £300,000.

According to the 2020 accounts, during the year building and repair grants totalled £60,000 and sundry grants totalled £177,100. Note: sundry grants included a number of grants to individuals, but we were unable to determine the exact value.

Only beneficiaries of grants over £1,000 were listed in the trust's 2020 accounts.

Beneficiaries included: St Machar's Cathedral (£15,000); Glasgow City Church and St Peter's Episcopal Church (£10,000 each); Lochgilhead Parish Church (£7,000); Buckie Baptist Church (£5,000); Tarbert Free Church (£3,000); Ferryhill Parish Church and The Filling Station (£2,000 each).

Exclusions

According to the trust's application form for repairs and/or new build funding, the trust does not support:

- Churches with adequate unrestricted and/or designated funds that could cover the costs
- Work that is already underway or has already taken place
- Applications without some contribution from the congregation

Applications

Application forms can be downloaded from the trust's website and must be accompanied by the latest annual report and accounts. Submissions are usually by either email or post; however, at the time of writing (March 2022) postal applications were not being received due to the closure of the trust's office.

Sources of information

Accounts; annual report; funder's website; OSCR record; trust's application form.

The Ballinger Charitable Trust

Older people and health, development and well-being of young people

The North East

£1.64 million (2020)

CC number: 1121739

Correspondent: Joanne Thomas, Co-ordinator, PO Box 166, Ponteland, Newcastle upon Tyne, Tyne and Wear NE20 2BL (tel: 07578 197886; email: info@ballingercharitabletrust.org.uk)

 www.ballingercharitabletrust.org.uk

 facebook.com/ballinger.charitabletrust.3

 @Ballinger_CT

General information

The Ballinger Charitable Trust was founded in 1994 by Martin Ballinger using part of his shares and dividend income from the Go-Ahead Group plc. It was registered with the Charity Commission in 2007. The trust makes grants to charities, social enterprises, voluntary organisations and community groups whose activities support young people and older people.

The trust currently makes grants to organisations with specific projects in the North East, with priority given to those working in areas of deprivation.

The trust has two funding streams for requests of less than £5,000 and those greater than £5,000. The trust's grants are wide-ranging in size, typically from £250 to £500,000. Previous grants have been for core costs, salaries, capital costs and project costs.

At the time of writing (February 2022), the trust's website stated:

> **COVID-19 – Important Notice**
>
> Please note that our usual online grant application process remains on hold for now. This decision has been reached due to the on-going uncertainty over our income during the current period.
>
> The above will be monitored closely, and reviewed by the Trustees **on a quarterly basis**, although it is likely that this situation will continue throughout 2022.

Financial information

Year end	31/12/2020
Income	£2,180,000
Assets	£31,320,000
Grants to organisations	£1,640,000
No. of grants	98+

Further financial information

Due to the COVID-19 pandemic, the trust paused its usual grant programmes and prioritised its existing multi-year grantees. It also made 87 COVID-19 grants of between £250 and £1,000 totalling £53,300. Only beneficiaries of grants over £20,000 were listed in the accounts (11 grants).

Beneficiaries included: Save the Children (two grants totalling £111,300); Dementia Matters (£95,000); Age UK North Tyneside (£90,000); Stanley All Together Consortium (£80,000); Streetwise (£25,000); First Stop Darlington and Silverline Memories CIO (£20,000 each).

Exclusions

The trust does not make grants to individuals.

Applications

The trust has an eligibility checker on its website. Online application forms will become available on the trust's website once its grant programmes re-open. Check the website for updates.

Sources of information

Accounts; annual report; Charity Commission record; funder's website.

Bally's Foundation

Mental health

UK; Malta; Gibraltar; Sweden; Ukraine; Manilla; USA; Canada; Hong Kong

£1.44 million (2020)

CC number: 1188099

Correspondent: The Trustees, 10 Piccadilly, London WJ10 0DD (email: a contact form is available on the foundation's website)

Trustees: Christina Southall; Anita Iwugo; Kevin Hopgood; Neil Goulden; Holly Spiers.

 www.ballysfoundation.org

General information

The Bally's Foundation (formerly known as The Gamesys Foundation) was established in February 2020 by Gamesys Group who are now owned by Bally's Corporation, a global casino and entertainment company. The foundation supports the well-being of individuals experiencing mental health conditions.

Grants are made to UK-based organisations with a minimum annual income of £50,000, or the equivalent for territories outside the UK. Funding is prioritised for countries where Gamesys plc either trades or has offices. These include: United Kingdom, Malta, Gibraltar, Sweden, Ukraine, Manilla, USA, Canada and Hong Kong

Financial information

Year end	31/12/2020
Income	£2,290,000
Assets	£805,900
Grants to organisations	£1,440,000

Beneficiaries included: Women's Aid (£843,000); Media Trust (£150,000); Sue Ryder and Red Cross (£100,000 each); Clubhouse Gibraltar (£26,300); Kinetic Foundation (£2,000).

Exclusions

According to the foundation's eligibility document, it does not usually fund:

- Organisations dealing with physical health care, research, treatment and rehabilitation. For example, this includes areas such as cancer research and treatment, heart disease, dementia, epilepsy and so on
- Applications relating to sports, such as sports scholarships, sponsorship or sporting events
- Organisations or activities which preach or spread religious beliefs or attempt to convert people to their own belief or religious views
- Organisations or activities which adopt a partisan political stance, or which are party political
- Organisations that advocate the use of violence to campaign or influence public opinion
- One-off conferences or workshops even within the mental health field, as it is difficult to demonstrate the impact that such events are likely to achieve. Funding can still be made available for conferences, workshops and other gatherings as long as they form part of longer-term projects
- Appeals for the funding of study or the attainment of qualifications, whether by an individual or group sponsorship, or sporting events
- Organisations or applications focused solely or primarily on raising public awareness of mental health issues via marketing campaigns. Funding can still be made available for such campaigns as part of a larger-scale project which will deal mainly with the alleviation, support and treatment of mental health
- Services that fall under the government's responsibility. Exceptions may be made in this case when specific services are not in place or are not available to the community. In these exceptional cases, low-cost alternatives can be used as an interim measure, along with setting a realistic plan of action for ensuring sustainability when the investment ends

Applications

Apply via the foundation's website.

Sources of information

Accounts; annual report; Charity Commission record; funder's website.

The Bamford Charitable Foundation

General charitable purposes

UK and overseas, but mainly within a 40-mile radius of Rocester

£409,000 (2020/21)

CC number: 279848

Correspondent: The Trustees, J. C. Bamford Excavators Ltd, Lakeside Works, Denstone Road, Rocester, Uttoxeter, Staffordshire ST14 5JP (tel: 01889 593140)

Trustees: Lord Bamford; Lady Bamford.

General information

The foundation was established in 1979. It provides support for a wide range of charitable purposes, with a preference for causes located within a 40-mile radius of Rocester, Staffordshire.

Financial information

Year end	31/03/2021
Income	£27,300
Assets	£1,670,000
Grants to organisations	£409,000
No. of grants	19

Beneficiaries included: Medical Detection Dogs (£100,000); Child Bereavement UK (£50,000); Lakeland Autistic Charity (£20,000); Help For Heroes (£10,000); Alabare Christian Care Centres (£5,000); Morton in Marsh Croquet Club (£1,000); Young Minds (£500).

Applications

Apply in writing to the correspondent. The 2020/21 annual report states: 'Successful applicants are required to demonstrate to the trustees that the receipt of the grant is wholly necessary to enable them to fulfil their own objectives.' The trustees also proactively identify potential grant recipients.

Sources of information

Accounts; annual report; Charity Commission record.

The Roger and Sarah Bancroft Clark Charitable Trust

General charitable purposes; Quaker causes; education; heritage

UK, with a preference for Somerset

£124,500 (2020)

CC number: 211513

Correspondent: The Trustees, c/o C. and J. Clark Ltd, Box 1, 40 High Street, Street, Somerset BA16 0EQ (tel: 01458 842121; email: mel.park@clarks.com)

Trustees: Alice Clark; Martin Lovell; Caroline Gould; Priscilla Goldby; Robert Robertson.

General information

The Roger and Sarah Bancroft Clark Charitable Trust was established in 1960 to make grants to charitable organisations. The trust's 2020 annual report states:

> The Charity invites applications for grants from the public and the Trustees meet regularly to decide which applications to support. In the past grants have been made to Religious Society of Friends and associated bodies, charities connected

> with Somerset and education. However, the Trustees will consider other applications for funding.

Financial information

Year end	31/12/2020
Income	£66,700
Assets	£7,740,000
Grants to organisations	£124,500

Further financial information

Grants have totalled over £300,000 in previous years.

Beneficiaries included: The Alfred Gillett Trust (£57,400); Quaker Council for European Affairs and The Society for Protection of Ancient Buildings (£4,000 each); Retreat York Ltd (£3,000).

Applications

Apply in writing to the correspondent. The trustees meet regularly to consider applications.

Sources of information

Accounts; annual report; Charity Commission record.

The Band Trust

General charitable purposes; armed forces; children and young people; disability; disadvantaged individuals; education and arts; older people; nursing care

UK

£4.3 million (2020/21)

CC number: 279802

Correspondent: Richard Mason, Trustee, BM Box 2144, London WC1N 3XX (tel: 020 7702 4243; email: rjsmason32@gmail.com)

Trustees: Richard Mason; Bartholomew Peerless; The Hon. Nicholas Wallop; The Hon. Mrs Nicholas Wallop; Victoria Wallop; Henry Wallop.

 www.bandtrust.co.uk

General information

The trust was established in 1976 for general charitable purposes and it supports registered charities in the UK.

The trustees proactively identify organisations that they wish to support.

Financial information

Year end	31/03/2021
Income	£719,000
Assets	£23,090,000
Grants to organisations	£4,350,000

Further financial information

Grants were broken down as follows:

People with disabilities	£1.57 million
Museums and art institutions	£900,000
Educational	£592,100
Children and young people	£420,000
Disadvantaged	£310,000
Miscellaneous	£250,000
Emergency Coronavirus grants	£115,000
Older people	£64,000
Church	£60,000
Veterans	£50,000
Miscellaneous (up to £2,000)	£23,800
Individuals	£18,600

Note that ordinarily the trust does not support individuals.

Beneficiaries included: Seashell Trust (£500,000); The British Exploring Society (£150,000); The PACE Centre Ltd (£120,000); The Royal Academy of Culinary Arts (£30,000); The Sick Children's Trust (£25,000); The Bolingbroke Trust (£10,000); Friends of the Courtauld Institute (£1,100).

Exclusions

The trust will not provide support for the following: individuals, political activities, commercial ventures or publications, retrospective grants or loans, direct replacement of statutory funding or activities that are primarily the responsibility of central or local government.

Applications

The trustees identify potential recipients themselves and do not accept unsolicited applications.

The website states:

> The Trust is unable to accept unsolicited applications. Due to the increase in postage costs The Band Trust will not acknowledge unsolicited applications.
>
> All the available funds are allocated pro-actively by the trustees. They are keen that applicants do not waste any charity money or The Band Trust's equally limited resources by submitting applications that have no chance of success.

Sources of information

Accounts; annual report; Charity Commission record; funder's website.

Veronica and Lars Bane Foundation

Young people and education; livelihoods and human rights; health and well-being; arts and culture

UK and overseas, including South Africa, Europe, Nepal and Kenya

£305,000 (2020)

CC number: 1183391

Correspondent: The Trustees, 98 Frognal, London NW3 6XB (tel: 07921 894842; email: grants@banefoundation.org)

Trustees: Georg Kjallgren; Lars Erik Bane; Martin Wiwen-Nilsson; Veronica Bane.

 https://banefoundation.org

General information

The foundation was established in 2019 by Veronica and Lars Bane, philanthropists from Sweden. It provides support in the following areas:

- Youth and education
- Livelihoods and human rights
- Health and well-being
- Arts and culture

Financial information

Year end	31/12/2020
Income	£2,080,000
Assets	£4,100,000
Grants to organisations	£305,000

Beneficiaries included: Biteback2030; EMpower; Fistula Foundation; Hand-in-Hand; London Academy of Excellence; Roundhouse.

Applications

Unsolicited applications are not accepted.

Sources of information

Accounts; annual report; Charity Commission record; funder's website.

The Banister Charitable Trust

Physical and natural environment

UK

£1.64 million (2020)

CC number: 1102320

Correspondent: The Trustees, Ludlow Trust Co. Ltd, Tower Wharf, Cheese Lane, Bristol BS2 0JJ (tel: 0117 313 8200; email: charitabletrusts@ludlowtrust.com)

Trustees: Huw Banister; Christopher Banister; Ludlow Trust Company Ltd.

General information

The primary objective of this trust is to promote the conservation, protection and improvement of the physical and natural environment in the UK.

Financial information

Year end	31/12/2020
Income	£196,300
Assets	£9,750,000
Grants to organisations	£1,640,000

Beneficiaries included: RSPB Scotland (£200,000); Amphibian and Reptile Conservation Trust (£55,000); Zoological Society of London (£10,000); Future Trees Trust (£5,000); Species Recovery Trust (£3,600).

Applications

Apply in writing to the correspondent. The trust's 2020 annual accounts state:

> Applications must be made in writing setting out the project details and either the budgeted cost or the amount being requested. The trustees pledge funds based on the relevance to the trust's aims and the benefit to the environment.

Sources of information

Accounts; annual report; Charity Commission record.

Bank of Scotland Foundation

Social exclusion and disadvantage

Scotland

£4.35 million (2020)

OSCR number: SC032942

Correspondent: Sinead Finnie, Grants Manager, The Mound, Edinburgh EH1 1YZ (tel: 0131 300 9007; email: enquiries@bankofscotlandfoundation.co.uk)

Trustees: Philip Grant; Martin Fleming; Graham Blair; Alison Macdonald; Graeme Thompson; Karen Watt.

 www.bankofscotlandfoundation.org

 facebook.com/bankofscotlandfoundation

 @bofsfoundation

General information

The Bank of Scotland Foundation was established in 2002 to disperse funds from an annual donation from Lloyds Banking Group to charities across Scotland. Over the past decade, the foundation has awarded over £14 million to almost 2,000 charities through its various grant programmes.

Eligibility

Eligible organisations must be a charity registered in Scotland, operational for more than one year. Organisations must have all regulatory returns up-to-date with OCSR and Companies House. See the foundation's grant programmes on its website for specific criteria.

Grant programmes

Launched in 2019, Supporting Positive Change Across Scotland is the foundation's five-year strategic plan which aims to focus its funds and impact on charities that address social exclusion or disadvantage. Charities supported may be addressing disadvantages such as: homelessness, mental health, poverty, debt issues, learning disabilities, illiteracy, unemployment or health issues. They may also be addressing exclusionary challenges for minority groups including people with disabilities, LGBTQ+ people, people with substance misuse issues, institutional care leavers, older people or young people.

Currently, the foundation has three grant programmes:

- **Reach:** charities with an annual income of £1 million or less can apply for grants of between £1,000 and £25,000 to enable them to address social disadvantage or exclusion
- **Change:** charities with an income of between £500,000 and £2 million can apply for capital costs, project costs or unrestricted core costs of between £50,000 and £100,00 per annum, over the course of one to two years. In response to the COVID-19 pandemic, this programme is allowing charities to apply for whatever is their greatest priority and area of need. Grants should enable charities to offer continued and reliable support to people across Scotland
- **Invest:** charities with an income of between £50,000 and £1 million can apply for grants of between £10,000 and £50,000 per year for between two and five years. The grants, either for project, capital or core costs, aim to support different themes each year. In 2022, the programme aims to support charities recovering from the COVID-19 pandemic

Further information on each of the funding streams is available on the foundation's website.

Employees of Lloyds Bank in Scotland can also claim up to £1,000 in matched-giving funding. Up to £500 is available for fundraising events and up to £500 for voluntary time given.

Financial information

Year end	31/12/2020
Income	£5,310,000
Assets	£2,450,000
Grants to organisations	£4,350,000
No. of grants	363

Further financial information

In 2020, the foundation made 351 grants ranging from £200 to £145,200 under the theme of social exclusion and disadvantage. In addition, it awarded matched funding to 12 charities supported by employees.

Only beneficiaries of grants over £20,000 were listed in the 2020 accounts. A full list of beneficiaries can be found on the foundation's website.

Beneficiaries included: The Moira Anderson Foundation (£145,200); REACH Lanarkshire Autism (£64,200); Beaston Cancer Charity (£40,000); Cerebral Palsy Scotland (£26,900); Rosemount Lifelong Learning (£20,900); Macmillan Cancer Support (£7,300); Musselburgh Windsor Community Football Club (£4,300).

Exclusions

The foundation does not support the following organisations and causes:

- Political organisations
- Individuals
- Animal welfare
- The promotion of religion
- Medical research
- Charities that redistribute funding for subsequent grant-making to other organisations and/or individuals
- Advertising
- Sponsorship
- Foreign trips
- Overseas projects

Applications

Applications can be made via an online portal on the foundation's website. Applicants will be expected to submit one A4 page explaining how the grant will be used and how it will benefit the applicant's beneficiaries/community. Check the foundation's website for current deadlines and programme opening dates. A Hints and Tips application guidance document can also be found on the website.

Sources of information

Accounts; annual report; funder's website; OSCR record.

The Barbour Foundation

Social welfare; education; employability; homelessness; children and young people; older people; health; medical research; the environment; heritage; national and international crisis

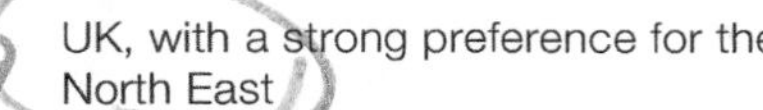

UK, with a strong preference for the North East

£2.75 million (2020/21)

CC number: 328081

Correspondent: Edith Howse, Executive Secretary, Simonside, South Shields, Tyne and Wear NE34 9PD (tel: 0191 427 4217; email: barbour.foundation@barbour.com)

Trustees: Helen Barbour; Dame Margaret Barbour; Nichola Bellaby.

 www.barbour.com/uk/the-barbour-foundation

General information

The foundation was established in 1988 and is the corporate charity of British luxury clothing and lifestyle brand, J. Barbour and Sons Ltd. It was set up by Dame Margaret Barbour, with a gift of 20% of the company shares. According to its website, the foundation supports charities and causes primarily in the North East (i.e. Tyne and Wear, Northumberland, Durham, South Tyneside).

Areas of work

The foundation's website states:

> The Foundation has a diverse collection of objectives, including;
>
> - The relief of persons in the North East of England who are in conditions of need, by reasons of their social and

economic circumstances, hardship or distress.
- To assist organisations that provide services/projects for those with special needs.
- To help improve the employment prospects of young people and to alleviate their problems of homelessness in the North East of England.
- The promotion of research into the cause and treatment of chronic illnesses or diseases and the provision of medical equipment.
- The protection and preservation for the benefit of the public in the North East of England such features of cities, towns. Villages and the countryside as are of special environmental, historical and architectural interest.
- National and international crisis

Grants are available in the following categories: main grants of over £2,000 and small grants of up to £2,000.

Financial information

Year end	05/04/2021
Income	£609,100
Assets	£13,170,000
Grants to organisations	£2,750,000

Beneficiaries included: Newcastle University Faculty of Medical Sciences (£1 million); North Music Trust (£150,000); Hospitality and Hope (£30,000); Veterans At Ease (£10,000); Single Homeless Action Initiative Durham and Versus Arthritis (£5,000 each); Together For Short Lives (£3,000); National Kidney Federation, Theatre Space and Wallsend Sea Cadets (£1,000 each).

Exclusions

According to its website, the foundation will not give for the following:
- Requests from outside the geographical area
- Requests from educational establishments
- Capital grants for building projects
- Applications for/from individuals

Applications

Apply in writing to the correspondent. Full details of what should be included in an application can be found on the foundation's website. Applications for the main grants are considered at quarterly meetings and applications for the small grants applications are considered at meetings every six weeks.

The website states the following:

> In addition to the Grant Meetings, consideration is given to requests for prizes for charitable events. If successful a voucher will be issued. Applications for prizes should be made in writing to the correspondence address. Applications must include the full address, date and full details of the event.

Sources of information

Accounts; annual report; Charity Commission record; funder's website.

Barcapel Foundation Ltd

Health; heritage; young people

UK, mainly Scotland

£93,600 (2020)

OSCR number: SC009211

Correspondent: Mia McCartney, Secretary, Third Floor, 3 Hill Street, New Town, Edinburgh EH2 3JP (tel: 0131 381 8111; email: admin@barcapelfoundation.org)

 www.barcapelfoundation.org

General information

The foundation was established in 1964 after the sale of the family business, Scottish Animal Products. The following information is taken from the foundation's website:

> Our three priority areas of interest for funding are **health**, **heritage** and **youth**.
>
> **Health** – all areas of medicine and healing are supported by the foundation, with a particular interest in complementary and alternative therapies.
>
> **Heritage** – we are committed to preserving and protecting our artistic and cultural heritage, especially with reference to the built environment.
>
> **Youth** – the foundation supports all areas of development for young people especially those from socially disadvantaged backgrounds.

Further detail about each of the foundation's priority areas is given on its website.

Grants are generally awarded to registered charities, although non-registered charitable organisations and individuals may occasionally be considered. The foundation's website states: 'It is highly unusual that a single donation will exceed £100,000 and all potential awards over £20,000 are assessed by a team operating independently of the Directors.'

Financial information

Year end	31/12/2020
Income	£55,500
Assets	££3,040,000
Grants to organisations	£93,600
No. of grants	9

Further financial information

In 2020, the foundation awarded grants totalling £93,600. The foundation's 2020 annual report notes that 'During the year, as a result of the pandemic, the Charity made a number of smaller grants in respect of each of the three priority areas'. In 2019 the foundation awarded grants totalling £419,500 and in 2018 grants totalled £385,600.

Beneficiaries included: A list of beneficiaries was not available. Previous beneficiaries include: The Little Sparta Trust (£30,000); Grassmarket Community Project (£20,000); Prince's Trust for Scotland (£15,000) Versus Arthritis (£10,000); Scottish Opera (£8,000); The Daisy Garland (£5,000); Tall Ships Youth Trust (£3,000).

Exclusions

Support is not given for:
- Individual applications for travel or similar
- Organisations or individuals engaged in promoting religious or political beliefs
- Applications for funding costs of feasibility studies or similar

Support is unlikely to be given for local charities whose work takes place outside the British Isles.

Applications

A preliminary application form can be downloaded from the foundation's website, and should be returned via email with a copy of your latest annual accounts and a covering letter. If an initial application is assessed as being likely to receive support from the trustees, the secretary will contact you for more information. The trustees typically meet in June and November to consider applications; upcoming deadlines are posted on the foundation's website.

Sources of information

Accounts; annual report; funder's website; OSCR record.

The Baring Foundation

The arts; international development; strengthening civil society and the voluntary sector

UK and Africa

£4.29 million (2020)

CC number: 258583

Correspondent: The Trustees, 8–10 Moorgate, London EC2R 6DA (tel: 020 7767 1348; email: baring.foundation@uk.ing.com)

 https://baringfoundation.org.uk

 @Baring_Found

General information

The foundation was established in 1969 as the corporate charity of Barings Bank. The foundation aims to improve the quality of life of people experiencing disadvantage and discrimination by making grants.

Grant programmes

The arts: according to the website, funding opportunities are likely to vary but the major focus of the programme will be on participatory art, 'where training artists work with people without their training to develop their creative skills'. Since 2020, funding in this area has focused on promoting the role of creativity in the lives of people with mental health problems. The programme is anticipated to run for at least five years, with up to £1 million in funding available each year. All funding rounds are announced on the website.

International development: this programme supports front-line civil society organisations and local grant-makers in sub-Saharan Africa working to end discrimination and disadvantage based on gender, sexual orientation or gender identity. Applications to this programme are by invitation only, unless otherwise advertised.

Strengthening Civil Society: this programme supports the use of law and human rights-based approaches. The programme is a collaboration with the Legal Education Foundation and Esmée Fairbairn Foundation. It aims to boost engagement and to support organisations within broader civil society to embrace legal and human rights-based approaches as effective tools for achieving change for individuals and communities. It also aims to build sustainable collaborations, partnerships and networks that leverage existing expertise within the sector to ensure the use of these approaches is as effective as possible.

The foundation is committed to supporting racial justice through all its grant programmes. Also, within its funding themes, the foundation aims to respond flexibly to the effects of the COVID-19 pandemic.

Grants are typically made for core costs and unrestricted funding is also available.

Financial information

Year end	31/12/2020
Income	£2,230,000
Assets	£120,000,000
Grants to organisations	£4,290,000
No. of grants	161

Further financial information

According to the 2020 accounts, the foundation gave a greater sum of money in 2020 than at any time in the last two decades. Overall, 161 new grants were agreed. There is a full list of the grants made during the year on the foundation's website.

Beneficiaries included: The All Party Parliamentary Group for Global LGBT+ Rights (£148,600); COVID-19 Bereaved Families for Justice UK (£40,000); Just for Kids Law (£25,700); Headspace Bolton (£12,000); Paisley Opera and The VC Gallery (£8,000 each); Hospice UK (£5,000); Minority Ethnic Carers of Older People Project (£4,500).

Applications

Applications must be made using the online system on the foundation's website. Prospective applicants should check the website to see when programmes open and for application opening/closing dates. Applicants may wish to sign up to the foundation's e-newsletter, to be notified when funding rounds open. Note: applications for international development grants are by invitation only. Also note that due to the number of enquiries the foundation receives, it does not have capacity to reply to unsolicited correspondence.

Sources of information

Accounts; annual report; Charity Commission record; funder's website.

The Barker-Mill Foundation

General charitable purposes; education; health; performing arts and culture; sport and leisure; animal welfare

UK, with a strong preference for the south-west of Hampshire, including Southampton

£14 (2020/21)

CC number: 1045479

Correspondent: Christopher Gwyn-Evans, Trustee and Administrator, The Estate Office, Longdown, Marchwood, Southampton, Hampshire SO40 4UH (tel: 023 8029 2107; email: info@barkermillfoundation.com)

www.barkermillfoundation.com

facebook.com/BarkerMFoundation

General information

The Barker-Mill Foundation was established in 1995 from funds provided by members of the Barker-Mill family in memory of their father and grandfather, Peter Barker-Mill. Previously known as the Peter Barker-Mill Memorial Charity, the foundation makes donations to charities, schools and organisations primarily in south-west Hampshire.

According to its website, the foundation makes around 80 donations each year, predominantly to those in the areas where the family has owned land for generations: the Lower Test Valley, Nursling, Ashurst, Colbury, Hounsdown, Longdown and Marchwood. Other than in exceptional circumstances, the foundation does not normally make one-off grants over £5,000.

Financial information

Year end	31/03/2021
Income	£48,100
Assets	£2,650,000
Grants to organisations	£14

Further financial information

The foundation had a particularly low grant total in 2020/21 but notes in its annual report:

> The usual operation of the Charity was effectively suspended between late March 2020 and early June 2021 as a result of both the COVID-19 pandemic, which impacted significantly on the investment portfolio valuation and the death in December 2020 of Trustee Tim Jobling

In the previous year (2019/20), the foundation awarded grants totalling £320,600.

Beneficiaries included: A list of beneficiaries was not available. Previous beneficiaries include: The Murray Parish Trust, Southampton Hospital Charity (General intensive Care Unit) (£100,000 each); Breast Cancer Haven (£24,000); Hampshire and Isle of Wight Wildlife Trust (£10,000); Raybell Charters (£4,000); Friends of Hazel Wood (£2,000); Colbury Memorial Hall Remembrance Concert (£500).

Exclusions

The foundation will typically not consider applications for funding from:

- Individuals
- National charities
- Charities with no connection to Hampshire

Applications

Applications should be made via the foundation's website, where guidelines are also available. The trustees meet quarterly to consider applications, usually in January, April, July and October.

Sources of information

Accounts; annual report; Charity Commission record; funder's website.

Lord Barnby's Foundation

General charitable purposes

UK

£211,900 (2020/21)

CC number: 251016

Correspondent: The Trustees, PO Box 442, Market Drayton, Shropshire TF9 9EQ (tel: 07835 441168; email: lordbarnbyfoundation@gmail.com)

Trustees: Laura Greenall; The Hon. George Lopes; The Countess Peel; Mr E. J. Smith-Maxwell; David Cecil.

General information

The settlor of the charity was the late The Rt Hon. Vernon, Baron Barnby. Following the death of Lady Barnby on 2 November 1988 the residue of her estate, after payment of certain legacies, was added to the foundation.

The foundation has established a permanent list of beneficiaries that it supports each year, with the remaining funds then distributed to other charities.

Financial information

Year end	31/03/2021
Income	£227,700
Assets	£5,270,000
Grants to organisations	£211,900

Further financial information

During 2020/21 grants totalled £190,100; however, in previous years the trust has made grants totalling over £300,000.

Beneficiaries included: Guy's and St Thomas' Charity (£12,000); Country Food Trust (£10,000); Heel and Toe Children's Charity (£5,000); The Garden Classroom (£2,000); FareShare Sussex (£1,000); Kate's Home Nursing (£750); Brain Tumour Charity (£500).

Exclusions

Grants are not given to individuals.

Applications

Applications will only be considered if they are received in writing and accompanied by a set of your latest accounts. Contact the correspondent for further information.

Sources of information

Accounts; annual report; Charity Commission record.

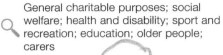

The Barnes Fund

General charitable purposes; social welfare; health and disability; sport and recreation; education; older people; carers

Ancient parish of Barnes only (broadly the SW13 postal district)

£347,700 (2020)

CC number: 200103

Correspondent: Katy Makepeace-Gray, Executive Director, PO Box 347, Hampton TW12 9ED (tel: 07484 146 802 (Monday to Thursday); email: executivedirector@thebarnesfund.org.uk)

Trustee: The Barnes Fund Trustee Ltd.

 https://thebarnesfund.org.uk

General information

The Barnes Fund (formerly known as the Barnes Workhouse Fund) was registered with the Charity Commission in 1961 and makes grants to organisations that benefit residents of the ancient parish of Barnes (this is, broadly speaking, the SW13 postal district).

The website states:

> Your organisation is likely to be providing one or more of the following to support the needs of the people of Barnes:
> - Support to **older people** or their carers
> - The relief of those on **low income** or in financial hardship
> - Relief and support to people who are **disabled, or in poor physical or mental health,** or their **carers**
> - facilities for **recreation** and other leisure pursuits, to improve the physical and mental wellbeing of all Barnes residents
> - **Educational facilities and opportunities**
>
> You do not need to be based in Barnes, but you do need to reach and assist Barnes people.

The fund considers applications for:

- Core funding and capital revenue grants
- Grants for specific one-off projects, schemes or equipment

The fund also makes grants to individuals through referral agencies for educational purposes and for the relief of financial hardship.

Financial information

Year end	31/12/2020
Income	£721,500
Assets	£13,510,000
Grants to organisations	£347,700
No. of grants	42

Further financial information

During the year 81% of the grants made to organisations were for core costs and 19% were for specific projects.

Grants were awarded in a wide range of categories, including social isolation; physical and mental health; end of life care; hardship; disability; carers; older people; children, parenting and families; education; the arts; community; access to nature; advice and advocacy.

Beneficiaries included: Barnes Methodist Church (£50,000); Richmond Citizens Advice (£38,600); Crossroads Care (£19,700); Barnes Community Arts Centre (£12,000); Richmond Aid (£5,000); Crossways Pregnancy Crisis Centre (£3,000); Barnes Music Society (£1,300); Power Station Youth Club (£500).

Exclusions

The fund does not provide grants to national charities.

Applications

Organisations can apply using an online form on the fund's website and are advised to first read the eligibility guidelines on the website. There are separate application forms for core funding and project funding. Applications from organisations are considered at trustee meetings in February, May, July and October each year. Applications must be received by the 6th of the month preceding a meeting to be considered.

Sources of information

Accounts; annual report; Charity Commission record; funder's website.

The Max Barney Foundation

General charitable purposes and unemployment, particularly within the Jewish community

England; Wales; Israel

£1.06 million (2020/21)

CC number: 1164583

Correspondent: The Trustees, 4th Floor, 168 Shoreditch High Street, London E1 6HU (tel: 020 7583 5555; email: shraga@maxbarney.com)

Trustees: Alexander Bard; Michael Goldstein; Gary Phillips.

General information

The foundation was registered with the Charity Commission in November 2015 and primarily makes grants to organisations for the relief of unemployment through vocational training and job creation. Preference is given to organisations focusing on the Jewish community. Grants may be awarded to charities, social enterprises or businesses.

Financial information

Year end	31/05/2021
Income	£1,020,000
Assets	£706,400
Grants to organisations	£1,060,000

Further financial information

Grants were distributed as follows:

Relief of unemployment through job creation	£549,800
Relief of unemployment through vocational training	£321,400
General charitable causes	£188,700

Beneficiaries included: A list of beneficiaries was not available. Previous beneficiaries include: The Work Avenue and World Jewish Relief (£100,000 each); London School of Jewish Studies (£50,000); Employment Resource (£42,000); Community Security Trust (£25,000); One Voice (£20,000).

Applications

Apply in writing to the correspondent.

Sources of information

Accounts; annual report; Charity Commission record.

Barnwood Trust

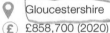

Improving the quality of life of people with disabilities and mental health conditions; sports equipment; holidays and play schemes; community spaces

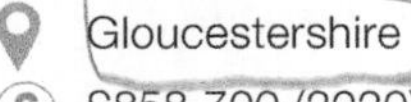

Gloucestershire

£858,700 (2020)

CC number: 1162855

Correspondent: The Grants Team, Overton House, Overton Road, Cheltenham GL50 3BN (tel: 01242 539935; email: grants@barnwoodtrust.org)

Trustees: Dr Jean Waters; Suzanne Beech; Shaun Parsons; Edward Playne; Benjamin Preece-Smith; Ann Santry; Patricia Jay; Philippa Jones; Colin Smith.

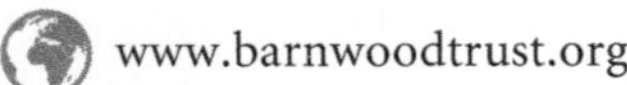

www.barnwoodtrust.org

facebook.com/BarnwoodTrust

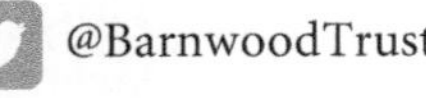

@BarnwoodTrust

@barnwoodtrust

General information

Barnwood House Trust was established in its original form in 1792 and its current endowment arises principally from the sale of the land upon which Barnwood House Hospital stood until 1969. It is one of Gloucestershire's largest charities providing assistance to people with disabilities, including those with mental health conditions, who live in the county.

The trust makes grants to organisations to support charitable work in Gloucestershire. The trust can support core costs, activity/project costs, equipment costs or refurbishment costs. At the time of writing (February 2022), we were unable to access the trust's funding guidelines through its website. Previous research suggests that all organisations are advised to contact the strategic development manager in their area of Gloucestershire to discuss their ideas.

The trust also makes grants to individuals. See its website for details.

Eligibility

The trust's website states:

> Charities, Community Interest Companies, social enterprises and other groups who work in Gloucestershire's local communities and not-for-profits can all apply for funding. You do not need to be a 'constituted' organisation or group to apply but if your organisation or group does not have a bank account, you may need to work with another organisation which can accept the funds awarded on your behalf.

Financial information

Year end	31/12/2020
Income	£3,020,000
Assets	£100,000,000
Grants to organisations	£858,700

Further financial information

During the year, small grants to organisations totalled £858,700 and grants to individuals and small groups totalled £1.68 million. Only the organisations that received grants of over £10,000 were listed in the accounts. Grants of under £10,000 totalled £400,000.

Beneficiaries included: Access Social Care (£50,000); Gloucester City Homes (£20,000); Bromford Housing Association (£15,000); Young Gloucestershire (£12,500); Cotswold Counselling and Independence Trust (£10,000 each).

Exclusions

People or organisations outside Gloucestershire.

Applications

Applicants must first contact their local strategic development manager (listed on the trust's website) to discuss their ideas. Applications can then be made via an online portal on the trust's website. Be aware that applications are considered first by Gloucestershire Funders, a partnership of funding organisations that works together to support local initiatives in Gloucestershire's communities.

Sources of information

Accounts; annual report; Charity Commission record; funder's website.

Robert Barr's Charitable Trust

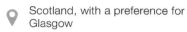

General charitable purposes; welfare; health; the arts; conservation; research

Scotland, with a preference for Glasgow

£749,000 (2020/21)

OSCR number: SC007613

Correspondent: The Trustees, c/o Dentons UK and Middle East LLP, 1 Regent Street, Glasgow G2 1RW

General information

The Robert Barr Charitable Trust makes grants to UK-registered charities, with a preference for those based in Glasgow. Grants are made for general charitable purposes including welfare, health, the arts, conservation and research.

The trustees have a policy of not normally supporting any charity more than once every three years and favour capital projects rather than contributions to running costs.

Grants vary in size, ranging from £5,000 to £75,000. Funding is often phased over a number of years.

Financial information

Year end	05/04/2021
Income	£250
Grants to organisations	£749,000

Further financial information

Full accounts were not available to view on the OSCR website due to the trust's low income. We have therefore estimated the grant total based on the trust's total expenditure.

Beneficiaries included: A list of beneficiaries was not available. Previous beneficiaries include: Keep Scotland Beautiful (£100,000); The Royal College of Surgeons of Edinburgh (£50,000); The Mark Scott Foundation (£40,000); Linlithgow Community Development Trust (£30,000); Team Jak Foundation and The Bread Maker (£20,000 each); The Fraser Centre Community Trust (£15,000); Provan Hall Community Trust (£10,000); Islay and Jura Community Enterprises Ltd (£5,000).

Applications

Apply in writing to the correspondent.

Sources of information

Accounts; annual report; OSCR record.

The Paul Bassham Charitable Trust

General charitable purposes

Norfolk

£313,900 (2020/21)

CC number: 266842

Correspondent: The Trustees, c/o Howes Percival LLP, Flint Buildings, 1 Bedding Lane, Norwich, Norfolk NR3 1RG (tel: 01603 762103)

General information

The trust was established in 1973 to support a wide range of charitable causes. Preference is given to charities and charitable causes in Norfolk; however, applications would be considered from national/international charities for projects benefitting Norfolk and its residents.

Financial information

Year end	05/04/2021
Income	£346,300
Assets	£14,330,000
Grants to organisations	£313,900

Further financial information

The list of beneficiaries only shows grants of over £5,000. Grants under £5,000 totalled £258,900.

Beneficiaries included: Norfolk and Norwich Festival and Soul Foundation (£10,000 each); Harleston Information Plus, Matthew Project and Norfolk Wildlife Trust (£5,000 each).

Exclusions

The trust does not make grants directly to individuals or to unregistered charities.

Applications

Apply in writing to the correspondent. The trustees will only consider written applications and meet quarterly to discuss such applications.

Sources of information

Accounts; annual report; Charity Commission record.

The Batchworth Trust

Medical causes; youth charities; welfare

Worldwide

£682,500 (2020/21)

CC number: 245061

Correspondent: James Peach, c/o Kreston Reeves LLP, Springfield House, Springfield Road, Horsham, West Sussex RH12 2RG (tel: 01293 776152; email: james.peach@krestonreeves.com)

General information

The trust mainly supports general charitable purposes both in the UK and overseas, with a particular interest in medical research, young people and social welfare. The 2020/21 annual report states:

> Grants to smaller charities remained a priority of the Trust during the year and in most cases the distributions so made were provided to support an innovation or a critical issue. Support for larger or national charities was predominantly to support either the ongoing work of the organisation or a particular initiative.

Financial information

Year end	05/04/2021
Income	£8,350,000
Assets	£21,970,000
Grants to organisations	£682,500
No. of grants	70

Further financial information

Grants were awarded to 70 charities during the year.

Beneficiaries included: Mind (£30,000); Christian Aid (£22,500); Off the Record (£20,000); RSABI (£15,000); St Peter's Hospice (£10,000); Action Ethiopia (£7,000); Cruse Bereavement Care (£5,000); St George's Kidney Patients Association (£3,000).

Applications

Apply in writing to the correspondent.

Sources of information

Accounts; annual report; Charity Commission record.

The Battersea Power Station Foundation

General charitable purposes, including community services and development

Lambeth; Wandsworth

£150,100 (2020)

CC number: 1161232

General information

The foundation was established in 2014 by the shareholders who are redeveloping Battersea Power Station. The foundation works with local organisations to support projects that improve the quality of life for people who live in Lambeth and Wandsworth.

There are two grant programmes administered by the foundation:

The Spring Fund

The following information has been taken from the foundation's website:

> The Spring Fund helps communities in Lambeth and Wandsworth with projects that bring together residents, volunteers, businesses and local authorities to strengthen neighbourhood bonds, create new opportunities and transform lives. It's about funding smaller, grassroots community efforts that energise neighbourhoods and deliver on local goals.
>
> Communities in both boroughs have been awarded grants that support civic activism, generate new cultural events, organise community members towards a common goal, create welcoming green spaces, build new opportunities for young people, improve community safety, and much more.
>
> Organisations applying for Spring Fund grants should show strong community ties to Lambeth or Wandsworth and meet some of these funding requirements in their proposals:
>
> - Encourage better connections between, and amongst local communities, so people feel a greater sense of ownership and responsibility for the places where they live
> - Improve the wellbeing of local people by building their confidence and strength of character
> - Open up new economic opportunities for residents
> - Create locally-based solutions to improve community conditions
> - Motivate residents to join in with neighbourhood activities
> - Improve the capabilities of local organisations to deal with neighbourhood issues.

The Evolve Fund

Grants from this fund are made on a proactive basis, with the fund identifying organisations which match its own long-term vision.

Further details about the funding priorities and grant programmes can be found on the foundation's website.

Financial information

Year end	31/12/2020
Income	£1,010,000
Assets	£730,100
Grants to organisations	£150,100

Further financial information

In previous years grants have totalled around £1 million.

Beneficiaries included: Walcot Foundation (£25,000); Hestia (£9,600); Caius House and Junction Community Trust (£5,000 each); Providence House (£2,000); NSPCC (£1,000).

Exclusions

According to its website the foundation will not fund the following:

- Individuals or causes that will benefit only one person, including student grants or bursaries
- General and round-robin appeals
- Promotion of religion and places of worship
- Replacement or subsidy of statutory funding, or for work we consider should be funded by government, such as residential and day care, housing provision, individual schools, nurseries and colleges, or a combination of any of these
- Individual campaigns
- Organisations seeking to distribute grants or funds to others
- Capital developments and individual items of equipment
- One-off events and/or any type of sponsorship, such as conferences, seminars, galas, or summer schools
- Educational initiatives linked to the national curriculum
- Medical research or treatment, including drug and alcohol rehabilitation services
- Counselling and psychotherapy services
- Animal welfare, zoos, captive breeding and animal rescue centres
- Retrospective funding, meaning support for work that has already taken place
- Work that is not legally charitable
- Organisations who have applied unsuccessfully within the previous 12-months

Applications

Applications for the Spring Fund can be made through the foundation's website. Detailed guidance, FAQs and other information is provided on the website. The Evolve Fund is a closed programme and does not accept unsolicited applications.

Sources of information

Accounts; annual report; Charity Commission report; funder's website.

Bauer Radio's Cash for Kids Charities

Disadvantaged children and young people up to the age of 18

UK

£1.98 million (2020)

CC number: 1122062

Correspondent: The Trustees, Hampdon House, Unit 3 Falcon Court, Preston Farm, Stockton on Tees, County Durham TS18 3TS (email: info@cashforkids.uk.com)

Trustees: Sally Aitchison; Martin Ball; Sean Marley; Danny Simpson; Susan Voss; Gary Stein; David Tighe; Sarah Barnes.

 www.cashforkids.uk.com

 facebook.com/cashforkidsuk

 @cashforkids

General information

The charity supports children (up to 18 years of age) who have a disability or are ill or otherwise disadvantaged. Grants are made to individuals, charities, organisations and community groups across the UK.

Financial information

Year end	31/12/2020
Income	£12,940,000
Assets	£3,440,000
Grants to organisations	£1,980,000

Further financial information

A further £8.75 million was donated in gifts-in-kind through the Mission Christmas appeal.

Beneficiaries included: A list of beneficiaries was not available.

Exclusions

A list of exclusions is available in the Eligibility Criteria document (see main website).

Applications

To apply for a grant, first visit the locations page of the charity's website to find your local radio station and grant team. Application forms, eligibility criteria and deadlines are available on the local websites.

Sources of information

Accounts; annual report; Charity Commission record; funder's website; guidelines for applicants.

Bay Charitable Trust

Social welfare; the advancement of traditions of the Orthodox Jewish religion and the study of Torah

UK and overseas

£184,400 (2020)

CC number: 1060537

Correspondent: Ian Kreditor, Trustee, 21 Woodlands Close, London NW11 9QR (tel: 020 8810 4321)

Trustees: Ian Kreditor; Michael Lisser.

General information

According to its 2020 annual report, the objects of the trust are:

> To give charity for the relief of poverty and sickness and for the advancement of traditions of the Orthodox Jewish Religion and the study of Torah.

Financial information

Year end	31/12/2020
Income	£137,000
Assets	£45,200
Grants to organisations	£184,400

Further financial information

In 2020, the trust awarded grants totalling £184,400; however, in previous years the trust has awarded higher amounts. For example, in 2019 the trust awarded grants totalling £791,000.

Beneficiaries included: A list of beneficiaries was not available.

Applications

Apply in writing to the correspondent.

Sources of information

Accounts; annual report; Charity Commission record.

BBC Children in Need

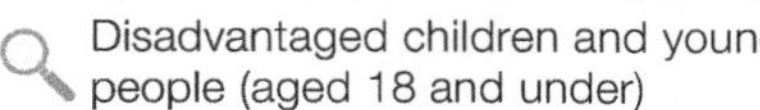
Disadvantaged children and young people (aged 18 and under)

UK

£49.85 million (2020/21)

CC number: 802052

Correspondent: Grants Team, Grants, PO Box 649, Salford, Greater Manchester M5 0LD (tel: 0345 609 0015 (select option 2); email: pudseygrants@bbc.co.uk)

Trustees: Bob Shennan; M[illegible] Jo Berry; Rosemary Millard; K[illegible] Imafidon; Trevor Bradley; Kieran Clifton; Rhona Burns; Jonathan Munro; Ade Adepitan; Suzy Lamb; James Fairclough; Sandeep Bhamra.

 www.bbcchildreninneed.co.uk

 facebook.com/bbcchildreninneed

 @BBCCiN

 @bbccin

General information

This charity, registered in 1989, distributes the proceeds of the BBC's annual Children in Need appeal (first televised in 1980). The charity's vision is that every child in the UK has a safe, happy and secure childhood and the chance to reach their potential. The charity awards grants each year to organisations working to improve the lives of disadvantaged children and young people in the UK.

Grant programmes

At the time of writing (March 2022), the charity's website explained that its main and small grant programmes were paused to applications while the charity developed a new grant-making strategy. The new strategy was set to be launched in spring 2022, with grant programmes expected to open in September 2022. Previously, the main grants programme awarded grants over £10,000 for up to three years, and the small grants programme awarded grants up to £10,000 for up to three years.

In March 2022, the charity was only awarding grants through the following programmes:

Youth Social Action Fund
In partnership with the #iwill Fund and The Hunter Foundation, the charity is delivering this £3 million fund to support organisations to embed youth social action across the UK.

Emergency Essentials
The charity also funds the Emergency Essentials programme which provides items to meet the most basic needs of individual children who are living in severe poverty. The programme is administered by Family Fund Business services. See www.familyfundservices.co.uk for further information.

Financial information

Year end	30/06/2021
Income	£65,100,000
Assets	£50,120,000
Grants to organisations	£49,850,000
No. of grants	1,429

Further financial information

In 2020/21, the charity awarded grants totalling £49.85 million to 1,429 organisations. Of the total amount awarded, £42.6 million was direct responsive funding (including 362 new main and small grants totalling £14.8 million).

Beneficiaries included: A list of beneficiaries was not available.

Exclusions

Each grants programme may have specific exclusion criteria, so check the relevant guidance on the charity's website.

Applications

Applications can be made via the charity's website which also has details of guidelines, application deadlines and exclusions. If you have a general enquiry or are looking for support regarding your application contact the charity via phone or email. You can also contact your local regional or national office.

Sources of information

Accounts; annual report; Charity Commission website; funder's website; guidelines for applicants.

BC Partners Foundation

Community development; environmental conservation; the arts; education

UK and overseas

£442,700 (2020)

CC number: 1136956

Correspondent: The Trustees, BC Partners LLP, 40 Portman Square, London W1H 6DA (tel: 020 7009 4800)

Trustees: Nikos Stathopoulos; Cedric Dubourdieu; Francesco Loredan; Jan Kengelbach; Matthew Evans.

www.bcpartners.com/about/foundation

General information

This foundation was established in 2010 and is the corporate charity of the private equity firm, BC Partners.

The firm's website states that the foundation focuses primarily on providing 'financial contributions to non-for-profit organisations worldwide that are important to the employees of BC Partners'.

The foundation is not restrictive in terms of the causes it supports; however, its funding priorities are:

- Community development including infrastructure advancements, development aid, healthcare improvements
- Conservation of the environment including endeavours related to pollution reduction, natural preservation, clean technologies
- The arts and education including support for educational, scholastic or artistic programmes

The foundation also matches donations made by employees.

Financial information

Year end	31/12/2020
Income	£396,600
Assets	£528,000
Grants to organisations	£442,700
No. of grants	29

Beneficiaries included: BCPF Inc (£238,200); Private Equity Foundation (£110,500); Dolphin Society (£25,000); American School in London Foundation (£15,000); Kids Welcome (£3,600); MS Society (£950); Hertford College (£500); Northern Ireland Children's Hospice (£100).

Applications

The foundation does not accept unsolicited applications. Charities are nominated by BC Partners employees or trustees of the foundation.

Sources of information

Accounts; annual report; Charity Commission record; funder's website.

Beauland Ltd

Social welfare and the advancement of the Orthodox Jewish faith and Jewish religious education

Worldwide, with some preference for the Manchester area

£256,700 (2020/21)

CC number: 511374

Correspondent: Maurice Neumann, Trustee, 32 Stanley Road, Salford, Greater Manchester M7 4ES (tel: 0161 720 6188)

Trustees: Henry Neumann; Pinchas Neumann; Maurice Neumann; Mr Neumann; Esther Henry; Janet Bleier; Miriam Friedlander; Rebecca Delange; Hannah Roseman.

General information

Beauland Ltd was registered with the Charity Commission in 1981. According to its Charity Commission record, its objectives are:

- To foster, assist and promote the charitable activities of any institutions professing and teaching the principles of traditional Judaism
- To advance religion in accordance with the Orthodox Jewish Faith
- To give aid to and support needy persons in general

Financial information

Year end	05/04/2021
Income	£861,900
Assets	£11,210,000
Grants to organisations	£256,700

Beneficiaries included: Talmud Torah Machzikei Hadass Trust (£100,000); Chortkov Trust (£30,000); Choimel Dalim (£25,500); Beenstock Home (£11,500); Chai Institute (£10,000); Asser Bishvil Foundation (£4,700).

Applications

Apply in writing to the correspondent.

Sources of information

Accounts; annual report; Charity Commission record.

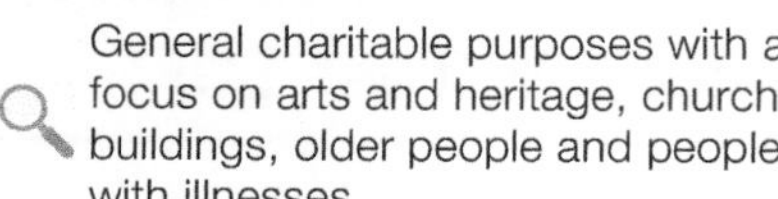

The Beaverbrook Foundation

General charitable purposes with a focus on arts and heritage, church buildings, older people and people with illnesses

England

£294,800 (2019/20)

CC number: 1153470

Correspondent: Jane Ford, Secretary, 19 Crown Passage, London SW1Y 6PP (tel: 020 3325 3987; email: jane@beaverbrookfoundation.org)

www.beaverbrookfoundation.org

General information

The foundation was originally established in 1954 by the first Lord Beaverbrook, a Canadian-British politician and newspaper publisher.

Grants are made at the discretion of the trustees for a range of charitable purposes including those that would have reflected the interests of the first Lord Beaverbrook, including:

- The erection or improvement of the fabric of any church building
- The purchase of books, papers, manuscripts, or works of art
- Care for older people or people with illnesses

Grant-making policy

Grants are made for capital expenditure, revenue and running costs, and towards special projects. The trustees are keen to support matched-funding initiatives and may make payment conditional upon the applicant obtaining the remaining funding from other sources. The foundation is able to support all faith organisations but applications are only accepted from registered charities.

Financial information

Year end	30/09/2020
Income	£78,200
Assets	£13,860,000
Grants to organisations	£294,800

Beneficiaries included: Northwood House (£40,000); English National Ballet and RAF Museum – Hendon(£25,000 each); World House Welfare (£20,000); Battle of Britain Memorial Trust (£10,000); PDSA (£7,500); Charlotte's BAG (£6,500).

Exclusions

Grants cannot be made for retrospective costs.

Applications

Applications can be made via the foundation's website.

Sources of information

Accounts; annual report; Charity Commission record; funder's website.

The Beaverbrooks Charitable Trust

General charitable purposes; education; welfare; health; mentoring and self-development; Jewish and Israeli charities

UK and Israel

£1.4 million (2020/21)

CC number: 1142857

Correspondent: The Trustees, Adele House, Park Road, St Annes-on-Sea, Lancashire FY8 1RE (tel: 01253 721262; email: Charitable.Trust@beaverbrooks.co.uk)

www.beaverbrooks.co.uk/100/enriching-lives

General information

This trust was registered with the Charity Commission in 2011. It is the corporate charity of Beaverbrooks the Jewellers. The trust supports a wide range of causes throughout the UK and Israel. The trust's website states:

> One of the ways we enrich lives is through our charity work. We are very proud to be able to support over 250 charities every year and to give our people the opportunity to support the causes close to their hearts.
>
> We're very proud to say that since the year 2000 we have donated over £17 million to over 750 charities.

Financial information

Year end	30/04/2021
Income	£363,600
Assets	£7,340,000
Grants to organisations	£1,400,000

Beneficiaries included: The M. and A. Brown Charitable Trust (£400,000); United Jewish Israel Appeal (£120,000); Manchester Jewish Museum (£50,000); Prevent Breast Cancer (£25,000); Magden David Adorn (£20,000); Grief Encounter (£10,000); Hale Concerts Society (£9,000); Royal Exchange Theatre (£7,000); Royal Northern College of Music (£5,000).

Applications

Contact the trust for more information.

Sources of information

Accounts; annual report; Charity Commission record.

The Becht Family Charitable Trust

Biodiversity and the environment, mainly marine conservation

Worldwide

£4.77 million (2020)

CC number: 1116657

Correspondent: The Trustees, c/o Rawlinson and Hunter, 6 New Street Square, London EC4A 3AQ (tel: 020 7842 2000; email: thebfct@rawlinson-hunter.com)

https://bfct.org

General information

Established in 2006, the trust provides support focusing on the following areas:

- Protection and restoration of the natural environment through marine conservation
- Humanitarian aid

The trust's website states: 'BFCT allocates grants to activities or organizations which neutralize, reverse or at least materially mitigate [negative impacts on the environment] in an attempt to preserve or restore our planet's biodiversity. Within this broad area, the main focus is marine conservation.'

The criteria for funding is as follows:

- Projects must clearly align with the trust's mission
- Projects must have measurable key performance indicators and specific outcomes that are a clear step forward in marine conservation
- Applicants must include a phased budget alongside a timetable for the achievement of the key performance indicators

The trust considers restricted and unrestricted funding.

Financial information

Year end	31/12/2020
Income	£4,440,000
Assets	£335,770,000
Grants to organisations	£4,770,000
No. of grants	20

Further financial information

The financial figures were converted from US dollars using the exchange rate at the time of writing (February 2022).

Beneficiaries included: Save the Children (£1.84 million); Blue Ventures Conservation (£740,000); Oceana Inc (£369,100); St George's Hospital Charity (£135,800); Sightsavers (£46,000); Oxford Hospitals (£9,200); Impatience 25 (£2,400).

Exclusions

Grants are not made to/for:

- Individuals
- Scholarships or tuition assistance for undergraduate or postgraduate students

Applications

An online application form is available on the trust's website. The trustees only reply to successful applicants.

Sources of information

Accounts; annual report; Charity Commission record; funder's website.

The John Beckwith Charitable Trust

Education; social welfare; overseas aid; young people; medical research; social welfare

UK and overseas

£258,500 (2020/21)

CC number: 800276

Correspondent: The Trustees, 124 Sloane Street, London SW1X 9BW (tel: 020 7225 2250; email: info@beckwithlondon.com)

Trustees: Sir John Beckwith; Heather Beckwith; Christopher Meech.

General information

This trust was established by Sir John Beckwith in 1987 with the aim of supporting a wide range of charitable organisations. Sir John Beckwith is the founder and Chair of Pacific Investments, a multi-asset fund management group and has a number of charitable commitments, namely as founder and President of the Youth Sport Trust.

Financial information

Year end	05/04/2021
Income	£144,800
Assets	£1,530,000
Grants to organisations	£258,500
No. of grants	50

Further financial information

During 2020/21, grants were distributed as follows:

Social welfare	44	£142,500
Sport	1	£100,000
Medical Research	4	£11,000
Education	1	£5,000

Beneficiaries included: Youth Sport Trust (£100,000); The Meath School (£11,000); National Domestic Helpline (£10,000); Lady Garden Foundation (£5,000); St John Ambulance (£4,000); Horses Trust and The Listening Place (£1,000 each); Children's House (£500).

Applications

Apply in writing to the correspondent. The trustees aim to meet once a year to review grant applications.

Sources of information

Accounts; annual report; Charity Commission record.

AJ Bell Trust

Children and young people; disability; social welfare and inclusion; skills development; education and training; health and medical research

UK

£296,600 (2019/20)

CC number: 1141269

Correspondent: Esther Speksnijder, Secretary, Blythe Hall, Blythe Lane, Lathom, Ormskirk, England L40 5TY (email: moorhall@outlook.com)

Trustees: Andrew Bell; Tracey bell; Paul Clements; Paul Barrow.

www.ajbell.co.uk/about-us/corporate-social-responsibility

General information

The trust has awarded grants and in-kind donations since 2011 and focuses on providing help and relief to people who are in need as a result of their age, financial hardship, poor health, disability, or other disadvantage. The trust's primary focus is on children and young adults under 25 years of age.

The trust supports social welfare and inclusion in the following ways:

- Providing grants, goods and services to individuals and/or charities and organisations that work to prevent or relieve financial hardship
- Providing for people's care and upbringing, including the provision of accommodation
- Skills development and education and training, including the study of art, culture, heritage or science
- Employment advice and assistance
- Providing or subsidising recreational and leisure activities and encouraging participation in amateur sports
- Promoting healthcare projects and medical research

Financial information

Year end	30/09/2020
Income	£684,900
Assets	£2,360,000
Grants to organisations	£296,600

Beneficiaries included: A list of beneficiaries was not available.

Applications

Apply in writing to the correspondent.

Sources of information

Accounts; annual report; Charity Commission record.

Benefact Trust Ltd

Churches; social welfare; homelessness; mental health; social exclusion; people who have offended; community health and well-being; substance misuse; heritage

UK and Ireland

£23.31 million (2020)

CC number: 263960

Correspondent: Iain Hearn, Benefact House, 2000 Pioneer Avenue, Gloucester Business Park, Brockworth, Gloucestershire GL3 4AW (tel: 01452 873189; email: info@benefacttrust.co.uk)

Trustees: Sir Laurence Magnus; Canon Michael Arlington; Timothy Carroll; Stephen Hudson; Caroline Banszky; The Ven. Karen Lund; The Revd Jane Hedges; Chris Moulder; The Revd Paul Davis; Sir Stephen Lamport; David Smart.

https://benefacttrust.co.uk

facebook.com/benefacttrust

@benefacttrust

General information

Formerly known as the Allchurches Trust, this trust was established in 1972. Its income is derived from its wholly owned subsidiary company the Benefact Group (formerly known as Ecclesiastical Insurance Group). According to its Charity Commission record, the trust's aims are 'to promote the Christian religion, to contribute to the funds of any charitable institutions, associations, funds or objects and to carry out any charitable purpose'.

Grant-making

Grants are available to churches and Christian charities, schools and colleges from all of the UK and Ireland, particularly areas of deprivation. The trust's grant programmes are outlined below. Grants are typically for capital projects and equipment, not salaries or running costs, with the exception of the trust's Transformational grants programme.

General grants

The General grants programme supports projects that demonstrate an impact on people and communities. These are typically capital grants that support the repair, restoration, protection and improvement of churches, cathedrals and other places of Christian worship where changes support wider community use and enable greater impact. The programme also supports projects that help tackle social issues, for example homelessness, poverty, climate change and cultural cohesion, and projects that support Christian leaders to share the Christian faith.

These grants range from £1,000 up to £15,000 for projects with a total cost of up to £1 million.

Brighter Lives

At the time of writing (May 2022) the trust's website stated: "Brighter Lives' is our new thematic grants programme. It's focused on helping Christian organisations to respond to the long-term impact throughout society of COVID-19 on people's mental health – whatever their faith, or none. [...] this programme will help enable churches and Christian charities across the UK and Ireland to provide increased mental health support'.

Methodist grants

The Methodist grants programme offers grants of up to £60,000 for building development projects that focus on church growth, community engagement and improving accessibility. Individual Methodist churches who are part of the Methodist Connexion are able to apply, along with Methodist Circuits and Districts and some key Methodist heritage sites.

Transformational grants

According to the trust's website, the 'Transformational Grants Programme provides funding for Christian organisations to make a step change in their capacity, reach, impact and spiritual growth, enabling them to forge connections with many more people and communities who will benefit from their work.' Grants can be for capital costs and salaries. Applications are considered on a rolling basis.

Roof alarm grants

The trust's Roof Protection Scheme 'provides grants to help churches install roof alarms in response to the issue of metal theft, which continues to be a very challenging issue across the UK', as stated on its website.

For more details on the trust's specific grant programmes see its website.

Financial information

Year end	31/12/2020
Income	£6,410,000
Assets	£556,050,000
Grants to organisations	£23,310,000
No. of grants	800+

Further financial information

The following geographical analysis of grants was provided in the trust's 2020 accounts:

England	£17.3 million
National projects	£2.74 million
Ireland	£1.9 million
Wales	£716,000
Scotland	£596,000
Other	£46,000

According to the trust's accounts, under the trust's general grants programme, 750 small grants were awarded totalling £2.4 million and 41 large grants were awarded totalling £1.5 million.

Only beneficiaries of grants of £100,000 and above were listed in the accounts.

Beneficiaries included: Methodist Connexion (£1.4 million); The Diocese of London (£403,000); The Diocese of Leeds (£302,000); The Cinnamon Network (£201,000); Betel UK – Birmingham (£120,000); Just Finance Foundation and The Keswick Convention Trust (£100,000 each).

Exclusions

According to the trust's website it will not normally fund the following:

- Non-Christian charities
- Overseas projects or charities
- Charities with a political association
- Projects that benefit only a small part of a community
- Multiple applications from the same organisation in a 24-month period

Applications

Applications for the General grants programme should be submitted via the trust's website using its online application form. Applications can be submitted at any time.

To apply for one of the trust's specific programmes, the relevant application form on the dedicated web page should be completed.

Sources of information

Accounts; annual report; Charity Commission record; funder's website.

Benesco Charity Ltd

Medicine; education; welfare; Jewish community

UK

£6.11 million (2020/21)

CC number: 269181

Correspondent: Michael Franks, Secretary, 8–10 Hallam Street, London W1W 6NS (tel: 020 7079 2506)

Trustees: Jonathan Ragol-Levy; Hon. Andrew Wolfson; David Wolfson; Mikael Breuer-Weil.

General information

Benesco Charity Ltd is a registered charity established in 1970. The majority of its grant expenditure is given to The Charles Wolfson Charitable Trust (Charity Commission no. 238043). Grants are also made to charitable organisations selected by the trustees and preference is given to organisations that address the needs of the Jewish community. Grants are made under the following categories:

- Medicine
- Education
- Welfare

In addition to making grants, the charity provides premises to operational charities on a reduced-rent or rent-free basis and occasionally makes interest-free loans.

Financial information

Year end	05/04/2021
Income	£9,840,000
Assets	£206,510,000
Grants to organisations	£6,110,000

Further financial information

Grants were broken down as follows: welfare (£306,000); medicine (£4,600). A grant of £5.8 million was also made to The Charles Wolfson Charitable Trust.

Beneficiaries included: The Charles Wolfson Charitable Trust (£5.8 million); Jewish Care (£200,000); Work Avenue (£100,000).

Exclusions

Individuals are not supported.

Applications

Apply in writing to the correspondent.

Sources of information

Accounts; annual report, Charity Commission record.

The Berkeley Foundation

Supporting young people in the areas of housing and homelessness; education, training and employment; health and well-being

Greater London; Berkshire; Birmingham; Buckinghamshire; Hertfordshire; Oxfordshire; Surrey; Kent; Hampshire; West Sussex; Warwickshire

£2.14 million (2020/21)

CC number: 1152596

Correspondent: The Trustees, Berkeley House, 19 Portsmouth Road, Cobham, Surrey KT11 1JG (tel: 01932 584551; email: info@berkeleyfoundation.org.uk)

Trustees: Robert Perrins; Wendy Pritchard; Elaine Driver; Alison Dowsett.

 www.berkeleyfoundation.org.uk

 @berkeleyfoundation

General information

This foundation was established in 2011 and became a registered charity in 2013. It is the corporate charity of the Berkeley Group, a property development company based in London.

The foundation aims to help young people and their communities across London, Birmingham, and the south of

England. According to its website, the foundation provides funding through the following channels:

Strategic Partnerships
Long-term, high value partnerships which operate on multiple levels.

Community Investment Fund
Targeting funding, aimed at supporting innovation and building evidence of what works.

Designated Charities
Partnership between Berkeley offices and local charities, focused on fundraising, volunteering and in-kind support.

The foundation also operates a Capacity Building Fund, available to all current charity partners, which 'aims to build your resilience and capacity, enabling you to overcome organisational challenges and operate more effectively.'

Registered charities and CICs can apply for funding under the foundation's Community Investment Fund, which has the following focus areas:

- A safe place to call home
- The skills to succeed
- Access to employment
- Health and well-being

Financial information

Year end	30/04/2021
Income	£2,593,000
Assets	£1,820.00
Grants to organisations	£2,140,000

Beneficiaries included: Imperial College (£600,000); The Change Foundation (£230,100); Richard House (£180,000); New Horizon Youth Centre (£150,000); Khulisa (£120,000); MAC-UK (£102,300); Oaresome Chance (£15,000); No.5 Young People (£10,000).

Exclusions

The foundation does not make grants to individuals.

Applications

Applications are typically made online through the foundation's website. The foundation welcomes expressions of interest at any time during the year.

Sources of information

Accounts; annual report; Charity Commission record; funder's website.

Ruth Berkowitz Charitable Trust

General charitable purposes; social welfare, education and security needs in the Jewish community; cancer research

UK and Israel

£398,600 (2020/21)

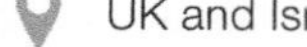

CC number: 1111673

Correspondent: The Trustees, PO Box 864, Gillingham ME8 1FE (tel: 020 7408 8888; email: admin@ruthberkowitztrust.org)

Trustees: Brian Beckman; Philip Goodman.

General information

This trust was established through the will of Ruth Berkowitz in 2001 and was registered with the Charity Commission in 2005. The purpose of the trust is to provide grants for general charitable purposes to registered charities in the UK and in Israel. The current grant-making policy is to award modest amounts to a number organisations. There is a preference for Jewish causes.

Financial information

Year end	05/04/2021
Income	£10,100
Grants to organisations	£398,600

Further financial information

Full accounts were not available to view on the Charity Commission's website due to the trust's low income. We have therefore estimated the trust's grant total based on its total expenditure.

Beneficiaries included: A list of beneficiaries was not available. Previous beneficiaries include: University Jewish Chaplaincy (£50,000); World Jewish Relief (£45,000); Community Security Trust (£40,000); London School of Jewish Studies (£30,000); Marie Curie Cancer Care (£15,000); Aleh Charitable Foundation and Camp Simcha (£10,000 each); British Friends of United Hatzalah Israel and The Z.S.V. Trust (£7,500 each); Rimon Jewish Primary School (£5,000).

Applications

Previous research suggests that unsolicited applications are not usually accepted.

Sources of information

Accounts; annual report; Charity Commission record.

The Bernicia Foundation

Social and economic inclusion

The North East

£465,200 (2020/21)

CC number: 1190094

Correspondent: The Trustees, Oakwood Way, Ashwood Business Park, Ashington NE63 0XF (tel: 0344 800 3800; email: foundation@berniciafoundation.com)

Trustees: Claire-Jane Rewcastle; Avril Gibson; Carol Meredith; Beth Hazon.

https://berniciafoundation.com

General information

The foundation is the corporate charity of Bernica, a housing provider based in the North East.

Inclusion Grants Programme

According to its website, the foundation's Inclusion Grants Programme supports initiatives that encourage:

Social inclusion:

- Reducing isolation and loneliness
- Promoting independence
- Building citizenship, confidence and aspiration

Economic inclusion:

- Removing barriers to employment, training and volunteering
- Reducing child poverty
- Tackling Fuel Poverty
- Improving financial wellbeing

The foundation's Inspiration Grants Programme also provides grants for talented individuals aged 24 or under.

Financial information

Year end	31/03/2021
Income	£503,000
Assets	-£6,000
Grants to organisations	£465,200

Beneficiaries included: South Tyneside Citizens Advice (£10,000); North Tyneside Disability Forum Ltd (£9,900); Chrysalis Club Tynedale (£7,500); Teams and Bensham Community Care (£6,100); Pennywell Neighbourhood Centre (£5,000).

Exclusions

The foundation's website states:

Our Inclusion and Inspiration Grant Programmes will not fund:

- Organisations with an annual income of over £750,000
- Organisations with unrestricted reserves that exceed 6 months running costs
- Contributions to general appeals or circulars
- Religious/political activity, which is not for the wider public benefit
- Routine building or equipment repairs and maintenance
- Activities that have already taken place/retrospective funding
- Grant-making by other organisations/ third – party funding
- Privately owned and profit-distributing companies or limited partnerships
- Projects and initiatives operating outside of the North East
- CICs and other non-charity enterprises with the costs of continuing services, which should be financed by the sale of goods and services in line with the governance model they have chosen

Applications

Applications can be made via the foundation's website.

Sources of information

Accounts; annual report; Charity Commission record; funder's website.

Bideford Bridge Trust

General charitable purposes; amateur sports; health; education; social welfare; business start-ups

The parish of Bideford, Devon and the immediate neighbourhood

£288,400 (2019/20)

CC number: 204536

Correspondent: The Steward, 23A The Quay, Bideford, Devon EX39 2PS (tel: 01237 473184; email: info@bidefordbridgetrust.org.uk)

Trustees: Oliver Chope; Peter Christie; Angus Harper; Eric Hubber; William Isaac; Elizabeth Junkison; Sally Ellis; Jamie McKenzie; Ruth Craigie; Jude Gubb; Peter Sims.

 www.bidefordbridgetrust.org.uk

General information

Registered with the Charity Commission in 1962, the trust aims to benefit the residents of Bideford in Devon and the surrounding neighbourhood. According to the trust's website, the trustees deem this beneficial area to be 'the Parish of Bideford and the area up to and including Hartland to the North, up to but excluding Torrington to the East and up to and including Instow to the South.' The trustees will only consider applications from organisations that substantially benefit the people in this area.

The trust makes grants to local charities and organisations to support the following areas:

- General charitable purposes
- Amateur sports
- Music
- Heritage and culture
- Health
- Disability
- Education
- Religious activities
- Recreational activities

Types of grant

Grants to organisations

- Annual grants are made to organisations with a charitable purposes (not necessarily a registered charity)
- Urgent grants are awarded to assist with an urgent need
- Swimming grants are awarded annually to local schools to assist with the costs of swimming lessons and associated travel costs
- One-off significant grants are considered every so often for organisations with a particular purpose that benefits the public at large

The trust also makes grants to individuals in need for welfare, education and transport needs. It can also offer business start-up grants of up to £500.

Full details on each grants programme can be seen on the trust's website.

Financial information

Year end	21/12/2020
Income	£854,100
Assets	£19,190,000
Grants to organisations	£288,400
No. of grants	36+

Further financial information

Only organisations that received grants over £1,500 were listed in the accounts. Grants under £1,500 totalled £29,000. In previous years, the trust has awarded over £300,000 to organisations.

Beneficiaries included: North Devon Hospice (£16,000); Marie Curie (£10,000); Home-Start Torridge and North Devon (£5,000); Appledore Maritime Heritage Trust (£4,200); Lavington United Reform Church (£2,500); Instow Primary School (£2,000); Bideford Pilot Gig Club (£1,000); Bideford Amateur Boxing Club (£850).

Exclusions

The trust does not make grants for political causes, personal computers, debts previously incurred or deposits for lettings.

Applications

Application forms for each type of grant are available to download from the trust's website. Completed forms should be sent by post to the correspondent. Applications for annual grants are accepted between 1 June and 31 July each year. For significant grants and swimming grants a written letter is required.

Sources of information

Accounts; annual report; Charity Commission record; funder's website.

Biffa Award

Biodiversity; community buildings; recreation

UK. Projects should be located near a Biffa operation and any licensed landfill site. There is a postcode checker on the website.

£3.62 million (2020/21)

Correspondent: The Grants Team, The Wildlife Trusts, The Kiln, Mather Road, Newark, United Kingdom NG24 1WT (tel: 01636 670000; email: biffa-award@wildlifetrusts.org)

Trustees: Andrew Moffat; Patience Thody; Simon Rutledge; Jackie Doone; Mick Davis; Debbie Tann.

 www.biffa-award.org

 @BiffaAward

General information

Biffa plc is a waste management company headquartered in High Wycombe. The Biffa Award is an environmental fund managed by Royal Society of Wildlife Trusts (RSWT) and funded through landfill tax credits donated by Biffa Waste Services.

Main grants scheme

The main grants scheme makes grants under four main themes, details of which have been taken from the organisation's guidance notes:

- **The Community Buildings theme** aims to improve community buildings such as village halls, community centres and church halls to act as mechanisms for community involvement
- **The Rebuilding Biodiversity theme** supports a variety of living things and includes all species of plants and animals and the natural systems (or habitats) that support them.
- **The Recreation theme** generally covers projects which will benefit people within their free time, but also includes renovations of clubhouses which have a wider community use outside of sporting activities.
- **The Cultural Facilities** theme aims to improve recreation, interest and education. The project could be based within a theatre, gallery, museum, concert hall, arts or heritage centre. It must be open to the general public for published periods of not less than 104 days each year and must attract tourists or day visitors.

Grants are for between £10,000 and £75,000 for projects with a total cost of less than £200,000 including VAT.

Partnership projects

Grants of between £250,000 and £750,000 are available for partnership projects. Organisations should work in partnership on brand new projects of regional or national significance which look to improve the built or natural environment.

Each grant scheme has its own eligibility criteria – see the organisation's website for further details.

Financial information

Grants to organisations	£3,620,000
No. of grants	30

Further financial information

Full financial information was not available as the organisation is not registered with the Charity Commission.

According to its annual review, during 2020/21 the organisation funded 25 main grants scheme projects across three themes: community buildings (£667,900 in 13 grants); rebuilding biodiversity (£337,700 in seven grants); recreation (£252,400 in five grants). In addition, the organisation awarded five partnership grants totalling £2.3 million.

Beneficiaries included: Winchester Science Centre (£292,400); Staffordshire Wildlife Trust (£75,000); Swannington Play Area (£64,300); Stourbridge Scout Hut (£12,400).

Exclusions

For full exclusions see the organisation's guidance notes.

Applications

The main grants programme is a rolling programme with no deadlines. Applicants must first submit an expression of interest form on the organisation's website. If successful, within five days you will be invited to submit a full application, which must be submitted within six weeks of the invitation being made. If you have been unsuccessful, you will receive an email.

Sources of information

Annual Report; funder's website.

The Percy Bilton Charity

General charitable purposes, particularly in support of: older people; children or adults with learning or physical disabilities or mental health conditions; children and young people who are socially or educationally disadvantaged

UK

£1 million (2020/21)

CC number: 1094720

Correspondent: The Trustees, Bilton House, 7 Culmington Road, Ealing, London W13 9NB (tel: 020 8579 2829; email: information@percybiltoncharity.org)

 www.percy-bilton-charity.org

General information

The charity was founded in 1962 and supports both individuals and organisations throughout the UK.

According to its website the charity will consider capital funding for the following projects and schemes:

1. **Disadvantaged/underprivileged young people (persons under 25)** Supported housing schemes and educational and training projects to encourage disadvantaged young people who may be homeless and/or unemployed away from crime, substance/alcohol misuse and homelessness. Facilities for recreational activities and outdoor pursuits specifically for young people who are educationally or socially underprivileged or disadvantaged
2. **People with disabilities (physical or learning disabilities or mental health problems)** Residential, respite care, occupational and recreational establishments for children, young people and adults with physical or learning disabilities or enduring mental health problems
3. **Older people (aged over 60)** Day centres, nursing and residential homes, sheltered accommodation and respite care for the frail or sufferers from dementia or age related disorders

Grants for organisations

The charity runs two programmes for organisations:

- **Large grants:** one-off grants for capital expenditure of approximately £2,000 and over (the majority of grants fall within the range of £2,000 to £5,000)
- **Small grants:** grants of up to £500 to assist smaller organisations with immediate funding for equipment and furniture (excluding office items)

Grants for individuals

In addition to its grant programmes for organisations, the charity also provides grants to individuals. Previously assistance has included the provision of food parcels, clothing, white goods, beds and other essential household items. See the charity's website for full details of their individual grant programmes.

See the website for further information on eligibility criteria for all programmes.

Financial information

Year end	31/03/2021
Income	£785,100
Assets	£31,430,000
Grants to organisations	£1,000,000

Beneficiaries included: A list of beneficiaries was not available.

Exclusions

According to the charity's website, the trustees will not consider applications for the following:

- Running expenses for the organisation or individual projects
- Salaries, training costs or office equipment/furniture
- Projects for general community use e.g. community centre and church halls
- Disabled access to community buildings
- Publication costs e.g. printing/distributing promotional and information leaflets
- Projects that have been completed
- Items that have already been purchased
- Provision of disabled facilities in schemes mainly for the able-bodied
- General funding/circularised appeals
- Pre-schools or playgroups (other than predominantly for disabled children)
- Play schemes/summer schemes
- Holidays or expeditions for individuals or groups
- Trips, activities or events
- Community sports/play area facilities
- Exterior works such as paving, roofing and garden landscaping
- Consumables (e.g. stationery, arts and crafts materials)
- Refurbishment or repair of places of worship/church halls
- Research projects
- Mainstream pre-schools, Schools, Colleges and Universities (other than special schools)
- Welfare Funds for individuals
- Hospital/medical equipment
- Works to premises not used primarily by the eligible groups

Other exclusions may apply, see the charity's website for full details.

Applications

Applications can be made via the charity's website.

Sources of information

Accounts; annual report; Charity Commission record; funder's website.

Binks Trust

General charitable purposes; arts; music; social welfare

Scotland

£2 million (2020/21)

OSCR number: SC008849

Correspondent: The Trustees, 61 Dublin Street, Edinburgh EH3 6NL

General information

The Binks Trust registered with the Scottish Charity Regulator in 1973 to make grants to a wide variety of charitable purposes in Scotland.

Financial information

Year end	05/04/2021
Income	£616,100
Assets	£10,850,000
Grants to organisations	£2,000,000

Beneficiaries included: University of Edinburgh Development Trust (£1.24 million); Greyfriars Kirk (£395,000); David Parr House (£25,000); Textile Conservation Trust (£15,000); Dunedin Concerts Trust (£14,500); Cross Reach (£10,000).

Applications

Apply in writing to the correspondent.

Sources of information

Accounts; annual report; OSCR record.

The Birmingham Diocesan Board of Finance

Christianity; churches; community regeneration; religious education

The Diocese of Birmingham

£868,000 (2020)

CC number: 249403

Correspondent: Dr Jan Smart, Diocesan Secretary, 1 Colmore Row, Birmingham, West Midlands B3 2BJ (tel: 0121 426 0400; email: diocesansecretary@cofebirmingham.com)

Trustees: Steven Murray Skakel; The Revd Sarah Hayes; Patricia Williams; Anesu Mayambi; The Revd Jeremy Allcock; Christine Price; The Revd Geoffrey Lanham; Guy Hordern; The Revd Louise Shaw; The Revd William Routh; Prebendary Jennifer Tomlinson; The Revd Rebecca Stephens; The Revd Bamidele Sotonwa; Jonathan Goll; Jennifer Clark; Matt Thompson; The Revd Catherine Grylls; Trevor Lewis; The Revd Anne Hollinghurst; Ven Simon Heathfield; Deirdre Moll; Julian Phillips; The Revd Canon Priscilla White; The Rt The Revd David Urquhart.

www.cofebirmingham.com

General information

Grants are mainly made for the benefit of Church of England organisations and schools, as well as for the education and welfare of children and young people in the beneficial area.

According to the 2020 annual report, the charity's grant programmes 'help parishes to further engage and service their local communities. This may be mission activities, community regeneration, church maintenance, schools and world mission.'

Financial information

Year end	31/12/2020
Income	£12,260,000
Assets	£46,070,000
Grants to organisations	£868,000

Beneficiaries included: A list of beneficiaries was not available.

Applications

Apply in writing to the correspondent. The trustees meet regularly throughout the year.

Sources of information

Accounts; annual report; Charity Commission record; funder's website.

The Michael Bishop Foundation

General charitable purposes; arts, culture and heritage; human rights and social justice; health and medicine; education and training

Worldwide

£3.83 million (2020/21)

CC number: 297627

Correspondent: The Trustees, Staunton House, Ashby-de-la-Zouche, Leicestershire LE65 1RW (tel: 01530 564388; email: jo.furlong@btconnect.com)

Trustees: Grahame Elliott; Baron Glendonbrook of Bowdon; Timothy Bye; Martin Ritchie.

General information

The Michael Bishop Foundation was registered with the Charity Commission in 1987. According to its Charity Commission record, it supports a broad range of organisations in different areas, mainly:

- Heritage
- Arts and culture
- Human rights and social justice
- Health and medicine
- Education and training

Other areas may be considered from time to time.

Financial information

Year end	05/04/2021
Income	£3,850,000
Assets	£42,620,000
Grants to organisations	£3,830,000

Beneficiaries included: Margaret Thatcher Scholarship Trust (£284,400); British Council (280,000); Governor Phillip Scholarship (£179,900); British Red Cross (£150,000); Saltdean Lido Trust (£100,000); Mill Hill School Foundation (£80,000); Iris Prize Outreach Ltd (£60,000); Just Like Us (£50,000); Miltons Cottage (£25,000); Palace Theatre Et Opera House Trust (£10,000); Place2Be (£1,000).

Applications

The trustees do not accept unsolicited applications.

Sources of information

Accounts; annual report; Charity Commission record.

Asser Bishvil Foundation

Jewish causes

Greater Manchester and London

£7.87 million (2020/21)

CC number: 1112477

Correspondent: Daniel Orzel, Trustee, 7 Bevendon Square, Salford M7 4TF (tel: 0161 792 1813; email: enquiries@asserbishvil.org.uk)

Trustees: Rabbi Daniel Orzel; S. Orzel; Chaim Simche Ehrenteu.

http://asserbishvil.org.uk

General information

The Asser Bishvil Foundation was registered in 2005. According to its 2020/21 accounts, the foundation makes grants for: the relief of poverty among the Jewish community; advancement of Jewish education; and advancement of the Jewish faith.

Financial information

Year end	05/04/2021
Income	£9,420,000
Assets	£2,870,000
Grants to organisations	£7,870,000

Further financial information

Grants were broken down as follows: relief of poverty (£4.96 million); education (£2.04 million); religion (£863,500).

Beneficiaries included: A list of beneficiaries was not available.

Applications

According to its 2020/21 annual report:

> the charity invites applications for funding through contacting local philanthropists to contribute towards projects that both the trustees and the philanthropists feel are appropriate for the charities objects.

Sources of information

Accounts; annual report; Charity Commission record.

Maria Bjornson Memorial Fund

General charitable purposes, with a focus on the performing, visual and creative arts

UK

£387,600 (2019)

CC number: 1126096

Correspondent: The Trustees, c/o Charles Russell Speechlys LLP, 5 Fleet Place, London EC4M 7RD (tel: 020 7227 7000)

Trustees: Simon Weil; Sir Richard Eyre; Robert Crowley; Ida Levine.

www.mbmf.org.uk

General information

The charity was established in 2008 in memory of Maria Björnson, who was a theatre, ballet and opera designer who died suddenly in 2002 at the age of 53. The charity's website states it will support artistic enterprises, arts-related activities and individual artists. In 2019 the charity's grant-making had a strong focus on the performing arts. Previous grants have been for core running costs and project costs.

According to its 2019 annual report, the causes the charity can support include:

- The advancement of education by promoting medical and scientific research
- The relief of hardship and suffering by promoting medical care and assistance to disabled and sick individuals and their carers
- The advancement of education by providing assistance to both individuals and organisations working in the areas of the performing arts and the visual and creative arts

Financial information

Year end	31/12/2019
Income	£446,200
Assets	£13,960,000
Grants to organisations	£387,600
No. of grants	18

Further financial information

The charity's 2020 accounts were not available to view at the time of writing (May 2022); therefore, we have used the charity's 2019 accounts.

Beneficiaries included: New English Ballet Theatre (£80,000); Belarus Free Theatre (£40,000); Diverse Abilities (£10,000); Carers Trust (£5,000); Humanity and Inclusion (£1,500).

Applications

Apply in writing to the correspondent.

Sources of information

Accounts; annual report; Charity Commission record.

The John Black Charitable Foundation

Medical research into prostate cancer and Parkinson's disease

UK and Israel

£3.5 million (2020/21)

CC number: 1143431

Correspondent: The Trustees, 24 Old Burlington Street, London W1S 3AW (tel: 020 7734 0424)

General information

The foundation makes grants for medical research into prostate cancer and Parkinson's Disease in the UK and Israel, as well as other charitable causes in the UK.

Financial information

Year end	31/03/2021
Income	£4,940,000
Assets	£84,990,000
Grants to organisations	£3,500,000

Further financial information

Grants were broken down as follows:

Parkinson's and prostate cancer	£2.2 million
Other purposes	£917,000
COVID-19 projects	£357,300

Beneficiaries included: A list of beneficiaries was not available.

Applications

Apply in writing to the correspondent.

Sources of information

Accounts; annual report; Charity Commission record.

The Blagrave Trust

Developing disadvantaged young people's skills, experience and capabilities; supporting young people's social change efforts; influencing policy

South-east Hampshire and the Isle of Wight, Sussex, Wiltshire and Berkshire. Occasionally, Somerset or Oxfordshire

£1.64 million (2020)

CC number: 1164021

Correspondent: Jo Wells, Director, c/o Cripplegate Foundation, 13 Elliotts Place, London N1 8HX (tel: 020 7399 0370; email: jo.wells@blagravetrust.org or grants@blagravetrust.org)

 www.blagravetrust.org

 @blagravetrust

General information

The Blagrave Trust was registered with the Charity Commission in 2015. On its website, the trust describes its purpose as:

> bringing lasting change to the lives of young people investing in them as powerful forces for change and acting upon their right to be heard in pursuit of a fair and just society.

Funding

The trust has two types of funding: ongoing funding opportunities (mainly unrestricted grants), and time-limited funding opportunities.

As stated on the trust's website, funding is primarily delivered in three areas of work:

Investing in youth organisations

The trust's regional funding programme funds youth organisations (charities and registered CICs only) working with young people aged 16+ in deprived areas of Berkshire, Hampshire, the Isle of Wight, Sussex and Wiltshire. The regional programme offers small grants to organisations working on the frontline providing vital support to young people, as well as partnership grants for long running, strategic partnerships. Both offer unrestricted funding for three years. Regional funding is available on an ongoing basis

Alongside its regional funding, the trust funds work on a national level, which supports listening and accountability practices within the youth sector. See the trust's website for open funding rounds.

Investing in better youth policy

The trust's website states: 'We fund work that aims for better youth policy outcomes and is directly informed by young people's experiences of systemic disadvantage.' The trust's website defines policy work as 'influencing government funding decisions, guidance, consultation outcomes, position papers or statements of intent; party manifestoes; or any legislative process'. See the trust's website for open funding rounds.

Investing in young people directly

Grants are given directly to young people (aged 16–25) engaged in social justice projects in England.

Financial information

Year end	31/12/2020
Income	£2,070,000
Assets	£41,560,000
Grants to organisations	£1,640,000
No. of grants	91

Further financial information

Grants were broken down as follows:

Core grants – supporting young people facing disadvantage; policy and influencing	£1.57 million
Challenge and Change Fund*	£179,700
Opportunity Fund	£63,400

*According to the accounts, these grants were primarily to individuals and collectives; therefore, we have not included these grants in the grant total to organisations.

Beneficiaries included: Peace First (£95,000); Just for Kids Law (£50,000); British Youth Council (£35,000); Children England (£25,000); Yellow Brick Road (£20,000); Youth Engagement (£10,000); Radical Restart (£6,000); Diaspora Dialogues (£4,000).

Exclusions

The trust's regional funding programme does not fund:

- Unconstituted groups
- Individuals
- Work outside the UK
- The promotion of religion
- Major capital appeals

See the trust's open funding rounds on its website for other specific exclusions.

Applications

For the trust's ongoing funding opportunities, applicants should complete the brief outline proposal form on the trust's website. The trust then invites successful applicants to complete the next steps, including a (virtual) meeting and sharing business, planning and financial documentation. Applications for grants over £20,000 are then reviewed by trustees in March, July or November, meanwhile applications for grants under £2,000 are reviewed within four weeks.

Separate online application forms for time-limited funding opportunities can be found on the trust's website, along with deadline dates.

Sources of information

Accounts; annual report; Charity Commission record; funder's website.

The Sir Victor Blank Charitable Settlement

Jewish causes; education; the arts; health; medicine; general charitable purposes

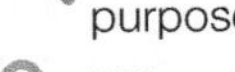
UK and overseas

£554,000 (2020/21)

CC number: 1084187

Correspondent: The Trustees, 2nd Floor, Regis House, 45 King William Street, London EC4R 9AN (tel: 020 7403 1877; email: enquiries@sirvictorblankcharitablesettlement.com)

Trustees: Lady Sylvia Blank; Simon Blank; Sir Maurice Blank.

General information

Established in 1979, the charity makes grants to Jewish organisations and for general charitable purposes. There is some preference for the arts, health charities and cross-community work.

Financial information

Year end	05/04/2021
Income	£187,500
Assets	£2,840,000
Grants to organisations	£554,000
No. of grants	40+

Further financial information

Only beneficiaries of grants over £1,000 were listed in the accounts (41 grants). Grants under £1,000 totalled £10,100.

Beneficiaries included: Oxford University Development Trust (£266,700); Wellbeing of Women (£50,000); Jewish Care (£25,000); United Jewish Israel Appeal (£12,500); Crisis (£4,000); Deafblind UK (£2,000); Noah's Ark Children's Hospice (£1,000).

Applications

Apply in writing to the correspondent.

Sources of information

Accounts; annual report; Charity Commission record.

Bloodwise

Research into blood cancers

UK

£2.2 million (2020/21)

CC number: 216032/SC037529

Correspondent: Research Team, Blood Cancer UK, 39–40 Eagle Street, London WC1R 4TH (tel: 020 7269 9018; email: research@bloodwise.org.uk)

Trustees: John Ormerod; Simon Guild; Dr Jane Stevens; Prof. Fran Balkwill; Julia Whittaker; Steven Prescott-Jones; Tim Gillbanks; Aileen Thompson; Gemma Peters.

https://bloodcancer.org.uk/research/funding/apply

facebook.com/bloodwise.uk

@bloodwise_uk

@bloodwise

General information

The charity was established in 1960 by the Eastwood family of Middlesbrough following the tragic death of their daughter Susan, aged seven at the time. According to its website, the charity's mission is 'to stop people dying from blood cancer, to make patients' lives better and to stop blood cancers happening in the first place'.

Bloodwise funds world-class research into leukaemia, lymphoma, myeloma, and other blood cancers, which is carried out by researchers at universities and hospitals across the UK. The charity's website explains: 'Our blood cancer research grants include long and short term projects, career development awards and basic research through to phase III clinical trials.'

The following information on research grants is taken from the charity's website:

Research projects:

- **Project grants** – Project grants are awarded for up to £250,000 and up to three years, for clearly defined research projects addressing key questions in the field of blood cancer
- **Programme continuity grants** – Current or recent holders of Bloodwise programme grants can apply for support to maintain core elements of their research programme, including but not limited to the retention of key research personnel.

Clinical trials:

- **Early Phase Clinical Trial grants** – This scheme provides up to £400,000 of funding to support early phase academic trials to evaluate blood cancer treatments, with the aim of funding research which translates into further studies to evaluate clinical efficacy. Applications are expected to be developed with the involvement of a relevant clinical trials unit.
- **Trial-associated research projects** – Applications requesting support for laboratory-based research projects that are integral to clinical trials and essential for the analysis of primary and/or secondary end points and clinical outcome can be submitted through our standard project grant scheme and will be considered by our Research Committee.

Training and career development awards:

Training and career development award applications are considered by our Training and Career Development sub-Committee, which makes funding recommendations to our Research Committee.

Financial information

Year end	31/03/2021
Income	£12,500,000
Assets	£13,220,000
Grants to organisations	£2,200,000

Beneficiaries included: A list of beneficiaries was not available. Previous beneficiaries include: University of Birmingham (£2.34 million); University of Oxford (£845,000); CRUK Centre for Drug Development – London (£493,000); University College London (£250,000); University of Leeds (£102,000); UK Biobank – Salford (£15,000).

Applications

See the website for full information on the charity's funding schemes. All applications must be made through the online grant tracker. Grants that have been approved must be administered through a UK institution.

Sources of information

Accounts; annual report; Charity Commission record; funder's website.

The Bloom Foundation

Community development; Jewish causes; health and medical research; social welfare; international development

UK, with a preference for Brighton; overseas, with a preference for Israel

£4.22 million (2019/20)

CC number: 1166112

Correspondent: The Trustees, 34/36 Jamestown Road, London NW1 7BY (tel: 020 3014 9861; email: info@thebloomfoundation.com)

Trustees: Linda Bloom; Marc Sugarman; Marcelle Lester; Adam Franks; Anthony Bloom; Philip Saunders; Simon Johnson.

General information

The foundation was established by Tony Bloom, an online gambling entrepreneur, who is also the owner of Brighton and Hove Albion FC and a well-known poker player.

According to its 2019/20 accounts the objects of the foundation are:

- Strengthen and educate communities and improve lives through charitable contributions, volunteering and fundraising
- Mainstream a preventative approach to health, with a particular focus on research and life-style based interventions
- Create a more cohesive society in Israel, particularly through common purpose programs and advocacy, that brings together different parts of society
- Strengthen the UK Jewish community and the local Brighton community through supporting key service organisations

Grants can also be made for general charitable purposes.

Financial information

Year end	30/06/2020
Income	£5,080,000
Assets	£7,630,000
Grants to organisations	£4,220,000

Further financial information

Grants were broken down as follows:

Brighton	£1.93 million
Medical research and welfare	£830,900
Jewish community	£755,300
Israel	£392,700
Disaster relief	£130,000
Social welfare	£86,800
International development	£60,000
Other	£34,300
Animal welfare	£1,500

Beneficiaries included: Brighton and Hove Hebrew Congregation (£1.66 million); Overcoming Multiple Sclerosis (£600,000); Jewish Women's Aid Ltd (£110,000); Plan International UK (£100,000); The Central British Fund for World Jewish Relief (£90,000); The Work Avenue Foundation (£60,000); The Lautman Foundation (£50,000); Sufra NW London (£30,000); Solace Women's Aid (£20,000).

Applications

Contact the foundation for further information.

Sources of information

Accounts; annual report; Charity Commission record.

The Bloomfield Charitable Trust

General charitable purposes

UK

£354,200 (2020/21)

CC number: 1145866

Correspondent: The Trustees, Ludlow Trust Co. Ltd, Tower Wharf, Cheese Lane, Bristol BS2 0JJ (tel: 0345 304 2424)

Trustees: Martin Hellawell; Mandy Hellawell; Ludlow Trust Company Ltd.

General information

The trust was established in February 2012 by Martin Hellawell, managing director of Softcat, an IT and software licensing company and government contractor. The trust makes grants for general charitable purposes in the UK. There appears to be a preference for supporting organisations working with children and young people.

Financial information

Year end	06/02/2021
Income	£1,760,000
Assets	£6,220,000
Grants to organisations	£354,200
No. of grants	7

Further financial information

In 2020/21, the trust awarded 13 grants to seven organisations.

Beneficiaries included: The Raspberry Pi Foundation (£198,200 in two grants); Action for Kids Charitable Trust (£50,000 in four grants); National Autistic Society (£48,800 in two grants); School-Home Support (£26,700); The Markfield Project (£15,500); The Friends of Harrington Scheme (£10,000 in two grants); Resources for Autism (£5,000).

Applications

Apply in writing to the correspondent.

Sources of information

Accounts; annual report; Charity Commission record.

The Bluston Charitable Settlement

General charitable purposes; education of children; social welfare; health; research; Jewish causes

Mostly UK

£271,700 (2020/21)

CC number: 256691

Correspondent: The Trustees, 20 Gloucester Place, London W1U 8HA (tel: 020 7486 7760)

Trustees: Anna Jose; Daniel Dover; Martin Paisner.

General information

The Bluston Charitable Settlement was established in 1968. It makes grants to support a wide range of organisations.

The annual report for 2020/21 states that during the year the charity supported the following:

- Children's education
- Capital expenditure projects for schools and other educational establishments
- Social welfare
- Hospitals and medical institutions
- Universities, for specific research projects

Analysis of the grants the trust awarded suggests a preference for Jewish organisations/causes.

Financial information

Year end	05/04/2021
Income	£235,200
Assets	£21,210,000
Grants to organisations	£271,700

Further financial information

The trust's income was significantly lower in 2020/21. In previous years grants have totalled over £700,000.

Beneficiaries included: British Institute of International and Comparative Law (£50,000); Ohel Torah Beth David (£30,000); Jaffa Institute (£25,000); British Library and Camden Psychotherapy Unit (£10,000 each); Jerusalem Foundation (£6,700).

Applications

Apply in writing to the correspondent. The trustees meet twice a year to consider applications.

Sources of information

Accounts; annual report; Charity Commission record.

The BNA Charitable Incorporated Organisation

General charitable purposes

UK, with a strong preference for Newark, Nottinghamshire, Lincoln, Lincolnshire and the surrounding area

£615,100 (2020/21)

CC number: 1182500

Correspondent: The Trustees, c/o Wright Vicar Ltd, 15 Newland, Lincoln LN1 1XG (email: phillipa.cridland@wrightvigar.co.uk)

Trustees: Richard Vigar; Paul Simpson; Herman Kok; Susan Fisher; Keith Girling.

www.bnacharity.com

General information

The charity supports general charitable purposes in the UK, with a preference for Newark, Nottinghamshire, Lincoln, Lincolnshire and the surrounding area.

Financial information

Year end	30/06/2021
Income	£402,400
Assets	£21,270,000
Grants to organisations	£615,100

Beneficiaries included: Nottinghamshire Hospice (£110,000); Children's Hospital (£100,000); Defence Medical Rehabilitation Charity (£85,000); Beaumond House Community Hospice (£60,900); Salvation Army (£25,000); Rosie May Foundation (£12,000); Carriages Cafe (£5,000).

Exclusions

According to its website, the charity is unable to fund the following:

- Projects outside the UK Organisations under the control of the UK or Scottish government
- Projects which are primarily intended to promote political or religious beliefs
- General appeals or circulars, including contributions to endowment funds

Applications

Applications can be made via the charity's website.

Sources of information

Accounts; annual report; Charity Commission record; funder's website.

The Boltini Trust

General charitable purposes; overseas causes; people who are disadvantaged or have a disability; community and education; medical research and institutions; disaster relief; environmental causes; arts and musical organisations (particularly those involved in contemporary music)

UK, particularly Surrey and West Sussex, but also other home counties; overseas including Africa, Asia and the West Indies

£378,300 (2020/21)

CC number: 1123129

Correspondent: The Trustees, Woolbeding Glebe, Woolbeding, Midhurst, West Sussex GU29 9RR (tel: 01730 817324; email: boltinitrust@gmail.com)

Trustees: Sarah Bolton; Benjamin Bolton; Oliver Bolton; Anthony Bolton; James Nelson; Emma Nelson; Fiona Bolton; Phoebe Bolton.

General information

The Boltini Trust was established in 2008 and makes grants to organisations supporting a wide range of charitable causes.

The trust has a strong preference for supporting organisations based in Surrey and West Sussex, but also considers funding organisations based more widely in the home counties (Berkshire, Buckinghamshire, Essex, Hertfordshire, Kent and Middlesex) and overseas (in particular, Africa, Asia and the West Indies).

Financial information

Year end	31/03/2021
Income	£471,300
Assets	£14,420,000
Grants to organisations	£378,300

Further financial information

Grants were broken down as follows:

Music	£125,400
Community and educational institutions	£74,000
International	£60,000
Adults who have a disability or are disadvantaged	£40,400
Children and young people who have a disability or are disadvantaged	£38,800
Disaster relief	£30,000
Medical research	£28,500
Environmental causes	£20,000

Beneficiaries included: Island Academy – Antigua (£32,900); Save the Children (£20,000); Electric Umbrella and Hope for Tomorrow (£10,000 each); Home-Start (£5,000); KidsCamp (£4,300); RNIB (£1,000).

Applications

Apply in writing to the correspondent.

Sources of information

Accounts; annual report; Charity Commission record.

The Booth Charities

Social welfare; health; education; recreation and leisure

Salford

£327,200 (2020/21)

CC number: 221800

Correspondent: The Trustees, c/o Butcher and Barlow LLP, 3 Royal Mews, Gadbrook Road, Northwich, Cheshire CW9 7UD (tel: 01606 334309; email: jaldersley@butcher-barlow.co.uk)

Trustees: John Willis; Barbara Griffin; Philip Okell; Richard Kershaw; Roger Weston; William Whittle; Richard Fildes; James Tully; Alan Dewhurst; Jonathan Shelmerdine; Stephen Cheshire.

General information

The Booth Charities comprises two charities supporting people in Salford. Together, grants are made to both individuals (particularly in the form of pensions) and charitable organisations working within Salford, or those working outside the area of benefit with beneficiaries in Salford.

Areas of work

Humphrey Booth the Elder's Charity was established to benefit the residents of Salford. The 2020/21 annual report states that its objects are:

- The relief of older people (i.e. those over the age of 60 years)
- The relief of distress and sickness
- The relief of those experiencing financial hardship
- The provision and support of facilities for recreation/leisure
- The provision and support of educational facilities

Humphrey Booth the Grandson's Charity was established for repair and maintenance of the Church of Sacred Trinity in Salford. Once the needs of the church are met, any surplus income will be applied to further the objects set by the Humphrey Booth the Elder's Charity.

The 2020/21 annual report states that the overall mission of the combined charities is 'to have a real impact on the ability of organisations and individuals, to improve the quality of life and general well-being of Salford inhabitants'.

Grant-making policy

The charity's 2020/21 annual report states that trustees consider the following when reviewing applications:

- All grants must fall within one or more of the charity's statutory objects of distribution

- Beneficiaries must be Salford inhabitants
- Whether the application has merit
- Whether there are sufficient funds
- The grant benefit in terms of the 'greatest good for the greatest number'
- Socio-economic and other deprivation factors in Salford
- Whether the stated aims of the projects are susceptible to measurement and evaluation
- The sustainability of the project and whether there is an 'exit' strategy in place from charitable funding
- Wherever reasonable grant applications will be required to secure match funding
- The history of grants funding from Booth Charities
- The availability of statutory and other potential sources of funding
- Whether the application qualifies for statutory funding

Financial information

Year end	31/03/2021
Income	£1,520,000
Assets	£47,100
Grants to organisations	£327,200
No. of grants	52

Further financial information

The charities make an annual grant to Sacred Trinity Church (£23,300 in 2020/21). Grants were broken down as follows:

Sickness and distress	£131,300
Educational facilities	£83,000
Recreation and leisure	£48,900
Social welfare	£26,700
Other	£14,000

Beneficiaries included: Salford City Council (£40,000); Salford Royal NHS Foundation Trust (£33,000); Maggie's Manchester (£15,000); Ronald McDonald House Charities (£11,600); Salvation Army, Swinton North (£3,000); This is it, Salford (£1,000).

Applications

Apply in writing to the correspondent.

Sources of information

Accounts; annual report; Charity Commission record.

Boots Charitable Trust

Health; lifelong learning; community development; social care

Nottinghamshire

£250,000 (2019/20)

CC number: 1045927

Correspondent: The Trustees, Boots UK Ltd, D90E S09, 1 Thane Road West, Nottingham, Nottinghamshire NG90 1BS (email: feelgoodworks@boots.co.uk)

Trustees: Lucy Reynolds; Stuart Buchanan; Peter Bowrey; Andrew Caplan; Felicity Walton-Bateson.

www.boots-uk.com/corporate_social_responsibility/boots-charitable-trust.aspx

General information

Boots Charitable Trust was registered with the Charity Commission in 1995 and is wholly funded by Boots UK Ltd, a health and beauty retailer and pharmacy chain.

It provides funding to registered charities that benefit the people of Nottinghamshire, the location of the first Boots store and head office. The trust also makes grants to smaller voluntary organisations in the county that are too small to qualify for charitable status, but still need support.

Around 50 grants are awarded per year ranging from £100 to £10,000; however, applications for larger amounts will be considered.

The trust's charitable giving policy states:

> 'The Trust will consider applications for funding for most expenditure items, including salary and running costs. Where a general overhead allocation is part of the funding requested, the method of calculation must be included. Generally, large building or construction projects will not be funded although minor structural improvements and refurbishments would be considered.'

To be considered for support, applicants must meet at least one of the trust's funding priorities. Current priorities are as follows:

- Health
- Lifelong learning
- Community development
- Social care

Financial information

Year end	31/08/2020
Income	£266,800
Assets	£0
Grants to organisations	£250,000

Further financial information

Grants were broken down as follows:

Health	11	£102,000
Social care	9	£69,400
Lifelong learning	5	£49,200
Community development	3	£29,400

Beneficiaries included: Broxtowe Youth Homelessness (£10,000); Defence Medical Welfare Service (£9,700); Bulwell Forest Garden (£9,500); Open Minds (£6,400); Cornwater Evergreens (£5,000); Re-engage (£4,900); St Jude's Church – Mapperley (£3,000).

Exclusions

The trust's charitable giving policy states that it will not fund the following:

- Projects benefitting those people outside of Nottinghamshire
- Individuals
- Organisations which are not registered charities and have an income or expenditure of more than £5,000 per year
- Charities seeking funds to re-distribute to other charities
- Projects for which there is a legal statutory obligation or which replace statutory funding

Applications

Applications can be made using an online application form on the website, where further guidance and eligibility criteria are also available to view. Paper application forms can also be requested by contacting feelgoodworks@boots.co.uk.

The trustees review applications on a bi-monthly basis. Applications should be received by the 7th day of February, April, June, August, October and December.

Sources of information

Accounts; annual report; Charity Commission record; funder's website; guidelines for applicants.

The Borrows Charitable Trust

General charitable purposes

England and Wales

£385,600 (2020/21)

CC number: 1140591

Correspondent: The Trustees, c/o Kingston Smith and Partners LLP, Devonshire House, 60 Goswell Road, London EC1M 7AD (tel: 020 7566 4000)

Trustees: Sally Borrows; Simon Borrows.

General information

The Borrows Charitable Trust was registered with the Charity Commission in 2011. The trust awards grants to a wide variety of charitable causes.

Financial information

Year end	31/03/2021
Income	£538,800
Assets	£7,430,000
Grants to organisations	£385,600

Beneficiaries included: Museum of London (£50,000); Footsteps International (£35,500); Prostate Cancer UK (£10,000); Orpheus (£7,000); Learning Skills Research (£5,000).

Applications

Apply in writing to the correspondent.

Sources of information

Accounts; annual report; Charity Commission record.

The Boshier-Hinton Foundation

Work with children and adults with special educational or other needs

England and Wales

£206,100 (2020/21)

CC number: 1108886

Correspondent: The Trustees, Whitegates, 32 Lower Street, Horning, Norfolk NR12 8AA (tel: 01692 630695; email: boshierhinton@yahoo.co.uk)

Trustees: Thea Boshier; Dr Peter Boshier; Colin Flint; Susanne McEwen.

www.boshierhintonfoundation.org.uk

General information

Set up in 2005, the Boshier-Honton Foundation makes grants to organisations which advocate for, support and provide facilities for children and adults with special educational needs and other disabilities, and their families. The foundation's website states:

> The Founding Trustees are experienced in working and caring for children and adults with special needs and their families. It is also their experience that funding for projects to promote the welfare of individuals and groups of individuals continues to be difficult to obtain as grants have become more restricted and limited in recent years. The purpose of this Charity is to identify areas of need and make appropriate grants, where possible.

The foundation's application guidelines state that it welcomes projects which are 'innovative and developmental'. Although the foundation will consider funding the whole of a project, it prefers to part-fund projects in partnership with other contributors.

The foundation mostly funds services or equipment. At the time of writing (January 2022), the maximum grant available was £2,000 – check the application guidelines for updates.

Financial information

Year end	31/03/2021
Income	£114,800
Assets	£1,250,000
Grants to organisations	£206,100
No. of grants	63

Further financial information

In 2020/21 the foundation awarded grants totalling £206,100; however, in previous years it has given more. In 2019/20 grants totalled £238,600 and in 2018/19 grants totalled £305,200.

Beneficiaries included: Deaf Academy (£35,800); British Paralympic Association and Open Up Music (£15,000 each); Crossroads and Royal Philharmonic Orchestra (£2,000 each); Animal Antiks (£1,000); Walkabout Foundation (£500).

Exclusions

No repeat grants are made within two years. The foundation does not fund salaries, capital projects, core costs or costs that should be covered by statutory funding.

Applications

Application forms can be downloaded from the website and should be returned by post *and* email. The correspondent can also be contacted via telephone or email for further information. There are no deadlines.

Sources of information

Accounts; annual report; Charity Commission record; funder's website.

Alan Boswell Group Charitable Trust

Community sport and leisure; health and medical causes; social welfare; education; children and young people

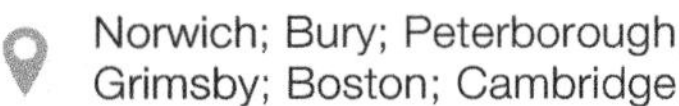
Norwich; Bury; Peterborough; Grimsby; Boston; Cambridge

£338,900 (2020/21)

CC number: 1183272

Correspondent: The Trustees, Prospect House, Rouen Road, Norwich NR1 1RE (tel: 01603 218000; email: contact@alanboswelltrust.com)

Trustees: Christopher Gibbs; Alexandra Bartram; Alan Boswell; Sarah Lusher; Alastair Drew; Lisa Adams.

www.alanboswell.com/about/corporate-social-responsibility

General information

The trust was established by and receives its funding from the Alan Boswell Group, an independent group of insurance brokers and financial planners. The trust supports good causes local to its offices.

Financial information

Year end	31/03/2021
Income	£349,000
Assets	£32,000
Grants to organisations	£338,900

Further financial information

Grants were broken down as follows:

Social and welfare	£139,800
Youth and educational causes	£89,400
Health and medical causes	£70,500
Heritage	£25,500
Community sport and leisure	£13,800

Beneficiaries included: A list of beneficiaries was not available.

Applications

Apply in writing to the correspondent.

Sources of information

Accounts; annual report; Charity Commission record; funder's website.

The Bothwell Charitable Trust

General charitable purposes; children's causes; hospices; medical research; disability and social welfare

UK

£336,000 (2020/21)

CC number: 299056

Correspondent: The Trustees, 69 Burrell Road, Compton, Newbury, Berkshire RG20 6QX (tel: 01925 757702; email: bct1987aa@gmail.com)

Trustees: Paul James; Crispian Howard; Theresa McGregor.

General information

This trust was established in 1988 for general charitable purposes and usually makes grants towards medical research, disability, hospices, social work and children's causes.

Financial information

Year end	05/04/2021
Income	£131,300
Assets	£3,920,000
Grants to organisations	£336,000

Further financial information

Grants were awarded as follows:

Disability/social work	£127,000
Medical research	£83,000
Children's causes	£64,000
Hospices	£52,000
Other causes	£10,000

Beneficiaries included: A list of beneficiaries was not available.

Exclusions

No grants are awarded to individuals.

Applications

Contact the correspondent for further information.

Sources of information

Accounts; annual report; Charity Commission record.

Bourneheights Ltd

Orthodox Jewish causes

UK

£1.6 million (2019/20)

CC number: 298359

Correspondent: Schloime Rand, Trustee and Secretary, Flat 10, Palm Court, Queen Elizabeth's Walk, London N16 5XA (tel: 020 8800 1572)

Trustees: Chaskel Rand; Erno Berger; Yechiel Chersky; Schloime Rand.

General information

This charity was established in 1984. According to its 2019/20 accounts the charity was initially established 'for the advancement of the education of persons expressing the Orthodox Jewish faith, the advance the Orthodox Jewish faith, and the relief of poverty in the Orthodox Jewish community'.

Financial information

Year end	30/11/2020
Income	£2,680,000
Assets	£11,610,000
Grants to organisations	£1,600,000
No. of grants	32+

Further financial information

Only beneficiaries of grants over £10,000 were listed in the accounts. Grants under £10,000 totalled £253,200.

Beneficiaries included: Mosdos Chernobil (£138,100); Start Upright (£122,500); Tchabe Kollel Ltd (£100,000); College for Higher Rabbinical Studies (£50,000); The Gevurath Ari Torah Academy Trust (£30,000); Clapton Support and Advice (£15,300); Ezra Umarpeh Ltd (£10,000).

Applications

Apply in writing to the correspondent.

Sources of information

Accounts; annual report; Charity Commission record.

The Bowland Charitable Trust

Religion; education; culture; rehabilitation of people who have offended; recreation; the environment; young people

North West England

£1.41 million (2019)

CC number: 292027

Correspondent: Carole Fahy, Bowland House, Philips Road, Blackburn, Lancashire BB1 5NA (tel: 01254 688051; email: carole.fahy@cannco.co.uk)

Trustees: Tony Cann; Carole Fahy; Hugh Turner.

General information

This trust, established with several large donations from the Cann family, invites applications for funding of projects from individuals, institutions and charities in particular (but not exclusively) for the promotion of education. Although its beneficial area covers the whole of the UK, in practice grants are mainly awarded in the North West. Most of the trust's grants are one-off, but some projects are funded over longer periods.

Financial information

Year end	31/12/2019
Income	£1,940,000
Assets	£7,020,000
Grants to organisations	£1,410,000

Further financial information

The 2019 annual report was the latest available at the time of writing (May 2022).

Beneficiaries included: A list of beneficiaries was not available. Previous beneficiaries include: Ron Clark Academy (£660,000); LEB Partnership (£306,000); The Brantwood Trust (£75,000); North Music Trust (£50,000); The Rosemere Cancer Foundation (£30,000); Blackburn Cathedral Trust (£25,000); Bowland High School (£20,000); Nazareth Unitarian Chapel (£15,000); The Lowry Centre Trust (£2,000); Ribble FM (£1,000).

Applications

Applications can be made in writing directly to the trustees, who meet regularly to assess them.

Sources of information

Accounts; annual report; Charity Commission record.

G. and K. Boyes Charitable Trust

The environment; education; medical research, in particular into dementia and brain tumors; health; heritage

UK

£400,000 (2020/21)

CC number: 1166015

Correspondent: Joanne Lee, c/o Cripps Harries Hall LLP, 22 Mount Ephraim, Tunbridge Wells, Kent TN4 8AS (tel: 01892 765431; email: joanne.lee@cripps.co.uk)

Trustees: Mark Cannon-Brookes; Mrs A. Dalmahoy; Mr R. A. Henderson; Cripps Trust Corporation Ltd.

General information

The trust was registered with the Charity Commission in 2016 and according to its 2019/20 accounts its objects are:

- The conservation, preservation, protection, and improvement of the physical and natural environment, including its woodland, rivers, lakes, flora, and fauna including birds; encouraging research into the same of publication of that research
- Promoting good citizenship amongst the public by supporting the maintenance and improvement of the grounds of the National Memorial Arboretum in Alrewas, Staffordshire
- Promoting, for the public benefit, education (including musical, social, and physical training)
- Promoting medical research for the public benefit generally and in particular in the areas of dementia and brain tumours and the publication of the results of that medical research
- Supporting the relief of those suffering from both physical and mental ill health
- The preservation, for the benefit of the nation, of land and buildings of beauty or historic interest and the preservation of furniture, pictures, and chattels of any description having national, historic, or artistic interest

Financial information

Year end	05/04/2020
Income	£5,000
Grants to organisations	£400,000

Further financial information

Full accounts were not available to view on the Charity Commission website due to the trust's low income. We have therefore estimated the grant total based on the trust's total expenditure.

Beneficiaries included: A list of beneficiaries was not available. Previous beneficiaries include: Royal Marsden Cancer Charity (£260,000); English National Ballet (£155,000); Susan's Farm (£62,200); London Zoological Society (£50,000); Cherubim (£30,000); Holland Park Opera (£20,000); David Shepherd Wildlife Trust (£10,000).

Applications

Apply in writing to the correspondent. The 2019/20 accounts state:

> Donation requests are collated by Cripps Pemberton Greenish who act on behalf of the trustees in relation to the administration of the Charity. Requests which meet the objectives of the Trust are put to the trustees for further consideration.

Sources of information

Accounts; annual report; Charity Commission record.

The William Brake Charitable Trust

General charitable purposes

UK, with a preference for Kent

£598,300 (2020/21)

CC number: 1023244

Correspondent: Michael Trigg, Chair and Trustee, c/o Gill Turner Tucker Solicitors, Colman House, King Street, Maidstone, Kent ME14 1JE (tel: 01622 759051; email: michael.trigg@gillturnertucker.com)

Trustees: Philip Wilson; Deborah Isaac; Penelope Lang; Michael Trigg.

General information

The William Brake Charitable Trust was established in 1993 with an initial gift from the late William Brake. The trust makes grants for general charitable purposes in the UK with a preference for local charities in Kent.

Financial information

Year end	31/03/2021
Income	£169,800
Assets	£13,490,000
Grants to organisations	£598,300

Beneficiaries included: The Whitley Fund for Nature (£60,000); Leonard Cheshire Disability Foundation (£15,000); NSPCC (£10,000); The Sam West Foundation (£1,000).

Applications

Apply in writing to the correspondent. The foundation's 2020/21 annual report notes that 'the charity invites applications from the William Brake family for funding of worthy registered charities each year, with a particular emphasis on local charities where the family know the charity's representative.' The trustees hold two formal meetings each year to consider grants.

Sources of information

Accounts; annual report; Charity Commission record.

The Liz and Terry Bramall Foundation

Christian causes; urban and rural regeneration; health; arts and culture; education; the environment; social welfare

UK, with a strong preference for Yorkshire

£5.35 million (2020/21)

CC number: 1121670

Correspondent: The Trustees, c/o Raworths LLP, Eton House, 89 Station Parade, Harrogate, North Yorkshire HG1 1HF (tel: 01423 566666; email: bramallfoundation@raworths.co.uk)

Trustees: Dr Terence Bramall; Elizabeth Bramall; Suzannah Allard; Rebecca Bletcher; Rachel Tunnicliffe; Anthony Sharp.

 www.bramallfoundation.org

General information

Established in 2007, this is the foundation of Terence Bramall, former chair of Keepmoat, a social housing building company in northern and central England.

Support is given to a wide range of charitable causes including Christian causes, education, social welfare, heritage, the environment, the arts, crime prevention and so on. A detailed list of supported areas can be found on the foundation's website.

The foundation prefers to support organisations that are based and work in Yorkshire.

Financial information

Year end	05/04/2021
Income	£2,160,000
Assets	£114,850,000
Grants to organisations	£5,350,000

Beneficiaries included: Leeds University (£395,900); West Yorkshire Playhouse (£200,000); The Message Trust (£100,000); St Margaret's Church (£70,000); South Yorkshire Community Foundation (£50,000); SUDEP Action (£20,000); Survive (£5,000); The David and Jane Richards Foundation (£1,000).

Applications

Applications should be made in writing to the correspondent and should include a paragraph of no more than 120 words. Details of what to include can be found on the website. Applications should be sent via post or email and will be acknowledged within ten working days. The trustees meet four times a year usually in January, April, August, and November, although this can be subject to change. The acknowledgment letter will note the date on which the application will be considered.

The 2020/21 annual report states:

> Unsolicited requests from national charities will generally only be considered if there is some public benefit to the Yorkshire region.

Sources of information

Accounts; annual report; Charity Commission record; funder's website.

The Breadsticks Foundation

Healthcare and education

UK; Africa; Asia

£222,800 (2019/20)

CC number: 1125396

Correspondent: The Trustees, 35 Canonbury Square, London N1 2AN (email: info@breadsticksfoundation.org)

Trustees: Beatrix Payne; Dr Paul Ballantyne; Beatrice Roberts.

 www.breadsticksfoundation.org

General information

The Breadsticks Foundation makes grants for the provision of quality healthcare and education to marginalised and vulnerable people. The trustees have a particular interest in supporting projects that enable good mental health or that work with young people.

The foundation aims to build long-term partnerships and, where possible, offers long-term core funding. It will also provide project-related grants.

The foundation currently works in the UK, South Sudan, Uganda, Kenya, South Africa and India.

Financial information

Year end	30/09/2020
Income	£200,400
Assets	£2,390,000
Grants to organisations	£222,800

Further financial information

The foundation made grants totalling £222,800 in 2019/20; however, in previous years the foundation has awarded grants totalling over £700,000.

Beneficiaries included: Basic Need, Basic Rights – Kenya (£80,600); Brighton Oasis (£48,400); Three2Six (£37,000); School Home Support (£20,000); St Mary Islington Community Partnership (£8,000).

Exclusions

The foundation does not support:

- Individuals
- Animal welfare
- Medical research
- Capital and building projects
- Faith-based programmes, unless they work with beneficiaries from all faiths or no faith

Applications

Applications are by invitation only; unsolicited applications will not be considered. See the foundation's website for more details.

Sources of information

Accounts; annual report; Charity Commission record; funder's website.

Breast Cancer Now

Research into breast cancer

UK; Ireland; USA

£11.47 million (2019/20)

CC number: 1160558

Correspondent: The Research Team, 5th Floor, Ibex House, 42–47 Minories, London EC3N 1DY (tel: 0333 207 0300; email: grants_admin@breastcancernow.org)

Trustees: Dr Marion Lewis; Mark Astaire; Barbara Brown; Susan Gallone; Christopher Copeland; Pascale Alvanitakis-Guely; Prof. Powles; Prof. Adrian Harris; Ann Pickering; Jill Thompson; Andrew Moore; Sonia Gayle.

 www.breastcancernow.org

 facebook.com/breastcancernow

 @breastcancernow

 @breastcancernow

General information

Breast Cancer Now was formed by the merger of Breakthrough Breast Cancer and Breast Cancer Campaign on 31 March 2015. The charity funds research into breast cancer, in particular research that supports improvements in the prevention, detection and treatment of all forms of breast cancer.

Grant programmes

At the time of writing (March 2022) the charity offered the following grant programmes:

Project grants – grants of up to £250,000 are available to established researchers in the UK or Ireland who have a strong track record in their field. Funding is intended to support scientific excellence and innovative research into breast cancer.

PhD studentships – studentships are available to established researchers in the UK and Ireland who have a strong track record in their field and have previous experience in supervising PhD students. PhD grant awards are for three or four years and can cover student stipends, student fees, college fees (where applicable), research expenses and essential equipment.

Further information on the charity's grant programmes is available on its website.

Financial information

Year end	31/07/2020
Income	£40,040,000
Assets	£16,090,000
Grants to organisations	£11,470,000

Beneficiaries included: Institute of Cancer Research (£6.67 million); Queen Mary University of London (£1.02 million); King's College London (£847,000); Beatson Institute of Cancer Research (£600,000); University of Manchester (£330,000); University of Cardiff (£230,000); University of Leeds (£219,000).

Applications

Applications can be made online through the charity's website. Refer to the website for application deadlines and guidelines.

Sources of information

Accounts; annual report; Charity Commission record; funder's website.

The Brelms Trust CIO

General charitable purposes

Yorkshire

£424,900 (2019/20)

CC number: 1153372

Correspondent: The Trustees, Stringer House, 34 Lupton Street, Leeds, West Yorkshire LS10 2RU (email: admin@brelmstrust.org.uk)

Trustees: Mary Cornish; Stephen Stroud; Lesley Faithful; Juliet Kemp; Alan Wallace; Susan Brown; Jillian Malcomson.

 www.brelmstrust.org.uk

General information

The Brelms Trust CIO was established in 2007. The trust offers grants to a wide variety of charities and community groups in Yorkshire. According to its website, the trust aims to support 'charities working at the heart of communities to tackle disadvantage and to provide sustainable benefit to the community'.

The trust supports registered charities with an annual income of less than £300,000 and usually with unrestricted reserves of six months or less. Grants are made for core costs and project costs.

The trust's website states:

> We are interested in funding charities which address community issues such as:
> - Arts, education and sport
> - Carers
> - Conservation
> - Debt and benefits advice
> - Domestic abuse and sexual violence
> - Excluded young people
> - Homelessness
> - Older people facing isolation
> - Physical and learning disabilities
> - Physical and mental health
> - Prevention of re-offending
> - Refugees, asylum-seekers and ethnic minorities
> - Rural isolation
> - Substance misuse
> - Support in bereavement
> - Support for disadvantaged

Financial information

Year end	30/11/2020
Income	£386,900
Assets	£2,410,000
Grants to organisations	£424,900

Beneficiaries included: Sight Support Ryedale (£15,000); City of Sanctuary (£14,600); Beverley Community Lift (£9,000); Esk Moors Active (£4,000); Sheffield Disabled Fishing Group (£3,000); York Women's Counselling Service (£2,700).

Exclusions

According to its website, the trust cannot make grants to or for the following:

- Organisations without charitable status.
- Organisations not registered at the Charity Commission.
- Large charitable organisations which currently have an annual income of £500,000 or more.
- National charities, unless the project is based in Yorkshire and for the specific benefit of the Yorkshire Community. Embedded local management by a board of Trustees and financial control of all budgetary spending must be evidenced, usually by a set of Accounts.
- Applications from individuals or student gap year costs.
- Charities requesting donations for specific or general appeals.
- Organisations which advance religion or promote faith-based activities as stated within the charitable objects registered at the Charity Commission. If this does not in any way apply to the Project for which you are applying for funding, then it is your responsibility to demonstrate to us within your application that such is the case.
- Party political organisations.
- Animal welfare.
- Medical research.
- Work requiring retrospective funding.

Applications

Applications can be made via the trust's website.

Sources of information

Accounts; annual report, Charity Commission record, funder's website.

The Brenley Trust

Social welfare; education

UK; southern Africa

 £369,200 (2020/21)

CC number: 1151128

Correspondent: The Trustees, 17 Princes Drive, Oxshott, Leatherhead, Surrey KT22 0UL (tel: 01372 841801; email: patrick.riley@btinternet.com)

Trustees: Patrick Riley; Mary-Louise Brenninkmeyer; Robbert Zoet.

General information

The trust was established in 2013 and its 2020/21 accounts state: 'The trust's objectives are to support independent charities and individuals in relation to the reduction of poverty and hardship, and the improvement of education. Grants will mainly be administered in the United Kingdom and Southern Africa.'

Financial information

Year end	31/01/2021
Income	£92,900
Assets	£11,790,000
Grants to organisations	£369,200

Beneficiaries included: Bridge House School (£139,300); Tayntons (£80,100); Stellenbosch University (£53,100); Wemmershoek School (£32,400); Mandel Gwebu (£19,800); Celtic Foundation (£10,000); Flame Introductions (£7,000); Help2Read (£3,000).

Applications

Apply in writing to the correspondent.

Sources of information

Accounts; annual report; Charity Commission record.

Bridgepoint Charitable Trust

Education; the environment; health

UK; Europe; USA

£2.83 million (2020)

CC number: 1134525

Correspondent: The Trustees, 95 Wigmore Street, London W1U 1FB (tel: 020 7034 3500)

Trustees: James Murray; Michael Walton; William Paul; Benjamin Marten; David Nicolson; Vanessa Delaage; Paul Koziarski; Christina Magnusson.

www.bridgepoint.eu/investing-responsibly/giving-back

General information

This trust was registered with the Charity Commission in February 2010 and is linked to the international private equity firm Bridgepoint. The trust's 2020 annual report states:

> Bridgepoint Charitable Trust ('BCT') is the charitable foundation of the international private equity group Bridgepoint. Formed and funded by the Firm and its employees, it focuses on giving to organisations in the broad areas of education, the environment and health within Europe. Its aims are simple: to provide support to adopted charities in the countries where Bridgepoint operates as well as giving tactical support to the charitable activities of individual team members.

Financial information

Year end	31/12/2020
Income	£3,370,000
Assets	£1,150,000
Grants to organisations	£2,830,000

Further financial information

During the year the trust's grant total was higher than usual as it launched a £3.3 million COVID-19 relief fund during the year to be spent in 2020 and 2021. Only beneficiaries of grants over £25,000 were listed in the accounts. Grants under £25,000 totalled £399,500. We were unable to determine the exact portion of grants awarded in the UK, but from the beneficiary list in the accounts we found that over £700,000 was donated in the UK.

Beneficiaries included: Football Beyond Borders (£92,600); Royal Marsden Cancer Hospital (£78,000); The UK Sepsis Trust (£75,000); The Felix Project (£50,000); Interfaith Medical Centre (£46,700); University of Birmingham (£30,000); Bookmark Reading and St Wilfrid's Hospice (£25,000 each).

Applications

Unsolicited applications are not accepted. The trust's website states that it 'provides support to charities nominated by [its] teams across [its] network and considered by trustees who are drawn from across the Firm.'

Sources of information

Accounts; annual report; Charity Commission record.

The BRIT Trust

Music; performing arts; young people

UK

£1.1 million (2020)

CC number: 1000413

Correspondent: The Trustees, British Phonographic Industry, Riverside Building, County Hall, Westminster Bridge Road, London SE1 7JA (email: brittrust@bpi.co.uk)

Trustees: Geoff Taylor; Tony Wadsworth; David Sharpe; William Rowe; David Munns; Angela Watts; Gerald Doherty; Rita Broe; Henry Semmence; Paul Burger; Caroline Dollimore; Mulika Sannie; Kwame Kwaten.

www.brittrust.co.uk

facebook.com/thebrittrust

@thebrittrust

General information

Established in 1989, The BRIT Trust is entirely funded by the British music industry and receives a large part of its income from the profits of the annual BRIT Awards. Its mission is 'improving lives through the power of music and the creative arts', which it does principally through its commitments to the BRIT School in Croydon – the UK's only non-fee-paying performing arts school – and to Nordoff Robbins, which is the UK's leading independent provider of music therapy.

The trust mainly supports The Brit School and Nordoff Robbins. However, if possible the trustees sometimes make smaller donations to support additional charitable organisations and activities. These applications are considered at the November meeting of the trust.

Financial information

Year end	31/12/2020
Income	£1,690,000
Assets	£12,620,000
Grants to organisations	£1,100,000

Beneficiaries included: Nordoff Robbins Music Therapy (£542,500); The BRIT School (£452,000); Day One Trust (£60,000); Music Support (£30,000); Key4Life (£20,000).

Applications

Application forms can be downloaded from the trust's website.

Sources of information

Accounts; annual report; Charity Commission record; funder's website.

John James Bristol Foundation

Education; health; older people; general charitable purposes

Bristol

£2.37 million (2020/21)

CC number: 288417

Correspondent: Louise O'Donnell, Chief Executive, 7 Clyde Road, Redland, Bristol BS6 6RG (tel: 0117 923 9444; email: info@johnjames.org.uk)

Trustees: Elizabeth Chambers; John Evans; Dr John Haworth; David Johnson; Joan Johnson; Andrew Jardine; Andrew Webley; Peter Goodwin; Nicola Parker; Julia Norton.

www.johnjames.org.uk

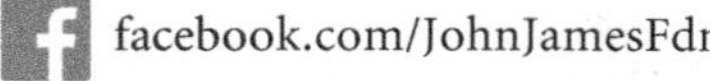
facebook.com/JohnJamesFdn

@JohnJamesFdn

General information

The foundation was established in 1983 by John James, a businessman and philanthropist, who was born and lived in Bristol until his death in 1996. It makes grants to charitable organisations whose work benefits residents of Bristol. According to the settlor's sentiments, the foundation's main aim is to benefit as many residents of the city as possible and so the trustees make every effort to grant money diversely in each financial year.

The main areas of focus for the foundation are education, health and older people, which were all supported by John James during his life. The website stresses that 'links with the past are however coupled with a strong vision for the future needs of Bristol and its residents'. To be eligible to apply, applicants must be a registered charity, exempt charity, not-for-profit social enterprise or CIC.

As well as awarding grants to organisations, the foundation also makes grants to clubs and organisations in Bristol that arrange Christmas or New Year parties for their members who are older or living with a disability and resident in Bristol. The foundation also runs a theatre ticket scheme where pensioners can apply for tickets to amateur dramatic shows.

Financial information

Year end	30/09/2021
Income	£2,190,000
Assets	£89,490,000
Grants to organisations	£2,370,000
No. of grants	404

Further financial information

During the year, the foundation received 493 applications, of which 404 were successful. Grants were broken down as follows:

Health	£1.34 million
Education	£659,600
Older people	£373,900
General	£3,000

Only beneficiaries of grants over £3,000 were listed in the accounts.

Beneficiaries included: The Park (£250,000); St Peter's Hospice (£105,000); Royal West of England Academy (£76,300); Clifton High School (£30,000); Brain Tumour Support (£13,600); Church Homeless Trust (£5,000); Queen Elizabeth's Hospital (£1,500).

Applications

Apply in writing to the correspondent by post or email. Full information on what should be included in an application can be found on the foundation's website.

Sources of information

Accounts; annual report; Charity Commission record; funder's website.

The Britford Bridge Trust

Social welfare; education; health; arts, science, culture and heritage; community development; sport; the environment

UK and overseas

£760,100 (2020/21)

CC number: 1160012

Correspondent: The Trustees, c/o Brodies LLP, Brodies House, 14–17 Atholl Cresent, Edinburgh EH3 8HA (tel: 01224 392264; email: thebritfordbridgetrust@brodies.com)

Trustees: Brodies and Co (Trustees) Ltd; Adrian Frost; Dr Margaret MacDougall.

General information

This trust, registered in January 2015, supports registered charities working in a wide range of areas worldwide.

According to the trust's website, grants are awarded to charitable organisations in accordance with the following objectives:

- The prevention or relief of poverty
- The advancement of education
- The advancement of health or the saving of lives
- The advancement of the arts, culture, heritage or science

The trust also has a secondary focus on the following areas:

- The advancement of citizenship or community development
- The advancement of amateur sport
- The advancement of environmental protection or improvement
- The relief of those in need, by reason of youth, age, ill-health, disability, financial hardship or other disadvantage.

Financial information

Year end	05/04/2021
Income	£500,320
Assets	£29,510,000
Grants to organisations	£760,100

Further financial information

The trustees typically make grants of between £10,000 and £50,000. Larger amounts may be available in exceptional circumstances.

Beneficiaries included: Addenbrooke's Charitable Trust (£75,000); London Handel Society (£50,000); Scottish Seabird Centre (£10,000); Peer Productions (£5,000); GreenSeas Trust (£4,400).

Applications

Application forms can be downloaded from the trust's website. The trustees meet to review applications every three months.

Sources of information

Accounts; annual report; Charity Commission record.

The British Academy

Humanities and social sciences

UK and overseas

£54.4 million (2020/21)

CC number: 233176

Correspondent: Grants Team, 10 Carlton House Terrace, London SW1Y 5AH (tel: 020 7969 5200; email: grants@britac.ac.uk)

Trustees: Prof. Bencie Woll; Prof. Simon Keay; Prof. Chakravarthi Ram-Prasad; Prof. Charles Tripp; Prof. Diarmaid MacCulloch; Prof. Dauvit Bron; Prof. Michael Moriarty; Prof. Jane Humphries; Prof. Andrew Hurrell; Prof. Ingrid De Smet; Prof. Sarah Birch; Prof. Sally Shuttleworth; Prof. Aditi Lahiri; Prof. Joanna Bourke; Prof. Simon Swain; Prof. Jane Millar; Prof. Tony Manstead; Prof. Conor Gearty; Prof. Hamish Scott; Prof. Isobel Armstrong; Prof. Annett Volfing; Prof. Genevra Richardson; Prof. Simon Goldhill; Prof. Sir David Cannadine; Sarah Whatmore; Prof. Rana Mitter; Prof. Christina Boswell; Prof. Angela McRobbie.

 www.britac.ac.uk

 facebook.com/TheBritishAcademy

 @britishacademy_

General information

The academy's website states:

> The British Academy provides a variety of grants and fellowships to support academic research, career development and wider engagement across the full range of the humanities and social sciences. Funding opportunities cover UK and international research from the postdoctoral level upwards, supporting the best ideas, individuals and intellectual resources.

Awards given include those for research grants, international joint initiatives, appointments and conferences.

There are various different funding opportunities available; for full, up-to-date details of each of the funding programmes, visit the academy's website.

Financial information

Year end	31/03/2021
Income	£63,030,000
Assets	£38,790,000
Grants to organisations	£54,450,000

Beneficiaries included: University of Oxford (£6.2 million); University College London (£2.8 million); University of Edinburgh (£1.7 million); London School of Economics (£1.2 million); University of York (£988,000); Durham University (£713,100); Imperial College London (£235,000); De Montfort University (£227,100).

Exclusions

No loans for graduate studies. All awards are at postdoctoral level only.

Applications

Applications are made through the academy's online grant portal. For details of the application process and criteria visit the academy's website.

Sources of information

Accounts; annual report; Charity Commission record; funder's website.

The British and Foreign School Society

Access to education or the quality of education for vulnerable or deprived children and young people under the age of 25

UK and overseas

£756,300 (2020)

CC number: 314286

Correspondent: The Trustees, 7–14 Great Dover Street, London SE1 4YR (email: grants@bfss.org.uk)

Trustees: Peter Miller; Anood Al-Samerai; Janice Miller; Charlotte Cashman; Timothy Andrew; David Baron; Vic Craggs; Jane Creasy; Prof. Joy Cooper; Leslie Stephen; Karen Hughes.

www.bfss.org.uk

facebook.com/pages/British-Foreign-School-Society/515588405261569

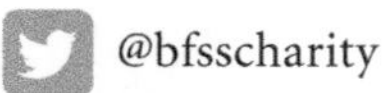

@bfsscharity

General information

This charity, established by Royal Charter in 1906, gives grants to UK-registered charities advancing educational opportunity in the UK and financially developing countries.

Grants to organisations

The BFSS supports charitable organisations running UK and international projects to improve access to education or the quality of education for vulnerable or deprived children and young people under the age of 25.

In the UK the charity will currently only consider applications to improve the educational outcomes and life chances of young carers and looked-after children for the foreseeable future.

Internationally the BFSS supports projects to improve the quality, sustainability and access to education for young people within international marginalised and deprived communities.

Financial information

Year end	31/12/2020
Income	£647,000
Assets	£26,920,000
Grants to organisations	£756,300

Beneficiaries included: Children on the Edge (£40,000); Teach A Man To Fish (£29,900); Temwa (£8,200); Scotswood Natural Community Garden (£2,500); Omushana (£600).

Applications

Apply via the BFSS website.

Sources of information

Accounts; annual report; Charity Commission record; funder's website.

British Eye Research Foundation (Fight for Sight)

Research into sight loss

UK

£2.41 million (2020/21)

CC number: 1111438

Correspondent: Andy Cottell, Director of Finance and Operations, 18 Mansell Street, London E1 8AA (tel: 020 7264 3904; email: grants@fightforsight.org.uk)

Trustees: Roy Quinlan; Louisa Vincent; Thomas Bjorn; Prof. Maria Cordeiro; Jennifer Williams; Alina Kessel; Sylvester Oppong.

www.fightforsight.org.uk

facebook.com/fightforsightuk

@fightforsightUK

@fightforsightuk

General information

Fight for Sight, previously known as the Prevention of Blindness Research Fund, funds pioneering research to prevent sight loss and treat eye disease.

The charity has the following research goals (taken from its website):

- **Understanding:** increasing understanding of how eye diseases and conditions start and develop
- **Prevention:** preventing eye diseases and conditions
- **Early Diagnosis:** enabling eye diseases and conditions to be detected earlier
- **Treatment:** developing new and improved treatments for eye diseases and conditions

Fight for Sight's primary way of delivering its goals is through funding medical research. Between 2017 and 2022 the charity focused the majority of funding across four strategic programmes, while also continuing to fund research into all eye conditions:

1. Age-related macular degeneration
2. Glaucoma
3. Inherited eye diseases
4. Sight loss linked to other diseases (multi-morbidities)

Grant schemes

The charity has a number of different grant schemes which open and close at differing times during the year. Its funds are allocated to research teams attached to UK academic or medical institutions. The research may be undertaken in the UK or overseas. Current funding opportunities can be found on the charity's website. Previous schemes have included:

- **Small Grants**: grants of up to £15,000 for clinical and pilot/feasibility research studies in ophthalmology and vision science
- **PhD Studentships**: grants of up to £100,000 awarded to PhD supervisors for three year PhD studentships
- **Project Grants**: grants of up to £250,000 for three years (or pro rata for shorter projects) for clinical and non-clinical scientists for research relevant to Fight for Sight's charitable aims

For further information, eligibility criteria, deadlines and guidance, refer to the charity's website.

Financial information

Year end	31/03/2021
Income	£6,420,000
Assets	£8,220,000
Grants to organisations	£2,410,000

Further financial information

Grants paid in 2020/21 totalled £2.41 million. New grants awarded in the period amounted to £1.97 million.

Beneficiaries included: King's College London (£830,000); London School of Hygiene and Tropical Medicine (£95,000); Anglia Ruskin University Higher Education Corporation (£36,000); University of Birmingham (£27,000); University of Cambridge (£15,000); The University of Edinburgh (£4,000).

Exclusions

Each individual scheme may have its own exclusion criteria. See the charity's website for further information.

Applications

Applications must be made through the charity's online portal, available through its website.

Sources of information

Accounts; annual report; Charity Commission record; funder's website.

British Gas Energy Trust

Fuel debt advice

England; Wales; Scotland

£3.56 million (2020/21)

CC number: 1179578

Correspondent: The Trustees, Farrer and Co., 65–66 Lincoln's Inn Fields, London WC2A 3LH (tel: 020 3375 7496; email: contact@britishgasenergytrust.org.uk)

Trustees: Helen Charlton; William Gillis; Albert Chong; Sheila Wheeler; Laurie Lee; Colin Trend; Hardial Bhogal;

Christina Thwaite; Mark McGillicud; Susan Deacon.

 www.britishgasenergytrust.org.uk

General information

The British Gas Energy Trust, which incorporates the Scottish Gas Energy Trust, was established in 2004 and is funded entirely by British Gas.

Organisational grants

The trust's website states:

> The Trust funds a number of organisations across England, Wales and Scotland to provide a wide range of specialist fuel debt advice services including:
> - Budget planning
> - Benefit / income maximisation checks
> - Energy supplier / tariff switching exercises
> - Resolution of energy debt problems
> - Negotiating with energy suppliers
> - Completing applications to British Gas Energy Trust and other grant giving schemes, e.g. Warm Home Discount and ECO schemes and energy companies' Priority Services Registers
> - Desktop Home Energy Efficiency Surveys and specific energy efficiency advice
> - Generalist advice on subjects including housing, employment and discrimination, helping to overcome other barriers to financial well-being.

Grants to individuals

Both British Gas customers and non-customers can apply for grants to clear domestic gas and electricity debts owed to British Gas or suppliers other than British Gas.

Financial information

Year end	31/01/2022
Income	£6,000,000
Assets	£2,620,000
Grants to organisations	£3,560,000

Beneficiaries included: A list of beneficiaries was not available.

Applications

Application forms are available on the trust's website.

Sources of information

Accounts; annual report; Charity Commission record; funder's website.

British Heart Foundation (BHF)

Clinical and non-clinical cardiovascular research

 UK

£51.9 million (2020/21)

CC number: 225971

Correspondent: Research Funds Department, Greater London House (4th Floor), 180 Hampstead Road, London NW1 7AW (tel: 020 7554 0434; email: research@bhf.org.uk)

Trustees: Dr Doug Gurr; Prof. David Lomas; Prof. John Iredale; Peter Phippen; Daryl Fielding; Dr Sarah Clarke; Timothy Howe; Karen Frank; Prof. Jill Pell; Mark Fitzpatrick; Sir Prof. Munir Pirmohamed; Sir John Hood; Dr Annalisa Jenkins.

 www.bhf.org.uk

 facebook.com/bhf

 @TheBHF

 @the_bhf

General information

The British Heart Foundation's vision is: 'A world free from the fear of heart and circulatory diseases', as stated on its website. The foundation looks to achieve this by funding pioneering cardiovascular research to prevent, treat and cure all heart and circulatory diseases, including heart attacks, strokes and vascular dementia, and risk factors like high blood pressure and diabetes.

Its annual report for 2020/21 states that the foundation remains 'the largest independent funder of research into heart and circulatory diseases in the UK'.

Grant programmes

There are multiple different grant types, all with their own specific guidelines. They are broken down into the following broad categories:

- Clinical and non-clinical cardiovascular researchers at all career stages
- Short and long-term research projects
- Essential infrastructure
- Strategic initiatives

For full and up-to-date details on the foundation's funding opportunities visit the 'Information for researchers' page on the foundation's website.

Financial information

Year end	31/03/2021
Income	£122,400,000
Assets	£79,600
Grants to organisations	£51,900,000

Further financial information

Only the top 50 grants made during the year were listed in the foundation's 2020/21 accounts.

Beneficiaries included: University of Oxford (£6.3 million in nine grants); Imperial College London (£3.1 million in five grants); University of Glasgow (£1.2 million in three grants); The Francis Crick Institute (£700,000); University of Leicester (£300,000).

Applications

Applicants are asked to prepare a detailed research proposal (in Arial font, size not smaller than 12 points) that complies with the instructions and eligibility criteria outlined in the specific grant guidelines. All applications, except for those to the Strategic Initiatives programme, must be submitted online using the Grants Management System (GMS) available via the foundation's website. New users will need to register before they submit an application.

For paper applications for the Strategic Initiatives programme, refer to the foundation's website.

Applications for funding are sent to independent peer reviewers before being assessed by the relevant research grant committee. According to the foundation's website 'decisions are based on factors such as relevance to cardiovascular disease, scientific merit, timeliness, relationship to other work in the field, adherence to the principles of the NC3Rs guidance for reduction, refinement and replacement of use of animals, and value for money'. Each of the foundation's research grant committees meets four times a year other than the Clinical Studies Committee and the Translational Awards Committee which meet twice a year.

For full details of all current grant programmes as well as information regarding eligibility criteria, application processes and deadlines, refer to the foundation's website.

Sources of information

Accounts; annual report; Charity Commission record; funder's website.

British Motor Sports Training Trust

Education and training in motor sports and safety in motorsports

 UK

£212,400 (2020)

CC number: 273828

Correspondent: Allan Dean-Lewis, Secretary, Birds Nest, 28 Tan y Bryn Road, Llandudno LL30 1UU (tel: 07801 591332; email: gensec@bmstt.org)

Trustees: Jim Morris; Hugh Chambers; Mr Nicky Moffitt; Dominic Ostrowski; Katherine Traxton; Roderick Parkin; Philip Parkin; Benjamin Shippey.

 www.bmstt.org

General information

This trust was established in 1977 to support safety and training initiatives in four-wheeled motor sport. According to the 2020 annual report, the objects of the trust are 'to provide funds for education and training particularly of volunteer officials, and other grants to further improve safety in the sport, including the best practice use of relevant equipment in order to prevent and reduce the incidence and gravity of accidents in motor sport generally'.

Grants are made through two programmes:

BMSTT Safety Development Fund – this fund is open to applications from Motorsport UK registered clubs or other Motorsport UK registered or licensed organisations (at the discretion of the trustees). Priority will be given to applications which are considered most likely to further improve safety aspects of motor sport. This programme includes, but is not limited to, the following:

1
- Closed road event safety grants: to assist clubs running 'closed road' events, providing funds for purchase of spectator safety and control equipment, and statutory safety signage. The maximum grant available is £600 per year (and £300 in a second year).
- Rally safety grants: grants towards the purchase of safety management radios and fire extinguishers

2. Venue safety and sustainability improvements
3. Rescue units and equipment
4. Recovery units and equipment

Volunteers and Marshals Training Day Programme – provides block grant aid funding each year for safety training projects (including but not limited to marshals training days, rescue and recovery training days, medical training days).

Financial information

Year end	31/12/2020
Income	£115,700
Assets	£3,700,000
Grants to organisations	£212,400

Further financial information

The trust awarded grants totalling £212,400 during the year; however, in previous years it has given over £300,000.

Beneficiaries included: British Automobile Racing Club (£16,500); Northern Ireland Motor Club (£11,000); Midland Centre of the British Racing and Sports Car Club (£8,000); South East Motor Sport Rescue (£5,400); Emergency Mobile Medical Unit (£1,000).

Applications

Application forms and further guidelines on the application process can be found on the trust's website. Application forms can either be downloaded and sent to the correspondent or be completed online.

Sources of information

Accounts; annual report; Charity Commission record; funder's website.

The J. and M. Britton Charitable Trust

Education and social welfare

Bristol

£289,000 (2020/21)

CC number: 1081979

Correspondent: The Trustees, 3A Merlin Haven, Wotton-under-Edge, Gloucestershire GL12 7BA (tel: 01453 498044)

Trustees: Robert Bernays; Annie Bernays; Richard Bernays; Caroline Duckworth; Alison Bernays; Lady Merrison.

General information

Established in 2000, the trust makes grants to local charities and individuals for education and social welfare purposes.

Financial information

Year end	05/04/2021
Assets	£3,610,000
Grants to organisations	£289,000

Beneficiaries included: A list of beneficiaries was not available. Previous beneficiaries include: Bristol Music Trust (£145,000); Quartet Community Fund (£20,000); The Matthew Tree Project (£5,000); Clifton College (£4,000); Alabare Gloucestershire Homes for Veterans (£2,500); Penny Brohn Cancer Care (£2,000); Kinergy (£1,300).

Applications

Apply in writing to the correspondent. According to the trust's 2020/21 annual report, the trustees 'meet regularly to consider what grants they will make.'

Sources of information

Accounts; annual report; Charity Commission record.

The Bromley Trust

Human rights and prison reform

UK

£820,500 (2020/21)

CC number: 801875

Correspondent: The Trustees, Studio 5, Unit G03, The Leather Market, 11/13 Weston Street, London SE1 3ER (email: enquiries@thebromleytrust.org.uk.)

Trustees: Dr Judith Brett; Anne-Marie Edgell; Fiona Cramb; Terrence Davies; Adam McCormack; Susan Silk; Helen Curtis; Rod Clark.

www.thebromleytrust.org.uk

General information

According to the trust's website, in 1989 Frederick Keith Bromley, also known as Toby, set up the Bromley Trust to 'offset man's inhumanity to man'.

The Bromley Trust funds UK charities through two grant programmes focusing on human rights and prison reform.

Human rights

The trust's current human rights focus areas are:

1. Torture and abuse
2. Detention
3. Human rights protection

Prison Reform

The trust's current prison reform focus areas are:

1. Prison education and skills training
2. Prison reform

Financial information

Year end	31/03/2021
Income	£326,900
Assets	£17,130,000
Grants to organisations	£820,500

Further financial information

Grants were broken down as follows: human rights (£410,000); prison reform (£410,500).

Beneficiaries included: Prison Reform Trust (£30,000): Birth Companions (£25,000); Room to Heal (£15,000); Detention Action (£10,000); Yorkshire Youth and Music (£5,500).

Exclusions

The trust's website states:

> What we don't fund:
> - Organisations that are not UK registered charities.
> - Organisations working entirely outside of the UK
> - Small organisations working at a local level unless they are also having a significant regional or national impact
> - Individuals
> - General Appeals
> - Emergency funding
> - Capital Projects
> - Academic research
> - Promotion of religion
> - International development work
> - Disaster relief
> - Conflict or post-conflict work
> - Drug or alcohol rehabilitation services
> - Housing projects
> - Domestic abuse projects
> - General mentoring programmes
> - Criminal Justice projects that do not work in prisons or directly benefit current prisoners
> - Newly established organisations without a full year's audited or independently examined accounts
> - Organisations with no (or very low) reserves

- Organisations which have more than one year's worth of unrestricted reserves
- Organisations who have made an unsuccessful application to the Trust in the last two years
- We no longer accept applications for environmental projects

Applications

Application forms and guidelines are available from the trust's helpful website.

Sources of information

Accounts; annual report; Charity Commission record; funder's website.

The Brook Trust

Social welfare and support of survivors of domestic and sexual abuse

UK

£708,900 (2020/21)

CC number: 1123562

Correspondent: The Trustees, PO Box 161, Cranbrook, Kent TN17 9BL (email: info@brooktrust.org)

Trustees: Tim Bull; Rosalind Riley; Dr Elinor Cleghorn.

 www.brooktrust.org

General information

The Brook Trust was established in 2008. According to the trust's website, the trust has two areas that support is concentrated on:

- Support of victims of domestic and sexual abuse
- Early intervention programmes with children and families aiming to break cycles of social and economic deprivation and dysfunction

Financial information

Year end	05/04/2021
Income	£87,300
Assets	£5,330,000
Grants to organisations	£708,900

Beneficiaries included: Refuge (£125,000); Young Minds (£50,400); Action Aid (£22,000); Child Autism UK (£5,000); Brighton and Hove City Council (£2,000).

Applications

The Brook Trust will not consider unsolicited funding applications. However, the trustees will consider initial enquiries which must be made by email to info@brooktrust.org.

Sources of information

Accounts; annual report; Charity Commission record; funder's website.

The Rory and Elizabeth Brooks Foundation

International development; poverty research; higher education in the UK; social justice; visual arts

 UK and overseas

£589,600 (2020/21)

CC number: 1111587

Correspondent: Robyn Bryson, Orion House, 5 Upper St Martin's Lane, London WC2H 9EA (tel: 020 7024 2217; email: RBryson@mmlcapital.com)

Trustees: Elizabeth Brooks; Roderick Brooks; Bridget Fury.

 www.brooks-foundation.org.uk

General information

The foundation was established in 2005 and receives its income through donations and legacies. The foundation currently provides support in the following areas:

- Global development and poverty research
- Higher education in the UK
- Visual arts
- Social justice

According to the website, the areas of focus of the foundation are a reflection of the life experiences and interests of the founding trustees Rory and Elizabeth Brooks. Rory is an advocate for philanthropy in higher education and he is the Chair of the University of Manchester's Global Leadership Board. Elizabeth is a previous Chair of the Tate Patrons Executive Committee.

Partnership is a key consideration for the foundation and in each area of focus there are one or more partners with which Rory and Elizabeth work. Current partners include; The Rugby Portobello Trust, Justice and Care; Manchester University Global Development Institute.

Financial information

Year end	31/01/2021
Income	£601,300
Assets	£273,000
Grants to organisations	£589,600

Beneficiaries included: University of Manchester (£355,000); Tate gallery and connected organisations (£154,600).

Applications

Apply in writing to the correspondent.

Sources of information

Accounts; annual report; Charity Commission record; funder's website.

The Broomton Foundation

General charitable purposes

East Anglia

£242,900 (2020/21)

CC number: 1125386

Correspondent: The Trustees, Providence House, 141–145 Princes Street, Ipswich, Suffolk IP1 1QJ (tel: 01473 232300; email: admin@broomton.org)

Trustees: Benedicta Chamberlain; Julius Chamberlain; Robert Chamberlain; Kate Lewis.

General information

The foundation was established in 2008 and makes grants for general charitable purposes throughout East Anglia.

Financial information

Year end	05/04/2021
Income	£1,420,000
Assets	£15,430,000
Grants to organisations	£242,900

Further financial information

In previous years grants have totalled around £400,000.

Beneficiaries included: Pancreatic Cancer UK (£150,000); Walnut Tree (£13,600); Find Ipswich (£10,000); Pawsitive Squad (£6,000).

Applications

Apply in writing to the correspondent.

Sources of information

Accounts; annual report; Charity Commission record.

The Brothers Trust

General charitable purposes; social welfare; health

 UK; USA; overseas

£347,900 (2020/21)

CC number: 1172675

Correspondent: The Trustees, c/o SA Ledgers Ltd, 57 Canbury Park Road, Kingston upon Thames, Surrey KT2 6LQ (tel: 020 7388 7000)

Trustees: Nicola Holland; Dominic Holland; Thomas Holland; Gregory Cook; Janine Cook.

 www.thebrotherstrust.org

 facebook.com/thebrotherstrust

 @Tbrotherstrust

 @thebrotherstrust

General information

This trust was registered with the Charity Commission in April 2017. It was established by Nikki and Dom Holland who are parents to four brothers Sam, Harry, Paddy and English actor and celebrity, Tom Holland. The trust uses Tom's platform and reach to run a number fundraising events throughout the year, with the donations being given to charities that the trust supports. Previous events have included a private screening of *Avengers Infinity War* with Tom Holland himself, which raised over £50,000.

The trust wishes to support charities that are able to demonstrate that their funds effectively benefit the beneficiaries in need, rather than being used on administration costs. Additionally, the trust states on its website that it wishes to 'shine a light on charities who struggle to be heard' in the charity sector.

The trust has provided regular support to charities both in UK and abroad for a range of causes including health, social welfare, children and support for people experiencing homelessness.

Financial information

Year end	31/03/2021
Income	£432,800
Assets	£117,400
Grants to organisations	£347,900

Beneficiaries included: Momentum (£77,000); DEBRA (£44,800); Tear Fund (£30,600); Mama Biashara (£20,000); Warm Heart Worldwide (£10,600); Shebach Ministry (£5,000); Dr Gary Burnstein Community Health (£1,000).

Applications

Apply in writing to the correspondent. The trust's Charity Commission record states that it both 'identifies needs itself and considers unsolicited applications for funds'.

Sources of information

Accounts; annual report; Charity Commission record; funder's website.

Bill Brown 1989 Charitable Trust

Social welfare; health, including research into blindness, other medical research and hospices; the care of older people and people who have disabilities

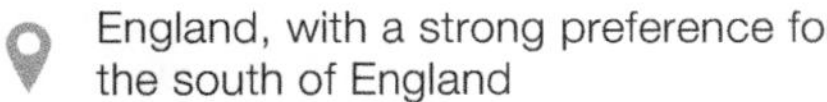

England, with a strong preference for the south of England

£184,300 (2019/20)

CC number: 801756

Correspondent: The Trustees, BM Box 4567, London WC1N 3XX (tel: 020 7465 4300)

Trustees: Anthony Barnett; Graham Brown.

 www.billbrowncharity.org

General information

This trust was founded in 1989 by Percy William Ernest Brown, a civil engineer and businessman who also served in the RAF during the Second World War.

The trust's 2019/20 accounts state that the trustees aim to make annual distributions of approximately £475,000, excluding substantial bursary commitments, which are usually made to the University of Bristol.

The trustees are particularly interested in supporting projects in the following areas of charitable work:

- Research into blindness
- Other medical research
- People who are deaf and blind
- Care of older people
- Care of people with disabilities
- General welfare
- Hospices

Financial information

Year end	30/06/2020
Income	£625,200
Assets	£12,920,000
Grants to organisations	£184,300
No. of grants	16

Further financial information

Grants paid in 2019/20 totalled £184,300; however, in previous years it has given around £500,000.

Beneficiaries included: Charities Aid Foundation (£75,000); Macmillan Cancer Support (£15,000); Alzheimer's Society, Crohn's and Colitis UK and Treloar Trust (£7,500 each); Blind Veterans UK (£5,000); Richmond Borough Mind (£3,800).

Exclusions

According to the trust's website, grants are not made for or to:

- Individuals
- Animal welfare
- Small (local) charitable causes
- Appeals from regional branches of national charities
- Wildlife and environmental conservation
- Maintenance of buildings
- Religious charities

Applications

Applications should be sent in writing to the correspondent with a copy of the latest annual report and accounts. Applications must be received by the end of April or the end of September to be sure of consideration at the summer and winter trustee meetings. Information on what to include in the application can be found on the trust's website.

Sources of information

Accounts; annual report; Charity Commission record; funder's website.

The Brownsword Charitable Foundation

Children and young people; the arts; older people; community work; learning difficulties; education; medical causes

Bath and surrounding areas

£414,900 (2020)

CC number: 1012615

Correspondent: The Trustees, 4 Queen Square, Bath, Somerset BA1 2HA (tel: 01225 339661)

Trustees: Andrew Brownsword; Robert Calleja; Peter Matthews; Alessandra Brownsword-Matthews.

General information

The trust was established in 1992. Its main operational area is the city of Bath.

The charity supports:

- Children and young people
- The arts
- Older people
- Community and neighbourhood work
- Physical and learning difficulties
- Educational projects
- Medical projects

Financial information

Year end	31/12/2020
Income	£504,900
Assets	£9,170,000
Grants to organisations	£414,900

Beneficiaries included: Forever Friends Appeal – Royal United Hospital (£200,000); Bath Abbey (£100,000); University of Exeter (£10,000); Jessie May Trust (£5,000); Merchant Venturers (£2,000).

Applications

Apply in writing to the correspondent.

Sources of information

Accounts; annual report; Charity Commission record.

The Jack Brunton Charitable Trust

General charitable purposes

North Riding of Yorkshire – prior to the boundary changes in 1974

£283,700 (2020/21)

CC number: 518407

Correspondent: David Swallow, Administrator and Trustee, Commercial House, 10 Bridge Road, Stokesley, North Yorkshire TS9 5AA (tel: 01642 711407; email: margaretc@swallco.co.uk)

Trustees: Derek Noble; James Lumb; David Swallow; Caroline Dickinson; Andrew Dickins.

 www.jackbruntontrust.co.uk

General information

The trust was formed with funds gifted by local farmer Jack Brunton. The trust is for the benefit of the population of the rural villages and towns within the North Riding of Yorkshire prior to the boundary changes in 1974.

The website states:

> While most contributions will go to established charities, all good causes will be considered and fully investigated.

Previous beneficiaries have included:

- Community groups providing play equipment etc. for local children
- Social enterprises empowering adults with disabilities to achieve their potential
- Hospital departments sourcing funds to purchase specialist equipment
- Animal welfare groups
- Drama societies, theatre groups and musical groups
- Outdoor centres
- Village halls
- Mountain rescue teams
- Organisations supporting visually impaired people with talking and listening books
- Schools
- Accessible transport services for older people
- Football teams, rugby/bowls/cricket clubs requiring financial assistance to purchase equipment and kit
- Churches needing help with refurbishment costs, DDA upgrades and building works
- Scout and girl guide groups in need of equipment
- Respite and leisure opportunities for children and young people

Financial information

Year end	05/04/2021
Income	£302,200
Assets	£11,930,000
Grants to organisations	£283,700

Beneficiaries included: Great North Air Ambulance (£45,500); Yorkshire Air Ambulance (£39,000); Peat Rigg Outdoor Training Centre (£10,000); Candlelighters Trust – North Yorkshire (£7,500); Northallerton Town Football Club (£5,000); Tang Hall Community Centre (£4,000); InterActive Whitby and District (£3,000); St Leonard's Hospice (£2,500); St Hilda's Church, Bilsdale Priory (£2,300).

Applications

Apply in writing to the trust administrator. Application forms are available to download from the website. The trustees meet on a quarterly basis to consider applications. Enquiries can be emailed to the trust's secretary, Margaret Culley at margaretc@swallco.co.uk.

Sources of information

Accounts; annual report; Charity Commission record.

Brushmill Ltd

Jewish education and places of worship for the Jewish community; social welfare; education

UK and overseas

£272,100 (2020/21)

CC number: 285420

Correspondent: Mrs M. Getter, Secretary, 76 Fairholt Road, London N16 5HN (tel: 020 8731 0777; email: mail@cohenarnold.com)

Trustees: Mr C. Getter; Mrs E. Weinberger; Mr J. Weinberger.

General information

Established in 1982, this charity gives grants for the advancement of the Orthodox Jewish religion, the relief of poverty and general charitable purposes. It would appear that the charity mainly supports Jewish organisations.

Financial information

Year end	31/03/2021
Income	£258,700
Assets	£33,700
Grants to organisations	£272,100

Further financial information

Only beneficiaries receiving grants of over £4,000 were listed in the accounts. Grants of less than £4,000 totalled £48,100.

Beneficiaries included: Friends of Boyan Trust (£106,400); North London Cost Shop (£24,300); Zoreya Tzedokos (£18,000); Bais Rizhin Trust (£17,500); Chasdei Aharon Ltd (£16,800); Yad Shlomo Trust (£12,000); Here 2 Help (£10,000); Sharei Chesed – London (£9,300); CMZ Ltd and Yesamach Levav (£5,000 each).

Applications

Apply in writing to the correspondent. The charity's 2020/21 accounts state:

> 'The Trustees consider all requests which they receive and make donations based on the level of funds available.'

Sources of information

Accounts; annual report; Charity Commission record.

The Buffini Chao Foundation

The education and training of children and young people

UK and overseas

£567,300 (2020/21)

CC number: 1111022

Correspondent: Alison Taylor, Foundation Secretary, PO Box 1427, Northampton, Northamptonshire NN1 9FP (email: trustees@buffinichao.com)

Trustees: Lady Buffini; Sir Damon Buffini; Maria Hindmarsh; Sue Gutierrez.

 www.buffinichao.com

General information

The foundation was established by Sir Damon Buffini and his wife Debbie in 2005. It is focused on promoting education and opportunities for children and young people in the UK and overseas.

Financial information

Year end	05/04/2021
Income	£2,470,000
Assets	£10,840,000
Grants to organisations	£567,300

Beneficiaries included: Royal National Theatre (£250,000); Community Foundation for Surrey (£30,000); Royal Ballet School (£20,000); Build Africa/Street Child (£16,200); Chance to Shine (£14,000); Envision (£10,000); Schoolreaders (£5,000).

Applications

The foundation's support is primarily determined through experience, personal networks and its own research. Charities that meet the foundation's core objectives can get in touch with the correspondent.

Sources of information

Accounts; annual report; Charity Commission record.

Bulb Foundation

Climate change

UK and overseas

£677,400 (2020/21)

CC number: 1183235

Correspondent: The Trustees, 155 Bishopsgate, London EC2M 3TQ (email: bulbfoundation@bulb.co.uk)

Trustees: Amit Gudka; Dr Amal-Lee Amin; Sophie Pullan; Hayden Wood; Dr Alexander Edwards.

 https://bulb.co.uk/foundation

General information

This foundation registered with the Charity Commission in May 2019 and is the corporate charity of Bulb Energy Ltd which is a green energy supplier. The company donates £2 to the foundation every time a new member switches to Bulb. The foundation supports projects that address the climate crisis.

Financial information

Year end	31/03/2021
Income	£1,110,000
Assets	£1,280,000
Grants to organisations	£677,400

Beneficiaries included: 350.org (£175,000); Stand.Earth (£100,000); Both ENDS (£75,000); Third Generation Environmentalism (£58,000).

Applications

The foundation's website states:

> We don't accept unsolicited applications for funding. Instead, we develop projects with partners that fit our strategic approach.

Sources of information

Accounts; annual report; Charity Commission record; funder's website.

The Bulldog Trust Ltd

General charitable purposes

UK

£1.94 million (2020/21)

CC number: 1123081

Correspondent: The Trustees, 2 Temple Place, London WC2R 3BD (tel: 020 7240 6044; email: info@bulldogtrust.org)

Trustees: Brian Smouha; Alex Williams; Charles Hoare; Charles Jackson; Hamish McPherson.

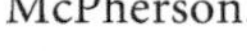

www.thefore.org or http://bulldogtrust.org/grant-making

General information

The Bulldog Trust has provided financial and advisory assistance to charities for over 30 years. In March 2017, the trust launched its new grant-making initiative, The Fore Trust.

The Fore Trust provides unrestricted development grants and pro bono strategic support to early-stage charities and social enterprises. The trust's website states:

> For its Spring 2022 funding round The Fore is offering 6–18 month grants of up to £15,000. We make unrestricted grants which have the potential to have a transformational impact on an organisation. Transformational impact includes helping organisations become more sustainable, more efficient, to grow significantly or enabling an organisation to take a major step forward of some kind.
>
> We see our grants as investments in the organisations we support.
>
> The Fore is particularly looking to fund small organisations working with marginalised groups and led by people in the community that may have found it hard to access trust and foundation funding in the past. We want to be different. Our funding process is specifically designed to level the playing field and give no advantage to those with fundraising experience or connections.
>
> Any registered charity, CIC, CIO or Community Benefit Society with turnover of under £500,000 in the last financial year is eligible to apply.

Financial information

Year end	30/06/2021
Income	£2,550,000
Assets	£278,000
Grants to organisations	£1,940,000

Beneficiaries included: ReMade Wigan (£30,000); Lifting Limits (£26,000); BelEve (£20,000); Plan Your Future (£15,000); Azuko (£13,300); Rory's Wells (£10,000).

Applications

Apply via The Fore Trust's website where application deadlines can also be found.

Sources of information

Accounts; annual report; Charity Commission record; funder's website.

The Burberry Foundation

Education; educational equality; waste reduction; social and economic development

Worldwide, with a strong preference for communities where Burberry employees live and work

£3.62 million (2020/21)

CC number: 1154468

Correspondent: Pamela Batty, Secretary, Burberry Ltd, Horseferry House, Horseferry Road, London SW1P 2AW (tel: 020 7806 1328; email: enquiries@burberryfoundation.com)

Trustees: Christopher Holmes; Edward Rash; Dr Gerard Murphy.

www.burberryplc.com/en/responsibility/policies/communities/the-burberry-foundation.html

General information

The Burberry Foundation was established in 2008 by Burberry Group plc, the British luxury fashion house.

According to its website, the foundation wishes to promote a sustainable future in communities that are affected by the luxury fashion industry. Its grant-making policy is focused on supporting the communities located in key Burberry supply chain locations.

The foundation has partnered with leading organisations to address educational inequality, support social and economic development, reduce waste and promote the STEAM (science, technology, engineering, the arts and mathematics) agenda.

The 2020/21 annual report states that, when considering requests for support the foundation will consider projects that:

- are managed competently through accountability, cost effectiveness, strong leadership and creativity
- provide a significant and measurable impact
- are located in a community where Burberry Group employees live and work
- have the potential to offer volunteering opportunities for Burberry Group employees

Financial information

Year end	31/03/2021
Income	£2,550,000
Assets	£3,590,000
Grants to organisations	£3,620,000

Further financial information

In 2020/21 the foundation awarded grants totalling £3.62 million. Within this, £2.79 million was awarded in the UK.

Beneficiaries included: Oxfam (£839,300); Royal College of Art (£412,700); Teach First (£300,000); London Youth (£285,000); MyKindaCrowd (£69,700); King's College (£50,000); California Association of Foodbanks (£5,000).

Applications

Apply in writing to the correspondent.

Sources of information

Accounts; annual report; Charity Commission record; funder's website.

The Burdett Trust for Nursing

Nursing and healthcare

UK

£4.04 million (2020)

CC number: 1089849

Correspondent: Lauren George, Rathbone Trust Company Ltd, 8 Finsbury Circus, London EC2M 7AZ (tel: 020 7399 0102; email: Lauren.George@rathbones.com)

Trustees: Dame Christine Beasley; Alan Gibbs; Andrew Smith; Evy Hambro; Prof. David Sines; Dr Michael Gormley; Andrew Gibbs; Audrey Ardern-Jones;

Prof. Charles Butterworth; Prof. Mary Lovegrove; Dame Donna Kinnair; Rachael Corser; Janice Stevens.

 www.btfn.org.uk

General information

The Burdett Trust for Nursing is an independent charitable trust named after Sir Henry Burdett KCB, the founder of the Royal National Pension Fund for Nurses. The trust was established in 2002 with the following charitable objects:

> To promote and advance education, research and training within the nursing and other healthcare professions for the benefit of the public and to promote public awareness of nursing and health issues; provide for the relief of hardship and mental or physical ill-health among nurses and other health-care professionals, and their dependants; and promote and advance the provision of nursing and other health services for the benefit of the public.

Grant programmes

In addition to its Proactive Grants programme (see below), the trust runs annual funding rounds focused on a specific area of interest. Calls for these rounds are advertised on the trust's website.

Proactive Grants

This programme aims to create opportunities to engage nursing stakeholders in collaborative problem-solving and programme development. Through the programme, the trustees work with a wide range of public and private partners to advance the foundation's long-term goals. All proactive grants are initiated by the Burdett Trust for Nursing and the trustees do not accept unsolicited applications.

Financial information

Year end	31/12/2020
Income	£1,270,000
Assets	£80,230,000
Grants to organisations	£4,040,000

Beneficiaries included: Institute of Health Visiting (£64,800); Barts Health NHS Trust (£24,200); Paintings in Hospitals (£20,000); Mesothelioma UK (£10,000); Oxford School of Nursing and Midwifery (£2,000).

Applications

See the trust's website for information on the current grant programmes and details on how to apply.

Sources of information

Accounts; annual report; Charity Commission record; funder's website.

The Clara E. Burgess Charity

The education, health and well-being of children and young people (with some preference for children under ten years)

 UK and overseas

£286,500 (2019/20)

CC number: 1072546

Correspondent: The Trustees, c/o Ludlow Trust Company Ltd, 1st Floor, Tower Wharf, Cheese Lane, Bristol BS2 0JJ (tel: 0117 313 8200; email: charitabletrusts@ludlowtrust.com)

Trustee: Ludlow Trust Company Ltd.

General information

The charity was registered in 1998 and makes grants to registered charities where children are the principal beneficiaries.

According to the 2019/20 annual report, grants are made towards 'the provision of facilities and assistance to enhance the education, health and physical well-being of such children, in order that their conditions of life may be improved, but having particular regard to children under the age of ten and those who have lost either one or both parents'.

Financial information

Year end	30/10/2020
Income	£202,900
Assets	£11,460,000
Grants to organisations	£286,500

Beneficiaries included: Children in Need (£120,000); Royal Manchester Children's Hospital (£10,000); Bethany Christian Trust (£6,000); Tom's Trust (£5,000).

Applications

Applications can be made in writing to the correspondent and are considered in January, April, July and October.

Sources of information

Accounts; annual report; Charity Commission record.

Byrne Family Foundation

 General charitable purposes, including disadvantaged children and young people

 UK

£361,500 (2020/21)

CC number: 1137878

Correspondent: Kevin Byrne, Trustee, Thrive Wellness Centre, Ellis Square, Selsey, Chichester, West Sussex PO20 0AF (tel: 07967 350212; email: kevin@byrneproperty.co.uk)

Trustees: Kevin Byrne; Ruth Byrne; Lisa Byrne; David Harland; Emily Maple; Rachel Byrne.

General information

The Byrne Family Foundation was established in 2010 and was formerly known as the Checkatrade Foundation. According to its 2019/20 accounts, the foundation supports a wide range of charitable purposes. These include, 'the support of disadvantaged young people and adults, by way of financial deprivation, illness or disability or any cause where lack of aid affects quality of life'.

Financial information

Year end	31/05/2021
Income	£124,000
Assets	£5,370,000
Grants to organisations	£361,500

Beneficiaries included: Hope House (£240,700); St Wilfrid's Hospice (£100,000); Global Compassion (£17,000).

Applications

Apply in writing to the correspondent.

Sources of information

Accounts; annual report; Charity Commission record.

The Edward Cadbury Charitable Trust

The arts and culture; community projects; social welfare; the environment and conservation; religious activities, such as interfaith and multifaith relations; education and training; medical research

The Midlands region, including Herefordshire, Shropshire, Staffordshire, Warwickshire and Worcestershire

£791,400 (2020/21)

CC number: 1160334

Correspondent: Susan Anderson, Trust Manager, Rokesley, University of Birmingham – Selly Oak, Bristol Road, Selly Oak, Birmingham, West Midlands B29 6QF (tel: 0121 472 1838; email: ecadburytrust@btconnect.com)

Trustees: Nigel Cadbury; Dr William Southall; Charles Gillett; Andrew Littleboy; Robert Marriott.

 www.edwardcadburytrust.org.uk

General information

The Edward Cadbury Charitable Trust was first established in 1945 by Edward Cadbury, the grandson of the founder of the chocolate company, and is linked to The Edward and Dorothy Cadbury Trust (Charity Commission no. 1107327). The trust supports charities in the Midlands region, including Herefordshire, Shropshire, Staffordshire, Warwickshire and Worcestershire.

The trust's website states that the founder's interests in 'education, religion and social welfare, together with the Quaker values of simplicity, equality, justice, peace and care of the environment, have helped shape the current grant-making policy of the Trust.' The trust awards grants within the following areas, as stated on its website:

- Arts and culture
- Community projects and integration
- Compassionate support
- Conservation and environment
- Interfaith and multi-faith relations
- Education and training
- Research

Grants normally range from £500 to £10,000 and are awarded on a one-off basis for a specific purpose or as part of a project. The trustees only make larger grants on an exceptional basis.

Financial information

Year end	05/04/2021
Income	£1,220,000
Assets	£52,780,000
Grants to organisations	£791,400

Beneficiaries included: New Model Institute for Technology and Engineering (£53,200); Father Hudson's Charity (£20,000); Action Medical Research (£10,000); Birmingham Disability Resource Centre (£5,000); Criminon UK (£3,000); Normandy Day UK (£2,000).

Applications

Applications can be made in writing to the correspondent by post or email. Alternatively, applications can be made online through the trust's website. Applications are accepted all year round and are normally considered within a three-month timescale. Letters of application should provide a clear and concise description of the project requiring funding as well as the outcomes and benefits that are likely to be achieved. The trustees also require an outline budget and explanation of how the project is to be funded initially and in the future together with the latest annual report and accounts for the charity.

Sources of information

Accounts; annual report; Charity Commission record; funder's website.

William A. Cadbury Charitable Trust

Locally: social welfare; education; the environment; health; the arts; penal reform. Nationally: Quaker charities and international development

West Midlands, especially Birmingham, and, to a lesser extent, the UK, Ireland and elsewhere overseas

£582,100 (2020/21)

CC number: 213629

Correspondent: The Trustees, Rokesley, University of Birmingham, Bristol Road, Selly Oak, Birmingham, West Midlands B29 6QF (tel: 0121 472 1464; email: info@wa-cadbury.org.uk)

Trustees: Margaret Salmon; Rupert Cadbury; Sarah Stafford; Katherine Cadbury; Adrian Thomas; John Penny; Sophy Blandy; Janine Cobain; Victoria Mohan.

 www.wa-cadbury.org.uk

General information

This trust was established in 1923. According to the trust's website:

> The William A Cadbury Charitable Trust is a Birmingham based grant making charity which provides funding to other charitable organisations working principally in the West Midlands. If you are thinking of applying to us for funding please review our Grant Programmes to see if your project qualifies for our support.

The trust has four main grant programmes, details of which have been taken from its website:

> **1. Birmingham and the West Midlands (Worcestershire, Warwickshire, Staffordshire and Herefordshire)**
>
> *Community Action*
>
> Community based and organised schemes (which may be centered on a place of worship) aimed at solving local problems and improving the quality of life of community members.
>
> *Vulnerable Groups*
>
> Vulnerable groups include the elderly, children and young people, the disabled, asylum seekers and similar minorities.
>
> *Advice, Mediation and Counselling*
>
> Applicants must be able to point to the rigorous selection, training and monitoring of front line staff (particularly in the absence of formal qualifications) as well as to the overall need for the service provided.
>
> *Education and Training*
>
> Trustees are particularly interested in schemes that help people of working age develop new skills in order to re-enter the jobs market.
>
> *Environment and Conservation*
>
> Projects which address the impact of climate change and projects to preserve buildings and installations of historic importance and local interest.
>
> *Medical and Healthcare*
>
> Hospices, self help groups and some medical research which must be based in and be of potential benefit to the West Midlands.
>
> *The Arts*
>
> Music, drama and the visual arts, museums and art galleries.
>
> *Penal Affairs*
>
> Restorative Justice, prison based projects and work with ex offenders aimed at reducing re-offending. (Penal reform used to be supported on a UK wide basis but, because of the volume of appeals received, this programme is now restricted to the West Midlands)
>
> **2. United Kingdom**
>
> *The Religious Society of Friends*
>
> Projects with a clear Quaker connection and which support the work of the Religious Society of Friends in the UK.
>
> **3. Ireland**
>
> Peace and Reconciliation.
>
> **4. International Development**
>
> The International grant programme is heavily oversubscribed and since the Trust can only support a small proportion of the appeals received trustees have decided to concentrate available funds on organisations with which the Trust has close and well established links. Ad hoc appeals are unlikely to be successful. All applicants must have UK charity registration.
>
> The International Development programme is concentrated on West Africa and work to reduce poverty on a sustainable basis in both rural and urban communities. Schemes that help children access education are also supported

Grants are available for core costs and development or project funding. Unregistered or exempt charitable groups can apply but must be properly constituted with an elective committee.

Financial information

Year end	31/03/2021
Income	£986,500
Assets	£54,530,000
Grants to organisations	£582,100
No. of grants	164

Further financial information

Grants were broken down as follows:

Vulnerable groups	£119,900
Medical causes and healthcare	£97,800
Community action	£90,300
Education and training	£63,600
Advice/meditation/counselling	£47,500
Ireland – peace and reconciliation	£35,500
Alan Cadbury Trust	£32,800
The environment and conservation	£29,000
United Kingdom	£27,800
The arts	£21,300
Penal affairs	£14,500
International development	£2,300

Beneficiaries included: Children in Crossfire (£25,000); The Mary Stevens Hospice (£20,000); The Springboard Charity (£15,000); Birmingham Contemporary Music Group (£12,000); Prisoners' Advice Service (£10,000); Women Acting in Today's Society (£5,000); Home From Hospital Care (£4,000).

Exclusions

According to the trust's website, the trust does not fund the following:

- Individuals (whether for research, expeditions, educational purposes or medical treatment)
- Projects concerned with travel, adventure, sports, or recreation
- Organisations which are based outside the UK

Applications

Applications can be made online using a form on the trust's website. Alternatively, applications can be sent by post. According to the trust's website, postal applications should include the following information:

- Charity registration number
- A description of the charity's aims and achievements
- An outline and budget for the project for which funding is sought
- The grant programme for which the organisation is applying
- Details of the projects previously funded by the trust (if applicable)
- Details of funds raised to date and the current shortfall

Small grants (up to a maximum of £2,000) are awarded monthly. The trustees meet in May and November to award large grants ranging in value from £10,000 to £20,000 with an occasional maximum of £50,000. The cut-off for applications to the May meeting is early March while for November the cut-off is early to mid-September.

Sources of information

Accounts; annual report; Charity Commission record; funder's website.

The Cadbury Foundation

Skills development and health

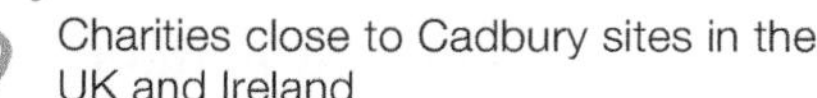

Charities close to Cadbury sites in the UK and Ireland

£437,500 (2020)

CC number: 1050482

Correspondent: Kelly Farrell, Community Affairs Manager, PO Box 12, Bourneville, Birmingham, West Midlands B30 2LU (tel: 0121 787 2421; email: kelly.farrell@mdlz.com)

Trustees: Eoin Kellett; Lisa Crane; Louise Stigant; Clive Jones; Joshua Townson; Denise Chester.

www.cadbury.co.uk/cadbury-foundation

General information

The Cadbury Foundation was established in 1935 in recognition of the founders of the Cadbury's chocolate company George and Richard Cadbury. In 2010 Kraft Foods Inc. gained control of Cadbury plc, and two years later divided the corporation into Kraft Food Group plc and Mondelez, the latter of which now funds the Cadbury Foundation.

According to its website, the foundation's ethos is 'helping people to help themselves'. It achieves this by supporting a number of charities in the UK and Ireland that are located in the communities in which the company operates.

The foundation's website states:

> Investment is focused in three key areas:
>
> **Health and wellbeing** – We encourage local communities to lead healthier lifestyles through cooking, food growing, physical activity and social cohesion.
>
> **Skills** – We inspire the next generation of talent by developing their transferable skills to help them succeed in the workplace.
>
> **Colleague Passions** – We care about the local charities our employees are passionate about, supporting local causes close to their hearts through our 'Your Charity Your Choice' and 'Cashmatch' programmes.

Financial information

Year end	31/12/2020
Income	£649,600
Assets	£264,900
Grants to organisations	£437,500

Further financial information

Grants were distributed as follows: health and well-being (£285,800); colleague passions (£131,600); skills (£20,000).

Beneficiaries included: Health for Life in Primary Schools (£100,000); Grocery Aid (£50,000); Downs Syndrome Ireland (£45,800); Pieta House (£5,000); Kingfisher Foodbank (£2,500); Irish Guide Dogs (£1,600).

Applications

The foundation actively seeks out projects to support and therefore does not accept any unsolicited requests for funding.

Sources of information

Accounts; annual report; Charity Commission record; funder's website.

The Barrow Cadbury Trust

Criminal justice; migration; social and economic justice

UK and overseas, with a preference for Birmingham and the Black Country (Wolverhampton, Dudley, West Bromwich, Smethwick or Sandwell)

£9.45 million (2020/21)

CC number: 1115476

Correspondent: The Trustees, Kean House, 6 Kean Street, London WC2B 4AS (tel: 020 7632 9075; email: general@barrowcadbury.org.uk)

Trustees: Nicola Cadbury; Erica Cadbury; Tamsin Rupprecheter; Henry Serle; Anna Southall; John Serle; Steven Skakel; Catherina Pharoah; Esther McConnell; Omar Khan.

www.barrowcadbury.org.uk

@BarrowCadbury

General information

The trust was established by Barrow Cadbury and his wife Geraldine in 1920. Barrow was the son of John Cadbury, founder of the Cadbury chocolate business. Barrow and Geraldine were inspired by Quaker beliefs and used their wealth to tackle social problems including juvenile crime and urban poverty.

Charitable activities

The trust promotes social justice through grant-making, research, influencing public policy and supporting local communities. The following themes are prominent across the trust's work, as stated on its website:

- Strengthening civil society
- Putting equality at the heart of everything we do
- Addressing gender based disadvantage
- Addressing racism in all its forms.
- Promoting sustainable development

Grant programmes

The programme priorities for 2016–22 are based on social objectives that are of particular concern to the trust. These are based on the existing strengths of work previously funded and current or possible areas of policy development. Projects will be chosen that the trust believes will help to achieve tangible shifts in policy and practice.

The trust's work is divided into three main areas of interest:

- Criminal justice
- Migration
- Economic justice

The trust is particularly interested in hearing from Birmingham-based organisations working in these areas that wish to undertake projects that influence policy and practice in Birmingham and the surrounding area (or nationally).

Criminal justice

According to the website, the aim of this programme is to 'strengthen the evidence base for structural and practical change for young adults to support rehabilitation and desistance from crime'.

The trust is interested in projects that:

- Add to its existing Transition to Adulthood (T2A) evidence base, especially new work on policing, courts and probation stages of the 'T2A Pathway'
- Address the specific challenges faced by young adults involved in crime
- Address the over-representation of young minority ethnic, Muslim and Gypsy/Traveller people in the criminal justice system
- Enable the voices of young adults and/or women and/or people from minority ethnic communities involved in the criminal justice system to be heard by policy makers, commissioners and service leaders
- Pilot projects or research that focus on the distinct needs of young adult women involved in the criminal justice system

All projects funded in this programme will be expected to include the voices or views of people directly affected by the criminal justice system.

Migration

According to the website:

> The Barrow Cadbury Trust believes that migrants and refugees should be treated in a fair and dignified manner. The aim of the migration programme is to promote an immigration system that is fair to both migrants and established residents and facilitate a policy and public debate on migration and integration that is based on shared values as well as evidence.
>
> Our current objectives are:
>
> - To promote greater understanding within communities and promote the fair and dignified treatment of refugees, asylum seekers and migrants.
> - To broaden and deepen the public debate on migration and integration and ensure that it draws on shared values as well as evidence.
> - To inform public policy and promote workable policies in relation to immigration and integration.
>
> **We are particularly interested in the following areas:**
>
> - Work promoting positive interaction between different groups in order to counter xenophobia, racism and Islamophobia.
> - Supporting migrant organisations, campaigners and others to influence national policy and promote the fair and dignified treatment of asylum seekers, refugees and migrants, particularly undocumented migrants.
> - Ensuring a broad range of voices is heard in the debate about migration and integration, including those affected by injustice.
> - Supporting work to deepen understanding of public attitudes and concerns about immigration and integration and develop appropriate responses.
> - Funding research and policy work on discrete areas of public policy with a view to developing fair and workable solutions to policy challenges.

Economic justice

At the time of writing (May 2022), the trust's website stated the following:

> The Trust undertook a strategic review during the year 2021–22, with our Trustees deciding to take a place-based approach to our Economic Justice work, focusing entirely on Birmingham and the surrounding area. We are currently co-developing the programme with local partners.

The programme is expected to reopen late in 2022. Check the website for further updates.

Connect Fund

The Connect Fund is a £6 million fund that makes grants to intermediaries and infrastructure organisations with the aim of strengthening the social investment market in England to better meet the needs of charities and social enterprises.

Financial information

Year end	31/03/2021
Income	£8,480,000
Assets	£83,830,000
Grants to organisations	£9,450,000
No. of grants	291

Further financial information

Grants were distributed as follows:

Migration	223	£6.22 million
Criminal justice	20	£1.08 million
Economic justice	21	£1.05 million
Connect Fund	13	£679,000
Cross-cutting themes and promoting philanthropy	13	£415,000
Fair By Design campaign	1	£20,000

Beneficiaries included: A list of the trust's funded projects is provided on its website.

Exclusions

See the trust's website for the relevant exclusions for each grants programme.

Applications

Applicants should fill in the online enquiry form available on the trust's website. If invited to complete a full application form, applicants should do so via the application portal available online. You may also get in touch with the trust to discuss your eligibility. The trust does not accept unsolicited applications for work outside the UK.

Sources of information

Accounts; annual report; Charity Commission record; funder's website.

The George Cadbury Trust

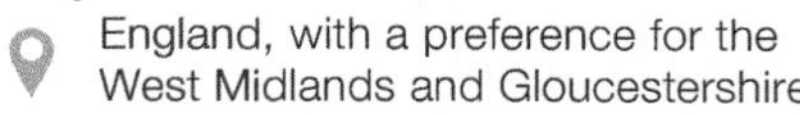

General charitable purposes

England, with a preference for the West Midlands and Gloucestershire

£465,300 (2020/21)

CC number: 1040999

Correspondent: The Trustees, c/o BDO LLP, 2 Snow Hill, Birmingham B4 6GA (tel: 0121 265 7288)

Trustees: Angela Cadbury; Mark Cadbury; Roger Cadbury; Benedict Cadbury; Timothy Cadbury.

General information

The trust was set up in 1924 to make grants to charitable organisations for general charitable purposes. Although the charity's area of benefit is undefined, the majority of grants are awarded in England, particularly in the West Midlands and Gloucestershire. Grants may be awarded up to the value of £25,000.

Financial information

Year end	05/04/2021
Income	£381,200
Assets	£18,960,000
Grants to organisations	£465,300

Beneficiaries included: Dean and Chapter Gloucester Cathedral For Dorothea Hoyland Choral (£25,000); Blood Bikes (£20,000); Avoncroft Museum (£13,000); UNICEF (£10,000); Worgan Trust (£5,000); Warwickshire Wildlife Trust (£3,000); Feedback Madagascar (£1,000).

Applications

Apply in writing to the correspondent.

Sources of information

Accounts; annual report; Charity Commission record.

Cadent Foundation

Social welfare; the environment; community development; sustainable energy projects

North West England; East of England; West Midlands; North London

£3.88 million (20201)

CC number: 327489

Correspondent: Julia Dwyer, Cadent Foundation Director, Pilot Way, Ansty Park, Coventry CV7 9JU (email: enquiries@cadentfoundation.com)

Trustees: Advisory Board: Sir Adrian Montague; Dr Catherine Bell; Mark Braithwaite; Linda Minnis.

 https://cadentgas.com/cadent-foundation

 @cadentfund

General information

The Cadent Foundation was established in March 2020. The Charities Trust administers the foundation and manages the grant applications and giving process. Cadent owns and manages four gas distribution networks and projects must take place in the following regions: North West England; East of England; West Midlands; North London.

Grants

According to its website, the foundation makes grants in the following areas:

- **Research and Innovation (R&I)** – Projects that help eliminate harmful emissions and support sustainable energy
- **People** – Projects that help alleviate suffering and hardship of people in vulnerable situations
- **Environment** – Projects that will help protect and preserve the environment
- **Communities** – Projects that provide a better and healthier community to live in and use

Partnerships

The foundation will also partner with organisations that are working to advance sustainable energy and create innovative ways to tackle the climate crisis.

Financial information

Year end	31/12/2021
Grants to organisations	£3,880,000
No. of grants	45

Further financial information

Full financial information was not available as the foundation is administered by the Charities Trust and is not a registered charity. The foundation's grant total has been taken from its 2021 Impact Report.

Grants were broken down as follows:

North West England	£1.05 million
West Midlands	£1 million
North London	£931, 800
East of England	£893,500

Beneficiaries included: A list of beneficiaries was not available.

Exclusions

The foundation's website states:

> Unfortunately, we cannot accept applications or grant funds to any of the following groups or related:
> - Animal groups
> - The benefit of individuals
> - The purpose of repaying loans
> - Sponsorship of events or activities
> - Religious or faith-based groups
> - Overseas travel or groups
> - Political or lobbyists groups
> - Sporting groups
> - Natural disaster relief
> - Heritage and historic buildings
> - Projects that are not sustainable
> - Refurbishment of buildings (we may consider community spaces)
> - Schools
> - Medical
> - Projects that are outside Cadent's region

Applications

Applications for grants can be made through the online form. There are detailed grant application guidelines available on the website. For partnership projects contact the foundation via email, including an outline of your project idea and purpose, details of your organisation and the breakdown of costs.

Sources of information

Cadent Impact Report 2021; funder's website.

The Cadogan Charity

Social welfare; medical research; military charities; animal welfare; education; conservation and the environment

UK, with a preference for London and Scotland

£2.48 million (2020/21)

CC number: 247773

Correspondent: Paul Loutit, Secretary to Trustees, 10 Duke of York Square, London SW3 4LY (tel: 020 7730 4567; email: paul.loutit@cadogan.co.uk)

Trustees: Rt Hon. The Earl Cadogan; Viscount Chelsea; William Cadogan; Countess Cadogan; Lady Anna-Karina Thomson.

General information

The charity was established in 1966 for general charitable purposes. The charity currently operates two funds, the General Fund and the Rectors' Fund. The Rectors' Fund was created with a gift from Cadogan Holdings Company in 1985 to pay an annual amount to one or any of the rectors of Holy Trinity Church – Sloane Street, St Luke's Church and Chelsea Old Church. The General Fund provides support for registered charities in a wide range of areas. These grants are only given to recognised national charities, particularly those based in London and Scotland.

Financial information

Year end	05/04/2021
Income	£2,590,000
Assets	£54,880,000
Grants to organisations	£2,480,000
No. of grants	41

Further financial information

Grants were broken down as follows in 2020/21:

Social welfare	£1 million
Military charities	£460,500
Medical research	£380,000
Animal welfare	£296,000
Education	£273,000
Conservation and the environment	£65,000

Beneficiaries included: Natural History Museum (£250,000); Royal College of Surgeons (£100,000); Missing Salmon Alliance (£50,000); Prince's Trust (£20,000); See Saw (£5,000); Dogs Trust (£1,000).

Applications

The charity's 2020/21 annual report states: 'Although the trustees make some grants with no formal applications, they normally require organisations to submit a request saying how the funds could be used, what would be achieved, and how this would add to public benefit.'

Sources of information

Accounts; annual report; Charity Commission record.

The Calleva Foundation

Education and academic research; children's holidays; social services; medical research and equipment; international relief; the environment; the arts; animal welfare

London; Hampshire

£8.88 million (2020)

CC number: 1078808

Correspondent: The Trustees, PO Box 22554, London W8 5GN (tel: 028638653; email: contactcalleva@btopenworld.com)

Trustees: Caroline Butt; Stephen Butt.

General information

Registered with the Charity Commission in January 2000, the foundation supports community-based projects in London and Hampshire.

Financial information

Year end	31/12/2020
Income	£8,190,000
Assets	£3,930,000
Grants to organisations	£8,880,000

Further financial information

Grants were broken down as follows:

Academic research	£7.32 million
Social services	£733,700
Education	£406,000
Overseas/international relief	£263,500
Education (international)	£74,900
Children's holidays	£36,500
The environment	£33,000
Medical research	£16,000
Instruments	£2,000
Animal welfare/other	£1,000

A small sample of beneficiaries was available in the 2020 accounts.

Beneficiaries included: Natural History Museum – Centre for Human Evolution (£535,000); Reading University (£100,000); Chalke Valley History Trust (£30,000); House of Good Health (£24,000); University of Cape Town Trust (£15,000); Silchester Playground Association (£3,000).

Applications

The trust does not accept unsolicited applications.

Sources of information

Accounts; annual report; Charity Commission record.

Camden Giving

General charitable purposes, particularly social and economic inequality

Camden

£1.32 million (2020/21)

CC number: 1174463

Correspondent: The Grants Team, 5–7 Buck Street, Camden Town, London NW1 8NJ (tel: 078 7253 4079 or 077 1759 5605; email: admin@camdengiving.org.uk)

Trustees: Rose Alexan[illegible] Mohammed; Mahfuz [illegible] Sutherland; Dominic [illegible] Pitkeathley; Sue Wilb[illegible] Tom Holliss; Nathan [illegible] Mujib.

www.camdengi[illegible]

facebook.com/[illegible]

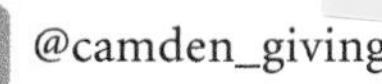

@camden_giving

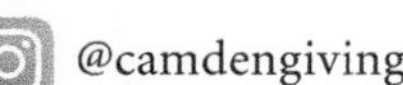

@camdengiving

General information

This charity was registered with the Charity Commission in August 2017. According to its 2020/21 annual report, it aims to 'address inequality of wealth, opportunity, health, well-being and influence for Camden's residents'. It does this by making grants to organisations that support people in Camden.

Grant programmes

Currently, the charity has the following programmes:

Equality fund: this fund provides support to small charities and social enterprises that are supporting women, families, care leavers, people with disabilities, people from BAME communities, and young people. Each year, two grants of £30,000 will be awarded by a panel of Camden residents.

The Future Changemakers fund: grants are awarded for projects that will improve the safety of young people (aged 16–25) in Camden. Eligible projects must either provide opportunities for young people to have positive/relatable role models or raise awareness of mental health and/or drugs, as well as signposting people to available support.

Inclusive Community fund: proposals of up to £20,000 are welcomed under this programme, for innovative and practical solutions to create new or improve existing spaces, services and activities that encourage community cohesion, inclusive participation and better access for adults with disabilities. Eligible organisations must *not* identify as a disability organisation and have an annual income of less than £500,000.

Social Action fund: the fund intends to bring together different groups and communities to help improve their lives and tackle local inequality in Camden by achieving one or more of the following aims: increasing social action; supporting community cohesion; creating community resilience.

Further information about each scheme can be found on the charity's website.

[illegible]rmation

[illegible]	31/03/2021
[illegible]	£3,170,000
[illegible]	£946,600
[illegible]nisations	£1,320,000

[illegible]ncluded: London Wildlife [illegible]); Chance UK (£72,300); [illegible] Community Association [illegible]VS Homeless Project [illegible]ban Community Projects [illegible]ur Bike Project CIC (£10,000); The Sapphire Foundation (£5,000); Mitzvah Day UK (£1,500).

Exclusions

A full list of exclusions for each grants programme can be found on the website.

Applications

Information on eligibility and opening dates for funding rounds can be found on the website. The charity strongly advises that prospective applicants get in touch before making an application, to talk through the criteria for funding. This can be done by attending one of the charity's events, booking an appointment or by emailing admin@camdengiving.org.uk.

Sources of information

Accounts; annual report; Charity Commission record; funder's website.

M. J. Camp Charitable Foundation

Conservation; canals and inland waterways; the welfare of horses, ponies and donkeys; preservation of historical vehicles and steam trains; community transport

UK, with a preference for Hayling Island

£325,000 (2019/20)

CC number: 1085654

Correspondent: The Trustees, Lower Tye Farm, Copse Lane, Hayling Island, Hampshire PO11 0RQ (tel: 023 9246 4276; email: info@sthermans.co.uk)

Trustees: Ann Rogers; Christopher Driscoll; Richard Weekes.

General information

The foundation was established by Michael James Camp in 2000. The foundation received the whole of the issued share capital of St Hermans Estate Co. Ltd following the death of Mr Camp in 2013.

Areas of work

According to its 2019/20 accounts, the objects of the charity are:

- To promote for the benefit of the public the recording, study and protection of places and objects of natural beauty or of ornithological, botanical, silvicultural, geological, zoological, archaeological, historical or scientific interest in the United Kingdom and in Hayling Island in particular and to advance public education in the conservation of such places and objects.
- To promote, encourage and assist the restoration to good and navigable order and the maintenance and improvement of canals and other inland waterways of the United Kingdom for the public benefit and to educate the public about inland waterways, their history, construction, use, development and operation.
- To relieve the suffering of horses, ponies and donkeys which are unwanted, sick or neglected or are in need of care as a result of cruelty or ill-treatment and to support (financially or otherwise) the establishment or maintenance of rescue homes or sanctuaries for the care and rehabilitation of such animals.
- To advance the education of the public by promoting interest in and appreciation of and preserving for public benefit historic vehicles and in particular steam trains, and all equipment, buildings and other items of general transport or historic interest which may have been used in connection with such vehicles.
- To establish or support community transport schemes for the benefit of the inhabitants of local communities in the United Kingdom.

- Such other charitable purposes as the Trustees may from time to time in their discretion decide.

Financial information

Year end	30/09/2020
Income	£1,280,000
Assets	£16,260,000
Grants to organisations	£325,000

Beneficiaries included: Hampshire and Isle of Wight Air Ambulance (£160,000); The Wey and Arun Canal Trust (£100,000); Royal National Lifeboat Institution (£30,000); Bumblebee Conservation Trust (£2,000); Surfers Against Sewage (£2,000); The Donkey Sanctuary (£1,000).

Applications

Apply in writing to the correspondent. The trust's 2019/20 annual accounts state:

> The Trustees intend that the Foundation will continue its operations of identifying and making grants to charities which are in accordance with the Foundation's objects and will also provide public benefit.
>
> In order to carry out this plan more effectively the Trustees would welcome applications for funding from any charities which meet or are likely to meet the objects contained in this report.

Sources of information

Accounts; annual report; Charity Commission; record.

Canary Wharf Contractors Fund

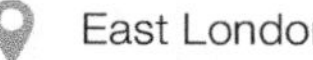

Communities; social welfare; education; people engaged in the construction industry; sport and recreation

East London

£297,300 (2019/20)

CC number: 1097007

Correspondent: Alan Ruddy, Secretary, Ruddy Joinery Ltd, Enterprise Way, Flitwick, Bedford MK45 5BS (tel: 07803 730360)

Trustees: Giles Woolley; Nicholas Curran; Alec Vallintine.

@cwc_fund

General information

Registered with the Charity Commission in 2003, this is a corporate charity of Canary Wharf Group plc. The fund supports those working in the construction industry, as well as community organisations in East London.

According to its 2019/20 accounts, the objects of the charity are as follows:

- the relief of poverty generally but with special regard to persons and their dependent families who have been or are employed in the building and engineering trades and professions
- the relief of sickness and distress of persons, who by reason of their work in or association with the building and engineering trades, have become partially or totally incapacitated through injury or illness
- to support the bereaved families of persons working in the building and engineering trades or who have retired but had previously worked in the building or engineering trades
- to foster and promote high educational and training standards in the fields of building, engineering and architecture
- to support young people in the local community in education, training, citizenship and sport
- to support families in the community whose children are ill or are life limited
- to support institutions in the community who provide welfare and healthcare support

Financial information

Year end	31/03/2021
Income	£407,300
Assets	£241,600
Grants to organisations	£297,300

Further financial information

The 2019/20 annual report was the latest available at the time of writing (May 2022).

Beneficiaries included: University College Hospital Cancer Fund (£40,000); London Air Ambulance (£20,000); Spread a Smile (£13,400); Construction Youth (£10,000); Oasis Hub Waterloo (£5,000); Stoke Newington Cricket Club (£4,000); South London Special League (£1,300).

Applications

Apply in writing to the correspondent.

Sources of information

Accounts; annual report; Charity Commission record.

Cancer Research UK

Cancer research

UK

£273.7 million (2020/21)

CC number: 1089464

Correspondent: Niamh O'Sullivan, Company Secretary, 2 Redman Place, London E20 1JQ (tel: 020 7242 0200; email: grants.helpline@cancer.org.uk)

Trustees: Prof. Sir Leszek Borysiewickz; Prof. Moira Whyte; Joanne Shaw; Prof. Sir Mike Richards; Prof. Sir Bruce Ponder; Tracy De Groose; Andrew Palmer; Bayo Adelaja; Carolyn Bradley; Catherine Brown; Peter Chambré; Dr Robert Easton; Prof. Nic Jones; Prof. Pamela Kearns

www.cancerresearchuk.org

facebook.com/cancerresearchuk

@CR_UK

@cr_uk

General information

Cancer Research UK is a leading cancer charity that funds research into finding cures for every type of cancer.

Grants

The charity makes a wide variety of grants to research institutions, including Cancer Research UK Centres, universities and hospitals, working in the following research areas, as stated on the charity's website:

- **Discovery** – research which will transform our fundamental understanding of cancer
- **Translational** – innovation in therapeutic discovery and development
- **Clinical** – supporting a broad portfolio of clinical studies which maximise patient impact
- **Prevention and population** – behavioural research, epidemiology, intervention studies, public health and research into cancer prevention

Most research grants are awarded for several years and may then be renewed to support the next stage in the research process.

Open funding schemes are advertised on the charity's website, each with their own criteria and guidelines.

Financial information

Year end	31/03/2021
Income	£581,900,000
Assets	£292,000,000
Grants to organisations	£273,700,000
No. of grants	28

Beneficiaries included: University of Cambridge (£45.6 million); University College London (£21.34 million); University of Oxford (£15.67 million); University of Southampton (£5.06 million); Dana Farber Cancer Institute (£1.12 million).

Exclusions

See the charity's website for details of exclusions under each specific funding scheme.

Applications

Applications can be made on the charity's online grants management system. Each funding scheme has its own application guidelines and deadlines, which are detailed on the charity's website.

Sources of information

Accounts; annual report; Charity Commission record; funder's website.

Cannon Charitable Trust

Religious education and social welfare

UK and overseas

£982,500 (2020/21)

CC number: 1080818

Correspondent: The Trustees, Unit 2A Berol House, 25 Ashley Road, Tottenham Hale, London N17 9LJ (tel: 020 8885 9430)

General information

The Cannon Charitable Trust was registered with the Charity Commission in 2000. According to its 2020/21 accounts the primary objective of the trust is 'to promote, encourage and provide finance for religious education and social welfare both in the United Kingdom and worldwide'.

Financial information

Year end	31/01/2021
Income	£1,520,000
Assets	£718,000
Grants to organisations	£982,500

Beneficiaries included: A list of beneficiaries was not available. Previous beneficiaries have included: Wlodowa Charity and Rehabilitation Trust (£80,000); The ABC Trust (£62,000); Karen Hatzolas Doros Alei Siach (£45,000); Bels Ruchel D'Satmer London (£34,500); Amut Hatzdokoh Trust (£33,000).

Applications

Apply in writing to the correspondent.

Sources of information

Accounts; annual report; Charity Commission record; funder's website.

Card Factory Foundation

General charitable purposes

UK

£237,000 (2020/21)

CC number: 1180081

Correspondent: The Trustees, Centrury House, Brunel Road, Wakefield 41 Industrial Estate, Wakefield, West Yorkshire WF2 0XG (tel: 07933 399645; email: trustees@cardfactoryfoundation.org)

www.cardfactoryinvestors.com/foundation

General information

The foundation was registered with the Charity Commission in September 2018 as the corporate charity of Card Factory, a national retailer of greetings cards based in Wakefield.

The foundation has three funds, details of which have been taken from the foundation's website:

Community Grant Fund

Card Factory Foundation supports projects and charitable causes to benefit the communities of our colleagues and stores. The Trustees welcome applications that support the Foundation's funding priorities from not-for-profit organisations, community groups and individuals based in the United Kingdom.

The maximum award for a Community Funding application is £2,500. Applications over £2,500 will be made at the discretion of the Charity Trustees.

All funding awarded by the Foundation must be used to cover the costs of the charitable activities the Trustees have agreed to fund. Funds will not be provided to meet salary or overhead costs.

Match Fund

Card Factory Foundation provide match-funding contributions for money raised by colleagues for charitable causes. Match funding is available to all colleagues who are directly employed by a Card Factory group company or an agency engaged by Card Factory.

Applicants must raise a minimum of £50 to be eligible for match funding and the maximum contribution for each successful application is £2,500. Applications for match funding beyond £2,500 shall be made at the discretion of the Charity Trustees.

Family Fund

Card Factory Foundation is committed to offering a helping hand to colleagues and their families in time of hardship. If you or your family have experienced or are experiencing hardship following a life-changing event. The maximum award for a Family Fund application is £2,000.

Financial information

Year end	31/01/2021
Income	£711,400
Assets	£1,640,000
Grants to organisations	£237,000

Further financial information

According to its annual statement, the foundation donated £131,500 between the Alzheimer's Society, British Heart Foundation, Macmillan and the NSPCC. In addition, it awarded £130,300 in COVID-19 grants to organisations during the year.

Beneficiaries included: Alzheimer's Society; British Heart Foundation; Macmillan; NSPCC.

Applications

Applications can be made via the foundation's website.

Sources of information

Charity Commission record; funder's website.

CareTech Foundation

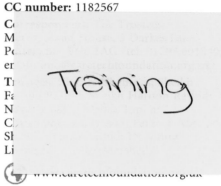

Disability; skills development; local communities

UK and Pakistan

£525,000 (2020/21)

CC number: 1182567

[illegible]

facebook.com/CareTechFoundation

@CareTechFdn

General information

Established in 2017, this foundation is the corporate charity of CareTech Holdings plc, which provides social care for children and adults below retirement age. The foundation's current areas of work are physical and learning disabilities and mental health, skills development (in the care sector), and local communities.

Grant programmes

There are four types of funding available. These are:

- Partnership grant-giving – the foundation supports a small number of significant partnerships with charities and social enterprises which coincide with its three focus areas
- Matched funding – CareTech staff can apply for matched funding of up to £350 per year for any charitable fundraising activity undertaken
- Community grants – under this grant scheme, CareTech staff can apply for funding for causes in their local communities. Previous beneficiaries have included Addaction Dumfries, Dudley Town FC, Edmonton Scouts and Sport Birmingham

- Staff hardship fund – CareTech staff experiencing significant hardship, or at risk of hardship, can apply for a grant from the foundation. This grant scheme is also open to previous staff who may have recently left the company

Financial information

Year end	30/09/2021
Income	£1,440,000
Assets	£7,100,000
Grants to organisations	£525,000
No. of grants	13+

Further financial information

Grants awarded to organisations were broken down as follows in 2020/21: skills and development in the care sector (£248,200); disabilities and mental health (£229,900); supporting communities (£47,000). In addition, grants totalling £145,100 were awarded to individual CareTech employees.

Beneficiaries included: Birkbeck College (£83,300); Barnardo's (£75,000); British Asian Trust (£50,000); Autistica (£37,500); Care First (£22,000); Open University (£20,000); Onside Youth Zones (£12,500); Birmingham Disability Recourse Centre (£11,300).

Applications

Each grants programme has an eligibility test, which should be completed by prospective applicants before making an application. If deemed eligible, applications can be made online. Paper or digital/word copies of the application form can be requested by email. The foundation can also offer applicants support filling in the application.

Sources of information

Accounts; annual report; Charity Commission record; funder's website.

David William Traill Cargill Fund

General charitable purposes

UK and overseas

£314,900 (2019/20)

OSCR number: SC012703

Correspondent: The Trustees, c/o Miller Beckett and Jackson Ltd, 190 St Vincent Street, Glasgow G2 5SP

General information

The charity was established with a gift from David William Traill Cargill. It has the same address as two other trusts – W. A. Cargill Charitable Trust and W. A. Cargill Fund – although they all operate independently.

The 2019/20 annual report states that the charity supports 'any hospitals, institutions, societies or others whose work in the opinion of the trustees is likely to be beneficial to the community'.

Financial information

Year end	30/11/2020
Income	£306,700
Assets	£10,540,000
Grants to organisations	£314,900

Beneficiaries included: A list of beneficiaries was not available. Previous beneficiaries include: City of Glasgow Society of Social Service; Colquhoun Bequest Fund for Incurables; Crathie Opportunity Holidays; Glasgow and West of Scotland Society for the Blind; Glasgow City Mission; Greenock Medical Aid Society; Lead Scotland; North Glasgow Community Forum; Scottish Maritime Museum – Irvine; Scottish Episcopal Church; Scottish Motor Neurone Disease Association; Three Towns Blind Bowling/Social Club.

Exclusions

Grants are not given to individuals.

Applications

Apply in writing to the correspondent.

Sources of information

Accounts; annual report; OSCR record.

The W. A. Cargill Fund

The prevention or relief of poverty; education; religion; the advancement of health; citizenship or community development; arts, culture and heritage; science; relief of older people; ill health; disability; social and economic disadvantage

Glasgow and the west of Scotland

£366,200 (2019/20)

OSCR number: SC008456

Correspondent: The Trustees, c/o Miller Beckett and Jackson Ltd, 190 St Vincent Street, Glasgow G2 5SP

General information

This charity has the same address and trustees as two others, the David William Traill Cargill Fund and W. A. Cargill Charitable Trust, although they all operate independently.

It supports a wide remit of causes in the west of Scotland, particularly in Glasgow.

Financial information

Year end	30/11/2020
Income	£523,200
Assets	£20,100,000
Grants to organisations	£366,200

Beneficiaries included: A list of beneficiaries was not available.

Applications

Apply in writing to the correspondent, including a copy of your charity's latest accounts or details of its financial position.

Sources of information

Accounts; annual report; OSCR record; SCVO Funding Scotland.

Carlee Ltd

Orthodox Jewish causes

Worldwide

£425,700 (2020/21)

CC number: 282873

Correspondent: The Trustees, 32 Paget Road, London N16 5NQ (tel: 020 8802 4782; email: admin@carleeltd.org)

Trustees: Bernard Stroh; Alexander Singer; Ephraim Bleier; Esther Kahn.

General information

The trust was established in 1981 to support Orthodox Jewish causes and social welfare for the Orthodox Jewish communities including Talmudical scholars and widows and families.

Financial information

Year end	31/03/2021
Income	£459,100
Assets	£1,500,000
Grants to organisations	£425,700

Further financial information

During 2020/21, grants were distributed as follows:

Poverty relief	£130,700
Education	£126,700
Religion	£114,300
Health and social welfare	£54,000

Beneficiaries included: Mifal Hachesed Vehatzedokoh (£30,000); Toldos Ahron Trust (£24,000); Friends of Beis Chinuch Lebonos (£22,000); Tevini Ltd (£20,000); Edupoor Ltd (£15,000); Congregation Sharei Sholom Tchabe Ltd (£14,000); Kids Care Ltd (£12,000).

Applications

Apply in writing to the correspondent.

Sources of information

Accounts; annual report; Charity Commission record.

The Antonio Carluccio Foundation

Education and training, and the prevention and relief of hunger and poverty

UK and overseas

£674,700 (2019/20)

CC number: 1167646

Correspondent: The Trustees, Chamberlain Berry, 27–28 New Road, Chippenham SN15 1HS (tel: 01249 461999; email: trustees@theantoniocarlucciofoundation.org)

Trustees: Andrea Stevenson; Steven Berry; Simon Kossoff.

General information

The foundation was registered with the Charity Commission in June 2016 and was founded by the late Antonio Carluccio, an Italian chef, restauranteur, and food expert.

According to the foundation's 2019/20 annual report, its objectives are 'the prevention and alleviation of hunger and training of chefs and cooks along with grants towards the expenses of training'. It makes grants to charities in the UK and overseas that meet its objectives, specifically by:

- providing grants to projects that feed those who are suffering poverty and/or malnutrition
- financing projects that seek to educate those suffering poverty and/or malnutrition in a way that they can apply the knowledge to feed themselves and others in a healthy, sustainable manner
- financing projects and individuals undertaking training of chefs and cooks, so as to extend Antonio's legacy to future generations

Financial information

Year end	30/06/2020
Income	£19,200
Assets	£319,600
Grants to organisations	£674,700

Beneficiaries included: Action Against Hunger (£25,000); Magic Breakfast (£10,000); Community Drug and Alcohol Recovery Services (£9,000); Activiteens (£8,500); Body and Soul (£5,000); Clothe and Feed (£2,500); Nurture through Nature (£1,500); Sherbourne (£1,000).

Applications

Apply in writing to the correspondent.

Sources of information

Accounts; annual report; Charity Commission record.

The Carnegie Trust for the Universities of Scotland

Scottish universities

Scotland

£1.98 million (2019/20)

OSCR number: SC015600

Correspondent: The Trustees, Andrew Carnegie House, Pittencrieff Street, Dunfermline, Fife KY12 8AW (tel: 01383 724 990 (answer phone only); email: a contact form is available on the trust's website)

Trustees: The Rt Hon. Lord Eassie; Dr Alison Fielding; Prof. Nigel Seaton; Prof. Craig Mahoney; Prof. Andrea Nolan; Prof. Sally Mapstone; Prof. Dame Anne Glover; Prof. George Boyne; Ray Perman; Dr Bridget McConnell; Alan McFarlane; Donald MacDonald; Sara Parkin; Mary Duffy.

www.carnegie-trust.org

facebook.com/pages/Carnegie-Trust-for-the-Universities-of-Scotland/545023725553882

@CarnegieUni

General information

This trust was established by Andrew Carnegie to improve and expand opportunities for both study and research in the universities and higher education institutions of Scotland.

The trust's 2020/21 annual report states:

> In accordance with Andrew Carnegie's wishes, the Royal Charter enables the Trust to support the staff and students of the 15 Universities of Scotland, the Glasgow School of Art and the Royal Conservatoire of Scotland.

The trust delivers the following schemes, full details of which can be found on its website:

- Undergraduate Tuition Fee Grants
- Carnegie Vacation Scholarship (for students wishing to undertake research in the summer vacation)
- Carnegie PhD Scholarships

All grants are awards to individuals, but mainly paid to their relevant educational institution.

Financial information

Year end	30/09/2021
Income	£3,310,000
Assets	£75,810,000
Grants to organisations	£1,980,000
No. of grants	17

Further financial information

During the year the trust received 636 applications and made 389 grants to 17 organisations. Grants were broken down as follows:

PhD scholarships	51.6%
Undergraduate tuition fee grants	27.7%
Vacation scholarships	13.4%
Study support grants	7.3%

Beneficiaries included: University of Aberdeen; University of Dundee; University of Edinburgh; University of Stirling; University of the Highlands and Islands.

Exclusions

See the trust's website for full exclusion criteria.

Applications

Applications can be made online via the trust's website, where deadlines can also be found.

Sources of information

Accounts; annual report; funder's website; OSCR record.

The Carpenters' Company Charitable Trust

Education; woodworking; general charitable purposes

UK

£1.19 million (2019/20)

CC number: 276996

Correspondent: Brigadier T. J. Gregson, Clerk to the Carpenters' Company, Carpenters' Hall, 1 Throgmorton Avenue, London EC2N 2JJ (tel: 020 7588 7001; email: info@carpentersco.com)

Trustees: Michael Mathews; Martin Samuel; Alistair Gregory-Smith; Rachel Bower.

www.carpentersco.com/pages/charities/carpenters_company_charitable_trust1

General information

The trust was established in 1978 for general charitable purposes. The Carpenter's Company itself was originally established as a medieval trade guild to safeguard the welfare and interests of carpenters in the City of London.

The trust's website provides the following information:

> The Carpenters' Company is a City of London Livery Company. It received its first royal charter in 1477, and was granted a coat of arms in 1466.
>
> The Company was originally established as a medieval trade guild to safeguard the welfare and interests of carpenters in the City of London. Today, charitable activities and support for the craft of woodworking through scholarships, competitions and the Building Crafts College are the two cornerstones of its work.
>
> The Carpenters' Company is the senior construction trade company amongst the City Livery Companies, and maintains close links with the carpentry profession and other building trades.

The trust's income is derived from a capital sum gifted by the company's corporate fund, supplemented when warranted by further grants from that fund. The majority of the trust's income each year goes to the Building Crafts College, but the trust also maintains long-standing commitments to numerous other organisations, mainly in the Greater London area. The craft of woodworking receives a high priority when awards are considered.

Financial information

Year end	30/06/2020
Income	£1,190,000
Assets	£32,870,000
Grants to organisations	£1,190,000

Further financial information

Grants were broken down as follows in 2019/20:

Craft activities	£1.14 million
Miscellaneous	£20,000
Young people and children's organisations	£14,700
City of London	£13,000
Religious organisations	£1,200

Beneficiaries included: Building Crafts College (£1.03 million); Norton Folgate Trust (£42,000); Carpenters and Dockland Centre (£15,000); Carpenters Primary School (£11,000); Institute of Carpenters (£6,000).

Exclusions

Grants are not normally made to individual churches or cathedrals, or to educational establishments that have no association to the Carpenters' Company. No grants (except educational grants) are made to individual applicants. Funds are usually only available to charities registered with the Charity Commission or exempt from registration.

Applications

Contact the correspondent for more information on the application process. The Charitable Grants Committee meets three times each year to consider applications. Day-to-day management of the trust is the responsibility of the clerk to whom correspondence should usually be addressed.

Sources of information

Accounts; annual report; Charity Commission record; funder's website.

The Castansa Trust

Education; children and young people; support for those diagnosed with dementia or cancer; social inclusion; arts and culture; health; the environment

The Lothians; Glasgow; Dumfries and Galloway

£350,200 (2020/21)

OSCR number: SC037414

Correspondent: The Trustees, c/o Turcan Connell, Princes Exchange, 1 Earl Grey Street, Edinburgh EH3 9EE

 www.turcanconnell.com/the-castansa-trust

General information

The trust was established in 2008 and, according to its website, its key funding motivations are: 'to provide early stage/catalyst funding, for our contribution to make a difference, to encourage a business approach to philanthropy and to enable action'.

The trust makes grants to charities working in the following fields:

- Education
- Children and teenagers (specifically leadership courses and help with employment)
- Support for those diagnosed with cancer or dementia and for their families
- Social inclusion
- Culture and the arts
- Environmental conservation

Grants are usually between £5,000 and £15,000, although larger grants and multi-year commitments may be occasionally considered. The trust also provides smaller community grants which are distributed by Foundation Scotland, the Women's Fund for Scotland and Inspiring Scotland.

Financial information

Year end	25/07/2021
Income	£43,900
Assets	£1,850,000
Grants to organisations	£350,200

Beneficiaries included: MidSteeple Quarter (£100,000); Queen of the South Community Trust (£40,000); Marie Curie (£10,000); Apex Scotland (£5,000); Wigtown Book Festival (£4,000).

Applications

The trust no longer accepts unsolicited applications 'due to a significant number of existing commitments'.

Sources of information

Accounts; annual report; funder's website; OSCR record.

Cattanach

Children up to the age of three and their families, carers and communities

Scotland

 £1.12 million (2020)

OSCR number: SC049833

Correspondent: Jemma Slater, Grants and Relationships Officer, Mansfield Traquair Centre, 15 Mansfield Place, 502 Gorgie Road, Edinburgh EH3 6BB (tel: 0131 474 6155; email: info@cattanach.org.uk)

Trustees: Andrew Millington; Ian McLaughlan; Mafe Marwick; Steven Murray; Rory Marsh; Heather Coady; Jennifer Corrigan; Patricia Jackson; Caroline Murray.

 www.cattanach.org.uk

 @cattanachscio

 @cattanachscio

General information

Cattanach SCIO (formerly known as Cattanach Charitable Trust) was founded in 1992 by Miss Phyllis Cattanach of Grantown-on-Spey, with the family wealth she had inherited from interests in the whisky industry. Following her death in 2008, Miss Cattanach left the 'residue' of her estate to the trust, as stated on the charity's website. Though it was established with broad purposes, the trustees have since focused the charity's grant-making criteria.

Grant-making criteria

The charity's website states:

> - You must be a charity registered in Scotland
> - You must be working with young children (pre-birth to 3) and their parents/carers
> - The main beneficiaries have a background of relative deprivation: this ranges from poverty to additional support needs to lack of opportunity due to lack of services
> - Children and their carers have to be actively involved in the proposed activity or service
>
> Families experiencing deprivation or in crisis will be given priority. "Deprivation" can mean low income, poor housing, unemployment, isolation, disability or health problems, lack of family support, young parenthood, contact with the justice system, substance abuse, violence etc.
>
> Cattanach is particularly interested in parenting, attachment, family support, and communication within the family, as it impacts on the healthy emotional and physical development of young children. The SCIO wishes to encourage training for staff and volunteers, and may recommend training or evaluation help.

Grants can be given for projects or, for smaller organisations, core costs (including salaries). The trust prefers to fund revenue costs, and any capital funding will only be associated with another aspect of revenue funding.

Amounts range between £3,000 and £25,000 (though most are around £10,000) per year and may be given for one, two or three years. Where fourth and fifth years are funded, the award will decrease in the final years. The trust prefers to fund a significant proportion of a project rather than just a small contribution, and can support matched funding within a project budget. In most cases, only one grant will be awarded to a particular organisation in a year.

Financial information

Year end	31/12/2020
Income	£615,200
Assets	£286,800
Grants to organisations	£1,120,000
No. of grants	59

Further financial information

Grants were broken down as follows:

Core grants	13	£531,800
COVID-19 grants	10	£424,200
Strategic grants	2	£60,000
Community well-being fund	15	£30,000
Other micro grants	3	£30,000
Bridging grants	5	£20,900
COVID-19 micro grants	11	£20,000

Beneficiaries included: The Promise (£100,000); Stepping Stones Edinburgh North (£76,500); Scottish Adoption (£30,000); Starcatchers (£24,000); Children in Scotland (£10,000); Youth Scotland (£5,000); Healthy Valleys (£2,100); Craigmillar Literacy Trust (£500).

Exclusions

The charity does not support: individuals; personal study or travel; hospices and palliative care (unless focused on attachment-related activities); animal charities; appliances for illness or disability; organisations concerned with specific diseases; large capital projects (of more than £100,000); projects costing less than £3,000; crèches where parents are not involved; organisations or activities where religious content is compulsory for users; general appeals.

Applications

Applicants must first register on the charity's website and will then be sent a link to the application form via email. The application form contains instructions and help, although there is also a useful list of FAQs on the charity's website. Applications must be made online (those sent on paper or by email are not accepted) and must be submitted along with the supporting documents listed on the form. The trustees meet four times a year, usually in February, May, August and November – meeting dates are posted on the charity's website.

Sources of information

Accounts; annual report; funder's website; OSCR record.

The Joseph and Annie Cattle Trust

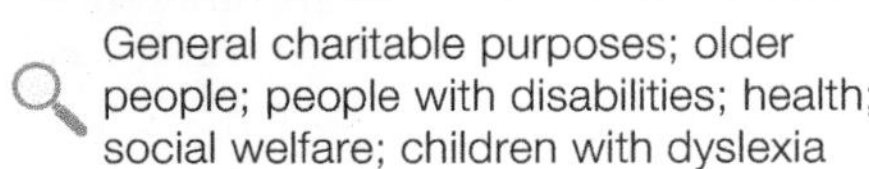

General charitable purposes; older people; people with disabilities; health; social welfare; children with dyslexia

Hull and East Yorkshire

£268,000 (2020/21)

CC number: 262011

Correspondent: The Administrator, PO Box 23, Patrington, Hull, East Yorkshire HU12 0WF (tel: 01964 671742; email: rogercattletrust@protonmail.com)

Trustees: Mr S. C. Jowers; Paul Edwards; Christopher Munday; Ann Hughes.

www.jacattletrust.co.uk

General information

According to its website, the trust was established 'to help vulnerable people change their lives in the Hull and East Riding of Yorkshire, by providing financial support.' Support is given for projects/groups that help following:

- Older people
- People with disabilities
- People who are underprivileged
- Children with dyslexia

The trust also accepts applications made by charitable or statutory bodies on behalf of individuals or families.

Financial information

Year end	30/06/2021
Income	£472,300
Assets	£12,940,000
Grants to organisations	£268,000

Beneficiaries included: A list of beneficiaries was not available.

Applications

Application forms are available from the trust's website. Application forms should be printed, completed in handwriting and submitted to the trust by post or fax.

Sources of information

Accounts; annual report; Charity Commission record; funder's website.

The Thomas Sivewright Catto Charitable Settlement

General charitable purposes

UK and overseas

£334,200 (2020/21)

CC number: 279549

Correspondent: The Trustees, PO Box 47408, London N21 1YW (tel: 020 7370 0058; email: office@tscatto.org.uk)

Trustees: Lord Catto; Olivia Marchant; Zoe Richmond-Watson.

General information

The trust was established in 1979 by the surviving children of The Rt Hon. Thomas Sivewright Catto, to commemorate the 100th anniversary of his birth.

The trust makes a large number of smaller grants (£500) to a wide range of organisations and a few larger grants for music scholarships at selected colleges and conservatoires.

Applications are invited from UK-registered charities. The trustees also invite suggestions for funding from other members of the First Baron Catto of Cairncatto's family.

Financial information

Year end	05/04/2022
Income	£135,700
Assets	£15,080,000
Grants to organisations	£334,200

Beneficiaries included: MS Society (£40,000); National Emergencies Trust (£20,000); Royal Conservatoire of Scotland (£12,000); Dementia UK (£5,100); Listening Books (£1,000); Health Poverty Concern (£750); Pain Concern (£500).

Applications

Apply in writing to the correspondent. The trustees meet quarterly to consider applications and distribute funding.

Sources of information

Accounts; annual report; Charity Commission record.

The Cayo Foundation

General charitable purposes; medical research; crime prevention; armed forces; children and young people; education; the arts

UK

£539,500 (2019/20)

CC number: 1080607

Correspondent: The Trustees, Ground Floor, 3 Devonshire Square, London EC2M 4YA (tel: 020 7248 6700)

Trustees: Angela McCarville; Stewart Harris.

http://cayofoundation.org.uk

General information

The Cayo Foundation provides grants and loans to registered charities for a range of charitable purposes. According to the foundation's website, the trustees are particularly interested in charities involved with 'medical research and training, the military, crime fighting, children and young people, education and the arts.' According to its 2019/20 accounts, the foundation also supported animal welfare and wildlife conservation during the year.

Financial information

Year end	30/09/2020
Income	£354,600
Assets	£3,740,000
Grants to organisations	£539,500
No. of grants	12

Beneficiaries included: Crimestoppers Trust (£151,900). A full list of beneficiaries was not available.

Applications

Apply in writing to the correspondent.

Sources of information

Accounts; annual report; Charity Commission record; funder's website.

CEO Sleepout

 Homelessness

UK

£155,300 (2020/21)

CC number: 1154963

Correspondent: The Trustees, Boho Number One, Bridge Street West, Middlesbrough, North Yorkshire TS2 1AE (tel: 07922 478994; email: info@ceosleepoutuk.com)

Trustees: Andy Preston; Niklas Tunley; Abu Ali.

 www.ceosleepoutuk.com

General information

The charity was established in 2013 to work to eradicate homelessness and poverty. Sleepout events take place across the country during which business and community leaders sleep outdoors for one night to raise funds and awareness. The money raised is distributed to local charities supporting people who are experiencing homelessness and poverty within a few miles of each CEO Sleepout, as well as national charities.

Financial information

Year end	31/03/2021
Income	1£40,000
Assets	£58,600
Grants to organisations	£155,300

Further financial information

During 2020/21 grants totalled £155,300; however, in previous years the charity has awarded grants totalling over £300,000. The charity's 2020/21 accounts state: 'Despite a challenging year the charity has managed to maintain its support of organisations through its existing funds. It is envisaged that the regular fundraising events will return once restrictions and National circumstances allow.'

Beneficiaries included: Stay at Home (£31,400); Grants Northumberland (£21,200); Grants Harrogate (£16,100); The Big Christmas Sleepout (£11,000); Grants London (£2,500); Saltburn Appeal (£1,400); Grants Halifax (£1,100).

Applications

Contact the correspondent for further information.

Sources of information

Accounts; annual report; Charity Commission record; funder's website.

Chalfords Ltd

 Advancement of the Orthodox Jewish religion; advancement of Jewish religious education; social welfare; grants to grant-making charities

England and Wales

£2.49 million (2020)

CC number: 287322

Correspondent: The Trustees, New Burlington House, 1075 Finchley Road, London NW11 0PU (tel: 020 8455 6075)

Trustees: Irwin Weiler; Riki Weiler; Mr A. Weiler; Mr M. Weiler.

General information

Established in 1983, the charity provides financial support to Jewish charitable organisations and institutions of learning for:

- The advancement of the Orthodox Jewish religion
- The advancement of Jewish religious education
- Social welfare

The charity also makes grants to other grant-making charities.

Financial information

Year end	31/12/2020
Income	£4,990,000
Assets	£58,430,000
Grants to organisations	£2,490,000

Further financial information

Grants were made in the following categories:

Grants to other grant-making charities	£1.6 million
Jewish education	£523,700
Jewish religion	£194,200
General charitable purposes	£94,700
Relief of poverty	£75,200

Only beneficiaries of grants of £20,000 and above were listed in the accounts. Grants under £20,000 totalled £170,700.

Beneficiaries included: LPW Ltd (£1.45 million); Rise and Shine Ltd (£126,000); Care All Ltd (£97,100); Support The Charity Worker (£61,000); Edupoor Ltd (£36,000); Bait Limud Vchesed and Community Concern London (£20,000 each).

Applications

Apply in writing to the correspondent.

Sources of information

Accounts; annual report; Charity Commission record.

The Chalk Cliff Trust

 Children and young people; social welfare; older people; disability; overseas aid; the environment; arts and culture

East Sussex

£807,700 (2020/21)

CC number: 1139102

Correspondent: The Trustees, 18 Keere Street, Lewes, East Sussex BN7 1TY (tel: 01273 525354; email: apply@chalkclifftrust.org)

Trustees: Sarah Hunter; Robert Senior; Justine Senior; Rachel Senior; Hannah Senior.

 www.chalkclifftrust.org

General information

The Chalk Cliff Trust provides support to organisations in East Sussex that work in the following areas:

- Youth schemes and activities (e.g. youth centres, clubs or arts-focused projects)
- Children's activities (e.g. playgroups, clubs, education and welfare)
- Older people (e.g. transport, events and activities)
- Activities for people with learning difficulties or disabilities
- Work overseas (e.g. education, medicine or projects focused on malnutrition)
- The care and preservation of the environment
- Regional arts, music, literature and cultural projects, especially related to the groups mentioned above
- Other types of community initiatives

The majority of grants fall within the £3,000 to £5,000 range. Larger grants will be considered, and small, one-off payments may be awarded for smaller concerns with low running costs or for a specific event. Grants can be used for projects, capital or core costs, administration costs, emergency funding and so on. The trust's website states that 'donations will normally be made to registered charities, however organisations pending registration or pressure groups will also be considered'.

Financial information

Year end	31/03/2021
Income	£4,150,000
Assets	£12,740,000
Grants to organisations	£807,700

Further financial information

Only organisations receiving grants of over £4,000 were listed as beneficiaries in the trust's accounts. Grants under £4,000 totalled £224,400.

Beneficiaries included: Glyndebourne Productions Ltd (£45,000); Charleston

Trust (£28,000); The Cinema Museum (£10,000); Active Children, Autism Stress Alert CIC and Street Child (£5,000 each); Brighton Food (£4,800); Sussex Wasps (£4,100).

Applications

Application forms can be downloaded from the trust's website and should be submitted with supporting documents by email.

Sources of information

Accounts; annual report; Charity Commission record; funder's website.

Chapman Charitable Trust

Physical and mental well-being; conservation of the natural environment; sustainability; improving access to the arts, especially for young people

National charities operating across the UK; local charities operating in North Wales or South East England

£258,000 (2020/21)

CC number: 232791

Correspondent: Richard Chapman, Trustee, c/o RPG Crouch Chapman LLP, 5th Floor 14–16 Dowgate Hill, London EC4R 2SU (tel: 020 3697 7147; email: cct@chapmancharitabletrust.org.uk)

Trustees: Richard Chapman; Guy Chapman; Bryony Chapman; Thomas Williams; Gregory Chapman.

www.chapmancharitabletrust.org.uk

General information

The trust was established in 1963 and makes grants to UK-registered charities. According to its website, the trust will support charities that are undertaking the following activities:

- promoting physical and mental wellbeing
- conserving our natural environment and promoting the sustainable use of resources
- increasing the accessibility of the arts, especially for young people

Support is given to registered charities, mainly national charities, but local charities working in North Wales and South East England are also supported.

Grants are usually for £1,000 or £2,000; however, according to the trust's website, larger grants are made to charities that fall under two headings:

- those where the current trustees have a special oversight
- those originally supported by our benefactor, Marjorie Chapman

The trust prefers to support charities that address the root causes of problems and it welcomes applications for research projects.

Financial information

Year end	05/04/2021
Income	£265,300
Assets	£8,190,000
Grants to organisations	£258,000

Further financial information

Grants awarded during the year can be broken down as follows:

The environment	£71,000
Well-being	£68,500
Care	£67,000
Arts	£51,500

Beneficiaries included: Pesticide Action Network UK (£10,000); Action for Children, A Rocha UK and Care for Veterans (£6,000 each); British Film Institute (£4,000); Cherry Trees (£3,000); Surrey Wildlife Trust and The Yard Theatre (£2,000 each); FoodCycle (£1,000); Amgueddfa'r Môr Porthmadog Maritime Museum (£500).

Exclusions

The following information has been taken from the trust's website:

> We only support **registered UK charities** and if you are not a UK charity then regretfully we cannot consider an application from you (unless you are an educational or research establishment with charitable status).
>
> Examples of applications we will not consider include those related to:
>
> - Individuals and their welfare, whether in the UK or abroad, including sponsorship of education, research or travel
> - Community Interest Companies (CICs)
> - Community Amateur Sports Clubs (CASCs)
> - Cooperative Societies and not-for-profit organisations

Applications

Apply online via the trust's website. The trustees meet twice a year in March and September to consider applications.

Sources of information

Accounts; annual report; Charity Commission record; funder's website.

P. F. Charitable Trust

General charitable purposes; health; the arts, culture, heritage or science; education; community development; advancement of religion; armed forces and emergency services; animal welfare; human rights

England; Wales; Scotland

£1.84 million (2020/21)

CC number: 220124

Correspondent: The Secretary, c/o RF Trustee Co. Ltd, 15 Suffolk Street, London SW1Y 4HG (tel: 020 3696 6721; email: charities@rftrustee.com)

Trustees: Philip Fleming; Rory Fleming; Matthew Fleming.

General information

The trust was established in 1951 to make grants to religious and educational charities and for general charitable purposes. The trust now makes grants to a wide range of causes and states that its policy is to continue to make a substantial number of small grants to charitable organisations both on a one-off and recurring basis.

Financial information

Year end	31/03/2021
Income	£2,230,000
Assets	£133,780,000
Grants to organisations	£1,840,000
No. of grants	334

Further financial information

334 grants were awarded during the year. Grants were broken down as follows:

Advancement of health/saving of lives	170	£1.04 million
Education	31	£151,500
Relief of those in need	46	£144,000
Advancement of art/culture/heritage/science	31	£127,800
Citizenship/community development	14	£100,000
Armed forces/police/fire rescue/ambulance services	4	£85,000
Relief of poverty	15	£77,000
Religion	3	£37,500
Environmental protection/improvement	7	£29,000
Amateur sport	6	£28,000
Animal welfare	6	£17,000
Advancement of human rights	1	£2,500

Beneficiaries included: ABF The Soldiers' Charity (£80,000); Institute of Cancer Research (£50,000); Scar Free Foundation (£40,000); Alice Marshall Hall (£30,000).

Exclusions

The trustees will not consider applications from individuals or non-registered charities and will not fund salaries.

Applications

Apply in writing to the correspondent. The trustees usually meet monthly to consider applications and approve grants.

Sources of information

Accounts; annual report; Charity Commission's record.

The Charities Advisory Trust

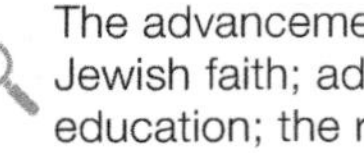

General charitable purposes

UK and overseas

£384,300 (2019/20)

CC number: 1040487

Correspondent: Dame Hilary Blume, Director, Radius Works, Back Lane, Hampstead, London NW3 1HL (tel: 020 7794 9835; email: people@charitiesadvisorytrust.org.uk)

Trustees: Rowena Dunn; David Russell; Leila Mactavish.

 www.charitiesadvisorytrust.org.uk

General information

The Charities Advisory Trust (originally called the Charity Trading Advisory Group) was established in 1979 by Dame Hilary Blume using funds from the Home Office to provide impartial information on all aspects of trading and income generation for charities. Today the trust runs a wide range of projects, many of which are intended to help build capacity in the voluntary sector.

According to its Charity Commission record, the objects of the trust are: to relieve poverty throughout the world; advance education; to preserve buildings and monuments of architectural merit; to assist charities so that they may make better use of their assets and resources both generally and in relation to trading and/or fundraising activities; and to advance any other charitable purposes.

Financial information

Year end	30/06/2020
Income	£753,100
Assets	£2,920,000
Grants to organisations	£384,300

Further financial information

Grants were broken down as follows in 2019/20: Good Gifts Catalogue (£372,300); direct awards programme (£7,200); Card Aid (£4,700).

Beneficiaries included: A list of beneficiaries was not available.

Exclusions

The trust has stated that it very rarely gives grants to individuals or to large fundraising charities. The promotion of religion is not supported.

Applications

Contact the correspondent for further information.

Sources of information

Accounts; annual report; Charity Commission record; funder's website.

Charitworth Ltd

The advancement of the Orthodox Jewish faith; advancement of Jewish education; the relief of poverty

Worldwide, mainly UK and Israel

£1.17 million (2020/21)

CC number: 286908

Correspondent: The Trustees, New Burlington House, 1075 Finchley Road, London NW11 0PU (tel: 020 8731 0777)

Trustees: Samuel Halpern; Sidney Halpern; David Halpern; Relly Halpern.

General information

This charity was established in 1983 and makes grants to support the advancement of the Orthodox Jewish faith and the relief of poverty. Our research suggests that support is given almost exclusively to Jewish organisations.

Financial information

Year end	31/03/2021
Income	£1,460,000
Assets	£41,190,000
Grants to organisations	£1,170,000

Beneficiaries included: Zichron Nachum (Europe) Trust (£165,000); Friends of Mercaz Hatorah Belz Macnivka (£75,000); Friends of Beis Chinuch Lebonos Trust (£60,000); Friends of Wiznitz Ltd and Rise and Shine (£50,000); British Friends of Mosdos Tchernobel (£40,000); Friends of Beis Soroah Schneirer (£30,000).

Applications

Apply in writing to the correspondent.

Sources of information

Accounts; annual report; Charity Commission record.

The Lorna and Yuti Chernajovsky Biomedical Research Foundation

 Biomedical research into autoimmunity, inflammation, infectious diseases and ageing

 UK

£785,100 (2020/21)

CC number: 1184405

Correspondent: The Trustees, PO Box 1198, Whitstable, Kent, CT5 9DW (email: a contact form is available on the foundation's website)

Trustees: Prof. Yuti Chernajovsky; Dr Lorna Chernajovsky; Prof. Paul Tak.

 www.chernajovskyfoundation.org.uk

General information

The foundation was established in 2019 to improve public health by providing grants to support high-quality biomedical research into the development of new targeted biomedical therapies in the fields of autoimmunity, inflammation, infectious diseases and ageing. The foundation's income comes from royalties from beta interferon.

Financial information

Year end	05/04/2021
Income	£717,900
Assets	£2,170,000
Grants to organisations	£785,100

Beneficiaries included: British Society for Research on Ageing (£143,800); MS Society (£106,800); University of Surrey (£83,500); British Immunology Society (£20,000).

Applications

See the foundation's website for information on its latest grant calls.

Sources of information

Accounts; annual report; Charity Commission record; funder's website.

Cheshire Freemasons' Charity

The relief of Masons and their dependants; Masonic charities; general charitable purposes

Cheshire; Stockport; Tameside; Trafford; Wirral

£210,300 (2020/21)

CC number: 219177

Correspondent: The Trustees, Ashcroft House, 36 Clay Lane, Timperley, Altrincham, Cheshire WA15 7AB (tel: 0161 980 6090; email: enquiries@cheshiremasons.co.uk)

Trustees: Graham Scott; Peter Carroll; Leo Saunders; Michael Ireland; Dennis Talbot; Jonathan Shasha; Paul Crudge.

 www.cheshiremasons.co.uk

 facebook.com/ProvinceofCheshireFreemasons

 @CheshirePGL

 @cheshirepgl

General information

According to the charity's 2020/21 annual report, its objects are:

- To relieve in cases of need Freemasons of the Province of Cheshire and their dependants in such ways as the Trustees think fit, which may include the granting of annuities or loans to such persons and the payment

of education, apprenticeships and advancement in life of such persons.
- To make grants to the Royal or other Masonic Charities.
- To provide charitable assistance to such other Masonic and non-Masonic Charitable objectives as the trustees shall decide.

Financial information

Year end	30/04/2021
Income	£336,700
Assets	£5,400,000
Grants to organisations	£210,300

Further financial information

In previous years grants have totalled over £300,00.

Beneficiaries included: A list of beneficiaries was not available.

Applications

Apply in writing to the correspondent.

Sources of information

Accounts; annual report; Charity Commission record; funder's website.

The Childhood Trust

Child welfare

London

£1.51 million (2019/20)

CC number: 1154032

Correspondent: Laurence Guinness, Chief Executive and Secretary, 18 Buckingham Palace Road, London SW1W 0QP (tel: 07507 880109; email: info@childhoodtrust.org)

Trustees: Rebecca Jacques; David Rhodes; Galiema Cloete; Karelia Ashman; Lesley O'Mara; Sonal Shenai; Grant Gordon; Dr Mathias Hink; Nicola Horlick; Andrei Popescu.

 www.childhoodtrust.org.uk

 facebook.com/ChildhoodTrust

 @ChildhoodTrust

 @childhoodtrust

General information

The Childhood Trust, which was registered with the Charity Commission in 2013, is a fundraising and grant-making charity that funds and facilitates projects run by charities, community groups and social enterprises that improve the lives of disadvantaged children of school age (4–18 years) who are living in poverty in London.

The trust has an informative website, which explains: 'We believe every London child deserves the possibility of a happy, safe childhood, and so we fund the very best initiatives and projects, run by charities and grassroots organisations – both large and small – that deliver vital support to the communities they serve.'

How the trust works

Funding local projects – the trust funds projects delivered by grassroots children's charities through its bi-annual matched funding campaigns. The campaigns are delivered through the online fundraising platform, The Big Give campaign participants receive matched funds from The Childhood Trust in the form of a grant.

There is typically a funding round in December, via The Christmas Give campaign and June, via the Summer Give campaign. In 2020 and 2021, the Summer Give campaign was replaced with the Champions for Children campaign, aimed at providing unrestricted funding to children's charities delivering critical services during the COVID-19 pandemic. Details of current campaigns can be found on the foundation's website.

Additional support – the trust also offers additional support, such as workshops on successful campaigning, skills training and marketing advice, free of charge to its partner organisations.

Supporting children through volunteering – the trust works with 'corporations, registered children's charities, and local authorities' Social Services teams to run two different volunteer programmes that provide immediate, practical support to vulnerable families and local youth projects'. See details of current projects on the website.

Advocating for disadvantaged children – the trust raises public awareness of children's experiences of living in poverty through advocacy projects, research and events.

Grant-making policy

The trust channels its funding into three thematic areas:

- **Practical – Ready to learn**: ensuring that children have access to the basic necessities
- **Emotional – Safe, secure, supported**: offering emotional support and motivation to break the cycle of poverty
- **Inspirational – Thriving, not just surviving**: providing opportunities to try new experiences and develop new skills

Full information on these three funding areas, including examples of the kind of projects that can be supported, is detailed on the website.

Eligibility

According to its website, the trust is looking for charities 'that have an existing supporter base and an appetite to engage with [the trust] and with the general public. In order to be successful in [the trust's] campaigns, it is helpful for charities to have an active trustee board or major donors who are prepared to make pledges to kickstart the project.'

Applicants are required to:

- Be registered with the Charity Commission
- Have one year of filed annual accounts
- Have over £25,000 income (as shown in your last annual accounts)
- Have three months of reserves
- Have strong financial processes and be legally compliant
- Have a robust governance structure
- Have solid safeguarding processes

Your project must:

- Have a clear focus on children and young people (4–18 years) from low-income families in London
- Have a budget of between £4,000 and £100,000
- Be completed within 12 months of the campaign

Financial information

Year end	30/06/2020
Income	£2,110,000
Assets	£298,500
Grants to organisations	£1,510,000
No. of grants	127

Beneficiaries included: Greenhouse Sports Ltd (£75,000); Mayor's Fund for London (£50,000); Safe Families for Children (£30,000); IntoUniversity (£25,000); Refugee Support Network (£15,000); Lives Not Knives (£10,000); London Chamber Orchestra Trust (£5,000); The Kids' Cookery School (£2,000); Young Roots (£1,000); Immediate Theatre (£220).

Exclusions

The trust does not:

- Fund activities that are aimed at services provided by the state
- Fund religious groups
- Offer grants other than the regular fundraising programmes that it curates
- Sponsor individuals
- Fund capital costs, trips abroad or accommodation for children and families experiencing homelessness

Applications

According to the website, 'all applications for The Childhood Trust's campaigns are processed through the Big Give platform.' To begin your application go to the 'Apply for funding' page of the trust's website and click 'begin application'.

The application process comprises the following steps:

1. Charities upload their project details onto The Big Give platform and submit their pledge donations
2. The Big Give and The Childhood Trust carry out checks on applicant charities

3 Funding offers are sent out to the successful charities and the campaign begins

Contact the correspondent for any further information or use the contact form available on the website.

Sources of information

Accounts; annual report; Charity Commission record; funder's website; further information provided by the funder.

Children with Cancer UK

Research into childhood cancer and welfare projects for young cancer patients and their families

 UK

£6.98 million (2020)

CC number: 298405

Correspondent: The Trustees, 51 Great Ormond Street, London WC1N 3JQ (tel: 020 7404 0808; email: research@childrenwithcancer.org.uk)

Trustees: Virna Midgley; David Gibbs; Caroline Randerson; Phil Hall; Alex Leitch.

 www.childrenwithcancer.org.uk

 facebook.com/childrenwithcanceruk

 @CwC_UK

 @childrenwithcanceruk

General information

According to its 2020 annual report, the charity's objects are:

- To promote the relief of children and young people suffering with leukaemia or any other form of cancer (and allied disorders) and of their families
- To raise public awareness and knowledge in matters relating to leukaemia or any other form of cancer (and allied disorders) affecting children and young people
- To promote research into the causes, alleviation, prevention, treatment and cure of leukaemia or any other form of cancer (and allied disorders) affecting children and young people and to publish the useful results of such research.

It provides funding for research into the causes, prevention and treatment of childhood cancer as well as funding innovative welfare projects to provide better care for young cancer patients and their families.

Grant-making policy

The following information has been taken from the charity's 2020 annual report:

> **Welfare grants** – There is no open application process for welfare grants and no welfare grants are given to individuals. The Trustees determine which organisations are to be supported.
>
> **Research grants** – The Trustees aim to award an increasing proportion of the charity's grants to scientific and medical research in child and young person cancer. The funding is directed in two areas of concern:
>
> - Research into treatment and survival
> - Research into prevention and causes

The charity also funds some five-year postdoctoral fellowships and clinical PhD studentships on these topics at leading research institutions regarding child and young adult cancer.

Financial information

Year end	31/12/2020
Income	£13,760,000
Assets	£9,300,000
Grants to organisations	£6,980,000

Further financial information

Grants were broken down as follows:

Research into treatment	£4.13 million
Research into prevention and causes	£1.56 million
Welfare	£1.29 million
Raising awareness	£6,800

Beneficiaries included: Cancer Research UK (£1.29 million); Teenage Cancer Trust (£1 million); Newcastle University (£348,800); Macarena Oporto Espuelas (£220,000); Institute of Cancer Research (£10,000); University of Edinburgh (£450).

Applications

For information on current research funding opportunities and how to apply, refer to the charity's website. There is no open application process for welfare grants, the trustees determine which organisations are to be supported. At the time of writing (May 2022), the charity was unable to say when the next funding call would be announced. Check the website for the latest information.

Sources of information

Accounts; annual report; Charity Commission record; funder's website.

Childs Charitable Trust

Supporting Christian organisations that actively share the Christian gospel

UK and overseas

£513,000 (2020)

CC number: 1153327

Correspondent: Melanie Churchyard, Chief Executive Officer, 40 Chapel Road, Pawlett, Bridgwater, Somerset TA6 4SH (tel: 01323 417944; email: info@childstrust.org)

Trustees: Christopher Large; Steve Puttock; Melanie Churchyard; Robert Peake.

 http://childscharitabletrust.org

General information

The Childs Charitable Trust's values are based on the Christian faith. It makes grants to mission organisations and charities working to promote the Christian gospel in the UK and overseas. As well as project costs, the trust accepts applications for funds to help develop policy, advocacy and research.

Financial information

Year end	31/12/2020
Income	£358,400
Assets	£10,050,000
Grants to organisations	£513,000
No. of grants	85

Further financial information

Only beneficiaries of grants over £10,000 were listed in the accounts. We were unable to determine the exact portion of grants awarded in the UK. During the year, the trust received 393 normal applications and 209 emergency requests for funding. It made grants to 85 organisations, of which 33 were for emergency funding.

Beneficiaries included: Off the Fence (£82,000); Middle East Media (£12,500); Kings Community Church, Stand by Me and Youthscape (£10,000 each).

Exclusions

The trust does not fund: new builds, repair, refurbishment or renovation projects, foodbanks, street pastors/wardens or gap year projects.

Applications

An online application form can be accessed on the trust's website, where application deadlines can also be found. Alternatively, an application form can be downloaded and returned by post or email. All applications must include your organisation's latest set of accounts.

Organisations with a turnover over £5 million should contact the trust prior to submitting an application to check eligibility.

Sources of information

Accounts; annual report; Charity Commission record; funder's website.

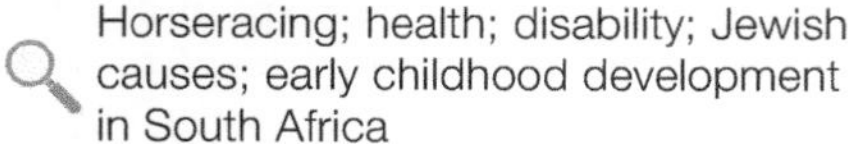

The Childwick Trust

Horseracing; health; disability; Jewish causes; early childhood development in South Africa

The south and south-east of the UK. A full list of the counties supported can be found on the trust's website. The trust also operates in South Africa

£3.72 million (2020/21)

CC number: 1150413

Correspondent: Kirsty Jones, Trust Administrator, 9 Childwick Green, Childwicksbury, St Albans, Hertfordshire AL3 6JJ (tel: 01727 844666; email: kirsty@childwicktrust.org)

Trustees: Clare Maurice; Mark Farmar; John Wood; Peter Anwyl-Harris; Dr Alan Stranders; Michael Fiddes.

 www.childwicktrust.org

General information

The trust was established in 1985 by the settlement of assets of the late founder, Mr H. J. Joel – racehorse owner and breeder.

Areas of work

Assistance is given exclusively to registered charities working in the counties listed on the website. The trust has four main focus areas:

Health charities

Grants are made to organisations offering care and support to people with serious illness, older people, adults and children with learning disabilities, mental health problems or physical disabilities, and ex-Service personnel who are in need of care or support. Some grants may also be made for medical research.

Grants (typically between £5,000 and £20,000) can be given towards purposes such as special equipment, respite care, holidays, education and other purposes. Salaries and core costs can be supported, as well as grants towards building or refurbishment projects if at least half the total budget is already met. Hospices in the South East are also supported, including running costs.

Horse racing

Support is given towards the welfare of those in the racing industry who are older and retired, injured, on a low income, or young people who need support. Other applications may be considered as long as they are related to either the welfare of people in the industry or connected to the welfare of thoroughbred race horses.

Jewish charities

The founder of the trust was Jewish and his wish was to benefit charities which promote the Jewish faith and to help Jewish people in need. The trust offers some support to charities which promote the Jewish faith and help the Jewish community – particularly older people, people with disabilities and children and young people. Grants are only made to charities in the UK, not Israel.

South Africa

In South Africa support is predominantly given to early childhood development projects with applications being administered through the Jim Joel Fund. As stated in the trust's objects, assistance is also provided 'to support the education of people resident in the Republic of South Africa', including the provision of grants and scholarships for individuals.

Financial information

Year end	31/03/2021
Income	£1,970,000
Assets	£87,040,000
Grants to organisations	£3,720,000

Further financial information

According to the 2020/21 accounts, grants made in the UK totalled £2.92 million and grants made in South Africa totalled £695,600. In addition, 'pensioner's welfare costs' totalled £101,300.

Grants were distributed as follows:

Health	69.8%
Education (South Africa)	18.7%
Jewish causes	7.4%
Pensioner's welfare	2.6%
Horseracing	1.5%

A list of beneficiaries can be found on the trust's website on the 'About Us' page. Only beneficiaries of grants of £15,000 and above were detailed.

Beneficiaries included: UK beneficiaries included: Rennie Grove Hospice Care (£38,300); Riding for the Disabled Association (£30,000); New West End Synagogue (£25,000); Deafblind UK (£20,000); Canine Partners and Jewish Policy Research (£15,000 each).

Exclusions

As stated on the website, grants are not made for:

- Complementary health and therapy projects
- Charities offering legal advice
- Charities offering counselling
- NHS Hospitals and other statutory bodies
- Universities – academic research, scholarships and bursaries
- Homelessness charities
- Projects related to drugs or alcohol addiction
- HIV/Aids related projects
- Charities which are part of a nationwide network – only those who are based within the South East can apply
- Individuals or organisations applying on behalf of an individual (other than in relation to South African educational grants)
- Students seeking sponsorship for educational or gap year projects
- Animal charities unless they are connected to thoroughbred racehorses
- National appeals
- Conferences and seminars
- Causes outside the UK (apart from South Africa)
- Organisations that have received a grant within the previous two years

Applications

The Childwick Trust – applications can be made using the online form on the trust's website when funding rounds are open. Deadlines can be found on the website.

The Jim Joel Fund – potential applicants should refer to the website for details of open funding rounds. Applications will need to be submitted online, typically by the end of April. Full guidelines for this fund may be requested from Giuliana Bland (PO Box 271, Jukskei Park, 2153, South Africa; tel: +27 011 704 6539; email: giuliana.jjf@iafrica.com).

Sources of information

Accounts; annual report; Charity Commission record; funder's website.

CHK Foundation

Children and young people (aged 11 to 24) at risk due to involvement in the criminal justice system, addictions or leaving the care system

UK

 £2.65 million (2020/21)

CC number: 1050900

Correspondent: The Trustees, PO Box 277, Royston, 8 St James's Square, London SG8 1EX (tel: 07592 806521; email: admin@chkcharities.co.uk)

Trustees: Joanna Prest; Katherine Loyd; Lucy Morris; Rupert Prest; Dr Edward Peake; Diana Acland; Pandora Morris; Charles Kirwan-Taylor; Susanna Peake; Camilla Peake; Elisalex de Castro Peake.

 www.chkcharities.co.uk

General information

CHK Foundation, formerly CHK Charities Ltd, was established in 1995. It makes grants to registered charities across the UK.

Main grants programme

From 2019 to 2024 CHK Foundation aims to focus on charities working throughout the UK in a targeted way to improve the lives and prospects of young people aged between 11 and 24 who are at risk as a result of:

- Involvement in the criminal justice system
- Addiction
- Leaving the care system

Other grants

CHK Mission Grants – grants under this programme are to support the protection of the environment

CHK Discretionary Grants – grants under this programme are made at the discretion of the trustees in line with their philanthropic interests

CHK Emergency/Disaster Grants – grants under this programme provide financial support for charitable work both nationally and internationally in response to natural disasters and humanitarian crises.

Financial information

Year end	31/01/2021
Income	£2,940,000
Assets	£138,580,000
Grants to organisations	£2,650,000

Beneficiaries included: Charities Aid Foundation (£245,000); Amber Foundation (£75,000); Baca Charity (£50,000); British Museum (£30,000); Big Change (£25,000); Making it Out (£10,000); Food4Heroes (£5,000).

Applications

The foundation's website states the following:

> Applications for funding are not invited. CHK Foundation undertakes its own research to identify the charities it wishes to support.

Sources of information

Accounts; annual report; Charity Commission record; funder's website.

Church Burgesses Trust

Ecclesiastical purposes and general charitable purposes

Sheffield

£711,500 (2020)

CC number: 221284

Correspondent: Ian Potter, The Law Clerk, c/o Wrigleys Solicitors LLP, Derwent House, 150 Arundel Gate, Sheffield S1 2FN (tel: 0114 267 5588; email: ian.potter@wrigleys.co.uk)

Trustees: Dr Julie Banham; Mr D. F. Booker; The Revd Hunter; Nicholas Hutton; Mr D. Stanley; Ian Walker; David Quinney; Stephen Eccleston; Elizabeth Brownhill; Dr Susan Gentle.

www.sheffieldchurchburgesses.org.uk

General information

The Church Burgesses Trust was established in 1554 with a gift of land and property from Queen Mary to the city of Sheffield.

It provides grants to support general charitable purposes for the benefit of the people of Sheffield and to support the religious and other charitable work of the Church of England in Sheffield.

Grant programmes

Ecclesiastical grants

Applications from Church of England churches in Sheffield are considered by the Ecclesiastical Grants Committee. Only Anglican churches within the four Sheffield deaneries (Attercliffe, Ecclesall, Ecclesfield and Hallam) are eligible to apply.

According to the website, grants can be given to support 'any activity which furthers the objectives of the Church of England', which often involves building repairs or the employment of parish-based staff. Applications from churches of other denominations can be considered by the General Charitable Purposes Committee. See the website for more information.

The trust also provides funding for ordained clergy serving in a ministry role within the Sheffield Deaneries of the Church of England to attend training courses, retreats and sabbaticals.

Other charitable support

The General Charitable Purposes Committee considers applications from a wide range of charities and groups whose activities are carried out within the city of Sheffield to the benefit of local residents. According to the website, there is a particular emphasis on:

- The relief for those who are aged, ailing, disabled, poor or otherwise disadvantaged.
- The relief of distress and sickness.
- The provision and support of facilities for recreation and other leisure time occupation.
- The provision and support of educational facilities

Grants range from £500 to £10,000 and can be used towards a complete scheme or a contribution towards a larger project.

Financial information

Year end	31/12/2020
Income	£1,650,000
Assets	£39,000,000
Grants to organisations	£711,500

Beneficiaries included: Age UK – Sheffield (£8,000); Emmaus (£5,000); Assist – Sheffield (£3,000); British Liver Trust (£2,000); Back Up Trust and Datic Trust (£1,000 each).

Exclusions

Grants are not made to individuals, although individuals who are under the age of 25 may be able to apply for educational assistance from the Church Burgesses Educational Foundation.

Applications

Application forms can be downloaded from the relevant page on the trust's website.

Sources of information

Accounts; annual report; Charity Commission record; funder's website.

Church of Ireland Priorities Fund

Church of Ireland

The Republic of Ireland and Northern Ireland

£400,100 (2021)

Correspondent: The Administrator, Church of Ireland House, Church Avenue, Rathmines, Dublin DO6 CF67 (tel: 0035314125607; email: priorities@ireland.anglican.org. A contact form is also available on the charity's website)

Committee members: Roy Totten; Joan Bruton; Hazel Corrigan; Bishop George Davison; The Revd Peter Ferguson; Glenn Moore; The Revd Lynda Peilow; Adrian Wilkinson,

www.priorities.ireland.anglican.org

General information

This grant-maker was established in 1980 to fund Church of Ireland projects anywhere in Ireland. Funds are donated by individual parishes and are then allocated to causes.

The following information on the grant-maker's criteria has been taken from its website:

> **Areas Currently Supported By The Fund**
>
> - **Training – Lay and Ordained –** Training in the following areas:– post–ordination, clergy in–service, lay ministry, youth ministry, children's ministry, student chaplaincy.
> - **Christian Education –** Development of RE in schools, children's ministry, youth work, adult education.
> - **Outreach Initiatives –** To encourage creative and innovative projects, which reach out to the communities our parishes serve, including church plants and missional areas.
> - **Innovative Ministry in a Rural Context –** To encourage creative and innovative ministry projects in the sparsely populated areas of the country, in rural or village settings.

Maximising The Effect Of Grants From The Priorities Fund

In order to spread the money from the Fund as widely and fairly as possible, we try to adhere to certain conditions.

We encourage:–
- Applications for grants for 'seed capital'.
- Applications for grants which will have a significant influence in attracting other funding.

Applications Requiring Recommendations

It is necessary for most projects to be vetted before they reach the Priorities Fund Committee.

These applications are recommended or not recommended by:–
- Church of Ireland Youth Department (youth projects).
- The appropriate Diocesan Council (diocesan and parish projects).

Financial information

Grants to organisations	£400,100
No. of grants	37

Further financial information

Grants awarded in 2021 were broken down as follows in the grant-maker's 2021 allocations document (available to download from the grant-maker's website):

Outreach initiatives	£254,200
Innovative ministry in rural contexts	£80,900
Training – lay and ordained	£38,900
Christian education	£26,100

Note: the financial figures have been converted from euros using the exchange rate at the time of writing (May 2022).

Beneficiaries included: Faughanvale (47,300); Donagh Parish (£21,200); Agherton Parish (£11,400); St Andrews Ballyhalbert (£7,100); St Katherine's (£4,100); COI Clergy Pension Fund (£1,100).

Exclusions

According to the grant-maker's website, it 'tries to avoid' funding:
- Projects which are still at the planning stage, including feasibility studies
- Recurrent grant aid
- Funding for salaries
- Financing debts
- Restoration projects for cathedrals and church buildings
- Routine renovations and repairs

Applications

Application forms are available from the grant-maker's website along with criteria and guidelines. Applications must be made by 31 October each year. The website states: 'It is advisable for applicants to check with the Administrator whether a project is required to be vetted BEFORE submitting an application.'

Sources of information

Funder's website; guidelines for applicants.

The City Bridge Trust (Bridge House Estates)

Social welfare; the environment; mental health; homelessness; older people; children and young people; food poverty

Greater London

£57.4 million (2020/21)

CC number: 1035628

Correspondent: The Grants Team, City of London Corporation, PO Box 270, Guildhall, London EC2P 2EJ (tel: 020 7332 3710; email: citybridgetrust@cityoflondon.gov.uk)

Trustee: The City of London Corporation.

www.citybridgetrust.org.uk

@citybridgetrust

General information

The primary objective of Bridge House Estates is the maintenance and support of five of the bridges that cross the Thames into or by the City of London – Tower Bridge, London Bridge, Southwark Bridge, Blackfriars Bridge and Millennium Bridge.

In 1995 a scheme was agreed by the Charity Commission which enabled the trustees to use the charity's surplus income (after meeting its responsibilities for the maintenance and replacement of the bridges) for charitable purposes benefitting the inhabitants of Greater London.

The trust works collaboratively to meet its objectives through four key areas of activity, namely:
- Grant-making
- Social investment
- Encouraging philanthropy
- Strategic initiatives

Grant-making

The trust has three main funding programmes, details of which have been taken from its website:

Connecting the Capital
- Voice and leadership
- Growing, greening and environmental projects
- Arts, sports, health and/or well-being projects for older people

Positive Transitions
- Specialist support services working with children and young people
- Specialist support services for older people
- Services which improve the accessibility and range of mental health support and services for people who are experiencing or at risk of homelessness or are vulnerably housed

Advice and Support
- Provision of advice and support to disadvantaged individuals
- Food poverty

Each of these programmes is cross-cut by our two over-arching priorities of **Reducing Inequalities** and **Enabling Voice and Representation**. You will need to demonstrate how your proposal sits within one of the funding programmes and how it will:
- Reduce inequality (especially the additional prejudices that those experiencing inequality can face, such as people who are LGBTQI experiencing mental health issues being less able to access the right services and support).
- Enable voice and representation for people who are disadvantaged.

Financial information

Year end	31/03/2021
Income	£47,400,000
Assets	£1,640,000,000
Grants to organisations	£57,400,000
No. of grants	1,617

Beneficiaries included: A list of beneficiaries was not available. Previous beneficiaries include: Federation of London Youth Clubs (£390,000 over three years); Kingston Voluntary Action (£303,600 over two years); British Refugee Council (£220,800 over three years); Afghanistan and Central Asian Association (£121,000 over three years); Magpie Dance (£100,000 over three years); Fulham Good Neighbour Service (£28,200); Cripplegate Foundation (£25,000); The Spitz Charitable Trust (£9,400); Migrants Rights Network (£5,100); St Barnabas Parochial Church Council (£980).

Exclusions

The trust's website states:

We cannot fund:
- Political parties
- Party political campaigning / lobbying
- Non-charitable activities
- Work which does not benefit the inhabitants of Greater London.

We do not fund:
- Individuals (except through our nominated agencies)
- Grant-making bodies to make grants on our behalf (except through our nominated agencies)
- Schools, PTAs, universities or other educational establishments
- Work taking place in schools, except for the delivery of non-statutory mental health services
- Medical or academic research
- Churches or other religious bodies where the monies will be used for religious purposes
- Hospitals or primary healthcare providers

- Community amateur sports clubs
- Projects which have already taken place or building work which has already been completed
- Statutory bodies, such as local authorities
- Profit-making organisations, except social enterprises
- Charities established/registered outside the UK
- Festivals or events which last no longer than a few days
- Activities or projects which incorporate an overnight stay
- Residential care services
- Residential facilities (except where they provide short-term emergency accommodation)

Applications

Applications must be made through the online portal on the trust's website. To access the online form, you must first complete the eligibility quiz.

Sources of information

Accounts; annual report; Charity Commission record; funder's website.

The Clore Duffield Foundation

The arts, culture, heritage and museums; Jewish charities; health and social welfare

UK. The larger grants go to London-based organisations

£5.6 million (2020)

CC number: 1084412

Correspondent: The Trustees, Studio 3, Chelsea Manor Studios, Flood Street, London SW3 5SR (tel: 020 7351 6061; email: info@cloreduffield.org.uk)

Trustees: Dame Vivien Duffield; David Harrel; James Harding; Melanie Clore; Richard Oldfield; Jeremy Sandelson.

www.cloreduffield.org.uk

General information

According to its website, 'The Clore Foundation was founded in 1964 by the late Sir Charles Clore, one of Britain's most successful post-war businessmen and one of the most generous philanthropists of his day.' Following his death in 1979, his daughter, Vivien Duffield, became chair of the foundation and created her own foundation in 1987 with the aim of continuing and consolidating her family's history of philanthropy. The two charities were merged in 2000 to become the Clore Duffield Foundation.

The foundation concentrates its grant-making on performing and visual arts, culture and heritage, with a particular interest in engaging children and young people with art and culture. In particular, it funds learning spaces within arts and heritage organisations, museums and galleries which provide access to cultural activities for people who would not normally take part. Some support is also given towards health and social welfare. Support towards enhancing Jewish life is mainly focused on JW3: London's Jewish Community Centre.

Grant programmes

Clore Learning Spaces: Since 2000 the foundation has funded more than 65 museums, gallery, heritage and performing arts learning spaces across the UK. These range from £2.5 million Clore Learning Centres in national museums, to grants of less than £50,000 to fund small Clore Studios with local museums.

Main grants: The foundation does occasionally provide grants for some health and social welfare projects, although the majority of support is directed towards the cultural sector.

Other initiatives: As well as making grants, the foundation runs a number of other initiatives. These include the Clore Leadership Programme, which aims to strengthen leadership across the cultural sector; the Clore Social Leadership Programme, which aims to support third sector leadership; and JW3: London's Jewish Community Centre. It has also undertaken research into areas relevant to its work.

Financial information

Year end	31/12/2020
Income	£10,500
Assets	£48,210,000
Grants to organisations	£5,600,000
No. of grants	94

Further financial information

Full accounts were not available to view on the Charity Commission website due to the foundation's low income. However, the 2020 accounts are available to view on the foundation's website. Grants were broken down as follows:

Arts, heritage and education	£4.27 million
Leadership training	£749,100
Health and social care	£438,600
Jewish support	£137,400

Beneficiaries included: Royal Opera House Covent Garden Foundation (£500,000); Imperial War Museums (£330,500); Jewish Care (£100,000); National Museum Wales (£55,000); Royal Institute of British Architects (£30,000); English National Ballet (£15,000); Elias Ashmole Trust (£2,000).

Exclusions

The foundation does not support:

- Projects outside the UK
- Individuals
- General appeals or circulars

Applications

Clore Learning Spaces

At the time of writing (February 2022) the website stated that the foundation is currently focused on supporting existing Clore Learning Spaces and is making very few new donations.

Main grants

At the time of writing, the foundation was no longer accepting unsolicited applications for its main grants programme. Any updates will be posted on the website.

Sources of information

Accounts; annual report; Charity Commission record; funder's website.

The Clothworkers' Foundation

People with disabilities; disadvantaged young people and minority communities; older people; domestic and sexual violence; homelessness; visual impairment; alcohol and substance misuse; prisoners and ex-offenders

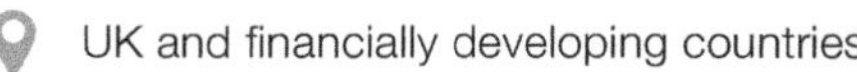

UK and financially developing countries

£9.2 million (2020)

CC number: 274100

Correspondent: The Trustees, Clothworkers' Hall, Dunster Court, Mincing Lane, London EC3R 7AH (tel: 020 7623 7041; email: foundation@clothworkers.co.uk)

Trustees: Michael Jarvis; Dr Lucy Rawson; Andrew Blessley; Hanif Virji; Susanna O'Leary; Philip Portal; Denis Clough; Thomas Stoddart-Scott; Charles Hutchins; Neel Patani; Emma Clark; Chloe Holness; Ola Opoosun; Oonagh Smyth.

www.clothworkersfoundation.org.uk

@ClothworkersFdn

General information

The Clothworkers' Company is an ancient City of London livery company, founded in 1528. One of the functions of livery companies was to support their members in times of need. As they grew wealthier, they were also able to benefit outsiders. The Clothworkers' Company acquired a number of trusts, established by individual benefactors for specific charitable ends. These totalled over 100 by the twentieth century. In addition, the company has always made payments to charitable causes from its own funds.

The Clothworkers' Foundation was set up in 1977 by the company as the independent arm for the whole of its charitable work. During its first 40 years, the foundation has made grants totalling around £125 million.

The foundation runs an open grants programme, open to UK-registered charities, CICs and other registered UK non-for-profit organisations, offering funding towards capital projects (defined as buildings, fittings, fixtures, equipment and vehicles). Work must fit into one or more of the specified programme areas:

- Alcohol and substance misuse
- Disadvantaged minority communities
- Disadvantaged young people
- Domestic and sexual abuse
- Homelessness
- Older people
- People with disabilities
- People who have offended
- Visual impairment

The size of grant awarded is dependent upon a number of factors, including the size of the organisation, and cost and scale of the project.

The foundation also runs a proactive grants programme, with the aim of offering more strategic multi-year revenue funding. Work must fit into one of the following themes, as stated on the website:

- Better futures
- Care leavers
- Conservation
- Dramatic arts
- Social investment
- Tech vs abuse
- Visual impairment in financially developing countries

See the website for full details on each programme area.

Financial information

Year end	31/12/2020
Income	£9,290,000
Assets	£232,700,000
Grants to organisations	£9,200,000

Further financial information

All beneficiaries relate to the Proactive Grants Programme.

Beneficiaries included: National Youth Theatre (£490,000); Vision Aid Overseas (£366,000); UK Youth (£150,000); Society of London Theatre (£50,000); Sam-Culture (£10,000).

Exclusions

See the foundation's website for a full list of exclusions.

Applications

Applications can be made through the foundation's website where guidelines and an eligibility quiz can also be found.

Sources of information

Accounts; annual report; Charity Commission record; funder's website.

Cloudesley

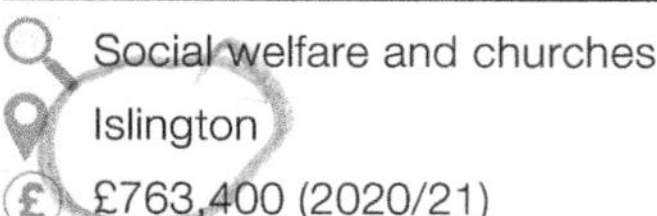

Social welfare and churches

Islington

£763,400 (2020/21)

CC number: 205959

Correspondent: Grants Committee, Office 1.1, Resource for London, 356 Holloway Road, London N7 6PA (tel: 020 7697 4094; email: info@cloudesley.org.uk)

Trustee: Richard Cloudesley Trustee Ltd.

 www.cloudesley.org.uk

General information

The charity was founded in 1517 under the will of Richard Cloudesley, an Islington resident. It operates as an independent charitable trust that makes grants to individuals, organisations and churches within the Borough of Islington.

Grant programmes

Health grants programme – this is a five-year programme running from 2019 to 2024 that aims to reduce health inequalities in Islington. Grants are awarded to organisations that support the physical and mental health of Islington residents who are in need. The programme consists of:

- Principal grants fund – larger, multi-year grants are awarded to established voluntary sector organisations with a track record of delivering positive health outcomes for local residents. Grants can be given for core costs or towards specific projects
- Development fund – provides local organisations with initial funding to develop specific projects to test a new approach to tackling health inequalities or to address a gap in local service provision
- Strategic grants fund – the charity has agreed multi-year grants for organisations supporting Islington residents through providing outreach and advice services
- Grants support fund – additional support beyond grant funding to organisations supported by the charity

Church grants programme – support is given to eligible Church of England churches in the Islington Deanery. Funding is given towards the upkeep and repair of buildings and maintenance of services.

The charity also makes grants to individuals, via Cloudesley Partners.

Further information about each grants programme can be found on the charity's website.

Financial information

Year end	30/06/2021
Income	£1,490,000
Assets	£58,700,000
Grants to organisations	£763,400

Beneficiaries included: Holloway Neighbourhood Group (£90,000); Manor Gardens Welfare Trust (£47,000); Healthwatch Islington and Islington Mind (£10,000 each); Help on Your Doorstep (£6,500).

Applications

Applications can be completed online during open funding periods; applicants are advised to regularly check the charity's website for more information.

Sources of information

Accounts; annual report; Charity Commission record; funder's website.

Clydpride Ltd

Advancement of the Orthodox Jewish faith; relief of poverty; general charitable purposes

Worldwide

£1.03 million (2019/20)

CC number: 295393

Correspondent: Mrs T. Faust, Secretary, c/o Rayner Essex LLP, Entrance D, Tavistock House South, Tavistock Square, London WC1H 9LG (tel: 020 8731 7744)

Trustees: Mr A. Faust; Jonathan Weinstein; Jacob Halpern; Leon Faust.

General information

Clydpride Ltd was registered with the Charity Commission in November 1986 and its 2019/20 annual accounts state that it has the following objectives:

- the advancement of religion accordance with the Orthodox Jewish Faith
- the relief of poverty, and
- for such other purposes as are recognised by English Law as charitable and in furtherance of the aforementioned objects.

Financial information

Year end	24/12/2020
Income	£3,200,000
Assets	£41,400,000
Grants to organisations	£1,030,000

Further financial information

Grants to organisations were broken down as follows:

Advancement of religion	£466,900
Relief of poverty	£411,500
Benefit of the Jewish community	£156,500

Only beneficiaries of grants over £30,000 were listed in the 2020 accounts. Grants under £30,000 totalled £420,700.

Beneficiaries included: Yad Eliezer Trust (£250,000); Tomchei Yoitzei Anglia

(£56,000); Friends of Dr Adlers Surgery (£50,000); Gateshead Talmudical College (£35,000); Side by Side (Children) Ltd (£33,300).

Applications

Apply in writing to the correspondent. The charity considers all grant requests from organisations that fall within the criteria of its objects.

Sources of information

Accounts; annual report; Charity Commission record.

CMZ Ltd

Jewish causes; relief of poverty; religious education

London; Israel; USA

£2.63 million (2020/21)

CC number: 1087870

Correspondent: Mr B. Goldberg, Secretary, 206 High Road, London N15 4NP (tel: 020 8801 6038)

Trustees: Mr P. Schneebalg; Samuel Steinmetz; Chaim Gottesfeld.

General information

The charity's 2020/21 annual report states:

> The charity's objects are the advancement of the Orthodox Jewish religion, to aid in the provision of, and improvement of, educational facilities and to assist in the alleviation of poverty of, in particular, the Orthodox Jewish community.
>
> The charity's funds are utilised in supporting other charities with similar objectives especially in helping persons in conditions of need, hardship and distress in the Orthodox Jewish community and the advancement of the Orthodox Jewish religion.

Financial information

Year end	31/03/2021
Income	£2,820,000
Assets	£324,700
Grants to organisations	£2,630,000

Further financial information

Only beneficiaries of grants of £45,000 and above were listed in the charity's 2020/21 accounts. Grants of under £45,000 totalled £1.17 million. A full list of beneficiaries can be requested from the charity's correspondent.

Beneficiaries included: The Rehabilitation Trust (£204,700); Edupoor (£138,000); Support the Charity Worker (£132,000); Care All Ltd (£69,300); Binyen Torah Ltd (£56,300); Viznitz Institutions Trust (£45,000).

Applications

According to the charity's 2020/21 annual report:

> Grants are made at the trustees' discretion from their knowledge of the various institutions, applications by individuals must be accompanied by a letter of recommendation by the applicant's minister or other known religious leader that meets the criteria as defined by its charitable objectives. The charity also operates a voucher system whereby each donor is given the equivalent amount of vouchers out of which the donor makes donations to charitable entities and individuals of their choice that meets the criteria as defined by CMZ Limited's charitable objects.

Sources of information

Accounts; annual report; Charity Commission record.

The Coalfields Regeneration Trust

Community regeneration; social welfare; health; employment, education and skills; young people; older people

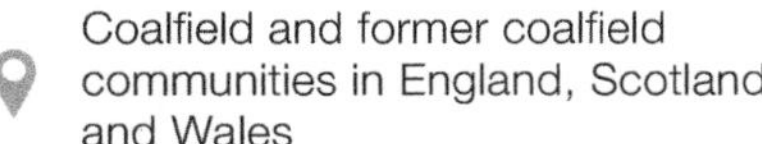

Coalfield and former coalfield communities in England, Scotland, and Wales

£2.49 million (2020/21)

CC number: 1074930

Correspondent: The Trustees, 1 Waterside Park, Valley Way, Wombwell, Barnsley, South Yorkshire S73 0BB (tel: 01226 270800; email: info@coalfields-regen.org.uk)

Trustees: Dawn Davies; Peter McNestry; Wayne Thomas; Sylvia Wileman; Nicolas Wilson; Michael Clapham; Robert Young; Nicky Stubbs; Trudie McGuinness; Linda Rutter; Judith Kirton-Darling; Keith Cunliffe.

 www.coalfields-regen.org.uk

 facebook.com/CRTEngland

 @coalfieldsregen

 @CoalfieldsRegen

General information

The Coalfields Regeneration Trust is an independent charity dedicated to the social and economic regeneration of coalfield communities in England, Scotland and Wales. It was set up in 1999 in response to a recommendation by the government's Coalfields Task Force Report. The report highlighted the dramatic effects that mine closures had, and continue to have, on communities in coalfield areas.

The trust provides advice, support and financial assistance to community and voluntary organisations which are working to tackle social issues at a grassroots level within coalfield communities. It is closely connected with the areas it serves, operating through a network of staff based at offices located within coalfield regions themselves. As stated on its website, the trust's mission is: 'to champion and strengthen coalfield communities, generate resources to respond to their needs and deliver programmes that make a positive and lasting difference.'

Key themes

According to its website, the trust's work falls into the following themes:

- Health and well-being
- Employment
- Skills

The trust runs a number of programmes providing grants, community investment programmes and voluntary sector support in England, Scotland and Wales. For full and detailed information on the trust's various programmes, see the website.

Financial information

Year end	31/03/2021
Income	£6,570,000
Assets	£38,330,000
Grants to organisations	£2,490,000
No. of grants	511

Beneficiaries included: A list of beneficiaries was not available. Previous beneficiaries include: Aylesham Neighbourhood Project (£210,000); Haswell and District Mencap Society – The Community Anchor (£98,000); Derbyside Rural Community Council – Wheels to Work (£89,000); The Cornforth Partnership (£75,000); Nottinghamshire Independent Domestic Abuse Link Workers (£66,000); Stoke-on-Trent and District Gingerbread Centre Ltd (£37,000); St John's Church – A Building in Which to Serve Our Community (£10,000); Mansfield and Dukeries Irish Association (£5,000); City of Durham Air Cadets (£3,800); Thornycroft Art Club (£520).

Exclusions

Check the trust's website for programme specific exclusions.

Applications

Application details are different for each programme; details can be found on the trust's website, where guidance notes are also available. Applicants can contact their regional team to find out more information or to discuss an application.

Sources of information

Accounts; annual report; Charity Commission record; funder's website.

The John Coates Charitable Trust

Education; the arts; medicine and healthcare; heritage, conservation and the environment; societal and community cohesion

London; Cambridge; Norfolk; Devon; Surrey; West Sussex

£462,000 (2020/21)

CC number: 262057

Correspondent: The Trustees, c/o The Trust Partnership Ltd., 6 Trull Farm Buildings, Trull, Tetbury, Gloucestershire GL8 8SQ (tel: 01285 719595; email: johncoates@thetrustpartnership.com)

Trustees: Claire Cartledge; Catharine Kesley; Rebecca Lawes; Susan Down; Antonia Youngman; Elspeth McGregor.

https://johncoatescharitabletrust.org.uk

General information

The trust was established in 1969 and mainly makes grants to large national charities or to small charities that are of personal or local interest to the trustees.

The trust only supports charities that deliver projects in the following geographical areas:

- London-wide or work focused on North Kensington, Lambeth, Merton, Wandsworth
- Cambridge or the surrounding area
- North West Norfolk
- North Devon
- Surrey
- West Sussex

Grants are made for general charitable purposes, with some preference for the following:

- Education
- The arts
- Medicine and healthcare (including supporting service-users and funding research)
- Heritage and the environment
- Societal and community cohesion

Typical grants are between £5,000 and £10,000 but in exceptional circumstances, awards may be higher. Only one grant will be awarded to any organisation within a 12-month period but the trustees may choose to renew their support in subsequent years.

Financial information

Year end	05/04/2021
Income	£430,700
Assets	£15,400,000
Grants to organisations	£462,000
No. of grants	78

Beneficiaries included: The British Heart Foundation (£15,000); Sebastian's Action Trust (£10,000); Teenage Cancer Trust (£7,500); Cambridge Literary Festival, Schoolreaders and South West Coast Path Association (£5,000 each); North Devon Hospice (£4,000); Nordoff Robbins Music Therapy (£3,000).

Exclusions

The trust is unlikely to support applications from individuals or regional offices of national organisations. Its website states that it is unlikely to support the following:

- Projects delivered overseas
- Advocacy
- Animal welfare
- Business ventures
- Capital projects
- Campaigning or lobbying
- Churches and religious causes and activities
- Conferences or seminars
- Endowments
- Exhibitions
- Festivals (apart from those dedicated to the arts)
- HIV charities
- Hospitals for operational services
- International travel
- Overseas projects
- Retrospective funding
- Routine maintenance of buildings
- Schools, colleges and universities (apart from specialist establishments, for example those for pupils with disabilities or those dedicated to the arts such as conservatoires)
- Statutory services
- Well-supported causes

Applications

Applications can be made through the trust's website. The trustees meet twice a year usually in January and July to consider applications.

Sources of information

Accounts; annual report; Charity Commission record; funder's website.

Denise Coates Foundation

Education and training; health and welfare; arts and culture; medical research and development; community development; disaster recovery

UK and overseas

£6.03 million (2020/21)

CC number: 1149110

Correspondent: The Trustees, bet365 House, Media Way, Stoke-on-Trent, Staffordshire ST1 5SZ (tel: 0845 600 0365)

Trustees: John Coates; Peter Coates; Denise Coates; James White; Simon Galletley; Oliver Adams.

General information

The foundation registered in September 2012. It formerly shared its name with Bet365 (Ltd), which was set up by Denise Coates. Her father, Peter Coates, also a trustee, is Chair of Stoke City FC, of which Bet365 Ltd is also a major shareholder.

The foundation's Charity Commission record states that it distributes 'funds in support of local, national and international charitable activities, exclusively charitable according to the laws of England and Wales'.

The foundation's objects are to support general charitable purposes. Previously, support has been given to the following causes:

- Health and welfare
- Education and training
- Community development
- Medical research and development
- Disaster recovery/emergency relief
- Arts and culture

Financial information

Year end	28/03/2021
Income	£103,810,000
Assets	£568,340,000
Grants to organisations	£6,030,000

Further financial information

During 2020/21, grants were distributed as follows:

Health and welfare	£2.27 million
Education and training	£1.83 million
Medical research and development	£1.33 million
Community development	£589,000

Beneficiaries included: University Hospitals of North Midlands Charity (£1.9 million in three grants); Stonyhurst Foundation (£1.6 million); Chronic Disease Research Foundation (£1.29 million in three grants); Douglas Macmillan Hospice (£322,000); Kick4Life (£250,000); Newcastle-under-Lyme School (£231,000); The Land Trust (£155,000); New Vic Theatre (£100,000).

Applications

The foundation's 2020/21 annual report states:

> The Foundation identifies charities that it wishes to support, these charities are then invited to present proposals to the Foundation's Trustees detailing how a grant would be used and the benefits that it would deliver. The Trustees assess how the proposal aligns to the Foundation's objectives in order to determine whether or not to award a grant.

Sources of information

Accounts; annual report; Charity Commission record.

The John S. Cohen Foundation

The arts; conservation and the environment; education; health and welfare

UK

£393,200 (2020/21)

CC number: 241598

Correspondent: Diana Helme, Administrator, PO Box 21277, London W9 2YH (tel: 020 7286 6921)

Trustees: Olivia Qizilbash; Dr Imogen Cohen; Jillian Barker.

General information

The foundation awards grants to organisations for general charitable purposes, mainly in the UK, but also worldwide. According to its 2020/21 annual report, the foundation is particularly active in supporting higher education, music, the arts and the built and natural environment. The foundation also makes awards for social and medical purposes.

Financial information

Year end	31/03/2021
Income	£630,100
Assets	£12,080,000
Grants to organisations	£393,200
No. of grants	63

Further financial information

During 2020/21, grants were distributed as follows: education (67%); the arts (22%); conservation and the environment (11%).

Beneficiaries included: Royal Botanical Gardens, Kew (£19,600); Westminster Abbey Foundation (£15,000); Imperial War Museums (£9,000); Academy of Ancient Music (£5,000); University of York Music Press (£3,000); Mahogany Opera Group (£2,500); Twentieth Century Society (£1,400).

Applications

Apply in writing to the correspondent.

Sources of information

Accounts; annual report; Charity Commission record.

The R. and S. Cohen Foundation

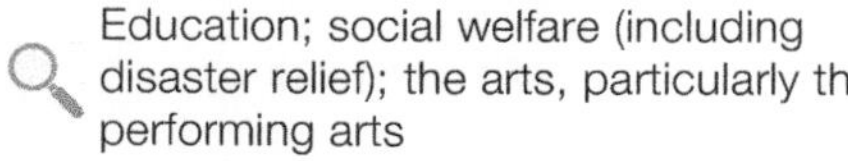

Education; social welfare (including disaster relief); the arts, particularly the performing arts

Worldwide, particularly the UK and Israel

£700,000 (2020)

CC number: 1078225

Correspondent: The Trustees, 3–4 Stanley Crescent, London W11 2NB (tel: 020 7182 7800)

Trustees: Lady Sharon Harel-Cohen; Sir Ronald Cohen; Tamara Harel-Cohen; David Marks; Jonathan Harel-Cohen.

General information

The R. and S. Cohen Foundation was established for general charitable purposes in 1999 by Sir Ronald Cohen and his wife Lady Sharon Harel-Cohen. He is the chair of Global Steering Group for Impact Investment, The Portland Trust and the Impact-Weighted Accounts Initiative at Harvard Business School. He is also co-founder of Social Finance UK, USA and Israel, Bridges Fund Management and Big Society Capital.

The objectives of the foundation, as detailed in the trust deed, are as follows:

- The advancement of education
- The relief of persons who are in conditions of need, hardship or distress as a result of local, national or international disaster or by reason of their social and economic circumstances
- In promoting and encouraging for the public all aspects of the arts, including painting, sculpture, theatre and music

Financial information

Year end	31/12/2020
Income	£8,600
Grants to organisations	£700,000

Further financial information

Full accounts were not available to view on the Charity Commission website due to the foundation's low income. We have therefore estimated the foundation's grant total based on its total expenditure.

Beneficiaries included: A list of beneficiaries was not available. Previous beneficiaries include: The Portland Trust (£492,500); Tate Foundation (£100,000); Fight for Peace International (£75,000); B Lab UK (£50,000); Ashoka (£24,000); Victoria and Albert Museum (£15,000); Norwood (£12,500); West London Synagogue Charitable Fund (£3,000); Royal Academy of the Arts (£1,000).

Exclusions

The foundation does not provide grants to individuals.

Applications

Our previous research suggests that unsolicited applications are unlikely to be successful, as the trustees prefer to support charities with which they have personal contact.

Sources of information

Charity Commission record; previous years' accounts; Sir Ronald Cohen (website).

The Coles-Medlock Foundation

International development; the empowerment and education of young girls; social welfare

UK and overseas (projects must be in financially developing countries)

£446,000 (2020/21)

CC number: 1132780

Correspondent: The Trustees, St George's Lodge, 33 Oldfield Road, Bath, Somerset BA2 3ND (tel: 01225 946226; email: office@coles-medlock.org)

Trustees: Mark Goodman; David Medlock; Jacqueline Medlock; Peter Medlock.

www.coles-medlock.org

General information

The foundation was established in 2009 and makes grants to UK-registered charities carrying out projects overseas. Its 2020/21 annual report states:

> The foundation's aim is to facilitate support and assistance for those in need due to youth, ill health, disability or financial deprivation both in the UK and overseas.
>
> A key focus is alleviating the impact of extreme poverty throughout the developing world through sustainable food provision, improved infrastructure, healthcare and education and independent financial progress.
>
> We work with UK registered charities and their international partners to fulfil our objectives.
>
> We award grants of between £150 and £140,000 but the large majority are worth £5,000 to £10,000.

The foundation's website states that it is currently focusing its giving on the empowerment and education of young girls.

Financial information

Year end	31/07/2021
Income	£292,700
Assets	£36,800
Grants to organisations	£446,000
No. of grants	98

Further financial information

A total of 98 grants were made to organisations in 2020/21, ranging from £1,000 to £25,000.

Beneficiaries included: Bath Festivals (£25,000); Children on the Edge and Pratham UK (£10,000 each); The Asian Students Christian Trust (£7,000); African Promise (£5,000); International Refugee Trust (£3,000); World Bicycle Relief UK (£2,100); Magic Bus (£1,000).

Exclusions

Applicants must be UK-registered charities. Grants will not be awarded for charitable projects being carried out in the UK. The foundation does not support individuals.

Applications

Applications can be made using an online form on the foundation's website. The trustees meet quarterly. The foundation's website states:

> When assessing potential grants, we look for the applicants to address the following points:
> - What is the need for the work that they are doing; how and why this need is not currently being met.
> - How the organisation intends to address that need.
> - The impact the work will have both in terms of numbers of people helped and the improvement to those peoples' lives both now and in the future.
> - What plans and procedures are in place for both qualitative and quantitative impact reporting.
> - A forecast budget for the work to demonstrate the short term and long term sustainability.
> - The last annual report and accounts of the charity.

Sources of information

Accounts; annual report; Charity Commission record; funder's website.

The Colt Foundation

 Occupational and environmental health research

 UK

£500,000 (2020)

CC number: 1190167

Correspondent: Tash Heydon, Director, Unit E, The Old Bakery, Petworth, West Sussex GU28 0AP (tel: 01798 342831; email: tash@coltfoundation.org.uk)

Trustees: Prof. David Coggon; Clare Gilchrist; Patricia Lebus; Dr Ira Madan; Prof. Anthony Taylor; Dr Alex Jones; Christina Fitzsimmons.

 www.coltfoundation.org.uk

General information

The foundation was established in 1978 by the O'Hea family with gifts of shares in Colt International and Associated Companies Ltd. According to its website the foundation funds 'high quality research projects in the field of occupational and environmental health, particularly those aimed at discovering the cause of illnesses arising from conditions at the place of work.' The foundation provides project grants and PhD fellowships.

Financial information

Year end	31/12/2020
Income	£742,800
Grants to organisations	£500,000

Further financial information

Full accounts were not available to view on the Charity Commission website as the foundation has recently re-registered. We have therefore estimated the grant total based on the foundation's total expenditure.

Beneficiaries included: A list of beneficiaries was not available. Previous beneficiaries include: University of Edinburgh (£85,900); UCL/London School of Hygiene and Tropical Medicine (£64,900); Imperial College (£52,000); University of Southampton (£40,600); British College – Nepal (£10,100); St Mary's Cathedral Workshop (£3,900).

Applications

Apply in writing to the correspondent. Full details of what should be included in an application can be found in the 'grants' section of the foundation's website. The trustees meet twice a year to review applications, in the spring and in the autumn. Applications normally need to be received approximately eight weeks beforehand to be considered at the meetings.

Sources of information

Accounts; annual report; Charity Commission record; funder's website.

Colwinston Charitable Trust

 The arts, with a preference for opera, music, the visual arts and library and archive projects

 UK, with a preference for Wales

£772,000 (2020/21)

CC number: 1049189

Correspondent: Mrs A. McMurray, Consultant Director, 14 Hanover Court, Midhope Road, Woking, Surrey GU22 7UX (tel: 020 7842 2000; email: colwinston.trust@ntlworld.com)

Trustees: Mathew Prichard; Martin Tinney; Sian Williams; Lucinda Prichard; Rebecca Evans.

 www.colwinston.org.uk

General information

The Colwinston Charitable Trust was established in 1995 and derives its income from the royalties from the West End production of *The Mousetrap*, the Agatha Christie play, which opened in 1952. The trust's General Guidelines set out its grant-making aims:

- Through its grant-making, the Trust seeks to sustain and support high quality artistic activities that add to the cultural life and experiences available in the UK and especially in Wales where over 80% of its grants are directed.
- The funding focus is particularly, but not exclusively, directed to the support of the live performing arts, the visual arts, plus library and archive projects in Wales.
- Other areas may also be supported on occasion, at the discretion of the trustees.

The trust makes grants to UK-registered charities for activities that take place in the UK. The types of activities it is most likely to fund are described in the guidelines:

- Projects that demonstrate excellence in terms of the creative ambition – through the quality of the artistic product, the calibre of the participating artists, and the value of the artistic experience for audiences and/or participants
- Collaborative projects that assist organisations to share skills and expertise, and extend the range and reach of the funded activity
- Projects designed to develop new audiences, make the art form more widely accessible, and help embed the art form in the community
- Projects that specifically target families and younger people, and which help them to better understand and engage with the arts
- Arts educational and outreach projects associated with high quality work
- Distinctive, high quality festivals and events, that impact beyond a purely local level
- Projects that help to fill an existing gap in artistic provision in Wales
- The commissioning of new work, particularly to develop the careers of emerging and midcareer Welsh artists, when professionally mounted presentations of the work form part of the project
- Projects that may assist organisations to increase their financial sustainability

The guidelines state that:

- The majority of grants will be in the range of £5,000 to £20,000.
- Larger grants are generally only awarded to organisations where a funding relationship with the Trust has been developed over several years
- Larger grants are more likely to be offered to fund activities that deliver strategic initiatives, and that would be unlikely to occur without the assistance of the Trust
- Larger grants are generally limited to organisations delivering high quality artistic activity in Wales

Financial information

Year end	05/04/2021
Income	£4,900
Grants to organisations	£772,000
No. of grants	12

Further financial information

The trust was not required to file accounts for the 2020/21 financial year due to its low income. According to the trust's website, it awarded grants totalling £772,000 to 12 organisations in 2020/21.

Beneficiaries included: Welsh National Opera (£500,000); Artes Mundi 9 (£140,000); Horatio's Garden (£50,000); National Dance Company of Wales (£20,000); Presteigne Festival (£10,000); National Opera Studio (£5,000); Agatha Christie Festival (£2,500).

Exclusions

See the trust's General Guidelines for a full list of exclusions.

Applications

Application forms and guidelines can be downloaded from the trust's website. The completed grant application and budget with any enclosures should be sent to the correspondent by post using ordinary postage only. Applications should be received no later than 30 September, for consideration at the November meeting, or 31 March for consideration at the May meeting of trustees.

Organisations wishing to discuss making an application for a larger grant (£20,000 plus) should contact the trust prior to making an application.

Sources of information

Accounts; annual report; Charity Commission record; funder's website; guidelines for applicants.

Colyer-Fergusson Charitable Trust

Disadvantaged young people; disadvantaged families; community development; the rehabilitation of people who have offended

Kent and Medway

£3.35 million (2020/21)

CC number: 258958

Correspondent: Gilly Green, Grants Assessor, 34 Hill Street, Richmond, Surrey TW9 1TW (tel: 020 8948 3388; email: grantadmin@cfct.org.uk)

Trustees: Nicholas Fisher; Ruth Murphy; Barbara Long; Rosalind Riley; James Thorne; Navprit Rai; Julia Megone.

 www.cfct.org.uk

 @ColyerFergusson

General information

Established by Sir James Colyer-Fergusson in 1969, this trust's overarching aim is to improve the lives of people in Kent and Medway, and in particular those who are most disadvantaged.

Funding programmes

The trust funds the following causes, details of which have been taken from the trust's website:

> **Investing in young people** – Making grants to support disadvantaged young people living at the margins of society to improve their skills, build their confidence and break down the barriers to their employment.
>
> **Investing in families** – Making grants to support Kent 'families' in the most inclusive sense of the word, living at the sharp end of chronic socio-economic problems or facing a financial or emotional crisis.
>
> **Investing in communities** – Making small grants to community groups and local charities to strengthen their resilience and build their capacity to deliver sustainable services to people at the margins of society.
>
> **Investing in rehabilitation** – Making grants to support the rehabilitation of offenders and to help reduce the collateral consequences of their imprisonment for their families, with the aim of reducing reoffending.
>
> **Grants to individuals** – Making small grants to disadvantaged young people for practical items such as interview clothes, course fees, tools, travel costs etc. All grants are made via a trusted referral partner.
>
> **Investing locally** – Funds allocated to this programme have been re-directed to other grant programmes to support charities struggling to meet the challenges of the coronavirus pandemic.

See the trust's website for guidance material about the range of grants available in each programme.

Financial information

Year end	31/03/2021
Income	£810,300
Assets	£32,970,000
Grants to organisations	£3,350,000

Further financial information

In 2020/21, grants paid totalled £3.35 million. Grants committed during the year (406 grants) totalled £2.64 million and were broken down as follows:

Investing in communities	107	£905,500
Proactive grants	1	£500,000
Investing in families	11	£425,500
Investing in rehabilitation	8	£359,600
Investing in young people	10	£351,000
Hardship awards	269	£95,700

Beneficiaries included: Age UK – Kent (£156,000); Construction Youth Trust (£135,600); Forward Trust (£70,000); Kent High Weald Partnership (£39,300); Taylor Made Dreams (£24,000); Oasis Domestic Abuse Service (£16,500); Stepping Out with Carers CIC (£7,500); SeeAbility (£1,000).

Exclusions

According to its website, the trust cannot support:

- Individuals – unless they are made as part of our 'Hardship Awards' Programme
- Statutory bodies and anything deemed to be the responsibility of the State
- Nurseries, schools and colleges
- Hospitals and health authorities
- Medical care, medical equipment or medical research
- Academic research, scholarships or bursaries
- Animal charities
- The promotion of religion
- The restoration or conservation of buildings
- Annual or one-off events and festivals
- Work outside of Kent
- Endowment appeals
- Work that has already taken place i.e. retrospective funding
- Round-robin, widely circulated appeals
- National charities without a base or planned project within Kent or Medway – unless applying to our Investing in Rehabilitation fund

Applications

Online application forms along with full guidance notes on each specific programme are available to download from the trust's website.

Sources of information

Accounts; annual report; Charity Commission record; funder's website.

Comic Relief 

Tackling poverty and social injustice; children and young people; women and girls; community development; mental health

UK and overseas (Bangladesh, Ghana, India, Kenya, Malawi, Nepal, Nigeria, Sierra Leone, South Africa, Rwanda, Tanzania, Uganda, Zambia and Zimbabwe)

£65.8 million (2020/21)

CC number: 326568

Correspondent: The Trustees, 1st Floor, 89 Albert Embankment, London SE1 7TP (tel: 020 7820 2000; email: a contact form is available on the charity's website)

Trustees: Saul Klein; Dr Sue Black; Tom Shropshire; Tessy Ojo; Rupert Morley; Charlotte Moar; Matt Hyde; Jenny Hodgson; Jacqueline Onalo; Gautam Raju; Eric Salama; Fiona Campbell.

 www.comicrelief.com

 facebook.com/comicrelief

 @comicrelief

 @comicrelief

General information

Since 1985 Comic Relief has raised around £500 million to tackle poverty and social injustice in the UK, Africa, and more recently in some of the poorest countries in other parts of the world. This entry is primarily concerned with its grant-making in the UK.

Comic Relief's vision is 'A Just World Free from Poverty, where everyone is safe, healthy educated and empowered' which it looks to achieve by 'working in partnership with people and organisations to create solutions to challenges together', as stated on its website.

The charity principally receives its income through the generosity of the public via its Red Nose Day fundraising event. This campaign is now held every year in partnership with the BBC, and the extent of the grant-making depends entirely on the success of this event.

In 2002, Comic Relief started a second initiative, Sport Relief. No longer a bi-annual event, Sport Relief is evolving into a year-round celebration linked with major sport events and partnerships throughout the year. Funds raised help projects in the UK that are using sport to increase social cohesion and inclusion.

Grants Strategy

The grants strategy, which has four key issue areas, connects the charity's work in the UK and internationally. The four key issue areas, which are described in full on the Comic Relief website, are:

- A World Where Children Survive and Thrive
- Improving Mental Health
- Gender Justice
- A Safe Place to Be, for Everyone

Funding Initiatives

Details of current open funding initiatives, including eligibility criteria, important dates and application processes, in the UK and around the world, can be found on the informative Comic Relief website. Examples of funds which were listed on the website at the time of writing (March 2022) included: Tech for Good 2021: Build; Change Makers; and Supporting and Sustaining Specialism.

Financial information

Year end	31/07/2021
Income	£74,080,000
Assets	£90,570,000
Grants to organisations	£65,800,000

Further financial information

In 2020/21, grants awarded in the UK totalled £41.56 million, and grants awarded overseas totalled £24.24 million. Grants awarded in the UK were broken down as follows under the theme of tackling poverty and social justice:

Multi-themed	£23.64 million
Safe places	£5.88 million
Mental health	£5.58 million
Gender justice	£3.74 million
Children Survive and Thrive	£2.72 million

Beneficiaries included: A list of beneficiaries was not available.

Exclusions

The charity's website states:

> Comic Relief does not fund:
> - **Activities which evangelise** (the practice of preaching or spreading religious beliefs) **or proselytise** (the practice of trying to convert people to one's own belief or religious views).
> - Organisations which adopt a **partisan political stance** or activities which are party political. Comic Relief will not support organisations that advocate the use of violence to campaign or influence public opinion.
> - **One-off conferences or workshops**, as it is difficult to demonstrate what impact such events are likely to achieve. We can fund conferences, workshops and other gatherings as part of longer-term projects or work.
> - General appeals, **individual and group sponsorship**, marketing appeals, proposals for bursaries from individuals or proposals from individuals for the funding of study or attainment of qualifications.
> - Work where the **long-term institutional care** of children or young people is a preferred way of working over the longer-term (e.g. setting up or running orphanages). Where short-term, temporary institutional care is used as part of an intervention to support children and young people, applicants will need to demonstrate how the work they propose seeks to develop and implement community-based alternatives.
> - **The delivery of services that are normally government's responsibility.** The only exceptions would be when specific services are simply not in place, and are fundamental to delivering the programme's results as specified in the call for proposals. In this case, low-cost alternatives can be used as an interim measure, along with a realistic plan for ensuring sustainability when the investment ends, for example through community ownership.

Applications

Open funding opportunities are listed on the charity's website as they arise. Applications can be made online via the charity's website, where full guidance is also provided. Potential applicants must register and complete a stage one proposal via the charity's grant management system. Shortlisted applicants will then be invited to submit a stage two proposal.

Sources of information

Accounts; annual report; Charity Commission record; funder's website; guidelines for applicants.

The Comino Foundation

 Educational and personal development activities for young people

UK

£378,200 (2020/21)

CC number: 312875

Correspondent: Sarah Mareschall, Administrator, 137 Thetford Road, Brandon, Suffolk IP27 0DB (tel: 07443 875920; email: john.dakin@cresswells.co.uk)

Trustees: Anna Comino-James; David Perry; Amrit Singh; Mumtaz Bashir-Hanid; Prof. Jose Chambers.

 www.cominofoundation.org.uk

General information

The foundation was established in 1971 by Demetrius Comino, who was an engineer and inventor, and his daughter Anna, who further endowed the foundation several years later. According to its website, the foundation 'looks for better ways of developing young people's capabilities, their capacity and desire to make things happen', focusing on the UK education system and changing attitudes to industry, particularly manufacturing.

The foundation has three current priority areas, which are explained on its website as follows:

> - Social opportunity – which to the Foundation means finding approaches/initiatives which help young people, whatever their background, to live fulfilling and productive lives in whatever ways have meaning and value for them
> - Personal capabilities – developing approaches which enhance young people's personal capacity to cope with the demands of growing up and with adult life
> - Improving practical capability – especially that which relates to designing and making, to innovation and to manufacturing.

It supports 'innovative ventures designed to enable people to function effectively and thrive'.

The website states that it has a number of longer-term commitments and has limited capacity to make further grants, so only considers applications that 'provide evidence showing that the new proposal will have an extremely close fit to existing work'.

The website also states:

> Proposals must, therefore, be clearly related to the Foundation's vision

statement. Preference is given to innovative and enterprising small scale ventures which, once their effectiveness has been demonstrated over a period, will have a chance of changing national policy and practice.

Further information about the foundation's areas of work can be found on its website.

Financial information

Year end	05/05/2021
Income	£388,400
Assets	£3,810,000
Grants to organisations	£378,200

Beneficiaries included: RSA Tipton Academy (£38,300); Knowle West Media Centre (£31,500); 5x5x5 = Creativity (£20,500); Potential Trust (£6,000); Pepperneck (£3,000); Parliament and Scientific Committee (£1,200).

Exclusions

Funding is not given for research or activities outside the UK or to individuals.

Applications

The foundation has a number of long-term commitments; potential applicants should first therefore refer to the foundation's website, where advice is given about what is currently being considered by the trustees. If, having read this advice, you think that your project is suitable, you should apply to the trust's administrator (sarah@cominofoundation.org.uk), following the guidance on the website about what to include.

Sources of information

Accounts; annual report; Charity Commission record; funder's website.

Community First

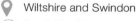

Community, built heritage and environmental projects; community transport; sport and leisure; jobs and business development

Wiltshire and Swindon

£512,800 (2020/21)

CC number: 288117

Correspondent: The Trustees, Unit C2 Brecon Business Centre, Hopton Park, Devizes, Wiltshire SN10 2EY (tel: 01380 722475; email: grants@communityfirst.org.uk)

Trustees: Steve Boocock; Edward Heard; James Moody; Piers Dibben; Jane James; Leah Campbell; Victoria Walsh; Sanjeen Payne-Kumar; Merope Sylvester.

 www.communityfirst.org.uk

 facebook.com/CommunityFirstWiltshire

 @commfirstwilts

General information

Community First was founded in 1965 as the Community Council for Wiltshire and later registered as a charity in 1983. It is part of the Rural Community Action Network (ACRE). The charity has two grant programmes:

The Landfill Communities Fund (LCF) – capital funding for local community, heritage and environmental projects in specific areas where local landfill operators sites or depots are located. Applications can be for any amount, but most range from £2,000 to £15,000. Examples of successful projects include: village halls, play areas, sports and leisure facilities and cycle paths.

Wiltshire Community Transport Development Fund – support for existing community and voluntary transport groups to provide a wider range of services, enable communities to trial new services which assist local people to better access local facilities and support the establishment of wholly new community and voluntary transport groups. The maximum amount for this grant is £1,000. Particular priority will be given to enabling community and voluntary transport to provide services that cater for the general public, especially where they wholly or partially replace subsidised public transport services that are no longer financially sustainable.

Financial information

Year end	31/03/2021
Income	£2,210,000
Assets	£1,780,000
Grants to organisations	£512,800

Beneficiaries included: Westbury Community Project (£52,000); Atworth Village Hall (£33,000); Purton PCC (£27,000); Goatacre Cricket Club (£15,200); Ashton Keynes Village Hall (£10,000).

Exclusions

Grants are not awarded to individuals or private companies. General appeals for non-specific works are not eligible.

Applications

Landfill Communities Fund – in the first instance download and complete the expression of interest form from the website then email it to grants@communityfirst.org.uk. If you have been advised that your project is eligible for LCF funding, then download and complete the application form on the website and submit it with supporting documents as specified in the form.

Wiltshire Community Transport Development Fund – for further information contact the Community Transport team at Community First on 01380 722475 or email: transport@communityfirst.org.uk.

Sources of information

Accounts; annual report; Charity Commission record; funder's website.

Congregational and General Charitable Trust

Protestant churches, in particular those of the United Reformed and Congregational denominations

UK

£523,200 (2019/20)

CC number: 297013

Correspondent: Trish Thorpe, Trust Administrator, PO Box 1111, Lincoln, Lincolnshire LN5 0WJ (email: enquiries@candgtrust.org.uk)

Trustees: Margaret Atkinson; The Revd Pamela Ward; John Holmes; The Revd David Coote; The Revd Margaret Tait; Alastair Forsyth; The Revd Richard Turnbull; Susan Austin; The Revd David Grosch-Miller.

 www.candgtrust.org.uk

General information

The trust was established in 1956 as the charitable arm of the Congregational and General Insurance Company and was reformed in 1987 as a separate entity, but still receives support from the company. In 2016, the trust became completely independent of the company.

The aim of the trust is to make grants for building maintenance and towards the capital costs of community projects to support Protestant churches, in particular those of the United Reformed and Congregational denominations. Each year the trust awards around £500,000 in grants.

Grants

Grants are given for capital projects involving building work, repairs, improvements and extensions. The trust can also make grants to church community projects for capital costs.

Amounts range between £1,000 and £25,000 and are usually given for around 25% of the total project cost; projects with a total cost of over £1 million are not considered.

The website states that the trust will fund professional advice on capital projects for churches planning and executing building projects – from architects or quantity surveyors, for example.

Financial information

Year end	31/01/2020
Income	£472,300
Assets	£16,690,000
Grants to organisations	£523,200
No. of grants	40+

Further financial information

A full list of beneficiaries was unavailable. A small list of beneficiaries (without grant totals) was listed in the accounts.

Beneficiaries included: Christ Church – Erith; Castle Hill URC; St Augustine's – Scisset; St Boniface – Quinton; St Martin's Church; St Peter's – Cleasby; Sykes Methodist Church.

Exclusions

The trust's website and annual accounts state that it will not fund:

- Running costs of the church
- Organ and church bells restoration
- Conservation/restoration of works of art
- Manse works
- Graveyard maintenance
- Solar panels
- Projects costing over £1 million
- Organisations based outside the UK

Applications

Application forms can be downloaded from the trust's website, where upcoming deadlines are also posted along with guidance on what to include in your application.

Sources of information

Accounts; annual report; Charity Commission record; funder's website.

The Connolly Foundation

Community facilities; education; older people

Bedfordshire

£1.95 million (2020/21)

CC number: 1109135

Correspondent: The Trustees, Manor Farm Court, Lower Sundon, Luton, Bedfordshire LU3 3NZ (email: a contact form is available on the foundation's website)

Trustees: Michael Callanan; Andrew Rowe; Shyam Ashoka; Nigel Croft; Vanessa Connolly; Simon White; David Wilkins.

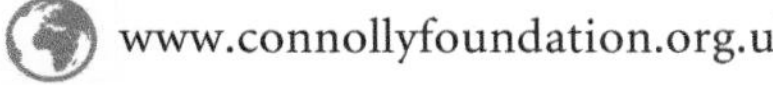

www.connollyfoundation.org.uk

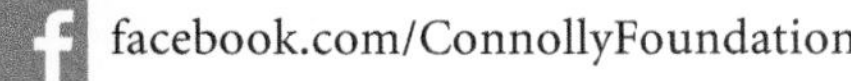

facebook.com/ConnollyFoundation

General information

The foundation receives its funding from its shareholding in Connolly Homes plc which was given to it by Michael Connolly. Grants are made to organisations and individuals in Bedfordshire.

The foundation awards grants in three specific areas:

- Community facilities
- Education
- Support for older people

Financial information

Year end	31/05/2021
Income	£15,020,000
Assets	£88,750,000
Grants to organisations	£1,950,000

Beneficiaries included: Bedford College (£750,000); Keech Hospice (£150,000); Youthscape (£56,500); Alzheimer's Research (£10,000); Harrold Cricket Club (£250).

Applications

Apply in writing to the correspondent.

Sources of information

Accounts; annual report; Charity Commission record; funder's website.

The Ernest Cook Trust

Outdoor learning

UK

£1.79 million (2020/21)

CC number: 1146629

Correspondent: The Trustees, The Estate Office, Fairford Park, Fairford, Gloucestershire GL7 4JH (tel: 01285 712492; email: grants@ernestcooktrust.org.uk)

Trustees: Andrew Christie-Miller; Harry Henderson; Simon Eliot; Sir Bertie Ross; Mary Riall; Jennifer Greenwood.

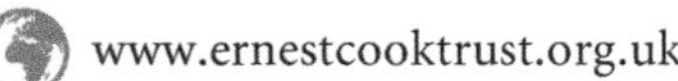

www.ernestcooktrust.org.uk

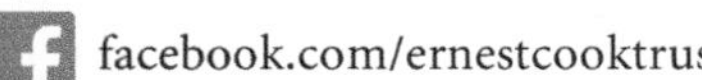

facebook.com/ernestcooktrust

@ernestcooktrust

General information

The trust was founded by the philanthropist Ernest Cook in 1952 to support outdoor learning, conservation and the management of the countryside. The trust makes grants for outdoor learning projects that benefit children and young people. The trust also owns over 9,300 hectares of land and property in Cumbria, Buckinghamshire, Dorset, Gloucestershire, Leicestershire and Oxfordshire

Financial information

Year end	31/03/2021
Income	£5,410,000
Assets	£193,020,000
Grants to organisations	£1,790,000

Beneficiaries included: A list of beneficiaries was not available. Previous beneficiaries include: City of Bradford YMCA and Farms for City Children (£15,000 each); The Smallpeice Trust (£11,000); Earth Trust (£10,000); Future Roots (£8,400); City and Guilds of London Art School and Salisbury Cathedral (£4,000 each).

Applications

See the website for information on the application processes for each funding stream.

Sources of information

Accounts; annual report; Charity Commission record; funder's website.

The Catherine Cookson Charitable Trust

General charitable purposes; education and training; health and medical causes; children and young people; religion; animal welfare; disability; arts and culture

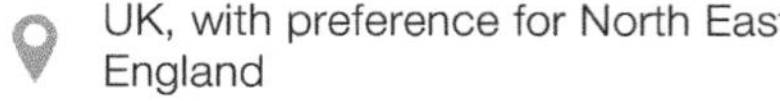

UK, with preference for North East England

£1.03 million (2020/21)

CC number: 272895

Correspondent: The Trustees, c/o Thomas Magnay and Co., 8 St Mary's Green, Whickham, Newcastle upon Tyne, Tyne and Wear NE16 4DN (tel: 0191 488 7459; email: enquiries@thomasmagnay.co.uk)

Trustees: Peter Magnay; David Hawkins; Hugh Marshall; Daniel Sallows.

http://catherinecookson.com/trust

General information

The trust was established in 1977 and endowed by the late Catherine Cookson, a famous author and keen philanthropist.

Areas of work

The trust supports causes that the trustees feel coincide with the wishes expressed by the settlor during her lifetime. The trust's primary areas of interest are:

- Education and training
- Environment and conservation
- Arts and culture

However, the trust's website states that it supports a wide range of general charitable purposes. Recent examples include health, disability, religious activities and animal welfare.

Grant-making policy

Organisations can apply for funding of between £250 and £100,000. Applications are invited from all parts of the UK, and are particularly welcomed from the settlor's native North East England.

Financial information

Year end	05/04/2021
Income	£1,000,000
Assets	£34,430,000
Grants to organisations	£1,030,000
No. of grants	185

Further financial information

Grants were broken down as follows:

Education and training	£222,700
Disability	£200,000
Medical, health and sickness	£171,200
Art and culture	£145,200
Religious activities	£128,100
Other charities	£105,900
Children and young people	£56,300
Animal welfare	£3,900

Beneficiaries included: Newcastle High School for Girls (£120,000); Kidney Research UK (£50,000); The Royal Marsden Cancer Charity (£35,000); Castletown Scout Group (£5,000); Church Army (£1,300); Northumbrian Hedgehog Rescue Trust (£100).

Applications

There is no standard application form but written applications, enclosing an SAE, should be sent to the correspondence address provided. There is no set format or time limit for applications. Charities interested in applying should complete the short online form which is available on the trust's website.

Sources of information

Accounts; annual report; Charity Commission website; funder's website.

The Alice Ellen Cooper Dean Charitable Foundation

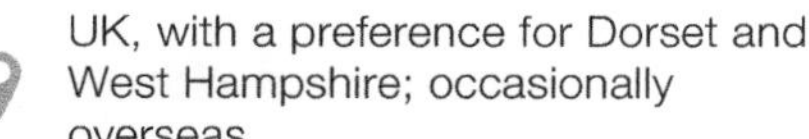

General charitable purposes; education; social welfare; religion

UK, with a preference for Dorset and West Hampshire; occasionally overseas

£731,000 (2020/21)

CC number: 273298

Correspondent: The Trustees, c/o Edwards and Keeping, Unity Chambers, 34 High East Street, Dorchester, Dorset DT1 1HA (tel: 01305 251333; email: cooperdean@edwardsandkeeping.co.uk)

Trustees: Emma Blackburn; John Bowditch; Linda Bowditch; Douglas Neville-Jones; Richard Wedgwood; Richard King.

General information

The foundation was established in 1977 with the following objects:

- The relief of poverty
- The advancement of education and religion
- The advancement of other charitable purposes of benefit to the community

Applications are welcomed for projects and appeals from local and national charities who are UK-registered. Preference is given to applications which will benefit the community of Dorset and West Hampshire.

Grants are also made for overseas appeals, particularly for education, healthcare and social welfare needs following conflict or natural disasters.

Financial information

Year end	31/03/2021
Income	£1,250,000
Assets	£37,740,000
Grants to organisations	£731,000
No. of grants	109

Beneficiaries included: Lantern Trust (£20,000); Action for Children Dorset Nightstop (£15,000); Melplash Agricultural Society (£14,000); Weymouth Skatepark Association (£10,000); Action for Kids (£5,000); Fine Cell Work (£3,000); Silverlinks (£1,000).

Exclusions

Grants are not awarded to individuals or non UK-registered charitable organisations.

Applications

Apply in writing to the correspondent. Applications should include a summary of the project, together with costings, financial accounts and details of fundraising activities. Occasionally, a trustee of the foundation will visit an applicant before awarding a grant.

Sources of information

Accounts; annual report; Charity Commission record.

Co-operative Community Investment Foundation

Disadvantaged communities; youth loneliness; community enterprise

UK

£3.44 million (2020)

CC number: 1093028

Correspondent: Ella Smyth, Funding and Partnerships Manager, 9th floor, 1 Angel Square, Manchester M60 0AG (tel: 0161 692 1877; email: foundation@coop.co.uk)

Trustees: Saleem Chowdhery; Daniel Crowe; Jamie Ward-Smith; Sheila Malley; Sharon Jones; Lois McClure; Michael Fletcher; Hope Levy-Shepherd; Ewansiha Imafidon.

 www.coopfoundation.org.uk

 facebook.com/Co-op-Foundation-156348321640279

 @Coop_Foundation

General information

Established in 2000, the Co-operative Community Investment Foundation is administered by the Co-operative Group and funded by its members who have agreed to donate some of their profit share to the foundation. The foundation's goals are:

- To champion young people's ability to contribute positively to their communities and help to strengthen their sense of belonging
- To invest in disadvantaged communities' capacity to overcome their social, economic or environmental challenges

Visit the foundation's website to see current funding and support available.

Financial information

Year end	31/12/2020
Income	£3,390,000
Assets	£24,490,000
Grants to organisations	£3,440,000

Further financial information

Grants were broken down as follows:

Youth	£2.49 million
Community spaces	£643,000
Equal voices	£153,800
Digital capacity building	£147,900
Volunteering	£5,900

Beneficiaries included: A list of beneficiaries was not available. Previous beneficiaries include: Envision (£132,500); The Children's Society (£69,800); Women's Technology Centre (£50,000); White Rock Neighbourhood Ventures (£40,000); Changing Our Lives (£35,000); Scotswood Garden (£21,200); UK Youth (£20,000).

Applications

Funding rounds for specific programmes open periodically during the year and will be advertised on the foundation's website. Alternatively, subscribe to the foundation's blog for updates.

Sources of information

Accounts, annual report, Charity Commission record, funder's website.

The Gershon Coren Charitable Foundation

General charitable purposes and Jewish causes

UK; Israel

£583,000 (2020/21)

CC number: 257615

Correspondent: Graham Weinberg, c/o Manna UK, Winston House, 303 Dollis Park, London N3 1HF (tel: 020 7429 4100)

Trustees: Anthony Coren; Graham Weinberg.

General information

This foundation, established in 1968, makes grants to registered charities, particularly Jewish organisations, for a wide range of charitable purposes. Grants are typically awarded up to £12,000, although a few larger grants are awarded each year.

Financial information

Year end	05/04/2021
Income	£234,300
Assets	£62,500,000
Grants to organisations	£583,000
No. of grants	38

Beneficiaries included: Jewish National Fund Charitable Trust (£180,000); Manna UK (£30,000); Jewish Futures Trust (£15,000); Campaign Against Antisemitism (£10,000); Institute of Jewish Policy Research (£5,000); Prostate Cancer and RNLI (£3,000 each).

Applications

Apply in writing to the correspondent.

Sources of information

Accounts; annual report; Charity Commission record.

The Evan Cornish Foundation

Human rights; social and economic inequality; education; health; criminal justice system; older people; refugees and asylum seekers; homelessness

UK, with a preference for the north of England; overseas

£1.35 million (2020/21)

CC number: 1112703

Correspondent: Nat Loftus, Charity Administrator, The Innovation Centre, 217 Portobello, Sheffield, South Yorkshire S1 4DP (tel: 0114 224 2230; email: contactus@evancornishfoundation.org.uk)

Trustees: Rachel Cornish; Barbara Ward; Sally Cornish.

 www.evancornishfoundation.org.uk

General information

The Evan Cornish Foundation was established in 2002 by the widow and four daughters of businessman Evan Cornish, with the aim of achieving equality and justice for all by supporting the most marginalised and promoting human rights. The foundation provides grants to charitable organisations in both the UK and overseas.

UK grants

Applications are accepted from charities, not-for-profits and CICs. Projects should benefit people living in the north of England and meet the aims of the foundation.

The foundation has seven main aims, details of which have been taken from its website:

Human Rights:

- fight injustice by combating violations of Human Rights (as defined by the Universal Declaration of Human Rights)
- support the victims of these violations and their dependants
- empower people to protect their own human rights Social and Economic Inequality
- work towards food sovereignty; through improvements to local food production and markets, movement building and/or policy work
- address the root causes of social and economic inequality and advocate for policy change, empowering people and communities
- support sustainable livelihoods
- address gender inequality

Education

- benefit excluded children or those at risk of exclusion
- address the gender gap in access to education
- support enrichment of education to promote human rights and social cohesion and improve young people's self-esteem

Health

- support people with mental health issues, promote better understanding, address inequality and work to eradicate stigma
- support women's health
- improve maternal and newborn health
- work to avoid sight loss, improve vision impairment and support a better quality of life for people with sight issues and blindness

Criminal Justice System

- promote prisoners' wellbeing, ensuring people are treated humanely and with dignity
- inspire prisoners and enrich their lives through creative and innovative programmes
- assist vulnerable people at risk of imprisonment, particularly women and young people
- work with people on their transition from prison, helping them to resettle and become independent from the Criminal Justice System

Elderly People

- support the wellbeing of older people with particular emphasis on maintaining independence and alleviation of isolation
- improve the quality of life of older people through home-based services, social networks and meeting places

Refugees and Asylum Seekers

- advocate on behalf of refugees and asylum seekers
- improve the quality of life for asylum seekers, destitute asylum seekers, refugees and vulnerable migrants
- promote social and community cohesion

Homelessness

- engage and support the vulnerable who are homeless or at risk of becoming homeless
- provide crisis support
- improve people's quality of life, relieving hardship and distress

Organisations from the rest of England and the UK can apply if:

- Your project is unique in the UK
- Your project involves advocacy/policy work
- Your project affects people in the UK prison system

Overseas grants

International applications will be prioritised that promote tolerance and equality for women and combat human rights violations. International applicants must have a registered UK office.

First-time applicants may apply for up to £5,000. Other applicants may apply for £5,000 to £10,000 or more.

Financial information

Year end	05/04/2021
Income	£171,500
Grants to organisations	£1,350,000
No. of grants	199

Beneficiaries included: Lincolnshire Community Foundation (£35,000); Food Hall Project (£25,000); The Reader (£10,000); Albert Kennedy Trust (£8,500); Burnley FC in the Community (£5,000); Chase Africa (£3,000); Behati Foundation (£1,000).

Exclusions

The foundation is unable to support the following activities:

- Building work or repairs
- Political activities and purpose
- Animal welfare
- Academic research
- Medical research
- Individuals/gap year students
- Holiday club providers
- Flight costs
- Religious organisations/religious or evangelical causes
- Organisations who discriminate internally or externally based on faith

The trustees will consider applications from organisations that grew from a religious basis but now have a multi-faith and secular approach.

Applications

Applications must be made through the foundation's website. Applicants should submit the following:

- A copy of your most recent accounts
- A copy of your project budget
- Details of an independent, UK-based referee not affiliated with your organisation
- Supporting information about your project

The trustees meet three times per year. Check the website for application deadlines.

Sources of information

Accounts; annual report; Charity Commission record; funder's website.

The Duke of Cornwall's Benevolent Fund

Social welfare; provision of almshouses, hospitals and hospices; education and training; arts and culture; religion; heritage and historic buildings

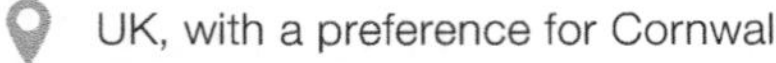

UK, with a preference for Cornwall

£303,200 (2019/20)

CC number: 269183

Correspondent: Terry Cotter, Secretary, Duchy of Cornwall, 10 Buckingham Gate, London SW1E 6LA (tel: 020 7834 7346)

Trustees: Sir James Leigh-Pemberton; Alastair Martin; Catherine Mead; Col. Edward Bolitho.

General information

The Duke of Cornwall's Benevolent Fund was established in 1975. Its main objectives are as follows:

- Social welfare
- Provision of almshouses, hospitals and convalescent homes
- Education
- The arts
- Religion
- Heritage and conservation of lands and buildings

Financial information

Year end	30/06/2020
Income	£124,900
Assets	£6,630,000
Grants to organisations	£303,200

Beneficiaries included: Cornwall Community Foundation (£100,000); Plantlife (£75,000); Cornwall Historic Churches Trust (£35,000); Bosence Farm and Urban Diversity CIC (£5,000 each); Friends of Bude Sea Pool (£1,000).

Applications

Apply in writing to the correspondent.

Sources of information

Accounts; annual report; Charity Commission record.

The Corporation of Trinity House of Deptford Strond

The education, safety, support and welfare of mariners and their dependants

UK

£1.73 million (2020/21)

CC number: 211869

Correspondent: Vikki Muir, Head of Charitable Giving, Trinity House, Tower Hill, London EC3N 4DH (tel: 020 7481 6903; email: victoria.muir@trinityhouse.co.uk)

Trustees: Capt. Roger Barker; Capt. Ian McNaught; Capt. Nigel Hope; Capt. Stephen Gobbi; Rear Admiral David Snelson; Cdre William Walworth; Richard Sadler; Malcolm Glaister; Cdre Robert Fimarest; Cdr Nigel Mrin.

www.trinityhouse.co.uk/supporting-seafarers/maritime-charity

facebook.com/trinityhouseuk

@trinityhouse_uk

General information

The charity was incorporated by Royal Charter in 1514. According to its website, the charity is 'dedicated to safeguarding shipping and seafarers, providing education, support and welfare to the seafaring community with a statutory duty as a General Lighthouse Authority to deliver a reliable, efficient and cost-effective aids to navigation service for the benefit and safety of all mariners'.

Grants are made to charities through a linked charity, The Trinity House Maritime Charity (THMC). The charity's website states:

> The Trinity House Maritime Charity (THMC) is one of the UK's largest-endowed maritime charities, committed to the education, safety, support and welfare of mariners and their dependants. We welcome applications from charities and organisations whose work aligns with our charitable objectives and who can demonstrate support of seafarers in the areas below:
>
> a. Support, maintenance and provision of Alms Houses and Annuities
>
> b. Advancing the education and training of officers, cadets and seamen (inc. grants and bursaries)
>
> c. Advancing the education of the public, including assisting schools and other institutions providing education
>
> d. Advancing public safety and the safety of shipping
>
> e. Relieving the need of mariners and former mariners of all ranks, and their families
>
> f. Publishing and disseminating information in any form relating to navigation, shipping and seamanship.

Financial information

Year end	31/03/2021
Income	£9,000,000
Assets	£271,200,000
Grants to organisations	£1,730,000

Further financial information

In 2020/21 grants were broken down as follows: welfare (£925,000); opportunities and training for young people (£715,100); public safety and education (£90,600). Note that the grant total includes grants to individuals.

Beneficiaries included: The Shipwrecked Mariners' Society (£110,000); Royal Alfred Seafarers Society (£100,000); Sailors' Children's Society (£68,200); London Nautical School (£40,000); Combat Stress (£25,000); Care for Veterans (£10,000).

Applications

Applicants are first asked to contact the correspondent for an informal chat to introduce themselves, their organisation and their proposal. Full information on how to apply for a grant can be found on the charity's website.

Sources of information

Accounts; annual report; Charity Commission record; funder's website.

Corra Foundation

Social welfare; children and young people; homelessness; families affected by substance abuse; international development (in Zambia, Rwanda, Malawi and Pakistan)

Scotland and Africa

£56.09 million (2020)

OSCR number: SC009481

Correspondent: Grants Team, Riverside House, 502 Gorgie Road, Edinburgh EH11 3AF (tel: 0131 444 4020; email: hello@corra.scot)

Trustees: Luke McCullough; Jude Turbyne; Joy Barlow; Elizabeth Carmichael; Claire Gibson; David Johnson; Fiona Sandford; Richard Martin; Christine McLaughlin; Mildred Zimunya; Michaela Collins.

www.corra.scot

facebook.com/CorraFoundation

@corrascot

General information

The foundation was previously known as Lloyds TSB Foundation for Scotland until it rebranded in August 2017. The foundation received its last payment from Lloyds Banking Group in February 2018 and now receives a large proportion of its income from the Scottish government.

What the foundation does

The foundation works to improve the lives of disadvantaged individuals and communities with the following mission: to make a difference to the lives of individuals and communities in Scotland, by encouraging positive change, opportunities, fairness and growth of aspirations, which improve quality of life. According to the foundation's website, the foundation's 2020–30 strategy aims to achieve the following:

Voice and Participation – strengthening people's voices and shifting power to communities. This includes flexible support for communities and participatory approaches within grant programmes.

People in Place – developing relationships with people and organisations in Scottish places and supporting communities to connect with each other to use their voice and power to influence wider systemic change.

Families affected by drugs and alcohol – creating lasting change by delivering partnership work and funding, at the heart of which is a promise to listen to children and young people.

Partnership – sharing expertise with, and working alongside a wide range of people, including communities, charities and other grant-makers to make a difference towards shared goals. The foundation will manage grants on behalf of others, often working closely to make sure the money has a wider impact on policy and practice.

Grant programmes

Henry Duncan grants

The theme for Henry Duncan grants in 2022 is supporting children and young people facing challenges. Charities can apply during 2022 for funding to support projects that address this theme and that last between one and five years. Organisations with an income up to £50,000 can apply for micro grants up to £1,000 through this programme. Unrestricted funding is made available wherever possible.

The theme for 2023 will be increasing opportunities for people with disabilities and long-term conditions, and the 2024 theme will be supporting people experiencing inequality or discrimination.

Partnership Drugs Initiative

Partnership Drugs Initiative (PDI) promotes voluntary sector work with children, young people and families affected by substance misuse. For funding opportunities in this area, see the foundation's website.

Other grant programmes

The foundation has several other grant programmes, including those related to housing/homelessness and children and young people. See its website for updates.

The foundation also administers funds for the Scottish Government's International Development Fund which aims to support and empower its partner countries: Malawi, Rwanda, Zambia and Pakistan.

Financial information

Year end	31/12/2020
Income	£59,600,000
Assets	£30,240,000
Grants to organisations	£56,090,000

Further financial information

Grants were broken down as follows:

Main grant programmes	£39.64 million
Maximising expertise	£16.37 million
Development and Sustainability	£56,000
Place-based programme	£7,000

The grant total includes £34.8 million of COVID-19 emergency funding.

Beneficiaries included: A list of beneficiaries was not available.

Exclusions

Exclusion criteria differs between grant programmes. See the website for further details.

Applications

Ongoing programmes and open funding rounds are advertised on the foundation's website, where applications can be made.

Sources of information

Accounts; annual report; funder's website; OSCR record.

Countypier Ltd

Promotion of the Orthodox Jewish faith and the relief of poverty in the Orthodox Jewish community

UK

£415,300 (2020/21)

CC number: 295399

Correspondent: The Trustees, Greenwood Student House, 29–31 Station Road, London N22 6UX (tel: 020 8881 3080)

Trustees: Ahron Halpern; Esther Halpern; Chana Klein.

General information

Countypier Ltd was registered with the Charity Commission in 1986. According to its Charity Commission record, Countypier Ltd makes grants for the promotion of the Orthodox Jewish faith and the relief of poverty.

Financial information

Year end	31/03/2021
Income	£796,300
Assets	£6,520,000
Grants to organisations	£415,300

Beneficiaries included: Notzar Chesed (£96,500); Friends of Boyan Trust (£92,000); Keren Hatzolas Doros Alei Siach (£48,000); Shir Chesed Beis Yisroel (£43,000); Torah Chesed Refuah Cio (£20,000).

Applications

Apply in writing to the correspondent.

Sources of information

Accounts; annual report; Charity Commission record.

Coutts Charitable Foundation

Women and girls, and projects empowering young people through the performing arts

UK

£784,700 (2020/21)

CC number: 1150784

Correspondent: The Trustees, c/o Coutts & Co., 440 Strand, London WC2R 0QS (tel: 020 7753 1000; email: coutts.foundation@coutts.com)

Trustees: Lord Waldegrave of North Hill; Dr Linda Yueh; Alison Rose-Slade; Peter Flavel; Camilla Stowell; Rachel Harrington; Judith McNeill; Laura Lines; Francesca Barnes.

www.coutts.com/coutts-foundation.html

General information

Established in 2013, this foundation is the corporate charity of Coutts & Co., a private bank and wealth manager. Coutts & Co. is one of the world's oldest banks (founded 1692) and is wholly owned by the Royal Bank of Scotland Group.

The foundation's website states:

> The mission of the Coutts Foundation is to support sustainable approaches to tackle the causes and consequences of poverty, focussing on the communities where Coutts has a presence. This mission builds on the legacy of Angela Burdett-Coutts, the grand-daughter of Thomas Coutts, who was a progressive 19th-century philanthropist concerned with breaking cycles of poverty and providing basic human needs.

According to its website, the foundation's current focus is 'UK organisations or programmes that support women and girls and organisations that empower young people through the performing arts, with a particular focus on addressing the causes and consequences of poverty'. The foundation makes grants to a small number of organisations that reflect its mission.

Financial information

Year end	01/04/2021
Income	£316,300
Assets	£3,400,000
Grants to organisations	£784,700
No. of grants	15

Further financial information

In 2020/21, the foundation awarded 16 grants to 15 organisations, of which 9 were COVID-19 emergency grants.

Beneficiaries included: Contact and Immediate Theatre (£150,000 each); The Magdalene Group (£128,200 in two grants); Clore Social Leadership Programme (£24,000); The Theatre Artists Fund (£20,000); The Nelson Trust (£10,000); Women Resource Centre (£250).

Applications

The foundation does not accept unsolicited applications. However, if you wish to bring your organisation to the foundation's attention there is an information submission form which can be downloaded from the foundation's website and emailed or posted to the correspondent. The trustees will then be in touch if it wishes to learn more about your organisation. Refer to the foundation's helpful website for more details.

Sources of information

Accounts; annual report; Charity Commission record; funder's website.

The Elizabeth Creak Charitable Trust

Agricultural education; life sciences education; research into agriculture, horticulture and food processing

UK, with a preference for Warwickshire

£1.25 million (2020/21)

CC number: 286838

Correspondent: John Hulse, Trustee, 27 Widney Road, Knowle, Solihull, West Midlands B93 9DX (tel: 01564 773951; email: creakcharity@hotmail.com)

Trustees: John Hulse; Johnathan May; Nicholas Abell.

General information

The Elizabeth Creak Charitable Trust was established in 1983 and supports agricultural education in the UK, with a preference for Warwickshire. The trust was established by the late Elizabeth Creak, who passed away in 2013. Elizabeth was well respected among the farming community and was invited on the boards of many charitable organisations including the Royal Agricultural Society, The Stoneleigh Abbey Trust and the Stratford Society. She was also the first female chair of the National Farmers Union in Warwickshire and became the first female High Sheriff of Warwickshire. Elizabeth was also interested in and a keen supporter of local craftsmen, artists and the theatre.

As stated in the 2020/21 annual report:

> The principal aim of the Trust is to provide support and encourage new blood in farming through education and other means and finance projects to help agriculture succeed and ultimately thrive in a challenging modern environment.

The trust provides grants to organisations for agri-food-related courses, training and research. Each year the trust awards approximately £200,000 to UK universities for student scholarships. The trust also funds four university chairs.

Preference is given to organisations that have a proven track record of supporting agricultural causes, although approximately 2% of funds each year are awarded to local, non-agricultural charities.

Financial information

Year end	31/03/2021
Income	£1,120,000
Assets	£32,000,000
Grants to organisations	£1,250,000

Further financial information

During 2020/21, grants were distributed as follows:

Life sciences education	£904,400
Agricultural national support	£408,000
Other local projects	£44,500

Only beneficiaries receiving grants of over £25,000 were listed in the trust's accounts. Grants of less than £25,000 totalled £161,700.

Beneficiaries included: Circular Economy Investment Fund (£715,000); Hartpury College (£250,000); Nuffield Farming Scholarship and Studley College (£30,000 each); Harper Adams, Newcastle University and University of Reading (£25,000 each).

Applications

Apply in writing to the correspondent. The trustees usually meet every two months to consider grant applications.

Sources of information

Accounts; annual report; Charity Commission record.

Creative Scotland

The arts, film and creative industries

Scotland

£139.52 million (2020/21)

Correspondent: Enquiries Service, Waverley Gate, 2–4 Waterloo Place, Edinburgh EH1 3EG (tel: 0345 603 6000 (unavailable at the time of writing in May 2022 due to office closure – email to request a call back); email: enquiries@creativescotland.com)

Trustees: Robert Wilson; Malath Abbas; Ewan Angus; Yahya Barry; David Brew; Duncan Cockburn; Stephanie Fraser; Duncan Hendry; Philip Long; Carol Main; Sarah Munro; Elizabeth Partyka; David Strachan.

 www.creativescotland.com

 facebook.com/CreativeScotland

 @creativescots

General information

Creative Scotland is a public body supporting the arts, screen and creative industries across the whole of Scotland, on behalf of everyone who lives, works or visits there. It redistributes income from two primary sources – the Scottish Government and the UK National Lottery – having taken on the funding responsibilities and investment strands of the Scottish Arts Council in 2010.

Funding streams

The following information on Creative Scotland's funding has been taken from its website:

> **Our Funding Routes**
>
> Creative Scotland's funding is split into three main types of support, consisting of:
>
> - **Open Fund**
>   - **Open Fund: Sustaining Creative Development** for organisations
>   - **Open Fund for Individuals**
> - **Regular Funding** for organisations for at least three years
> - A small number of **targeted funds** which have specific priorities or shared goals with other agencies. Within this will be a number of funds – sometimes called 'devolved funds' – which are delivered by partner organisations on behalf of Creative Scotland.
>
> **Open Fund: Sustaining Creative Development**
>
> The Open Fund: Sustaining Creative Development was launched in March 2020 in the midst of the Coronavirus pandemic to focus support on helping individuals and organisations to sustain themselves.
>
> - Funding available for between £1k and £50k
> - The fund aims to enable individuals and organisations to explore ways of working that will help them to adapt

and respond to the current changing circumstances
- The fund is Open all year round, with no deadlines and can support activity for up to 12 months.

Regular Funding
Regular Funding provides stable support for a range of organisations and consortia across Scotland who make an important contribution to the development of the arts, screen and creative industries, enabling them to plan and deliver activities over a 3-year period.

Financial information

Year end	31/03/2021
Income	£3,460,000
Assets	£29,760,000
Grants to organisations	£139,520,000

Further financial information

Grants awarded in 2020/21 were broken down as follows:

COVID-19 response funds	£66.22 million
Regular funded organisations	£33.21 million
Scottish Government – restricted funds	£16.13 million
Targeted funding	£8.93 million
Open project funding	£4.02 million

Note: the grant total may include grants awarded to individuals.

Beneficiaries included: Youth Music Initiative (£12.15 million); Platform for Creative Excellence (£1.97 million); Royal Edinburgh Military Tattoo (£240,000); Festivals Edinburgh (£197,000); Demarco Archive (£20,000).

Applications

Application forms can be downloaded from Creative Scotland's website. For all information regarding grant applications visit the website.

Sources of information

Accounts; annual report; funder's website.

Credit Suisse EMEA Foundation

The education and training of children and young people

Countries where Credit Suisse has offices – in Europe, the Middle East and Africa

£1.49 million (2020)

CC number: 1122472

Correspondent: Corporate Citizenship Team, Credit Suisse, 1 Cabot Square, London E14 4QJ (tel: 020 7888 8888; email: emea.corporatecitizenship@credit-suisse.com)

Trustees: Colin Hely-Hutchinson; Mark Ellis; Marisa Drew; Marc Pereira-Mendoza; Guy Varney; Sean Alleyne; Ian Hale; Nicola Kane; Karen Newton; Caroline Waddington; Matthew Weston; Katarzyna Jozefowicz; Aneta Kocemba-Muchowicz; Annabel Morris.

www.credit-suisse.com/about-us/en/our-company/corporate-responsibility/economy-society/emea.html

General information

The foundation was established by Credit Suisse AG and channels the group's corporate citizenship activities in Europe, the Middle East and Africa. It supports general charitable purposes in the areas where the company has a presence, but has a preference supporting organisations that improve the educational attainment, employability and aspirations of disadvantaged young people. The foundation has a core grant-making programme and a UK Small Grants programme. It also makes grants to the employee-nominated Credit Suisse Charity of the Year.

UK Small Grants programme
This programme was launched in 2018 to fund early-stage organisations supporting the education and employability of young people. In 2020 the programme was suspended due to the COVID-19 pandemic, but in the previous year the programme supported the following themes:
- Mental health and well-being
- Disability
- Career opportunities, including the use of arts, culture and sports to develop skills, strengthen well-being and provide alternative education and employment paths

The foundation's 2020 annual report states the following about its grant-making:

> The Foundation will support proposals, which meet its priority areas of work. This may be a specific project or ongoing costs including staff salaries and overheads. It also encourages any organisation seeking funding to include a reasonable amount of core costs to cover overheads if applying for project funding. [...] The foundation looks for opportunities to provide multi-year funding over one to five years where possible.

Financial information

Year end	31/12/2020
Income	£1,440,000
Assets	£1,650,000
Grants to organisations	£1,490,000
No. of grants	14

Beneficiaries included: City Year UK (£350,000); St Giles Trust (£220,000); Centre for Citizenship Education (£100,000); Ambition Institute and Learning with Parents (£50,000 each); Children's University Foundation (£40,000); Get Further (£30,000).

Exclusions

According to the foundation's 2020 annual report, it will not support applications:
- that directly replace or subsidise statutory funding;
- that are the primary responsibility of statutory funders such as local and central government and health authorities;
- for administration and costs not directly associated with the application;
- from individuals, or which are for the benefit of one individual;
- for the promotion of religious or political causes;
- for holidays;
- for work that has already taken place;
- for general appeals;
- for animal welfare;
- for festivals, sports and leisure activities.

Exceptions may be made to the above exclusions in relation to Credit Suisse's Charity of the Year and under other exceptional circumstances.

Applications

Contact the correspondent for further information.

Sources of information

Accounts; annual report; Charity Commission record; funder's website.

England and Wales Cricket Trust

Encouragement of healthy recreation by providing facilities for playing cricket and supporting amateur cricket clubs

England and Wales

£18.86 million (2020/21)

CC number: 1112540

Correspondent: The Trustees, Lord's Cricket Ground, London NW8 8QZ (tel: 020 7432 1200; email: kate.hailstone@ecb.co.uk)

Trustees: Scott Smith; James Wood; Ebony Rainford-Brent; Tom Harrison; Ian Lovett.

www.ecb.co.uk/be-involved/club-support/club-funding

General information

Established in 2005, the England and Wales Cricket Trust is the charity of the England and Wales Cricket Board (ECB). The ECB website states:

> The England and Wales Cricket Trust (EWCT) promotes community participation in cricket as a means of promoting and improving health – which is a charitable purpose. The EWCT also promotes work to improve the provision of cricket in schools, clubs, and other youth cricket activities. Activities funded by the EWCT must benefit the community, not just a

small group or elite. This is a primary obligation of an applicant when applying for the funds provided by EWCT.

Interest-Free Loan Scheme

According to the England website, 'The England and Wales Cricket Trust (EWCT) Interest-Free Loan Scheme provides finance to clubs for capital projects to help them build and ensure a sustainable future.' Loans are given in support of projects within the following areas: buildings, equipment, fine turf, land purchase for cricketing purposes and non-turf. A minimum of 10% partnership funding is required from the applicant.

All ECB-affiliated cricket clubs and other organisations that can demonstrate achievement/delivery of the trust's charitable aims can apply. The ECB website further states that 'ECB Clubmark registration or accreditation is not a requirement'.

Detailed information on all current schemes, including guidance notes and application forms can be found on the ECB's website.

Financial information

Year end	31/01/2021
Income	£27,370,000
Assets	£45,900,000
Grants to organisations	£18,860,000

Beneficiaries included: A list of beneficiaries was not available.

Applications

An application form is available on the trust's website.

Sources of information

Accounts; annual report; Charity Commission record; funder's website.

Cripplegate Foundation

General charitable purposes; young people; social isolation; mental health and well-being; advice and access to services; support to families; financial inclusion

London borough of Islington and part of the City of London

£1.77 million (2020)

CC number: 207499

Correspondent: Programme Team, 13 Elliott's Place, Islington, London N1 8HX (tel: 020 7288 6940; email: grants@cripplegate.org.uk)

Trustee: Cripplegate Foundation Ltd.

 www.cripplegate.org

 @CripplegateFdn

General information

The first recorded gift to the Church of St Giles-without-Cripplegate was by the Will of John Sworder dated 2 April 1500. Cripplegate Foundation was established in 1891 by a Charity Commission Scheme which amalgamated all the non-ecclesiastical charitable donations previously administered as separate trusts. The early governors of the foundation built an institute on Golden Lane, containing reading and reference libraries, news and magazine rooms, classrooms, a theatre and even a rifle range. The institute was run until 1973, when it was closed and the foundation became a grant-making charity. In 2008 the foundation's area of benefit was extended to cover the whole of Islington.

Cripplegate Foundation is an independent charity with the vision 'of a society where everyone has the opportunity to live a rewarding and fulfiled life free from poverty and inequality', as stated on the website. By funding voluntary organisations and working in partnership with others, the charity works to bring about change which will positively transform the lives of Islington's most disadvantaged residents. In 2010, Cripplegate Foundation was part of a collaboration which launched Islington Giving, a restricted fund of the foundation that makes grants to local organisations.

The foundation's priorities are:

- Improving the voluntary sector's ability to serve local residents
- Building the resilience of vulnerable residents
- Increasing the resources available in Islington
- Influencing policy and practice that affects Islington

Eligibility

To apply for funding through the foundation's own or partner programmes, organisations must be one of the following:

- A registered charity
- A registered CIC
- A registered CIO
- A charitable company or social enterprise
- A constituted organisation
- An unincorporated organisation with a management committee of at least three people

Grant programmes

There are several grant programmes administered by the foundation:

- **Main grants programme** – provides organisations with substantial, flexible and often long-term support
- **Islington Council's Community Chest** – a fund provided through a partnership between Islington Council and Cripplegate Foundation. Funding of up to £5,000 a year is available for voluntary organisations with a turnover less than £100,000 that work with Islington residents who are experiencing poverty and/or isolation
- **Islington Giving** – awards grants to voluntary organisations providing support and activities to Islington residents
- **Development Partners** – offers five-year core funding to organisations to work in a partnership with the foundation. At the time of writing (January 2022) all the programme spaces were filled; check the foundation's website for updates

The foundation's key programmes typically fund core and project costs, and typically offer multi-year funding between two and three years.

The charity funds individuals through the London Borough of Islington's Resident's Support Scheme. The foundation donates £55,000 a year to the scheme to support emergency one-off payments to people in crisis or to fund furniture and white goods for people on low incomes.

For full details regarding each fund visit the foundation's helpful website.

Financial information

Year end	31/12/2020
Income	£2,320,000
Assets	£44,190,000
Grants to organisations	£1,770,000

Further financial information

Grants were broken down as follows:

Investing in young people	£537,300
Advice and access to services	£464,700
Mental health and well-being	£279,200
Supporting families	£174,600
Financial inclusion and capability	£141,100
Social isolation	£131,600

No grants were made directly to individuals during the year.

Beneficiaries included: Help on Your Doorstep (four grants totalling £351,400); Islington Law Centre (£76,700); Solace Women's Aid (£30,100); Islington Chinese Association (£19,000); Crafts Council (£10,600); Memory Gardens (£5,000); Talk for Health (£3,000); Hillside Clubhouse (£1,100); Rough Sleeping Local Authority Team (£890).

Exclusions

The following list of exclusions is taken from the foundation's website:

- Political parties
- Political lobbying
- Churches or other religious bodies where the monies will be used for religious purposes/ promotion of religion
- Work which does not benefit Islington residents
- Individuals (except through our identified Partners)
- Medical or academic research
- Expenses that have already been incurred, projects that have already taken place

- Residential care services or residential facilities
- General appeals
- Trips/outings (unless part of a bigger project)
- Debts

Applications

Applications for each programme can be made through the foundation's website. Details of the application process, eligibility guidelines, deadlines and FAQs for each programme can also be found here.

Sources of information

Accounts; annual report; Charity Commission record; funder's website.

Crisis UK

Homelessness

England; Scotland; Wales

£3.62 million (2019/20)

CC number: 1082947

Correspondent: The Trustees, 66 Commercial Street, London E1 6LT (tel: 0300 636 1967; email: enquiries@crisis.org.uk)

Trustees: Terrie Alafat; Martin Cheeseman; Ann McIvor; Julia Goldsworthy; Damien Regent; Geetha Rabindrakumar; Robert Weston; Tamsin Stirling; Victoria Fox; Alison Wallace; Rob Perrins; Tristia Harrison.

 www.crisis.org.uk

 facebook.com/crisis.homeless

 @crisis_uk

 @crisis_uk

General information

Crisis UK is the national charity for people experiencing homelessness. The charity's website provides the following summary of its activities:

> We provide vital help so that people can rebuild their lives and are supported out of homelessness for good. We offer one to one support, advice and courses for homeless people in 12 areas across England, Scotland and Wales. How we help someone depends on their individual needs and situation. It could be with finding a home and settling in, getting new skills and finding a job, or help with their health and wellbeing. We use research to find out how best to improve our services, but also to find wider solutions to homelessness. Together with homeless people and Crisis supporters, we campaign for the changes needed to end homelessness for good.

The following information about the charity's recent grant programmes is taken from its 2019/20 annual report:

Crisis Changing Lives: 'is a grants programme providing financial awards to people who are or have been homeless so that they may achieve their vocational goals, fulfil their potential and become independent. Grant applications can be made by individuals who are supported by a coach working at a Crisis Skylight centre to access training, buy tools for work or set up a business where a robust business plan is presented.'

Tackling homelessness for women survivors of modern day slavery: 'is a project funded by the Department for Digital Culture, Media and Sport through the Tampon tax fund. The project aims include enabling homelessness charities to identify, protect and support female victims of modern day slavery as well as developing the national understanding of homelessness and modern day slavery affecting women through development of a national database. Grants were made to two organisations with an average grant of £196,810'.

European Union settlement scheme: 'Crisis is leading a pan-London partnership project funded by the Home Office to deliver a coordinated approach supporting vulnerable and at-risk EU citizens to make EU Settlement Scheme applications. The partnership is formed of expert organisations working with EU citizens across the homelessness and migration sectors in 12 London boroughs. Grants were paid to eight organisations with an average grant of £60,631.'

In This Together: 'As a direct response to the Coronavirus pandemic, Crisis launched the 'In this together' grants programme to support local homelessness organisations across the United Kingdom to respond to the emergency [...] Grant awards were made to 216 organisations with an average grant award of £8,552.'

Tackling multiple disadvantage: was 'a project partnership targeting some of the most socially and economically excluded people in east, north and west London giving them skills, confidence and motivation to engage with the labour market and make an active contribution to the economy and society as a whole.' The programme was completed in March 2020.

Innovation grants programme: funding for new initiatives that address homelessness, particularly those that are focused on hard-to-reach and vulnerable groups. Themes include homelessness prevention, rapid rehousing, welfare and employability as well as migrant homelessness.

The charity advertises open funding programmes on its website, so check the site for up-to-date information. The charity's website states: 'We are keen to develop relationships with charitable and corporate trusts and foundations that are committed to fighting homelessness and social exclusion. If you are interested in partnering with us, have any questions about anything on this page, or want to visit one of our Skylight Centres, contact us via trusts@crisis.org.uk or 020 7036 2841.'

Financial information

Year end	30/06/2020
Income	£63,420,000
Assets	£36,120,000
Grants to organisations	£3,620,000

Further financial information

Grants awarded to organisations in 2019/20 were distributed through the following programmes:

In This Together	£1.85 million
Innovation grants programme	£736,000
European Union settlement scheme	£485,000
Tackling homelessness for women survivors of modern day slavery	£394,000
Other	£97,000
Tackling multiple disadvantage programme	£64,000

A sample of beneficiaries was taken from the charity's website.

Beneficiaries included: Ashley Community Housing; Birmingham and Solihull Women's Aid; Churches Housing Action Team; Emmaus Bristol; Justlife; Only a Pavement Away; Spitalfields Crypt Trust; YMCA Dulverton Group.

Exclusions

Grant programmes may have specific exclusion criteria – check the charity's website for details.

Applications

Refer to the charity's website for application forms and deadlines for any current grants schemes.

Sources of information

Accounts; annual report; Charity Commission record; funder's website.

The Cross Trust

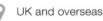

 The advancement of religion; religious education; social welfare

UK and overseas

£1.08 million (2020/21)

CC number: 1127046

Correspondent: The Trustees, Cansdales, Bourbon Court, Nightingales Corner, Amersham, Buckinghamshire HP7 9QS (tel: 01494 765428; email: mailto@cansdales.co.uk)

Trustees: David Lilley; Jenny Farmer; Douglas Olsen; Michael Farmer.

General information

The objects of the trust are to make grants for religious or secular education, social welfare and to advance the Christian faith in the UK or overseas.

Financial information

Year end	05/04/2021
Income	£81,900
Assets	£2,270,000
Grants to organisations	£1,080,000

Beneficiaries included: Luckley House (£639,500); London City Mission (£100,000); George Whitefield College – Africa (£50,000); Christian Youth Enterprises Sailing Centre (£5,000).

Applications

Apply in writing to the correspondent.

Sources of information

Accounts; annual report; Charity Commission record.

The Peter Cruddas Foundation

Disadvantaged and disengaged young people aged 16 to 30

England and Wales

£313,300 (2020/21)

CC number: 1117323

Correspondent: Stephen Cox, Company Secretary and Foundation Administrator, 133 Houndsditch, London EC3A 7BX (email: s.cox@petercruddasfoundation.org.uk)

Trustees: Lord Peter Cruddas; Martin Paisner; The Rt Hon. Lord Young of Graffham.

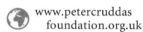

www.petercruddasfoundation.org.uk

General information

Established in December 2006, this is the charitable foundation of Peter Cruddas, founder of the UK-based financial trading group CMC Markets plc, who has pledged to donate at least £100 million to good causes during his lifetime.

The foundation's website provides the following information about its funding:

> The foundation supports programmes designed to help disadvantaged and disengaged young people in the age range of 16 to 30, to pursue pathways to Education, Training and Employment with the ultimate aim of helping them to become financially independent.
>
> Preference will be given to the support of projects undertaken by charitable organisations registered with The Charity Commission of England and Wales benefitting young people in England and Wales only.

The foundation's priority funding streams are listed on its website as:

- Pathways/support for young disadvantaged or disengaged young people in the age range 16 to 30 into education, training or employment
- Work experience/skills projects for young people aged 16 to 30
- Youth work in London; particularly evening work for disadvantaged young people aged 16 to 30

Financial information

Year end	31/03/2021
Income	£437,500
Assets	£161,500
Grants to organisations	£313,300

Beneficiaries included: The Scout Association (£100,000); Great Ormond Street Hospital Charity (£35,000); The Amber Trust (£10,000); Yes Futures (£5,000); Tall Ship Youth Trust (£3,000); The Childhood Trust (£2,000).

Applications

The foundation operates an invitation-only application scheme. At the time of writing (January, 2022) the foundation's website stated:

> At a recent Trustee meeting, concern was raised over the time it takes a charity to apply to The Foundation and subsequently receive a decision on their application. With this in mind and wishing to avoid any lengthy period between application submission and receiving an outcome, it has been decided that from 1st September 2021, The Foundation will go to an 'Invitation Only' application scheme.
>
> The current backlog of applications received prior to this date will be processed and then The Foundation will review past applications as a resource to reach out to those charities working in our area of interest. This will be the case for the foreseeable future.
>
> We know this will be a disappointment to charities only recently finding The Peter Cruddas Foundation but we hope you will understand this as a necessary step to take following an unprecedented time caused by COVID-19. Please do revisit the website for future updates.

Sources of information

Accounts; annual report; Charity Commission record; funder's website; guidelines for applicants.

Cruden Foundation Ltd

Social welfare; medical support and research; arts; education; conservation

Scotland

£305,300 (2020/21)

OSCR number: SC004987

Correspondent: The Trustees, 16 Walker Street, Edinburgh EH3 7LP

Trustees: John Rafferty; Kevin Reid; Alison Paul; Dr Angus Campbell.

https://crudenfoundation.org

General information

Cruden Foundation Ltd is the corporate charity of Cruden Ltd, one of the largest independent development and construction groups in Scotland.

The object of the foundation is to support and contribute to institutions for the benefit of the community. According to the Cruden Ltd website, the foundation makes donations to small and medium-sized charities in Scotland, with a focus on community welfare, medical support and research, the arts, education and conservation.

The foundation's website states:

> The Trust is keen to support charities involved in one, or more, of the following areas:
>
> - Activities relating to community healthcare services including home care, aftercare, sufferers of long-term medical conditions and the continuing care of disabled people.
> - Health education and prevention – promoting knowledge and awareness of specific diseases or medical conditions.
> - Research in preventative or curative medicine.
> - Lifelong learning projects helping people of any age to achieve their educational potential through supplementary schools, literacy and numeracy projects, community education, vocational/restart education for the unemployed, and alternative education for excluded school pupils.
> - Community development by helping groups to organise and respond to problems and needs in their communities.
> - Social services including organisations assisting individuals or families to overcome social deprivation e.g. people who are homeless or disabled and their carers, single parent and childcare groups and other family support groups.
> - Social preventive schemes covering activities which prevent crime, 'dropping out' and general delinquency, provide social care outreach services, deliver social health and safety awareness schemes.
> - Community social activities which promote social engagement for vulnerable people, mitigating against isolation and loneliness.
> - Artistic activities that are supportive of cultural enhancement in the community.
> - Advancing public participation in a sport that involves physical skill and physical exertion.

Financial information

Year end	31/07/2021
Income	£265,700
Assets	£14,100,000
Grants to organisations	£305,300

Further financial information

Grants were distributed as follows:

Social welfare	£108,500
Arts	£96,300
Medical	£64,500
Education	£26,500
Heritage conservation	£6,500

Beneficiaries included: Edinburgh International Festival (£25,000); Pitlochry Festival Theatre (£20,000); Marie Curie Cancer Care (£13,000); Lintel Trust and Sepsis Research (£2,500 each).

Applications

Applications can be made via the foundation's website.

Sources of information

Accounts; annual report; corporate website; OSCR record.

CSIS Charity Fund

UK organisations that are wholly or partly devoted to assisting civil and public servants and their families with social welfare or health needs

UK

£736,000 (2020)

CC number: 1121671

Correspondent: Kevin Holliday, Secretary, 1st Floor, Gail House, Lower Stone, Kent ME15 6NB (tel: 07843 342889; email: secretary@csischarityfund.org)

Trustees: Charles Cochrane; Rebecca Gooch; Sally Bundock; Tunde Ojetola; Ray Flanigan; Angelos Pampos; Sun-Hee Park; Ian Albert; Gaby Glasener-Cipollone; Deborah Terry; Michael Duggan; Colin Birch; Mary Jeffrey.

www.csischarityfund.org

General information

The CSIS Charity Fund was originally a benevolent fund established over 100 years ago by the name of the Civil Service Widows and Orphan's Fund. Its aim was to provide grants to support the dependants of deceased policy holders of the Civil Insurance Society (CSIS), a not-for-profit insurance intermediary that provides insurance products to civil and public servants.

Grants

The main focus of the charity is supporting the main public service charities with annual grants. However, the charity will consider requests to support projects where there is a clear and direct impact on serving or former or retired civil and public servants in need, such as funding helplines or developing services.

Beneficiaries

The charity's website states:

> CSIS Charity Fund is a small, highly focused organisation with the welfare of serving, retired and former civil and public servants at its heart. Our charitable Objects, and our whole purpose, is the relief of need, hardship and distress amongst our client group.
>
> We are able to interpret the term "civil or public servant" in our Objects quite widely. Those who may benefit from our help include:
>
> - Employees of government departments
> - Government agencies and non-departmental public bodies
> - The armed forces
> - All employees working in the NHS and care services
> - NHS Retirement Fellowship members
> - Teachers and teaching assistants
> - The police, fire and other emergency services
> - Local government employees
> - Employees of privatised bodies that were formerly part of the civil service such as BT, the Post Office and the railways, whose pensioners were civil servants when they were working

Financial information

Year end	31/12/2020
Income	£311,800
Assets	£1,520,000
Grants to organisations	£736,000

Beneficiaries included: The Charity for Civil Servants (£200,000); BT Benevolent Fund (£60,000); Railway Benefit Fund (£30,000); Fire Fighters Charity (£10,000); Carers Network (£5,000).

Applications

Application forms can be requested from the correspondent.

Sources of information

Accounts; annual report; Charity Commission record; guidelines for applicants; funder's website.

Cullum Family Trust

General charitable purposes and specialist education targeted at children in Surrey who are on the autism spectrum

Surrey and Sussex

£1.2 million (2020/21)

CC number: 1117056

Correspondent: Peter Cullum, Chair, Wealden Hall, Parkfield, Sevenoaks, Kent TN15 0HX (tel: 01622 809471)

Trustees: Ann Cullum; Claire Cullum; Peter Cullum; Simon Cullum.

General information

The trust was established in 2006 by the entrepreneur Peter Cullum. According to the 2020/21 annual report, grant-making is carried out in partnership with:

- The National Autistic Society 'to provide specialist education targeted at children who are on the autism spectrum, but who typically have good cognitive ability'
- The Sussex Community Foundation to support charity and community groups across East and West Sussex and Brighton and Hove that work with children and young people, community support and development, homelessness, hospices, animals, and older people
- Cass Business School, which 'helps develop the skills and connections needed to make great business ideas succeed'

Financial information

Year end	05/04/2021
Income	£787,400
Assets	£35,200,000
Grants to organisations	£1,200,000

Beneficiaries included: The National Autistic Society (£815,100); Five Acre Wood School (£331,400); The Sussex Community Foundation (£50,000).

Applications

Apply in writing to the correspondent.

Sources of information

Accounts; annual report; Charity Commission record.

Itzchok Meyer Cymerman Trust Ltd

The advancement of the Orthodox Jewish faith; education; social welfare; the relief of sickness; general charitable purposes

UK and Israel

£559,700 (2020/21)

CC number: 265090

Correspondent: Mrs H. F. Bondi, Trustee and Secretary, 497 Holloway Road, London N7 6LE (tel: 020 7272 2255)

Trustees: Mrs H. F. Bondi; Sara Heitner; Leonard Bondi; Ian Heitner; Bernard Hoffman; Michael Cymerman; Sylvia Cymerman.

General information

The trust was established in 1972 and its objectives are the advancement of religion and education in accordance with the Orthodox Jewish faith, the relief of people who are sick and in need, and general charitable purposes. Almost all of the trust's grants are awarded to Jewish charitable organisations.

Financial information

Year end	31/03/2021
Income	£1,550,000
Assets	£18,990,000
Grants to organisations	£559,700

Further financial information

Grants were broken down as follows in 2020/21:

Education	£272,400
Relief of poverty	£144,300
Advancement of religion	£119,500
General charitable purposes	£14,800
Medical causes	£8,800

Only beneficiaries of grants of £30,000 and above were listed in the accounts. Grants of under £30,000 totalled £189,700.

Beneficiaries included: Russian Immigrant Aid Fund Ltd (£110,000); M. D. and S. Charitable Trust (£85,000); Ichud Mosdos Gur Ltd (£75,000); CMZ Ltd and Dencommon Ltd (£35,000 each); Gur Foundation (£30,000).

Applications

The trustees tend to select organisations based on their personal knowledge of the organisation's work. Although applications are not actively invited, the trust's 2020/21 annual report states that the trustees 'are always prepared to accept any application which will be carefully considered and help given according to circumstances and funds then available'.

Sources of information

Accounts; annual report; Charity Commission record.

The D'Oyly Carte Charitable Trust

The arts; medical and social welfare; the environment

UK

£1.78 million (2020/21)

CC number: 1112457

Correspondent: Grants Administrator, 6 Trull Farm Buildings, Tetbury, Gloucestershire GL8 8SQ (tel: 020 3637 3003; email: info@doylycartecharitabletrust.org)

Trustees: Henry Freeland; Andrew Jackson; Dr Michael O'Brien; Julia Sibley; Andrew Wimble; Amelia Beringer; Nina Camilleri.

www.doylycartecharitabletrust.org

General information

The trust was founded in 1972 by Dame Bridget D'Oyly Carte, granddaughter of the founder of both the Savoy Theatre and the Savoy Hotel. The trust supports the arts, medical welfare and the environment. Certain charities in which the founder took a special interest continue to be supported on a regular basis.

The D'Oyly Carte Charitable Trust is entirely separate from the aims and objectives of The D'Oyly Carte Opera Trust Ltd (Charity Commission no. 200024).

Grant programmes

The trust has three main funding priorities for 2021–23, details of which have been taken from the trust's Guidelines for Applicants:

The arts

- Promotion of access, education, excellence, and diversity in the arts with emphasis on choral singing for children and young people to encourage recruitment into choirs
- Performance development opportunities in the performing arts for those in the early stages of their careers, encouraging involvement in the community through performances and workshops for the benefit of those with special needs and those who would otherwise have no opportunity to hear or participate in a live performance
- Support for charities seeking to engage with, and inspire, young people on the fringes of society through music and drama projects to improve their employability and diminish the risk of social exclusion

Medical welfare

- Provision of music and art therapy to improve quality of life
- Support for charities concerned with alleviating the suffering of adults and children with medical conditions who have difficulty finding support through traditional sources
- The welfare of those who care for others through the provision of breaks for carers and projects and schemes that allow young carers to enjoy being children

The environment

- Conservation of the countryside and its woodlands, with emphasis on the encouragement of voluntary work and active involvement in hands-on activities, particularly activities that bring about positive changes in the lives of young people and help them to experience the value of nature
- Rural crafts and skills in heritage conservation, with emphasis on increasingly rare skills that would otherwise be lost
- Social and therapeutic horticulture: projects that use gardening or other environmental activities to bring about positive changes in the lives of those who are living with disabilities or ill-health

Grants typically range from £500 to £6,000 and the majority of grants are one-off. The trustees will consider applications for core costs or projects.

Eligibility

Applicants must be UK-registered charities (or exempt charities) operating in the UK for the benefit of UK residents and their annual returns must be up-to-date.

Financial information

Year end	31/03/2021
Income	£1,300,000
Assets	£63,470,000
Grants to organisations	£1,780,000
No. of grants	510

Further financial information

The annual report gave the following breakdown of grants paid: the arts (217 grants totalling £770,100); medical and social welfare (224 grants totalling £762,700); the environment (69 grants totalling £250,100).

Beneficiaries included: Hospice UK (£15,000); British Youth Opera and Canine Partners for Independence (£5,000 each); Carer Support Wiltshire (£4,000); City of Birmingham Symphony Orchestra (£3,500); Historic Chapels Trust (£2,500); Imagine The Day (£1,500); Rowans Hospice (£1,000); Oxford Conservation Volunteers (£300).

Exclusions

The guidelines state that the trust is unlikely to support the following:

- Advocacy
- Animal welfare
- Campaigning or lobbying
- Capital projects (unless a specific element falls within the trust's remit)
- Community transport organisations or services
- Conferences and seminars
- Counselling and psychotherapy services
- Drug abuse or alcoholism rehabilitation
- Educational projects linked to the National Curriculum
- Endowments
- Exhibitions
- Expeditions and overseas travel
- Feasibility
- Festivals (other than those dedicated to the arts)
- General and round-robin appeals
- Grant-making organisations
- Individuals
- Large national charities
- Medical research
- NHS hospitals for operational services
- Nurseries and playgroups
- Organisations that are not registered charities (or accepted as exempt charities)
- Projects taking place or benefitting people outside the UK
- Recordings and commissioning of new works
- Religious causes and activities
- Routine maintenance of religious or historic buildings
- Sport
- Statutory services including state schools (other than those for pupils with disabilities)
- Umbrella organisations

- Universities, colleges and schools (other than those dedicated to the arts)

The trustees do not consider requests from charities that have had an application turned down until two years after the date of rejection.

Applications

Apply online via the trust's website. The trust's website lists the relevant submission dates and has detailed guidelines on how to apply. The trustees usually consider applications three times a year in March, July and November.

Sources of information

Accounts; annual report; Charity Commission record; funder's website; further information provided by the funder.

The Daiwa Anglo-Japanese Foundation

British–Japanese relations

UK and Japan

£210,500 (2020/21)

CC number: 299955

Correspondent: The Trustees, Daiwa Foundation Japan House, 13/14 Cornwall Terrace (Outer Circle), London NW1 4QP (tel: 020 7486 4348; email: grants@dajf.org.uk)

Trustees: Takashi Hibino; Stephen Barber; Prof. Richard Bowring; Paul Dimond; Yoko Dochi; Sir Tim Hitchens; Jessie Turnbull; Yusuke Kawamura; Prof. Sachiko Kusukawa; Masaki Orita; Prof. Hirotaka Takeuchi.

 www.dajf.org.uk

 facebook.com/DaiwaFoundation

 @DaiwaFoundation

 @daiwafoundation

General information

The Daiwa Anglo-Japanese Foundation was established in 1988 with a benefaction from Daiwa Securities Co. Ltd. The foundation's purpose is to support closer links between Britain and Japan. It does this by:

- Making grants available to individuals, institutions, and organisations to promote links between the UK and Japan in all fields of activity
- Enabling British and Japanese students and academics to further their education through exchanges and other bilateral initiatives
- Awarding of Daiwa Scholarships for British graduates to study and undertake work placements in Japan
- Organising a year-round programme of events to increase understanding of Japan in the UK

Daiwa Foundation Japan House, the London-based headquarters, acts as the centre in Britain by offering a wide programme of lectures, seminars, book launches, courses and exhibitions, as well as meeting rooms for Japan-related activities and facilities for visiting academics.

The foundation is represented in Japan by its Tokyo office, which provides local assistance to Daiwa scholars and administers grant applications from Japan. It also handles general enquiries and forms part of the network of organisations supporting links between the UK and Japan.

The foundation awards grants to individuals and organisations in the UK and Japan in all areas of the visual and performing arts, the humanities, the social sciences, science and engineering, mathematics and business studies. Educational insitutions, grassroots and professional groups are also supported.

The foundation's website provides a useful summary of its grant-making programmes:

> **Daiwa Foundation Small Grants**
> Grants of £2,000-£7,000 are available to individuals, societies, associations or other bodies in the UK or Japan to promote and support interaction between the two countries. Daiwa Foundation Small Grants can cover all fields of activity, including educational and grassroots exchanges, research travel, the organisation of conferences, exhibitions, and other projects and events that fulfil this broad objective. New initiatives are especially encouraged.
>
> **Daiwa Foundation Awards**
> Awards of £7,000-£15,000 are available for collaborative projects that enable British and Japanese partners to work together, preferably in the context of an institutional relationship. Daiwa Foundation Awards can cover projects in most academic, professional, arts, cultural and educational fields. (Applications in the field of science can also be considered.)
>
> **Daiwa Adrian Prizes**
> The Daiwa Adrian Prizes have been discontinued.
>
> **Daiwa Foundation Art Prize**
> The Daiwa Foundation Art Prize has been discontinued.

Financial information

Year end	31/03/2021
Income	£215,600
Assets	£45,120,000
Grants to organisations	£210,500

Further financial information

The foundation awarded grants totalling £210,500 during the year; however, in previous years it has given over £300,000.

Beneficiaries included: Loughborough University (£10,000); University of Leeds (£7,000); University of Glasgow (£4,000); Southbank Centre, Mugen Taiko Dojo and Global Street Art (£3,000 each); King's College London (£2,500); Manchester Metropolitan University, Royal Scottish National Orchestra and University of Birmingham (£2,000 each).

Exclusions

See the foundation's website for detailed exclusions for each grants programme.

Applications

Application forms are available to download from the foundation's website where you can also find details of deadlines, further guidance, and eligibility criteria. For Daiwa Foundation Small Grants and Daiwa Foundation Awards, there are two application deadlines each year, 31 March (for a decision by 31 May) and 30 September (for a decision by 30 November). However, the foundation encourages applicants to submit their applications as early as possible.

Applications for the Daiwa Foundation Small Grants should be sent to the Daiwa Foundation Tokyo Office, and applications for the Daiwa Foundation Awards and the Daiwa Adrian Prizes should be sent to the Daiwa Foundation Japan House in London.

According to the foundation website:

> UK-based applicants can apply using the online application facility. Applications to the Tokyo Office must be sent by post or delivered by hand.

Sources of information

Accounts; annual report; Charity Commission record; funder's website; guidelines for applicants.

Baron Davenport's Charity

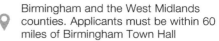

Almshouses; hospices; residential homes for older people; children and young people; older people

Birmingham and the West Midlands counties. Applicants must be within 60 miles of Birmingham Town Hall

£617,100 (2020)

CC number: 217307

Correspondent: Kate Slater, Charity Administrator, Portman House, 5–7 Temple Row West, Birmingham, West Midlands B2 5NY (tel: 0121 236 8004; email: enquiries@barondavenportscharity.org)

Trustees: William Colacicchi; Sue Ayres; Lisa Bryan; Peter Horton; Alec Jones;

Victoria Milligan; Lynn Clark Redwood; Victoria Smith; Mohammed Sajid.

 www.barondavenports charity.org

General information

The charity was established in 1930 by Mr Baron John Davenport who was the chair of Davenport's Brewery. The charity supports organisations in the Birmingham and West Midland counties within 60 miles of Birmingham Town Hall. The charity awards grants in four categories, details of which have been taken from the charity's website:

- **Homes and hospices** – The Charity gives grants to residential homes for older people, almshouses and hospices (for children and adults).
- **Children's Organisations** – The Charity gives grants to organisations established for the benefit of children and young people under the age of 25.
- **Older People's Organisations** – The Charity gives grants to organisations supporting older people in their retirement.
- **Various Grants to Individuals** – Twice yearly grants to single ladies in their retirement and living alone. Emergency grants to single ladies and fatherless children.

Financial information

Year end	31/12/2020
Income	£877,600
Assets	£36,180,000
Grants to organisations	£617,100

Further financial information

Only grants of over £10,000 are included in the beneficiaries list.

Beneficiaries included: Acorn Children's Hospice Trust (£22,000); John Taylor Hospice (£20,000); Compton Care, Donna Louise Trust and Severn Hospice (£10,000 each).

Exclusions

According to its website, the charity will not fund the following:

- Statutory services including state schools and academies (unless these are specifically for pupils with disabilities), local authorities, prisons, NHS hospitals or services.
- Universities and further education colleges.
- Nurseries and pre-schools.
- Parent teacher associations.
- Uniformed groups participating in international camps or jamborees.
- Start up organisations that have not yet produced their first year's audited accounts.
- Retrospective expenditure.
- Capital appeals for places of worship unless these are primarily for community use, such as an adjoining church hall or clearly defined community area within a place of worship.
- Medical research.

Applications

Applications can be made through the charity's website.

Sources of information

Accounts; annual report; Charity Commission record; funder's website; further information provided by the funder.

The Manny and Brigitta Davidson Charitable Foundation

 Purchasing, holding, maintaining and exhibiting works of art; capital and infrastructure projects; social welfare

UK and Israel

£1.11 million (2020/21)

CC number: 1175058

Correspondent: The Trustees, OGR Stock Denton LLP, 2nd Floor, Winston House, 2 Dollis Park, London N3 1HF (tel: 020 8349 5500)

Trustees: Emanuel Davidson; Brigitta Davidson; Gerard Cohen; Richard Denton; Jeremy Sandelson; Ilan Rappaport; Lord Jonathan Kestenbaum.

General information

The foundation was registered with the Charity Commission in 2017 and, according to its 2020/21 annual accounts, has the following objectives:

1. the advancement of education, the arts, culture and heritage primarily but not exclusively by: (i) providing support for capital and infrastructure projects in the United Kingdom and Israel; and (ii) purchasing, holding, maintaining and exhibiting works of art; and
2. the relief of those in need by reason of youth, old age, ill-health, disability or financial hardship by the provision of support for organisations in the United Kingdom and Israel

Financial information

Year end	31/03/2021
Income	£933,000
Assets	£126,800
Grants to organisations	£1,110,000

Beneficiaries included: Emunah (£300,000); Noah's Ark (£200,000); Bowel and Cancer Research (£100,000); The London Academy of Music and Dramatic Art (£60,000); The Noam Primary School Ltd (£50,000); University of Oxford (£25,000); Dennington Synagogue (£13,000).

Applications

Apply in writing to the correspondent.

Sources of information

Accounts; annual report; Charity Commission record.

The Davidson Family Charitable Trust

 Jewish causes and general charitable purposes

UK and Israel

£438,700 (2020/21)

CC number: 262937

Correspondent: The Trustees, 58 Queen Anne Street, London W1G 8HW (tel: 020 7224 1030)

Trustees: Gerald Davidson; Maxine Davidson.

General information

Established in 1971, this is the trust of Gerald Davidson, director of Queen Anne Street Capital and Wolfe Properties, and his family. The trust makes grants for a wide range of purposes and, in the main, supports Jewish organisations. The 2020/21 annual report states that the trust 'continues to make donations towards larger capital projects'.

Financial information

Year end	05/04/2021
Income	£675,100
Assets	£417,000
Grants to organisations	£438,700

Beneficiaries included: The Jerusalem Foundation (£308,200); Community Security Trust (£42,000); City Pregnancy Counselling and Psychotherapy (£20,000); Israel Philharmonic Orchestra Foundation UK (£10,000); Bodleian Libraries – University of Oxford (£5,000); The Chicken Soup Shelter (£1,000); Sinai Jewish Primary School (£500).

Applications

Apply in writing to the correspondent.

Sources of information

Accounts; annual report; Charity Commission record.

Margaret Davies Charity

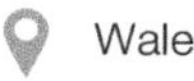 Visual and performing arts; education; young people; health; social welfare; general charitable purposes

Wales

£244,400 (2020/21)

CC number: 235589

Correspondent: The Trustees, Plas Dolerw, Milford Road, Newtown, Powys SY16 2EH (tel: 01686 625228; email: daviescharities@gmail.com)

Trustees: Daniel Davies; Dr Denis Balsom; Dr Janet Lewis; Thomas Williams; Elinor Gilbey.

General information

The charity was established by the Davies sisters in 1934. The daughters of an industrialist and philanthropist, the sisters began to collect art while travelling in Europe before the outbreak of the First World War. They amassed a sizeable collection of impressionist and post-impressionist art which they bequeathed to the National Museum of Wales. In the early 1920s the sisters bought Gregynog Hall in Montgomeryshire where they founded a press and started hosting the Gregynog Music Festival, which celebrated classical music and poetry. Margaret donated Gregynog to the University of Wales for use as an arts centre. As well as being patrons of the arts, the sisters volunteered with the Red Cross during the First World War and opened their home to artists fleeing the war.

The charity continues to support projects that were started by the sisters or inspired by them. Grants are awarded to organisations benefitting the people of Wales and Welsh-based registered charities supporting the following:

- Visual and performing arts
- Education
- Projects for young people
- Health and social welfare

Financial information

Year end	05/04/2021
Income	£1,530,000
Assets	£9,790,000
Grants to organisations	£244,400

Beneficiaries included: Welsh National Opera (£10,000); Montgomeryshire Family Crisis Centre, Artes Mundi and St David's Catholic Church (£5,000 each).

Applications

Apply in writing to the correspondent. The trustees meet quarterly to consider new applications.

Sources of information

Accounts; annual report; Charity Commission record.

The Hamilton Davies Trust

Education; sport and recreation; community development and regeneration

Irlam; Cadishead; Rixton-with-Glazebrook

£228,700 (2020/21)

CC number: 1106123

Correspondent: The Trustees, Hamilton Davies House, 117C Liverpool Road, Cadishead, Manchester M44 5BG (tel: 0161 222 4003; email: hello@hamiltondavies.org.uk)

Trustees: Neil McArthur; Graham Chisnall; Frank Cocker.

 www.hamiltondavies.org.uk

General information

The Hamilton Davies Trust is a grant-making charity which supports projects within the communities of Irlam, Cadishead and Rixton-with-Glazebrook. According to its website, the trust makes grants in four areas:

- **Community:** grants are awarded for a wide variety of community purposes, such as improvements to community buildings and facilities, rent, running costs and events. Funding can also be given towards the costs of uniforms or football kits
- **Education:** the trust supports after school clubs, educational trips and other extra-curricular activities in schools
- **Recreation:** grants are given to groups such as choirs, dance troupes and community organisations for various activities which support social inclusion and friendship. The trust has also supported young people with contributions towards equipment, holiday programmes and competitions
- **Regeneration:** the trust works in partnership with Salford City Council and other stakeholders to boost regeneration in the local area. They provide grants to grassroots community organisations to improve local facilities and enhance the area

Further information on eligibility can be found on the trust's website.

In addition to its main grant programmes, the trust also administers the Chris Stocks Fund with provides small value grants to support young people to develop their skills and benefit their future employability. For full details see the trust's website.

Financial information

Year end	05/04/2021
Income	£210,600
Assets	£3,280,000
Grants to organisations	£228,700

Further financial information

During 2020/21 grants totalled £228,700; however, in previous years the trust has made grants totalling over £300,000.

Beneficiaries included: A list of beneficiaries was not included in the most recent accounts. Previous beneficiaries have included: Newton-Le-Willows Boys' and Girls' Club (£270,000); Manchester Technology Trust (£180,000); Manchester United Foundation (£25,000); Lady James' Hall (£8,000); St Helen's Primary School (£6,200); 2nd Irlam Scout Group (£3,500); Preston Hall (£3,000); Hollins Green Bowling Club (£900); Irlam Junior Football Club (£500).

Applications

For applications for over £150, application forms can be downloaded from the trust's website. There are separate application forms for requests up to £10,000 and for requests over this amount.

The trust's website states that applications for under £150 should be made in writing to the correspondent detailing the following:

- A brief outline of the project and its benefits
- Who will be involved?
- How many people will be involved?
- Who will benefit?
- How many will benefit?
- What area will the project benefit?
- The amount of financial support required?
- Details of any other funding received or applied for

Sources of information

Accounts; annual report; Charity Commission record; funder's website.

The Davis Foundation

Jewish causes; personal development; care of older people; education in music and opera; horticulture; environmental conservation; religious education; religious harmony and research into racism

UK and overseas, including Israel and the Middle East

£1 million (2020/21)

CC number: 1152998

Correspondent: The Trustees, 3 Beechworth Close, London NW3 7UT (tel: 020 7389 9512; email: applications@thedavisfoundation.com)

Trustees: Sir Michael Davis; Lady Barbara Davis; Sarah Davis.

General information

The trust was registered with the Charity Commission in 2013 to support social welfare and community cohesion.

According to its 2020/21 annual report and accounts, the objects of the charity are:

- Financial support for Jewish people (particularly young people) for activities that will help them grow as members of society
- To support organisations which provide support and care for people who are elderly or have a disability and are in need
- Educating the general public in the areas of opera; music; and other creative or performing arts

- To promote the study of horticulture; gardening; and garden design, and also the appreciation of ecology, conservation, and the study of flora and fauna
- Promoting religious harmony
- Promoting social inclusion
- Supporting organisations which provide security, advice and training to those who are involved with religious based schools or places of worship
- Supporting organisations who promote good relationships between Jewish people and the rest of the community
- To promote good citizenship
- Relief for victims of racial or religious harassment
- Providing support for organisations that research racism

Financial information

Year end	05/04/2021
Income	£882,800
Assets	£440,900
Grants to organisations	£1,000,000

Beneficiaries included: A list of beneficiaries was not available.

Applications

Apply in writing to the correspondent.

Sources of information

Accounts; annual report; Charity Commission record.

Dawat-E-Hadiyah Trust (United Kingdom)

Advancement of the Islamic religion; education; social welfare

UK and overseas

£1.32 million (2020)

CC number: 294807

Correspondent: The Trustees, 6 Mohammedi Park Complex, Rowdell Road, Northolt, Middlesex UB5 6AG (tel: 020 8839 0750; email: farazdaq@dawatuk.org)

Trustee: The 53rd Dai Al-Mutlaq, His Holiness Syedna Mufaddal Saifuddin.

General information

The trust was registered with the Charity Commission in 1986 and supports the causes chosen by the Dai al-Mutlaq, the spiritual leader of the Dawoodi Bohra community.

According to its 2020 annual report, the trust's objects are:

> To carry out such charitable purposes for the relief of poverty and the advancement of education or religion or otherwise for the benefit of mankind anywhere in the world as His Holiness, the Dai al-Mutlaq shall from time to time determine. These include the advancement, safeguard and protection of the Islamic religion; the advancement of learning and education in their widest connotations; the relief of poverty and help to the poor and needy; the grant and aid of medical relief and the advancement of such other religious and charitable objects as the Dai al-Mutlaq shall determine.

The trust makes grants to charities in the UK and overseas, as well as to individuals in need.

Financial information

Year end	31/12/2020
Income	£8,700,000
Assets	£87,230,000
Grants to organisations	£1,320,000

Further financial information

A list of beneficiaries was unavailable. Grants were awarded in the following categories: medical aid (£1.17 million); religious schools (£64,000); building repairs (£16,500); community kitchens (£12,400). An additional £50,300 was awarded to individuals.

Applications

Apply in writing to the correspondent. The trust's 2020 accounts state that the 'grant-making policy is to identify those charities and persons in need based on the objects of the Trust'.

Sources of information

Accounts; annual report; Charity Commission record.

The Roger De Haan Charitable Trust

Arts and culture; education; health and welfare of older people; sports; community development, heritage and regeneration in Folkestone; social welfare

Folkestone

£6.58 million (2020/21)

CC number: 276274

Correspondent: Sir Roger De Haan, Trustee, Strand House, Pilgrims Way, Monks Horton, Ashford, Kent TN25 6DR (email: a contact form is available on the trust's website)

Trustees: Sir Roger Haan; Joshua Haan; Benjamin Haan; Lady De Haan.

www.rdhct.org.uk

facebook.com/rdhct.org.uk

@RDHCT

General information

The Roger De Haan Charitable Trust was established in 1978 by Sir Roger De Haan, former Chair of Saga Group, and his father Sidney, Saga's founder. The trust supports a wide range of charitable causes and activities, mainly in the area around Folkestone, Hythe and the Romney Marsh in Kent.

Grants are made to a range of charities and community groups under the following categories:

- Education
- Arts and culture
- Heritage and regeneration
- Community and young people
- Sport
- Health and welfare
- Other causes at the trustee's discretion

Financial information

Year end	05/04/2021
Income	£904,000
Assets	£13,600,000
Grants to organisations	£6,580,000

Further financial information

During 2020/21 grants were distributed as follows:

The arts	£5.21 million
Sport	£1.1 million
Health and welfare	£123,000
Community development	£89,400
Schools and academies	£45,100
Heritage	£11,000

Beneficiaries included: Creative Folkestone (£5.18 million); Cheriton Road Sports Ground Trust – Athletics Track (£958,400); Shepway Sports Trust (£98,500); Chichester Memorial Hall (£5,000); Rotary Club of the Channel (£3,000); LASS Theatre CIC (£1,800); Broadstairs Folk Week (£500); Nordoff Robbins Music Therapy (£100).

Exclusions

Applications that are unlikely to receive support from the trust include:

- Those where a grant would replace or subsidise statutory funding
- The development of business ventures, publications or websites
- Conferences
- Those that would primarily benefit an individual
- Requests from students for the purpose of study or travel
- Funding for expeditions or overseas travel
- Projects that promote political or religious beliefs
- Animal welfare charities
- National charities, unless there is a significant benefit to a local office or project
- Organisations that have already applied within the last 12 months

The trustees will not normally consider unsolicited applications for medical research grants.

Applications

An application form can be downloaded from the trust's website, or requested in writing. Applicants can also apply online through the foundation's online application. The trustees meet multiple times a year to consider grants and deadlines for the meetings can be found on the trust's website.

Sources of information

Accounts; annual report; Charity Commission record; funder's website.

The de László Foundation

The arts and education

UK and worldwide

£731,000 (2020/21)

CC number: 327383

Correspondent: The Trustees, 5 Albany Courtyard, Piccadilly, London W1J 0HF (tel: 020 7437 1982; email: damon@delaszlo.com)

Trustees: Lucy Birkbeck; Damon László; Robert László; William Laszlo.

General information

Established in 1987 in honour of the painter Philip de László, the foundation has the following objects:

- To promote the education and interest in the visual arts, especially the works of contemporary painters, in particular those of the late Philip de László
- To encourage research into the restoration of works of art and their preservation and the location of suitable venues for them
- To acquire and maintain a collection of the works of art of the late Philip de László and other works of art of the same or any other period
- To advance education and research generally in the areas of arts, science, economics and medicine
- To encourage the study, reproduction and cataloguing of works of art and the publication of books and literature in that respect
- To promote the founding of scholarships and prizes related to the objects above

Financial information

Year end	05/04/2021
Income	£1,300,000
Assets	£3,660,000
Grants to organisations	£731,000
No. of grants	24

Further financial information

Grants were distributed as follows:

Education	£188,200
Medicine	£172,900
Archive Trust	£170,000
Arts	£94,700
Scholarships and grants	£62,500
Science	£36,600
Economics	£5,500
Other charities	£770

Only organisations receiving grants of over £10,000 were listed as beneficiaries in the charity's accounts. Grants of under £10,000 were awarded to 17 organisations.

Beneficiaries included: The de Laszlo Archive Trust (£170,000); City and Guilds of London Art School (£25,000); Action for ME (£21,000); The Brain Tumour Charity, Liver Research Trust and Treloar Trust (£15,000 each).

Applications

The 2020/21 annual report states:

> Grants are made based on research by the Trustees and the Trust's advisors and requests received by the Trustees. Grants are formally considered and made on an annual basis at Trustee meetings and informally on regular occasions during the year.

Sources of information

Accounts; annual report; Charity Commission record.

William Delafield Charitable Trust

Restoration of records or archives of historical societies/bodies and restoration of churches

Oxfordshire; Buckinghamshire; Bedfordshire

£510,100 (2020/21)

CC number: 328022

Correspondent: Tom Gilman, Trustee, Royds Withy King, Godstow Court, Minns Business Park, 5 West Way, Oxford OX2 0JB (email: tom.gilman@roydswithyking.com)

Trustees: Thomas Gilman; Bianca Silva; Christopher John.

General information

The trust supports the restoration of records or archives of historical societies/bodies and the restoration of churches.

Financial information

Year end	31/03/2021
Income	£569,400
Assets	£26,190,000
Grants to organisations	£515,100

Beneficiaries included: Ashmolean Museum (£105,000); Pitt Rivers Museum (£85,000); Brasenose College (£50,000); Oxford Preservation Trust (£45,000).

Applications

Apply in writing to the correspondent.

Sources of information

Accounts; annual report; Charity Commission record.

The Desmond Foundation

General charitable purposes, with a particular focus on children and young people; Jewish causes; social welfare; health

UK and overseas

£1 million (2020)

CC number: 1014352

Correspondent: The Trustees, The Northern & Shell Building, 10 Lower Thames Street, London EC3R 6EN (tel: 020 7308 5320; email: michael.downer@norshell.co.uk)

Trustees: Richard Desmond; Northern & Shell Services Ltd; Northern & Shell Media Group Ltd.

General information

The Desmond Foundation was established in 1992. Originally called the RD Crusaders Foundation, it was renamed the Desmond Foundation in 2013. The trustees of the foundation are Richard Desmond (owner of Express Newspapers and founder of Northern & Shell), Northern & Shell Services Ltd and Northern & Shell Media Group Ltd.

In recent years the foundation has awarded the majority of its grants to children's and Jewish charities in the UK. Children's charities remain the focus of the foundation but consideration is given by the trustees to worthy causes outside this area.

Financial information

Year end	31/12/2020
Income	£12,400
Grants to organisations	£1,000,000

Further financial information

Full accounts were not available to view on the Charity Commission due to the foundation's low income. We have therefore estimated the foundation's grant total based on its total expenditure.

Beneficiaries included: A list of beneficiaries was not available. Previous beneficiaries include: Noah's Ark Children's Hospice (£500,000); Imperial War Museum (£333,000); Greenhouse Sports (£333,000 in two grants); Barnet Youth Zone (£100,000); Jewish Blind and Disabled (£10,000); The Chicken Soup Shelter (£1,000).

Applications

Apply in writing to the correspondent.

Sources of information

Accounts; annual report; Charity Commission record.

The Duke of Devonshire's Charitable Trust

General charitable purposes

Projects in areas which are local or relevant to Chatsworth, Bolton Abbey and the other Devonshire Group estates (Lismore Castle and Careysville Fishery in the Republic of Ireland)

£352,100 (2020/21)

CC number: 213519

Correspondent: Mollie Moseley, Chatsworth, Bakewell, Derbyshire DE45 1PP (email: mollie.moseley@chatsworth.org)

Trustees: Duke of Devonshire; Duchess of Devonshire; Oliver Stephenson; William Cavendish.

 www.ddct.org.uk

General information

The Duke of Devonshire's Charitable Trust is a small family charity established by the 11th Duke of Devonshire in 1949. It supports a wide range of charitable organisations which are local or relevant to the Chatsworth, Bolton Abbey and the Devonshire Group estates. Support further afield may be agreed at the trustees discretion.

Grants can be made to UK-registered charities (including exempt charities such as churches and hospitals), CIOs and CICs. Grants are typically made for one year although the trust does sometimes make funding commitments over several years. Grants are usually in the region of £250 to £10,000. The trustees anticipate the organisations will have secured a significant proportion of the funding prior to applying.

Financial information

Year end	05/04/2021
Income	£249,400
Assets	£16,320,000
Grants to organisations	£352,100

Beneficiaries included: Derby Museum Endowment Fund (£20,000); Addingham Youth Council (£1,500); Skipton Baptist Church (£1,000); Life Cycle UK (£500); St John Ambulance (£190).

Exclusions

The following information has been taken from the trust's website:

> What the Trust is unlikely to fund:
>
> 1. The Trust will not consider any funding request made within 12 months of the outcome of a previously unsuccessful application or 2 years of a successful one. This is to ensure that the Trust can assist as wide a spread of worthwhile organisations as possible.
>
> 2. The Trust only considers applications from UK registered charities, Charitable Incorporated Organisations (CIOs) and Community Interest Companies (CICs). Your registration number must be included in your application (unless you have exempt status as a church, educational establishment, hospital etc.).
>
> 3. The Trust does not typically fund projects outside the UK, even if the organisation is a registered charity within Britain.
>
> 4. The Trust is not able to accept applications from individuals or for individual research or study. This includes gap year activities, study trips, fundraising expeditions and sponsorship.
>
> 5. The Trust does not make funding commitments over several years – grants made are typically for a single year with few exceptions.
>
> 6. It is unusual for the Trust to consider making a grant to organisations who cannot demonstrate significant progress with fundraising, so please bear this in mind when considering the timing of your application.
>
> 7. Applications will not be considered without all information requested being provided and accounts being included.

Applications

Application forms and deadlines can be found on the trust's website.

Sources of information

Accounts; annual report; Charity Commission record; funder's website.

The Laduma Dhamecha Charitable Trust

General charitable purposes, including medical equipment for hospitals and education (particularly education in rural areas)

UK and overseas

£1.89 million (2020/21)

CC number: 328678

Correspondent: Pradip Dhamecha, Trustee, c/o The Dhamecha Group, 2 Hathaway Close, Stanmore, Middlesex HA7 3NR (tel: 020 8903 8181; email: info@dhamecha.com)

Trustees: Pradip Dhamecha; Shantilal Dhamecha; Manish Dhamecha.

General information

The trust was founded by the Dhamecha family who founded and operate the Dhamecha cash and carry group based in Greater London. The trust supports a wide range of organisations in the UK and overseas.

According to the trust's 2020/21 annual report, its aims are:

- To provide relief for sickness by provision of medicines and medical equipment and/or improving the facilities at the hospitals as the trustees determine
- To provide for the advancement of education and/or educational establishment in rural areas so as to make children self sufficient in the longer term
- Such other charitable purposes as the trustees shall determine

Financial information

Year end	31/03/2021
Income	£1,790,000
Assets	£2,240,000
Grants to organisations	£1,890,000

Further financial information

Grants awarded in the UK totalled £679,400 and grants awarded overseas totalled £1.2 million.

Beneficiaries included: A list of beneficiaries was not available.

Applications

Apply in writing to the correspondent.

Sources of information

Accounts; annual report; Charity Commission record.

Diabetes UK

Diabetes research

UK

£5.91 million (2020)

CC number: 215199

Correspondent: Research Department, Wells Lawrence House, 126 Back Church Lane, London E1 1FH (tel: 01345 123 239; email: research@diabetes.org.uk)

Trustees: Sir Peter Dixon; Dr Robert Young; Helen McCallum; Janice Watson; Prof. Mohamed Hanif; Robin Swindell; Ian King; Rosemary Thomas; Dr Wendy Thomson; Melanie Gray; Prof. Linda Bauld; Alexandra Lewis; Dr Asiya Yunus; Michael Gibbs.

 www.diabetes.org.uk

 facebook.com/diabetesuk

 @DiabetesUK

 @diabetesuk

General information

Diabetes UK was established in 1934 by H. G. Wells and Dr R. D. Lawrence, both of whom had diabetes. It is the UK's leading charity for people with diabetes, and the UK's leading charitable funder of diabetes research.

Grant programmes

According to its website, the charity provides the following grants:

- **Project grants –** To provide support for diabetes research projects for up to five years.
- **Early-Career Small grants –** To enable early-career researchers to

undertake small research projects or pilot studies.

- **Harry Keen Intermediate Clinical Fellowship –** To allow outstanding medically qualified professionals, and other clinically qualified professionals to establish themselves as independent researchers, with a view to a long-term career as a clinical research leader in the field of diabetes. This includes nurses, pharmacists and members of the Allied Health Professions, who have gained a PhD or equivalent (e.g. MD (Res)).
- **Sir George Alberti Research Training Fellowship –** To enable graduates currently working in the NHS to study for a PhD or MD in diabetes research and develop a career in research. Applications are invited from individuals working in a patient-facing role including, but not limited to, doctors, nurses, midwives, psychologists and dietitians.
- **NIHR/Diabetes UK Doctoral Fellowship –** To fund a Doctoral Fellowship which supports individuals to undertake a PhD in an area of diabetes related research.
- **RD Lawrence Fellowship –** To provide personal support enabling postdoctoral researchers to establish their independence in diabetes research.
- **PhD Studentship –** To enable experienced researchers to recruit outstanding science graduates to study for a PhD in the field of diabetes-related research.

Financial information

Year end	31/12/2020
Income	£37,660,000
Assets	£17,770,000
Grants to organisations	£5,910,000

Beneficiaries included: University of Exeter (£549,000); The University of Manchester (£383,000); Academy of Medical Sciences (£184,000); University of Southampton (£103,000).

Applications

Prospective applicants should first read the general guidelines for research grant applicants on the charity's website. Applications should then be submitted online using the charity's online grants management system.

Sources of information

Accounts; annual report; Charity Commission record; funder's website.

The Djanogly Foundation

Jewish causes; arts and culture; education; medicine; welfare of older and younger people

UK and Israel

£175,000 (2020/21)

CC number: 280500

Correspondent: The Trustees, 3 Angel Court, London SW1Y 6QF (tel: 020 7930 9845)

Trustees: Sir Harry Djanogly; Michael Djanogly; Jonathan Djanogly.

General information

The foundation was established in 1980 by Sir Harry Djangoly, a textile manufacturer from Nottingham. He is a well-known benefactor of the arts.

The foundation's 2020/21 annual report states:

> The donations policy of the trustees is to sponsor developments in medicine, education, social welfare and the arts. Grants will also be made to fund project to relieve distress and to promote the welfare of the aged and the young.
>
> The charity is particularly concerned with the funding of projects that are new and may require a number of years to establish. In such cases the grant making activity will be related to the development phases of these projects.

The foundation also supports Jewish organisations/causes.

Financial information

Year end	05/04/2021
Income	£44,500
Assets	£4,280,000
Grants to organisations	£175,000

Further financial information

The foundation awarded grants totalling £175,000 in 2020/21; however, in previous years the foundation has had the capacity to give more. For example in 2019/20 the foundation awarded grants totalling £700,000.

Beneficiaries included: Royal Drawing School (£75,000); Westminster Abbey Foundation (£50,000); Imperial War Museum (£25,000); St Lawrence College (£9,600); Chicken Shed Theatre Company (£1,000).

Applications

Apply in writing to the correspondent.

Sources of information

Accounts; annual report; Charity Commission record.

The Ken Dodd Charitable Foundation

Social welfare and the advancement of public education and appreciation in the performing arts

UK, with a preference for Merseyside

£515,300 (2020/21)

CC number: 1179779

Correspondent: The Trustees, Barristers Chambers, 3 Field Court, London WC1R 5EP (tel: 020 3693 3700)

Trustees: Lady Sybilanne Dodd; Peter Vaines; John Lewis.

General information

The foundation was established by an initial gift from comedian Sir Kenneth Dodd in 2013. Since his death the foundation has received substantial gifts from his estate and his wife Lady Sybil Anne Dodd.

Areas of work

The following information has been taken from the foundation's 2020/21 annual accounts:

> The purposes of the charity are to advance the education of the public in the performing arts, to further the development of the public appreciation and understanding of performing arts by the support and encouragement of the work of young artists, to provide for the relief of poverty of persons in the United Kingdom and elsewhere who are in conditions of need, hardship or distress by reason of their social or economic circumstances by providing advice and financial assistance to those in need and to provide financial assistance to any other exclusively charitable organisation.

Financial information

Year end	31/03/2021
Income	£459,500
Assets	£11,630,000
Grants to organisations	£515,300

Further financial information

Grants were awarded to 14 organisations during the year.

Beneficiaries included: St John the Evangelist Church (£335,000); Christ Church Parochial Church Council and Alder Hey Children's Hospital League of Friends (£50,000 each); The Parish Church of St Anne (£20,000); Overseas Plastic Surgery Appeal (£10,000); British Music Hall Society (£1,000); The Liverpool Heart and Chest Hospital Charity (£250).

Applications

Apply in writing to the correspondent.

Sources of information

Accounts; annual report; Charity Commission record.

Dollond Charitable Trust

Jewish causes

UK and Israel

£2.05 million (2020/21)

CC number: 293459

Correspondent: Brian Dollond, Trustee and Secretary, 3rd Floor, Hathaway House, Popes Drive, Finchley, London N3 1QF (tel: 020 8346 6446)

Trustees: Adrian Dollond; Jeffrey Milston; Melissa Dollond; Brian Dollond; Rina Dollond.

General information

The trust was registered with the Charity Commission in January 1986. The trust operates a broad grant-making policy; however, the activities are often focused on health, education and religious activities. The annual report for 2020/21 states that although 'the constitution of the charity is broadly based, the trustees have adopted a policy of assisting in Jewish communities in Britain and Israel'.

Financial information

Year end	31/03/2021
Income	£1,090,000
Assets	£50,990,000
Grants to organisations	£2,050,000

Further financial information

Grants were broken down as follows:

Education and training	£551,000
Religious education	£450,000
Relief of poverty	£368,000
Disability	£332,500
Medical, health and sickness	£303,000
Religious activities	£50,000

Beneficiaries included: A list of beneficiaries was not available.

Applications

Apply in writing to the correspondent.

Sources of information

Accounts; annual report; Charity Commission record.

The Dorfman Foundation

General charitable purposes, including Jewish causes and the arts

Worldwide

£1.27 million (2020/21)

CC number: 1120714

Correspondent: The Trustees, 22 Manchester Square, London W1U 3PT (tel: 020 7725 1221; email: charity.correspondence@bdo.co.uk)

Trustees: Amy Lux; Sophie Dorfman; Sir Lloyd Dorfman; Anthony Wagerman; Lloyd Dorfman; Sarah Dorfman; Peter Leach; Charles Dorfman.

General information

The foundation was registered with the Charity Commission in August 2007 and has general charitable purposes, although there is a preference for Jewish causes and the arts.

Financial information

Year end	05/04/2021
Income	£166,513
Assets	£5,050,000
Grants to organisations	£1,270,000

Beneficiaries included: Friends of St Paul's (£283,000); Royal Opera House (£200,000); Cygnet Training Theatre Et Cygnet Research Library (£180,000); Jewish Care (£100,000); British Council Benevolent Fund (£50,000); Norwood Ravenswood (£35,000); Migration Museum Project (£15,000); Holocaust Education (£12,500).

Applications

Apply in writing to the correspondent.

Sources of information

Accounts; annual report; Charity Commission record; funder's website.

The Doughty Charity Trust

Orthodox Jewish causes, religious education and the relief of poverty

England and Israel

£706,600 (2020)

CC number: 274977

Correspondent: The Trustees, 22 Ravenscroft Avenue, London NW11 0RY (tel: 020 8209 0500)

Trustees: Mr G. Halibard; Mrs M. Halibard.

General information

The Doughty Charity Trust makes grants to alleviate poverty and advance religion and religious education. In the past, grants have been awarded to Orthodox Jewish schools and organisations.

Financial information

Year end	31/12/2020
Income	£987,200
Assets	£894,100
Grants to organisations	£706,600

Beneficiaries included: A list of beneficiaries was not available.

Applications

The trust has stated that its funds are fully committed and therefore it does not accept unsolicited applications.

Sources of information

Accounts; annual report; Charity Commission record.

Drapers' Charitable Fund

Social welfare; education and young people; textiles and heritage

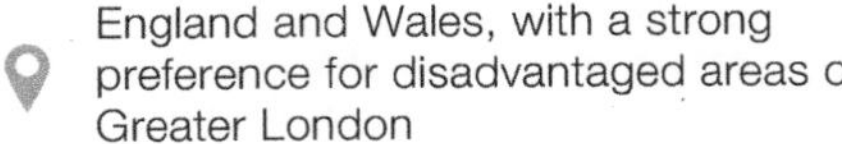

England and Wales, with a strong preference for disadvantaged areas of Greater London

£2.58 million (2019/20)

CC number: 251403

Correspondent: Head of Charities, The Drapers' Company, Drapers' Hall, Throgmorton Avenue, London EC2N 2DQ (tel: 020 7588 5001; email: charities@thedrapers.co.uk)

Trustee: The Drapers' Company.

https://thedrapers.co.uk/drapers-charitable-fund

General information

This charity was established in 1959. The charity's primary aim is to 'improve the quality of life and expectations of people and their communities, especially those disadvantaged or socially excluded', as stated in its 2019/20 annual report. The charity has a strong preference for Greater London, where the company has its historical roots.

Areas of work

Grant-making is concentrated in three areas:

- **Social welfare** – particularly causes relating to homelessness, prisoners, ex-Service personnel, disability, as well as support services in areas of high deprivation in Greater London
- **Young people and education**
- **Textiles and heritage** – particularly textile conservation projects, certain projects within the textile industry (see website) and the preservation of museums, memorials and monuments related to the armed forces, the history of London or the textile trade

Grants awarded are normally for sums up to £15,000 but larger grants may be awarded. Organisations must be registered charities with a total annual income of less than £10 million. Funding is mainly for core costs, including salaries and/or project costs, to enable organisations to maintain and develop their work/services.

For full details of the types of projects supported by the charity, see its website.

Financial information

Year end	31/07/2020
Income	£2,880,000
Assets	£72,510,000
Grants to organisations	£2,580,000

Further financial information

Grants awarded from the charity's General Fund totalled £1.92 million (174 grants to 160 organisations). The remaining grants were awarded from the charity's restricted funds.

Beneficiaries included: Bancroft's School (£70,000 in two grants); Bangor University (£40,000); Veterans Aid (£30,000); Future Youth Zone (£25,000); In2Change (£18,000); Havering Women's Aid (£15,000); Royal College of Music (£8,000); Canal and River Trust (£2,000).

Exclusions

The charity does not support the following:

- Organisations that are not registered charities (unless exempt from registration)
- Organisations with an annual income of over £10 million
- Branches of national charities or movements, or charities which are part of a federal structure
- Schools, colleges or universities
- Churches or other places of worship
- Almshouses
- Hospitals, medical centres or hospices
- Individuals (or organisations applying on their behalf)
- Capital projects, appeals or major refurbishments
- Projects which do not support all members of the targeted community
- Physical disabilities, medical research or medical conditions (including substance misuse or HIV)
- Arts projects (unless able to demonstrate an impact on prisoners, older people or those with less visible disabilities)
- Projects supporting those experiencing domestic violence, trafficking or sexual exploitation
- Projects where the main focus is tolerance and understanding between faiths and communities, promotion of religious beliefs or social cohesion
- Charities whose principal objective is campaigning, lobbying or raising awareness
- Holidays or trips
- Preschool projects
- Animal welfare
- Projects taking place or whose beneficiaries are situated outside the UK
- Work that has already taken place

Applications

Applications can be submitted by email. Applicants should send a detailed proposal document explaining what your organisation does, how you intend to spend the money and your most recent financial accounts and trustees report, along with a completed application summary sheet (see the charity's website). The committee meets five times a year to consider applications. Details of upcoming meeting dates, with full guidelines, can be found on the charity's website.

Sources of information

Accounts; annual report; Charity Commission record; funder's website; guidelines for applicants.

Dromintee Trust

Social welfare; children and young people; health and health education; medical research

UK and overseas, with a preference for Leicestershire

£497,200 (2020/21)

CC number: 1053956

Correspondent: Hugh Murphy, Trustee, 1 Westmoreland Avenue, Thurmaston, Leicester, Leicestershire LE4 8PH (tel: 0116 260 3877; email: dromintee trust@gmail.com)

Trustees: Robert Smith; Hugh Murphy; Margaret Murphy; Paul Tiernan; Mary Middleton; Patrick Murphy; Joseph Murphy.

General information

Established in March 1996, this Leicestershire-based trust principally supports organisations working in the areas of: social welfare, children's welfare, health and research into rare diseases. Grants are made to organisations operating locally, nationally and overseas, particularly in financially developing countries. Previously the trust has also supported a number of Catholic organisations.

Financial information

Year end	31/03/2021
Income	£533,500
Assets	£3,330,000
Grants to organisations	£497,200

Beneficiaries included: Ratcliffe College Catholic Bursary (£80,00); The Good Counsel Network (£50,000); The National Brain Appeal (£36,000); March for Life (£35,000); Don Bosco (£30,000); Let The Children Live (£20,000); Missio (£10,000).

Applications

Apply in writing to the correspondent. The 2020/21 annual report states: 'The trustees consider all written applications for grants at trustees' meetings. Applications are considered on merit based on how closely the activities of the applicant fit with the objectives of the charity.'

Sources of information

Accounts, annual report, Charity Commission record.

The Dulverton Trust

Youth opportunities; general welfare; conservation; heritage; peace and disaster preparedness; community development and wildlife conservation in Kenya and Uganda

The UK (excluding Greater London and Northern Ireland); Kenya; Uganda

£3.78 million (2020/21)

CC number: 1146484

Correspondent: Eleanor Hingley, Grants Manager, 5 St James's Place, London SW1A 1NP (tel: 020 7495 7852; email: grants@dulverton.org)

Trustees: The Lord Dulverton; Christopher Wills; The Lord Hemphill; Richard Howard; Dame Mary Richardson; Tara Douglas-Home; Sir Malcolm Rifkind; Robert Wills; Dr Catherine Wills

 www.dulverton.org

General information

This is one of the trusts deriving from the tobacco-generated fortune of the Wills family. It has an endowment worth £85 million and a body of trustees which combines family members and others.

Funding

The trust offers both project and core funding. Applicants are advised to apply for the amount they need; however, as a guide, the average grant is between £25,000 and £35,000 per year.

Eligibility

The trust prioritises medium-sized (income of £200,000 to £3 million) UK charities and CIOs that have a national footprint and do not receive a significant proportion of income from government or local authority contracts.

Areas of work

The trust awards funding across five categories, details of which have been taken from its website:

> *Youth opportunities*
> This is our largest category and supports work that engages people primarily on the basis that they are from lower-income backgrounds (the charities we fund tend to work with children in receipt of Free School Meals or Pupil Premium funding, or live in geographies that sit in the 20% most deprived on the IMD scale). We fund initiatives that support young people to develop the life skills (e.g. employability skills, skills to succeed at school, improving social and emotional skills) to enable them to thrive.
>
> As of May 2021, we are also accepting applications for the Dulverton Trust #iwill Fund under our Youth Opportunities category. Applications can be submitted through our online application form. [The fund] is open to applications from charities which meet our criteria and are

working to create youth social action opportunities for young people in England aged 10–20 years old. We have identified two areas of focus for the Fund: heritage and issues facing rural communities. We are particularly interested in projects which create youth social action opportunities for children and young people aged 10–14.

General welfare

We support a wide range of charities that benefit disadvantaged people and communities, with particular interest in:

- strengthening and supporting family relationships
- work with offenders, especially young offenders, with a focus on desistance
- helping young homeless people to move forward
- maintaining active living and independence for older people (note: this does not include help with medical and mental health)
- the welfare of those who care for others
- developing tolerance and understanding between faiths and communities and the promotion of social cohesion

Conservation

We support charities working to support the health and resilience of the UK's wildlife habitat. This work focuses on:

- protecting, planting and sympathetically managing trees and native woodlands
- protecting coastal and marine environments

Please note that we rarely consider applications for projects concerned with a single species.

Heritage

We support the development of craftsmanship in the traditional techniques of repair and restoration and have a strong interest in:

- heritage skills training, particularly where it may benefit a disadvantaged group
- cathedrals (Trustees generally make one award to a cathedral per year)

Please note that annual grants are awarded to the National Churches Trust to disburse to churches on our behalf, and as such, we are not able to support applications from individual churches.

Kenya and Uganda

This category is currently restricted to UK registered charities operating in Kenya or Uganda, which already have a long association with the Trust. Our priorities in these locations are:

- community development (in particular, the provision of water and power, and the encouragement of farming, common market gardening and enterprise)
- wildlife conservation

International Stability and Reconstruction

The Trust does not normally contribute to disaster relief appeals. Instead we fund charities that:

- (a) Provide support facilities or expertise to organisations engaged in disaster preparedness
- (b) Are engaged in peace intervention

Community foundation partnerships

Small grants of up to £5,000 are awarded to local UK charities (with annual incomes of below £200,000) on behalf of the trust by community foundations. The trust rotates its partnerships with these foundations with the intention that over time most regions in the UK will be covered.

In-kind support

Grantees are offered additional non-financial help such as advice, advocacy, referral to pro bono support, and free access to the trust's boardroom.

Financial information

Year end	31/03/2021
Income	£3,210,000
Assets	£113,580,000
Grants to organisations	£3,780,000
No. of grants	74

Further financial information

Grants paid during the year totalled £3.78 million. Grants committed during the year were broken down as follows:

General welfare	31	£1.46 million
Youth opportunities	25	£925,300
Heritage	5	£559,200
Africa	5	£217,500
Conservation	2	£80,000
Local appeals	5	£28,000
Trustee exception (a grantee outside the trust's criteria)	1	£25,000

During the year, 58% of grants were awarded for core costs and 42% were awarded for project costs.

Beneficiaries included: National Churches Trust (£450,000); Action on Poverty (£105,000); Children and Families Across Borders (£75,800); Access to Justice Foundation (£50,000); Child Bereavement UK (£30,000); Heritage Crafts Association (£21,200); Break the Silence (£5,000); Cotswold Friends (£1,000).

Exclusions

The trust is very unlikely to support research. Grants are not given to charities benefitting residents of Northern Ireland or London. Grants to UK charities operating in Kenya and Uganda are restricted to those with whom the trust has an existing relationship.

Applications

Applicants must first complete the eligibility quiz on the trust's website. If you are eligible, you will be provided with a link to the online application form. Applications are accepted all year round but the trustees make decisions in February, June and October. If your application is progressed, the trust will arrange a visit or online meeting. All applicants are notified of the outcome of their application via email.

Applicants to the #iwill Fund are encouraged to contact the trust's office for an informal conversation in advance of making a full application.

Sources of information

Accounts; annual report; Charity Commission record; funder's website.

Dunard Fund

Classical music; architecture; visual arts; to a lesser extent, environmental and humanitarian projects

UK, mainly Scotland

£11.91 million (2020/21)

OSCR number: SC046889

Correspondent: The Trustees, J. & H. Mitchell W. S., 51 Atholl Road, Pitlochry, Perthshire PH16 5BU

General information

The charity has close links with Dunard Ltd and has previously received donations from the company. Ms Carol Colburn Grigor, a trustee of the Dunard Fund, is both a director and a shareholder of Dunard Ltd.

The charity mainly supports classical music, architecture, visual arts and environmental and humanitarian projects. The trustees tend to make large grants for long-term development projects.

Financial information

Year end	31/03/2021
Income	£9,300,000
Assets	£75,880,000
Grants to organisations	£11,910,000

Further financial information

During 2020/21, grants were distributed as follows:

Architecture	£5.55 million
Classical music	£5.02 million
Visual arts	£1.33 million
Humanitarian and environmental causes	£10,000

Beneficiaries included: Pitlochry Festival Theatre (£3.2 million); Edinburgh International Festival (£800,000); Royal Opera House (£500,000); St Mary's Music School (£200,000); Dunedin Consort (£150,000); The Marian Consort (£50,000); Royal Drawing School (£25,000); Refuge (£10,000).

Applications

Apply in writing to the correspondent.

Sources of information

Accounts; annual report; OSCR record; Companies House.

The Dunhill Medical Trust

Research into improving the quality of life, functional capacity and well-being of older people

UK

£3.94 million (2020/21)

CC number: 1140372

Correspondent: The Trustees, Fifth Floor, 6 New Bridge Street, London EC4V 6AB (tel: 020 7403 3299; email: admin@dunhillmedical.org.uk)

Trustees: Prof. Alison Petch; Deborah Dunn-Walters; James Lorigan; Keith Shepherd; Prof. Thomas Kirkwood; Michael Bellamy; Prof. Bernard Conway; Prof. Stuart Parker; Eren Osman; Dominic Jones; Prof. Carmel Hughes.

 www.dunhillmedical.org.uk

 @DunhillMedical

General information

The Dunhill Medical Trust (DMT) was established in 1950 by the will left by Herbert Dunhill. The trust, which was formally registered as a charity in the 1980s, was established with charitable objects focused on medical research.

Grants are given to universities, community organisations and not-for-profit organisations. The trust focuses on research aimed at understanding the mechanisms of age-related medical issues and improving the health and well-being of older people.

According to its website, the trust's funding covers a variety of academic disciplines, including biological and biomedical sciences, health, social care, the built environment, engineering, behavioural science and others.

Financial information

Year end	31/03/2021
Income	£2,580,000
Assets	£157,210,000
Grants to organisations	£3,940,000

Beneficiaries included: Social Care Institute for Excellence (£316,600); University of Sheffield (£200,000); Queen's Nursing Institute (£105,000); Sensory Trust and Woven Nest Theatre (£31,000 each); Curriculum and Language Access Services (£27,000); Life Cycle UK (£600).

Applications

Check the trust's website for open funding calls. Applications can be made through the trust's online grants portal.

Sources of information

Accounts; annual report; Charity Commission record; funder's website.

The Charles Dunstone Charitable Trust

General charitable purposes; arts and culture; children and young people; community care; education and training; health and disability; social welfare; heritage and restoration

 UK

£169,100 (2020/21)

CC number: 1085955

Correspondent: The Trustees, H. W. Fisher and Company, Acre House, 11–15 William Road, London NW1 3ER (tel: 020 7388 7000; email: jtrent@hwfisher.co.uk)

Trustees: Adrian Bott; Denis Dunstone; John Gordon; Robert Clarkson.

General information

Established in 2001 for general charitable purposes, this is the charitable trust of Charles Dunstone, co-founder of the Carphone Warehouse.

Financial information

Year end	05/04/2021
Income	£931,600
Assets	£495,800
Grants to organisations	£169,100

Further financial information

During 2020/21 grants totalled £169,100; however, in previous years the trust has made grants totalling over £300,000. Grants were distributed as follows:

Children and youth	£160,000
Medical and disability	£8,000
Other	£1,000
Community care and ethnic organisations	£100

Beneficiaries included: A list of beneficiaries was not available. Previous beneficiaries include: Brighton Belle (£500,000); Prince's Trust (£150,300); Royal Museum Greenwich (£100,000); Make a Wish (£20,000); Lady Garden (£18,000); Comic Relief (£5,000); The Fulwood Academy (£2,200).

Applications

The 2020/21 annual report states:

> The trust is currently supporting a small number of charities with whom it has an existing relationship. The trustees continue to respond to solicited applications only and strongly advise against submitting unsolicited applications.

Sources of information

Accounts; annual report; Charity Commission record.

Dushinsky Trust Ltd

Alleviation of poverty and furtherance of Orthodox Jewish education abroad

UK and Israel

£563,200 (2020/21)

CC number: 1020301

Correspondent: Simon Reisner, Secretary, 23 Braydon Road, London N16 6QL (tel: 020 8802 7144)

Trustees: Simon Reisner; Zvi Levine; Mosche Schischa.

General information

The charity was established in 1992 with the aim 'to assist in the alleviation of poverty and the furtherance of Orthodox Jewish education in the UK and abroad'. Particular emphasis is given to the Dushinsky and Minchas Yizchok institutions based in Israel.

Financial information

Year end	31/03/2021
Income	£660,800
Assets	£52,300
Grants to organisations	£563,200

Further financial information

Grants were broken down as follows: advancement of education (£312,300); advancement of religion (£179,600); relief of poverty (£71,300).

Beneficiaries included: A list of beneficiaries was not available.

Applications

The trust does not accept unsolicited applications.

Sources of information

Accounts; annual report; Charity Commission record.

The Dyers' Company Charitable Trust

 Education; children and young people; health; social welfare; armed forces; arts; the church

UK

£681,900 (2019/20)

CC number: 289547

Correspondent: Assistant Clerk, Dyers' Hall, 11–13 Dowgate Hill, London EC4R 2ST (tel: 020 7236 7197; email: office@dyerscompany.com)

Trustee: The Dyers Company.

 www.dyerscompany.co.uk/charitable-activity

General information

The trust was established in 1984 and makes a large number of grants to registered charities in support of general charitable purposes. The trust gives to UK-registered charities for both one-off and long-standing projects. The trust does not consider applications unless they are sponsored by a member of the Dyers' Company. The trust has several commitments to educational bursaries with schools and universities, including Norwich School, that it reviews annually.

Financial information

Year end	31/10/2020
Income	£1,340,000
Assets	£19,700,000
Grants to organisations	£681,900

Beneficiaries included: University of Leeds (£21,800); The Trussell Trust (£15,000); Chemin Neuf Community (£2,000); Above and Beyond (£1,000); Axminster Heritage (£500).

Exclusions

Grants are not made to individuals or international charities.

Applications

The trust does not accept unsolicited applications, but members of the company can nominate charities for support.

Sources of information

Accounts; annual report; Charity Commission record; funder's website.

The James Dyson Foundation

Medical research; engineering education; projects in Malmesbury

Worldwide, with a preference for the UK and in particular the local area around the Dyson company's UK headquarters in Malmesbury, Wiltshire

£733,200 (2020)

CC number: 1099709

Correspondent: The Trustees, Tetbury Hill, Malmesbury, Wiltshire SN16 0RP (tel: 01666 746802; email: info@jamesdysonfoundation.com)

Trustees: Lady Deirdre Dyson; Sir James Dyson; Valerie West.

www.jamesdysonfoundation.com

facebook.com/JamesDysonFoundation

@JDF

@jamesdysonfoundation

General information

The James Dyson Foundation is the charitable foundation of the British technology company Dyson Ltd. The foundation was established in 2002 to promote charitable giving, especially to charities working in the fields of science, design, engineering education and medical research. The foundation is almost exclusively funded by donations from Dyson Ltd.

Charitable support

According to its website, the foundation can provide small financial donations to charitable causes that fall within its three areas of focus:

- Engineering education
- Medical or scientific research
- Projects and organisations in Malmesbury, Wiltshire, where Dyson's head office is based

The James Dyson Award

The foundation runs the James Dyson Award, an annual international design competition that aims to inspire and encourage the next generation of design engineers. The award is open to current and recent design engineer students.

Financial information

Year end	31/12/2020
Income	£1,010,000
Assets	£187,700
Grants to organisations	£733,200

Further financial information

Grants were distributed as follows: education and training (£575,800); science and medical research (£131,600); social and community welfare (£25,800).

Beneficiaries included: A list of beneficiaries was not available.

Exclusions

According to its website, the foundation will not fund any of the following:

- Animal welfare
- Loans or funding for individuals or companies
- Sports team sponsorship

Applications

To apply, organisations should complete the online contact form on the foundation's website. The foundation aims to respond within two weeks.

Sources of information

Accounts; annual report; Charity Commission record; funder's website.

The James and Deirdre Dyson Trust

The arts; healthcare; education; sport

England and Wales

£450,900 (2020)

CC number: 1160919

Correspondent: The Trustees, Dyson Ltd, Tetbury Hill, Malmesbury SN16 0RP (tel: 01666 827258; email: info@jamesanddeirdredysontrust.com)

Trustees: Lady Deirdre Dyson; Sir James Dyson; Weybourne Corporate Trustee Ltd.

www.jamesanddeirdredysontrust.com

General information

The trust was established by James and Deirdre Dyson, who also sit as trustees. James Dyson is an inventor, designer and the founder of Dyson Ltd.

The trust supports charitable projects relating to the arts, healthcare, education and sport.

Financial information

Year end	31/12/2020
Income	£22,990,000
Assets	£4,930,000
Grants to organisations	£450,900

Beneficiaries included: Cure EB (£433,600); The Burma Star Memorial Fund (£10,000); Batheaston Village Hall (£500); World Sports (£100).

Applications

Unsolicited applications are not accepted.

Sources of information

Accounts; annual report; Charity Commission record.

The Earley Charity

Arts, culture and heritage, and social welfare

The ancient liberty of Earley (i.e. the central, eastern and southern parts of Reading, Earley and Lower Earley, northern Shinfield, Winnersh, Sonning and Lower Caversham)

£315,500 (2020)

CC number: 244823

Correspondent: Jane Wittig, Clerk to the Trustees, St Nicolas Centre, Sutcliffe, Earley, Reading RG6 7JN (tel: 0118 926 1068; email: ec@earleycharity.org.uk)

Trustees: Robert Ames; Tahir Maher; David Sutton; Elizabeth Terry; Philip Hooper; Mary Waite; Dr Deborah Jenkins.

www.earleycharity.org.uk

General information

The Earley Charity was founded in 1990 and is one of the largest local grant-making charities in central southern England. The charity makes grants to charitable and community organisations and to individuals in need. According to the website, the charity's object is 'the relief of need among elderly, disabled or poor people living in [its] area of benefit. The Charity's terms of reference also make it possible for [it] to fund community, educational, informational, cultural, sporting, recreational and social initiatives.'

Grants are made to a wide variety of organisations within the charity's area of benefit. Applications should be for one-off non-recurrent funding for specific projects or equipment. Grants normally range from £500 to £5,000. Larger grants may be awarded to organisations that the trustees know well.

Arts, culture and heritage

The charity has a specific programme for arts, culture and heritage. Its website states:

> The Earley Charity is keen to promote all aspects of cultural life within our area of benefit.
>
> To enable this, the Arts, Culture and Heritage category of grant-making has been set up to fund group activities. Through this programme we aim to:
> - promote all aspects of art, culture and heritage within our area of benefit
> - bring people together
> - promote the sharing of skills and knowledge
> - encourage people of all ages and backgrounds to try new things

Further information on what the charity will fund can be found on the website.

Financial information

Year end	31/12/2020
Income	£262,300
Assets	£12,300,000
Grants to organisations	£315,500

Beneficiaries included: Readipop (£80,000); Berkshire Women's Aid (£41,100); Aspire2 (£22,000); Launchpad Reading (£7,000); Me2 Club (£2,000); Readifolk (£500).

Applications

Application forms can be requested via email or by completing the online enquiry form. Application forms and supporting documents should be returned to the charity by post. See the charity's website for application deadlines.

Sources of information

Accounts; annual report; Charity Commission record; funder's website.

Sir John Eastwood Foundation

General charitable purposes, including children with special needs, older people and people with disabilities

Nottinghamshire

£320,000 (2020/21)

CC number: 235389

Correspondent: The Trustees, PO Box 9803, Handley Arcade, Leeming Street, Mansfield, Nottinghamshire NG18 9FT (tel: 07970 438740; email: sirjohneastwoodfoundation@talktalk.net)

Trustees: Valerie Hardingham; David Marriott; John Mudford; Victoria Cottingham.

General information

The aim of the charity is to make grants to other registered charities, with priority being given to local registered charities that benefit Nottingham. However, applications from organisations outside Nottingham will still be considered.

According to the trustees' report for 2020/21, 'particular emphasis is given to charities which help the disabled, the elderly and children with special needs'.

Financial information

Year end	31/03/2021
Income	£289,900
Assets	£10,360,000
Grants to organisations	£320,000

Further financial information

During the year the charity made a total of 135 grants of between £500 and £10,000.

Beneficiaries included: Nottinghamshire Hospice (£14,000); Warsop Youth Club, Newark and Nottinghamshire Agricultural Society, Loughborough Bell Foundry Trust (£10,000 each); Mansfield Street Pastors, Harrington Junior School and Macmillan Cancer Support (£5,000 each).

Exclusions

The foundation does not make grants to individuals.

Applications

Apply in writing to the correspondent.

Sources of information

Accounts; annual report; Charity Commission record.

EBM Charitable Trust

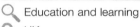

Youth development; animal welfare; social welfare

UK

£1.37 million (2019/20)

CC number: 326186

Correspondent: Lynne Webster, Moore Family Office Ltd, 42 Berkeley Square, London W1J 5AW (tel: 020 7318 0845; email: Lynne.Webster@moorefamilyofficegroup.com)

Trustees: Stephen Hogg; Michael MacFadyen; Richard Moore; Francis Moore; Lucy Forsyth.

General information

The EBM Charitable Trust was established in 1982 by the late Eric Blechynden Moller. The trustees' 2019/20 annual report states that the trust aims 'to support a wide variety of beneficiaries including charities involved in animal welfare and research, relief of poverty and youth development'. However, the report also notes 'the trustees do not tend to support research projects as research is not a core priority but there are exceptions'.

Financial information

Year end	30/06/2020
Income	£1,400,000
Assets	£57,400,000
Grants to organisations	£1,370,000

Beneficiaries included: British Racing School (£120,000); Animal Care Trust (£100,000); Amy Winehouse Foundation (£50,000); Camp Mohawk (£15,000); Chartwell Cancer Trust (£10,000); Lake District Calvert Trust (£7,500); Animal Health Trust (£3,000).

Applications

The 2019/20 annual report states:

> Unsolicited applications are not requested as the trustees prefer to support donations to charities whose work they have researched and which is in accordance with the wishes of the settlor.

Sources of information

Accounts; annual report; Charity Commission record.

Edge Foundation

Education and learning

UK

£155,000 (2020)

CC number: 286621

Correspondent: The Trustees, 44 Whitfield Street, London W1T 2RH (tel: 020 7960 1540; email: enquiry@edge.co.uk)

Trustees: Neil Bates; Prof. Colin Riordan; Pauline Daniyan; Tobias Peyton-Jones; Andrew Stevens; Prof. Ann-Marie Bathmaker; Michael Butler; Elaine Lilley; Stephen Gray.

 www.edge.co.uk

 facebook.com/ukedge

 @UKedge

General information

The Edge Foundation is an independent education charity working to transform young people's experience of learning so everyone has the opportunity to fulfil their potential and thrive. The foundation is also a registered company (company no. 286621).

The Edge Grant Fund

Open funding rounds are advertised on the foundation's website with full guidance. In previous years the foundation has awarded around £1 million of funding biennially to support innovation in education. Grants are typically of £30,000 to £100,000.

In 2020 the foundation focused its attention on existing projects undertaken in previous funding rounds. It also launched a one-off post-COVID-19 recovery grant fund with the aim of supporting educational institutions to prepare to 'build back better' post pandemic, as stated on the foundation's website. Four projects were given grants of between £10,000 and £50,000.

Financial information

Year end	31/12/2020
Income	£1.080,000
Assets	£26,390,000
Grants to organisations	£155,000
No. of grants	4

Further financial information

Due to the COVID-19 pandemic, the foundation's expenditure on grants was much lower than usual. It made four COVID-19 recovery grants during the year totalling £155,000. As the foundation has given much more in the past (grants totalled £902,000 in 2019 and £742,000 in 2018), we have chosen to include it in this edition of the guide.

Beneficiaries included: Skills Builder Partnership (£50,000); Warwickshire College Group (£46,000); Baysgarth School (£35,000); Warwickshire College Group (£24,000).

Applications

Check the foundation's website for funding round deadlines.

Sources of information

Accounts; annual report; Charity Commission record; funder's website.

D. M. H. Educational Trust Ltd

The Orthodox Jewish religion; relief of poverty; general charitable purposes

England and Wales

£184,100 (2020/21)

CC number: 271437

Correspondent: David Halpern, Trustee, 31A The Park, London NW11 7ST (tel: 020 8731 0777; email: dh@dominionltd.net)

Trustees: Samuel Halpern; Sidney Halpern; David Halpern; Relly Halpern.

General information

This trust was registered with the Charity Commission in 1976. It gives grants to organisations for Orthodox Jewish causes, the prevention or relief of poverty and general charitable purposes.

Financial information

Year end	31/03/2021
Income	£215,000
Assets	£2,050,000
Grants to organisations	£184,100

Further financial information

During 2020/21, the trust awarded grants totalling £184,100. However, in previous years grants have totalled over £300,000.

Beneficiaries included: Keren Hatzolas Doros Alei Siach (£35,000); Rise and Shine and Keren Chochmas Shloma Trust (£25,000 each); Support the Charity Worker (£20,000); Mechinah Golders Green Ltd (£6,600); Beis Yaakov Primary School Foundation (£6,000); Kollel Torah Ve Yirah Ltd (£5,000).

Applications

Apply in writing to the correspondent.

Sources of information

Accounts; annual report; Charity Commission record.

Edupoor Ltd

Education and training; the relief of poverty; older people; physical and mental health; disability; general charitable purposes

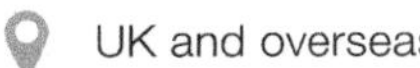

UK and overseas

£938,400 (2020/21)

CC number: 1113785

Correspondent: Meir Amitay, Secretary, Flat 10, 125 Clapton Common, Stamford Hill, London E5 9AB (tel: 07947 249515)

Trustees: Alan Shelton; Michael Shelton; Benjamin Levy.

General information

Set up in 2006, the charity is constituted as a company limited by guarantee (company no. 05576948). According to its 2020/21 accounts, the charity's objects are:

- The advancement in education and training through the world
- The relief of poverty, old age, illness, both mental and physical and the relief of persons suffering from any disability, and such other charitable purpose as the association may time to time authorise

Financial information

Year end	30/06/2021
Income	£937,100
Assets	£96,800
Grants to organisations	£938,400

Further financial information

We were unable to determine the figure for of grants given in the UK.

Beneficiaries included: A list of beneficiaries was not available.

Applications

Contact the correspondent for further information.

Sources of information

Accounts; annual report; Charity Commission record.

The Eighteen Fund

General charitable purposes; education and training; advancement of health or saving of lives; disability; prevention or relief of poverty; religious activities

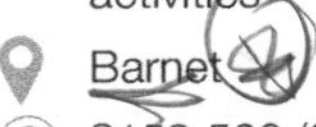

Barnet

£159,500 (2020/21)

CC number: 1135961

Correspondent: Jacqueline Rashbass, Trustee, 17 Wykeham Road, London NW4 2TB (tel: 07974 151494; email: jacquelinerrashbass@gmail.com)

Trustees: Jacqueline Rashbass; Andrew Rashbass; Elie Rashbass.

General information

The trust was established in May 2010, originally as the Rashbass Family Trust. The trust supports general charitable purposes, with a focus on education, religion, health and the relief of need.

Financial information

Year end	31/03/2021
Income	£250,000
Assets	£104,800
Grants to organisations	£159,500

Further financial information

During 2020/21 grants totalled £159,500; however, in previous years the charity has awarded grants totalling over £300,000.

Beneficiaries included: A list of beneficiaries was not available.

Applications

Apply in writing to the correspondent. The trustees meet regularly to consider applications.

Sources of information

Accounts; annual report; Charity Commission record.

The Eighty Eight Foundation

General charitable purposes; education; cancer and dementia research and care; Irish people who are underprivileged; underprivileged artists and photographers

UK; Ireland; South Africa

£1.67 million (2020/21)

CC number: 1149797

Correspondent: The Trustees, c/o Rawlinson and Hunter, Eighth Floor, 6 New Street Square, New Fetter Lane, London EC4A 3AQ (tel: 020 7842 2000; email: eighty.eight@rawlinson-hunter.com)

Trustees: Edward Fitzmaurice; Ann Fitzmaurice; Claude Slatner; Stuart Walker; Neelesh Heredia; Barry Fine.

General information

Established in 2012, the foundation makes grants for general charitable purposes. The foundation's key focus is on education and cancer and dementia research and care. According to its annual report for 2020/21, the trust also supports disadvantaged individuals who are Irish and 'exceptional underprivileged artists and photographers'.

The foundation makes grants to registered charities, non-registered charitable projects and individuals.

Financial information

Year end	31/03/2021
Income	£3,750,000
Assets	£20,020,000
Grants to organisations	£1,670,000

Beneficiaries included: UBS Optimus Foundation UK (£262,600); The Silver Line (£185,000); World Vision (£52,500); Wendell Park (£16,000); Motor Neurone Disease Association (£10,000).

Applications

The foundation's 2020/21 accounts state:

> The charity identifies worthy causes through its own research, the use of specialist research companies like NPC or the philanthropy units of UBS and Barclays. Once the potential charities are selected to progress to discussion by the trustees they need to submit a written proposal, showing how the grant will be spent, the phasing of the funds and the frequency and type of reporting. These proposals will then be discussed at meetings between the Board of Trustees with formal minutes being held.

Contact the correspondent for further information.

Sources of information

Accounts; annual report; Charity Commission record.

The George Elias Charitable Trust

Education; relief of poverty; promotion of the Jewish faith

UK and overseas

£489,500 (2020/21)

CC number: 273993

Correspondent: Stephen Elias, Trustee, Shaws Fabrics Ltd, 1 Ashley Road, Altrincham, Cheshire WA14 2DT (tel: 0161 928 7171; email: textiles@kshaw.com)

Trustees: Ernest Elias; Stephen Elias.

General information

The trust was established in 1977 by the late Mr George Elias. The trust's 2020/21 annual report states that it gives grants to charities supporting educational needs and the 'fight against poverty' as well as organisations promoting the Jewish faith. Support is given to organisations in the UK as well as overseas.

Financial information

Year end	05/04/2021
Income	£60,100
Assets	£689,200
Grants to organisations	£489,500

Beneficiaries included: A list of beneficiaries was not available.

Applications

Apply in writing to the correspondent.

Sources of information

Accounts; annual report; Charity Commission record.

The Gerald Palmer Eling Trust Company

Christianity, particularly the Orthodox church; medical research and the study of medicine; relief of sickness and poverty; local charities

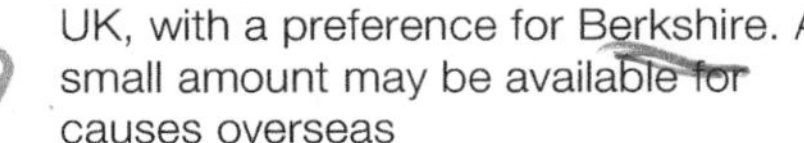

UK, with a preference for Berkshire. A small amount may be available for causes overseas

£368,500 (2020/21)

CC number: 1100869

Correspondent: D. J. Hill, Company Secretary, Eling Estate Office, Wellhouse, Hermitage, Thatcham, Berkshire RG18 9UF (tel: 01635 200268; email: charities@elingestate.co.uk)

Trustees: Desmond Harrison; Robin Broadhurst; James Gardiner; Kenneth McDiarmid; Angela Cropley.

General information

The charity was established in 2003. Its annual report for 2020/21 states that the policy of the trustees is to make grants in response to specific requests giving particular emphasis to:

- Advancing the Christian religion
- Advancing medical research
- Relieving sickness and poverty
- Supporting local charities.

The charity is also responsible for the management of the Eling Estate, which comprises of residential properties, farmland and woodlands.

Financial information

Year end	31/03/2021
Income	£1,690,000
Assets	£88,400,000
Grants to organisations	£368,500

Beneficiaries included: Brendoncare (£25,000); Recovery in Mind (£15,000); West Berkshire Mencap and Priors Court (£10,000 each); Autism Berkshire (£7,000); Cancer Research (£5,000).

Applications

Apply in writing to the correspondent.

Sources of information

Accounts; annual report; Charity Commission record.

The Marian Elizabeth Trust

Children with disabilities

UK

£1.09 million (2020/21)

CC number: 1166932

Correspondent: The Trustees, The Enterprise Centre, Priors Hall, Corby NN17 5EU (tel: 01536 560394; email: info@themarianelizabethtrust.org)

Trustees: Robert Rowley; Maureen Edwards; Michael Edwards; Rosemary Edwards.

General information

This trust was registered with the Charity Commission in May 2016. Its 2018/19 annual report, which was the latest available to view at the time of writing (June 2022), states: 'The charity makes grants to charitable organisations, such as hospices, which specialise in providing care to children with severe disabilities, with special focus on those with profound and multiple learning difficulties.'

Financial information

Year end	31/03/2021
Income	£1,200
Grants to organisations	£1,090,000

Further financial information

Full accounts were not available to view on the Charity Commission's website due to the trust's low income. We have therefore estimated the trust's grant total based on its total expenditure.

Beneficiaries included: A list of beneficiaries was not available. Previous beneficiaries include: Acorn Children's Hospice (£885,000); Rainbows Hospice (£600,000); Newlife Centre (£100,000); Rutland Rotoract Family Support Centre (£39,000).

Applications

Apply in writing to the correspondent.

Sources of information

Accounts; annual report; Charity Commission record.

The Maud Elkington Charitable Trust

General charitable purposes and social welfare

Northamptonshire and Leicestershire

£356,900 (2020/21)

CC number: 263929

Correspondent: Helen Pole, Administrator, c/o Shakespeare Martineau LLP, Two Colton Square, Leicester, Leicestershire LE1 1QH (tel: 0116 257 4462; email: helen.pole@shma.co.uk)

Trustees: Roger Bowder; Michael Jones; Katherine Hall.

General information

The trust was established in 1972 with the aim of making grants to organisations particularly, but not exclusively, in Desborough and the county of Northampton. Today, the trustees continue to focus their grant-making in Northamptonshire and Leicestershire, supporting general charitable purposes.

Funding is normally given to smaller charities where there will be a quantifiable difference to the recipients. Grants are only made to national charities when there is a benefit to the people of Northamptonshire and Leicestershire.

Grants to individuals are only made through a referring agency such as social services or the NHS. The trust is also committed to funding six pupils for the duration of their education at independent schools in Leicestershire and Northampton.

Financial information

Year end	31/03/2021
Income	£494,800
Assets	£34,520,000
Grants to organisations	£356,900
No. of grants	198

Further financial information

Grants paid in 2020/21 totalled £356,900. Grants varying from £300 to £5,000 were paid to 190 organisations, and grants of above £5,000 were paid to 8 organisations.

Beneficiaries included: A list of beneficiaries was not available. Previous beneficiaries include: Bromford Housing Association; Cancer Research UK; CARE Shangton; Charity Link – Northampton; Cynthia Spencer Hospice; Elizabeth Finn Care; Launde Abbey; Loughborough University; Multiple Sclerosis Society; Phoenix Furniture; Voluntary Action Northamptonshire.

Exclusions

The trustees only make grants to individuals in exceptional circumstances.

Applications

Apply in writing to the correspondent. The trustees meet bi-monthly, or more regularly if necessary, to consider applications.

Sources of information

Accounts; annual report; Charity Commission record.

John Ellerman Foundation

Performing arts; museums and galleries outside London; the environment; social action

UK; UK Overseas Territories (environmental work only)

£1.83 million (2020/21)

CC number: 263207

Correspondent: Dorothée Irving, Head of Grants, Aria House, 23 Craven Street, London WC2N 5NS (tel: 020 7930 8566 (general) or 020 7451 1471 (Head of Grants); email: enquiries@ellerman.org.uk or dorothee@ellerman.org.uk)

Trustees: Keith Shepherd; Geraldine Blake; Gary Steinberg; Peter Kyle; Tyfyal Choudhury; Annika Small; Becca Bunce; Jonathan Hughes.

 www.ellerman.org.uk

 @ellermanuk

General information

The foundation was established as a generalist grant-maker on the death of Sir John Ellerman in 1971. John Ellerman had inherited his substantial wealth from the business interests set up by his father, primarily the shipping business, Ellerman Lines. Throughout their lives, Sir John and his wife, Esther, fostered a profound interest in philanthropy.

The foundation funds UK-registered charities and museums and galleries. It also supports environmental work in UK Overseas Territories. The foundation prioritises charities with an annual income of between £100,000 and £10 million. The website states: 'If your income is greater than this we will only consider a grant if you are uniquely placed to help meet our funding objectives. We call this the 'only they can do it' test.'

Grants are made for core/revenue costs and project funding. These costs could include: staff salaries, training and expenses; day-to-day running costs; monitoring and evaluation; and communications and digital innovation.

Areas of work

The following information has been taken from the trust's website:

> **Arts**
>
> We concentrate our Arts funding under two separate headings:
>
> 1 ***Creators in the performing arts*** – we focus on the creation of the highest quality new work outside London, by funding organisations which collaborate with, commission or otherwise support artists to create or re-imagine work. We will prioritise applicants from outside the capital, but will consider those based in London where the proposal would bring significant benefits elsewhere. *(Organisations can apply at any time under this heading.)*
>
> 2 ***Curators in museums and galleries outside London*** – we aim to strengthen those institutions that focus on making use of curatorial skills to attract a wider public. We are keen to fund work which has a legacy within and beyond the organisation. We prioritise applications that aspire to achieve outcomes for people working in curatorial roles, the collections they work with and the institutions in which they work.
>
> **Environment**
>
> We concentrate our Environment funding under two main headings:
>
> 1 ***Protecting the seas*** – safeguarding and restoring the marine environment, through more and better managed protected areas; engaging coastal communities; reducing overfishing and tackling other harmful effects of human activity on the sea, such as pollution.
>
> 2 ***Creating richer, more sustainable places on land*** – building healthier ecosystems in urban or rural settings, through better management of these areas; experimenting with or linking together habitats; large-scale interventions that help restore places of special significance. We will also support work to reduce or prevent damaging effects of human activity, such as climate change, air pollution or pesticide use.
>
> **Social action**
>
> We want to support those with ambition to achieve positive change at scale while also creating benefits for those involved. We will therefore concentrate our funding in pursuit of a thriving society on work which:
>
> 1 ***Improves systems and institutions through policy, advocacy and campaigning*** – through building bridges between people and the establishment by creating opportunities for contact and dialogue; enabling those with experience of an issue to have a voice on what matters to them; ensuring professionals and their organisations listen and respond; using this

communication to advocate or campaign for improving policies, practices and systems
AND

2 ***Actively involves those with personal experience of the issue tackled*** – reflecting our belief that those closest to an issue understand it best. This means both people with direct personal experience of a problem, and those who have expertise and insight from working alongside them. A high priority will be finding new ways to draw on these experiences and skills, and engaging them in identifying and working on the change they want to bring about.

The foundation's website states that it wants its funding to make a difference and to have as wide an impact as possible; therefore, it supports work of 'national significance'. The definition of 'national significance' differs depending on the funding category being applied to. Details of how work of 'national significance' may look within each of the foundation's funding categories can be found on the website.

Financial information

Year end	31/03/2021
Income	£3,820,000
Assets	£149,700,000
Grants to organisations	£1,830,000

Further financial information

According to the accounts, grants paid in the year totalled £1.83 million; we have taken this figure as the grant total. Grants payable within one or more years totalled £3.9 million. This means that in total the foundation pledged £5.7 million of grants in 2020/21 in support of 64 organisations. Note: the beneficiary list includes beneficiaries of grants payable within one or more years.

Beneficiaries included: Refugee Action (£150,000); Opera Rara (£120,000); Carers UK (£100,000); North West Wildlife Trusts (£90,000); University of Oxford (£65,000); Local Trust (£25,000); Sheila McKechnie Foundation (£5,000).

Exclusions

The website states that grants are not made for the following purposes:

- individuals, including student grants or bursaries
- general and round-robin appeals
- capital developments and individual items of equipment
- promotion of religion or places of worship
- arts organisations and projects whose main focus is supporting and developing individuals, rather than when new work is part of an artistic programme
- learning and participation in the arts, where this is the primary focus of the application
- leisure or individual holiday schemes
- sport, where this is the core of the organisation's activities
- education, such as initiatives linked to the curriculum, arts or environmental educational projects
- animal welfare, captive breeding and animal rescue centres
- medical research or treatment, including drug and alcohol rehabilitation services
- prisons and offenders
- one-off campaigns
- one-off events, such as conferences, trips, seminars, master classes, summer schools, single commissions, or productions

The foundation does not consider applications from organisations that:

- have applied unsuccessfully within the previous 12 months
- focus on a single medical area, such as an individual disease, organ or condition
- are hospitals, hospices, schools, colleges or universities, unless the application is from a leading university specialist unit.

Applications

Before you apply, make sure to read the foundation's funding guidelines and complete the eligibility quiz on the website. The website states: 'We receive many more applications than we can fund. Unfortunately, this means that even if your work matches our areas of interest, we may not be able to make a grant.'

The foundation has a two-stage application process. Stage one involves a two-page proposal (headings are provided on the website). You will need to create an account on the online portal to submit your proposal and recent accounts. If your application proceeds to the second stage, you will be asked for a more detailed proposal and additional information. Then the foundation will arrange to meet you to find out more about your work.

Applications can be made at any time. Application timelines can be found on the website.

Sources of information

Accounts; annual report; Charity Commission record; guidelines for applicants; funder's website.

The Ellinson Foundation Ltd

Jewish causes; relief of poverty; religious education; general charitable purposes

London; North East England; overseas

£275,100 (2020/21)

CC number: 252018

Correspondent: Uri Ellinson, Company Secretary and Trustee, First Floor, Winston House, 349 Regents Park Road, London N3 1DH (tel: 020 3411 2001; email: u.ellinson@gmail.com)

Trustees: Alexander Ellinson; Uri Ellinson.

General information

The Ellinson Foundation Ltd was established in 1967. According to its 2020/21 annual report, the foundation was created 'to support the activities of religious Jewish organisations recognised as charitable by English Law both in the United Kingdom and abroad, especially those in the field of education and relief of poverty'.

Financial information

Year end	31/03/2021
Income	£368,500
Assets	£5,830,000
Grants to organisations	£275,100

Further financial information

During 2020/21 grants totalled £275,100. Only beneficiaries that received grants of over £5,000 were listed in the accounts. Grants of less than £5,000 totalled £3,800.

Beneficiaries included: Kesser Yehoshua (£109,500); Achisomoch (£57,000); Gateshead Kehilla (£50,000); Three Pillars (£37,800); Kollel Ohel Torah – Jerusalem (£9,000); British Friends of Rinat Aahron and Kupat Hair Karen Zaretsky (£5,000 each).

Applications

Apply in writing to the correspondent.

Sources of information

Accounts, annual report; Charity Commission record.

The Emerald Foundation

The performing arts; animal welfare; amateur sport; education; children

West Riding of Yorkshire

£1.43 million (2020)

CC number: 1127093

Correspondent: Sylvia Hall, Secretary, Howard House, Wagon Lane, Bingley BD16 1WA (tel: 07908 426823; email: shall@emeraldgroup.com)

Trustees: Peter Meredith; Karen Fojt; Martin Hasyn; Emma Tregenza; Melissa Tomlinson

https://careers.emeraldpublishing.com/community/the-emerald-foundation

General information

The Emerald Foundation was founded in 2008 as the charitable arm of the Emerald Group Holdings Ltd, of which four of the trustees are directors.

According to its website, the foundation supports charities that promote:

- The performing arts
- Animal welfare
- Sport – The Yorkshire Cricket Foundation and Leeds Rugby Foundation in particular

The foundation also provides opportunities for children living in disadvantaged areas to attend selected schools and universities in the areas of Leeds and Bradford.

Financial information

Year end	31/12/2020
Income	£1,200,000
Assets	£1,020,000
Grants to organisations	£1,430,000

Beneficiaries included: Opera North (£300,000); Whitehall Dog Rescue (£240,000); Howard Assembly Room (£100,000); Bradford Grammar School (£75,000); Geraldine Connor Foundation (£20,000); Left Bank (£5,000); One in a Million (£2,100).

Applications

Applications should be made in writing or via email to the correspondent. Applications are considered twice a year.

Sources of information

Accounts; annual report; Charity Commission record; funder's website.

EMI Music Sound Foundation

Access to music

UK and Ireland

£396,200 (2019/20)

CC number: 1104027

Correspondent: The Trustees, Universal Music, 4 Pancras Square, Kings Cross, London N1C 4AG (tel: 020 3932 6101; email: umuksoundfoundation@umusic.com)

Trustees: James Beach; Paul Gambaccini; Jo Hibbitt; Leslie Hill; Mr D. Hughes; Rupert Perry; Charles Ashcroft; Tony Wadsworth; Keith Harris; Adam Barker; Laura Arowolo.

www.emimusicsoundfoundation.com

facebook.com/The-EMI-Music-Sound-Foundation-119480934788116

General information

The EMI Music Sound Foundation was established in 1997 in celebration of the centenary of EMI Records with the purpose of improving access to music education in the UK and Ireland, with a particular focus on young people.

The foundation provides funding in two ways:

Instrument and equipment awards – grants of up to £1,500 towards the purchase of musical instruments and/or equipment for individuals who are in full-time education or schools that require the equipment to improve music education. Music teachers working within schools can apply for funding for courses and training.

Bursary awards – providing students with assistance with fees and/or living expenses. Every year the foundation awards bursaries to students at 11 chosen music colleges in the UK and Ireland – see the foundation's website for more information.

Financial information

Year end	31/07/2020
Income	£434,600
Assets	£7,020,000
Grants to organisations	£396,200

Further financial information

Grants awarded to organisations in 2019/20 were broken down as follows:

Donations to schools	£170,500
Schools Project*	£144,700
Bursaries (awarded to educational organisations on behalf of individuals)	£65,000
Institute of Education bursaries	£18,000

In addition, grants totalling £98,000 were awarded directly to individuals.

*In 2019/20 the foundation funded the Schools Project, offering grants of £6,000 to 25 secondary schools in need of support for music education.

Beneficiaries included: A full list of beneficiaries was not available. Bursaries were paid to organisations including: English National Opera; Liverpool Institute for Performing Arts; National Children's Orchestra; Royal Conservatoire of Scotland.

Exclusions

Specific exclusion criteria for the foundation's programmes can be found on its website.

Applications

Application forms for instruments and equipment grants can be downloaded from the foundation's website, along with guidance notes and deadlines. Applications should be submitted by email. The trustees review applications twice a year, in March and October.

Sources of information

Accounts; annual report; Charity Commission record; funder's website.

The Englefield Charitable Trust

General charitable purposes

Mainly the Berkshire area, as well as parts of Hackney and Inverness-shire which are connected with the Englefield Estate

£346,000 (2020/21)

CC number: 258123

Correspondent: The Trustees, Englefield Estate Office, Englefield Road, Theale, Reading, Berkshire RG7 5DU (tel: 07880 701138; email: charity@englefield.co.uk)

Trustees: Lady Elizabeth Benyon; Zoe Benyon; Richard Benyon; Catherine Haig; Melissa Owston; Richard Bampfylde; Richard Griffiths.

www.englefieldestate.co.uk/community/englefield-charitable-trust

General information

The trust was established in 1968 by Sir William Benyon. The trust supports a wide range of causes, including:

- Education
- Sport
- The arts
- Community
- Churches and faith groups
- Social welfare
- Medical support
- Agriculture and conservation
- Armed forces

Grant-making policy

Grants of between £500 and £5,000 are made (generally on a one-off basis) to organisations. Capital grants are preferred, but revenue grants will be considered.

Individuals are also eligible for grants of up to £350.

Financial information

Year end	31/03/2021
Income	£442,800
Assets	£16,980,000
Grants to organisations	£346,000

Further financial information

Grants awarded to organisations and individuals in 2020/21 were broken down as follows in the trust's accounts:

Young people, education and community	£186,100
Social, welfare and overseas support	£82,900
Church and religion	£47,000
Conservation, heritage and the arts	£18,000
Medical research and support	£9,300
Armed forces charities	£3,000

Beneficiaries included: A list of beneficiaries was not available.

Exclusions

Recipients of grants within the previous 12 months are advised not to reapply.

Applications

Applications can either be submitted directly to the trust or through the online fundraising platform The Good Exchange (www.thegoodexchange.com). Guidance notes, which are available to view in full on the trust's website, state that applications should include the following information as succinctly as possible:

- The name and address of your charity/cause, including a contact name, telephone and email and, if relevant, registered charity number
- What your organisation does
- Whether it is active in the favoured geographical areas
- What the grant is needed for
- The total cost of the project for which you are seeking funding
- How much you are asking the trust for
- How much you have raised already
- Any other funders you have applied to
- How many people will benefit from a grant from the trust, both directly and indirectly

A summary of your organisation's accounts/current financial situation should also be enclosed.

The trustees meet to consider applications twice a year, in early March and early October, and applications should be submitted by 1 February or 1 September, respectively. Your organisation's bank details should be included in your application as all grants are paid via BACS. Successful applicants will be informed as soon as possible. The trustees are unable to acknowledge every application or notify unsuccessful applicants.

Sources of information

Accounts; annual report; Charity Commission record; funder's website.

Entindale Ltd

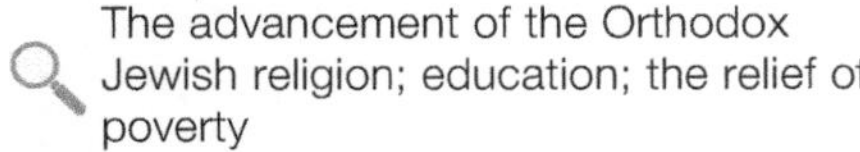

The advancement of the Orthodox Jewish religion; education; the relief of poverty

UK and Israel

£2.24 million (2019/20)

CC number: 277052

Correspondent: Joseph Pearlman, Chair, 8 Highfield Gardens, London NW11 9HB (tel: 020 8458 9266)

Trustees: Allan Becker; Barbara Peters; Joseph Pearlman.

General information

This charity was registered with the Charity Commission in June 1979. The trustees' 2019/20 annual report states that the charity's objects are to 'advance religion in accordance with the Orthodox Jewish faith.' The charity does this through its grant-making to charitable organisations with similar aims, which include the relief of poverty and the advancement of education.

Financial information

Year end	30/06/2020
Income	£1,350,000
Assets	£17,150,000
Grants to organisations	£2,240,000

Beneficiaries included: Tchabe Kollel Ltd (£85,000); Friends of Eida Chareidis Orthodox Council of Jerusalem (£72,000); Shir Chesed Beis Yisroel (£71,500).

Applications

Apply in writing to the correspondent.

Sources of information

Accounts; annual report; Charity Commission record.

Epilepsy Research UK

Epilepsy research

UK

£1.32 million (2020/21)

CC number: 1100394

Correspondent: Caoimhe Bennett, Head of Research, Can Mezzanine, 7–14 Great Dover Street, London SE1 4YR (tel: 020 3096 7887; email: caoimhe@eruk.org.uk)

Trustees: Barrie Akin; Dr John Hirst; Harry Salmon; Prof. Matthew Walker; Prof. Mark Richardson; Judith Spencer-Gregson; Mary Gavigan; Prof. Stephanie Schorge; Dr Rhys Thomas; Dr Anne Coxon; Prof. Michael Cousin; The Rt Hon. David Cameron; Thomas McLaughlan; Joseph Brice.

www.epilepsyresearch.org.uk

General information

Epilepsy Research UK was formed in 2007 through the merger of the Epilepsy Research Foundation and the Fund for Epilepsy. According to its website, the charity 'invests in clinical and fundamental scientific research investigating the causes, diagnosis and clinical management of epilepsy and associated conditions'.

There are three types of grant awarded by the charity:

- **Project grants:** Grants of up to £200,000 awarded to a team with a track record in epilepsy research to investigate a research question based on prior evidence
- **Pilot study grants:** Grants of up to £30,000 awarded to a research team to test a novel research idea and provide evidence to leverage larger funding amounts
- **Fellowship awards:** Grants of up to £300,000 awarded to an early-career researcher to develop their skills and knowledge in order to become a leader in epilepsy research

Financial information

Year end	31/03/2021
Income	£1,230,000
Assets	£1,970,000
Grants to organisations	£1,320,000

Beneficiaries included: University College London (£290,000); University of Edinburgh (£250,000); University of Sheffield (£50,000); Newcastle University (£49,600).

Applications

Application forms, together with criteria, guidelines and application deadlines, are available to download from the charity's website.

Sources of information

Accounts; annual report; Charity Commission record; funder's website.

The EQ Foundation

Disadvantaged people and social mobility

Worldwide, with a preference for the UK

£623,100 (2020/21)

CC number: 1161209

Correspondent: John Spiers, Trustee, Centennium House, 100 Lower Thames Street, London EC3R 6DL (tel: 020 7488 7110; email: info@eqfoundation.org.uk)

Trustees: Mark Kenner; Jeannie Boyle; John Spiers.

https://eqfoundation.org.uk

General information

The foundation was registered with the Charity Commission in April 2015 and was set up by EQ Investors, an investment management organisation.

The objective of the foundation is to reduce the cost of raising funds for organisations that can demonstrate they are achieving above-average impact. The 2020/21 annual report states:

> The foundation purposely does not define the groups it may make grants to but these are likely to include children, the elderly, people with disabilities, people of particular ethnic or racial origin and other Charities or voluntary bodies.

Financial information

Year end	30/04/2021
Income	£3,670,000
Assets	£3,790,000
Grants to organisations	£623,100

Further financial information

The foundation made grants to 39 charitable organisations during the year.

Beneficiaries included: For Baby's Sake Trust (£50,000); Best Beginnings (£35,000); Excellent Developments (£26,900); Access Project (£25,000); West London Zone (£20,000); upReach (£15,000); The Big Issue (£10,000); The Big Give (£5,000).

Exclusions

According to its website, the foundation has a 'preference for registered charities in the size range £500,000-£4,000,000 and working in areas connected with Early Years, Climate Action or Ethnic Inequalities'.

Applications

Apply in writing to the correspondent.

Sources of information

Charity Commission record; funders website.

The Esfandi Charitable Foundation

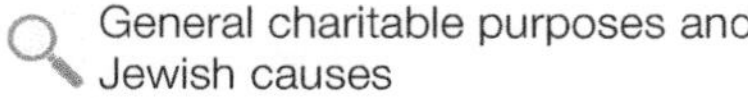

General charitable purposes and Jewish causes

UK and overseas

£822,000 (2020/21)

CC number: 1103095

Correspondent: The Trustees, 4 Fitzhardinge Street, London W1H 6EG (tel: 020 7629 6666)

Trustees: Denise Esfandi; Joseph Esfandi; Michael Esfandi; David Esfandi; Jonathan Esfandi.

General information

Set up in 2004, this foundation supports general charitable purposes, although it may have a preference for Jewish causes and organisations. The foundation's 2020/21 annual report states:

> The charity's objects are to apply general funds for general charitable purposes. No policies have been adopted regarding the level of income reserves nor the selection of the recipients of grants from the Trust

Financial information

Year end	05/04/2021
Income	£500,100
Assets	£74,400
Grants to organisations	£822,000

Beneficiaries included: Migdal Ohr (£218,700); Jewish Care (£150,000); Jewish Homes Emergency (£30,000); NSPCC (£10,000); The Chicken Soup Shelter and Noah's Ark (£2,500 each); Prism the Gift Fund (£1,000).

Applications

Apply in writing to the correspondent.

Sources of information

Accounts; annual report; Charity Commission record.

The Essex Youth Trust

Services for and the education of people under the age of 25

UK

£119,000 (2020/21)

CC number: 225768

Correspondent: Jonathan Douglas-Hughes, Clerk, c/o Gepp and Sons, 58 New London Road, Chelmsford, Essex CM2 0PA (tel: 01245 493939; email: douglas-hughesj@gepp.co.uk)

Trustees: Julien Courtauld; The Ven. Duncan Green; Claire Cottrell; William Robson; Lady Julia Denison-Smith; Michael Dyer; Michael Biegel; Julie Rogers; Jonathan McEachern.

https://sites.google.com/site/essexyouthtrust

General information

The Essex Youth Trust comprises three charities administered under a scheme of the Charity Commission dated 24 February 1993. The three charities are Essex Home School for Boys, The Charity of George Stacey Gibson and the Charity of George Cleveley.

The trust's website states:

> The object of the Charity is the education and advancement in life of young people under the age of 25 years who are in need of assistance so as to develop their physical, mental and spiritual capacities so that they may grow to full maturity as individuals and members of society, with a preference for those who, in the opinion of the Trustees, are in need of help by reason of being temporarily or permanently deprived of normal parental care or who are otherwise disadvantaged.

Financial information

Year end	31/03/2021
Income	£348,700
Assets	£8,800,000
Grants to organisations	£119,000

Further financial information

The trust awarded grants totalling £119,000 during the year; however, in previous years its grant-making exceeded £300,000.

Beneficiaries included: Cirdan Sailing Trust (£50,000); Essex Boys' and Girls' Clubs (£42,000); Chain Reaction Theatre Company (£15,000); North Avenue Youth Centre (£12,000); Lambourne End (£10,000); Sea Change Projects Ltd (£5,000).

Applications

The trust's website has a downloadable application form, which should be emailed to the correspondent after completion. Grants applications are considered by the trustees quarterly, in February, May, August and November. Applications made before the first day of the month in which a meeting is held will be considered at that meeting.

Sources of information

Accounts; annual report; Charity Commission record; funder's website.

The Ethos Foundation

General charitable purposes and community development

UK

£1.03 million (2019/20)

CC number: 1166697

Correspondent: The Trustees, 18 Buckingham Palace Road, London SW1W 0QP (tel: 07802 208276; email: ethosfoundation.uk@gmail.com)

Trustees: Grant Gordon; Brigitte Gordon; Lucy Blythe; Luka Gakic.

www.ethosfoundation.uk

General information

The foundation was established on 2016 by Grant and Brigitte Gordon. As stated on its website, the mission of the foundation is 'to support local communities and UK society in general'. Grants are normally made to registered UK charities or CIOs.

Financial information

Year end	30/09/2020
Income	£1,000,000
Assets	£563,400
Grants to organisations	£1,030,000
No. of grants	31

Further financial information

Grants of under £20,000 totalled £127,300. In 2019/20, the foundation made a larger number of small grants of under £20,000 in response to the COVID-19 pandemic.

Beneficiaries included: The Childhood Trust (£640); The Cabrach Trust (£185,000); National Trust for Scotland (£36,000); Beacon Fellowship (£20,000); City of London Sinfonia; Dogs Trust; Human Rights Watch; The Children's Society; Walnut Tree Health and Well-being CIC.

Exclusions

The foundation will generally not fund:

- Individuals
- Fundraising events
- Medical causes or scientific research
- Religious causes
- Animal-related causes

Applications

Unsolicited applications are not accepted. The foundation's website states:

> The Foundation normally applies its annual income to charitable causes proactively selected by its trustees. Grant-making decisions aim to honour the family's historical philanthropy and to make a positive impact going forward.
>
> From time to time, the Foundation may identify new focus areas and conduct research and due diligence to identify charities and programmes best placed to make a difference. Those identified will be invited to apply for support. The Foundation will work with prospective grantees in preparing materials and developing proposals for review by the trustees.

Sources of information

Accounts; annual report; Charity Commission record; funder's website.

Euro Quality Foundation

Emergency response and relief; education; social welfare; sustainable living; social projects; health and medicine

Shropshire; UK; overseas

£359,500 (2020/21)

CC number: 1119242

Correspondent: The Trustees, Euro House, Dale Street, Craven Arms, Shropshire SY7 9PA (tel: 01588 676318; email: hello@euroqualityfoundation.org)

Trustees: Mr M. N. Mansha; Rizvan Khalid; Sattar Khalid.

https://sites.google.com/euroqualityfoundation.org/eqf/home

General information

The foundation was established in 2007 and is the charitable arm of Euro Quality Lambs Ltd, a meat supplier based in Shropshire. The following information on the foundation has been taken from its website:

> The Foundation works with registered charities operating in a number of fields.
>
> Each application is considered on its own merits but we expect accountability, transparency and progress updates from recipients on funds received. The following sectors take precedence
>
> - Emergency Situations
> - Education
> - Poverty Relief
> - Sustainable Living
> - Social projects
> - Medical
>
> We broadly segment activities according to three overarching geographical regions.
>
> - Shropshire – giving locally where we are based
> - UK – giving nationally for the benefit of the country
> - Global – giving internationally for global development

Financial information

Year end	30/06/2021
Grants to organisations	£359,500

Further financial information

Grants were broken down as follows:

Education and training	£151,00
Social community welfare	£140,400
Emergency response and healthcare	£68,200

Beneficiaries included: A list of beneficiaries was not available.

Applications

Apply in writing to the correspondent.

Sources of information

Accounts; annual report; Charity Commission record; funder's website.

The Evelyn Trust

Medical research and health and well-being

Cambridgeshire

£1.19 million (2020/21)

CC number: 232891

Correspondent: Rebecca Wood, Charity Director, PO Box 1436, Willingham, Cambridgeshire CB24 5YX (tel: 01799 542708; email: rebeccawood@evelyntrust.com)

Trustees: Amy Agnew; Will Dawkins; Adrian Frost; Julia Squier; Jeremy Pemberton; Bill Pike; Catherine Thomas; Prof. Rebecca Fitzgerald; Jeremy Newsum; Dr Trevor Baglin.

www.evelyntrust.com

General information

Established as a charity in 1920, the Evelyn Trust owned and managed the Evelyn Hospital in Cambridge. The hospital was sold in 2003 and the funds invested. The investment income is used to make grants to support a broad range of projects, but mainly medical research and health and well-being projects that deliver transformational change.

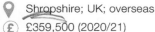

One-off grants are made to non-profit organisations for particular projects. Funding can be for capital and people costs relating to front-line work. The trust's website states: 'We seek projects for which funding from the Evelyn Trust is significant in the context of the project and makes the difference to the project's success.'

The trust has two main grant programmes:

Health and well-being grants: support is given for healthcare projects that support and inform population health and well-being in Cambridgeshire. The trust will consider supporting other projects; however, its website states that it particularly welcomes applications from organisations that:

- Support young people and families with mental health, alcohol, violence or substance abuse issues
- Assist working age adults with long-term conditions and healthcare communities that support these issues
- Enable older people to receive help and support in the community rather than needing to go into hospital or long-term care
- Work at a strategic level in the region to suggest new modes of improving health and well-being which can seed, inform and drive long-term policy and practice.

Grants are usually in the range of £10,000 up to a maximum of £250,000. There is also a rolling small grants programme under which applications in the range of £4,000 to £10,000 can be considered at any time.

Medical research grants: One-off grants are awarded for projects that benefit charitable or non-profit making organisations, rather than individuals. The trust is especially interested in projects with a clear clinical impact or that can deliver transformational change, especially demonstration or pilot projects. Grants are usually in the range of £10,000 up to a maximum of £250,000. As stated on the trust's website, medical grants are awarded for:

- Clinical research projects – towards the cost of specific, planned and well managed medical research programmes especially for younger researchers or newly established researchers seeking to obtain their first funding.
- Medical support staff and teams to achieve a step-change in service – towards the cost of medical/care teams and staff engaged in specific innovative, transformational programmes to provide medical and healthcare support to the public.

For more information and funding guidelines, visit the trust's website.

Financial information

Year end	31/03/2021
Income	£1,020,000
Assets	£29,240,000
Grants to organisations	£1,190,000

Beneficiaries included: University of Cambridge (£927,600 in nine grants); Cambridge Ethnic Community Forum (£50,000); 20Twenty Productions CIC

(£27,000); Versus Arthritis (£11,400); Disability Huntingdonshire (£5,000).

Exclusions

The exclusions are dependent upon the grants programme – refer to the relevant funding guidelines on the trust's website for full details.

Applications

Full details of how to apply to each grants programme can be found on the trust's website.

Sources of information

Accounts; annual report; Charity Commission record; funder's website.

Eversheds Sutherland (International) Charitable Trust

General charitable purposes

Charities local to the firm's UK offices

£628,800 (2020/21)

CC number: 1083594

Correspondent: Kath Pring, Eversheds, 1 Callaghan Square, Cardiff CF10 5BT (tel: 0845 498 7156; email: kathpring@eversheds.com)

Trustees: Jonathan Bowley; Naeema Choudry; Peter Scurlock; Mark Fletcher; David Beswick; Clare Whitaker; Kathryn Roberts; Michael Thompson.

www.eversheds-sutherland.com/global/en/where/europe/uk/overview/csr/charitable-giving.page

General information

The trust is the corporate charity of Eversheds Sutherland LLP, an international law firm. It receives its income from donations from the firm's partners and dormant client balances.

Financial information

Year end	30/04/2021
Income	£966,600
Assets	£1,140,000
Grants to organisations	£628,800

Beneficiaries included: End Youth Homelessness (£110,700); WaterAid (£50,100); Refuge (£20,000); National AIDS Trust (£5,000); CALM (£2,500); Unseen UK (£1,500).

Applications

The firm's website states: 'Each year the partners donate funds to the Eversheds Sutherland Business Lawyers Charitable Trust to create a significant pot of cash, the majority of which is allocated by reference to the number of people in each of our offices to support the various local charities chosen by each office.'

Sources of information

Accounts; annual report; Charity Commission record; funder's website.

The Eveson Charitable Trust

People with physical disabilities (including those who are blind or deaf); people with learning difficulties; hospitals and hospices; children who are in need; older people; people who are experiencing homelessness; medical research; mental health

Herefordshire, Worcestershire and the county of West Midlands (covering Birmingham, Coventry, Dudley, Sandwell, Solihull, Walsall and Wolverhampton)

£4.26 million (2020/21)

CC number: 1032204

Correspondent: Denise Bradley, Grants Assistant, 3 Sansome Place, Worcester WR1 1UQ (tel: 01905 905085 or 07859 393380; email: grants@eveson.org.uk)

Trustees: Richard Mainwaring; Louise Woodhead; Bill Wiggin; Judith Millward; Vivien Cockerill; Tamsin Clive; The Rt Revd Richard Jackson; Mark Taylor; Dr David Rees.

www.eveson.org.uk

General information

The trust was established in 1994 through a legacy of £49 million from Mrs Violet Eveson. It supports registered charities whose work benefits residents in Herefordshire, Worcestershire and the West Midlands. Causes in the following areas are supported:

- People with physical disabilities (including those who are blind or deaf)
- People with learning difficulties
- Mental health
- Hospitals and hospices
- Children and young people in need
- Older people
- People who are experiencing homelessness
- Medical research

Grants can be given for core costs, project costs and capital projects. While most funding is awarded to registered charities, the trust will consider applications from special needs schools and colleges.

Financial information

Year end	31/03/2021
Income	£1,550,000
Assets	£113,430,000
Grants to organisations	£4,260,000
No. of grants	303

Further financial information

Grants were broken down as follows:

Hospices	16	£600,300
Homelessness	20	£598,300
Other disabilities	78	£539,100
Disadvantaged children	59	£517,300
Children with disabilities	36	£343,300
Older people	29	£339,400
People with blindness or deafness	12	£132,000
Medical research	4	£75,000
Hospitals	7	£67,700

A further £1.05 million was awarded in 42 grants to causes falling under two or more of the above categories.

Beneficiaries included: Herefordshire Vennture (£750,000); St Anne's Hostel (£220,000); Acorns Children's Hospice Trust (£80,000); Age UK – Herefordshire and Worcestershire (£30,000); Herefordshire Night Shelter (£22,000); Brain Tumour Support (£10,000); Dyspraxia Education (£8,000); The Honeypot Children's Charity (£5,100).

Exclusions

The trust does not consider applications from individuals and will not provide retrospective funding.

Applications

Initial enquiry forms can be completed on the trust's website. If eligible, applicants will receive a full application form. The trustees meet regularly to consider grant applications.

Sources of information

Accounts; annual report; Charity Commission record; funder's website.

The Exilarch's Foundation

Jewish causes; social welfare; education; health and medical research; community development

Worldwide, with a preference for the UK, Israel, USA and Iraq

£3.69 million (2020)

CC number: 275919

Correspondent: The Trustees, 4 Carlos Place, Mayfair, London W1K 3AW (tel: 020 7399 0850)

Trustees: David Dangoor; Robert Dangoor; Elie Dangoor; Michael Dangoor.

General information

The foundation was established in 1978 by Sir Naim Dangoor, who was an Iraqi Jewish businessman. During his life, Sir Naim Dangoor gave away millions of pounds to educational, health and religious causes. After he passed away aged 101 in November 2015, his son David took over the role of the foundation's 'exilarch'.

The foundation, which was established with general charitable purposes, has the following aims: 'the eventual re-establishment of a Jewish community in Iraq through setting up educational and religious institutions' (for which the trustees have designated a £10 million fund) and to use its resources to support other charitable purposes.

The foundation has made grants to a wide range of charitable organisations under the following headings: social welfare (subcategories: community development; monotheism project; hospitals, medical education and research; ethics; and general); and education (subcategories: university/college and sundry).

Financial information

Year end	31/12/2020
Income	£6,500,000
Assets	£101,900,000
Grants to organisations	£3,690,000

Beneficiaries included: Cancer Research UK (£1.2 million); Jewish Leadership Council (£200,000); Woolf Institute (£72,000); Jewish Book Week (£20,000); Global Leadership Foundation (£10,000).

Applications

Apply in writing to the correspondent.

Sources of information

Accounts; annual report; Charity Commission record.

Extonglen Ltd

The advancement of the Orthodox Jewish religion; education; the relief of poverty

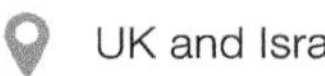

UK and Israel

£1.61 million (2020)

CC number: 286230

Correspondent: The Trustees, New Burlington House, 1075 Finchley Road, London NW11 0PU (tel: 020 8731 0777; email: ml@rowdeal.com)

Trustees: Meir Levine; Chaya Levine; Isaac Katzenberg.

General information

Registered with the Charity Commission in January 1983, this charity accepts applications from representatives of Orthodox Jewish charities and educational institutions. The charity has a particular focus on the Orthodox Jewish religion, education and the relief of poverty.

The charity continues to be involved in the educational programme Kol Halashon, which provides lectures and other educational material, and the majority of the charity's funding is given to support the programme every year.

Financial information

Year end	31/12/2020
Income	£1,140,000
Assets	£31,000
Grants to organisations	£1,610,000

Beneficiaries included: Kol Torah Ltd – towards the Kol Halashon programme (£1.56 million). Previous beneficiaries have included: Ahavas Chesed (£95,000); Pikuach Nefesh (£50,000); Kupath Gemach Chaim Bechesed Viznitz Trust (£40,000); British Friends of Nishmat Yisrael (£12,000); Children's Town Charity (£3,600).

Applications

Apply in writing to the correspondent.

Sources of information

Accounts; annual report; Charity Commission record.

Esmée Fairbairn Foundation

Preservation of species and habitat; freshwater; sustainable and ethical food; injustice and structural inequality; young leaders and artists; community development; local economies; art and culture

UK

£53.53 million (2020)

CC number: 200051

Correspondent: The Grants Team, Kings Place, 90 York Way, London N1 9AG (tel: 020 7812 3700; email: info@esmeefairbairn.org.uk)

Trustees: Tom Chandos; John Fairbairn; Beatrice Hollond; Kate Lampard; Sir Jonathan Phillips; Joe Docherty; Eleanor Updale; Edward Carter; Prof. David Hill; Stella Manzie; Flora Fairbairn; Prof. Claire Alexander; Dr Wanda Wyporska.

www.esmeefairbairn.org.uk

@esmeefairbairn

General information

Ian Fairbairn established the foundation in 1961. He was a leading City figure and his company, M&G, was the pioneer of the unit trust industry. Ian Fairbairn endowed the foundation with the greater part of his own holding in M&G, and in the early years the majority of grants were for economic and financial education.

The foundation's interest in financial education stemmed from the founder's concern that most people had no access to stock exchange investment, and were therefore precluded from investing their savings in equities and sharing in the country's economic growth. It was precisely this concern that had led him into the embryonic unit trust business in the early 1930s.

The foundation was set up as a memorial to Ian Fairbairn's wife Esmée, who had played a prominent role in developing the Women's Royal Voluntary Service and the Citizens Advice before being killed during an air raid towards the end of the Second World War. Her sons Paul and Oliver Stobart contributed generously to the original trust fund, as co-founders.

The foundation's website and its annual report and accounts provide a wealth of information for anyone with an interest in its work.

Aims

The website provides the following information:

> Esmée Fairbairn Foundation aims to improve our natural world, secure a fairer future and strengthen the bonds in communities in the UK.
>
> We support people and organisations with brilliant ideas who are doing everything they can to bring about the change they want to see.
>
> Under this strategy we are changing our approach. In addition to funding organisations with larger, longer grants, we will take a more active role ourselves. Working in collaboration with others, we will use all our tools to unlock change – not just grants and investments – but our influence, endowment, and our ability to broker alliances and remove barriers.

Grant-making strategy

The foundation's strategy is focused on three interdependent aims, details of which have been taken from the foundation's website:

Our Natural World

Impact goals by 2030, and priorities for the first five years:

1. Preserved and improved species health and habitat
   - Peat
   - Space for nature
2. Clean and healthy freshwater
   - Freshwater
3. Sustainable and ethical food
   - Family friendly farming
   - Fishing in tandem with nature

A Fairer Future

Impact goals by 2030, and priorities for the first five years:

1. Injustice and structural inequality is challenged and changed
   - Acting early on the root causes of problems
   - Children and young people's rights
   - Young people leaving care
   - Tackling injustice
2. A new inclusive generation of leaders and artists
   - Removing barriers to creative careers
   - Cultural education

Creative, Confident Communities

Impact goals by 2030, and priorities for the first five years:

1 Communities take an active role in decisions that affect them
   - Communities working together for change

2 Local economies work better for the people who live there
   - Community ownership and regeneration

3 Everyone can access the benefits of culture and creativity
   - Creativity transforming lives
   - Culture restoring communities

Further information on each aim can be found on the foundation's website.

Types of support

Support is given in three ways – grants, social investment and Funding Plus – which are outlined on the foundation's website.

- **Grants**: unrestricted, core and project grants for charitable work in the UK
- **Social investment**: the foundation provides charities and other not-for-profit organisations with investments of between £100,000 and £2 million. The investments should help to achieve the foundation's three impact goals
- **Funding Plus**: the foundation provides additional support for recipients of its grants and social investments and enables organisations to make the most of opportunities and to receive support they might not otherwise be able to afford or prioritise

Financial information

Year end	31/12/2020
Income	£4,790,000
Assets	£1,140,000
Grants to organisations	£53,530,000
No. of grants	905

Further financial information

In 2020, grants were broken down as follows:

A Fairer Future	115	£17.6 million
COVID-19 emergency grants	555	£16.1 million
Our Natural World	58	£12.8 million
Creative, Confident Communities	38	£4.6 million
Infrastructure and New Ideas	13	£1.1 million
TASK Fund (Trustees' Areas of Special Knowledge)*	114	£880,000
Funding in partnership	12	£450,000

*This fund is not open to applications.

In addition, the foundation provided 12 social investments in the following categories (these have not been included in the grant total):

Our Natural World	5	£2.3 million
A Fairer Future	3	£1.1 million
Social change	1	£230,000
Creative, Confident Communities	2	£183,000
Infrastructure and New Ideas	1	£100,000

Beneficiaries included: Soil Association (£675,500); Food Sense Wales (£234,200); Roots of Empathy (£195,000); The British Youth Council (£150,000); Best Beginnings (£60,000); Child Poverty Action Group (£39,900); UK Feminista (£17,500); Aurora Orchestra (£12,500); Friends of the Earth Scotland (£5,000).

Exclusions

The foundation's website states:

> We will not consider applications from/for:
> - Organisations with an annual turnover of less than £100,000 (as reflected in the latest set of accounts)
> - Organisations without at least three non-executive trustees or directors
> - Grants for less than £30,000
> - Social investments for less than £100,000 or more than £2m
> - Work that is not legally charitable
> - Work that does not have a direct benefit in the UK
> - Grants to individuals
> - Capital costs including building work, renovations, and equipment (grants only, we may make social investments for these)
> - Academic research – unless it can demonstrate real potential for practical outcomes
> - Healthcare with a clinical basis, including medical research, hospices, counselling and therapy, arts therapy, education about and treatment for drug and alcohol misuse
> - Work that is primarily the responsibility of statutory authorities
> - The promotion of religion

Applications

An eligibility quiz is available on the foundation's website. Expressions of interest can be submitted via the foundation's website. Applicants should receive a response to their expression of interest within four weeks.

Sources of information

Accounts; annual report; annual review; Charity Commission record; guidelines for applicants; funder's website.

The Lord Faringdon Charitable Trust

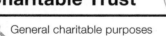

General charitable purposes

UK, with a preference for Oxfordshire

£190,100 (2020/21)

CC number: 1084690

Correspondent: Sharon Lander, Secretary, The Estate Office, Buscot Park, Faringdon, Oxfordshire SN7 8BU (tel: 01367 240786; email: estbuscot@aol.com)

General information

This trust was formed in 2000 by the amalgamation of the Lord Faringdon First and Second trusts.

According to the 2020/21 annual report, the trust supports a wide range of charitable purposes, with a preference for:

> - Educational Scholarships Grants
> - Hospitals and the provision of medical treatment for the sick
> - Purchase of antiques and artistic objects for museums and collections to which the public has access
> - Care and assistance of the aged and infirm
> - Development and assistance of Arts and Sciences, physical recreation and drama
> - Research into matters of public interest
> - Relief of poverty
> - Support of matters of public interest

The trust also supports The Faringdon Collection Trust (Charity Commission no. 203770).

Financial information

Year end	05/04/2021
Income	£272,300
Assets	£12,050,000
Grants to organisations	£190,100
No. of grants	113

Further financial information

During 2020/21 grants totalled £190,100; however, in previous years the trust has made grants totalling over £300,000.

Beneficiaries included: Loughborough Bell Foundry Trust (£10,000); FAI UK Italian Heritage (£5,000); Ashmolean Museum (£2,500); Brain Tumour Charity and Jubilee Sailing Trust (£1,000 each); Cherwell Theatre Company (£500); The Leprosy Mission (£250).

Exclusions

Grants are not made to individuals.

Applications

Apply in writing to the correspondent. The annual report for 2020/21 explains:

> Grant applications are accepted from registered charities and other recognised bodies. All grant applications are required to provide information on the specific purpose and expected beneficiaries of the grant. This information helps the charity assess how its programme of discretionary grant-making achieves a spread of benefit.

Sources of information

Accounts; annual report; Charity Commission record.

The Thomas Farr Charity

Education; young people; health; older people

Nottinghamshire

£355,600 (2020/21)

CC number: 328394

Correspondent: The Trustees, c/o Nottinghamshire Community Foundation, Pine House B, Ransom Wood Business Park, Southwell Road West, Mansfield, Nottinghamshire NG21 0HJ (tel: 01623 620202; email: enquiries@nottscf.org.uk)

Trustees: Rathbone Trust Company Ltd; Philip Pruden; Amanda Farr; Henry Farr.

 https://thomasfarrcharity.com

General information

The charity was established in 1989, following the sale of the Home Brewery in Nottingham, and has the aim of supporting areas where the Home Brewery had a presence. Support is given to a wide range of causes; however, the charity's main areas of focus are:

- Education
- Young people
- Health
- Older people

Preference is given to projects and activities in or benefitting the people of Nottinghamshire and the adjacent areas.

Financial information

Year end	05/04/2021
Income	£264,100
Assets	£9,380,000
Grants to organisations	£355,600

Further financial information

Grants were broken down as follows:

Community projects	£132,700
Disability	£89,800
Hospitals/health	£30,100
Older people	£21,400
Homelessness	£18,100
Children	£18,000
Education	£14,800
Sport	£14,800
Youth organisations	£9,000
Religion	£5,000
Museums/theatre	£2,000

Beneficiaries included: Portland College (£50,000); Reach Learning Disability (£20,000); Nottinghamshire Community Foundation (£10,000); Grace Enterprises Nottingham Ltd (£5,000); Nottinghamshire Clubs for Young People Ltd (£4,000); Disability Nottinghamshire (£2,000); Ellerslie Cricket Club (£250).

Exclusions

The charity does not make grants for the following:

- Loans or business finance
- Campaigning work and projects that are primarily political
- Retrospective costs
- General or mail shot appeals
- Replacing statutory funding
- Activities that are the responsibility of the local health authority, education authority or a similar body

Grants are not made to individuals.

Applications

Applications can be made via the Nottinghamshire Community Foundation website. The trustees meet three times a year to review applications, usually in March, July and November. For consideration in these meetings, applications must be received by 20 January, 20 May and 20 September, respectively.

Sources of information

Accounts; annual report; Charity Commission record; funder's website.

The February Foundation

General charitable purposes; health; end-of-life care; the environment; heritage

UK

£11.68 million (2020/21)

CC number: 1113064

Correspondent: Richard Pierce-Saunderson, Chief Executive, Spring Cottage, Church Street, Stradbroke, Suffolk IP21 5HT (tel: 01379 388200; email: rps@thefebruaryfoundation.org)

Trustees: James Carleton; Mark Clarke; Michael Moody.

 www.thefebruaryfoundation.org

General information

The foundation was established in 2006 for general charitable purposes and has a broad range of interests. According to its 2020/21 annual report, the foundation makes grants for:

- Charities which are for the benefit of persons who are making an effort to improve their lives
- Charities which are for the benefit of persons no longer physically or mentally able to help themselves
- Charities which have a long-term beneficial impact on the future of individuals, groups of individuals, or organisations
- Charities which protect the environment
- Small or minority charities where small grants will have a significant impact

The foundation can also make grants to companies where the acquisition of equity would be in line with the foundation's charitable objectives. There is no minimum grant. The maximum grant is usually £5,000 but awards are considered on a case-by-case basis.

Grants are made for project, core or capital costs. The foundation is happy to part-fund projects.

Financial information

Year end	28/02/2021
Income	£17,590,000
Assets	£117,510,000
Grants to organisations	£11,680,000
No. of grants	222

Further financial information

In 2020/21, the foundation awarded 235 grants to 221 organisations totalling £2.41 million. Grants were distributed in the following categories:

Healthcare and patient support	£1.03 million
End-of-life care	£782,200
Other	£394,000
Education	£204,600

In addition, the foundation donated investments with a market value of £9.34 million to a UK charity with general charitable purposes.

Beneficiaries included: A list of beneficiaries was not available.

Exclusions

The foundation's website states that it will not accept applications from or for the following:

- Animal charities (except those involving therapy or sportspeople with disabilities)
- Charities which are party-politically driven
- Charities with a commercial bias for a particular product or company
- Charities with an aggressive religious bias
- Childcare
- Citizens Advice Bureaux
- Community centres
- Education (including adult, further, higher and secondary education, and special educational needs)
- Housing associations
- Individuals
- Medical research
- Minibuses
- NHS trusts (or charities which support them)
- Non-departmental government bodies
- Outdoor activity centres
- Overseas projects
- Scouts, Guides, Brownies, Cubs and similar organisations
- Single-faith organisations
- Sports clubs, unless for people with mental or physical disabilities
- Village halls
- Youth clubs and centres

Applications

Apply in writing to the correspondent. The foundation's website states:

> Applications by email are given priority as the Foundation aims to operate on a paperless basis. Please send us the details and budget of the proposed project, how many people would benefit, how those benefits might be measured (not just financially), what the estimated cost of raising funds for the project is, and the full cost of raising voluntary income (especially if this is not detailed in your accounts). It is important to include in your email application full accounts for your most recent completed financial year.

Full details of what to include in an application can be found on the foundation's website. If you are applying on behalf of a hospice, consult the foundation's website for details of additional required information .

There are no application deadlines and applicants are normally informed of the trustees' decision within 12 weeks of submission.

Sources of information

Accounts; annual report; Charity Commission record; funder's website.

The Marc and Tania Feldmann Charitable Trust

Medical research

England and Wales

£402,600 (2020)

CC number: 1150832

Correspondent: The Trustees, 5 Durham Terrace, London W2 5PB (tel: 020 7792 2440)

Trustees: Prof. Sir Marc Feldmann; Lady Tania Feldmann; Prof. Sir Ravinder Maini.

General information

This trust was established in February 2013 and its primary objective is to promote effective research in the field of biology and medicine.

Financial information

Year end	05/04/2020
Income	£637,400
Assets	£1,270,000
Grants to organisations	£402,600

Beneficiaries included: A list of beneficiaries was not available.

Applications

The trustees do not consider unsolicited applications. The trust's 2019/20 annual accounts state:

> Strategies for achieving objectives will be by making donations, usually to other registered charities, which together can fulfil aims of the Charity. The Charity does not plan at present to invite applications, as this would dramatically change the ethos of the Trust.

Sources of information

Accounts; annual report; Charity Commission record.

Allan and Nesta Ferguson Charitable Settlement

Education; international friendship and understanding; world peace and development

UK and overseas

£1.58 million (2020)

CC number: 275487

Correspondent: Letitia Glaister, Trustee, c/o Tees Law, John Street, Royston, Hertfordshire SG8 9BG (tel: 01763 295850; email: Letitia.glaister@teeslaw.com)

Trustees: Elizabeth Banister; Prof. David Banister; Letitia Glaister; Eleanor Banister; Edmund Cairns.

 www.fergusontrust.co.uk

General information

The Allan and Nesta Ferguson Charitable Trust (registered as The Allan and Nesta Ferguson Charitable Settlement) was established in 1979 by their son and daughter-in-law, John and Elnora. Its objectives have closely followed the interests of the Ferguson family in their commitment to education, international friendship and understanding, and the promotion of world peace and development.

Eligibility

The following information has been taken from the trust's website:

> The Allan and Nesta Ferguson Charitable Trust primarily funds projects which support the Trust's interests of education, international friendship and understanding, and the promotion of world peace and development.
>
> The Trust aims to support projects both in the UK and abroad, and supports charitable organisations situated in the UK and overseas. However, all charitable organisations must be registered as a charity with the UK Charity Commission in order to be eligible for funding.
>
> Grants to charities will be on a matching funding basis only so that if the applicant has raised 50% of their budget the Trustees will consider awarding matching funding up to a maximum of 50%. However, if the applicant has raised less than 50% of their budget the Trustees will only consider awarding a maximum of 30% funding.

Financial information

Year end	31/01/2020
Income	£357,200
Assets	£29,070,000
Grants to organisations	£1,580,000

Beneficiaries included: Loughborough University (£60,000); University of Leeds (£45,700); Africa Educational Trust (£30,000); Barnardo's and Tearfund (£20,000 each); Scottish Love In Action (£15,000).

Applications

Apply online via the trust's website.

Sources of information

Accounts; annual report; Charity Commission record; guidelines for applicants; funder's website.

The Fidelity UK Foundation

Arts, culture and heritage; community; education; health; the environment

UK, with a preference for London, Kent and Surrey

£9.86 million (2020)

CC number: 327899

Correspondent: Head of Foundations, Beech Gate, Millfield Lane, Lower Kingswood, Tadworth, Surrey KT20 6RP (tel: 01732 777364; email: foundation@fil.com)

Trustees: Anthony Bolton; John Owen; Sally Walden; Abigail Johnson; Elizabeth Johnson; Dr Malcolm Rogers; Sanjeev Gandhi; Peter Goldsbrough; Edward Johnson.

 www.fidelityukfoundation.org

General information

The Fidelity UK Foundation is the charitable foundation of the financial services company Fidelity Worldwide Investments. The foundation was established in 1988 and primarily supports UK-registered charities based in the areas where Fidelity Worldwide Investment has corporate offices: London, Kent and Surrey. Applications are also considered from elsewhere in the UK, provided the organisation is a nationally recognised centre of excellence.

Grants are generally made to organisations with an annual operating budget in excess of £500,000.

According to its website, the foundation's charitable giving is mainly in the areas of:

> - **Arts, culture and heritage** – Including nationally significant heritage sites, internationally recognised museums and class leading organisations in the visual and performing arts

- **Community** – Particularly early interventions and charities which help young and/or disadvantaged people achieve their potential.
- **Education** – Particularly initiatives which improve education outcomes for the disadvantaged, from early years through to transition to work.
- **Health** – Including disability, palliative care and centres of excellence involved in ground-breaking research and treatments to address chronic illness (with a particular focus on investment in specialist equipment).
- **Environment** – Particularly preservation and sustainable initiatives that have a positive impact on the natural world.

Grants are typically directed to specific projects in the following categories:

Capital Improvements
Large-scale projects central to the overall growth and sustainability of the applicant, such as new construction, renovations, expansions, equipment and other initiatives that support the organisation's strategic vision.

Technology Projects
High-impact technology projects that can substantially increase an organisations efficiency, effectiveness and sustainability. Projects may include:

- the development of front and back office systems
- performance measurement systems
- on-line functionality
- staff training (ensuring appropriate allocation of training of staff to manage the system)
- financial accounting, inventory management, point-of-sale and other business systems.

Please note that funding is not provided for replacement of dated IT hardware, routine system upgrades or ongoing website content.

Organisational Development
Projects which seek to establish a new, transformational strategic path. This could include support for an initiative that helps a growing organisation achieve scale efficiencies, the development of a franchise model or helping charities to yield consolidation efficiencies through mergers.

Planning Initiatives
Funding for expert/external consultants to develop strategic, business, technology and other types of plans.

Grant size depends upon the impact and scope of the project. The majority of grants are of between £25,000 and £150,000, although in exceptional circumstances, the trustees may choose to exceed this amount. Grants are not normally intended to cover the entire cost of a project.

Grants are normally made towards significant, transformational projects with a total budget of £50,000 or more. Grants are one-off investments; they are rarely awarded for, or across, multiple years and will not normally be awarded to the same organisation in successive years.

The foundation has established two grant funds to award smaller grants (£5,000 to £20,000) to small and medium-sized registered charities in Kent and Surrey. The funds support charities helping socially disadvantaged young people achieve their potential, and grants are only awarded towards capital costs. The funds are administered by Kent Community Foundation and the Community Foundation for Surrey, respectively.

Fidelity also has three international foundations: The Fidelity Bermuda Foundation, The Fidelity Europe Foundation and The Fidelity Asia Pacific Foundation. They make grants to organisations in countries where the company has operations and which serve beneficiaries in Austria, Belgium, Ireland, Italy, France, Germany, Luxembourg, Netherlands, Poland, Spain, Sweden, Switzerland, Australia, Bermuda, China, Hong Kong, India, Japan, South Korea, Singapore and Taiwan.

Financial information

Year end	31/12/2020
Income	£4,360,000
Assets	£288,030,000
Grants to organisations	£9,860,000
No. of grants	50

Further financial information

Grants were broken down as follows:

Health	14	£3.57 million
Education	15	£2.87 million
Community development	16	£2.86 million
Arts, culture and heritage	4	£360,000
Cross sector	1	£200,700

Beneficiaries included: Mental Health Innovations (£600,000); Young Lives vs Cancer (£300,000); Future First (£153,300); NowTeach (£83,100); Vauxhall City Farm and WomenCentre (£20,000 each).

Exclusions

Grants are not generally made to:

- Start-up, political or sectarian organisations
- Organisations which have been running for less than three years
- Individuals
- Private schools

Grants are not generally made for:

- Sponsorships
- Scholarships
- Corporate memberships
- Advertising and promotional projects
- Exhibitions
- General running costs

Grants will not normally cover costs incurred prior to application and/or the grant being awarded.

Applications

The foundation used to accept applications; however, at the time of writing (January 2022) the foundation was not accepting new enquiries and was instead proactively identifying organisations to support.

Sources of information

Accounts; annual report; Charity Commission record; funder's website.

Doris Field Charitable Trust

General charitable purposes

UK, with a particular interest in Oxfordshire

£310,900 (2020/21)

CC number: 328687

Correspondent: Emily Greig, c/o Blake Morgan LLP, Seacourt Tower, West Way, Oxford, Oxfordshire OX2 0FB (tel: 01865 254286; email: emily.greig@blakemorgan.co.uk)

Trustees: John Cole; Mr N. Harper; Wilhelmina Church; Helen Fanyinka.

General information

The Doris Field Charitable Trust was established in 1990 following the passing of Doris Field in 1988. One-off and recurrent grants are given to large UK organisations and small local projects for a wide variety of causes, and are usually of below £3,000. The trust favours local causes in Oxfordshire.

Financial information

Year end	15/08/2021
Income	£413,700
Assets	£12,160,000
Grants to organisations	£310,900
No. of grants	272

Beneficiaries included: Prostate Cancer UK (£7,500); Witney Buttercross Scout Group (£2,500); Cecily's Fund (£2,000); Asthma Relief, Blind in Business and Prisoners' Education Trust (£1,000 each); Wantage Choral Society (£750); Lake Street Nursery and Wootton School (£500 each).

Applications

Potential applicants can obtain an application form from the correspondent. The trustees meet three times a year to consider applications but can respond to urgent appeals if necessary.

Sources of information

Accounts; annual report; Charity Commission record.

Sir John Fisher Foundation

General charitable purposes, with a preference for maritime causes; medicine; people with disabilities; education; music; the arts; community projects

UK, with a strong preference for charities in the Furness peninsula and Cumbria

£2.76 million (2020/21)

CC number: 277844

Correspondent: David Dawson, Executive Officer, c/o Hart Jackson and Sons, 8–10 New Market Street, Ulverston, Cumbria LA12 7LW (tel: 07464 504756; email: www.sirjohnfisherfoundation.org.uk)

Trustees: Diane Meacock; Daniel Tindall; Michael Shields; Thomas Meacock; Christopher Batten; Chris Tomlinson; Dr David Jackson.

www.sirjohnfisherfoundation.org.uk

General information

The foundation was registered with the Charity Commission in 1979 after it was established by Sir John and Lady Maria Fisher. The foundation is closely associated with James Fisher and Sons plc, which provides marine engineering services.

Areas of work

The foundation's website states that it supports charitable causes in the six following categories:

- Maritime
- Medical and disability
- Education
- Music
- Arts
- Community projects in Barrow-in-Furness and the Furness peninsula

Capital and revenue funding is available for up to three years. Most grants are of less than £30,000. In the past, larger grants have also been awarded for major one-off projects and research.

The foundation's website states:

> The Foundation gives priority to applying its income to projects and causes based in Barrow-in-Furness and the Furness Peninsula. Exceptionally, occasional community projects from the remainder of Cumbria and North Lancashire will be considered. Some projects are supported nationally, particularly Maritime projects and a few educational Music projects.

Financial information

Year end	31/03/2021
Income	£58,260,000
Assets	£124,480,000
Grants to organisations	£2,760,000
No. of grants	96

Further financial information

During 2020/21, grants were broken down as follows:

Lady Maria Fisher Foundation	2	£1 million
Community	46	£649,000
Medical research	6	£398,700
Medical	17	£242,900
Education	14	£251,700
Arts	6	£160,400
Maritime	3	£31,500
Music	2	£17,500

Beneficiaries included: The Lady Maria Fisher Foundation (£1.2 million); University of Cumbria (£240,600); The Neurological Research Trust (£110,000); Cumbria Community Foundation (£50,000); Hospice of St Mary of Furness (£40,000); The Birchall Trust (£20,000); Word Market (£300).

Exclusions

According to the foundation's website, it will not make grants for:

- Sponsorships
- Individuals
- Expeditions
- The promotion of religion or places of worship (except when acting as a community centre)
- Animal welfare
- Retrospective appeals
- Pressure groups
- Community projects outside Barrow-in-Furness and the Furness peninsula (except occasional projects in Cumbria or the north of Lancashire, or that fall within one of the other categories supported by the foundation)

Applications

Application forms are available from the correspondent or to download from the website, where guidelines can also be found. Applications should be made by submitting a completed application form, together with all relevant information (set out on the application form) to the secretary by email or post. The trustees meet at the beginning of May and the beginning of November each year. The closing dates for applications are posted on the foundation's website.

Sources of information

Accounts; annual report; Charity Commission record; funder's website.

Fishmongers' Company's Charitable Trust

Education in prisons; mental health; food and nutrition

City of London and the boroughs of Camden, Hackney, Islington, Lambeth, Southwark, Tower Hamlets, Newham and Westminster

£1.47 million (2019/20)

CC number: 263690

Correspondent: Amy Spolton, Grants Officer, The Fishmongers' Company, Fishmongers' Hall, London Bridge, London EC4R 9EL (tel: 020 7626 3531; email: charity@fishmongers.org.uk)

Trustee: The Fishmongers' Company.

https://fishmongers.org.uk/grants

General information

The Fishmongers' Company is one of the 12 great livery companies of the City of London, and is among the most ancient of the City guilds. It makes a significant contribution to the UK fishing sector and other non-fishery areas through its grants and philanthropy.

Currently, the trust operates a grants programme to support projects in the following areas:

- Education in prisons
- Mental health
- Food and nutrition

Eligibility

The trust's website states:

> An application will only be considered where it meets the following criteria:
>
> - Submitted by a Registered Charity, Social Enterprise or Community Interest Company
> - Clearly identifies key objectives and measurable outcomes
> - Is made by the organisation delivering the activity, service or project. i.e. applications cannot be made on behalf of a third party
>
> Preference will be given to applicants:
>
> - Whose annual income is not below £100,000 and does not exceed £5,000,000
> - Requesting funding for a **specific project** rather than for general funds and to those
> - Operating within the City of London and the Boroughs of Camden, Hackney, Islington, Lambeth, Southwark, Tower Hamlets, Newham or Westminster

Grants are typically of between £15,000 and £30,000 per year, for up to three years.

Financial information

Year end	31/01/2020
Income	£1,590,000
Assets	£36,210,000
Grants to organisations	£1,470,000

Further financial information

During the year, grants to organisations totalled £1.59 million; however, £121,000 of grants were cancelled. Note: the following breakdown of grants provided in the accounts does not take the cancellations into consideration:

Education	£884,000
Health and well-being	£376,000
Hardship	£203,000
Fisheries	£79,000
Civic grants	£44,000

In addition, grants to individuals for education and welfare totalled £44,000.

Only beneficiaries of grants of £1,000 and above were listed in the accounts.

Beneficiaries included: Free Cabs for NHS Staff (£277,000); The Gresham's Foundation (£198,000); Chefs in Schools (£95,000); The Listening Place (£45,000); FoodCycle (£31,000); First Aid Nursing Yeomanry (£11,000); RAF Marham (£4,000); The Soup Kitchen (£1,000).

Exclusions

Applications are not considered from individuals, or organisations applying on their behalf. Charities with political associations or purposes are also ineligible.

Applications

An online application form can be accessed on the trust's website.

The grants officer can be contacted using the online enquiry form on the trust's website. Remember to choose 'Philanthropy and Grants Team' for the enquiry type in the drop-down menu when filling out the form.

Sources of information

Accounts; annual report; Charity Commission record; funder's website.

The Fonthill Foundation

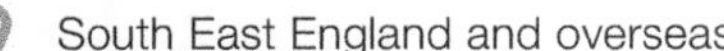

Children and young people's education

South East England and overseas

£282,200 (2019/20)

CC number: 325071

Correspondent: The Trustees, PO Box 261, Lewes BN7 9LS (email: enquiry@fonthill-foundation.org.uk)

Trustees: Stephen Wilkins; Victoria Henley; Margaret Lloyd; Niki Cannon; Adrian Carver.

 https://fonthill-foundation.org.uk

 facebook.com/Fonthill-Foundation-1555279228093304

 @fonthillcharity

General information

The foundation supports the education of children and young people in South East England and overseas.

The following information has been taken from the foundation's website:

UK Programme

Our UK programme focuses on helping those in need in the South East. We look to partner with local organisations that have clear educational objectives, and who are passionate about making a difference for young people.

Overseas Programme

Through our overseas programme we look to develop partnerships with organisations that fit with our Charity's aims and objectives. It is really important for us that our international partners demonstrate an established relationship with the communities in which they operate, and that they are truly committed to empowering the growth and development of those communities through education.

Small Community Grants Programme

As well as our larger programmes, each year we allocate a pot of funding for our small Community Grants Scheme. This fund is open to organisations in the South East of the UK supporting and promoting educational activities, who need a bit of a helping hand. Grants of up to £3,000 are available, with applications accepted throughout the year.

Financial information

Year end	31/08/2020
Income	£163,900
Assets	£5,760,000
Grants to organisations	£282,200

Beneficiaries included: IntoUniversity (£20,000); Steyning Grammar School (£10,000); The Crew Club Youth Centre (£8,800); Kyaninga Child Development Centre (£5,600); Migrant English Project (£3,000); Brighton Metropolitan College (£2,500); Family Support Work (£930).

Applications

The foundation's website states: 'We would love to hear about your organisation and the work you are doing. We're dynamic in constantly seeking out the best new partnerships, but note we don't take unsolicited applications for our UK or Overseas Programmes.' Application forms for small grants can be downloaded from the foundation's website.

Sources of information

Accounts; annual report; Charity Commission record; funder's website.

The Football Foundation

Grassroots and community football

England and Wales

£69.9 million (2020/21)

CC number: 1079309

Correspondent: Grant Management Team, 10 Eastbourne Terrace, London W2 6LG (tel: 0345 345 4555; email: enquiries@footballfoundation.org.uk)

Trustees: Michael Callanan; Andrew Rowe; Shyam Ashoka; Nigel Croft; Vanessa Connolly; Simon White; David Wilkins.

 www.footballfoundation.org.uk

 facebook.com/FootballFoundation1

 @FootballFoundtn

 @footballfoundation

General information

The Football Foundation is the UK's largest sports charity, receiving funding from The Football Association, the Premier League and the Department for Culture, Media and Sport via Sports England. It uses this money to leverage even more partnership funding, in order to deliver a programme of new and improved community sports facilities in towns and cities across the country.

According to its 2020/21 annual report the foundation's current objectives are to:

- Put into place a new generation of outstanding facilities in parks, schools, colleges and universities
- Provide capital and revenue support to increase participation in community football
- Strengthen the links between football and the community, and harness its potential as a force for good in society
- Work with other charities to help achieve the Foundation's objectives

A wide range of organisations are eligible for support, including:

- Football clubs (grassroots, professional and semi-professional) and their associated community charities
- Multi-sport clubs
- Local authorities
- County football associations
- Educational establishments (including schools)
- Registered charities
- Not-for-profit organisations

Financial information

Year end	31/05/2021
Income	£42,300,000
Assets	£27,920,000
Grants to organisations	£69,900,000

Beneficiaries included: Newcastle United Foundation (£2 million); The Futures Trust (£1.24 million); John Colet School (£599,600); Leek Town FC Ltd (£418,900).

Applications

New grant programmes open and close regularly, so potential applicants are advised to check the foundation's website for the latest information, including detailed application instructions and eligibility terms.

Sources of information

Accounts; annual report; Charity Commission record; funder's website.

The Forrester Family Trust

 General charitable purposes

 UK and overseas

£1.17 million (2020/21)

CC number: 1190231

Correspondent: The Trustees, 11 Whitecroft Way, Beckenham, Kent BR3 3AQ (tel: 020 8629 0089; email: admin@theforresterfamilytrust.org)

Trustees: Wendy Forrester; Hilary Porter; Melissa Jones; Thomas Walker; Fiona Cole.

 http://forrestertrusts.com/donald-forrester-trust

General information

The Forrester Family Trust was established in 2020 following the merging of Donald Forrester Trust and Gwyneth Forrester Trust. Both trusts have been supporting small charities since 1986.

Grants are given for a wide range of purposes. The trust's website states the following:

> Our strategy from 2021 to 2026 details the values and priorities which will help us work towards a just and equitable society, and support excellent charities to help people facing significant disadvantage.

Previously, Gwyneth Forrester Trust has provided grants under the following themes:

- Domestic violence
- Asylum seekers
- Mental health
- Education (children and young people)
- Homelessness
- Children in crisis
- Support for older people
- Helping young people and people who have offended into employment
- Hospices
- Mental health

Grants are also given towards disaster relief.

Financial information

Year end	31/03/2021
Income	£60,210,000
Assets	£43,080,000
Grants to organisations	£1,170,000

Further financial information

The Forrester Family Trust's 2020/21 annual report states 'No grants were paid in the period to 31 March 2021, as the charity establishes itself and accepts applications for grants to be made in the forthcoming year'. However, during 2020/21, £252,600 was awarded by Donald Forrester Trust and £916,400 by Gwyneth Forrester Trust. We have therefore used the combined total of £1.17 million as the grant total.

Beneficiaries included: NSPCC and British Heart Foundation (£10,000 each); Life Cycle UK, North Bristol Advice Centre and Read for Good (£5,000 each); Outward Bound Trust (£4,100); Congolese Association of Merseyside (£2,500); Blind in Business (£2,000); Swansea Music Art Digital (£500).

Applications

Details of how to apply will be made available on the trust's website by July 2022. Check the website for any updates.

Sources of information

Accounts, annual report, Charity Commission record; funder's website.

The Fort Foundation

Health; amateur sport; education; arts and culture; citizenship; community welfare; religion; environmental protection and improvement

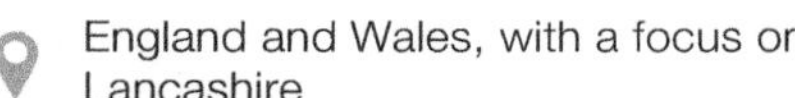

England and Wales, with a focus on Lancashire

£107,100 (2020/21)

CC number: 1028639

Correspondent: The Trustees, c/o Fort Vale Engineering Ltd, Calder Vale Park, Simonstone Lane, Simonstone, Burnley, Lancashire BB12 7ND (tel: 01282 440000; email: info@fortvale.com)

Trustees: Ian Wilson; Edward Drury; John Hartley; Peter Fort; Edward Fort.

General information

The Fort Foundation was registered with the Charity Commission in 1993. According to its Charity Commission record, the foundation gives grants to organisations and individuals, particularly those based in Lancashire, and its areas of interest are health, amateur sport, education, art and culture, citizenship, community welfare, religion, and environmental protection and improvement.

Financial information

Year end	28/02/2021
Income	£300,000
Assets	£1,700,000
Grants to organisations	£107,100

Further financial information

The foundation awarded grants totalling £107,100 during the year; however, in previous years its grant-making exceeded £300,000.

Beneficiaries included: Pendleside Hospice and The Outward Bound Trust (£10,000 each); Teenage Cancer Trust (£7,500); Lancaster University Formula Student Project (£6,000); Valley Heritage (£5,000).

Applications

Apply in writing to the correspondent.

Sources of information

Accounts; annual report; Charity Commission record.

The Foster Wood Foundation

Advancement of Christianity; relief of poverty; advancement of education; social welfare

 UK and overseas

£468,000 (2020/21)

CC number: 1101364

Correspondent: Geoffrey Hill, Trustee, 21–27 Lamb's Conduit Street, London WC1N 3GS (tel: 020 7935 3793; email: ghill@gsmaccountants.co.uk)

Trustees: Geoffrey Hill; Margaret Lodge; The Revd David Hodson.

General information

The Foster Wood Foundation was established in 2003. According to its 2020/21 annual report, the foundation primarily provides funding to organisations which fall into one of the following categories:

- Christian organisations
- Medical charities
- Charities relieving poverty
- Social welfare institutions

Financial information

Year end	05/04/2021
Income	£463,700
Assets	£63,000
Grants to organisations	£468,000

Further financial information

Grants were distributed as follows:

Christian organisations	£287,000
medical charities	£100,000
charities relieving poverty	£56,000
social welfare institutions	£25,000

Beneficiaries included: A list of beneficiaries was not available.

Applications

The foundation's 2020/21 annual report states the following: 'In the past applications have been invited from suitable charities able to demonstrate that they can use the funds they apply for in an effective manner to achieve their stated aims which must be consistent with the objects of the foundation. However, as it is the intention of the trustees to reduce the activities of the foundation, no applications are being sought from any other charity other than those already being supported.'

Sources of information

Accounts; annual report; Charity Commission record.

Four Acre Trust

Children and young people, and international eye and water projects

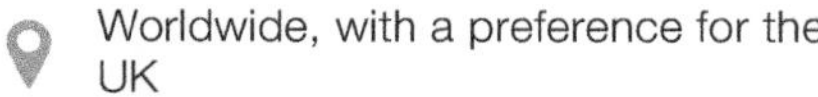

Worldwide, with a preference for the UK

£2.61 million (2020/21)

CC number: 1053884

Correspondent: The Trustees, Treferanon, St Weonards, Hereford, Herefordshire HR2 8QF (tel: 01981 580002; email: info@fouracretrust.org.uk)

Trustees: John Bothamley; Taymour Ezzat; Mary Bothamley; Marion Baker; Robert Carruthers.

www.fouracretrust.org.uk

General information

Four Acre Trust was founded in 1995 by John Bothamley with profits from the building industry. The trust supports charities that give children a better start in life. Its current programmes support schools' extracurricular projects, early intervention work, and international eye and water projects. There is an emphasis on supporting smaller and lower-profile charities, usually with a turnover of less than £1 million.

The trust aims to spend at least 20% of its total grant distribution on charities working internationally. Grants are mostly made for revenue/core costs with less than 10% given for capital projects.

Financial information

Year end	31/03/2021
Income	£2,060,000
Assets	£4,800,000
Grants to organisations	£2,610,000

Beneficiaries included: Dulverton Trust (£600,000); Bulldog Trust (£120,000); Onside Youth Zones HQ (£100,000); Impact Foundation (£50,000); Oakleaf Enterprise (£25,000); Coventry Boys and Girls Club (£20,000); Family Action (£18,000).

Applications

The trust's 2020/21 accounts state: '[the trust] is essentially closed to new applications preferring to seek out relevant charities thorough research. However applications from charities that mirror our existing recipients, and meet our other policies, might be acceptable and approaches should first be made to our Administrator with a very short synopsis of the support that is required.'

Sources of information

Accounts; annual review; Charity Commission record; funder's website.

Foux Foundation

Health; education; children and young people; the relief of poverty

Worldwide

£309,400 (2020/21)

CC number: 1177520

Correspondent: The Trustees, Gerald Edelman Chartered Accountant, 73 Cornhill, London EC3V 3QQ (email: hello@fouxfoundation.org.uk)

Trustees: Adam Ferguson; Mika Foux; Joshua Segal; Laura Ferguson.

www.fouxfoundation.org.uk

General information

The foundation was established by members of the Foux family in 2015. Grants are made to registered charities with incomes of less than £3 million per year.

According to its website the foundation has the following areas of focus:

- The relief of sickness and promotion of good health
- The advancement of education
- The advancement of disadvantaged young people
- The prevention or relief of poverty

Financial information

Year end	05/04/2021
Income	£250,000
Assets	£63,200
Grants to organisations	£309,400

Beneficiaries included: The Felix Project (£65,000); The Kids Network (£52,200); Food Forward (£32,500); Garden Library (£6,000); Not Standing By (£5,000).

Applications

Proposals can be submitted via the foundation's website.

Sources of information

Accounts; annual report; Charity Commission record.

Fowler Smith and Jones Trust

The arts; churches; community; health and medical causes; young people; general charitable purposes

Essex

£648,100 (2019/20)

CC number: 1132249

Correspondent: Penny Langran, Grant Administrator, Third Floor, Marlborough House, Victoria Road South, Chelmsford, Essex CM1 1LN (tel: 01245 809899; email: plangran@fsjtrust.org.uk)

Trustees: Nicholas Charrington; Richard Furlonger; Nicholas Jones; Philip Tolhurst; Lucy Bettley.

http://fsjtrust.org.uk

General information

The charity consists of three trusts established at different times by the Fowler Family, Albert and Florence Smith and Edward Cecil Jones, who all lived in the south-east of England.

One-off grants are made to groups and projects within Essex, either directly or through national charities working in the county. Grants are made towards core funding, project funding, the refurbishment of premises and equipment costs.

Grants are made in the following categories:

- The arts
- Churches
- Community
- Medical causes
- Young people
- Miscellaneous

Financial information

Year end	30/09/2020
Income	£738,500
Assets	£10.620,000
Grants to organisations	£648,100

Further financial information

Grants were broken down as follows:

Capital grants	£170,000
Young people	£156,700
Community	£133,900
Medical/health	£90,900
Miscellaneous	£87,100
Churches	£6,500
Overseas	£3,000

Only beneficiaries of grants over £10,000 were listed in the 2019/20 accounts. Grants of under £10,000 totalled £463,600.

Beneficiaries included: Chalkwell Bay Seascout Group (£30,000); St Peter's Church (£25,000); St Luke's Hospice (£22,500); Colchester Arts Centre (£20,000); Sport for Confidence (£10,000).

Exclusions

The charity's website states that it will not fund:

- Individuals directly
- Animal charities
- Political activities
- Commercial ventures
- Direct replacement of statutory funding or activities that are primarily the responsibility of local or central government

Applications

Apply in writing to the correspondent. Details of what should be included in an application can be found on the charity's website. The trustees meet three times a year to consider applications, in February, May and September. Deadlines can be found on the charity's website. All potential beneficiaries will require a visit from the administrator.

For large capital grants, contact the correspondent for an in-depth discussion prior to applying.

Sources of information

Accounts; annual report; Charity Commission record; funder's website.

The Foyle Foundation

The arts and culture; education; libraries

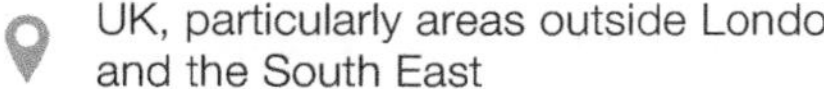

UK, particularly areas outside London and the South East

£6.75 million (2020)

CC number: 1081766

Correspondent: David Hall, Chief Executive, Rugby Chambers, 2 Rugby Street, London WC1N 3QU (tel: 020 7430 9119; email: info@foylefoundation.org.uk)

Trustees: Sir Peter Duffell; Michael Smith; Roy Amlot; James Korner; Vikki Heywood.

www.foylefoundation.org.uk

General information

The foundation was formed under the will of the late Christina Foyle, who was the daughter of William Foyle. Alongside his brother, William was a founder of the bookshop Foyles on Charing Cross Road, London, which Christina managed after her father's death. The foundation is an independent charity and there is no connection with Foyles bookshop. The foundation operates several funding programmes, which are outlined below by quotations taken from the foundation's helpful website.

In light of the COVID-19 pandemic, until further notice the foundation has revised the criteria of its funding programmes to include the following:

- One-year grants only to charities that can demonstrate ongoing financial stability for the next 12 months from the date of the application
- More grants to cover core costs, favouring those with no, or without significant, public funding
- Grants to cover the costs of essential equipment or re-equipping to enable ongoing service provision, homeworking, delivery of online digital services and education work
- Grants to enable minor works, or fund equipment, to enable social distancing within buildings
- Projects/schemes that employ or support skilled freelance and independent artists and practitioners
- Grants to support capital projects and building projects (discuss your situation with the foundation before applying)
- Projects/proposals that help reduce fixed or variable costs to promote efficiency savings, or which enable the generation of higher income or additional revenue streams. This can include environmental efficiency projects

Main grants scheme

The foundation gives financial support to UK-registered charities that operate in the fields of the arts and learning. Grants mostly range from £10,000 to £50,000.

> ***Arts:*** The foundation seeks applications that make a strong artistic case for support in either the performing or visual arts. [...] Typical areas of support include:
>
> - helping to make the arts more accessible by developing new audiences
> - encouraging new work and supporting young and emerging artists; skilled freelancers and independent practitioners
> - projects that encourage sustainability by reducing overheads or which help generate additional revenue. This might include environmental improvements to save energy and lower carbon emissions where a cost benefit can be demonstrated.
>
> ***Learning:*** The foundation will support projects which facilitate the acquisition of knowledge and which have a long-term strategic impact. Key areas for support are:
>
> - libraries, museums and archives;
> - special educational needs;
> - projects that encourage sustainability by reducing overheads or which help generate additional revenue;
> - projects and activities which increase access and widen the diversity of attenders/visitors.
>
> ***Schools:*** For state funded schools our main initiative will be The Foyle School Libraries Scheme [special guidance notes are available from the foundation's website]. Dedicated schools catering for those with Special Educational Needs (SEN) can be considered for educational projects.
>
> ***Universities:*** For Universities we will consider supporting arts, museum, archive or special collection projects, which meet a clear public benefit. All University projects should enable general and not just specialist use the majority of the time [...] In all cases we will expect Universities to be contributing to the project in financial and not just in-kind terms. Some grants may be offered on a matched funding basis.

The Foyle Schools Library Programme

The majority of the funding for this programme is directed towards primary schools, as there is no statutory requirement for schools to have a library. Secondary schools and sixth form colleges are eligible but are not the top priority. Priority will be given to funding library/reading books but not textbooks or curriculum books. Applications can be made for amounts of between £1,000 and £10,000. Further information and a detailed list of exclusions is available on the website.

Small grants scheme

Applications are accepted from charities with an annual turnover of less than £150,000 per annum. The scheme will make one-off, one-year grants of between £1,000 and £10,000 for core costs or essential equipment.

Financial information

Year end	31/12/2020
Income	£1,780,000
Assets	£64,230,000
Grants to organisations	£6,750,000
No. of grants	412

Further financial information

Grants paid in the year totalled £6.75 million. A full list of grants is available on the website. Grants were broken down as follows:

The arts	86	£3.13 million
Learning	40	£2.24 million
Small grants	205	£977,100
School library grants	81	£406,500

Beneficiaries included: City and Guilds Art School Property Trust (£275,000); National Portrait Gallery (£200,000); Bletchley Park Trust Ltd and Royal Opera House (£150,000 each); Help Musicians UK (£100,000); Courtyard Trust and Derby Museums (£75,000 each).

Exclusions

The foundation does not support individuals, CICs, community amateur sports clubs or social enterprises. It does not provide retrospective funding. See the website for funding guidelines and exclusions for each funding stream.

Applications

Guidelines and online application forms for each of the foundation's grants schemes can be downloaded from the website. Specific contacts for each grants scheme can also be found here.

Applications need to be submitted online through the application portal. Applications are accepted all year round; however, applications for large capital projects (over £75,000) will only be considered twice a year (in spring and autumn). Note that at the time of writing (February 2022) the website stated that applicants for large capital projects must first submit an enquiry form, which can be found on the website.

Sources of information

Accounts; annual report; Charity Commission record; funder's website.

The Elizabeth Frankland Moore and Star Foundation

General charitable purposes

UK

£345,000 (2020/21)

CC number: 257711

Correspondent: The Trustees, c/o Neuhoff and Co., 11 Towcester Road, Whittlebury, Towcester, Northamptonshire NN12 8XU (tel: 01327 858171; email: info@neuhoffandco.com)

Trustees: R. Griffiths; Anne Ely; Dr David Spalton; Janine Cameron.

General information

This foundation was established in 1969 and makes grants to other charities and individuals for general charitable purposes. According to the foundation's 2020/21 annual report, its current areas of interest are:

- Medical research
- Homelessness
- War veterans
- Human rights
- Hospices
- The arts
- Education
- Vulnerable members of society

Financial information

Year end	05/04/2021
Income	£345,700
Assets	£14,530,000
Grants to organisations	£345,000
No. of grants	37

Further financial information

In 2020/21 the trustees received 456 applications for grants from UK-registered charities, and of these 37 were accepted. Grants were broken down into the following categories:

Vulnerable people	£139,500
Homelessness	£68,800
Hospices	£49,100
Medical research	£32,000
War veterans	£20,000
National Star College	£15,000
Education and the arts	£10,000
Human rights	£10,000
Other	£600

Beneficiaries included: Salvation Army (£32,000); St Mungo's and The Trussell Trust (£20,000 each); Shelter Scotland and Turn2Us (£10,000 each); The Big Issue (£5,000); Kingston Churches Action on Homelessness (£3,000); UK Youth (£1,000).

Applications

Apply in writing to the correspondent. The trustees meet twice a year to consider grant applications.

Sources of information

Accounts; annual report; Charity Commission record.

The Hugh Fraser Foundation

Arts and culture; health and medical causes; the environment; education; children and young people; older people; people with disabilities

Scotland

£2.69 million (2020/21)

OSCR number: SC009303

Correspondent: The Trustees, c/o Turcan Connell, 180 St Vincent Street, Glasgow G2 5SG (tel: 0141 441 2111; email: hughfraserfoundation@turcanconnell.com)

Trustees: Patricia Fraser; Dr Kenneth Chrystie; Belinda Hanson; Andrew Harrow.

www.turcanconnell.com/the-hugh-fraser-foundation

General information

This foundation was established in 1960 by Hugh Fraser, who was responsible for developing his father's shop into the retail chain now known as House of Fraser.

The foundation's website states:

> The Foundation makes donations to registered charities which are active in such sectors as the arts and culture, medical and health, the environment and education, care and support of the young and elderly, people with disabilities and the under-privileged. So long as the object is charitable, the Trustees will consider any application from a registered charity.
>
> The Trustees' policy is to focus on applications relating to activities and projects in Scotland, particularly those parts of Scotland where the local economy and/or circumstances make fund-raising for charitable purposes difficult.
>
> Grants will only be made to organisations which are registered charities or community interest companies. The Trustees tend not to support highly-publicised national appeals and do not make grants to individuals.
>
> The Trustees are prepared to enter into commitments over a period of time by making grants in up to three successive years, often to assist in new initiatives which can maintain their own momentum once they have become established. Grants are frequently made by way of pledge where payment is conditional on the full funding and the commencement of the activities or project.

Financial information

Year end	31/03/2021
Income	£2,500,000
Assets	£89,120,000
Grants to organisations	£2,690,000
No. of grants	381

Further financial information

Only beneficiaries of grants of over £100,000 were included in the foundation's annual accounts.

Beneficiaries included: University of Glasgow (£300,000); Glasgow Science Centre (£200,000); Aberdeen Art Gallery and Museums Development Trust and Beatson Cancer Charity (£100,000 each).

Exclusions

Grants are only awarded to individuals in exceptional circumstances.

Applications

Letters of application should be submitted by email. A list of information that should be included in an application can be found on the foundation's website. The trustees usually meet in March, June, September and December. Applications should be submitted at the beginning of the month preceding the month of the meeting date.

Sources of information

Accounts; annual report; OSCR record; funder's website.

The Freelands Foundation Ltd

Support for artists; art education; cultural institutions

UK

£3.8 million (2020)

CC number: 1162648

Correspondent: The Trustees, 113 Regent's Park Road, London NW1 8UR (tel: 020 3598 7081; email: grants@freelandsfoundation.co.uk)

Trustees: Elisabeth Murdoch; Mark Devereux; Sarah Altenstadt; Keith Tyson.

http://freelandsfoundation.co.uk

facebook.com/FreelandsF

 @freelandsf

 @freelandsfoundation

General information

The foundation was registered with the Charity Commission in July 2015 and supports engagement in the arts. It was founded by Elisabeth Murdoch, who is the chair of trustees, and who also founded Shine Group, an independent television production company, as well as working for a number of film and television companies internationally.

According to its website, the foundation's current funding priorities are to 'support organisations and programmes that enable everyone, regardless of background or location, to access and take part in the creation and enjoyment of art'.

The foundation's funding criteria state that its grant-making strategy is focused on supporting programmes, projects and initiatives that:

- support artists in order to nurture their creativity, enhance their skills, exhibit their work and collaborate with diverse communities
- endeavour to increase access to visual arts for new audiences and to support organisations to engage with their local communities
- encourage young people to engage in the creation and enjoyment of art particularly through supporting teachers and teacher training, as well as developing the exploration of experimental approaches to art education
- research and articulate the value that art and culture bring to society

Financial information

Year end	31/12/2020
Income	£869,700
Assets	£70,970,000
Grants to organisations	£3,800,000

Beneficiaries included: The Artist Information Co. (£1.5 million); Artangel (£67,000); Gasworks (£47,100); Ikon Gallery (£16,000); University of Brighton (£12,500).

Exclusions

The foundation does not provide support for the following, as stated in its funding criteria:

- activity that does not have a charitable purpose or is not of public benefit
- organisations not based in the UK
- direct grants to individuals, including for travel, study or other similar purposes
- activity that generates significant personal profit
- building work or capital campaigns

Applications

Apply in writing to the correspondent.

Sources of information

Accounts; annual report; Charity Commission record; funder's website.

Charles S. French Charitable Trust

Older people; community and the arts; people with disabilities; people who are disadvantaged; medical causes; hospices; children and young people; education; sports and holidays (including respite breaks)

Essex and the north-east of London

£503,400 (2020/21)

CC number: 206476

Correspondent: The Trustees, 169 High Road, Loughton, Essex IG10 4LF (tel: 020 8502 3575; email: trustmanager@csfct.org.uk)

Trustees: Michael Foster; William Noble; Joanna Thomas; Christopher Noble; James Foster; Antonia McLeod; Edwin Cook.

 www.csfct.org.uk

General information

Established by Charles S. French in 1959, this trust has a policy of supporting local charities, mainly in Essex and north east London. Applications can also be considered from charities based outside this area if they can demonstrate benefit to residents within the north-east of London, Essex, or the immediate surrounding areas. Most grants are in the range of £1,000 and £5,000, although the trust sometimes provides larger grants for specific projects.

Financial information

Year end	31/03/2021
Income	£302,800
Assets	£11,630,000
Grants to organisations	£503,400

Further financial information

Grants were broken down as follows in 2020/21:

Medical activities	£103,400
Disability	£77,600
Community	£70,800
Sports/holiday	£62,100
Older people	£57,500
Education	£42,800
Disadvantage	£41,200
Young people	£27,000
Hospices	£21,000

Beneficiaries included: A list of beneficiaries was not available. Previous beneficiaries include: Essex Boys and Girls Clubs (£24,000); Epping Forest Foodbank (£10,000); Step by Step London (£5,000); Action for Family Carers (£3,000); Computers for the Disabled (£1,500); Foodcycle (£1,000); South West Essex Choir (£500).

Applications

Application forms and guidance notes can be downloaded from the trust's website. They should be submitted by email (not by post) along with a copy of your latest accounts. Applicants are advised to email with any questions about the application process.

Sources of information

Accounts; annual report; Charity Commission record; funder's website.

The Freshfield Foundation

Climate change; sustainable development; health; education; homelessness; research into motor neurone disease

UK and overseas

£2.36 million (2020/21)

CC number: 1003316

Correspondent: Paul Kurthausen, c/o BWM Chartered Accountants Ltd, Suite 5.1, 12 Tithebarn Street, Liverpool, Merseyside L2 2DT (tel: 0151 236 1494; email: paul.k@bwm.co.uk)

Trustees: Paul Kurthausen; Patrick Moores; Elizabeth Potter; Noland Carter.

General information

The foundation was established in 1991 and aims to support organisations involved in sustainable development, education and health.

Financial information

Year end	05/04/2021
Income	£1,550,000
Assets	£28,270,000
Grants to organisations	£2,360,000

Further financial information

During 2020/21, grants totalling £2.26 million were awarded for education, health and well-being, and grants totalling £100,000 were awarded for sustainable development and climate change control.

Beneficiaries included: Sustrans – Liveable Neighbourhoods (£2.24 million); Sustrans (£100,000); Motor Neurone Disease Association and St Mungo's Community Housing Association Ltd (£8,000 each).

Applications

The trust's 2020/21 annual report states that 'the trustees proactively research and identify those organisations and projects that will best achieve the Foundation's aims and objectives and make grants accordingly.'

Sources of information

Accounts; annual report; Charity Commission record.

The Raphael Freshwater Memorial Association

Jewish causes, including social welfare and education

UK and overseas

£3.61 million (2020/21)

CC number: 313890

Correspondent: Benzion Freshwater, Trustee, Freshwater Group of Companies, Freshwater House, 158–162 Shaftesbury Avenue, London WC2H 8HR (tel: 020 7836 1555)

Trustees: Benzion Freshwater; Richard Fischer; Solomon Freshwater; Mr D. Davis.

General information

The charity was registered with the Charity Commission in 1962. The charity's 2020/21 annual accounts provide the following information on its objectives:

> The Company was established to support the activities of religious Jewish organisations recognised as charitable by English Law both in the United Kingdom and abroad, especially those in the field of education and relief of poverty. The Trustees regularly support a significant number of institutions and organisations both in the United Kingdom and abroad which meet the Company's criteria.
>
> The Company is also supportive of organisations which are solely committed to the relief of poverty. Such organisations assist needy Jewish families through both financial and non-financial grants and distributions

Financial information

Year end	31/03/2021
Income	£9,100,000
Grants to organisations	£3,610,000

Beneficiaries included: Bobov Cheder Trust (£641,000); Rabinow Divrei Shir Kollel (£51,000); Edupoor Ltd (£26,000); Three Pillars Trust (£26,000).

Applications

Apply in writing to the correspondent.

Sources of information

Accounts; annual report; Charity Commission record.

Friends of Boyan Trust

The Orthodox Jewish faith, education and welfare

Worldwide

£507,700 (2020)

CC number: 1114498

Correspondent: Jacob Getter, Trustee, 23 Durley Road, London N16 5JW (tel: 020 8809 6051)

Trustees: Jacob Getter; Mordechai Freund; Nathan Kuflik.

General information

This trust was established in 2006 and makes grants to support the advancement of the Orthodox Jewish faith and religious education, and the relief of poverty in the Orthodox Jewish community.

Financial information

Year end	31/12/2020
Income	£643,000
Assets	£99,100
Grants to organisations	£507,700

Further financial information

Only beneficiaries of grants of over £8,000 were listed in the accounts. Grants of under £8,000 totalled £65,900.

Beneficiaries included: Yazoiree Boyan (£204,700); Mesifta Tiferet Yisroel (£151,100); Gomli Chesed Boyan (£31,700); Yeshiva Gedoila Zichron Moshe (£15,900); Bais Rizhin Trust (£12,100); Teens United (£8,900).

Applications

Contact the correspondent for further information.

Sources of information

Accounts; annual report; Charity Commission record.

Friends of the National Libraries

Written and print heritage

UK

£699,300 (2020)

CC number: 313020

Correspondent: Nell Hoare, Secretary, PO Box 4291, Reading, Berkshire RG8 9JA (tel: 01491 598083; email: admin@fnlmail.org.uk)

Trustees: Charles Sebag-Montefiore; Roland Keating; Prof. Richard Ovenden; Geordie Greig; Dr Jessica Gardner; Dr Emma Markiewicz; Pedr Llwyd; Felix Oyens; Joan Winterkorn; Mark Storey; Alexandra Sitwell; Stephen Clarke; Peter Mimpriss; Natalie Livingstone; Sybil Kretzmer; Dr Amina Shah.

 www.fnl.org.uk

 @FNL313

General information

Friends of the National Libraries (FNL) saves our written and printed heritage by giving acquisition grants to national, regional and specialist archives, libraries and collections. The charity also acts as a conduit for gifts of books and collections to collecting institutions.

According to the website, 'FNL's contribution to the UK's national book, manuscript and archive collections is unrivalled. It is the only UK charity focusing solely on supporting acquisitions in this area.'

Grants

Grants typically range from £200 to £20,000 and can be used towards the purchase of rare printed books; manuscripts; archives of historical, literary, artistic, architectural, musical or other interest; and fine bindings.

Institutions that are eligible to apply include:

- The national libraries and the libraries of national museums
- Record offices and archives services
- University and specialist libraries
- Any museum, gallery or collecting institution to which the public has reasonable access and which, in the opinion of the trustees, constitutes a proper repository for the proposed acquisition

Financial information

Year end	31/12/2020
Income	£1,220,000
Assets	£4,300,000
Grants to organisations	£699,300
No. of grants	40

Further financial information

During the year, 39 grants were awarded totalling £199,300. In addition, FNL gifted a book to University College Cork valued at £500,000 – this was included in the charity's grant total in the 2020 accounts.

Beneficiaries included: University College Cork (£500,000); Dorset History Centre (£18,200); The British Library (£15,000); Bangor University (£10,000); Ashmolean Museum – University of Oxford (£5,000); Cambridge University Library (£2,000); Balliol College (£900); Brighton and Hoe Record Office (£500).

Exclusions

The charity will not contribute to the purchase of an item already bought, or to the cost of conservation or cataloguing.

Applications

Applications are considered at trustees' meetings, which take place in March, June and November. Applications should be made by the first of each month using a form available on the website or by email.

Email applications should include:

- A description of the proposed acquisition, with information about its condition and provenance
- A brief statement of the significance of the acquisition for your collection

- A copy of the sale-catalogue entry if the item is to be auctioned, or if you are buying from a dealer, a copy of a dealer's catalogue entry if available
- If you are buying from a dealer or private individual, also state whether you have obtained, or will obtain, an independent valuation
- State what funding you will contribute yourself and what other funding you are seeking
- The amount of the grant you are seeking from FNL

If you have an auction or similar deadline approaching and your application cannot wait, you can apply at any time and your application will quickly be considered.

Where it can, FNL will suggest other sources of funding to which an institution might also apply, so informal contact is welcomed.

Eligible institutions can apply for grants as often as they wish.

Sources of information

Accounts; annual report; Charity Commission record; funder's website.

Friends of Wiznitz Ltd

Orthodox Jewish religious education; the advancement of the Orthodox Jewish religion; the relief of poverty; medical causes

Hackney; Haringey; Israel; USA

£6.93 million (2020/21)

CC number: 255685

Correspondent: The Trustees, 8 Jessam Avenue, London E5 9DU (tel: 020 8806 0017)

Trustees: Shulom Feldman; Henrich Feldman; Ephraim Gottesfeld.

General information

This charity supports the advancement of the Orthodox Jewish religion, Orthodox Jewish religious education and the relief of poverty. The charity also grants free use of its buildings to other Wiznitz charities in order to fulfil the above objectives.

This charity is mainly concerned with supporting major educational projects carried out by Orthodox Jewish institutions.

Financial information

Year end	31/03/2021
Income	£4,220,000
Assets	£2,680,000
Grants to organisations	£6,930,000

Further financial information

During 2020/21, grants were distributed as follows:

religious education	£5.93 million
relief of poverty	£830,100
advancement of religion	£140,100
social welfare	£35,000

Only beneficiaries that received grants of over £50,000 were listed in the charity's accounts. Grants of under £50,000 totalled £386,300.

Beneficiaries included: Mosdos Viznitz (£2.96 million); Igud Mosdot Wiznitz (£2.72 million); Lehachzikom UK (£485,600); Lehachzikom Velehachyosom (£328,000); Mosdos Viznitz USA (£55,500).

Applications

The 2020/21 accounts state:

> In general the trustees select the institutions to be supported according to their personal knowledge of work of the institution. Whilst not actively inviting applications, they are always prepared to accept any application which will be carefully considered and help given according to circumstances and funds then available. Applications by individuals must be accompanied by a letter of recommendation by the applicant's minister or other known religious leader.

Sources of information

Accounts; annual report; Charity Commission record.

Friends Provident Charitable Foundation

Sustainable economic development

UK

£3.06 million (2019/20)

CC number: 1087053

Correspondent: The Trustees, Blake House, 18 Blake Street, York YO1 8QG (tel: 01904 629675 (option 3); email: enquiries@friendsprovidentfoundation.org.uk)

Trustees: Joanna Elson; Paul Dickinson; Aphra Sklair; Kathleen Kelly; Stephen Muers; Abraham Baldry; Ann Bosco; Priya Lukka; Stephanie Maier.

www.friendsprovidentfoundation.org

 @fprovfoundation

General information

Friends Provident was a life insurance provider founded as a mutual Friendly Society for Quakers in 1832. The society was demutualised in 2001 and became a publicly listed company no longer linked to the Religious Society of Friends. As part of the demutualisation, the Friends Provident Foundation was endowed as an independent charity.

The foundation funds a range of organisations, from think tanks and universities to private non-profit enterprises, community groups and charities. It also invests in social enterprises and spends its money in line with its values.

The Developing a Fair Economy programme encourages thinking that deals with the cause of the problem, and seeks to change parts of our wider economic system. This could be working to realign the purpose of business away from profit maximisation, creating new ways of retaining value in a local area or tackling the financial drivers that are deepening the climate crisis. The scope is broad, as the economy is broad, but the focus is on changing the economic system for a better future that is more inclusive, fairer and respects the environment. There are two parts to the programme: systems change and local economies. See the foundation's website for further information.

Financial information

Year end	30/09/2020
Grants to organisations	£3,060,000

Further financial information

Grants paid during the year totalled £3.06 million, of which £2.3 million was committed in the year. The foundation received 39 applications and awarded 27 grants, of which 12 were to new grant holders.

According to the 2019/20 annual report, the themes covered by these grants included: 'communicating economic ideas; investor/corporate behaviour; community energy; local development; a fair transition to a low carbon economy; tax; community assets and convening, and diversity, equity and inclusion.' Six grants were made for unrestricted core funding.

Beneficiaries included: New Economics Foundation (£200,000); The Landworkers' Alliance (£144,000); Energy Garden (£97,000); Fairshare Educational Foundation (£80,000); Manchester Metropolitan University (£38,000); Behavioural Insights Ltd (£10,000); Stir to Action Ltd (£2,500).

Exclusions

The foundation will not fund activity that is not based in, or likely to have a tangible economic impact on, the UK.

Applications

The foundation has a two-stage application process. First, potential applicants should submit their proposal b making an outline application online. These applications are reviewed by an expert advisory group. Successful stage-one applicants will then be invited to submit a full stage two application. Applications can be submitted at any time.

Note: at the time of writing (March 2022), the foundation's website stated it was pausing its grants programme between January and August 2022 to review the programme and its priorities. Check the foundation's website for updated information and guidance.

Sources of information

Accounts; annual report; Charity Commission record; funder's website.

The Patrick and Helena Frost Foundation

General charitable purposes and children and young people

UK

£535,000 (2020/21)

CC number: 1005505

Correspondent: The Trustees, c/o Trowers and Hamlins LLP, 3 Bunhill Row, London EC1Y 8YZ (tel: 020 7423 8303; email: asorrell@trowers.com)

Trustees: Luke Valner; Dominic Tayler; Neil Hendriksen; Mark Hendriksen; Clare Armitage.

General information

The Patrick and Helena Frost Foundation was established in 1991. It makes grants to organisations for general charitable purposes, including the relief and welfare of disadvantaged individuals. It also provides support to smaller charities that rely on a considerable amount of self-help and voluntary effort.

Financial information

Year end	05/04/2021
Income	£483,100
Assets	£23,380,000
Grants to organisations	£535,000

Beneficiaries included: Ocean Youth Trust South and The Yard Theatre Ltd (£20,000 each); London Narrow Boat Project and WheelPower – The British Wheelchair Sports Foundation Ltd (£15,000 each); Childhood Tumour Trust and The London Children's Flower Society (£10,000 each); Action on Addiction (£7,500); Yeldall Christian Centres (£5,000); The Fforest Uchaf Horse and Pony Rehabilitation Centre Charitable Trust (£2,000).

Exclusions

The foundation does not make grants to individuals.

Applications

The 2020/21 annual report notes the following:

> the Trustees of the Foundation proactively seek and select organisations to which they wish to award grants. The Trustees kindly request that unsolicited applications are not submitted as, regretfully, they will not be considered or responded to.

Sources of information

Accounts; annual report; Charity Commission record.

The Fulmer Charitable Trust

The relief of suffering and hardship; education; religion; general charitable purposes

UK and overseas

£268,300 (2020)

CC number: 1070428

Correspondent: The Trustees, 8 The Parade, Marlborough, Wiltshire SN8 1NE (tel: 01672 515691)

Trustees: Caroline Mytum; John Reis; Sally Reis; The Revd Philip Bromiley; Julia Reis.

General information

The Fulmer Charitable Trust was registered with the Charity Commission in 1998. The trust supports a range of charitable organisations and causes both in the UK and overseas. The trust's 2020 accounts state the following:

> The Settlor expressed his wish that available income should be distributed under the following 'Heads of Charity' and broadly in the proportions indicated:
> - Relief of suffering hardship – 70%
> - Advancement of education – 10%
> - Advancement of religion – 10%
> - Other charitable purposes for the benefit of the community – 10%'

Grants are made to a wide range of organisations, often on a recurring basis.

Financial information

Year end	31/12/2020
Income	£214,000
Assets	£15,180,000
Grants to organisations	£268,300
No. of grants	281

Further financial information

During the year the trust made grants totalling £268,300 to 281 organisations. The trust's grant expenditure was lower than usual during the year. Typically the trust makes grants totalling around £500,000.

Beneficiaries included: Catstone PCC (£10,000); Swindon Women's Aid (£3,000); The Sequel Trust (£2,000); Hope Christian Trust (£1,500); Refuge (£1,000); Ambitious About Autism, British Red Cross and Street Child Africa (£750 each); Demelza House Children's Hospice (£500).

Applications

Apply in writing to the correspondent.

Sources of information

Accounts; annual report; Charity Commission record.

The Funding Network

General charitable purposes; human rights; health; education; inclusion; the environment; climate change; crime reduction; social change

UK and overseas

£583,400 (2020/21)

CC number: 1088315

Correspondent: The Trustees, Toynbee Hall, 28 Commercial Street, London E1 6LS (tel: 020 7846 4070; email: info@thefundingnetwork.org.uk)

Trustees: Michael Chuter; Adrian Coles; Samuel Lush; Kawika Solidum; Ailis Clarke; Shantanu Sinha; Fiona Johnston; Ofovwe Aig-Imoukhuede.

www.thefundingnetwork.org.uk

facebook.com/FundingNetwork

@FundingNetwork

General information

The Funding Network (TFN) is an open network that links donors to charitable causes and social entrepreneurs. The charity's 2020/21 accounts note that the charity aims to:

> - Raise money for organisations creating social change
> - Provide a public benefit by educating attendees at events about social change projects
> - Encourage an increasing number of people to engage in active, intelligent philanthropy
> - Help individuals make an impact by enabling them to combine their giving with others

The charity carries out its long-term objectives through hosting live crowdfunding events for charitable causes and social entrepreneurs. Within the UK, live crowdfunding events take place in London, Oxford, Bristol and Hertfordshire.

The charity invites non-profit organisations nominated by network members to apply for the opportunity to pitch for funds at its events, typically for amounts up to £10,000. The funds raised are then passed on to the organisation by the network in the form of grants. The charity supports organisations covering a wide range of sectors.

Financial information

Year end	31/03/2021
Income	£823,600
Assets	£127,200
Grants to organisations	£583,400
No. of grants	74

Beneficiaries included: Reprezent (£36,100); The Armitage Foundation (£24,500); Lightyear Foundation (£14,800); Elevated Minds (£10,600); Opening Doors London (£5,900); Dream

Green (£3,000); Romanian Diaspora Funding Network (£1,800); Untold (£45).

Exclusions

The charity does not support any of the following:

- Organisations that are involved in the promotion of religion or a political party
- Organisations with a turnover of over £1.2 million
- Fundraising challenges
- Individuals

Applications

To apply, organisations must first be sponsored by a Funding Network member. Members are notified when applications are being accepted for an event, and non-profits may then apply online. A selection panel will shortlist the strongest candidates and interview these candidates over Zoom. Non-profits are notified within 48 hours whether they have been selected or not. The charity does not share the details of its current members; however, organisations that do not know a current network member can ask somebody to become a member with a view to nominating them. This could be a trustee, volunteer or someone close to the organisation, but it cannot be somebody who is in paid employment of the organisation. Once they have signed up, new members are asked to attend and donate at a network event before being eligible to sponsor an organisation. Organisations can also submit a short expression of interest on the charity's website, which will be circulated to current members, who will get in touch if they want to know more.

Sources of information

Accounts; annual report; Charity Commission record; funder's website.

The Gale Family Charity Trust

General charitable purposes

UK, with a preference for Bedfordshire

£1.44 million (2020/21)

CC number: 289212

Correspondent: The Trustees, Northwood House, 138 Bromham Road, Bedford, Bedfordshire MK40 2QW (tel: 01234 354508; email: galefamilytrust@gmail.com)

Trustees: John Tyley; Alistair Law; Doreen Watson; Warwick Browning; Charles Codrington; David Fletcher; Russell Beard; John Cleverley; Alison Phillipson.

General information

This trust was founded in 1984 by Horace and Marjorie Gale. According to its 2020/21 accounts, the main object of the trust is:

> To apply funds to charitable causes, both locally for the benefit of the community, and to larger organisations with links across the UK. Funds are also donated to local churches to further their work.

Financial information

Year end	05/04/2021
Income	£101,800
Assets	£5,850,000
Grants to organisations	£1,440,000

Beneficiaries included: A list of beneficiaries was not available.

Applications

Apply in writing to the correspondent. The trustees meet every six months to award grants.

Sources of information

Accounts; annual report; Charity Commission record.

GambleAware

Education, prevention, treatment services and research aimed at minimising the negative impact of gambling

England, Scotland and Wales

£11.66 million (2020/21)

CC number: 1093910

Correspondent: The Trustees, Pennine Place, 2A Charing Cross Road, London WC2H 0HF (tel: 020 7287 1994; email: info@gambleaware.org)

Trustees: Kathryn Lampard; Dr Koravangattu Valsraj; Marina Gibbs; Mubin ul Haq; The Rt Hon. Baroness Armstrong; Rachel Pearce; Paul Simpson; Michelle Highman; Saffron Cordery; Prof. Sian Griffiths.

http://about.gambleaware.org

facebook.com/BeGambleAware

@begambleaware

@begambleawaregb

General information

GambleAware is dedicated to minimising the negative impact gambling has on individuals and societies. The charity's income is derived principally from donations from the gambling industry and is used to fund related education, prevention and treatment services as well as to commission research to promote awareness and understanding of the harm caused by gambling.

According to its website, the charity:

> is an independent, grant-making charity commissioning prevention and treatment services across England, Scotland and Wales in partnership with expert organisations and agencies, including the NHS, across three areas:
>
> - Commissioning the National Gambling Treatment Service
> - Producing public health campaigns on a national scale and providing practical support to local services
> - Commissioning research and evaluation to improve knowledge of what works in prevention.

Financial information

Year end	31/03/2021
Income	£33,660,000
Assets	£22,330,000
Grants to organisations	£11,660,000

Beneficiaries included: GamCare (£8.34 million); Central and North West London NHS Foundation Trust (£1.51 million); The Gordon Moody Association (£1.09 million); Leeds and York Partnership Trust (£698,300).

Applications

The 2020/21 annual report states:

> GambleAware does not offer funding in response to speculative applications, but from time to time does issue open tenders when there is the opportunity to bid for funding for innovative projects within a broader field.

Sources of information

Accounts; annual report; Charity Commission record; funder's website.

The Gannochy Trust

Community development; social welfare; employability; education; the natural and built environment

Scotland, with a strong preference for the Perth and Kinross area

£4.06 million (2020/21)

OSCR number: SC003133

Correspondent: Grants Team, Kincarrathie House Drive, Pitcullen Crescent, Perth, Perthshire PH2 7HX (tel: 01738 620653; email: grants@gannochytrust.org.uk)

Trustees: Jane Mudd; David Gray; Stephen Hay; Bruce Renfrew; Roland Bean; Alisa Macmillan; Ruth Ogston.

www.gannochytrust.org.uk

facebook.com/GannochyTrustOrg

@GannochyTrust

General information

The Gannochy Trust was founded in 1937 by Arthur Kinmond Bell, a whisky distiller and philanthropist, for charitable and public purposes for the benefit of the community of Perth and its immediate environs. The trust is also responsible for the management of the model housing estate built by Bell.

The trust's website states:

> A K Bell's belief, that "after you have a roof over your head and your bread and butter" you should look to invest any surplus for the benefit of your native town, has matured into a lasting legacy that has improved the quality of life of many thousands of people, not only in Perth but all over Scotland.

In 2019 the trust released a new grant-making strategy for 2019 to 2022 which is focused on the following themes:

- Improving the quality of life for people (Perth and Kinross only)
- Improving the availability or quality of the built and natural environment for wide community use (Perth and Kinross only)
- Developing and inspire young people (Scotland-wide)

There are three different levels of grants than can be applied for. Each stated figure is the grant amount per year, awarded for up to three years:

- Small: £1,000 to £10,000
- Main: Up to £30,000
- Major (Perth and Kinross only): Over £30,000

Grants can be awarded for:

- Project funding
- Core funding (Perth and Kinross only)
- Capital funding (Perth and Kinross only)

Financial information

Year end	30/06/2021
Income	£3,530,000
Assets	£224,340,000
Grants to organisations	£4,060,000

Further financial information

In 2020/21, grants awarded Scotland-wide to develop and inspire young people totalled £1.59 million. Grants made in Perth and Kinross were broken down as follows: capital projects (£1.14 million); improving the quality of live for people (£834,800); COVID-19 Recovery and Renewal Fund (£471,300). Other grants totalled £26,700.

Only beneficiaries of grants of £100,000 and above were listed in the accounts. Grants of under £100,000 totalled £2.72 million.

Beneficiaries included: Pitlochry Festival Theatre (£1 million); Live Active Leisure (£152,000); RSPB Scotland (£129,600); Perth and Kinross Countryside Trust and Perth and Kinross Heritage Trust (£100,000 each).

Applications

There are a number of documents that applicants must complete, including an application form. These are available to download from the trust's very informative website, where detailed guidance notes can also be found. Completed applications may be submitted by email or post. The trustees meet at least four times per year to consider applications, which may be submitted at any time. For capital funding, applicants must first complete a stage one project summary report, which should be returned by email.

Sources of information

Accounts; annual report; OSCR record; funder's website.

The Gatsby Charitable Foundation

Plant science; neuroscience; STEM education; Africa; public policy; the arts

Worldwide, with a preference for the UK and East Africa

£50.47 million (2020/21)

CC number: 251988

Correspondent: The Trustees, The Peak, 5 Wilton Road, London SW1V 1AP (tel: 020 7410 0330; email: contact@gatsby.org.uk)

Trustees: Joseph Burns; Sir Andrew Cahn; Judith Portrait.

 www.gatsby.org.uk

General information

This foundation is one of the Sainsbury Family Charitable Trusts, which share a common administration but work autonomously. The foundation was founded and endowed by David Sainsbury in 1967. The foundation operates in areas that the founder is particularly passionate about, which according to its Charity Commission record, includes the UK, Israel, the USA and Africa.

The foundation's objects, as given in the trust deed, are for general charitable purposes. However, the foundation's 2020/21 annual report states that the trustees' current fields of interest are:

- **Plant science** – to develop basic research in fundamental processes of plant growth and development and molecular plant pathology, and to encourage young researchers in the field of plant science in the UK.
- **Neuroscience** – to support world class research in the area of neural circuits and behaviour and theoretical neuroscience, and to support activities which enhance our understanding in these fields.
- **Science and engineering education** – to strengthen science and engineering skills in the UK by developing and enabling innovative programmes and informing national policy.
- **Africa** – to promote economic development in East Africa that benefits the poor through supporting the growth and sustainability of key sectors.
- **The arts** – to support the fabric and programming of institutions with which Gatsby's founding family has connections.
- **Public policy** – to support the Institute for Government as an independent centre available to politicians and the civil service focused on making government more effective, and the Centre for Cities which provides practical research and policy advice that helps cities understand how they can succeed economically.

The trustees occasionally support other charitable work which falls outside their main fields of interest. Many of the grants awarded help to fund long-term projects that the foundation has helped to initiate.

Financial information

Year end	05/04/2021
Income	£60,440,000
Assets	£517,050,000
Grants to organisations	£50,470,000

Beneficiaries included: University of Cambridge (£8.54 million); The Sainsbury Laboratory (£3.37 million); 2Blades Foundation (£777,000); Hebrew University of Jerusalem (£304,000); Royal Shakespeare Company (£268,000); Baker Dearing Educational Trust (£100,000); Engineering UK (£75,000).

Exclusions

Grants are not awarded directly to individuals.

Applications

The foundation's 2020/21 annual report states: 'Generally, the Trustees do not make grants in response to unsolicited applications.'

Sources of information

Accounts; annual report; Charity Commission record; funder's website.

The Gaudio Family Foundation (UK) Ltd

General charitable purposes; poverty relief, especially in urban areas; advancing and improving education, particularly for disadvantaged children

England and Wales

£5.03 million (2020)

CC number: 1157301

Correspondent: The Trustees, c/o Withers LLP, Third Floor, 20 Old Bailey, London EC4M 7AN (tel: 020 7597 6000; email: ac@fultonvittoria.com)

Trustees: Julius Gaudio; Belma Gaudio; Alfred Cavallaro.

General information

The Gaudio Family Foundation (UK) Ltd, formerly known as The Butters Foundation (UK), was registered in June 2014.

The foundation's Charity Commission record states that it makes grants for general charitable purposes to organisations in England and Wales. According to the foundation's 2020 annual report, it aims to provide grants in the following three areas:

- Relieving poverty, especially in urban areas
- Advancing and improving education, particularly for disadvantaged children in impoverished areas; and
- Various other charitable endeavours at the discretion of the Trustees.

Financial information

Year end	31/12/2020
Income	£15,410,000
Assets	£34,040,000
Grants to organisations	£5,030,000
No. of grants	16

Beneficiaries included: Gaudio Family Foundation (£3.2 million); West London Zone (£185,000); St Giles Trust (£180,000); Helpforce Community Trust and Mental Health Innovations (£160,000 each); Place2Be (£80,000); Société Des Amis National (£27,300).

Applications

Applications can be made in writing to the foundation. Grant recipients will be required to produce project reports.

Sources of information

Accounts; annual report; Charity Commission record.

The Robert Gavron Charitable Trust

Education; the arts; prison reform; human rights; social policy/research; disability

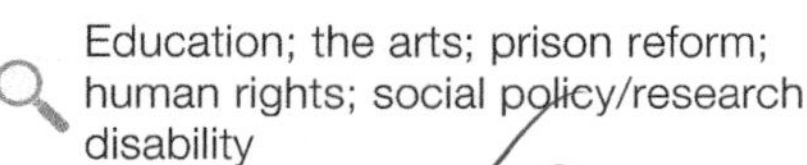

UK

£368,000 (2020/21)

CC number: 268535

Correspondent: The Trustees, 27 Maywin Drive, Hornchurch, Essex RM11 3ST (tel: 020 7400 4301; email: office@rgct.org.uk)

Trustees: Sarah Gavron; Charles Corman; Jessica Gavron; Dr Kate Gavron.

General information

The trust was established in 1974. Its 2020/21 annual report states that the trust has supported a similar range of charitable causes in recent years. These are:

- Education
- The arts
- Prison reform
- Human rights
- Charities for people with disabilities

One-off and recurrent grants are available. According to the 2020/21 annual report, the trustees prefer to make grants to organisations 'whose work they personally know and admire'; however, the trust does also welcome unsolicited applications.

Financial information

Year end	05/04/2021
Income	£104,200
Assets	£8,930,000
Grants to organisations	£368,000

Beneficiaries included: Arab Israel Children's Tennis Charity (£60,300); Morpeth School (£10,000); Arnott Catto Foundation (£8,000); Keen London (£5,000); The Respite Association (£3,000).

Applications

Apply in writing to the correspondent. The trustees meet formally approximately four times per year. The trust's 2020/21 accounts state:

> Research into certain grant applications and new projects to be supported is carried out by the Trust Administrator, who visits and reports on new applicants to assist the Trustees in making decisions.

Sources of information

Accounts; annual report; Charity Commission record.

Sir Robert Geffery's Almshouse Trust

Education of disadvantaged children and young people; ironwork projects; STEM

UK

£617,400 (2020/21)

CC number: 219153

Correspondent: The Trustees, Ironmongers' Hall, Barbican, London EC2Y 8AA (tel: 020 7776 2311; email: helen@ironmongers.org)

Trustee: The Ironmongers' Trust Company.

www.ironmongers.org/charitable-grants

General information

Sir Robert Geffery was twice Master of the Worshipful Company of Ironmongers and was Lord Mayor of London in 1685. The trust owns two almshouses and makes grants for educational projects.

The trust has five linked charities, which are collectively known as the Ironmongers' Charities. The charities make grants for the following:

- Grants to organisations – for educational activities for children and young people from disadvantaged backgrounds
- Iron projects – for the restoration of historic ironwork or creation of new decorative work in iron and steel
- STEM projects – for activities engaging students with materials science

Financial information

Year end	31/03/2021
Income	£2,260,000
Assets	£34,170,000
Grants to organisations	£617,400

Beneficiaries included: Make Believe Arts (£44,700); The Work Wise Foundation (£15,000); Face Front Inclusive Theatre Ltd (£10,000); Yellow Submarine Holidays (£7,500); Finding Rhythms (£6,000); Edmonton Community Partnership (£4,100); Sheriffs' and Recorders' Fund (£2,000); City of London Police Widows and Orphans Fund (£300).

Exclusions

- Projects that begin before the date of the relevant committee meeting (15 December and 31 July)
- Schools, unless they are a registered charity for children/young people with disabilities
- Large projects towards which a contribution from the trust would have a limited impact
- Research projects
- Projects for individuals over the age of 25
- Educational activities that do not develop learning, motivation, or skills
- Projects outside the UK

Applications

Application forms can be downloaded from the Ironmongers' website.

Sources of information

Accounts; annual report; Charity Commission record; funder's website.

General Charity (Coventry)

Social care and development, including services for children and young people, older people, people with disabilities and people who are experiencing homelessness; education; medical causes; healthcare, including the prevention and treatment of specific diseases

Within the boundary of the City of Coventry

£1.36 million (2020)

CC number: 216235

Correspondent: Susan Hanrahan, Clerk to the Trustees, Old Bablake, Hill Street, Coventry, Warwickshire CV1 4AN

(tel: 024 7622 2769; email: cov.genchar@btconnect.com)

Trustees: Edward Curtis; David Evans; Michael Harris; Marcus Lapsa; David Mason; Terry Proctor; Richard Smith; Vivien Kershaw; Catherine Miks; Julia McNaney; Cllr Ram Lakha; Dr Roger Davies; Cllr Joseph Clifford; Cllr Patricia Hetherton; Simon Sharpe.

General information

The charity's aim is to benefit people in need living in Coventry by awarding grants to local organisations, and grants and pensions to local residents.

According to the charity's 2020 accounts, grants were made in four main areas:

- **Education**
- **Medical**
- **Social care and development** – includes organisations providing human and social services to a community or target population, including services for children, young people, physically and mentally disabled, elderly people and homeless people.
- **Healthcare** – includes grants to organisations that focus on the prevention or treatment of specific diseases; the prevention or treatment of diseases generally and/or health problems; the rehabilitation of disabled individuals; residential nursing homes for the frail, elderly, severely disabled and those offering terminal care.

Financial information

Year end	31/12/2020
Income	£4,170,000
Assets	£13,630,000
Grants to organisations	£1,360,000

Further financial information

Grants were broken down as follows:

Social care and development	£384,600
Healthcare	£205,500
Medical	£81,100
Education	£57,500

In addition to the grants listed above, the charity also made a grant of £629,600 to Coventry School Foundation.

Beneficiaries included: Warwickshire and Northampton Air Ambulance (£90,000); Bond's Lodge (£35,000); Mercia MS Therapy Centre (£10,000); Happy Days (£4,000); Limbrick Wood School (£410).

Applications

Apply in writing to the correspondent.

Sources of information

Accounts; annual report; Charity Commission record.

The Generations Foundation

Children who are disadvantaged, ill or who have disabilities, and environmental protection and conservation projects

UK; the London Borough of Merton; financially developing countries

£311,700 (2020/21)

CC number: 1110565

Correspondent: The Trustees, 36 Marryat Road, Wimbledon, London SW19 5BD (email: generationstrust@mail.com)

Trustees: Bob Finch; Stephen Finch; Rohini Finch.

www.generationsct.co.uk

General information

The trust's website provides a useful overview of its activities:

> Set up by the Finch family in 2005, Generations supports numerous local causes in the Borough of Merton, where the family lives. But our contribution stretches much further than that. We also support projects in developing countries ranging from India and Sri Lanka to Romania, Madagascar and Paraguay. In addition, we support projects for environmental protection and conservation for future generations.

Grants range from £500 to £25,000 and causes are often supported for multiple years.

Financial information

Year end	05/04/2021
Income	£375,000
Assets	£122,800
Grants to organisations	£311,700

Beneficiaries included: British Red Cross Society (£50,000); Home-Start – Merton (£25,000); PAPYRUS (£12,500); Tennis for Free (£10,000); Launch It Trust (£7,500); Wimbledon Guild (£5,000).

Applications

Application forms are available to download from the website. Potential applicants should contact the foundation by email to before applying to gauge whether their application is likely to be successful.

Sources of information

Annual accounts; annual report; Charity Commission record; funder's website.

The Tara Getty Foundation

General charitable purposes; marine conservation; the environment; climate change; community development; education; health and saving lives; medical research; mental health; disaster relief; children and young people; research

UK and overseas

£65,800 (2020)

CC number: 1107895

Correspondent: The Trustees, 26 Curzon Street, London W1J 7TQ (tel: 020 7409 3900)

Trustees: Patrick Maxwell; Tara Getty; Louise Creasey.

General information

The Tara Getty Foundation was established as a grant-making charity in November 2004. It awards grants to UK-registered charities. According to its 2020 annual report, the foundation's original core focus was to:

- Revitalise existing charities and individual charitable projects that are failing in their objectives due to financial constraints and/or lack of exposure and publicity
- Fund projects that will alleviate poverty and financial hardship, relieve sickness and poor health

Following a review of these charitable objectives in 2019, according to its 2020 annual report, the foundation now aims to:

- Facilitate the empowerment and development of rural people living in or adjacent to conservation areas in different parts of the world, by forging unique partnerships between conservation initiatives and communities, working in the fields of education, health and income generating initiatives.
- Support environmental, educational and community projects that protect the environment and surrounding wildlife.
- Support sustainable marine conservation programs, protection of the oceans and climate change.
- Save lives, promote safety and rescue service efficiency, and provide relief from disaster at sea and on inland and flood waters, including the advancement of education in these areas.
- Support disadvantaged young people in their chance to succeed and transform their lives by developing their confidence and skills to live, learn and earn.
- Raise awareness, and distribute funding for, supporting orphaned and vulnerable children.

- Support those who are affected by poor health, both mental or physical incapacity as well as research programmes to shape policies and treatments thereof and relieve suffering.

Financial information

Year end	31/12/2020
Income	£107,200
Assets	£55,300
Grants to organisations	£65,800
No. of grants	17

Further financial information

In 2020 the foundation awarded grants totalling £65,800; however, in previous years it has awarded significantly more. In 2019 grants to organisations totalled £393,100 and in 2018 grants totalled £538,300.

Grants were broken down as follows:

Community	9	£41,000
Medical	3	£33,500
Marine conservation	1	£23,000
Young people	4	£7,700

Beneficiaries included: Fight for Sight; Leeway Domestic; Ocean Family Foundation; One Can Trust; The Jubilee Sailing Trust; Tom's Trust; Wellington College; Wycombe Homeless Connection.

Applications

Apply in writing to the correspondent. Shortlisted charities will be contacted for more detailed information. The foundation requests a full breakdown of the project, detailed financial statements and a breakdown of secured and projected income for the upcoming year.

Sources of information

Accounts; annual report; Charity Commission record.

The G. C. Gibson Charitable Trust

The arts; music; education; health; hospices; medical research; community; social projects; religion

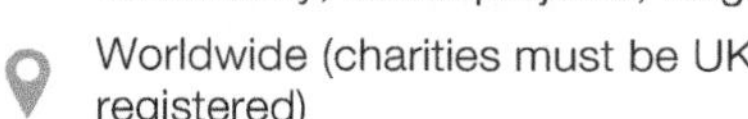

Worldwide (charities must be UK registered)

£691,600 (2020/21)

CC number: 258710

Correspondent: The Trustees, Durnsford Mill House, Mildenhall, Marlborough, Wiltshire SN8 2NG (tel: 07850 859824; email: gcgibsoncharity@gmail.com)

Trustees: Anna Dalrymple; Martin Gibson; Jane Gibson; Lucy Kelly; Edward Gibson; Thomas Homfray.

www.gcgct.org

General information

The trust was established in 1968 by George Gibson through a grant of shares in his shipping company, Atlantic Shipping.

The trust's website states that 'priority for support is given to charities that the trustees have previously worked with. However, the trust adds few new charities each year.'

For new applications, funding is given within particular themes. These themes can vary each year. In 2021, the priorities were education, social inclusion and physical and mental health. In 2021, the trust awarded 12 grants of up to £4,000 for capital and product purchases. The size and type of grant may vary between funding rounds, so check the trust's website for up-to-date information.

Eligibility

Charities must be UK registered but can operate anywhere in the world. The trust gives priority to small to medium-sized charities (with an annual income of less than £1 million) and to organisations that it has supported previously.

Financial information

Year end	31/03/2021
Income	£481,100
Assets	£16,360,000
Grants to organisations	£691,600
No. of grants	12

Further financial information

In 2020/21, grants were broken down as follows:

Nature conservation	£261,600
Civil society	£100,000
Health and medical research	£98,400
Art, music and entertainment	£52,600
Religion	£43,500
Care	£42,500
Hospices	£15,000

Beneficiaries included: A list of beneficiaries was not available.

Exclusions

For online applications, support is not given to the following, as the trust already supports these areas:

- The fabric of Christian churches
- Hospices
- Educational farms
- Riding and carriage driving for people with disabilities
- Cancer care and research
- Theatres
- Museums

Applications

If new to the trust, applications should be made using the online form on the trust's website only. Applications open on 1 August and close around the end of August each year. Prospective applicants are advised to read the guidelines before applying, as these may change with each funding round. If you have already received a grant from the trust, you do not need to complete the application form. Contact the charity directly to discuss your organisation's needs. Note: the trust does not respond to or acknowledge any correspondence sent by post.

Sources of information

Accounts; annual report; Charity Commission record; funder's website.

The Simon Gibson Charitable Trust

General charitable purposes, with a preference for conservation, education, religious purposes, young people and older people

Suffolk; Norfolk; Cambridgeshire; Hertfordshire; Glamorganshire; Gwent; Powys; Carmarthenshire

£783,000 (2020/21)

CC number: 269501

Correspondent: The Trustees, SGCT Applications, PO Box 609, Welwyn Garden City AL7 9QQ (tel: 07798 515812; email: info@sgctrust.org.uk)

Trustees: George Gibson; Deborah Connor; John Homfray.

www.sgctrust.org.uk

General information

The trust was established and endowed by Mr Simon Gibson in 1975.

Eligibility

UK-registered charities and CICs, either nationally or locally organised, that deliver benefit within the trust's designated geographical areas are eligible for funding. These are:

- Suffolk
- Norfolk
- Cambridgeshire
- Hertfordshire
- Glamorganshire
- Gwent
- Powys
- Carmarthenshire

The trust has a preference for organisations that support young and/or older people, and organisations with conservational, educational or religious purposes.

Funding

The trust makes grants of up to £20,000, with the typical grant being between £3,000 and £5,000. Awards are made towards core costs or for specific projects.

Financial information

Year end	05/04/2021
Income	£1,620,000
Assets	£22,230,000
Grants to organisations	£783,000

Beneficiaries included: Royal Welsh Agricultural Society Glamorgan Fund (£2,000); Wales Millennium Centre

(£15,000); Livery Company of Wales Charitable Trust (£10,000); Parkinson's UK (£5,000); Royal Agricultural Society (£3,000).

Exclusions

According to its website the trust does not support:

- Individuals (or organisations applying on behalf of individuals)
- Students seeking sponsorship for educational or gap year purposes
- Conferences, seminars or workshops
- Overseas charities (except conservation charities or those previously known to the trustees)

Applications

Application forms are available to download from the website and should be returned by post. Applications should be submitted between 1 January and 31 March each year.

Sources of information

Accounts; annual report; Charity Commission record; funder's website.

The Girdlers' Company Charitable Trust

Employability; carers; mental health; education, in particular literacy; people who have offended

England, with a preference for London and, in particular, Islington, Hammersmith and Peckham; New Zealand

£813,100 (2019/20)

CC number: 328026

Correspondent: Murray Whiteside, Clerk, Girdlers' Hall, Basinghall Avenue, London EC2V 5DD (tel: 020 7638 0488; email: clerk@girdlers.co.uk)

Trustee: The Girdlers' Company.

www.girdlers.co.uk

General information

Established in 1988, the trust's main areas of interest are:

- Increasing people's employability through vocational training
- Supporting carers
- Improving people's mental health
- Improving people's literacy
- Reducing the rate of re-offending

The trust operates throughout the UK, with a strong preference for London and, in particular, Islington, Hammersmith and Peckham. In 2009 the trust received the assets of the Geoffrey Woods Foundation, which was merged with The Girdlers' Company Charitable Trust.

To achieve its objectives, the trust makes donations under the following headings:

- Principal, Hammersmith and Peckham and general charities, and selected appeals
- New Zealand scholarships and fellowship
- Irish Guards
- Jock French Charitable Fund
- Christmas Court donations
- Master's Fund donations

Each year, around half of the trust's charitable expenditure is awarded to approximately 30 principal charities. These are organisations that the trust wishes to have enduring and close relationships with. Grants to principal charities are for up to £25,000 per year for three years.

Selected appeals are awarded to charities proposed by a member of the Girdlers' Company who has a close personal involvement.

The trust continues to support New Zealand undergraduate scholarships at Cambridge University and a medical research fellowship at Oxford University.

An annual donation goes to support the Irish Guards' Benevolent Fund and an amount is spent at the direction of the 1st Battalion's commanding officer to support guardsmen's welfare, adventurous training and sporting activities.

The Jock French Charitable Fund encourages charitable donations from livery members of the company. The subscribing members are invited to nominate charities to receive donations.

The Master's Fund is allocated an amount each year for the master to donate to charities of their own choice. A sum is also allocated to Christmas Court donations for members to nominate donations to charities of their individual choice at Christmastime.

The trust awards grants related specifically to leather matters through its Leather Fund in order to connect with the Girdlers' historic trade.

Many of the company's members have an interest in sailing, and for several years, the trust has also provided modest support to a number of sailing charities, especially those providing sail training to disadvantaged young people and individuals with disabilities.

According to the trust's website (March 2022), one-off grants of up to £10,000 can be applied for by organisations that deliver clearly defined outcomes and that support one of the trust's focus areas (employability; carers; mental health; literacy; people who have offended). Preference is given to smaller organisations where the grant will make a recognisable difference. Our research suggests this is the only funding stream which currently accepts unsolicited applications.

Financial information

Year end	29/09/2020
Income	£162,200
Assets	£4,840,000
Grants to organisations	£813,100

Further financial information

Grants were broken down as follows in 2019/20:

Principal charities	£312,000
New Zealand scholarships and fellowship	£132,800
COVID-19 emergency grants	£53,800
Enhanced selected appeals	£43,600
Hammersmith and Peckham charities	£36,000
The Irish Guards' Benevolent Fund	£25,000
Leather Fund	£22,800
Other	£10,000
Islington charities	£8,000
Selected appeals	£5,000
Entertainment	£4,100

Beneficiaries included: A list of beneficiaries was not available.

Applications

Applications for one-off grants of up to £10,000 can be made via the charity's website once an eligibility quiz has been completed. Applications are reviewed in mid-January and late June. Deadlines can be found on the trust's website. All applicants will be advised of the outcome, whether or not they have been successful. It appears that the trust does not accept unsolicited applications for its other funding streams.

Sources of information

Accounts; annual report; Charity Commission record; funder's website.

The Glass-House Trust

The built environment; child development; social research; the arts

UK and occasionally overseas

£370,500 (2020/21)

CC number: 1144990

Correspondent: The Trustees, The Peak, 5 Wilton Road, London SW1V 1AP (tel: 020 7410 0330; email: info@sfct.org.uk)

Trustees: Elinor Sainsbury; Alex Sainsbury; Judith Portrait.

www.sfct.org.uk/Glass-house.html

General information

This is one of the Sainsbury Family Charitable Trusts, which share a joint administration but work autonomously as independent legal entities. They have a common approach to grant-making and generally discourage applications from organisations not already in contact with the trust concerned, but some are open to unsolicited approaches.

The trust was established in 2011 and concentrates on supporting a small number of projects, usually in the following areas:

- Built environment
- Child development
- Social policy
- The arts

Financial information

Year end	05/04/2021
Income	£192,200
Assets	£10,500,000
Grants to organisations	£370,500
No. of grants	13

Beneficiaries included: Four Corner Books (£100,000); A Space (£55,000); MayDay Rooms (£50,000); Raven Row (£25,000); Transform Drug Policy Foundation (£15,000); The Sainsbury Archive (£5,000).

Exclusions

The trust does not support individuals, education fees or expeditions. Grants are made to projects initiated by the trustees, or jointly by the trustees and the beneficiary, and to other projects which the trustees proactively seek out.

Applications

Unsolicited applications are not accepted.

Sources of information

Accounts; annual report; Charity Commission record; funder's website.

The F. Glenister Woodger Trust

General charitable purposes

West Wittering

£427,400 (2020/21)

CC number: 1187947

Correspondent: The Trustees, The Pavilion, Rookwood Road, West Wittering, Chichester, West Sussex PO20 8LT (tel: 01243 513116; email: office@fgwoodgertrust.org)

Trustees: Rosamund Champ; William Craven; Maxine Pickup; Rosamund Gentle; Dr Adrian Gregory; Stuart Dobbin.

General information

The trust was established in 1989 with the object to improve the quality of life for people who live in West Wittering and the surrounding area. This object is met through the giving of grants to organisations working for general charitable purposes in the beneficial area.

Financial information

Year end	31/03/2021
Income	£1,410,000
Assets	£49,090,000
Grants to organisations	£427,400

Beneficiaries included: Local Primary Schools STEM Project (£225,000); The Aldingbourne Trust (£50,000); Chichester Information Shop for Young People (£30,000); Samaritans – Bognor, Chichester and District (£10,000); Stirlands Cricket Club (£3,000); Downview Community Hall (£1,500); RNIB (£1,000).

Applications

Apply in writing to the correspondent. The trustees meet quarterly to review grant applications.

Sources of information

Accounts; annual report; Charity Commission record.

The Gloag Foundation

General charitable purposes; people trafficking; advancement of Christianity; relief of poverty; health; education

UK and overseas

£902,900 (2020)

OSCR number: SC035799

Correspondent: The Trustees, The Steading, Kinfauns, Perth, Perthshire PH2 7JU (tel: 01738 633264)

www.gloagfoundation.org.uk

General information

The foundation was established by Dame Anne Gloag. It supports projects that prevent or relieve poverty and encourage the advancement of education, health and religion in the UK and overseas.

According to its 2020 annual report, new awards were made for the following purposes:

- Health
- Relief of poverty
- Anti-exploitation and people trafficking
- Advancement of Christianity
- Other purposes

Financial information

Year end	31/12/2020
Income	£665,500
Assets	£8,870,000
Grants to organisations	£902,900

Beneficiaries included: Freedom from Fistula Foundation (£668,600); Kenya Children's Homes (£58,000); Refuge (£15,000); Marks for Scotland (£10,000).

Applications

The foundation does not accept unsolicited applications or requests.

Sources of information

Accounts; annual report; OSCR record; funder's website.

Global Charities

Inclusion, diversity and equality; physical and mental health; safety and shelter; life skills; reducing isolation

UK

£2.36 million (2020/21)

CC number: 1091657

Correspondent: Grants Team, 30 Leicester Square, London WC2H 7LA (tel: 0345 606 0990; email: grants@makesomenoise.com)

Trustees: Gareth Andrewartha; Michael Connole; Jonathan Norbury; Joanne Kenrick; Ulrika Hogberg; Sally Cairns; Marcia Asare; Jennifer Stubbs; Shalni Sood; Martin Allen.

www.makesomenoise.com

facebook.com/globalsmakesomenoise

@makenoise

@globals_make_some_noise

General information

Global Charities is the charitable arm of Global, the media and entertainment group which operates some of the UK's largest and best known radio stations, including Heart, Capital and Classic FM.

Global's Make Some Noise

The charity's flagship grant-giving programme, Global's Make Some Noise, raises money from Global Radio listeners, customers, and the entertainment and music industries, which the charity then distributes to support projects undertaken by small community charities. Historically, the programme focused on supporting children and young people's charities; however, in response to the COVID-19 pandemic this remit was expanded to address the growing diverse needs of all communities in the UK.

The programme's four key outcome areas are:

- Providing safety and shelter
- Supporting physical and/or mental health
- Developing life skills
- Reducing isolation or improving inclusion

There is one funding round per year. At the time of writing (May 2022), the next funding round was planned to open on 1 April 2023. In 2022, the programme offered one-year grants of between £20,000 and £30,000. The programme does not award grants of more than 40% of a charity's annual income.

To be eligible for funding, applicants must be registered a charity delivering a project or service that addresses one or more of the programme's key outcomes. Charities must have been registered for at least one year, have an annual income of between £30,000 and £1 million and have at least one set of full submitted accounts. Full eligibility criteria are available on the charity's website.

Financial information

Year end	31/03/2021
Income	£4,580,000
Assets	£3,200,000
Grants to organisations	£2,360,000
No. of grants	91

Further financial information

In 2020/21, grants were broken down as follows:

Lack of opportunity	20	£441,600
Disability	17	£428,200
Illness	16	£422,700
Mental health	10	£353,800
Bereavement	9	£187,100
Carers	5	£143,900
Poverty	3	£100,000
Homelessness	4	£90,000
Domestic abuse	2	£80,000
Loneliness and isolation	3	£72,000
Other	2	£40,000

A full list of beneficiaries is available on the charity's website.

Beneficiaries included: Youth@Heart (£482,900); Sufra (£135,000); New Step for African Community (£55,000); Trafford Domestic Abuse Services (£30,000); Leeds Black Elders Association (£22,000); The Candlelighters Trust (£14,000); The Children's Respite Trust (£12,000); NE Youth (£8,000).

Applications

The charity has a three-stage application process. The stages are:

1. **Expression of interest:** an online form can be completed when funding rounds open
2. **Invitation to apply:** the grants team will shortlist charities to apply based on how well they meet the funding objectives. A full application form will need to be completed with relevant documents attached (including your safeguarding policy, current financial information and your constitution or governing document)
3. **Panel assessment:** Applications will be assessed by the grants panel. All applicants will be notified of the outcome and will be given feedback

Sources of information

Accounts; annual report; Charity Commission record; funder's website.

The Golden Bottle Trust

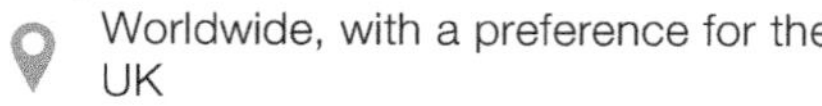

General charitable purposes

Worldwide, with a preference for the UK

£2.45 million (2019/20)

CC number: 327026

Correspondent: Hoare Trustees, c/o C. Hoare and Co., 37 Fleet Street, London EC4P 4DQ (tel: 020 7353 4522)

Trustee: Hoare Trustees.

www.hoaresbank.co.uk/golden-bottle-trust

General information

The trust was established in 1985 for general charitable purposes, by C. Hoare and Co. bankers, the oldest remaining private bank in the UK. The trust is managed by the company, Messrs. Hoare Trustees, and continues to receive most of its income from C. Hoare and Co.

The objective of the trust is the continuation of the philanthropic commitments and ideals of the Hoare family. According to the trust's 2019/20 annual report, traditionally the trust has supported causes in the spheres of:

- The arts
- Education
- Health
- The environment/sustainability
- Social investment

The trust's website states that in recent years its giving has focused on:

- Prisons and early intervention
- Financial and income inequality
- The refugee crisis
- The environment

The minimum grant is £250, rising to a maximum of £100,000, but occasionally larger sums are considered. The trust's 2019/20 annual report states that 'the preference of the trustee is to build trusted partnerships that allow for the donation of unrestricted funding.'

Financial information

Year end	30/09/2020
Income	£135,400
Assets	£16,960,000
Grants to organisations	£2,450,000

Further financial information

Grants paid during the year totalled £2.45 million. The following breakdown was provided:

Donations to related parties	£525,500
Education	£319,700
Citizenship and community development	£278,000
Arts, culture, heritage and science	£257,000
Health and saving lives	£256,200
The environment	£210,000
Staff matched giving	£186,300
Human rights, racial harmony and equality	£114,000
Religion	£105,600
Other	£55,000
Relief in need	£44,300
Prevention and relief of poverty	£40,800
Children	£39,000
Armed forces and emergency services	£7,500
Amateur sports	£7,000
Animal welfare	£1,500

Only beneficiaries of grants of £10,000 and above were listed in the accounts.

Beneficiaries included: The Fore (£310,000); Philanthropy Impact (£125,000); Buglife (£100,000); Henry C. Hoare Charitable Trust (£80,000); Global Cyber Alliance (£50,000); Royal Albert Hall (£26,500); Reach Charity (£20,000); Exeter Cathedral (£11,000); African Prisons Project and Dawlish Gardens Trust (£10,000 each).

Applications

The trust's website states that it prefers to work with trusted partners and networks to identify suitable causes to help. For this reason, unsolicited grant requests are not accepted.

Sources of information

Accounts; annual report; Charity Commission record; funder's website.

The Goldman Sachs Charitable Gift Fund (UK)

General charitable purposes; community development; education; health; social welfare; arts and culture; religion; humanitarian relief

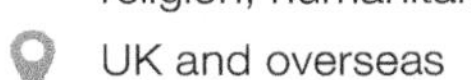

UK and overseas

£1.71 million (2019/20)

CC number: 1120148

Correspondent: The Trustees, Goldman Sachs International, 25 Shoe Lane, London EC4A 4AU (tel: 020 7774 1000)

Trustees: Jennifer Evans; Graham Shaw; Robert Katz; Peter Fahey.

General information

The Goldman Sachs Charitable Gift Fund (UK) was established in 2007 for general charitable purposes. It is the UK charity of the multinational investment bank and financial services company The Goldman Sachs Group Inc., and is the wholly owned subsidiary of the Goldman Sachs Charitable Gift Fund, which has been recognised by the United States Internal Revenue Service as a tax-exempt organisation.

Grants are awarded worldwide and are used to support a wide range of charitable activities, including community development, education, health, social welfare, arts and culture, and humanitarian relief.

According to the its 2019/20 annual report:

> The ongoing strategy of the Fund is to make grants pursuant to its objects from donated funds solicited from The Goldman Sachs Group, Inc, and its predecessors, subsidiaries, affiliates and successors ("Goldman Sachs"), and current and former senior employees of Goldman Sachs.

Financial information

Year end	30/06/2020
Grants to organisations	£1,710,000

Further financial information

A total of 86 grants were awarded during the year. According to the charity's annual report:

> Grants were made to support charities that build and stabilise communities, increase educational opportunities, advance health, relieve poverty, promote the arts and culture, provide humanitarian relief and to further other exclusively charitable purposes under English and Welsh law and American law. All grants were made to institutions.

Beneficiaries included: Columbia University (£737,500); Princeton University (£304,000); PeacePlayers International (£150,000); Noble and Greenough School (£100,000).

Applications

The charity's annual report explains that it 'operates as a donor-advised fund whereby the directors establish donor accounts for individual donors to make recommendations, although the ultimate decision for the distribution of funds rests solely with the directors of the fund'.

Sources of information

Accounts; annual report; Charity Commission record.

Goldman Sachs Gives (UK)

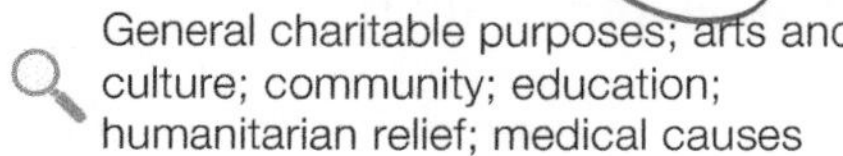

General charitable purposes; arts and culture; community; education; humanitarian relief; medical causes

Worldwide

£18.18 million (2019/20)

CC number: 1123956

Correspondent: Jenny Evans, Trustee, Goldman Sachs, Peterborough Court, 133 Fleet Street, London EC4A 2BB (tel: 020 7774 1000)

Trustees: Jenny Evans; Robert Katz; Graham Shaw; Peter Fahey.

www.goldmansachs.com/citizenship/goldman-sachs-gives

General information

Goldman Sachs Gives (UK) was established and registered with the Charity Commission in 2008. The income of the fund is made up of donations from affiliate and subsidiary companies of Goldman Sachs Group Inc., and also from past and present senior employees of these companies.

The charity's 2019/20 annual accounts state:

> The objects of the Fund are to promote for the public benefit the advancement of education, the relief of poverty, the advancement of religion and any other exclusively charitable purpose. In furtherance of those objects the Fund focuses on supporting charities and charitable activities that build and stabilise communities, increase educational opportunities, advance health, relieve poverty, promote the arts and culture, provide humanitarian relief and further any other charitable purposes.

Financial information

Year end	30/06/2020
Income	£23,360,000
Assets	£90,800,000
Grants to organisations	£18,180,000

Further financial information

There were a total of 653 grants made during the year.

Grants were broken down as follows:

Community	£6,100,000
Education	£4,540,000
Medical	£4,020,000
Other	£1,340,000
Humanitarian	£1,240,000
Arts and culture	£929,600

Beneficiaries included: Greenhouse Sports Ltd (£854,000); Mind (£590,000); Fondation de l'Assistance Publique (£518,000).

Applications

Apply in writing to the correspondent. Be aware, however, that this is a donor-advised fund. The trustees do not utilise key performance indicators to measure the activity of grant-making.

Sources of information

Accounts; annual report; Charity Commission record; funder's website.

The Goldsmiths' Company Charity

General charitable purposes; relief of poverty; advancement of education; prisoner resettlement; young people; mental health; older people

UK, with a preference for London

£4.08 million (2020/21)

CC number: 1175593

Correspondent: David Reddaway, Clerk and Correspondent, Goldsmiths' Hall, 13 Foster Lane, London EC2V 6BN (tel: 020 7606 7010; email: the.clerk@thegoldsmiths.co.uk)

Trustees: Lord Mark Bridges; Timothy Schroder; Edward Harley; Thomas Fattorini; Richard Agutter; George MacDonald; Dr Charles Mackworth-Young; Richard Reid; William Parente; Michael Prideaux; Edward Braham; Victoria Broackes; Judith Cobham-Lowe; Richard Fox; Neil Carson; Arthur Drysdale; Arthur Galsworthy; Jane Goad; Joanna Hardy; Hector Miller; Michael Wainwright; Brig Butler; Richard Madeley.

www.thegoldsmiths.co.uk/charities

facebook.com/TheGoldsmithsCompany

@GoldsmithsCo

@goldsmithsfair

General information

The Goldsmiths' Company Charity was created following the amalgamation of 57 separate trust funds which had been built up over the centuries within the Goldsmiths' Company. Today, the charity supports a wide range of charitable causes.

According to its website, the charity is currently focused on three areas: prisoner resettlement, young people and the ageing population. Two types of grant are available:

Small grants (of up to £5,000) for:

- General welfare (including homelessness, prisoners and substance misuse)
- Culture
- Medical welfare/people with disabilities

Large grants (of up to a maximum of £30,000) for:

- Disadvantaged young people, specifically young people leaving care, young carers, young people with mental health issues and youth homelessness (affiliated members of London Youth may be considered under the small grants category)
- The rehabilitation/resettlement of prisoners, particularly prisoner education and training, mentoring, employment opportunities, arts and music, women in prison and support for prisoners' families
- Charities working to combat isolation and loneliness among older people anywhere in the UK

COVID-19 update

At the time of writing (June 2022), the charity's website stated the following:

> Following a review of our priorities and due to the impact on our income as a result of COVID-19 pandemic and the

turbulent financial market, we have taken the decision to fund in our large grants category (specifically charities within the prisoner resettlement space) by invitation only. We are also no longer running a small grants programme until further notice. Any changes or updates to our funding position will be announced clearly on our webpages

The Goldsmiths' Company also sponsors a number of educational initiatives. These are typically directed towards primary and secondary education, the improvement of STEM subjects, community engagement and the well-being of teachers. Full details of all the charity's current education programmes can be found on the website. Unsolicited applications were not being accepted at the time of writing (June 2022).

Finally, the charity's Wardens' grants are directed towards discrete projects predominantly focused on support for: the advancement of the trade of goldsmithing and silversmithing; existing military associations; wider causes in the City of London; and strategic partnerships with cultural institutions. Unsolicited applications are not accepted for this programme.

The charity regularly reviews its grant-making policy and will update guidance on its website as necessary. As such, organisations are advised to check the website regularly for updates.

Financial information

Year end	31/03/2021
Income	£3,590,000
Assets	£162,800,000
Grants to organisations	£4,080,000

Further financial information

Support of the craft (including the COVID-19 Fund)	£2.71 million
Culture	£800,100
Prisoner resettlement	£513,500
Education	£309,700
Warden's grants	£208,500
General welfare	£108,100
Youth	£86,500
Ageing population	£67,000
Restricted funds	£53,300

Beneficiaries included: Goldsmiths University (£71,700); The National Literacy Trust (£24,900); Safer London (£20,000); Arts4Dementia (£10,000); The National Youth Choirs of Great Britain (£3,000); City of London Police Widows and Orphans (£1,000); City Giving Day (£30).

Exclusions

Applications are not accepted from any of the following:

- Individuals
- Overseas charities and projects taking place and/or benefitting people outside the UK
- Medical research
- Animal welfare
- Individual housing associations and tenant organisations
- Endowment schemes
- Individual churches, for maintenance of the fabric
- Individual hospices
- Individual schools or supporting associations
- Play schemes, nurseries or preschool facilities
- Local authorities, or work usually considered a statutory responsibility
- Major building projects, or capital funding
- One-off events (such as festivals, conferences, exhibitions and community events)
- Overseas projects or trips
- Campaigning or lobbying projects, or general awareness-raising work
- Membership organisations

Further programme specific exclusions may also apply. See the guidelines on the charity's website for full details.

Applications

At the time of writing (June 2022), applications for the charity's large grants category were accepted by invitation only. Organisations are advised to check the website regularly for updates.

Sources of information

Accounts; annual report; Charity Commission record; funder's website.

The Goodman Foundation

General charitable purposes; the relief of poverty; older people; illness and disability; children; overseas assistance and disaster relief

 UK and overseas

 £936,800 (2020/21)

CC number: 1097231

Correspondent: The Trustees, c/o ABP, Unit 6290, Bishops Court, Solihull Parkway, Birmingham Business Park, Birmingham B37 7YB (tel: 0121 717 2500)

Trustees: Laurence Goodman; Catherine Goodman; Philip Morgan.

General information

The Goodman Foundation was registered with the Charity Commission in 2003 for general charitable purposes. According to its Charity Commission record, its main objectives are:

- To help people on low incomes, older people, and those with disabilities or ill health
- To support other general charitable purposes

Financial information

Year end	31/03/2021
Income	£5,810,000
Assets	£75,310,000
Grants to organisations	£936,800
No. of grants	47

Further financial information

Grants were broken down as follows:

People who are poor, elderly and have a disability	19	£390,100
Children's charities	4	£276,200
Other charitable causes	19	£225,200
Financially developing countries and disasters	5	£45,300

Beneficiaries included: A list of beneficiaries was not available.

Applications

Apply in writing to the correspondent.

Sources of information

Accounts; annual report; Charity Commission record.

The Mike Gooley Trailfinders Charity

Medical research; community projects for young people; armed forces

UK

 £1.76 million (2019/20)

CC number: 1048993

Correspondent: The Trustees, 9 Abingdon Road, London W8 6AH (tel: 020 7938 3143)

Trustees: Fiona Gooley; Tristan Gooley; Bernadette Gooley; Michael Gooley.

General information

The charity was founded by Mike Gooley, the owner of the travel company Trailfinders Ltd. The charity was created in 1995 and, according to its 2019/20 annual report, supports:

- Medical research
- Community projects which encourage young people in outdoor activities
- Armed forces veteran organisations

Financial information

Year end	30/06/2020
Income	£637,100
Assets	£21,950,000
Grants to organisations	£1,760,000

Beneficiaries included: A list of beneficiaries was not available.

Applications

Apply in writing to the correspondent.

Sources of information

Accounts; annual report; Charity Commission record.

The Goshen Trust

Christian projects

England and Wales, with preference for North East England

£353,300 (2020/21)

CC number: 1119064

Correspondent: Company Secretary, PO Box 275, Stanley, County Durham DH8 1HH (email: admin@goshentrust.org)

Trustees: Jonathan Dicken; Alison Dicken; Pauline Dicken; Albert Dicken; Rachel Dicken.

General information

The trust has general charitable purposes but, according to its 2020/21 annual report, also 'encourages and develops Christian projects which otherwise would not be able to reach an effective operational conclusion as well as supporting those that are already well established'.

According to the trust's 2020/21 accounts:

> The charity invites written applications for grants from Christian organisations in England and Wales, although grants are made to other parts of the UK and overseas, and the trustees are particularly interested in supporting charities in the North East of England where possible. The charity receives many more applications than it has funds to support. It is the aim of the charity to encourage and develop Christian projects which otherwise may not be able to reach an effective operational conclusion as well as supporting those that are already well established.

Most awarded grants are in the range of £1,000 to £60,000.

Financial information

Year end	05/04/2021
Income	£309,900
Assets	£9,680,000
Grants to organisations	£353,300

Beneficiaries included: Urban Saints (£60,000); Teen Challenge (£43,100); Kiwoko Hospital (£30,000); Angel Foundation (£25,000); Sowing Seeds Ministries (£10,200); Reeth Evangelical (£5,000); Whitby Museum (£2,000); The Big Give (£1,500).

Applications

Apply in writing to the correspondent. The trustees meet several times a year to consider applications. All applications are acknowledged. If applicants do not receive any further communication from the trust, they should assume that they have been unsuccessful.

Sources of information

Accounts; annual report; Charity Commission record.

The Gosling Foundation Ltd

Education; relief of poverty; religion; general charitable purposes for community benefit

UK

£1.69 million (2020/21)

CC number: 326840

Correspondent: The Trustees, 2A Kempson Road, London SW6 4PU (tel: 020 7495 5599; email: Gosling.Foundation@conprop.co.uk)

Trustees: Hon. Capt. Adam Gosling; Peter Caplan; Nicholas Giles.

www.thegoslingfoundation.com

General information

The foundation was established in 1985 by Sir Donald Gosling, co-founder of NCP car parks and former seafarer. Sir Donald Gosling sadly passed away in 2019. The foundation's endowment derives from his personal fortune and its objects are the relief of poverty, education and general charitable purposes beneficial to the community. Grants are given each year to a wide range of charities, with naval and other service-related charities receiving substantial support.

Financial information

Year end	31/03/2021
Income	£4,030.00
Assets	£171,740,000
Grants to organisations	£1,690,000
No. of grants	48

Further financial information

Grants to organisations were distributed as follows: advancement of education (£851,700); relief of poverty (£617,500); community (£217,800).

Beneficiaries included: The Royal Naval Benevolent Trust (£500,000); The Greenwich Foundation for the Old Royal Naval College (£250,000); UK Youth (£100,000); The Felix Project (£65,000); Treloar Trust (£45,000); Tall Ships Youth Trust (£30,700); The Petersham and Ham Sea Scout Group (£25,000); Cowes Unit 118 of the Sea Cadet Corps (£5,000); The Hull C. U. Ltd (£2,500).

Exclusions

According to the foundations' website, support is not given for/to the following:

- Organisations that are not charities, CIOs or CICs registered in England, Wales, Scotland, or Northern Ireland.
- Core costs – salaries, running costs, training programmes, rent, utility bills
- Applications for less than £5,000
- Capital fees – building surveys, planning applications or feasibility studies
- Grants to individuals
- Churches or other religious bodies that are not registered charities/CIOs/CICs and that have no secular activity
- NHS hospitals or mainstream schools, colleges, or universities
- Heritage or conservation projects (the trustees occasionally fund naval heritage projects, but do not accept unsolicited applications for them)
- Medical or research medical equipment
- Organisations supporting those affected by sexual abuse, sexual violence, and rape
- Organisations supporting those affected by domestic violence
- Hospices
- Charities with an annual income of £30 million and over
- Newly established charities with [fewer] than two sets of annual accounts
- Applications made via post

Applications

Contact the correspondent for more information.

Sources of information

Accounts; annual report; Charity Commission record; funder's website.

The Edward Gostling Foundation

Disability; social welfare; long-term illness

UK

£3.75 million (2020/21)

CC number: 1068617

Correspondent: The Grants Manager, Suite 1, 61 Thames Street, Windsor, Berkshire SL4 1QW (tel: 01753 753900; email: info@theactfoundation.co.uk or use the contact form on the website)

Trustees: Michael Street; John O'Sullivan; Robert White; Denis Taylor; Christine Erwood; Russell Meadows; Colin Clarkson; Stephen O'Sullivan; Victoria Hoskins.

www.edwardgostlingfoundation.org.uk

General information

The Edward Gostling Foundation, formerly known as The ACT Foundation, was formed in 1994. According to its website, the foundation provides grants to UK-registered charities with the aim of 'enhancing the quality of life of people in need and, particularly, those on a low income and who have a physical and/or mental disability or long-term illness'.

Grants are awarded within four key themes, as detailed on the website:

- Health and Wellbeing – supporting access to community facilities to maintain, improve and enhance general welfare

- Independent Living at Home – helping people to live independently in their own home for as long as possible
- Respite – enabling carers to take a break from the responsibility of caring for a loved one
- Transition – supporting people beyond education and into employment, long-term volunteering or other meaningful daytime activity, housing and independent living

The foundation offers small grants of up to £25,000 to charities with an annual income of £1 million or less that are in need of immediate support to sustain an essential existing service. Capital grants of up to £250,000 are available to charities of any size. Funding is directed towards projects that either enhance or expand an existing service or bring about a transformational change in the way support and care are provided.

Financial information

Year end	31/03/2021
Income	£4,060,000
Assets	£104,950,000
Grants to organisations	£3,750,000

Beneficiaries included: Tees Valley Community Foundation (£50,000); The Katherine Low Settlement (£25,000); Rainbow Trust Children's Charity (£20,000); Halow Project (£10,000).

Exclusions

According to the foundation's website, applications are not accepted from:

- Individuals
- Charities that have not been registered with a UK Charity Commission for at least 3 years
- Overseas projects or organisations
- Community Interest Companies
- Exempt Charities not directly regulated by a UK Charity Commission
- CASC's or other sporting associations without a UK Charity Commission registration
- Social Enterprises without a UK Charity Commission registration
- Statutory organisations and charities that support them, including NHS hospitals or services, prisons and state funded or independent schools
- Organisations providing further education except where the facility is wholly for students with additional needs
- Community centres, youth clubs or other leisure activities, except where the main beneficiaries have a physical and/or a mental disability, are elderly or suffering from a long-term illness or are carers
- Campaigning, lobbying or other similar awareness raising campaigns

Applications

Small grants application forms can be downloaded from the foundation's website. There is no application form for capital grants. Full information on what to include in an application and how to apply can be found on the foundation's website.

Sources of information

Accounts; annual report; Charity Commission record; funder's website.

Grace Charitable Trust

General charitable purposes; social welfare; medical causes; Christian and church-based activities; education

UK and overseas

£860,000 (2020/21)

CC number: 292984

Correspondent: The Trustees, Swinford House GCT Office, Nortons Lane, Great Barrow, Chester, Cheshire CH3 7JZ (tel: 01928 740773; email: gracecharitabletrust@live.co.uk)

Trustees: Mark Mitchell; Eric Payne; Robert Quayle; Robert Wright; Angela Payne.

General information

Established in 1985, the trust makes grants for general charitable purposes but has a preference for Christian and church-based activities, social welfare, education and medical needs. Grants are only awarded to charities that are known to the trustees.

Financial information

Year end	30/04/2021
Income	£2,120,000
Assets	£3,940,000
Grants to organisations	£860,000

Further financial information

Grants were broken down as follows:

Christian causes	£450,000
Social and medical causes	£303,100
Education	£106,700
General charitable purposes	£11,500

Beneficiaries included: A list of beneficiaries was not available.

Applications

Unsolicited applications are not accepted. Grants are only made to charities known to the settlors.

Sources of information

Accounts, annual report, Charity Commission record.

The Grace Trust

Education; medical research; disability; humanitarian aid and disaster relief; relief of poverty; life preservation; advancement of Christianity

UK and overseas

£30.79 million (2020)

CC number: 257516

Correspondent: The Trustees, Noble House, Eaton Road, Hemel Hempstead, Hertfordshire HP2 7UB (tel: 020 3301 3806; email: enquiries@thegracetrust.org.uk)

Trustees: Scribefort Ltd; Aller Brook Ltd.

 www.thegracetrust.org.uk

General information

The Grace Trust was set up in 1968 by Mr John Dallow, a member of the Plymouth Brethren Christian Church, using a large proportion of the proceeds from the sale of his manufacturing business.

The trust donates to a large variety of UK-registered charities. It supports charities working nationally and locally in order to further its wide aims and objectives. The trust has a long tradition of supporting educational organisations but will also support charities involved in:

- Non-statutory emergency services and medical relief
- Disaster relief
- Childcare
- Disability support
- Essential medical research

Financial information

Year end	31/01/2020
Income	£127,450,000
Assets	£55,130,000
Grants to organisations	£30,790,000

Beneficiaries included: OneSchool Global UK (£23.94 million); Rapid Relief Team (£640,000); FareShare and Leeds Cares (£2,000 each); Hourglass and Lifeworks (£1,000 each); The Lin Berwick Trust (£500).

Applications

Apply in writing to the correspondent. The trust's 2020 annual report states:

> All applications are considered carefully by the Trustees, and recommendations are made by the grantmaking committee, comprising individuals who are not Trustees of the Grace Trust, for approval by the Trustees. This allows for additional scrutiny of applications, and unbiased opinions to be presented to the Board, therefore providing increased independence.

Sources of information

Accounts; annual report; Charity Commission record; funder's website.

Graff Foundation

General charitable purposes

UK and worldwide

£1.33 million (2020)

CC number: 1012859

Correspondent: Anthony Kerman, Trustee, Kerman and Co. LLP, 28–29 Albemarle Street, London W1S 4JA (tel: 020 7584 8571)

Trustees: Nicholas Paine; Mr L. Graff; Mrs F. Graff.

General information

The Graff Foundation is funded by Graff Diamonds Ltd, a multinational jeweller based in London. The foundation was established in 1992 and makes grants for general charitable purposes.

Financial information

Year end	31/12/2020
Income	£186,200
Assets	£3,290,000
Grants to organisations	£1,330,000

Beneficiaries included: COVID-19 Solidarity Response Fund (£807,600); Facet Foundation (£391,800); The Museum of Contemporary Art (£75,900); Guggenheim Museum (£22,800); Tate Foundation (£10,000); Chabad Jewish Community of Central London (£6,500).

Applications

Apply in writing to the correspondent.

Sources of information

Accounts; annual report; Charity Commission record.

The Grand Trust CIO

General charitable purposes

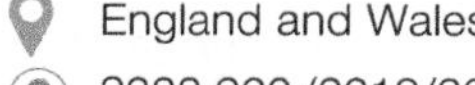

England and Wales

£388,900 (2019/20)

CC number: 1179280

Correspondent: The Trustees, c/o Brabners LLP, 55 King Street, Manchester M2 4LQ (tel: 0161 836 8949)

Trustees: Danielle Peet; Joanne Radcliff; Steven Appleton

General information

This trust was registered with the Charity Commission in July 2018 to make grants to organisations in England and Wales for general charitable purposes.

The trust makes grants in support of organisations that provide assistance to marginalised groups and those from disadvantaged backgrounds.

Financial information

Year end	30/06/2020
Income	£1,210,000
Assets	£1,030,000
Grants to organisations	£388,900

Beneficiaries included: A list of beneficiaries was not available.

Applications

Contact the trust for more information.

Sources of information

Charity Commission record.

The Grant Foundation

General charitable purposes; the advancement of the Christian faith; the education and welfare of children and young people; emergency overseas appeals

UK and overseas

£40,500 (2020)

CC number: 1084915

Correspondent: Anna Warner-McLoughlin, Trustee, The Entertainer, Broughton Business Park, Bell Lane, Amersham HP6 6GL (tel: 01494 737037; email: anna@thegrantfoundation.org.uk)

Trustees: Catherine Grant; Gary Grant; Duncan Grant; Stuart Grant; Anna Warner-McLoughlin; Alastair Grant.

General information

According to its 2020 annual report, the objectives of the foundation are to:

- Apply funds for such charitable purposes that the Trustees may from time to time select.
- [Advance] the Christian faith in the UK or overseas.
- [Advance the] education of children and young people, assisting with the provision of help to socially disadvantaged children and young people and assisting children and young people in financial need to receive support and training.

The foundation also makes grants in support of emergency appeals overseas and awards grants directly to individuals in need.

Financial information

Year end	31/12/2020
Income	£30,000
Assets	£285
Grants to organisations	£40,500
No. of grants	38

Further financial information

In 2020, the foundation awarded 38 grants to organisations, totalling £40,500. Of this amount, £8,000 was awarded in 3 grants to Christian Aid, and the remaining £32,500 was awarded to other organisations in 35 grants of less than £5,000 each.

Beneficiaries included: A list of beneficiaries was not available. Previous beneficiaries include: The Lambeth Trust (£40,000); Christians Against Poverty (30,000); Alpha International (£20,000); Just Love (£10,000) Food for the Hungry UK (£5,800); Citizens Advice Chiltern (£5,260); Autism Bedfordshire and Safe Families for Children (£5,000 each).

Applications

Apply in writing to the correspondent.

Sources of information

Accounts; annual report; Charity Commission record.

The Grantham Yorke Trust

Young people (under 25); education; social welfare; training; recreation

West Midlands

£261,000 (2020/21)

CC number: 228466

Correspondent: Chrissy Norgrove, Clerk to the Trustees, The Estate Office, Wharf Cottage, Broombank, Newham Bridge, Tenbury Wells, Worcestershire WR15 8NY (tel: 07799 784019; email: chrissy@granthamyorketrust.org.uk)

Trustees: The Revd Matthew Thompson; Fred Rattley; Howard Belton; Philip Smiglarski; Sue Butler; Tim Clarke; Hugh Sherriffe; Ruth Burgess; Beverley Momenabadi.

General information

According to its Charity Commission record, the trust supports the 'education, physical and social training, rehabilitation and recreational pursuits' of those under the age of 25 years who are in need. Grants are made to both individuals and organisations in the West Midlands region.

The trust's 2020/2021 annual report provides further details of its aims, as follows:

- Providing financial assistance, outfits, clothing, tools, instruments, equipment or books to help young people on leaving school, university or other educational establishment, to prepare for, or to enter, a profession, trade or calling
- Promoting or assisting the education or rehabilitation of such persons who are in need of physical, mental or moral care
- Assisting by way of education and training the prevention of juvenile delinquency, the abuse of drugs, alcohol and gambling, and the neglect or ill treatment of children

- Assisting parents with advice, education or training
- Providing young people with facilities for recreation and other leisure-time occupation in the interests of social welfare

Grants to organisations typically range from £1,000 to £10,000. Grants to individuals tend to be smaller, in the range of £150 to £1,500.

Financial information

Year end	05/04/2021
Income	£218,600
Assets	£7,010,000
Grants to organisations	£261,000

Further financial information

Grants were awarded to 96 organisations and 18 individuals during the year.

Beneficiaries included: A list of beneficiaries was not available. Previous beneficiaries include: Severn Valley Railway Charitable Trust (£10,000); Warley Baptist Church (£7,500); The Feast Youth Project and Touchstones Child Bereavement Support (£5,000 each); Birmingham Opera Company (£3,000); Kenelm Youth Trust and Shakespeare Hospice (£2,500 each); Queen Alexandra College (£1,500); 2nd Warwick Sea Scouts (£1,000).

Applications

Apply in writing to the correspondent. The trustees meet quarterly.

Sources of information

Accounts; annual report; Charity Commission record.

GrantScape

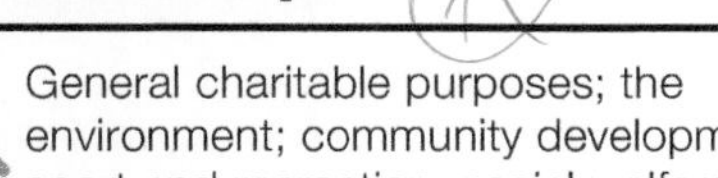

General charitable purposes; the environment; community development; sport and recreation; social welfare

UK

£2.75 million (2020/21)

CC number: 1102249

Correspondent: Kim Wilkinson, Grant Administrator, Office E, Whitsundoles, Broughton Road, Salford, Milton Keynes, Buckinghamshire MK17 8BU (tel: 01908 247630; email: info@grantscape.org.uk)

Trustees: Antony Cox; Michael Clarke; Philippa Lyons; Michael Singh; John Mills; Thomas Walker; Stuart McAleese.

www.grantscape.org.uk

@GrantScape1

General information

GrantScape is a grants management specialist whose main activity is to redistribute donations received from landfill operators under the Landfill Communities Fund. It also delivers grants and community benefit programmes on behalf of renewable energy companies from other sectors (e.g. wind and solar energy) and provides grants administration services to other organisations. GrantScape is a company limited by guarantee and is enrolled with ENTRUST as an accredited environmental body.

Financial information

Year end	31/03/2021
Income	£3,320,000
Assets	£2,500,000
Grants to organisations	£2,750,000

Beneficiaries included: Glapthorn Parish Council (£50,000); Lincolnshire YMCA (£29,800); Miles for Men (£20,000); NSPCC (£10,000); Cumbria Wildlife Trust (£1,300); Friends of Centre Vale Park (£400).

Exclusions

Each fund is subject to its own exclusions – for details, consult the fund listing on the website.

Applications

Applicants should visit the 'Grant and Project Finder' section of the charity's website to find information on all grant programmes currently available. Applications should be made online via the website.

Sources of information

Accounts; annual report; Charity Commission record; funder's website.

The Great Britain Sasakawa Foundation

Links between UK and Japan

UK and Japan

£771,200 (2020)

CC number: 290766

Correspondent: The Trustees, Lower Ground Floor, 24 Bedford Row, London WC1R 4TQ (tel: 020 7436 9042; email: grants@gbsf.org.uk)

Trustees: Prof. David Cope; Ambassador Fujii; Tatsuya Tanami; The Earl of St Andrews; Joanna Pitman; Prof. Yuichi Hosoya; Prof. Yoriko Kawaguchi; Prof. Janet Hunter; Prof. Ryuichi Teshima; Jeremy Scott; Prof. Izumi Kadono.

www.gbsf.org.uk

facebook.com/GBSasakawa

@gbsasakawa

General information

The foundation was established following a visit to London in 1983 by the late Ryoichi Sasakawa to discuss UK–Japanese relations. Its main aim is to enhance and promote a mutual appreciation of each culture.

Grants

The foundation can make grants for activities in the following areas:

- Arts and culture
- Humanities and social issues (including Japanese studies)
- The Japanese language
- Medicine and health
- Science, technology and the environment
- Sport
- Young people and education

The website states that although applications can be submitted in any of the above areas, the foundation is especially keen to support projects in science and technology, medicine and health, the environment and social issues, Japanese studies, and the Japanese language. Grants are made for pump-priming and not core funding of projects.

The following information is taken from the website, where you can find a more in-depth guide:

> - Grants are intended to be 'pump-priming' or partial support for worthwhile projects which would not otherwise be realised, and evidence of core funding should be available before any application is made for an award.
> - For projects involving travel between the UK and Japan, a maximum grant of £1,600 per person can be applied for towards flights, accommodation and subsistence, and a maximum of £2,000 per person for visits of two weeks or longer.
> - There are no set budgets for any category of activity, but emphasis is placed on innovative projects and on those involving groups of people in both countries (especially young people) rather than individuals. Awards do not normally exceed £5,000-£6,000 for larger-scale projects.
> - Projects originating in the UK should be submitted through the London office and those originating in Japan through the Tokyo office.
> - Applications for UK-Japan collaborations or exchanges should be submitted as a single project through Tokyo or London, and not as separate applications from the UK and Japanese partners.

Support of up to £1,000 will also be considered for fieldwork in Japan at PhD level only.

Butterfield Awards

As a lasting commemoration of a former trustee, Lord Butterfield, who was a distinguished medical researcher, the foundation launched the Butterfield Awards. The awards are intended to further collaboration between qualified professionals in the UK and Japan in the fields of medical research and public health practice. This includes investigation of scientific, clinical, social and economic aspects of medicine in any field. Grants may be used for travel expenses or to contribute to other costs as appropriate (but not for laboratory consumables).

The website states:

> A small number of awards of around £5,000 are offered annually. Proposals for continuous funding of up to £5,000 per annum. for a maximum of three years are acceptable. Applications for smaller – and, exceptionally, larger – sums can be considered. Substantial funds are also available for support of conferences and publications bringing together UK and Japanese expertise.

Financial information

Year end	31/01/2020
Income	£11,800,000
Assets	£41,140,000
Grants to organisations	£771,200
No. of grants	112

Beneficiaries included: A full list of beneficiaries can be found in the foundation's annual reports, available from its helpful website.

Exclusions

Grants are not made for the following purposes:

- Consumables, fees, salaries or the purchase of materials
- Capital projects, including the purchase, construction or maintenance of buildings
- Individuals/personal projects, apart from where there is clear evidence of organisational support and a project which furthers the foundation's aims
- Student fees or travel for study, apart from PhD fieldwork in Japan (limited to £1,000 maximum and only where it is necessary for the completion of the PhD thesis – applications must be accompanied by a letter of support from the supervisor)
- Completed or current projects

Applications

Full application details can be found on the website. Application forms to the London office can be downloaded from the website. Once completed they must be sent via email to grants@gbsf.org.uk.

Trustees make the final decisions on awards at meetings held in London three times a year (normally March, May and November) and Tokyo twice a year (normally April and October). The deadlines for London applicants are as follows: 15 December for a decision in March; 31 March for a decision in May; 15 September for a decision in November.

The annual deadline for the Butterfield Awards is 15 December.

To apply to the Tokyo office, applicants must email tokyo@gbsf.org.uk before making an application.

The foundation's website states that it normally receives three times as many requests than it is able to fund, and that around 75% of applicants receive funding, but may receive less than originally requested.

Sources of information

Accounts; annual report; Charity Commission record; funder's website.

The Kenneth and Susan Green Charitable Foundation

Social welfare; education; health; arts and culture; science

UK

£573,600 (2020)

CC number: 1147248

Correspondent: The Trustees, c/o Kenneth Green Associates, Hill House, Monument Hill, Weybridge, Surrey KT13 8RX (tel: 01932 827060)

Trustees: Kenneth Green; Philip Stokes; Susan Green; Sarah Scragg; Charlotte Garlick.

General information

The settlor of the foundation, Kenneth Green, is Chair of Kenneth Green Associates, a company that markets and distributes luxury brands. The foundation supports organisations with the following purposes:

- Social welfare
- Education
- Health
- The arts, culture, heritage and science

Financial information

Year end	31/12/2020
Income	£2,060,000
Assets	£7,350,000
Grants to organisations	£573,600

Beneficiaries included: Royal Opera House Covent Garden Foundation (£450,000); Royal Ballet School (£50,000); RNLI (£25,000); The Pepper Foundation (£20,000); Helford River Children's Sailing Trust (£10,000).

Applications

The foundation supports a few specific charities and does not seek new applications.

Sources of information

Accounts; annual report; Charity Commission record.

The Green Hall Foundation

Social welfare; medical causes; health; community projects; general charitable purposes

UK and overseas

£340,500 (2020/21)

CC number: 270775

Correspondent: The Trustees, 2nd Floor, International House, 41 The Parade, St Helier, Jersey JE2 3QQ (tel: 01534 487757; email: greenhallfoundation@fcmtrust.com)

Trustees: Margaret Hall; Sue Collinson; Nigel Hall; Peter Morgan; Charlotte Footer.

 www.greenhallfoundation.org

General information

The foundation was established by Constance Vera Green, a well-known philanthropist from Yorkshire. In 1976 she set up her own charitable trust, to which she donated substantial financial assets. Due to her involvement in charitable activities, Mrs Green was appointed to the Order of the British Empire (OBE) in 1986 before she died in 1992.

Following the death of Colonel Henry Robert Hall in 2012, one of the long-standing original trustees, additional assets were donated to the foundation. To commemorate the colonel's contribution, the trustees decided to adopt the name The Green Hall Foundation in May 2013.

The foundation makes grants to UK-registered charities working to improve the lives of older people, young people in need, and people with disabilities, illnesses and other disadvantages, particularly in the UK. Typical grants range from £1,000 to £10,000. Overseas projects are supported as long as the applicant charity is registered in the UK.

The trustees prefer to support applications in which the foundation can meet a significant proportion of the funding needed, or where specific equipment or building is required.

Financial information

Year end	05/04/2021
Income	£342,100
Assets	£11,030,000
Grants to organisations	£340,500

Further financial information

Grants were broken down as follows:

Older people and people with disabilities	£93,600
Children and young people	£89,700
Medical and social care	£67,200
Homelessness	£30,000
Church and community projects	£25,000

Beneficiaries included: The Connection at St Martin-in-the-Fields (£20,000); Alder Hey Children's Charity (£5,000); Gympanzees (£4,000); Ability North London (£3,000); Sudden Productions (£1,000).

Exclusions

The foundation does not make grants for general running costs or salaries.

Applications

Applications must be made online through the foundation's website. The trustees meet twice a year, in May and November. The opening dates for application cycles are detailed on the website. Only the first 200 applications received by the foundation will be taken forward to be considered by the trustees.

Sources of information

Accounts; annual report; Charity Commission record; funder's website.

The Green Room Charitable Trust

General charitable purposes; social welfare; human rights; social enterprises; ethical and social impact investment

 UK

£1.06 million (2019/20)

CC number: 1134766

Correspondent: The Trustees, Piccards Wood, Sandy Lane, Guildford GU3 1HF (tel: 07855 697603; email: thegreenroomct@yahoo.co.uk)

Trustees: Tom Prickett; Kelly Prickett; Andrew Ferry.

General information

This trust was registered with the Charity Commission in March 2010. According to its 2019/20 annual report, it makes grants to the following:

> registered UK and international charities, specifically focussing on the following areas: 1. poverty, human rights, social enterprises 2. ethical and social impact investment

Financial information

Year end	01/10/2020
Income	£1,160,000
Assets	£7,980,000
Grants to organisations	£1,060,000

Further financial information

The 2019/20 accounts were the latest available at the time of writing (May 2022).

Beneficiaries included: So Give Clean Air Task Force (£520,000); Médecins Sans Frontières (£155,000); International Rescue Committee UK (£50,000); The Funding Network (£30,000); Crisis (£15,000); Unseen UK (£5,000); Save the Children (£1,000); Freedom from Torture (£300).

Applications

Apply in writing to the correspondent.

Sources of information

Accounts; annual report; Charity Commission record.

Greenham Trust Ltd

General charitable purposes

 West Berkshire and specific ward areas of North Hampshire

£2.33 million (2020/21)

CC number: 1062762

Correspondent: Jaz Ghalley, Grants Administrator, Liberty House, The Enterprise Centre, Greenham Business Park, Newbury, Berkshire RG19 6HS (tel: 01635 736740; email: grantenquiries@greenhamtrust.com)

Trustees: David Bailey; Graham Mather; Sir Peter Michael; Malcolm Morris; Julian Cazalet; Charles Brims; Biddy Hayward; Zoe Benyon; Robert Woods; Fiona Spencer-Jones; Justyn Waterworth.

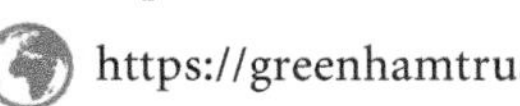 https://greenhamtrust.com

 facebook.com/GreenhamTrustLtd

 @greenham_trust

 @greenhamtrust

General information

Greenham Trust was established in 1997 with acquisition of the former Greenham Common airbase which the trust turned into a mixed-use business park.

Beneficial area

The trust provides support in West Berkshire plus the following ward areas of North Hampshire:

- East Woodhay
- Burghclere, Highclere and St Mary Bourne
- Kingsclere
- Tadley Central
- Tadley South
- Baughurst and Tadley North
- Pamber and Silchester

Areas of work

Causes supported by the trust historically include:

- Poverty
- Education
- Sport
- Health and well-being
- Community
- The arts, heritage and science
- Human rights and diversity
- The environment
- Helping disadvantaged people
- Wildlife
- Military and emergency services

Funding opportunities

Open funding opportunities are advertised on the trust's website. Examples of programmes open at the time of writing (April 2022) included:

Community grants: grants of up to £30,000 are awarded twice per year to a variety of good causes. The average grant size awarded is £1,750.

Surviving to Thriving: a £200,000 fund offering grants of up to £30,000 to help not-for-profit organisations in West Berkshire mitigate the impacts of the COVID-19 pandemic on people's mental health and well-being.

Major project funding: major grants of £30,000 and above for capital projects, awarded on a matched-funding basis.

Financial information

Year end	31/03/2021
Income	£10,050,000
Assets	£95,580,000
Grants to organisations	£2,330,000

Further financial information

In 2020/21, grants to organisations were broken down as follows:

Community	£834,400
Health	£501,600
Education	£404,700
Sport	£207,800
Young people	£88,600
Economic	£83,200
Disability	£75,000
The arts	£57,400
Diversity	£52,400
Nature and conservation	£17,500
Older people	£6,000

Grants made to individuals for education totalled £33,400.

Beneficiaries included: A list of beneficiaries was not available.

Exclusions

Programme-specific exclusions can be found on the trust's website.

Applications

All applications should be made through The Good Exchange. A link can be found on the trust's website.

Sources of information

Accounts; annual report; Charity Commission record; funder's website.

The Greggs Foundation

General charitable purposes; social welfare; community; inequality; health; children and young people; the environment; older people; disability

UK, with a preference for causes in the north-east of England (Northumberland, Tyne and Wear, Durham and Teesside) and in the regional divisions of Greggs plc

£3.1 million (2019/20)

CC number: 296590

Correspondent: Justine Massingham, Foundation Secretary, Greggs House, Quorum Business Park, Newcastle upon Tyne, Tyne and Wear NE12 8BU (tel: 0191 212 7626 or 0739 2195377 to contact the correspondent directly; email: grants@greggsfoundation.org.uk)

Trustees: Andrew Davison; Richard Hutton; Roisin Currie; Jane Hartley; Fiona Nicholson; Kate Bradley; Karen Wilkinson-Bell; Sanjay Singh; Steve Haines; Mick Thompson.

 www.greggsfoundation.org.uk

General information

The Greggs Foundation was registered with the Charity Commission in 1987. It is the corporate charity of Greggs plc, the food retail group known for its baked goods.

The foundation provides grants to charitable organisations with a focus on:

- Addressing issues of poverty and inequality
- Ensuring food is at the heart of communities
- Supporting local community organisations to make a real difference

According to its website, the foundation distributes 'over £3 million per year to charitable organisations throughout England, Scotland and Wales'.

Programmes

North East Core Fund: grants of up to £60,000 (up to £20,000 per year) are awarded to organisations working with the community's 'most deprived and excluded members' to help cover core running costs, as stated on the website.

Applications are particularly welcomed from organisations serving people with disabilities, people who are experiencing homelessness, voluntary carers, and older and isolated people.

Eligible organisations must be able to provide at least one full year's set of accounts. Applications from organisations with more than six months' running costs in free reserves will not be considered.

Local Community Projects Fund: small grants of up to £2,000 are made to help organisations based in local communities to 'deliver activities that they wouldn't otherwise be able to'. Note: this fund was suspended in 2020 due to the COVID-19 pandemic. Check the foundation's website for updates.

Breakfast clubs: the breakfast club programme was established to help primary schoolchildren get a nutritious start to their day. Through the scheme, schools are provided with fresh bread from their local Greggs store, as well as grants to support start-up and ongoing costs.

Community Holiday Club programme: the programme provides food and activities to children to reduce the impact of poverty and social deprivation during the school holidays.

Tackling Health programme: this programme is an interactive project for children which takes a holistic approach to teach children about their own health and well-being and about leading a healthy lifestyle.

Community Urban Rivers Regeneration Fund: this fund provides financial assistance to rivers trusts to run educational and community-based environmental projects focused on urban rivers.

Hardship fund: this fund provides grants to people in need in the north-east of England through recognised social organisations like housing associations, social services and registered charities that are acting on behalf of an individual or family in need.

The foundation also donates unsold food to local charities.

Financial information

Year end	31/01/2020
Income	£3,890,000
Assets	£23,370,000
Grants to organisations	£3,110,000

Further financial information

Grants were distributed as follows:

Hardship*	£749,600
COVID response and recovery	£633,800
Breakfast clubs	£568,100
Community	£350,000
Food poverty	£279,600
Health	£200,000
The environment	£200,000
North East Core Fund	£133,800

*Note: these are grants paid to organisations for distribution to individuals. During the year 2,747 hardship grants were awarded.

Beneficiaries included: A list of beneficiaries was not available.

Exclusions

A full list of exclusions for each grants programme can be seen on the website.

Applications

Each grants programme has its own detailed criteria, guidelines and application process. See the foundation's website for more information.

Sources of information

Accounts; annual report; Charity Commission record; funder's website.

The Grimmitt Trust

General charitable purposes; community development; children and young people; culture; education; medical causes; older people; overseas aid

The Birmingham, Dudley, Wolverhampton and Walsall postcode areas; overseas

£275,000 (2020/21)

CC number: 801975

Correspondent: Vanessa Welch, Secretary, 151B All Saints Road, Kings Heath, Birmingham, West Midlands B14 6AT (tel: 07576 195955; email: admin@grimmitt-trust.org.uk)

Trustees: Sue Day; David Owen; Tim Welch; Sarah Wilkey; Phil Smith; Trevor Jones; Emma Pardoe; Catherine Chase.

General information

The Grimmitt Trust was established by a trust deed in 1986. The trustees' report for 2020/21 states:

> The objective of the trust is the encouraging and strengthening of local communities, together with an awareness of national and international responsibilities particularly those within the active interest and geographical areas of the trustees and the Kite Connexion group employees.

The trust supports charities, organisations and individuals that seek funding for projects or activities in the following areas: community, children and young people, culture and education, medical causes, older people and overseas. Our research suggests that the trust also supports Christian causes and organisations.

Currently, the geographical areas covered are the Birmingham, Dudley, Wolverhampton and Walsall postcodes. Grants are typically one-off and are usually of less than £3,000. Larger or recurrent grants may be made on an exceptional basis.

Financial information

Year end	05/04/2021
Income	£303,600
Assets	£12,190,000
Grants to organisations	£275,000
No. of grants	171

Further financial information

During 2020/21, the trust processed 232 applications and made 171 grants to organisations. Grants were awarded in the following categories:

Community	£117,900
Children and young people	£54,100
Culture and education	£42,300
Overseas causes	£30,000
Medical causes	£20,500
Older people	£10,500

Only beneficiaries of grants of £2,000 and above were listed in the accounts. Grants of under £2,000 totalled £80,900.

Beneficiaries included: Christian Aid (£20,000); All We Can (£10,000); St Martin's Youth Centre (£4,000); Birmingham Centre for Art Therapies and Brierley Hill Samaritans (£3,000 each); Age Concern Birmingham (£2,500); Sport4Life, The Cotteridge Church and West Midlands Care Team (£2,000 each).

Exclusions

The trust does not normally support national charities, CICs or social enterprises.

Applications

Applicants should contact the secretary, who will advise on the best way to make a grant request and to ensure that all the necessary information is included. The trustees meet three times a year to consider applications.

Applicants must demonstrate how their project and the grant received are used in line with the trust's objectives.

Sources of information

Accounts; annual report; Charity Commission record.

The Grocers' Charity

Children and young people; disability; older people; the environment and conservation; health; heritage; military; social welfare; the arts; churches; education; health and medical research

UK

£830,000 (2019/20)

CC number: 255230

Correspondent: Michelle Molyneux, Charity Manager, Grocers' Hall, Princes Street, London EC2R 8AD (tel: 020 7606 3113; email: charity@grocershall.co.uk)

Trustee: The Grocers' Trust Company Ltd.

www.grocershall.co.uk

@grocerscompany

General information

The charity was established in 1968 and is administered by The Grocers' Trust Company Ltd. It makes one-off grants of up to £5,000 to a broad range of UK-registered charities, as well as providing regular support to a number of churches, schools and colleges with which it has historical links.

The charity's main priority is education; however, it also funds charities that are working in the following areas:

- **Relief of poverty** – increasing social mobility, empowering those who experience homelessness, revitalising community life and working within areas of high deprivation in the UK
- **Children and young people** – improving support for disadvantaged young people, investing in peer support and young leaders. The London Youth Quality Mark is recognised when considering applications
- **Older people** – ending social exclusion and loneliness
- **Disability and inclusion** – providing support and innovative projects for people with disabilities, and empowering marginalised and excluded individuals and groups
- **Health** – undertaking ethical research into specific conditions, purchasing equipment or materials and supporting people with rare medical conditions. Priority is given to charities with a turnover of no more than £15 million
- **Military** – providing opportunities for education and employment for ex-Service people, supporting the physical, emotional and mental well-being of ex-Service people and their families, and providing innovative projects and programmes
- **The arts and heritage** – the conservation of historical buildings (not places of worship), objects and paintings, engaging with marginalised audiences and providing opportunities for artists who have disabilities or financial disadvantages
- **The environment and conservation** – conservation on land and at sea, supporting the protection of plants and animals, connecting people with environmental issues and countering the effects of pollution

Funding is provided for core costs as well as new and existing projects that demonstrate a public benefit.

Financial information

Year end	31/07/2020
Income	£812,400
Assets	£24,640,000
Grants to organisations	£830,000
No. of grants	151

Further financial information

Grants were broken down as follows:

Education	£286,800
Relief of poverty/young people	£172,800
Older people and other grants	£107,400
Health	£75,700
Disability	£70,500
The arts and heritage	£64,200
Churches	£52,500

Only beneficiaries of grants of £2,000 and above were listed in the charity's accounts.

Beneficiaries included: Oundle School (£150,000); Mossbourne Community Academy (£20,000); Cavell Nurses' Trust (£10,000); The Listening Place (£7,500); St Mary and Holy Trinity – Bow (£7,000); Silverlining Brain Injury Charity (£5,000); The Country Food Trust (£2,500); Therapy Garden (£2,000).

Exclusions

Support is rarely given to the following unless there is a specific or long-standing connection with the Grocers' Company:

- Places of worship
- Educational establishments
- Hospices
- Charities whose beneficiaries are overseas
- Charities that are not registered in the UK
- Non-medical charities with a turnover of over £500,000, except for health/medical charities (up to £15 million turnover)
- Individuals

Applications

Application enquiries can be made through the Grocer's Hall website. If the initial application is successful, applicants will be sent a link to an online form within three weeks. This should be submitted along with the applying organisation's most recent financial information, the anticipated outcomes of the project and a full breakdown of the costs involved.

Current application deadlines can be found on the charity's website. The Education and Charities Committee usually meets four times a year to consider applications.

Sources of information

Accounts; annual report; Charity Commission record; funder's website.

M. and R. Gross Charities Ltd

The advancement of the Jewish religion and the advancement of Jewish religious education; the relief of poverty

UK and overseas

£2.15 million (2020/21)

CC number: 251888

Correspondent: The Trustees, c/o Cohen Arnold, New Burlington House, 1075 Finchley Road, London NW11 0PU (tel: 020 8731 0777; email: mail@cohenarnold.com)

Trustees: Rifka Gross; Sarah Padwa; Michael Saberski; Leonard Lerner.

General information

This charity makes grants to organisations within the Orthodox Jewish community in the UK and overseas.

According to the charity's 2020/21 annual report, its objects are:

- To foster, assist and promote the charitable activities of any institution professing and teaching the principles of traditional Judaism
- To advance religion in accordance with the Jewish faith
- To undertake, accept, execute and administer, without any remuneration, any charitable trust
- To give philanthropic aid to the Jewish needy

Financial information

Year end	31/03/2021
Income	£4,150,000
Assets	£55,370,000
Grants to organisations	£2,150,000

Beneficiaries included: A list of beneficiaries was not available. Previous beneficiaries include: Asser Bishvil Foundations (£118,000); United Talmudical Associates Ltd (£103,800); Yetev Lev London Jerusalem Trust (£36,200); The Rehabilitation Trust (£36,000); Beis Ruchel D'Satmar London Ltd (£35,400).

Applications

Contact the correspondent for further information. Applications are assessed regularly and many smaller grants are dealt with through a grant-making agency, United Talmudical Associates Ltd.

Sources of information

Accounts; annual report; Charity Commission record.

Groundwork UK

The environment; community places; education and training

UK

£19.65 million (2020/21)

CC number: 291558

Correspondent: The Trustees, Suite B2, The Walker Building, 58 Oxford Street, Birmingham, West Midlands B5 5NR (tel: 0121 236 8565; email: info@groundwork.org.uk)

Trustees: Graham Hartley; Claire Marshall; Patrick Hughes; Nigel Reader; Andrew Thurston; Stuart Bonham; Anne-Marie Simpson; Tony Berry; Jack White; Faiza Amin; Paul Roots; Jeff Greenidge; Antony Nelson; Michael Ormerod; Wendy Golland; Alan Smith; Catherine Culverhouse.

 www.groundwork.org.uk

 facebook.com/groundworkuk

 @groundworkuk

General information

The Federation of Groundwork Trusts is the national body of Groundwork Trusts, a group of independent registered charities that share a common set of aims, objectives and processes.

The following information on the organisation's Groundwork 2023 strategy has been taken from its website:

> By 2023 we will have mobilised 75,000 days of voluntary action to combat the climate and nature emergency. Improved people's wellbeing by connecting them with their community and with nature. Helped people to improve their life chances by accessing learning and work.

Grants

While Groundwork UK does not have its own grants scheme, it administers a number of grant programmes for other organisations. See the Groundwork website for the latest information on open grants schemes.

Financial information

Year end	31/03/2021
Income	£24,360,000
Assets	£5,520,000
Grants to organisations	£19,650,000

Beneficiaries included: A list of beneficiaries was not available.

Applications

Check the Groundwork UK website for details of grant programmes currently being administered.

Sources of information

Accounts; annual report; Charity Commission record; funder's website.

The Albert Gubay Charitable Foundation

Amateur sport; support for people facing disadvantage, ill health or hardship; medical research; religion

England; Wales; the Isle of Man; the Republic of Ireland

Around £10 million per year

CC number: 1193970

Correspondent: The Trustees, 3 Denmark Street, Goose Green, Altrincham WA14 2SS (tel: 0161 703 7992; email: enquiries@theagfoundation.org)

Trustee: The Albert Gubay Trustee Ltd.

 www.thederwentgroup.com/about-us/ag-foundation

General information

Albert Gubay was a Welsh businessman and philanthropist who made his fortune with the Kwik Save retail chain. He had similar ventures around the world and also owned Total Fitness, which was sold in 2004 for £70 million. The portfolio of properties he owned ultimately became The Derwent Group in 2005. Following the death of Albert Gubay in 2016, the Derwent Group was left to The Albert Gubay Charitable Foundation. The foundation registered with the Charity Commission in March 2021 but has been operational since 2016.

According to its website, the foundation has had the capacity to distribute about £10 million to good causes per annum. The foundation's website states: 'However, The Derwent Group's plans for the coming years should see a dramatic increase in donations to good causes.'

Funding

The foundation awards grants to registered charities in England, the Isle of Man, the Republic of Ireland and Wales for work carried out in one of those jurisdictions.

After temporarily adapting its funding priorities in response to the COVID-19 pandemic, at the time of writing (May 2022) the foundation had resumed its regular priorities. Its website stated the following:

> Our current funding priorities are as follows:
>
> 1 Amateur sport
> 2 Care leavers
> 3 Residential care for elderly people
> 4 Ex-offenders and their families
> 5 Homelessness
> 6 Medical research where the charity is a member of the Association of Medical Research Charities (AMRC)
> 7 People recovering from drug and substance misuse
> 8 People with intellectual disability

9 People with terminal illnesses/life limiting conditions and their carers
10 Worship and associated community outreach
11 Victims of domestic abuse
12 Victims of modern slavery

Financial information

Grants to organisations	£10,000,000

Further financial information

No financial information was available as the foundation had only recently registered with the Charity Commission at the time of writing (May 2022) and was therefore not required to file accounts yet.

Applications

To enquire about funding contact enquiries@theagfoundation.org.

Sources of information

Funder's website.

Calouste Gulbenkian Foundation – UK Branch

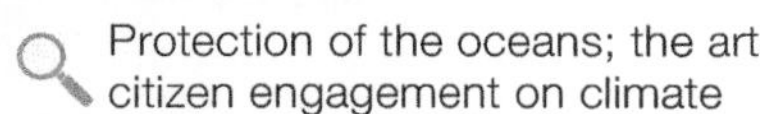
Protection of the oceans; the arts; citizen engagement on climate

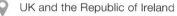

UK and the Republic of Ireland

£1.74 million (2020/21)

Correspondent: Louisa Hopper, Interim Director, 50 Hoxton Square, London N1 6PB (tel: 020 7739 1961; email: info@gulbenkian.org.uk)

Trustee: Martin Essayan.

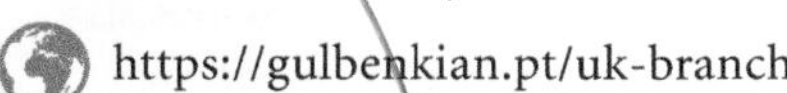
https://gulbenkian.pt/uk-branch

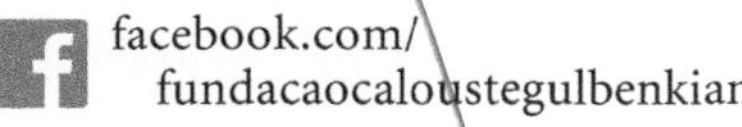
facebook.com/fundacaocaloustegulbenkian

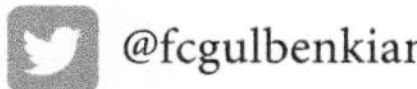
@fcgulbenkian

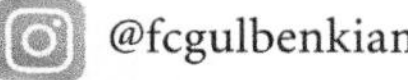
@fcgulbenkian

General information

The foundation was established in 1956 following the death of its founder Calouste Gulbenkian the year before. Calouste Gulbenkian was a British-Armenian businessman and philanthropist who played a major role in making Middle Eastern oil reserves open to Western development.

The following information has been taken from the foundation's website:

> The Calouste Gulbenkian Foundation is a Portuguese institution, established in perpetuity, with the statutory goal of undertaking charitable, artistic, educational and scientific activities. Committed to all humankind, its mission is to support sustainable development by actively promoting the wellbeing and quality of life of vulnerable groups in the population, and in balance with environmental protection and economic prosperity.
>
> **The UK Branch**
>
> We are focused on building coalitions to tackle complex global problems. Based in London, the UK Branch sits at the heart of a world centre for philanthropy which enables us to deliver on the Foundation's mission using our networks, experience and way of working. We look ahead, thinking globally and acting locally, to create the conditions for change by connecting across borders of all kinds – national, cultural, organisational, disciplinary and social. We prioritise the vulnerable and underserved in the UK and elsewhere.

The foundation's UK branch focuses on three programmes:

- **Valuing the Ocean** – connecting and building relationships designed to help protect our oceans
- **Citizen Engagement on Climate** – demonstrating what effective public engagement on climate looks like and creating conditions for its scaling
- **The Civic Role of Arts Organisations** – creating a movement of change-makers who want arts organisations to play a civic role in their communities, across the UK and internationally

The foundation tends to focus on early-stage funding.

Financial information

Year end	31/03/2021
Income	£1,880,000
Grants to organisations	£1,740,000

Further financial information

As the foundation is not a UK-registered charity, it does not have a record on the Charity Commission's website; however, the foundation files an annual review on its website. The 2020/21 annual review states that the UK branch's income was £1.88 million. It also details 'outgoings' for the year as follows: The Civic Role of Arts Organisations (£806,500); Valuing the Ocean (£554,900); Climate Engagement (£375,700). We have used the sum of these outgoings as the foundation's grant total for the year.

Beneficiaries included: A list of beneficiaries was not available. Previous beneficiaries include: Arts Homelessness International; Birmingham Royal Ballet; Climate Outreach; Common Vision; John Ellerman Foundation; Marine Alliance for Science and Technology for Scotland; Marine Conservation Society; Streetwise Opera; University of St Andrews; UK Health Alliance on Climate Change.

Applications

Unsolicited applications are not accepted. The foundation's website states:

> Our approach to funding is that we do not accept unsolicited applications. This is because we do not fund projects or organisations reactively. We think of our approach as being 'interactive' rather than 'reactive' or 'proactive'. [...] We identify the organisations that we want to work with through research, engagement in a wide range of networks and open consultations. We sometimes issue 'calls' for applications.

Sources of information

Annual review; funder's website.

The Guy Foundation

Quantum biology research

Worldwide

£567,300 (2020/21)

CC number: 1178782

Correspondent: The Trustees, The Estate Office, Chedington Court, Chedington, Beaminster DT8 3HY (tel: 0151 600 3341; email: info@theguyfoundation.org)

Trustees: Richard Brass; Dr Geoffrey Guy; Eric Dixon; Katherine Guy; Jonathan Laughton; Lord William Waldegrave.

www.theguyfoundation.org

General information

The foundation was established by Geoffrey and Kate Guy in 2018 to facilitate exploration into quantum biology and the role it could play in advancing medicine.

Project grants are available for novel and ambitious research in the field of quantum biology that has the potential to significantly advance our understanding of human biology, health and disease.

According to the foundation's website:

> Projects may take the form of bench research, but may also include the development of new hypotheses, in silico modelling of these ideas, or developing new technology.
>
> The research we fund:
>
> - Is closely aligned to our strategic aims and research priorities
> - Has potential impact in generating new knowledge and understanding, sparking interest and changing perceptions
> - Is undertaken by research teams that have talent, expertise and a track record
> - Fits into the integrated programme, and is undertaken by researchers willing to work in collaborative partnership with the Foundation
> - Probably wouldn't be funded elsewhere

Financial information

Year end	30/04/2021
Income	£5,000
Assets	£556,700
Grants to organisations	£567,300

Beneficiaries included: A list of beneficiaries was not available.

Exclusions

The foundation's website states that it will not fund the following:

- Indirect costs
- Overheads
- Salary recovery costs for staff funded full time by the employing organisation
- Fees for academic courses such as PhDs and other tuition fees
- Equipment that is not going to be used primarily for the project during the lifetime of the grant, or related costs such as maintenance and insurance
- Costs for capital building or refurbishment

Applications

Contact the foundation by email to request an application form.

Sources of information

Accounts; annual report; Charity Commission website; funder's website.

H. and T. Clients Charitable Trust

General charitable purposes

UK

£856,000 (2020/21)

CC number: 1104345

Correspondent: The Trustees, 64 New Cavendish Street, London W1G 8TB (tel: 020 7467 6300)

Trustees: Ronnie Harris; Neville Newman; Charlotte Harris; Jamie Taylor.

General information

Registered with the Charity Commission in 2004, the trust makes grants to charitable organisations for general charitable purposes. In addition, the trust administers a restricted fund to support individuals in need of specialist medical treatment for cancer that is not readily available on the NHS.

Financial information

Year end	05/04/2021
Income	£763,400
Assets	£863,600
Grants to organisations	£856,000

Beneficiaries included: A list of beneficiaries was not available. Previous beneficiaries include: Girls Rock Glasgow (£10,300); JA Africa (£7,800); Herts Homeless Support (£5,000).

Applications

Apply in writing to the correspondent.

Sources of information

Accounts; annual report; Charity Commission record.

H. C. D. Memorial Fund

Education; health; prisoner and refugee welfare; the environment, in particular climate change; community development; international development and peace-keeping

UK and overseas

£980,200 (2019/20)

CC number: 1044956

Correspondent: Susannah Drummond, Secretary, 24 Fern Avenue, Jesmond, Newcastle upon Tyne, Tyne and Wear NE2 2QT (tel: 0191 281 4228; email: hcdmemorialfund@gmail.com)

Trustees: Nicholas Debenham; Jeremy Debenham; Bill Flinn; Harriet Lear; Joanna Lear; Susannah Drummond.

General information

This fund was established in 1995 and makes grants to a wide range of organisations in the UK and overseas.

The trust's 2019/20 annual report gives the following information on its grant-making policy:

> The policy is to make grants as determined by the trustees at twice-yearly meetings, for all or any purposes which are charitable according to English law.
>
> The policy is flexible as regards donees, but currently:
>
> - maintains a balance between home and overseas grants
> - directs grants mainly towards (1) the relief of human need, whether due to poverty, ill-health, disability, want of education, or other causes, and (2) projects which aim to mitigate the effects of Climate Change
> - prefers projects which are small or medium-sized
> - permits the taking of risks in an appropriate case

Financial information

Year end	30/06/2020
Income	£933,700
Assets	£875,400
Grants to organisations	£980,200

Beneficiaries included: Centre for Alternative Technology (£64,500); Health Poverty Action – Guatemala (£35,000); Feedback Global and Key 4 Life (£25,000 each); Christian Aid – Lebanon (£24,000); Children Heard Not Seen (£20,000); Womankind (£15,000); Meals Behind the Wire (£10,800); Stand Against Sexual Exploitation (£10,000).

Applications

Apply in writing to the correspondent. Applicants should be aware, however, that the trustees prefer to seek out their own projects and will only very rarely respond to general or unsolicited appeals. Grants are considered by the trustees at meetings held twice a year.

Sources of information

Accounts; annual report; Charity Commission record.

HP Charitable Trust

General charitable purposes; advancement of Orthodox Judaism; poverty relief

UK and overseas

£432,400 (2020/21)

CC number: 278006

Correspondent: Aron Piller, Trustee, 26 Lingwood Road, London E5 9BN (tel: 020 8806 2432; email: apiller26@gmail.com)

Trustees: Arthur Zonszajn; Aron Piller; Hannah Piller; Isaac Freilich.

General information

The HP Charitable Trust was created by Hannah Piller in 1979 and makes grants to Orthodox Jewish charities.

According to the trustees' report for 2020/21, 'the charity was formed for general charitable purposes, in particular the advancement of religion in accordance with the Orthodox Jewish faith, the relief of poverty, and other charitable purposes.'

Financial information

Year end	30/06/2021
Income	£390,200
Assets	£5,730,000
Grants to organisations	£432,400

Beneficiaries included: Friends of Beis Chinuch Lebonos (£60,000); Lev Simcha Talmudical College (£50,000); Mercas Hatorah Belz Machnovke (£38,000); New Rachmastrivka Synagogue Trust (£25,000); Support The Charity Worker (£15,000); One Heart – Lev Echod (£12,000); Chevra Mo'oz Ladol (£10,000);

Applications

Contact the correspondent for further information.

Sources of information

Accounts; annual report; Charity Commission record.

The Hadfield Charitable Trust

Young people and employment; social welfare; older people; the arts; the environment

Cumbria

£241,800 (2019/20)

CC number: 1067491

Correspondent: Susan Berriman, Trust Administrator, Shoestone Cottage, Garnett Bridge, Kendal, Cumbria LA8 9AZ (tel: 01539 823112; email: admin@hadfieldtrust.org.uk)

Trustees: Cameron Ogden; Ann Mroz; Lord Jim O'Neill; Samantha Twiselton; Sarah Loftus; Mark Heffernan; Lorna Fitzsimons; Raksha Pattni; Kavita Gupta.

www.hadfieldtrust.org.uk

General information

The Hadfield Charitable Trust was established in 1997 and was endowed through the generosity of a family that had been resident in Cumbria for many years. It gives grants to charitable organisations in Cumbria, particularly to provide help for charitable projects in the fields of: social needs; young people and employment; help for older people; the arts; and the environment. The trustees wish to support projects that benefit as many people in as possible, in particular, those who are disadvantaged.

The trust can give grants of up to £5,000; however, the majority of awards range from £1,500 to £3,000. The trust usually has around £100,000 to distribute at each of its three rounds of funding annually, but its website notes that the trust normally receives 50–60 applications per funding round and therefore funding is competitive. Preference is given to capital funding requests, although revenue costs will be considered. Most grants are one-off, although two or three-year awards are considered occasionally for vital projects where their sustainability is at risk.

Applicants should ideally be a registered charity or applying to become one; however, any properly constituted body with charitable objectives can apply, although they should check with the administrator first. National charities can only apply if they can clearly evidence the work they do in Cumbria.

Financial information

Year end	31/08/2020
Income	£291,500
Assets	£8,550,000
Grants to organisations	£241,800
No. of grants	86

Further financial information

During the year, grants ranging from £500 to £6,800 were made to 86 organisations. These grants were broken down as follows:

Social needs	£157,900
Young people and employment	£53,900
The arts	£16,200
The environment	£7,000
Older people	£6,500
Other	£380

Beneficiaries included: Growing Well (£6,800); Church in The Barn and Hospice at Home Carlisle and North Lakeland (£5,000 each); Autism Support Allerdale and Copeland and Huntington's Disease Association (£3,000 each); Dent Reading Room (£1,000); Natland and Oxenholme Table Tennis (£500).

Applications

Application forms are available from the trust's website. The completed application form should be sent to the administrator by post or email along with supporting documents, details of which are on the trust's website. The application deadlines are 1 February, 1 June and 1 October, and applications must be received by midday on these dates to be considered. Applicants are encouraged to contact the trust before applying to discuss their plans with the administrator or assistant.

Sources of information

Accounts; annual report; Charity Commission record; funder's website.

The Hadley Trust

Crime and justice; young people (mainly those in care); disabilities; social investment; local causes; medical causes; welfare reform; work overseas; hospices

UK and overseas

£3.54 million (2020/21)

CC number: 1064823

Correspondent: Carol Biggs, Gladsmuir, Hadley Common, Barnet, Hertfordshire EN5 5QE (tel: 020 8447 4577; email: carol@hadleytrust.org)

Trustees: Lady Janet Hulme; Sir Philip Hulme; Thomas Hulme; Katherine Prideaux; Sophie Swift; Juliet Lyon.

General information

The trust was established in 1997 and makes grants to registered charities. Its 2020/21 annual report states the following:

> In practice, the main focus has been on helping people who are disadvantaged to improve their situation, either by involvement in project and support work or research into the causes of, and means to alleviate, hardship.

Occasionally the trust will also support organisations that are not registered charities.

The trust aims to make grants on a long-term basis; therefore, it does not take on many new funding commitments. However, the trustees will always consider and respond to proposals that fit the activities of the trust. The trust prefers to work with small to medium-sized organisations.

Financial information

Year end	31/03/2021
Income	£1,750,000
Assets	£287,220,000
Grants to organisations	£3,540,000
No. of grants	69

Further financial information

In 2020/21, criminal justice remained the trust's main area of activity. The following breakdown of causes supported during the year was provided in the trust's 2020/21 accounts:

Crime and justice	£1.45 million
Young people	£586,200
Social investment	£421,000
Hospices	£345,000
Local causes	£324,000
Medical causes	£226,400
Disabilities	£164,000
International	£30,000

Beneficiaries included: Coram Voice; Crest Advisory; Noah's Ark Children's Hospice; Policy Exchange; Prison Reform Trust; The Centre for Justice Innovation.

Applications

Although the majority of the trust's funds are already committed, it does nevertheless still accept and consider new applications made in writing to the correspondent.

Sources of information

Accounts; annual report; Charity Commission record.

Halifax Foundation for Northern Ireland

Social and community welfare; education and training; disability

Northern Ireland

£1.54 million (2020)

CCNI number: NIC101763

Correspondent: The Trustees, Clifton House Heritage Centre, 2 North Queen Street, Belfast BT15 1ES (tel: 028 9032 3000; email: grants@halifaxfoundationni.org)

Trustees: Paula Leathem; Áine McCoy; Gillian Boyd; Ken Simpson; Barry Connolly; Michael Prendergast; Melvin

Slaine; Brenda Kelly; Jenny Ebbage; Niall Parfitt; Dionne Darragh.

 www.halifaxfoundationni.org

General information

This foundation is one of four Lloyds Banking Group charities, which cover England and Wales, Scotland, Northern Ireland and the Channel Islands. Together, the four charities receive 0.5% of the group's pre-tax profits.

Areas of support

The foundation supports a wide range of activities and the following examples are listed on the website as a guide:

- **Advice services:** homelessness, addictions, bereavement, family guidance, money advice, helplines and suicide awareness
- **Community services:** family centres, youth clubs, older people's clubs, after-school clubs, self-help groups, childcare provision, preschools and playgroups
- **People with special educational needs:** residences, day centres, transport, carers, information, advice and advocacy
- **Promotion of health:** information and advice, mental health, hospices, day care, home nursing, independent living for older people
- **Civic responsibility:** young people at risk, crime prevention, promotion of volunteering, victim support, mediation and the rehabilitation of people who have offended
- **Cultural enrichment:** improving access and skills development in the arts and national heritage for disadvantaged people and those with special needs
- **Employment:** projects which help disadvantaged people develop their potential and secure employment
- **Life skills**: the promotion of life skills and independent living skills for people with special needs
- **Training and education:** accredited, vocational or personal development training
- **Employment**: projects which help disadvantaged people develop their potential and secure employment

Grant programmes

The Community Grants programme is the foundation's main focus through which grants are made within its funding objectives. Grants currently average between £3,000 and £4,000.

In order to be eligible to apply, organisations must have had an income of less than £1 million in the previous 12 months. For registered charities which have a headquarters based outside Northern Ireland, the foundation will use the figure of the income of their Northern Ireland operation to determine their eligibility.

Financial information

Year end	31/12/2020
Income	£1,590,000
Assets	£2,350,000
Grants to organisations	£1,540,000
No. of grants	469

Beneficiaries included: A list of beneficiaries was not available.

Exclusions

See the foundation's website for a full list of exclusions.

Applications

All applications must be made online via the foundation's website, where full guidelines, including a list of supporting documentation required, are available.

Sources of information

Accounts; annual report; funder's website; CCNI record; funding guidelines.

Paul Hamlyn Foundation

The arts; education; young people; social justice

UK and India

£40.27 million (2020/21)

CC number: 1102927

Correspondent: Grants Team, 5–11 Leeke Street, London WC1X 9HY (tel: 020 7812 3300; email: information@phf.org.uk)

Trustees: Claire Whitaker; Lord Anthony Hall; Jane Hamlyn; James Lingwood; Michael Hamlyn; Tom Wylie; Tim Bunting; Charles Leadbeater; Dr Janet McKenley-Simpson; Akeela Ahmed; Andrew Headley.

 www.phf.org.uk

 facebook.com/PaulHamlynFoundation

 @phf_uk

General information

Paul Hamlyn was a publisher and philanthropist. In 1987 he established the Paul Hamlyn Foundation and upon his death in 2001, bequeathed the majority of his estate to the foundation, making it one of the UK's largest independent grant-giving organisations.

According to its website, the mission of the foundation is to 'help people overcome disadvantage and lack of opportunity so that they can realise their potential and enjoy fulfiling and creative lives'. In particular, the foundation has an interest in supporting young people and a strong belief in the importance of the arts.

The foundation's current strategy, launched in September 2020, is built around five key funding priorities:

- Investing in young people
- Migration and integration
- Arts access and participation
- Education and learning through the arts
- Nurturing ideas and people

Under each of these themes the foundation offers a range of funds and grant programmes. At the time of writing (May 2022) the following information was available on the foundation's website:

> **Arts Access and Participation Fund**
>
> The Fund addresses inequalities of opportunity to access and participate in the arts. We want to support change in the way the arts are created, presented, accessed and experienced.
>
> - Grants from £30,000 – £400,000 and lasting between 12 months and 4 years
> - Rolling application cycle – no deadlines. Decision making panels meet approximately 5 times a year.
>
> **Arts-Based Learning Fund**
>
> This Fund supports work which enables pupils in formal education settings, particularly those experiencing systemic inequality or disadvantage, to thrive through engagement with high quality, arts-based learning.
>
> - Grants from £30,000 – £400,000 up to two or three years
> - Rolling application cycle – no deadlines
>
> **Teacher Development Fund**
>
> The purpose of the Teacher Development Fund is to support delivery of effective arts-based teaching and learning opportunities in the primary classroom, and to embed learning through the arts in the curriculum. It aims to do this through supporting teachers and school leaders to develop the necessary skills, knowledge, confidence and experience.
>
> - Grants up to £150,000 over two academic years
> - One deadline per year in the autumn
>
> **Shared Ground Fund**
>
> The Shared Ground Fund supports organisations to influence migration system reform, improve access to support services, strengthen civic participation and inform public understanding of migration and integration narratives.
>
> - Grants from £30,000 – £400,000 for work lasting up to 4 years
> - Rolling application cycle – no deadlines
>
> **Youth Fund**
>
> The Youth Fund supports organisations whose main purpose is working with and for young people (aged 14–25) who face complex transitions to adulthood.
>
> - Core funding grants up to £90,000 over three years
> - Rolling application cycle – no deadlines

India Open Grants Fund
The India Open Grants Fund seeks to enable vulnerable communities living in priority geographical areas to improve their lives. The Fund assists NGOs to design and develop programmes which assist vulnerable communities to build on their strengths.

We support work in the following states: Madhya Pradesh, Chhattisgarh, Odisha, Jharkhand, Bihar, West Bengal and Assam.

Applications can be made at any time, but are assessed biannually in March and October.

Financial information

Year end	31/03/2021
Income	£39,760,000
Assets	£9,010,000
Grants to organisations	£40,270,000

Beneficiaries included: Social Finance (£200,000); University of Manchester (£150,000); Women at the Well (£90,000); Islington Mill (£70,000); Migration Museum (£50,000); National Association for Voluntary and Community Action (£30,000); Racial Justice Network (£25,000); The Social Change Nest (£10,000); Nerve Centre (£600).

Exclusions

On its website, the foundation provides the following information regarding exclusions:

> We do not fund:
> - Activity that is not legally charitable
> - Activity that involves breaking any UK laws
> - Work that has already been delivered
> - Proposals that are only for the benefit of one individual
> - Individuals under the age of 18
> - Websites, publications or seminars, unless part of a wider proposal
> - General fundraising appeals, letters requesting donations and other non-specific funding requests
> - Proposals that have been considered from November 2020 and turned down. Applicants have to wait for 12 months before applying again, unless we have explicitly invited you to resubmit. Organisations that have submitted a proposal to one of our Funds which has been rejected may apply to another Fund for a different proposal
> - Proposals which are mainly about property or other capital items, including the restoration or conservation of buildings or habitats
> - Proposals which are mainly about equipment, although we know that certain costs related to overheads or facilities might be included in your budget as part of a broader application for core funding
> - Promotion of religion
> - Proposals that benefit people living outside the UK (except for the priority geographical areas of our India Programme)
> - Academic research, scholarships, bursaries, or student fees
> - Overseas travel, including expeditions, adventure and residential courses
> - Loan and/or debt repayments, or funds to reduce a deficit
> - Organisations working with children and young people or vulnerable adults, who don't have a Safeguarding Policy and active procedures in place, or are unable to show they are working towards this.

Further information about each specific fund and the types of grant that are unlikely to be supported is available on the foundation's website.

Applications

Applications can only be submitted via the online application process. The foundation does not accept any applications that have been sent in by mail. Applicants should first complete the eligibility quiz before submitting the form online. A comprehensive FAQs section on the foundation's helpful website outlines the application process in detail.

Sources of information

Accounts; annual report; Charity Commission record; funder's website.

The Helen Hamlyn Trust

Medical causes; the arts and culture; education and welfare; heritage and conservation in India; international humanitarian affairs; healthy ageing

Worldwide, with preference for the UK and India

£2.38 million (2020/21)

CC number: 1084839

Correspondent: John Roche, Director of Finance and Administration, Unit 1, Drayton House Court, Drayton St Leonard, Oxfordshire OX10 7BG (tel: 07969 811531; email: john.roche@helenhamlyntrust.org)

Trustees: Brendan Cahill; Dr Kate Gavron; Lady Hamlyn; Margaret O'Rorke; Dr Deborah Swallow; Dr Shobita Punja; Stephen Lewin; Dame Alison Peacock; Lord Ara Darzi.

www.phf.org.uk/our-work-in-the-uk/helen-hamlyn-trust

General information

The Helen Hamlyn Trust was established in 2000 and registered with the Charity Commission in January 2001. In April 2002 the assets and activities of the Helen Hamlyn 1989 Foundation were transferred to the trust. The trust's activities fall within the aims and broad objectives of the Paul Hamlyn Foundation (Charity Commission no. 1102927).

The trust's 2020/21 annual report states that its core aim is to 'initiate and support innovative medium to long-term projects which will effect lasting change and improve quality of life for the benefit of the public or sections of the public'. Grants are currently made in the following areas:

- **Medical causes:** supporting innovation in the medical arena
- **The arts and culture:** increasing access to the arts and supporting the professional development of artists from the fields of music and the performing arts
- **Education and welfare:** increasing intercultural understanding and providing opportunities for young people, including young people who have offended, to develop new interests and practical skills which will contribute to their education and future lives
- **Heritage and conservation in India:** conserving heritage in India for public access and cultural activities
- **International humanitarian affairs:** supporting examples of good practice in the humanitarian sector
- **Healthy ageing:** providing practical support to enable older people to maintain their independence for as long as possible

Additionally, the trust also awards small grants of up to £10,000 to a wide variety of small local and regional charities where a grant of this size can make a significant difference.

Financial information

Year end	31/03/2021
Income	£2,190,000
Assets	£5,980,000
Grants to organisations	£2,380,000

Further financial information

Grants paid in 2020/21 totalled £2.38 million. Grants committed in 2020/21 were broken down as follows:

Medical causes	£1.02 million
Education and welfare	£886,400
The arts and culture	£430,300
International humanitarian affairs	£97,500
Healthy ageing	£5,000

Only beneficiaries of grants of £3,000 and above were listed in the trust's accounts.

Beneficiaries included: Imperial College London (£1 million); UCL Institute of Education (£291,200); University of Oxford (£108,400); Mind and The Courtauld Institute (£10,000 each); Manorfield Charitable Foundation (£5,000).

Applications

Our previous research found that the trustees energies are focused on the initiation of projects and they do not accept unsolicited applications for major grants. Appeals for small awards (up to £10,000) may be directed to the correspondent. The trustees meet formally twice a year and informally throughout the year.

Sources of information

Accounts; annual report; Charity Commission record; funder's website.

Hammersmith United Charities

General charitable purposes; education and training; people with disabilities; the prevention or relief of poverty; accommodation and housing; community development; recreation; children and young people

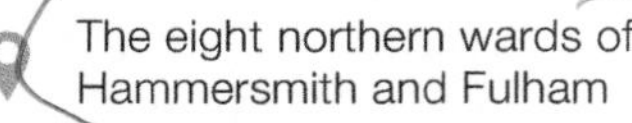

The eight northern wards of Hammersmith and Fulham

£379,600 (2020/21)

CC number: 205856

Correspondent: The Trustees, Sycamore House, Sycamore Gardens, London W6 0AS (tel: 020 8741 4326; email: grants@hamunitedcharities.com)

Trustee: Hammersmith United Trustee Company.

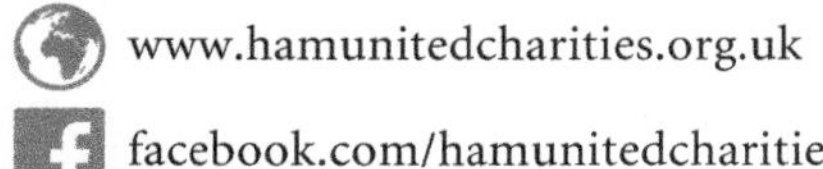

www.hamunitedcharities.org.uk

facebook.com/hamunitedcharities

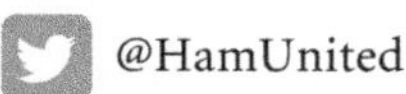

@HamUnited

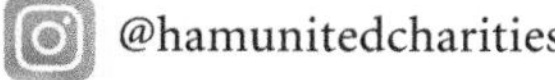

@hamunitedcharities

General information

The charity offers grants to organisations that are working to prevent or relieve hardship or distress within the area of benefit.

According to its website at the time of writing (March 2022), the charity's funding priorities were:

- Work with families and children (supporting parents, education, play, transition points, vulnerable children)
- Countering isolation (in any group and for any reason)
- Building confident individuals and communities
- Meeting basic needs (shelter, food, advice)

Grants

The grants committee meets in January, May and October to consider applications, with a grants budget of £400,000. The trustees are particularly keen to fund smaller, local organisations with a very strong connection to their beneficiaries and a good knowledge of the local area. Applications should be with the trustees four weeks before their meeting, the dates of which are published on the website.

The trustees also offer micro grants of up to £500 for one-off projects and activities, or for specific pieces of equipment. Micro-grant applications are assessed on a rolling basis and the application form is much simpler than that for larger grants. However, you are strongly advised to contact the charity before making an application.

The charity is open to applications from a wide range of organisations as long as they operate on a not-for-profit basis. According to the website, to be eligible for a grant 'you do not need to be a registered charity but you do need to be a constituted organisation (for example, a CIC), [with] some kind of management committee and an organisation bank account requiring at least two independent signatures.'

Community action

The charity helps bring together partnerships for the benefit of the local community, advocating on behalf of the organisations it supports and running its own community action projects.

Sheltered housing

The charity provides affordable sheltered housing in Hammersmith.

Financial information

Year end	31/03/2021
Income	£1,320,000
Assets	£34,340,000
Grants to organisations	£379,600

Further financial information

Grants were awarded to 40 community organisations during the year.

Beneficiaries included: Shepherds Bush Family Project (£20,000); Foodbank and Harrow Club W10 (£15,000 each); City Harvest and Urban Partnership Group (£10,000 each); White City Youth Theatre (£8,000); Funpact (£6,000); Grove Toddlers Group (£3,500); Bubblesqueakeat (£2,600).

Exclusions

Religious or political causes; causes primarily for the benefit of animals or the environment rather than for people; causes benefitting people who are not experiencing need of some kind; organisations whose work does not benefit the residents of the eight northern wards of Hammersmith and Fulham.

Applications

The charity welcomes initial grant enquiries by phone or email. The charity's website states, 'we like to meet new applicants to develop a better understanding of what they are doing and we are happy to give advice about potential projects'.

Grant application forms can be downloaded from the website. The charity has three grants committee meetings each year. The dates of these meetings and the dates by which forms must be received for each meeting are advertised on the website. Once completed, application forms must be emailed to the correspondent.

The foundation's helpful website provides a number of documents relating to grant-giving guidelines and the type of grants which the grant-maker is willing to award.

Sources of information

Accounts; annual report; Charity Commission record; funder's website; grant application guidelines.

Hampton Fund

Relief in need and social welfare

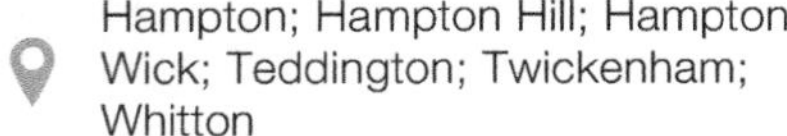

Hampton; Hampton Hill; Hampton Wick; Teddington; Twickenham; Whitton

£1.46 million (2019/20)

CC number: 211756

Correspondent: David White, Director, 15 High Street, Hampton, Middlesex TW12 2SA (tel: 020 8941 7866; email: david@hfac.co.uk)

Trustees: Hilary Hart; Dr James Brockbank; Dr Martin Duffy; Martin Seymour; The Revd Ben Lovell; Mark Boyle; David Meggitt; Geraldine Locke; Kim Loxton; Sharika Sharma; Adele Kimber; Laurence Sewell.

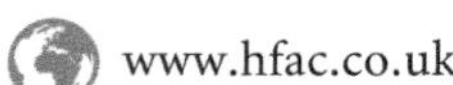

www.hfac.co.uk

facebook.com/Hampton-Fund-1637831249830683

@FundHampton

General information

This charity was established by an Act of Parliament in 1811 and exists to support people and families in need. It makes grants to individuals and organisations. The main aim of the charity is to ensure that local people will not suffer from fuel poverty.

Areas of support

The charity's objectives are:

- The relief of need, hardship or distress of those in the area of benefit
- Support for people who are sick, recovering from illness or who have a disability
- Promoting the education of children and young people
- Providing and supporting recreational and leisure-time activities to improve life condition in the interests of social welfare

Grants are made to individuals in need to improve their quality of life. Assistance is given with fuel costs, the purchase of essential household items and the costs of Year 6 school trips, for example. Full information on these grants is available on the charity's website.

Community grants are made to charities, voluntary sector organisations and community groups which provide services and activities to support people who live in the area of benefit. Grants are given to a wide range of organisations working in sectors including disability, older people, children and young people, carers, mental health and community activities.

Financial information

Year end	30/06/2020
Income	£1,940,000
Assets	£62,790,000
Grants to organisations	£1,460,000
No. of grants	76

Further financial information

Grants awarded to organisations in 2019/20 were broken down as follows:

Disability	16	£296,200
Health and well-being	13	£195,500
Children and young people	12	£174,800
Carers	8	£159,100
Advice, advocacy and outreach	5	£156,500
Older people	7	£131,400
Community activities		£109,100
oneRichmond initiative grants		£104,100
Education	5	£57,000
Housing and homelessness	2	£50,000
Other	1	£20,000
The arts, sport and recreation	1	£6,000

Beneficiaries included: Citizens Advice Richmond (£90,000 in two grants); Richmond upon Thames Crossroads Care (£40,000 in two grants); MTV Youth Hampton (£24,000); Kick London (£16,800); ADHD Richmond and Kingston (£10,000); OK Music Trust (£8,000); River Thames Boat Project (£4,800); Churches Together in Teddington (£900).

Exclusions

The charity is unlikely to support the following:

- Grants to individuals for private and post-compulsory education
- Adaptations or building alterations for individuals
- Holidays, except in cases of severe medical need
- Decoration, carpeting or central heating
- Anything which is the responsibility of a statutory body
- National general charitable appeals
- Animal welfare
- The advancement of religion and religious groups, unless they offer a non-religious service to the community
- Commercial and business activities
- Endowment appeals
- Projects of a political nature
- Retrospective costs, both capital and revenue
- Organisations whose free reserves exceed 12 months' running costs
- Non-charitable social enterprises

Applications

Applicants are first asked to contact the grants team on 0208 979 5555 to discuss eligibility. If deemed eligible, applicants will either be asked to complete an application form, or the charity will arrange a visit to the applicant's organisation. Application forms and guidance notes are available to download from the charity's website.

Sources of information

Accounts; annual report; Charity Commission record; funder's website; guidelines for applicants.

The Lennox Hannay Charitable Trust

 General charitable purposes

 England; Wales; Scotland

 £575,500 (2020/21)

CC number: 1080198

Correspondent: Mrs C. E. Scott, Company Secretary, c/o RF Trustee Co. Ltd, 15 Suffolk Street, London SW1Y 4HG (tel: 020 3696 6721; email: charities@rftrustee.com)

Trustees: Caroline Wilmot-Sitwell; Tara Douglas-Home; Joanne King; RF Trustee Co. Ltd.

General information

The Lennox Hannay Charitable Trust was established in 2000 for general charitable purposes. The trust makes grants to a wide variety of UK-registered charities. Grants have previously been awarding under the following categories:

- Education and training
- Health
- Disability
- Relief of poverty
- Overseas aid
- Religious activities
- Arts and culture
- Sports and recreation
- Environmental conservation
- Emergency services and armed forces
- Community development
- Human rights and equality
- Animal welfare
- Amateur sports
- Social welfare (including young and older people)

In 2020/21 the trustees continued with their policy of making a mixture of smaller (below £2,000), medium (up to £25,000) and larger grants.

Financial information

Year end	31/03/2021
Income	£716,400
Assets	£32,830,000
Grants to organisations	£575,500
No. of grants	127

Beneficiaries included: Westminster City School General Charitable Trust (£50,000); Fleming Wyfold Art Foundation, Game and Wildlife Conservation Trust, Missing Salmon Alliance and The Garden Museum (£25,000 each).

Applications

Applications can be made in writing to the correspondent via post. There are no deadlines. The trustees meet twice a year to discuss applications.

Sources of information

Accounts; annual report; Charity Commission record.

The Kathleen Hannay Memorial Charity

General charitable purposes; health; children and young people; the arts

UK and worldwide

£257,500 (2019/20)

CC number: 299600

Correspondent: Mrs H. D'Monte, Secretary to the Trustees, c/o Charles Russell Speechlys LLP, 5 Fleet Place, London EC4M 7RD (tel: 01242 246311)

Trustees: Simon Weil; Christian Ward; Jonathan Weil; Laura Watkins.

General information

The charity was established by the Reverend Robert Fleming Hannay in 1988. Its Charity Commission record states that it awards grants to organisations in the UK and overseas on a one-off and recurring basis. The charity supports a wide range of charitable purposes but appears to have a preference for supporting children and young people, and the arts.

Financial information

Year end	05/04/2020
Income	£227,500
Assets	£12,230,000
Grants to organisations	£257,500

Beneficiaries included: New English Ballet Trust (£50,000); Children's Burns Trust (£25,000); Cambridge House Opera Company (£15,000).

Exclusions

Grants are not made to individuals or non-registered charities.

Applications

Unsolicited applications are not accepted.

Sources of information

Accounts; annual report; Charity Commission record.

The Haramead Trust

Children's charities; social and medical assistance; homelessness; health education

UK, with a preference for the East Midlands; Republic of Ireland; financially developing countries

£1.12 million (2020/21)

CC number: 1047416

Correspondent: The Trustees, Park House, Park Hill, Gaddesby, Leicestershire LE7 4WH (tel: 01664 840908; email: harameadtrust@aol.com)

Trustees: Winifred Linnett; Robert Smith; Victoria Duddles; Dr Mary Hanlon.

General information

The Haramead Trust was established in 1995 for general charitable purposes. According to the annual report for 2019/20, the trust's grant-giving is focused on:

- The relief of people experiencing hardship or distress
- Children's welfare
- Education in relation to the advancement of health

Causes supported include children's charities, social and medical assistance, homelessness and educational needs.

Grants are also made to individuals and families in direct need of assistance.

Financial information

Year end	31/03/2021
Income	£656,900
Assets	£2,280,000
Grants to organisations	£1,120,000
No. of grants	149

Further financial information

In 2020/21, the trust received 426 requests for support and made 149 grants. Of these grants, 39 were of £10,000 and above, 101 were of between £5,000 and £10,000 and nine were of less than £5,000. Only beneficiaries of grants of £10,000 and above were listed in the accounts.

The following geographical breakdown of grants was provided: UK and Ireland (£627,500); financially developing countries (£285,000); local areas, including East Midlands (£208,500).

Beneficiaries included: Age Concern, Leicestershire Cares and The Ireland Fund (£25,000 each); Samaritans of Leicester and Rutland (£15,000); Action on Poverty, Canine Concern Scotland Trust and WaterAid (£10,000 each).

Applications

Contact the correspondent for information regarding the application process.

Sources of information

Accounts; annual report; Charity Commission record.

The Harbour Foundation

General charitable purposes; the relief of poverty; refugees; people experiencing homelessness; education and research, including scientific and technical postgraduate training; musical training

Worldwide. In practice, mostly the UK and occasionally Israel

£637,100 (2020/21)

CC number: 264927

Correspondent: Mr D. Abrahams, Secretary, 1 Red Place, London W1K 6PL (tel: 020 7456 8180)

Trustees: Dr Daniel Harbour; Susan Harbour; Edmond Harbour; Gideon Harbour; Harry Rich; Richard Hermer.

General information

The foundation was established in 1970 with the following objects, as stated in its 2020/21 annual report:

- The relief of poverty, suffering and distress among refugees and other homeless people
- The advancement of education, learning and research and the dissemination of the results of such research
- To make donations to any institution established for charitable purposes according to the law of England and Wales

Areas of work

According to its 2020/21 annual report, the foundation's grant-making contributes to the following:

- Enabling those in hardship to be educated where a potential students' education and future projects might otherwise be at risk
- Widening the pool of educated students in the field of science and medicine, giving opportunities for those in poverty and the further public benefit from the skills those students will bring to their working lives and communities
- Properly co-ordinated medical research into finding a cure or new treatment for illnesses, generating improvements in medical care to those who are sick
- Relief of poverty, support for refugees and support for victims of disasters affecting the international community regardless of race, religion or nationality
- Maintenance and improvement of the arts and the training of musicians to a high standard who might otherwise not succeed professionally or have opportunity to perform
- Bringing music training to underprivileged inner-London areas

In practice, there is no geographical restriction on awards made by the foundation; however, most grants are awarded to organisations in the UK and Israel. Grants typically range up to £200,000.

Financial information

Year end	31/05/2021
Income	£892,700
Assets	£20,020,000
Grants to organisations	£637,100
No. of grants	38

Further financial information

Grants were broken down as follows in 2020/21:

Education	7	£419,100
Social organisations	14	£106,000
The arts	6	£68,000
Relief in need	11	£44,000

Only beneficiaries of grants of £5,000 and above were listed in the 2020/21 accounts.

Beneficiaries included: Ben Gurion University Foundation and British Friends of Hebrew University of Jerusalem (£200,000 each); Royal College of Music (£28,000); Royal Society of Arts and The Wigmore Hall Trust (£20,000 each); Age UK (£10,000); National Emergencies Trust (£8,000); Salvation Army (£5,000).

Applications

The foundation's 2020/21 accounts state:

> One or more individual Director-Trustees research appropriate institutions or individuals to be recipients of grants, and then make recommendations to the Council for formal approval.

The council meets quarterly.

Sources of information

Accounts; annual report; Charity Commission record.

The David and Claudia Harding Foundation

Scientific research and education

UK

£538,900 (2020)

CC number: 1120878

Correspondent: The Trustees, Grove House, 27 Hammersmith Grove, London W6 0NE (tel: 020 8576 5800)

Trustees: David Harding; Claudia Harding; Steven Lindley.

General information

The foundation was established by David Harding, founder of the Winton Group and his wife Claudia in 2007. David also established Winton Philanthropies in 2005. Winton Philanthropies closed in October 2019 and all funds were transferred to the foundation.

The foundation's Charity Commission record states: 'The foundation's primary focus is on funding scientific research and education, particularly at Cambridge University and the UK's national Science Museum Group.'

Financial information

Year end	31/12/2020
Income	£25,010,000
Assets	£2,360,000
Grants to organisations	£538,900

Further financial information

Only grants of over £50,000 are included in the list of beneficiaries.

Beneficiaries included: Policy Exchange Ltd (£450,000); Greenhouse Sports (£50,000).

Applications

Unsolicited applications are not accepted.

Sources of information

Accounts; annual report; Charity Commission record.

William Harding's Charity

Education and social welfare

Aylesbury

£117,800 (2020)

CC number: 310619

Correspondent: John Leggett, Clerk to the Trustees, c/o Parrott and Coales LLP, 14 Bourbon Street, Aylesbury, Buckinghamshire HP20 2RS (tel: 01296 318501; email: doudjag@pandcllp.co.uk)

Trustees: Anne Brooker; William Chapple; Roger Evans; Les Sheldon; Penni Thorne; Lennard Wakelam; Susan Hewitt; Ranjula Takodra; Roy Collis.

General information

Under a scheme of 1978, Harding's Eleemosynary Charity and Harding's Educational Charity (both set up in the 18th century) merged to become William Harding's Charity. Its objects, limited to the town of Aylesbury, include:

- The provision of almshouses and other benefits for older people
- The provision of special benefits of any kind not normally provided by the local authority for any maintained school or any college of education or other institution of further education in or substantially serving the town of Aylesbury
- Awarding maintenance allowances tenable at any school, university or college of further education
- Relief in need and provision of general benefit in Aylesbury

According to the charity's web page (see www.leapwithus.org.uk/funding/william-hardings-charity):

> Grants are available for voluntary and community groups, clubs, charities, schools and individuals based in Aylesbury, towards education, one-off projects, relief in need and for the general benefit of Aylesbury town residents. Grants are made to assist young persons in education, including at an individual level, scholarships, maintenance allowances, travel awards and grants for equipment. At a wider level, grants are made to the LEA for Aylesbury schools to fund equipment in addition to that which can be provided by the authority. Relief in Need grants are awarded to persons suffering need, hardship or distress.

Financial information

Year end	31/12/2020
Income	£1,240,000
Assets	£38,030,000
Grants to organisations	£117,800

Further financial information

Due to the COVID-19 pandemic, the charity's expenditure on grants was lower than usual during the year. The accounts explain that the charity received fewer applications due to the closure of schools and educational organisations. Typically, grants to organisations total around £300,000. The accounts state that normal levels of giving should resume from 2021.

Grants to organisations were broken down as follows:

Relief in need	£51,500
Youth groups	£37,000
Schools and educational organisations	£17,600
Travel for clubs/societies/groups	£51,500

Beneficiaries included: Aylesbury Youth Action (two grants totalling £20,000); Queens Park Art Centre (£14,000); St Edward's Catholic Primary School (£9,000); Aylesbury Youth Motor Centre (£5,000); Aylesbury Child Contact Centre (£2,000); The Grange School (£1,000); Heritage Care (£200).

Applications

Application forms are available on request from the charity, either by collection or by sending an SAE. The trustees meet on a regular basis to consider applications.

Sources of information

Accounts; annual report; Charity Commission record; Leap (website).

The Hargreaves Foundation

Disadvantaged children and young people

UK

£335,300 (2020/21)

CC number: 1187297

Correspondent: The Trustees, The Old Surgery, Swan Barton, Sherston, Malmesbury, Wiltshire SN16 0LJ (email: info@thehargreavesfoundation.org)

Trustees: Louisa Hargreaves; Robert Hargreaves; Peter Hargreaves; Rosemary Hargreaves; Nigel Bence.

 www.thehargreavesfoundation.org

General information

The foundation was established by Peter Hargreaves and his family in 2020. Peter Hargreaves was the co-founder of Hargreaves London, one of the UK's largest financial services firms.

Areas of support

The foundation supports disadvantaged children under the age of 18. Its website states:

> The Foundation's objectives are underpinned by the desire to give those under the age of 18, and living with a mental health condition, disability, or growing up in poverty, the opportunity to fulfil their potential whilst improving wellbeing, self-esteem and independence.
>
> The Foundation can fund clearly defined projects, initiatives or the purchase of specific items that support one or more of the following:
>
> - Enables individuals to experience the mental and physical health benefits of participatory sport
> - Ensures participatory sport is accessible
> - Provides sporting or educational activities that foster life skills
> - Aims to improve academic engagement and attainment
> - Encourages the development of skills and personal attributes to aid future employability

Financial information

Year end	31/01/2021
Income	£91,550,000
Assets	£83,910,000
Grants to organisations	£335,300

Beneficiaries included: The Change Foundation (£39,100); The Literacy Pirates (£30,000); Independence at Home (£20,000); Bristol Down Syndrome Trust (£12,800); The Jack Hazeldine Foundation (£3,300).

Applications

An online application form is available on the foundation's website.

Sources of information

Charity Commission record; funder's website.

The Harpur Trust

 Education; relief of poverty, hardship or sickness; social welfare; recreation

 The borough of Bedford

 £1.18 million (2019/20)

CC number: 1066861

Correspondent: Lucy Bardner, Grants Manager, Princeton Court, The Pilgrim Centre, Brickhill Drive, Bedford, Bedfordshire MK41 7PZ (tel: 01234 369503; email: grants@harpurtrust.org.uk)

Trustees: Michael Womack; Philip Wallace; William Phillimore; Susan Clark; Tina Beddoes; Prof. Stephen Mayson; Hugh Stewart; Dr Jennifer Till; Dr Anne Egan; David Wilson; Rhian Castell; Linbert Spencer; Shirley Jackson; Harriett Mather; Mark Taylor; Sir Clive Loader; Sarah Wheeler; Terence Rigby; Abu Sultan; John Fordham; Neil Harris.

 www.harpurtrust.org.uk

 facebook.com/TheHarpurTrust

 @theharpurtrust

General information

The Harpur Trust (formerly known as the Bedford Charity) has been in existence since 1566 when it was founded by Sir William Harpur (1496–1573), a tailor from Bedford and later Lord Mayor of London, who created an endowment to sustain a school he had established in Bedford.

Today, the trust owns and runs four independent schools in Bedford – Bedford School, Bedford Girls' School, Bedford Modern School and Pilgrims Pre-Preparatory School. The trust is also a co-sponsor, along with Bedford College, of the new Bedford Academy, and manages almshouses which provide secure, affordable accommodation for a number of the borough's disadvantaged, older citizens.

Grants

Each year the trust awards grants totalling up to £1 million to organisations which fit one or more of its charitable objects: education, the relief of poverty, sickness or distress, and recreation with a social welfare purpose. Applicants must be a registered charity or other non-profit making body and must be based in the borough of Bedford and/or be conducting specific activities aiming to meet the needs of people who live in the borough. The borough comprises the town of Bedford and the surrounding area of North Bedfordshire. The trust's small grants programme offers grants of up to £5,000 for capital projects or up to £2,000 for any other project. Larger grants are also available.

In addition to grants for organisations, the trust also awards a small number of individual educational grants and university bursaries.

From time to time, the trust also offers additional grant programmes with separate requirements and application processes. Check the trust's website for the latest information.

Financial information

Year end	30/06/2020
Income	£53,870,000
Assets	£183,550,000
Grants to organisations	£1,180,000
No. of grants	65

Further financial information

Grants awarded to organisations in 2019/20 were broken down as follows: relief of poverty (£907,000); education (£186,000); recreation (£82,000).

Beneficiaries included: FACES and Link to Change (£143,800); Bedford Borough Council (£50,000); HMP Bedford (£30,000); CHUMS CIC (£20,200); Mark Rutherford School Trust (£15,400); YMCA Bedfordshire (£7,500); Bedford Daycare Hospice (£5,000); Wilstead Bowls Club (£1,000).

Exclusions

Grants are not provided for the following:

- Businesses
- Projects that promote a particular religion
- Projects considered to be the responsibility of the local authority or national government
- Projects that do not benefit the residents of the borough of Bedford
- Costs already incurred
- Trips, except in very limited circumstances

Applications

Organisations are encouraged to contact the trust informally for initial guidance on potential applications. The trust's main priorities, grant programmes and application process are also set out in the guidance notes, which are available by post, email and on the trust's helpful website.

Organisations applying to the small grants programme can submit a full application using an online form on the trust's website, or by downloading or requesting a form from the grants manager.

All other funding requests must follow the two-stage application process. The first stage of the formal application process is to submit a preliminary proposal form. Proposals are first considered by trustees before the trust writes to applicants to discuss the outcome, offer feedback and make an invitation to submit a formal, second-stage application if applicable.

The second-stage application may be completed online or by filling out a hard-copy form, downloadable from the website, and posting it back to the trust. Ensure you include the required additional information. The trust's guidelines detail what information is required depending on the size and type of grant requested. Decisions for these grants are usually made within three to six months.

Sources of information

Accounts; annual report; annual review; Charity Commission record; funder's website; guidelines for applicants.

The Peter Harrison Foundation

 Access to sport for people with disabilities; children and young people; education

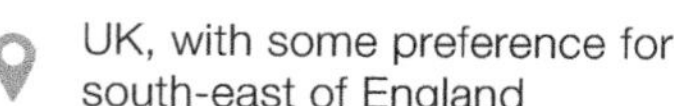 UK, with some preference for the south-east of England

£2.45 million (2020/21)

CC number: 1076579

Correspondent: The Trustees, Foundation House, 42–48 London Road, Reigate, Surrey RH2 9QQ (tel: 01737 228000; email: enquiries@peterharrisonfoundation.org)

Trustees: Julia Harrison-Lee; Peter Lee; Nicholas Harrison.

 www.peterharrisonfoundation.org

General information

The foundation was established by businessman Peter Harrison in April 1999. The foundation aims to maintain the value of this capital while distributing approximately £2.2 million of its annual income for charitable purposes.

According to its website, the foundation has three broad areas of need:

- Opportunities for self-development through participation in sport, including sport for disadvantaged and disabled people
- Care of children and young people with special needs
- Education, with a particular interest in supporting Harrison Scholarships and capital development at Reigate Grammar School

Grant programmes

At the time of writing (March 2022), the foundation had four grant programmes:

Opportunities through sport

This programme supports sporting activity or projects which provide opportunities for people who have a disability or are otherwise disadvantaged to fulfil their potential and to develop other personal and life skills. Grants will often be considered for capital, revenue or project funding.

The trustees welcome applications for the following types of project:

- Projects which provide a focus for skills development and confidence building through the medium of sport
- Projects that have a strong training and/or educational theme within a sporting activity
- Projects that provide sporting equipment or facilities for people with a disability or who are disadvantaged
- Projects with a high degree of community involvement
- Projects that help to engage children or young people at risk of crime, truancy or addiction

Special needs and care for children and young people

This programme is exclusively for charities in the south-east of England and applications are accepted only from charities meeting the needs of children and young people in the following counties: Berkshire; Buckinghamshire; East Sussex; Hampshire; Isle of Wight; Kent; Oxfordshire; Surrey; and West Sussex.

The foundation does not accept applications from charities based in or operating in London but may consider funding charities based in London for a specific project taking place in the South East that meets the foundation's criteria:

- Projects that work with or benefit children with a disability or chronic or terminal illness and provide support for their parents and carers
- Projects that help to engage children or young people at risk of crime, truancy or addiction
- Projects organised for young people at risk of homelessness or that provide new opportunities for young people experiencing homelessness

Education

This programme supports education initiatives, primarily in the South East, which are of particular interest to the trustees. The trustees also fund bursary places for children from Reigate and Redhill areas in Surrey, to enable them to attend Reigate Grammar School. **This programme does not accept unsolicited applications.**

Trustees' discretion

This programme supports projects that are of particular interest to the trustees that may fall outside the foundation's main aims. **This programme does not accept unsolicited applications.**

Financial information

Year end	31/05/2021
Income	£3,010,000
Assets	£51,030,000
Grants to organisations	£2,450,000

Beneficiaries included: Loughborough University (£100,000); Rose Road Association (£30,000); Lifecentre (£19,400); Friends of Gibside School (£12,000); Glasgow Eagles Sports Club (£1,000).

Exclusions

The foundation does not fund:

- Requests for retrospective funding
- Activities that are primarily the responsibility of central or local government
- Individuals
- CICs
- Exempt charities
- Overseas projects
- Adventure challenges or expeditions in the UK or abroad
- Projects that are solely for the promotion of religion

Applications

See the foundation's website for further information on how to apply. For its open grant programmes the foundation has a two-stage application process.

Sources of information

Accounts; annual report; Charity Commission record; guidelines for applicants; funder's website.

Edward Harvist Trust (The Harvist Estate)

General charitable purposes; health; social welfare; recreation and leisure; older people; education

The London boroughs of Barnet, Brent, Camden, Harrow and the City of Westminster

£376,600 (2020/21)

CC number: 211970

Correspondent: Hugh Peart, Honorary Secretary, London Borough of Harrow, Finance Department, PO Box 21, Civic Centre, Harrow, Middlesex HA1 2XY (tel: 020 8424 1450; email: treasurymanagement@harrow.gov.uk)

Trustees: Cllr Angela Harvey; Cllr Heather Johnson; Cllr Alex Prager; Cllr Nitin Parekh; Cllr Mary Daly.

General information

This trust dates back to 1610 and derives its income from its former ownership of estates on the line of the Edgware Road, which it has now sold. The income is currently distributed to the constituent authorities, namely the London boroughs of Barnet, Brent, Camden, Harrow and the City of Westminster, in proportion to the length of the Edgware Road passing through the local authorities' boundaries. Each local authority has a representative on the trustee body.

The trust does not make direct grants; each local authority is responsible for the charitable allocation of its grant for the following purposes: the relief of older and disadvantaged people; the relief of distress and sickness; the provision and support of recreational and leisure-time facilities (in the interests of social welfare); the provision and support of educational facilities; and any other purposes for the benefit of residents.

Financial information

Year end	31/03/2021
Income	£441,800
Assets	£10,780,000
Grants to organisations	£376,600
No. of grants	107

Further financial information

In 2020/21, grants were awarded to the following authorities for distribution to organisations:

London Borough of Barnet	£116,800
London Borough of Brent	£104,300
City of Westminster	£94,200
London Borough of Camden	£40,400
London Borough of Harrow	£21,100

Beneficiaries included: Somers Town Community Association (£12,500); Sidings Community Centre (£10,500); Westminster Arts (£8,000); Lebanese Welfare Centre (£5,000); The Flower Bank (£3,000); The Last Cuppa CIC (£1,500); Bereavement Care (£520).

Applications

Applications must be made through the appropriate local authority. Do not write to the correspondent. At the time of writing (April 2022) there was information on the trust (such as eligibility criteria and application procedures) available on each of the five borough councils' websites – this information could be found following a search for the trust's name using the websites' search bars. There may be different criteria and application procedures imposed by the five local authorities.

Sources of information

Accounts; annual report; borough councils' websites (Barnet, Brent, Camden, Harrow and City of Westminster); Charity Commission record.

The Charles Hayward Foundation

Heritage and conservation; older people; social and criminal justice; overseas aid

UK and the Commonwealth countries of Africa

£2.15 million (2020)

CC number: 1078969

Correspondent: Dorothy Napierala, Director, Hayward House, 45 Harrington Gardens, London SW7 4JU (tel: 020 7370 7063 (9.30am – 5.30pm weekdays); email: dorothy@charleshaywardfoundation.org.uk)

Trustees: Julia Chamberlain; Susan Heath; Alexander Heath; Brian Insch; John Leuven; Caroline Donald; Richard Griffith.

 www.charleshaywardfoundation.org.uk

General information

The Charles Hayward foundation was established in 2000, when two charitable trusts (the Hayward Foundation and the Charles Hayward Trust) founded by the businessman Sir Charles Hayward were combined.

Grant programmes

The foundation currently operates two separate grant programmes:

- **Main grants programme** – social and criminal justice, and heritage and conservation (for charities with an income of more than £350,000); and overseas aid (for charities with an income of between £150,000 and £5 million)
- **Small grants programme** – social and criminal justice and older people (for charities with an income of less than £350,000)

Both grant programmes are designed to cover project costs, including salaries and capital costs. Full guidelines for each of the foundation's grant programmes are provided on the website.

Financial information

Year end	31/12/2020
Income	£25,100
Assets	£73,170,000
Grants to organisations	£2,150,000
No. of grants	175

Further financial information

Grants paid during the year were broken down as follows:

Social and criminal justice	66	£1.49 million
Small grants	56	£254,100
Heritage and conservation	8	£182,000
Overseas	12	£178,200
Other	33	£42,300

Beneficiaries included: Early Years Scotland (£25,000); Manchester Youth Zone (£20,000); Coastal Forces Heritage Trust and Prisoners Abroad (£10,000 each); Arts 4 Dementia (£5,000); Light of the World Community Centre (£3,000); Welsh Air Ambulance (£1,000); Supporting Wounded Veterans (£500).

Exclusions

The foundation only supports UK-registered charities. The website notes further that generally funding is not given for the following purposes:

- Endowments
- General appeals
- Grant-making charities
- Individuals
- Loans or deficits
- Retrospective appeals (for costs already incurred prior to receiving a decision from the foundation)
- Unrestricted grants

Note that individual programmes may have their own additional exclusions.

Applications

Full information, including eligibility criteria and how to apply for a grant, is available on the foundation's website.

Applications to the small grants programme are accepted on a rolling basis and are considered every three months (usually in March, June September and December).

The main grants programme has a two-stage application process. Firstly, applications are considered by the grants committee, which recommends applications to be considered by the trustees at the second stage of the process. Trustee meetings usually take place in February, May, August and November, but check the website for exact deadlines.

Sources of information

Accounts; annual report; Charity Commission record; funder's website.

The Headley Trust

Arts and heritage; cathedral and church restoration; health; social welfare; education; overseas development

UK; sub-Saharan anglophone Africa; Ethiopia; Central and Eastern Europe

£2.75 million (2020/21)

CC number: 266620

Correspondent: The Trustees, c/o The Sainsbury Family Charitable Trusts, The Peak, 5 Wilton Road, London SW1V 1AP (tel: 020 7410 0330; email: info@sfct.org.uk)

Trustees: Judith Portrait; The Rt Hon. Sir Timothy Sainsbury; Timothy Sainsbury; Lady Susan Sainsbury; Camilla Sainsbury; Amanda McCrystal.

 www.sfct.org.uk/Headley.html

General information

The trust is one of the 17 grant-making charities that make up the Sainsbury Family Charitable Trusts.

Areas of work

According to its website, the Headley Trust is prepared to consider unsolicited applications as long as they closely match one of the areas of interest listed below:

Arts and heritage (UK)

- Regional museums and galleries (including local authority museums), with special consideration for curatorial support and acquisitions
- The display, study and acquisition of British ceramics
- Conservation of industrial, maritime and built heritage
- Archaeology
- Arts education including digitisation and outreach

Cathedrals and major churches

- Restoration or repair work to the fabric of ancient cathedrals, parish church cathedrals and large churches of 'exceptional architectural merit' that were built before 1850
- Conservation of monuments
- Applications for solar panels, energy-efficient measures and fire and burglar alarms

Parish churches

- Fabric repairs to listed medieval parish churches in rural areas in England and Wales and the provision of toilet facilities and disability access. Note: churches are considered by diocese on a rotational basis. See the website for current dioceses being supported/considered

Education

- Bursary support for vocational training in conservation and heritage skills and for UK graduate students (dance) and postgraduate students (music)
- Support for music projects in primary schools

Health and social welfare

- Support for older people to live independently for as long as possible
- Improving older people's quality of life in residential care homes, including support for people with dementia
- Support for carers of older people, both locally and nationally
- Support for disadvantaged families and young people

Arts and heritage (overseas)

- The conservation and recording of heritage (including ecclesiastical and vernacular architecture, archaeology and cultural artefacts), primarily in south-eastern Europe (Albania,

Bosnia-Herzegovina, Bulgaria, Croatia, Greece, Macedonia, Montenegro, Romania, Serbia and Slovenia) as well as Ethiopia

- Raising awareness of heritage issues in these countries; supporting the capacity of new heritage NGOs; training the next generation of conservation and heritage professionals; engaging young people in their heritage
- Priority is given to locally led organisations employing local experts

Financially developing countries

Development projects that focus on:

- Education and employment interventions for women and girls
- Water, sanitation and hygiene, and community health programmes in the poorest anglophone countries in Africa
- Priority is given to locally led organisations employing local experts

Financial information

Year end	05/04/2021
Income	£2,160,000
Assets	£79,440,000
Grants to organisations	£2,750,000
No. of grants	269

Further financial information

Grants were broken down as follows:

Arts and heritage – UK	124	£1.67 million
Health and social welfare	110	£557,800
Education	17	£235,800
Financially developing countries	11	£198,500
Arts and heritage – overseas	7	£87,100

Beneficiaries included: Art Fund (£100,000); Microloan Foundation (£42,500); Halifax Minster (£30,000); Beamish Museum (£20,000); Best Beginnings (£15,000); Zenica City Museum (£10,000); University of York (£5,000).

Exclusions

The trust will not support individuals, education fees or expeditions.

Applications

Applications can be made online using the form on the trust's website.

Sources of information

Accounts; annual report; Charity Commission record; funder's website.

The Health Foundation

Healthcare and public health research; training and development

UK

£20.17 million (2020)

CC number: 286967

Correspondent: Programmes Team, Salisbury Square House, 8 Salisbury Square, London EC4Y 8AP (tel: 020 7257 8000; email: info@health.org.uk)

Trustees: Melloney Poole; Sir David Dalton; Branwen Jeffreys; Prof. Rosalind Smyth; Sir Hugh Taylor; Eric Gregory; Loraine Hawkins; Dr Ruth Hussey; David Smart; Prof. Dawn Edge; Katherine Blacklock; Ravi Gurumurthy.

 www.health.org.uk

 facebook.com/thehealthfoundation

 @HealthFdn

General information

The Health Foundation aims to improve health and the quality of healthcare in the UK. It receives funding from an endowment, which came from a one-off charitable donation from the sale of the PPP Healthcare group in 1998 – one of the largest charitable donations in UK history. The website states:

> Our aim is a healthier population, supported by high quality health care that can be equitably accessed. We learn what works to make people's lives healthier and improve the health care system. From giving grants to those working at the front line to carrying out research and policy analysis, we shine a light on how to make successful change happen.
>
> As the second largest endowed foundation in the UK focusing on health, we spend around £37 million a year on improving health and health care.

The foundation's activities expand across five key strategic priorities:

- Promoting healthy lives for all
- Data analytics for better health
- Supporting health care improvement
- Making health and care services more sustainable
- Improving national health and care policy

The foundation works in partnership with others to ensure that the learning generated from its work helps to shape future health policy and practice. It works with individuals and organisations from across the UK health system, including clinicians and managers, charity sector and patient organisations, academics, national bodies and policy-makers. It also works with people and organisations from around the world that have an interest in how to improve the quality of healthcare.

Grant programmes

The foundation's grant-making activity is extremely wide ranging. Grants are categorised under the following headings:

- Funding for improvement projects
- Funding for research projects
- Funding for data analytics
- Funding for health promotion projects
- Fellowship opportunities

Funding programmes across the different streams vary throughout the year. Recent calls have been aimed at academic research, research projects, NHS trusts, GP practices and policy work. The amount of funding available varies hugely depending upon the project. Interested applicants working in healthcare should consult the foundation's 'Current Opportunities' web page for full and up-to-date information.

Financial information

Year end	31/12/2020
Income	£16,380,000
Assets	£1,110,000
Grants to organisations	£20,170,000

Further financial information

Grants were broken down as follows: improving health and care services (£12.1 million); other (£6.3 million, including £3.61 million of COVID-19 grants); promoting healthy lives for all (£1.73 million). These grants ranged from small one-off awards to multi-year projects and fellowships.

Beneficiaries included: Public Health Wales (£951,000); Lloyds Bank Foundation (£500,000); University of Manchester (£279,100); The Point of Care Foundation (£109,100); Longevity International (£50,000); Empathy Museum (£26,600); Business for Health (£10,000); Health Innovation Network (£5,500).

Exclusions

See the website for a full list of exclusions relevant to the grants programme being applied to.

Applications

The foundation does not consider unprompted requests or proposals for funding. Programmes open to applications are advertised on the foundation's website. These are likely to change frequently and candidates are advised to visit the website for the most up-to-date information. You may sign up for a website account to receive alerts when new funding opportunities go live. Application forms are available online, together with full guidelines and specific requirements and deadlines for each of the programmes. There is also a helpful FAQs page, which should be consulted by potential applicants.

Sources of information

Accounts; annual report; Charity Commission record; funder's website.

Heart Research UK

Medical research into the prevention, treatment and cure of heart disease

UK

£293,600 (2020)

CC number: 1044821

Correspondent: The Trustees, Suite 12D, Joseph's Well, Hanover Walk, Leeds, West Yorkshire LS3 1AB (tel: 0113 234 7474; email: info@heartresearch.org.uk)

Trustees: Richard Brown; Dr David Dickinson; Dr Catherine Dickinson; Anthony Knight; Paul Smith; Kevin Watterson; Paul Rogerson; Peter Braidley; Julie Fenwick; Pierre Bouvet; Christopher Newman; James Breeze; Linda Musonza.

 www.heartresearch.org.uk

 facebook.com/heartresearchuk

 @heartresearchuk

 @heartresearchuk

General information

Heart Research UK (formerly the National Heart Research Fund) was founded in 1967. The stated aims of the charity are 'funding ground breaking, innovative medical research projects at the cutting edge of science into the prevention, treatment and cure of heart disease. There is a strong emphasis on supporting clinical and surgical projects and young researchers on their first steps into research.'

The objects are fulfilled by funding medical research projects throughout the UK. All projects undertaken are allocated and controlled in line with the guiding principles of the Association of Medical Research Charities (AMRC).

At the time of writing (February 2022) the charity was offering the following medical research grant programmes:

- **Scotland grants:** up to £200,000 for research at hospitals and universities across Scotland
- **Translational Research Project grants:** up to £200,000 per award to help bridge the gap between scientific research and patient care, bringing about clinical benefits in the most efficient way
- **Novel and Emerging Technologies grants:** a maximum of £250,000 for research projects which focus on the development of new and innovative technologies to diagnose, treat and prevent heart disease and related conditions
- **PhD studentships:** one PhD studentship will be awarded each year to cover tuition fees, research consumables and a student stipend

The charity also offers Healthy Hearts grants of 'up to £10,000 to community projects across the UK that focus on heart health and promote healthier, happier longer lives'.

Financial information

Year end	31/12/2020
Income	£2,740,000
Assets	£6,910,000
Grants to organisations	£293,600

Beneficiaries included: University of Exeter (£102,000); University of Leeds (£53,600); University of Glasgow (£8,000); Sheffield Hallam University (£1,300).

Applications

Application forms, full guidelines and up-to-date deadlines for each programme can be found on the charity's website.

Sources of information

Accounts; annual report; Charity Commission record; funder's website.

The Heathcoat Trust

Relief of poverty; education and training; health; general charitable purposes

Local causes in and around Tiverton, Devon

£244,000 (2020/21)

CC number: 203367

Correspondent: Helen Isaac, Secretary to the Trustees, The Factory, West Exe, Tiverton, Devon EX16 5LL (tel: 01884 244296; email: heathcoattrust@heathcoat.co.uk)

Trustees: Mark Drysdale; Sir Ian Heathcoat-Amory; John Smith; Susan Westlake; Julian Morgan; Lee Sellens.

General information

This trust was established in 1945 and makes grants for the following causes:

- The relief of financial hardship
- Education and training
- Building or making grants to health organisations
- General charitable purposes

Grants are mainly awarded to organisations in Tiverton in Devon and its neighbourhood or in places where the firms John Heathcoat and Company Ltd and Lowman Manufacturing Company Ltd and their subsidiaries carry on business.

Financial information

Year end	05/04/2021
Income	£683,500
Assets	£27,590,000
Grants to organisations	£244,000

Further financial information

In previous years grants have totalled between £300,000 and £400,000.

Beneficiaries included: Devon Community Foundation (£15,000); Tiverton Museum (£5,000); Tiverton Swimming Club and Mid Devon Mobility (£1,000 each).

Applications

Apply in writing to the correspondent. The trustees meet regularly to consider applications.

Sources of information

Accounts; annual report; Charity Commission record.

Heathrow Community Trust

Community development; young people; education; skills and employment; sport and recreation; environmental protection

The areas surrounding Heathrow Airport (Ealing, Hillingdon, Hounslow, Richmond, Runnymede, Slough, South Bucks, Spelthorne and the Royal Borough of Windsor and Maidenhead)

£441,900 (2020)

CC number: 1183004

Correspondent: The Trustees, c/o Groundwork South, Colne Valley Park Centre, Denham Court Drive, Denham, Middlesex UB9 5PG (tel: 01895 839916; email: HCT@Groundwork.org.uk)

Trustees: Dr Prabhjot Basra; Nigel Milton; Aled Patchett; Jason Knight; David Cottrell; Alison Keeley; Gennie Dearman; Richard de Belder; Michael Murphy.

 www.heathrowcommunitytrust.org

General information

The trust is an independent charity which receives funding from Heathrow Airport Ltd, airline noise fines, other funders and airport staff. Its grant programmes look to improve the quality of life for communities near the airport.

Grant programmes

There are three routes to funding for external applicants:

- **Projects for Young People:** grants of up to £7,500 for projects that raise aspirations, increase resilience or increase employability in children and young people up to age 24

- **Environment and Sustainability**: grants of up to £7,500 for projects focused on the environment and sustainability
- **Communities Together**: grants of up to £2,500 for small community projects

More information on these programmes, including full eligibility criteria and guidelines, is available from the charity's website.

There are also two funds to which employees can apply for support with their own charitable involvement:

- **Heathrow Active People Initiative (HAPI)**: grants of up to £2,500 are open to Heathrow Airport employees who are regular volunteers with non-profit organisations anywhere in the UK
- **Matched funding**: employees are also supported in their fundraising with a matched funding scheme through which the trust will match funds raised for charity

Financial information

Year end	31/12/2020
Income	£543,400
Assets	£245,700
Grants to organisations	£441,900

Beneficiaries included: A list of beneficiaries was not available. Previous beneficiaries include: The Eikon Charity (£47,380); Finefutures (£45,200); Oxfordshire Crossroads (£22,500); West London River Group (£20,900); Stanwell Village Hall (£17,000); Slough West Indian People's Enterprise (£15,000); Spark! (£9,400); Victoria Junior School (£5,000); The Manor Friends Charity (£2,100).

Exclusions

Refer to the trust's website. Each of the grant programmes are subject to their own eligibility criteria and restrictions.

Applications

Application forms and guidance notes for each of the grant programmes are available from the trust's website.

Sources of information

Accounts; annual report; Charity Commission record; guidelines for applicants; funder's website.

The Heathside Charitable Trust

General charitable purposes; healthcare; education; social welfare

UK and overseas

£382,500 (2020)

CC number: 326959

Correspondent: The Trustees, 32 Hampstead High Street, London NW3 1QD (tel: 020 7431 7739)

Trustees: Geoffrey Jayson; Louise Jacobs; Juliet Solomon; Daniel Solomon; Sir Harry Solomon; Lady Judith Solomon; Sam Jacobs; James Jacobs.

General information

This trust was established in 1985 to support general charitable purposes. Our previous research suggests the trust has a preference for funding Jewish organisations and causes. According to its 2020 annual report, 'the objects of the charity are making available funds for the benefit of such charitable institutions, or for such charitable purposes, as the trustees shall decide.'

Financial information

Year end	31/12/2020
Income	£317,300
Assets	£5,000,000
Grants to organisations	£382,500
No. of grants	63

Further financial information

Grants were distributed as follows:

Education	37%
Healthcare	35%
Other	26%
Welfare	2%

Beneficiaries included: Only one beneficiary was noted in the accounts: The Portland Trust (£50,000).

Exclusions

The trust does not award grants to individuals.

Applications

Apply in writing to the correspondent. The trustees meet four times a year to discuss and approve existing and new grants.

Sources of information

Accounts; annual report; Charity Commission record.

The Charlotte Heber-Percy Charitable Trust

General charitable purposes; animal welfare; the environment; health and hospices; overseas aid; education; children; the arts and museums

UK and overseas

£286,200 (2020/21)

CC number: 284387

Correspondent: Linda Cousins, c/o Rathbone Trust Company Ltd, 8 Finsbury Circus, London EC2M 7AZ (tel: 020 7399 0820; email: linda.cousins@rathbones.com)

Trustees: Joanna Prest; Charlotte Heber-Percy.

General information

The trust was set up by a deed created in 1981 to support general charitable purposes. A wide range of causes are supported, including: animal welfare; the environment; medical causes and hospices; international charities; local charities; children and education; the arts and museums. Donations are made without any commitment to future funding and typically range from £1,000 to £20,000.

Financial information

Year end	05/04/2021
Income	£263,900
Assets	£8,290,000
Grants to organisations	£286,200

Further financial information

Grants were broken down as follows:

General charitable organisations	£106,000
Medical, cancer and hospices	£80,000
Animal welfare and the local environment	£67,000
The arts and museums	£20,200
Local organisations	£6,000
International charities	£5,000
Education and children	£2,000

Beneficiaries included: British Horse Society (£55,000); Horatio's Garden (£30,000); Dementia UK (£10,000); Gift Grenada (£5,000); St Peter's Church (£1,000).

Applications

Applications should be made in writing to the correspondent. The trustees meet on a quarterly basis to consider applications.

Sources of information

Accounts; annual report; Charity Commission record.

Ernest Hecht Charitable Foundation

Social welfare; advancement of the arts; education; people who are disadvantaged; older people; children and young people

UK

£2.68 million (2020)

CC number: 1095850

Correspondent: The Trustees, c/o Glazers, 843 Finchley Road, London NW11 8NA (email: info@ernesthechtcharitablefoundation.org)

Trustees: Robert Ward; Barb Jungr; Ben Barkow.

http://ernesthechtcharitablefoundation.org

General information

This foundation was registered in 2003 by Ernest Hecht, founder and managing director of the independent publishing house Souvenir Press.

The foundation's website explains:

> The Foundation's primary objective is to support the work of UK registered charities by awarding grants that benefit the disadvantaged and promote the advancement of the arts and education.
>
> It awards grants that will make a difference in a particular field, especially for the vulnerable, the young, and the elderly.

Financial information

Year end	31/12/2020
Income	£5,270,000
Assets	£4,060,000
Grants to organisations	£2,680,000

Beneficiaries included: Book Trade Charity (£150,000); Chickenshed (£50,300); Crisis UK (£10,000); Maggs Day Centre (£7,000); Equal Arts (£4,000); Northampton Hope Centre (£1,000).

Applications

At the time of writing (February 2022) the foundation's website stated: 'The Ernest Hecht Charitable Foundation's applications process is closed and will remain closed until further notice.' See the website for the latest information on applications.

Sources of information

Accounts; annual report; Charity Commission record; funder's website.

The Hedley Foundation

Disadvantaged young people; older people; people with a terminal illness; disability; carers; social welfare

UK

£179,100 (2020/21)

CC number: 262933

Correspondent: Lucy Janes, Appeals Secretary, Victoria House, 1–3 College Hill, London EC4R 2RA (tel: 020 7489 8076; email: ljanes@hedleyfoundation.org.uk)

Trustees: David Byam-Cook; Angus Fanshawe; Sir Andrew Ford; Patrick Holcroft; Lorna Stuttaford; Charles Bennett; Alexander Scully.

www.hedleyfoundation.org.uk

General information

Established in 1971, The Hedley Foundation is an endowed grant-giving charitable foundation that supports small to medium-sized UK-registered charities. The foundation aims to improve the quality of life of people in the UK, particularly those from disadvantaged backgrounds. This is achieved by making grants for the benefit of young people, people with disabilities, older people, people who are terminally ill and their carers. Grants typically range up to £5,000 but occasionally larger sums are awarded.

According to its website, the foundation supports four areas:

> **Youth Support** – raising the aspirations of disadvantaged young people and supporting youth projects through education, the arts, sport and adventurous activities.
>
> **Disabled Support** – improving the quality of life of those living with physical or mental disabilities, sensory impairment and learning difficulties.
>
> **Supporting the Elderly and Terminally Ill –** improving the quality of life of the elderly and those receiving end of life care.
>
> **Miscellaneous Support** – supporting other social welfare projects such as those for carers, the homeless and ex-offenders.

Financial information

Year end	31/03/2021
Income	£1,340,000
Assets	£39,120,000
Grants to organisations	£179,100
No. of grants	73

Further financial information

Due to the impact of the COVID-19 pandemic, the foundation adjusted its grants budget for 2020/21; however, the foundation's normal annual grants budget is £700,000. Grants were broken down as follows in 2020/21:

Disability	£76,200
Young people	£60,800
Terminal illness and hospices	£29,100
Other	£13,000

Beneficiaries included: A list of beneficiaries was not available. Previous beneficiaries include: In2Change South Yorkshire Ltd (£25,000); Edward James Foundation (£21,000); Young Musicians Symphony Orchestra (£15,000); English National Ballet School, Raleigh International and Tapping House Hospice (£10,000 each).

Exclusions

The foundation does not support:

- Organisations which are not UK-registered charities
- Individuals directly
- Churches, cathedrals and museums
- Exclusive charities (which only help people from specific groupings)
- Appeals for general running costs, transport, salaries or financial deficits
- Appeals for building or refurbishment projects
- Overseas projects

Applications

Application forms are available to download from the foundation's website and should be returned by post with the latest accounts. Dates of trustee meetings are listed on the foundation's website.

Sources of information

Accounts; annual report; Charity Commission record; funder's website.

The Helping Foundation

Orthodox Jewish causes

UK

£13 million (2020)

CC number: 1104484

Correspondent: The Trustees, Flat 1, Allanadale Court, Waterpark Road, Salford, Greater Manchester M7 4JN (tel: 01617 40116)

Trustees: Rachel Weis; Rabbi Aubrey Weis; David Neuwirth; Benny Stone; Sir Weis.

General information

The Helping Foundation was established in 2004, and is funded primarily by donations and investment income. According to its 2020 annual report, the objectives of the foundation are as follows:

- The advancement of education according to the tenets of the Orthodox Jewish faith
- The advancement of the Orthodox Jewish religion
- The relief of poverty among older people or people in need, hardship or distress in the Jewish community

The charity invites applications for funding for projects that the trustees feel are appropriate for the charity's objects.

Financial information

Year end	31/12/2020
Income	£21,360,000
Assets	£351,870,000
Grants to organisations	£13,000,000

Beneficiaries included: A list of beneficiaries was not available.

Applications

Apply in writing to the correspondent.

Sources of information

Accounts; annual report; Charity Commission record.

The Christina Mary Hendrie Trust

Young people charities; older people; veterans; hospices

Scotland and Canada

£246,800 (2020/21)

OSCR number: SC014514

Correspondent: Audrey Souness, Secretary, 1 Rutland Court, Edinburgh EH3 8EY (tel: 0131 270 7700)

www.christinamaryhendrietrust.com

General information

The trust was established in 1975 following the death in Scotland of Christina Mary Hendrie. The trust supports charities in both Scotland and Canada with a focus on:

- Veterans
- Older people
- Young people
- Hospices

The trust's website provides the following information about what the trustees favour when considering applications:

- Smaller local organisations will be preferred to larger well-funded ones
- Charities helping greater numbers of people will be preferred to those helping only a few. Group activity is preferred to individual support
- Charities involved in early intervention will be preferred
- Charities helping people with limited resources are preferred to those helping a broader range of the community
- Geographical spread is important both in Scotland and Canada
- Specific project funding is preferred to general funding but contributions to the cost of employing staff, community workers are acceptable
- Charities achieving aims through sport, organised physical activity, the arts, yoga and education are preferred
- Building projects are not generally supported
- Scottish charities will be preferred to England-based charities offering services in Scotland
- In Canada, applications relating to issues facing First Nation citizens and those in remote rural areas are invited

Financial information

Year end	31/03/2021
Income	£121,000
Assets	£8,630,000
Grants to organisations	£246,800

Further financial information

Only recipients of amounts exceeding more than 5% of the trust's grants total were listed in the accounts. Smaller grants totalled £186,100.

Beneficiaries included: Camphill Newton Dee and Wester Hailes Youth Agency (£30,000 each).

Exclusions

The trust does not usually support individuals or building projects.

Applications

Applications can be made online via the trust's website.

Sources of information

Accounts; annual report; OSCR record; funder's website.

The Alan Edward Higgs Charity

Disadvantaged young people; families and children; resource deprivation

Within 25 miles of the centre of Coventry only

£650,600 (2020/21)

CC number: 509367

Correspondent: Peter Knatchbull-Hugessen, Clerk, The Ricoh Arena, Judd's Lane, Longford, Coventry, Warwickshire CV6 6GE (tel: 024 7622 1311; email: clerk@higgscharity.org.uk)

Trustees: Marilyn Knatchbull-Hugessen; Rowley Higgs; Emily Barlow; Mark Franklin; Steven Cooke; Emma Bates; Alexander Barrett.

 www.higgscharity.org.uk

General information

The charity was established in 1979 in memory of Alan Higgs, a businessman from Coventry. It provides grants to organisations with a particular focus on:

- Disadvantaged young people
- Families and children
- Resource deprivation

Grants can only be made to organisations based within 25 miles of the centre of Coventry. However, those outside the area may still apply if the project will benefit people living in the beneficial area.

Financial information

Year end	05/04/2021
Income	£416,800
Assets	£19,740,000
Grants to organisations	£650,600
No. of grants	47

Further financial information

Grants were awarded to 47 organisations during the year.

Beneficiaries included: Heart of England Community Foundation (£250,000); Historic Coventry Trust (£60,100); Belgrade Theatre Trust (£45,000); Armonico Consort (£30,000); Valley House (£10,000); The Royal Society for Blind Children (£5,000); The Heart Theatre (£4,000); Tall Ships Youth Trust (£1,500); Myaware (£1,000).

Exclusions

According to its website, the charity will not fund the following:

- Individuals
- Statutory bodies or anything deemed to be the responsibility of the state
- Nurseries, schools and colleges
- Hospitals and health authorities
- Academic research, scholarships or bursaries
- Any promotion of religion
- Work outside the beneficial area
- Endowment appeals
- Restoration and conservation of buildings unless they are being repurposed for community use
- Work that has already taken place (i.e. retrospective costs)
- Round-robin, widely circulated appeals

Applications

Applications can be made online through the charity's website, where detailed guidelines are also available.

Sources of information

Accounts; annual report; Charity Commission record; funder's website.

The Hillier Trust

Development and support work for disadvantaged groups; Christian causes

 Worldwide

£274,300 (2020/21)

CC number: 1147629

Correspondent: Anthony Hillier, Trustee, Loose Court Farmhouse, Old Drive, Maidstone, Kent ME15 9SE (tel: 07767 775792; email: tonyhillier@zen.co.uk)

Trustees: Anthony Hillier; Susan Hillier; Elizabeth Jordan; David Hillier.

General information

The Hillier Trust was registered in June 2012, The Hillier Trust distributes grants to both organisations and individuals. The charity's 2019/20 accounts state:

> A substantial part of the trust expenditure goes to support the work of The Family Trust which is a Christian organisation operating in Kent, whose primary aim is to help children understand that Christianity is relevant to their daily lives. Other beneficiaries tend to be organisations, generally with a Christian ethos, who are carrying out development and support work among disadvantaged groups.

Grants to other organisations are typically in the range of £500 to £4,000.

Financial information

Year end	30/06/2021
Income	£51,200
Assets	£3,520,000
Grants to organisations	£274,300

Beneficiaries included: The Family Trust (£200,000); Embrace the Middle East (£14,000); 500,000 Churches (£10,000); Open Doors (£5,000); The Dandelion Trust (£3,000); South London Strings (£2,000); Salvation Army (£1,500); Amos Trust (£1,000).

Applications

Apply in writing to the correspondent. The trustees communicate regularly throughout the year to consider grant applications.

Sources of information

Accounts; annual report; Charity Commission record.

The Lady Hind Trust

Community healthcare; health education and prevention; lifelong learning; community development; personal social services; social preventative schemes; community social activities

Nottinghamshire and Norfolk

£485,800 (2020)

CC number: 208877

Correspondent: Trust Administrator, PO Box 10455, Nottingham, Nottinghamshire NG5 0HR (tel: 07710 639946; email: ladyhind@btinternet.com)

Trustees: Charles Barratt; Timothy Farr; Nigel Savory; John Pears.

www.ladyhindtrust.org.uk

General information

The trust was established in 1951 by Dame Lilian Francis Hind and has general charitable purposes. However, the trustees have historically given support in the following areas described on the trust's website:

- Charitable projects and activities in or benefiting the people of Nottinghamshire or Norfolk
- Activities relating to community healthcare services including home care, after care, sufferers of long term medical conditions and the continuing care of disabled people
- Health education and prevention – promoting knowledge and awareness of specific diseases or medical conditions
- Lifelong learning projects helping people of any age to achieve their educational potential through supplementary schools, literacy and numeracy projects, community education, vocational/restart education for the unemployed, and alternative education for excluded school pupils
- Community development by helping groups to organise and respond to problems and needs in their communities
- Personal social services including organisations assisting individuals or families to overcome social deprivation e.g. people who are homeless or disabled and their carers, single parent and childcare groups and other family support groups
- Social preventive schemes covering activities which prevent crime, 'dropping out' and general delinquency, provide social care outreach services, deliver social health and safety awareness schemes
- Community social activities which promote social engagement for vulnerable people, mitigating against isolation and loneliness

The Lady Hind Trust and The Charles Littlewood Hill Trust (Charity Commission no. 286350) share the same trustees and are administered together.

Financial information

Year end	31/12/2020
Income	£424,700
Assets	£22,000,000
Grants to organisations	£485,800

Further financial information

Grants of under £1,000 totalled £9,300. Grants of over £1,000 were broken down as follows:

Medical and disability	£155,500
Welfare	£144,000
Other	£44,500
Churches	£41,000
Education	£32,500
The environment	£19,500
The arts	£15,000
Heritage	£9,500
Groups/clubs	£9,000
Accommodation	£6,000

Only beneficiaries of grants of over £1,000 were listed in the accounts.

Beneficiaries included: Betel UK Nottingham (£40,000); Bromley House Library (£25,000); Maggie's Nottingham (£10,000); University of East Anglia (£4,000); Marine Conservation Society (£2,500); Autism East Midlands (£2,000); St Mary's Church – Arnold and The Almshouse Association (£1,000 each).

Exclusions

The trust will not support:

- Individuals
- Organisations working or based outside England
- Activities that are the responsibility of the local health authority, education authority or similar body

Applications

Applications should be made in writing via post to the correspondent. The website explains that applications must be received by 20 January, 20 May or 20 September, to be considered at the trustees' meetings held in March, July and November, respectively. Applicants should also provide their latest set of accounts. Full details of what should be included in an application can be found on the trust's website. Applications are not acknowledged, nor are unsuccessful applicants.

Sources of information

Accounts; annual report; Charity Commission record; funder's website.

The Stuart Hine Trust CIO

Evangelical Christianity and missionary work

UK and overseas

£371,900 (2020/21)

CC number: 1168500

Correspondent: Raymond Bodkin, Trustee, c/o Caladine Ltd, Chantry House, 22 Upperton Road, Eastbourne, East Sussex BN21 1BF (tel: 01323 843948; email: ray.bodkin@talktalk.net)

Trustees: Raymond Bodkin; Jonathan Juby; Leonard Chipping; Melanie Churchyard; Nigel Coltman; Robert Clark; Susan Wilmot.

https://stuarthinetrust.com

General information

The trust was established in 1985 and receives the royalties produced by the hymn 'How Great Thou Art' (the words of this hymn were written by the late Stuart K. Hine). It makes grants to evangelical Christian organisations, churches and missionary societies. A large portion of the trust's funding goes to Wycliffe Bible Translators and organisations supported by Stuart Hine during his lifetime.

Financial information

Year end	31/03/2021
Income	£386,500
Assets	£240,400
Grants to organisations	£371,900

Beneficiaries included: Wycliffe Bible Translators (£130,400); Retired Missionary Aid Fund (£26,400); Innovitsa (£15,000); Lifewords (£13,500); CLC International (£10,700); Breadline and Institute for Bible Translation (£10,000 each).

Applications

The trust's website states that 'all requests for grants should be made by email or by post'. The trustees meet several times a year and grants are usually considered at their meeting in the spring.

Sources of information

Accounts; annual report; Charity Commission record; funder's website.

The Hintze Family Charity Foundation

Education; arts and culture; advancement of the Christian faith; health

UK and overseas

£690,200 (2020)

CC number: 1101842

Correspondent: Gemma Rooney, 4th Floor, One Strand, London WC2N 5HR (tel: 020 7201 2444; email: enquiries@hfcf.org.uk)

Trustees: Sir Michael Hintze; Sir Michael Peat; Duncan Baxter.

General information

The foundation was established in 2003 by UK-based Australian businessman, philanthropist and political patron Sir Michael Hintze, the founder and head of CQS Management, a London hedge fund. Many of the organisations that receive larger grants are those to which the founder is closely connected.

The principal objectives of the foundation, according to its 2020 annual report, are:

- to advance education by supporting schools, colleges and universities;
- to support museums, libraries and art galleries and in particular to promote access for the general public to works of artistic, scientific, historic, architectural or cultural importance;
- to support the Christian faith and institutions;
- to relieve sickness and protect and preserve public health through projects to benefit the sick and terminally ill; and
- to further such other purposes which are charitable in accordance with the laws of England and Wales as the Trustees think fit provided that in so doing the charity shall not relieve any local authority or other body from its statutory obligations

Applications are invited from charities working in these areas. In the past, the foundation has provided support in the areas of education, culture and art, the armed services and health.

Financial information

Year end	31/12/2020
Income	£2,870,000
Assets	£1,020,000
Grants to organisations	£690,200

Further financial information

Only grants of over £50,000 are included in the list of beneficiaries.

Beneficiaries included: Institute of Economic Affairs Ltd (£150,000); Minderoo Foundation (£132,100); Royal Navy and Royal Marines Charity (£120,000); YouBelong (£80,700); British Council (£50,000).

Applications

The 2020 annual report explains that the foundation 'invites applications for grants from charities which further the objectives of the foundation. No specific format is required for applications. Applications and potential donations identified by the Chief Executive and the trustees are considered at trustees' meetings.'

Sources of information

Accounts; annual report; Charity Commission record; funder's website.

The Hiscox Foundation

General charitable purposes; education; medical science; the arts; independent living for older, disadvantaged or vulnerable members of society

Worldwide, primarily the UK

£1.34 million (2020/21)

CC number: 327635

Correspondent: The Trustees, Hiscox Underwriting Ltd, 1 Great St Helen's, London EC3A 6HX (tel: 020 7614 5299; email: hiscox.foundation@hiscox.com)

Trustees: Lucy Hensher; Nick Orton; Lee Turner; Craig Martindale; Robert Childs; Amanda Brown.

www.hiscoxgroup.com/hiscox-foundation-uk

General information

The Hiscox Foundation is the corporate charity of Hiscox Group, a specialist insurance provider.

According to its website, the foundation's charitable giving is divided into three key pillars:

- Social mobility and entrepreneurship
- Protecting and preserving the environment
- Causes that Hiscox employees are passionate about

Focus is given to education, medical science, the arts, and independent living for older, disadvantaged or vulnerable members of society.

Eligibility

Preference is given to organisations local to the Hiscox office (no more than around 25 miles away), or those that have a presence in the communities that it serves.

Although the foundation will fund organisations of all sizes, preference is given to those with an annual income of under £10 million.

The foundation will also provide match funding to its employees raising money for good causes.

Financial information

Year end	05/04/2021
Income	£1,030,000
Assets	£9,680,000
Grants to organisations	£1,340,000

Beneficiaries included: Alzheimer's Society (£101,500); Action for Children (£100,000); Crisis UK (£50,000); HART (£30,000); I CAN (£25,000); Masks for NHS Heroes (£20,500); KEEN London (£16,900); Andover RDA (£6,000); Barnardo's (£4,000); City Music Foundation (£2,000); Pancreatic Cancer UK (£500).

Exclusions

The foundation will not fund the following:

- Scholarships
- Event sponsorship
- New business start-up funding
- Carbon offset schemes
- Requests from other charitable foundations

Applications

Applications can be made at any time using the foundation's online application form. Unsolicited applications are not accepted for multi-year grants.

Sources of information

Accounts; annual report; Charity Commission record; funder's website.

Historic Environment Scotland

The protection and promotion of the historic environment

Scotland

£7.08 million (2020/21)

OSCR number: SC045925

Correspondent: Grants Team, Longmore House, Salisbury Place, Edinburgh EH9 1SH (email: a contact form is available on the charity's website)

www.historicenvironment.scot

facebook.com/historicenvscotland

@histenvscot

@histenvscot

General information

Historic Environment Scotland offers various grants and funding schemes. Individuals and organisations can apply for financial help with projects and works that benefit the historic environment of Scotland.

The charity's website states:

> Grants are offered to help protect and promote the historic environment, and to train people in skills needed in this area.

Our grants are in high demand, so we can't always give a grant to every eligible project.

When making grant decisions, we also consider the extent to which a project will:
- deliver benefits for communities
- promote public access
- promote quality
- develop knowledge and skills
- build capacity for local heritage management

Financial information

Year end	31/03/2021
Income	£93,660,000
Assets	£23,660,000
Grants to organisations	£7,080,000

Beneficiaries included: A list of beneficiaries was not available. Previous beneficiaries include: East Ayrshire Council (£1.12 million); Glasgow Life (£500,000); Archaeology Scotland (£30,000); Society of Antiquaries of Scotland (£3,000); Leadhills Heritage (£530).

Applications

Apply via the charity's website. Applicants are required to submit a brief expression of interest form before making an application.

Sources of information

Accounts; annual report; OSCR record; funder's website.

Historic Houses Foundation

Heritage

 England and Wales

£696,800 (2019/20)

CC number: 1111049

Correspondent: David Price, Secretary, Sheephouse Farm, Uley Road, Dursley, Gloucestershire GL11 5AD (tel: 01453 547124; email: info@historichousesfoundation.org.uk)

Trustees: Nicholas Barber; Norman Hudson; Sir Andrew Jardine; Mary King; Jeremy Musson; Sir John Parsons; Oliver Pearcey; Richard Compton.

 www.historichousesfoundation.org.uk

General information

The foundation was established in 2005 as the Country Houses Foundation. It changed its name to Historic Houses Foundation in 2019 following a merger with the Heritage Conservation Trust.

Its main aims are:
- To support the preservation of buildings of historic or architectural significance and their gardens and grounds
- To support the restoration and conservation of works of art in historic houses open to the public

According to the website, in order to qualify for a grant, you must be able to demonstrate that:
- there is a compelling need for the work you want to undertake to be done within the next 2 to 3 years;
- the project will enhance our historic environment;
- there will be appropriate public access;
- there is a financial need for the grant;
- the project can proceed within a reasonable time frame (i.e. 1–2 years).
- the project is sustainable with a suitable conservation and/or business plan. A grant is unlikely to be awarded without this information.

Financial information

Year end	30/06/2020
Income	£325,900
Assets	£11,230,000
Grants to organisations	£696,800

Further financial information

A total of 25 grants were awarded in 2020, with the average grant approved being £22,400.

Beneficiaries included: Highcliffe Castle (£70,000); Cobham Dairy (£50,000); Abercamlais Bridge (£30,000); Stonor Park (£24,000); Tickenham Court (£15,000); Gwydir Castle (£8,400); Sulgrave Manor (£6,000); Leighton Hall (£910).

Exclusions

According to its website, the foundation does not provide support for the following:
- Buildings and structures which have been the subject of recent purchase and where the cost of works for which grant is sought should have been recognised in the purchase price paid.
- Projects which do not principally involve the repair or conservation of a historic building or structure
- Churches and chapels unless now or previously linked to a country house or estate
- Alterations and improvements, and repairs to non historic fabric or services.
- Routine maintenance and minor repairs.
- General running costs.
- Demolition unless agreed as part of a repair and conservation programme.
- Rent, loan or mortgage payments.
- Conservation of furniture, fittings and equipment except where they are themselves of historic or architectural significance, have a historic relationship with the site, are relevant to the project, and can be secured long term from sale or disposal.
- Work carried out before a grant offer has been made in writing and accepted.

Applications

The foundation requires applicants to complete a pre-application form to confirm that projects fit its criteria. Pre-application forms and application forms, along with detailed guidelines regarding the application process, can be found on the foundation's website.

Sources of information

Accounts; annual report; Charity Commission record; funder's website.

The Henry C. Hoare Charitable Trust

General charitable purposes

UK

£433,100 (2019/20)

CC number: 1088669

Correspondent: Hoare Trustees, c/o C. Hoare and Co., 37 Fleet Street, London EC4P 4DQ (tel: 020 7353 4522)

Trustees: Henry Hoare; Hoare Trustees.

General information

This trust was established in 2001 with general charitable purposes. Grants have been awarded in the following categories: environmental protection and improvement; health; education; citizenship and community development; animal welfare; relief of those in need due to youth, age, ill health, disability or financial hardship; religion; public policy; and the arts. Both one-off and annual donations are made, with grants mostly ranging up to £15,000.

Financial information

Year end	30/09/2020
Income	£182,700
Assets	£5,020,000
Grants to organisations	£433,100

Further financial information

Grants were broken down as follows:

The environment	£126,000
Citizenship and community development	£102,000
Education	£72,300
Health	£61,000
Social welfare	£33,500
Animal welfare	£25,300
Relief of poverty	£8,000
The arts, culture, heritage and science	£4,000
Religion	£1,000

Only beneficiaries of grants of £10,000 and above were listed in the accounts.

Beneficiaries included: Soil Association (£45,000); Seeds 4 Success (£30,000); Royal Forestry Society and University of Oxford Development Trust (£20,000 each); Gillingham Youth Foundation and The Mindfulness Initative (£10,000 each).

Applications

The annual report for 2019/20 states that the trustees 'seldom grant funds to unsolicited requests for donations.'

Sources of information

Accounts; annual report; Charity Commission record.

The Hobson Charity Ltd

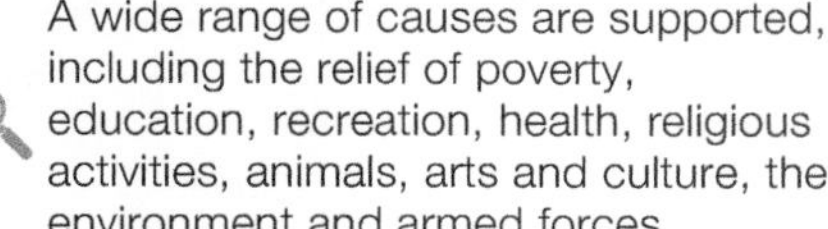

A wide range of causes are supported, including the relief of poverty, education, recreation, health, religious activities, animals, arts and culture, the environment and armed forces

UK

£1.59 million (2020/21)

CC number: 326839

Correspondent: The Trustees, PO Box 57691, London NW7 0GR (tel: 020 3880 6425; email: Post@HobsonCharity.org.uk or use the contact form on the website)

Trustees: Deborah Hobson; Lady Patricia Hobson; Jennifer Richardson; Elizabeth Kelsall; Emma Richardson.

https://hobsoncharity.org.uk

General information

The charity was established in 1985 as the charitable vehicle of the late Sir Ronald Hobson, founder of Central Car Parks and later co-owner of NCP car parks.

The charity's website states:

> The work of the Charity continues today with the same enthusiasm under the chairmanship of Lady Hobson, Sir Ron's wife. She is supported by four trustees, all of whom are family members.
>
> The charity supports a wide range of charitable causes and has the following objects:
>
> - The relief of poverty, suffering and distress amongst older and disadvantaged people and the provision of recreational facilities and other leisure time occupation in the interests of their social welfare
> - The advancement of education
> - The furtherance of other charitable purposes beneficial to communities in the UK
> - To make grants to associations, trusts, societies or corporations established for charitable purposes

In practice, a very wide range of causes are supported, including education, medicine, community, museums, hospices, veterans, animal welfare, the environment, mental health, the relief of poverty, and people with disabilities.

At the time of writing (May 2022), the trustees are continuing to focus their attention on urgent COVID-19-related applications from front-line service charitable organisations.

Financial information

Year end	31/03/2021
Income	£2,680,000
Assets	£47,120,000
Grants to organisations	£1,590,000

Beneficiaries included: Zoological Society of London (£100,000); Wildlife Hospital Trust (£50,000); Secret World Wildlife Rescue (£25,000); Hope Rescue (£18,000); Freedom of Spirit Trust for Border Collies (£10,000); Cuan Wildlife Rescue (£4,000); Cotswold Dogs and Cats Home (£1,000).

Exclusions

Unless there are exceptional circumstances, the charity will not support salaries, core costs or multi-year grants.

Applications

Applicants should first read the eligibility criteria and guidance on the charity's website. Applications may then be made using the online application form.

Sources of information

Accounts; annual report; Charity Commission record; funder's website.

Hockerill Educational Foundation

Education and training, and Christianity

UK and overseas, with a preference for the dioceses of Chelmsford and St Albans

£250,100 (2020/21)

CC number: 311018

Correspondent: The Trustees, 3 The Swallows, Harlow, Essex CM17 0AR (tel: 01279 420855; email: info@hockerillfoundation.org.uk)

Trustees: The Ven. Janet Mackenzie; Janet Scott; David Morton; Jonathan Longstaff; Tim Elbourne; Hannah Potter; The Ven Robin King; Colin Bird; Anthea Kenna; The Revd Dr Alan Smith; Judy King.

www.hockerillfoundation.org.uk

General information

This foundation was established in 1977, following the closure of Hockerill College. It makes grants within the field of education in three main areas, which are outlined on the website:

> - Individual grants to support the education and training of teachers
> - Grants to organisations to support teachers and research and development in religious education
> - Grants to develop the church's educational work in the dioceses of Chelmsford and St Albans

Grants to organisations are able to be renewed for up to three years, and occasionally up to five years.

Approximately two-thirds of the foundation's annual grants expenditure is allocated to the church's educational work in the two dioceses, and the remainder is given in organisational and individual grants. Awards are made both in the UK and internationally.

Financial information

Year end	31/03/2021
Income	£321,500
Assets	£7,740,000
Grants to organisations	£250,100

During the year, the two dioceses each received £110,000 in grants, with 'corporate grants' to organisations totalling a further £30,100.

Exclusions

According to the website, grants are not made for the following:

- General appeals for funds
- 'Bricks and mortar' building projects
- Purposes that are the clear responsibility of another body

Applications

Application forms for each type of funding are available from the foundation's website, along with full guidelines.

Applications are accepted from December for the following year. Applications received by the first deadline of 31 March will be considered in May and may stand a better chance of success. Applicants will normally find out the outcome of their application in May or June. The foundation welcomes contact from potential applicants before submission of the application.

Sources of information

Accounts; annual report; Charity Commission record; funder's website.

The Jane Hodge Foundation

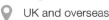

Medical care and research; education; religion; social welfare

UK and overseas

£273,600 (2019/20)

CC number: 216053

Correspondent: The Foundation Administrator, One Central Square, Cardiff CF10 1FS (tel: 029 2078 7674; email: contact@hodgefoundation.org.uk)

Trustees: Ian Davies; Jonathan Hodge; Karen Hodge; Helen Molyneux.

www.hodgefoundation.org.uk

General information

The foundation was established in 1962 by Sir Julian Hodge, an entrepreneur and banker in commemoration of his mother, Jane. It derives its income from businesses controlled or managed by the Hodge Family.

The foundation makes grants to UK-registered or exempt charities in the UK and overseas. According to its website, the foundation has donated over £16 million to worthwhile causes over the past six years

Areas of work

The foundation supports work in four main areas, details of which have been taken from the foundation's website:

> **Welfare** – The Foundation supports charities working with people who may be vulnerable or disadvantaged and who need assistance to improve their lives. This includes a variety of causes and groups including the elderly, homeless, disabled, special needs and those with mental health issues.
>
> **Education** – Importance is placed on support for education and learning, both within formal school settings and practical approaches to learning which support young people to fulfil their potential and thrive including those with special needs. The Foundation continues to support arts projects for education that encourage and inspire audiences across the UK and bring a range of benefits to people of all ages and backgrounds.
>
> **Medical** – The Foundation supports medical related charities specialising in the treatment and support for specific illnesses and research. The main focus has been on local hospices, children's care and university-based research in the fields of cancer and mental health.
>
> **Religion** – The Foundation supports communities by providing funds towards projects such as facilities in church buildings and inclusive activities for the wider community.

Financial information

Year end	30/09/2020
Income	£723,400
Assets	£40,970,000
Grants to organisations	£273,600
No. of grants	54

Beneficiaries included: Cardiff Business School; Cardiff University; St Fagans National Museum of History; Swansea University; The Aloud Charity; The Prince's Trust Cymru; Welsh National Opera.

Applications

Applications can be made via email. Full details of what should be included in the application can be found on the foundation's website. Applications sent by post not will not be accepted.

Sources of information

Accounts; annual report; Charity Commission record, funder's website.

The Holbeck Charitable Trust

Medical research and palliative care; education and training; advancement of the Christian religion; recreational facilities; emergency relief; heritage; the arts and culture

UK, with a preference for London and Yorkshire

£284,000 (2020/21)

CC number: 1146205

Correspondent: Gerry Morrison, Secretary, c/o Rollits LLP, Forsyth House, Alpha Court, Monks Cross, York, North Yorkshire YO32 9WN (tel: 01904 688500; email: gerry.morrison@rollits.com)

www.holbecktrust.com

General information

The Holbeck Charitable Trust is a grant-making charity, making awards to charitable organisations to support a wide variety of charitable aims for the benefit of the public. First founded in 2006, the trust was established as a company limited by guarantee and incorporated in 2012.

Organisations from across the UK are welcome to apply; however, priority is given to organisations that benefit people living in London and Yorkshire.

Areas of work

The trust's website states:

> We have power to award grants for any purpose recognised as charitable under English law, but our policy is to give priority to organisations which carry out one or more of the activities below:
>
> - advance medical research into the treatment and care of people suffering from mental or physical illness particularly those involved with cancer, circulatory or neurological conditions;
> - advance the education of people who are disadvantaged by reason of their social and/or economic circumstances;
> - relieve poverty and unemployment including by creating training and employment opportunities;
> - advance the Christian religion by providing facilities and services to enable believers to practice their faith and enlighten others about the Christian faith;
> - provide recreational facilities for those who by reason of their youth, age, infirmity or disablement, financial hardship or social and/or economic circumstances have need of such facilities;
> - help those in need in areas of social and economic deprivation affected by natural disasters or the relief of famine;
> - preserve buildings or sites of historical or architectural importance, so that future generations might appreciate and learn from them; and
> - arts and cultural activities which may also enhance or further any of the aims and activities above.

Types of funding

Grants can be made to support general funds, running costs and salaries. Most grants made to unsolicited applicants are between £500 and £5,000.

The trust also administers Holbeck Charitable Trust scholarships, which are designed to recognise exceptional academic performance from students across Yorkshire who are seeking places at competitive entry universities and are facing, or who have faced, significant adverse personal circumstances during the course of their secondary education.

Financial information

Year end	05/04/2021
Income	£81,000
Assets	£1,960,000
Grants to organisations	£284,000

Further financial information

Grants were broken down as follows:

Education	£130,000
Children and young people	£87,000
Medical research and palliative care	£48,000
Public amenities and recreation facilities	£9,000
Advancement of the Christian religion	£6,000
Provision of relief to deprived areas	£4,000

Beneficiaries included: A list of beneficiaries was not available. Previous beneficiaries include: Cardinal Hume Centre; Helmsley Arts Centre; National Railway Museum; The Poppy Factory Ryedale Festival Trust Ltd; Tommy's; Wilberforce Trust; Yorkshire Ballet Seminars Charitable Trust.

Exclusions

See the trust's website for a full list of exclusions.

Applications

Applications should be made through the trust's online portal. The trustees meet four times a year to consider applications, usually in February, May, August and November. Visit the trust's website for further information.

Sources of information

Accounts; annual report; Charity Commission record; funder's website.

The Holden Charitable Trust

Jewish causes; relief of poverty; religious education; general charitable purposes

UK

£265,700 (2020/21)

CC number: 264185

Correspondent: The Trustees, 1 Park Lane, Salford, Great Manchester M7 4HT (tel: 0161 832 8721; email: david.lopian@lopiangb.co.uk)

Trustees: Michael Lopian; Daniel Lopian.

General information

The trust was established in 1972 and, according to it its 2020/21 annual report, 'exists to distribute charitable donations to worthy causes primarily within the Jewish community'. Preference may be given to educational or religious charities.

Financial information

Year end	05/04/2021
Income	£204,400
Assets	£574,700
Grants to organisations	£265,700

Further financial information

In 2020/21 the trust awarded grants totalling £265,700. In previous years the trust has awarded grants totalling over £300,000.

Beneficiaries included: Ohel Bnei Yaakov (£50,000); Broom Foundation (£44,500); Hachno Kalo (£25,000); Friends of Beis Eliyohu Trust (£18,400); King David School (£3,000).

Applications

Apply in writing to the correspondent.

Sources of information

Accounts; annual report; Charity Commission record.

Hollick Family Foundation

General charitable purposes

No specific restrictions, although there is a preference for Kensington and Chelsea, Camden, East Sussex and Kent

£338,500 (2020/21)

CC number: 1060228

Correspondent: David Beech, Trustee, Prager Metis LLP, 5A Bear Lane, Southwark, London SE1 0UH (tel: 020 7632 1400; email: dbeech@pragermetis.com)

Trustees: Caroline Kemp; The Hon. Georgina Hollick; David Beech; The Hon. Abigail Benoliel; Lady Sue Woodford-Hollick; Lord Clive Hollick.

General information

The trust was established in 1997 with an initial donation of £750,000 and makes grants for general charitable purposes. The trust's policy, outlined in the annual report for 2020/21, is to support 'small and medium-sized charities, working predominantly with the most vulnerable in society'.

The report states:

> We focus on issues that reflect the passions and personal values of the trustees including education and skills, human rights, housing, mental health, women and children, and the arts. We support community-led organisations working directly with people at the margins of society and with charities in the early stages of development looking for seed funding.
>
> While we have no specific geographic restrictions, we look to support appropriate charities local to our trustees including Kensington and Chelsea, Camden, East Sussex and Kent. We make one off donations but prefer to commit to funding specific projects over a number of years.

Financial information

Year end	05/04/2021
Income	£248,000
Assets	£26,070,000
Grants to organisations	£338,500

Beneficiaries included: A list of beneficiaries was not available.

Applications

Apply in writing to the correspondent. The trustees meet at least twice a year.

Sources of information

Accounts; annual report; Charity Commission record.

Hollyhock Charitable Foundation

Social welfare; health and well-being; education; the promotion of Christianity

UK and overseas

£2.33 million (2020)

CC number: 1186232

Correspondent: The Trustees, c/o Rawlinson and Hunter, 8th Floor, 6 New Street Square, London EC4A 3AQ (tel: 020 7842 2000; email: hollyhock@rawlinson-hunter.com)

Trustees: Simon Brooks; Berta Arienza; Dr Simon Peck; Rupert Elwes; Simon Jeffries.

www.hollyhockfoundation.co.uk

General information

The foundation was registered with the Charity Commission in 2019. The foundation's website provides the following information about its objectives:

> To advance such charitable purposes (according to the law of England and Wales) as the trustees see fit from time to time, in particular by providing grants.
>
> These grants will in particular, but not exclusively, be used to:
>
> - (a) prevent or relieve poverty worldwide for individuals in need;
> - (b) advance the health and wellbeing of the general public (including preventing or relieving sickness, disease or suffering, as well as the promotion of good health);
> - (c) support programmes which promote and advance the education of the general public; and
> - (d) promote and support Christianity for the benefit of the general public.

Financial information

Year end	31/12/2020
Income	£2,410,000
Assets	£58,700
Grants to organisations	£2,330,000

Beneficiaries included: Hearing Dogs (£400,000); Breast Cancer Now (£150,000); Shelter (£100,000); Mind (£50,000); Feeding Britain (£50,000); KidsOut (£5,000).

Applications

Application forms can be downloaded from the foundation's website.

Sources of information

Accounts; annual report; Charity Commission; record; funder's website.

P. H. Holt Foundation

General charitable purposes in Merseyside, including community development, social welfare, education, the arts and the environment

Merseyside

£699,500 (2020/21)

CC number: 1113708

Correspondent: Anne Edwards, Trust Administrator, 151 Dale Street, Liverpool, Merseyside L2 2AH (tel: 0151 237 2663; email: administrator@phholtfoundation.org.uk)

Trustees: Ken Ravenscroft; Elspeth Christie; Ian Matthews; Amy Joia; Ian Bakewell; Lesley Martin-Wright; Christopher Evered; Michael Furniss; Grainne Cuerden.

www.phholtfoundation.org.uk

@phhfoundation

General information

This foundation makes grants to a wide range of projects in Merseyside. The foundation acts as sole corporate trustee to The Holt Education Trust, established in 1915, and the origins of both charities derive from Philip Henry Holt, one of the founders of the Liverpool-based Ocean Steam Ship Company Ltd.

The foundation's five core priority themes are:

- Creating opportunities for people to contribute to their local community
- Enabling people to overcome barriers
- Widening access to education for all ages
- Increasing engagement in the arts for excluded groups
- Encouraging care of the environment

Grants are for one year and range from £1,000 up to a maximum of £10,000 for exceptional work.

The foundation's website states:

> To be eligible for a grant, you must be a small or medium-sized charity headquartered in Merseyside with an income of under £1 million. There are certain things that we fund, namely:
>
> - Existing and new activities
> - Salaries and project expenses
> - Volunteer and beneficiary costs
> - Community and outreach initiatives
> - Arts, welfare and education programmes
> - Advice, information, and advocacy services
> - Resources and items of equipment

Financial information

Year end	31/03/2021
Income	£192,200
Assets	£22,470,000
Grants to organisations	£699,500
No. of grants	132

Further financial information

In 2020/21, grants were broken down as follows:

COVID-19 emergency grants*	£304,000
Community and overcoming barriers	£329,100
The arts	£39,400
The Holt Education Trust (bursaries)	£20,000
Education	£7,000

*Emergency grants were distributed in the following categories: community and overcoming barriers (£298,000); the arts (£6,000).

Beneficiaries included: Compass Counselling (£15,000); West Everton Community Council (£10,000); Ferries Family Groups (£7,800); Headway Wirral (£4,200); Bold Rangers Junior FC (£3,100); Sefton Advocacy (£2,500); Mathematical Education on Merseyside (£1,000).

Exclusions

The following exclusions have been taken from the foundation's application form:

- CIC's and social enterprises
- National charities and those enjoying high profile support*
- Intermediary charities with no direct services
- Individuals and uniform groups
- Work that has already taken place
- Medical research
- Religious and political causes
- Sponsorship of individuals or events
- General charity appeals
- Statutory responsibilities

*While we do not fund national charities, we may consider an appeal from a national charity headquartered in Merseyside, or whose federated structure allows for local autonomy of decision making and spending in the region.

Applications

Application forms are available to download from the foundation's website and should be returned by email to administrator@phholtfoundation.org.uk with a copy of your latest annual report and accounts, a copy of a recent bank statement and your safeguarding policy.

Applications are considered quarterly, with deadlines on the first day of January, April, July and October. Applicants should allow three months from the closing date to the funding decision being reached. Complex applications may take longer.

Sources of information

Accounts; annual report; Charity Commission record; funder's website.

The Holywood Trust

Disadvantaged young people

Dumfries and Galloway

£2.12 million (2020/21)

OSCR number: SC009942

Correspondent: Clare Hanna, Grants Officer, Hestan House, Crichton Business Park, Bankend Road, Dumfries, Dumfries and Galloway DG1 4TA (tel: 01387 269176; email: funds@holywood-trust.org.uk)

Trustees: Valerie McElroy; John Jencks; Ben Weatherall; Amy Agnew; Clara Weatherall.

www.holywood-trust.org.uk

facebook.com/HolywoodTrust

General information

The trust provides grants to organisations that work with and provide opportunities for young people aged 15–25 in Dumfries and Galloway. It gives grants to individuals and organisations, creating opportunities for young people in the region. Grants are made in the following areas, as stated on the website:

- Providing opportunities for the most disadvantaged and vulnerable young people in the region
- Encouraging talented young people in Dumfries and Galloway
- Helping improve sports and cultural opportunities across the region

The website also notes that the trust is 'particularly interested in helping to fill gaps in provision, and to support innovative ideas'.

The trust will occasionally consider supporting vulnerable younger children for preventative measures in relation to health or social disadvantage.

Examples of work the trust has previously supported includes: youth and sporting clubs; equipment; group development activities and residential trips; programmes for activities for young people; and cultural venues or arts programmes.

Financial information

Year end	05/04/2021
Income	£3,220,000
Assets	£116,160,000
Grants to organisations	£2,120,000

Beneficiaries included: A list of beneficiaries was not available. Previous beneficiaries include: Kirkcudbright Development Trust (£152,500); Aberlour Child Care Trust (£92,500); The Stove Network (£50,600); Independent Living Support (£35,000); Dumfries Table Tennis Club (£25,000); Lochside Community Association (£17,000); Chariots of Fire Equestrian Centre (£15,000); Step Forward Volunteering (£12,300); Lockerbie Academy (£10,000).

Applications

Applications can be made via the trust's website.

Sources of information

Accounts; annual report; OSCR record; funder's website.

Homelands Charitable Trust

General charitable purposes; general conference of the New Church; medical research; care and protection of children; hospices

UK

£321,000 (2020/21)

CC number: 214322

Correspondent: The Trustees, 4th Floor, Imperial House, 8 Kean Street, London WC2B 4AS (tel: 020 7240 9971)

Trustees: Nigel Armstrong; The Revd Clifford Curry; Robert Curry; Eleanor Maquire.

General information

The trust was established in 1962, the settlors were four members of the Curry family and the original endowment was in the form of shares in the Curry company.

The trust's 2020/21 annual report notes that the trust supports general charitable purposes with a bias towards:

- The General Conference of the New Church
- Medical research
- Care and protection of children
- Hospices including those for children

Financial information

Year end	05/04/2021
Income	£132,900
Assets	£9,360,000
Grants to organisations	£321,000

Beneficiaries included: A list of beneficiaries was not available. Previous beneficiaries include: The General Conference of New Church (£63,000); Broadfield Memorial Fund (£16,000); Friends of the Earth and RNLI (£3,000 each); Anorexia and Bulimia Care and SOS Children's Villages (£2,800 each); Benslow Music Trust, Edinburgh Young Carers Project, Riding for the Disabled and Sailors' Families Society (£1,800 each); St Luke's Hospice (£1,500); Womankind Worldwide (£1,000).

Applications

Apply in writing to the correspondent.

Sources of information

Accounts; annual report; Charity Commission record.

Sir Harold Hood's Charitable Trust

Roman Catholic charitable purposes

Worldwide

£832,500 (2020/21)

CC number: 225870

Correspondent: The Trustees, c/o Haysmacintyre, 10 Queens Street Place, London EC4R 1AG (tel: 020 7969 5500; email: hoodcharitabletrust@yahoo.co.uk)

Trustees: Dom Hood; Lord True; Lady True; Margaret Hood; Christian Elwes.

General information

The trust was established in 1962 by the late Sir Harold Hood, who died in 2005. Sir Harold was an influential editor and director of several Catholic publications during his lifetime, a philanthropist who was involved in a number of charities, and an early investor in an electronics company that later evolved into Vodafone. The trust supports Roman Catholic organisations only.

The trust's 2020/21 accounts show that grants were made across the following categories: single grants, aid, churches, education, homelessness, hospitals, leprosy, missionary, nursing, prisoners, retreat centre, schools, seminary, the Vatican, young people, special and emergency grants.

Financial information

Year end	05/04/2021
Income	£652,600
Assets	£34,920,000
Grants to organisations	£832,500

Beneficiaries included: Downside Abbey (60,000); Craig Lodge Trust (£50,000); Downside School (£40,000); Downside Fisher Youth Club (£30,000); Diocese of Brentwood (£12,000); Diocese of Hexham and Newcastle, St Bede's – Jarrow (£10,000); Catholic Marriage Care (£3,000).

Applications

Apply in writing to the correspondent.

Sources of information

Accounts; annual report; Charity Commission record.

The Thomas J. Horne Memorial Trust

Hospices; disability; health; social welfare

UK and overseas

£868,500 (2020/21)

CC number: 1010625

Correspondent: The Trustees, Kingsdown, Warmlake Road, Chart Sutton, Maidstone, Kent ME17 3RP (tel: 01622 842638; email: cc@horne-trust.org.uk)

Trustees: Jeff Horne; Jon Horne; Emma Horne.

General information

The trust was established in 1992. The vast majority of support is given to hospices, particularly children's hospices, and related medical support charities.

Financial information

Year end	31/03/2021
Income	£296,200
Assets	£22,270,000
Grants to organisations	£868,500

Beneficiaries included: North Yorkshire Hospice Care (£12,500); Together for Short Lives (£8,000); Lifelites (£6,000); The Amber Trust (£5,000); Involve Kent (£4,000); Whitby Dog Rescue (£1,000).

Applications

Apply in writing to the correspondent. The trust's 2020/21 annual report states:

> Grant making decisions are made at Trustees meetings, when applications received from charities will be discussed with a view to acceptance.

Sources of information

Accounts; annual report; Charity Commission record.

The Horse Trust

Health and welfare of horses

UK

£368,700 (2020)

CC number: 231748

Correspondent: Jan Rogers, Director of Research and Policy, Speen Farm, Slad Lane, Speen, Princes Riseborough, Buckinghamshire HP27 0PP (tel: 01494 488464; email: jan@horsetrust.org.uk)

Trustees: Prof. Josh Slater; Milly Soames; Rupert Neal; David Cook; Caroline Roddis; Bronwen Jones; Lord Rupert de Mauley; Prof. Peter Clegg; Dr Ian Bowen; Prof. Bruce McGorum; Christopher Marriott; Laura McGillycuddy.

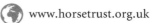

www.horsetrust.org.uk

facebook.com/HorseTrust

@horsetrust

@thehorsetrust

General information

The trust works to improve the quality of life of horses, ponies and donkeys in the UK. Its aim is to fund ethically approved, non-invasive research that advances knowledge of veterinary treatment, the optimal care of equines and the prevention of disease and suffering.

The trust accepts applications from all UK veterinary schools and will consider applications from other universities and organisations. Funding is available for research grants, PhDs, postgraduate studentships, pump-priming projects and other innovative proposals.

Financial information

Year end	31/12/2020
Income	£2,110,000
Assets	£26,410,000
Grants to organisations	£368,700

Beneficiaries included: University of Liverpool (£129,400); University of Edinburgh (£64,600); University of Bristol (£39,200); Roslin Institute (£20,100); Hartpury (£3,200).

Applications

Preliminary applications can be made in October each year. Those who are successful will be invited to complete a full application. Further details can be found on the trust's website.

Sources of information

Accounts; annual report; Charity Commission record; funder's website.

Hospice UK

Hospice and palliative care, and professional development for hospice staff

 UK

£258.5 million (2020/21)

CC number: 1014851/SC041112

Correspondent: Grants Team, 34–44 Britannia Street, London WC1X 9JG (tel: 020 7520 8200; email: grants@hospiceuk.org)

Trustees: Anthony Collins; Emma Reynolds; Catherine Tompkins; Stephen Roberts; Dr Michael Miller; Michelle Rollinson; David Smith; John Knight; Paul Jennings; Chloe Chik; Sharon Allen.

 www.hospiceuk.org

 facebook.com/hospiceuk

 @hospiceuk

 @hospice_uk

General information

Hospice UK's work is explained on its website as follows:

> Hospice UK is the national charity for hospice and end of life care. We work to ensure everyone affected by death, dying and bereavement gets the care and support they need, when they need it.

Grant programmes

Grants are made to organisations working in the UK, with the intention of having a lasting impact on the provision of hospice and palliative care. Grant programmes are funded by donations from external sources, including grant-making charities. The charity notes on its website that criteria for each grants programme are approved by the Hospice UK Governance Committee and by each individual funder. Each programme has its own specific application form, criteria, guidelines and deadlines.

In the UK, Hospice UK member organisations and their staff can apply for funding to enable them to undertake specific capital projects, develop new or existing services, and increase their expertise in the work that they do. Organisations that offer palliative care services but are not Hospice UK members can also apply for grants, depending on the criteria of the grants programme.

Financial information

Year end	31/03/2021
Income	£264,360,000
Assets	£7,430,000
Grants to organisations	£258,460,000
No. of grants	1432

Further financial information

During the financial year, grants were distributed as follows:

Grants to support the COVID-19 response in England	£257 million
Grants to develop bereavement services in hospices	£450,000
Grants for capital projects to enhance well-being	£312,000
Other grant programmes	£228,000
Professional development grants	£207,000
Grants to support the COVID-19 response in England – PPE	£165,000

Beneficiaries included: A list of beneficiaries was not available. Previous beneficiaries include: Saint Michael's Hospice – Harrogate (£39,900); Nottinghamshire Hospice (£20,300); Princess Alice Hospice – Surrey (£20,000); Mary Stevens Hospice – Stourbridge (£14,900); St Elizabeth Hospice – Ipswich (£12,900); Great Oaks, Dean Forest Hospice (£7,800).

Exclusions

Exclusion criteria vary according to the programme being applied to. See the charity's website for further information.

Applications

Full details of open grant programmes can be found on the Hospice UK website. The charity's grants team can also be contacted for further information.

Sources of information

Accounts; annual report; Charity Commission record; funder's website.

The Hospital Saturday Fund

Health, disability and medicine

 The UK, Isle of Man, Channel Islands and Republic of Ireland

£1.24 million (2020)

CC number: 1123381

Correspondent: The Trustees, 24 Upper Ground, London SE1 9PD (tel: 020 7202 1365; email: charity@hsf.eu.com)

Trustees: Jane Dalton; John Greenwood; John Randel; David Thomas; Mark Davies; Margaret Rogers.

 www.hospitalsaturdayfund.org

 facebook.com/hsfcharity

 @HSFCharity

 @hsfcharity

General information

The Hospital Saturday Fund is a healthcare cash plan organisation which was founded in 1873. In 1987 it established a charitable fund to support a wide range of hospitals, hospices and medical charities for care and research, as well as welfare organisations providing similar services. According to the charity's website, it can support:

- Individuals with a medical condition or disability who would benefit from assistance with the purchase of specialised equipment or from practical forms of treatment
- Registered health charities such as hospitals, hospices and medical organisations that are in need of grants for medical projects, care, research or support of medical training

The charity will also consider grants for running costs.

The Hospital Saturday Fund has two grant categories, standard grants (up to £2,000) and large grants (up to £10,000).

Large grant applications should be for specific projects, research or equipment rather than running costs.

Financial information

Year end	31/12/2020
Income	£31,300,000
Assets	£43,350,000
Grants to organisations	£1,240,000

Further financial information

Grants were broken down as follows:

Medical charities	£847,800
COVID-19 fund grants	£207,700
Grants to individuals	£90,800
Other welfare/medical organisations	£74,400

Beneficiaries included: Arthritis Ireland; British Liver Trust; Cerebra; Douglas Bader Foundation; Look Good Feel Better; Marie Keating Foundation; Sepsis Research.

Exclusions

The charity does not support: projects outside the UK, the Isle of Man, Channel Islands and the Republic of Ireland; unregistered organisations; organisations carrying out non-medical activities; or donations towards general fundraising appeals.

Applications

Applications should be made using the online system on the charity's website.

Sources of information

Accounts; annual report; Charity Commission record; funder's website.

The Sir Joseph Hotung Charitable Settlement

Medical causes/research; education; culture; human rights; climate change

UK and overseas, with some preference for London

£1.43 million (2020/21)

CC number: 1082710

Correspondent: Sir Joseph Hotung, Chair of Trustees, c/o Penningtons Manches LLP, 125 Wood Street, London EC2V 7AW (tel: 020 8940 3827; email: henry.painton@blueyonder.co.uk)

Trustees: Sir Joseph Hotung; Prof. Sir Robert Boyd; Peter Painton; Prof. Dame Jessica Rawson.

General information

The charity was set up in 2000 by Sir Joseph Hotung and still receives significant support by the settlor. It was established to support a range of general charitable purposes worldwide but mainly focuses on medical causes, education and human rights. According to the charity's 2020/21 accounts, the trust is also currently making grants towards addressing issues related to COVID-19 and climate change. In practice, the charity appears to have a preference for London-based organisations. The charity tends to support a small number of organisations, often on a regular basis.

Financial information

Year end	05/04/2021
Income	£1,110,000
Assets	£2,410,000
Grants to organisations	£1,430,000
No. of grants	10

Further financial information

During the year, the charity made 21 grants to 10 organisations. A substantial donation of £1 million was made to the Imperial College of Science, Technology and Medicine for vaccine research into the COVID-19 virus.

Beneficiaries included: Imperial College of Science, Technology and Medicine (£1 million); St George's University of London (£345,100); Who Cares? Scotland (£20,000); FareShare (£10,000); Strength and Learning Through Horses (£5,000); Spinal Research (12 grants totalling £1,200).

Applications

Apply in writing to the correspondent. Note that regular trustee meetings are not held as there are few new grant recipients each year.

Sources of information

Accounts; annual report; Charity Commission record.

The Reta Lila Howard Foundation

General charitable purposes, with a preference for children and young people up to the age of 16

UK and the Republic of Ireland

£718,000 (2020/21)

CC number: 1041634

Correspondent: The Trustees, Horsmonden Business Centre, The Business Centre, Green Road, Horsmonden, Tonbridge, Kent TN12 8JS (tel: 07852 924412; email: retalilahoward@gmail.com)

Trustees: Melissa Murdoch; Gregg Weston; Tamara Rebanks; Galvin Weston; Sarah Mitchell; Pilar Bauta.

General information

The foundation was established in 1994 to support general charitable purposes. Today the foundation primarily supports a few innovative projects that support the education or benefit the physical and emotional well-being of children up to the age of 16 within the UK and the Republic of Ireland. Funding is only awarded to registered charities. Beneficiaries also include Christian charities.

According the foundation's 2019/20 accounts, 'donations are intended to be given over a finite period', with the intention that the projects will be self-supporting once funding has ended.

Financial information

Year end	31/03/2021
Income	£84
Grants to organisations	£718,000

Further financial information

The foundation was not required to file accounts in 2020/21 due to its low income. We have therefore estimated the foundation's grant total based on previous years' accounts. Around 90% of the foundation's total expenditure is typically spent on grants. In 2019/20, the foundation awarded 22 grants totalling £725,000.

Beneficiaries included: A list of beneficiaries was not available. Previous beneficiaries include: Kids Run Free (£100,000); Action for Conservation (£60,000); Tree Council (£45,000): Camden Music Trust (£30,000); Walk Through the Bible UK (£26,000); Young Minds (£20,000); Woodland Trust (£15,300); The Bike Project (£10,000); Rose Road (£7,300).

Exclusions

According to the foundation's annual report for 2018/19, it does fund any of the following:

- Individuals
- Non-registered charities
- Core costs
- Fundraising activities
- Conferences
- Student aid
- General endowment funds
- Sole capital projects
- Budget deficits
- Annual charitable appeals

Applications

The foundation does not accept unsolicited applications.

Sources of information

Accounts; annual report; Charity Commission record.

The Hull and East Riding Charitable Trust

General charitable purposes

Hull and the East Riding of Yorkshire

£264,600 (2020/21)

CC number: 516866

Correspondent: John Barnes, Secretary, Greenmeades, Kemp Road, Swanland, East Yorkshire HU14 3LY (tel: 01482 634664; email: john.barnes@herct.org.uk)

Trustees: Adrian Horsley; Matthew Fletcher; Victoria Carver.

 www.herct.org.uk

General information

The trust was established in 1985 to give to charitable causes for the benefit of people living in Hull and the East Riding of Yorkshire. National charities may be supported but usually only if they carry out work in the local area.

The trust's website states:

> Participation by young people under the age of 18 years, in UK or overseas visits or projects with a leading organisation will be considered. Requests for notable buildings with a good level of community use will be evaluated.
>
> For significant community projects demanding major fund raising, support may be given by way of pledge, payment being conditional upon all other funds being sourced. Funding of both capital and revenue costs will be considered.

Financial information

Year end	05/05/2021
Income	£139,700
Assets	£8,400,000
Grants to organisations	£264,600

Beneficiaries included: St Paul's Boxing Academy (£10,000); East Riding County Council (£7,500); Butterflies Memory Loss Support Group (£5,000); Bransholme Trust (£3,000); Artlink Hull (£2,000); Asthma Relief in Hull and East Riding (£1,000); Christ Church – Bridlington (£500).

Exclusions

Grants are not awarded for education, political or religious purposes.

Applications

Apply in writing to the correspondent via post or email. A list of the required information is available on the trust's website.

Sources of information

Accounts; annual report; Charity Commission record; funder's website.

The Albert Hunt Trust

Health and well-being; hospices; homelessness

UK

£4.57 million (2020/21)

CC number: 1180640

Correspondent: The Trustees, The Hermitage, 15A Shenfield Road, Brentwood, Essex CM15 8AG (tel: 0330 113 7280; email: info@alberthunttrust.org.uk)

Trustees: Stephen Harvey; Bridget McGuire; Ian Fleming; Kate McGuire.

www.alberthunttrust.org.uk

General information

The Albert Hunt Trust was established in 1979 and supports charities throughout the UK. The trust re-registered as a CIO in November 2018.

Areas of work

The trust's website states that it will support organisations that:

- Provide hospice care
- Provide support for the homeless
- Promote health and well being – areas of support under this heading have included physical and learning disability, physical and mental health, plus social challenge and deprivation

Types of grant

According to its website, the trust will make the following types of grant:

- Single awards for capital projects (building/equipment/renovation)
- Grants for core funding to include staff costs
- Ongoing running costs for specific projects

Under the focus area of health and well-being, the trust looks to support organisations with an annual income of below £250,000. However, it will consider capital projects, such as equipment purchases or building works irrespective of income levels.

Financial information

Year end	05/04/2021
Income	£1,430,000
Assets	£61,860,000
Grants to organisations	£4,570,000
No. of grants	844

Beneficiaries included: Shelter (£50,000); Emmaus – Dover (£25,000); Church Army (£10,000); Barons Court Project (£5,000); Bread of Life Outreach (£1,000).

Exclusions

According to its website the trust does not fund:

- Animal welfare
- Arts/heritage
- Conservation/the environment
- Expeditions and overseas travel
- Individual and sports sponsorship
- Mainstream able-bodied sport (but it will consider disability sports projects)
- Promotion of religion
- Medical research

Applications

Applications can be made through the trust's website. Applications are reviewed on a monthly rolling basis.

Sources of information

Accounts; annual report; Charity Commission record; funder's website.

The Hunter Foundation

Prevention and relief of poverty; education; entrepreneurialism; economic equality

UK and overseas

£9.17 million (2020/21)

OSCR number: SC027532

Correspondent: The Trustees, Marathon House, Olympic Business Park, Drybridge Road, Dundonald, Ayrshire KA2 9AE (email: info@thehunterfoundation.co.uk or use the contact form on the foundation's website)

Trustees: Sir Tom Hunter; Lady Marion Hunter; Jim McMahon.

www.thehunterfoundation.co.uk

facebook.com/THunterFoundation

@THunterF

General information

The Hunter Foundation defines itself on its website as 'a proactive venture philanthropy that seeks to invest in determining model solutions, in partnership with others, to troubling systemic issues relating to poverty eradication and educational enablement'. The foundation's objectives are to support economic opportunity and equality by providing funding for education, entrepreneurship and the prevention and relief of poverty.

Grant-making

The foundation usually works in strategic partnerships with governments, agencies, funders and individuals but sometimes runs grant programmes such as The Innovation Fund itself.

Financial information

Year end	31/03/2021
Income	£30,820,000
Assets	£71,520,000
Grants to organisations	£9,170,000

Further financial information

During 2020/21, grants totalling £9.15 million were distributed in the UK and £30,900 was distributed overseas.

Beneficiaries included: Kiltwalk (£2.47 million); Scottish Football Association (£1.13 million); Mail Force Charity (£600,000); Music for Dementia (£500,000); The Prince's Foundation (£250,000); Street Soccer (£71,600); Cash for Kids (£50,000).

Applications

Contact the foundation using the contact form on the website. The foundation states that if a project appears to be of initial interest, it will contact the applicant to discuss taking the application further.

Sources of information

Accounts; annual report; OSCR record; funder's website.

Miss Agnes H. Hunter's Trust

Disability and the education and training of disadvantaged people aged 16 years or over who have left school

Scotland

£501,000 (2020/21)

OSCR number: SC004843

Correspondent: Sarah Wright, Trust Manger, Davidson House, 57 Queen Charlotte Street, Edinburgh EH6 7EY (tel: 0131 538 5496; email: s.wright@agneshunter.org.uk)

Trustees: Keith Burdon; Elaine Crichton; Norman Dunning; Duncan McEachran; Daljit Singh; Denise Spence.

www.agneshunter.org.uk

General information

The trust was established in 1954 to support registered charities delivering health and social welfare projects in Scotland.

Since January 2019, following the trustees' review of the grant-making policy, the trust has made grants to support these two broad areas:

- Charities that help people with disabilities

- Charities that assist with the education and training of disadvantaged people aged 16 years or over who have left school

The trust's website states:

> The Trust seeks to encourage inclusion, integration and independence. Priorities for the Trust include services or projects that focus on:
> - Self-management and awareness
> - Advice, support and information
> - Life-skills training
> - Employability, particularly in relation to IT, literacy and numeracy
> - Helping people participate and contribute to their community
>
> In addition, the Trust is particularly keen to hear from the following:
> - Smaller charities with a strong local community presence
> - Causes that do not have a strong public profile, including start-up organisations
> - Charities developing innovative approaches, including pilot projects.

Grants programme

This programme provides grants of between £3,000 and £15,000 per year (most grants are of between £5,000 and £10,000) to registered charities in Scotland. The trust welcomes termed applications for grants covering two or three years, as well as one-year grants. Grants can be used for core costs or direct project/service costs, including staff salaries and overheads. The trust's website states:

> The Trust looks to make maximum impact on the delivery of a project or service, and therefore the preference is to fund a greater proportion of the total project cost (TPC). Therefore, the Trust will only award grants that equate to **at least 10%** of the TPC.

Financial information

Year end	30/06/2021
Income	£579,300
Assets	£17,440,000
Grants to organisations	£501,000
No. of grants	45

Further financial information

In 2020/21, the trust awarded grants totalling £501,000 to 45 charities, of which 17 were first-time applicants. Grants were broken down as follows: disability (27 grants totalling £292,000) and education and training (18 grants totalling £209,000).

Beneficiaries included: The Brock Garden Centre SCIO (£30,000); Headway Highland (£22,000); Nourish Support Centre (£15,000); Deafblind Scotland (£10,000); MyBnk (£8,000); Friends of Seaview (£5,000); Musically Active Dudes (£3,600).

Exclusions

As the trust's website specifies, the following are not supported:

- Organisations that are not registered with OSCR
- Projects/services outside Scotland
- Charities with an annual income of over £2.5m
- Services designed solely to support children under the age of 14
- Organisations under the control of the UK or Scottish Government
- Projects which are primarily intended to promote political or religious beliefs
- Individuals – including students
- Expeditions, overseas travel or international projects
- General appeals or circulars, including contributions to endowment funds
- Statutory requirements of local authorities, hospitals, schools, universities and colleges
- Medical research
- Hospices
- Clinical work within hospitals
- Animal welfare
- The breeding and training of assistance/guide dogs for blind/disabled people
- Capital projects (buildings and equipment)
- Initiatives focused on sports, arts or the environment except where these are being used as a vehicle to engage with one of the Trust's key areas of support
- Normal youth club activities
- Holiday schemes
- Small UK charities supporting very limited numbers of people with rare disabilities/illnesses

Applications

Apply online via the trust's website. There are two grant decision meetings per year (in November and May/June). The application deadlines fall approximately 12 to 14 weeks before the meetings – visit the trust's helpful website for exact deadlines, as well as further application guidance. Potential applicants are welcomed to contact the trust manager for informal advice on the application process.

Sources of information

Accounts; annual report; OSCR record; funder's website.

Huntingdon Freemen's Trust

General charitable purposes, including the arts and sport

The area covered by Huntingdon Town Council, including Oxmoor, Hartford, Sapley, Stukeley Meadows and Hinchingbrooke Park

£331,500 (2020/21)

CC number: 1044573

Correspondent: The Trustees, 37 High Street, Huntingdon, Cambridgeshire PE29 3AQ (tel: 01480 414909; email: info@huntingdonfreemen.org.uk)

Trustees: Brian Bradshaw; John Hough; Jonathan Hampstead; Kate Parker; Juliet Cole; Jonas King; Tom Sanderson.

 www.huntingdonfreemen.org.uk

General information

Huntingdon Freemen's Trust was established in 1993 for the benefit of residents of Huntingdon, Cambridgeshire.

The trust supports local groups involved in sports and the arts. Grants are made for the purchase of equipment, project costs and training. Help is also available for trips, organised outings and recreational activities.

Grants are also made to individuals for welfare purposes and to students for accommodation costs while at university or college.

Financial information

Year end	30/04/2021
Income	£478,000
Assets	£18,540,000
Grants to organisations	£331,500

Beneficiaries included: A list of beneficiaries was not available.

Exclusions

The trust does not normally consider grants for the payment of rent, council tax, debts, fines or funerals.

Applications

Application forms for organisations and individuals are available on the trust's website. Forms should be returned to the correspondent.

Sources of information

Accounts; annual report; charity commission record; funder's website.

Hurdale Charity Ltd

Jewish causes

England and Wales

£1.8 million (2020/21)

CC number: 276997

Correspondent: Abraham Oestreicher, Trustee, 162 Osbaldeston Road, London N16 6NJ (tel: 020 8731 0770)

Trustees: David Oestreicher; Benjamin Oestreicher; Jacob Oestreicher; Abraham Oestreicher.

General information

The charity was set up in 1978 and supports charitable activities mostly concerned with the Orthodox Jewish faith, education, medical causes and the relief of poverty. Almost all of the support is given to Jewish organisations.

Financial information

Year end	30/04/2021
Income	£2,490,000
Assets	£30,620,000
Grants to organisations	£1,800,000

Further financial information

Only beneficiaries that received grants of over £25,000 were listed in the charity's accounts. Grants of less than £25,000 totalled £326,600.

Beneficiaries included: Moundfield Charities Ltd (£340,000); Springfield Trust Ltd (£315,000); Amud Hatzdokoh Trust (£101,000); Wlodowa Charity and Rehabilitation Trust (£65,000); British Friends of Tiferes Chaim (£40,000); Achisomoch Aid Company (£35,000); Kollel Viznitz (£25,000).

Applications

Apply in writing to the correspondent. The charity's 2020/21 annual report states that 'the trustees consider all requests which they receive and make donations based on the level of funds available.'

Sources of information

Accounts; annual report; Charity Commission record.

Hyde Charitable Trust

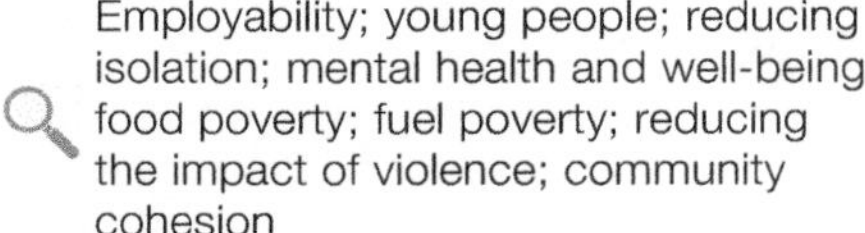

Employability; young people; reducing isolation; mental health and well-being; food poverty; fuel poverty; reducing the impact of violence; community cohesion

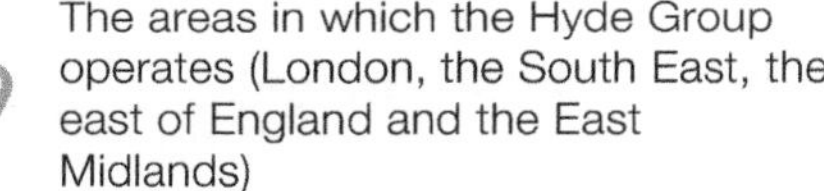

The areas in which the Hyde Group operates (London, the South East, the east of England and the East Midlands)

£1.14 million (2020/21)

CC number: 289888

Correspondent: The Trustees, Hyde Housing Association, 30 Park Street, London SE1 9EQ (tel: 020 3207 2762; email: zoe.ollerearnshaw@hyde-housing.co.uk)

Trustees: Jonathan Prichard; Patrick Law; Brid O'Dwyer; Katherine Rodgers; Jessica Skilbeck; Junior Moka; Clare Ferguson.

www.hyde-housing.co.uk/corporate/our-social-purpose/the-hyde-charitable-trust

General information

Hyde Charitable Trust (also known by its working name, Youth Plus) is a charitable company established in 1984. It works closely with Hyde Housing Association to help target its funds to the Hyde residents and communities most in need. In particular, it supports activities and services that:

- Prevent homelessness and help Hyde residents to maintain their tenancies
- Support Hyde residents to secure employment or become more employable
- Build community resilience, through its Successful Places grants

Successful Places grants

Grants are given to community organisations to support projects and programmes under the following themes: employment and skills; youth work; reducing isolation; mental health and well-being; food poverty; fuel poverty; reducing the impact of violence; and community cohesion.

Financial information

Year end	31/03/2021
Income	£5,330,000
Assets	£15,060,000
Grants to organisations	£1,140,000

Beneficiaries included: A list of beneficiaries was not available.

Applications

Apply in writing to the correspondent.

Sources of information

Accounts; annual reports; Charity Commission record; funder's website.

Hyde Park Place Estate Charity

Church maintenance; social welfare; health; education

City of Westminster

£316,100 (2020/21)

CC number: 212439

Correspondent: Yvonne Eddy, Clerk to the Trustees, St George's Church, The Vestry, 2A Mill Street, London W1S 1FX (tel: 020 7629 0874; email: hppec@stgeorgeshanoversquare.org)

Trustees: The Revd Roderick Leece; Mark Hewitt; Graham Barnes.

www.stgeorgeshanoversquare.org

General information

The charity registered with the Charity Commission in 1962. After paying for the cost of maintenance of the burial ground and repairs to the chapel of the parish church of St George, Hanover Square, the income of this charity is divided equally between the civil trustees and the ecclesiastical trustees to be distributed in the City of Westminster.

The civil trustees apply their allocated funds to people in need, whether through poverty, disadvantage or ill health, within the London Borough of the City of Westminster. The civil trustees have ongoing relationships with a number of organisations, including City of Westminster Social Services, St John's Hospice, Age UK Westminster and Home-Start Westminster.

The ecclesiastical trustees apply their allocated funds towards the preservation and maintenance of the district churches, or for any such ecclesiastical purposes as they see fit within the district.

Financial information

Year end	31/03/2021
Income	£475,800
Assets	£18,560,000
Grants to organisations	£316,100
No. of grants	41

Further financial information

In 2020/21, the charity made grants to around 41 charities, some of which received multiple grants.

Beneficiaries included: St George's Hanover Square (£71,300); The Grosvenor Chapel (£20,000); St George's School (£12,000); Church Homeless Trust, Listening Books, Motor Neurone Disease Association and Royal Trinity Hospice (£5,000 each); West End Community Trust (£3,400).

Applications

Apply in writing to the correspondent. The trustees meet four times a year.

Sources of information

Accounts; annual report; Charity Commission record; funder's website.

IBM United Kingdom Trust

An IT-driven approach to causes such as education, research, disability, poverty, health, the environment, the efficiency of the charitable sector and emergency response

UK; Europe; the Middle East; Africa

£2.78 million (2020/21)

CC number: 290462

Correspondent: The Trustees, IBM United Kingdom Ltd, 1PG1, 76 Upper Ground, London SE1 9PZ (tel: 020 7202 3608; email: wakefim@uk.ibm.com)

Trustees: Prof. Derek Bell; Naomi Hill; Anne Wolfe; Andrew Fitzgerald; Juliet Upton; Bryan Berry; Kuljit Takhar.

www.ibm.org

General information

This trust was established in 1984. It is the corporate charity of IBM, the global technology company specialising in hardware, software and cloud-based services.

According to its Charity Commission record and 2020/21 annual report, the trust strives to meet the following objectives through the use and

understanding of information technology:
- The advancement of education
- The advancement of research (with emphasis, although not exclusively, on information technology)
- The improvement of life for people with disabilities and/or those who are disadvantaged
- The relief of poverty
- Support for disaster relief efforts
- Encouraging the use/understanding of IT in the charitable sector
- The advancement of health in the community
- The preservation of the environment

Grant-making policy

The trust's grant-making falls into two key areas:
- The provision of grants to advance both the aims of the trust and support IBM programmes
- The provision of small grants in support of charitable organisations in the communities surrounding IBM sites

In 2020/21, the trust had one primary focus area: education and skills. It also had two secondary focus areas: health, and human trafficking and modern slavery.

While a crucial part of meeting the trust's objectives is to make direct financial contributions, it also encourages relationships between charitable organisations, educational organisations and IBM itself.

Note: the trust's 2020/21 annual report states that the trustees are likely going to wind down the trust because its principal source of income, the IBM International Foundation, will no longer be providing funding. However, the annual report states that 'this will not take within 12 months from the date of signing these financial statements'.

Financial information

Year end	31/03/2021
Income	£95,000
Assets	£916,000
Grants to organisations	£2,780,000
No. of grants	206+

Further financial information

Grants awarded to organisations in 2020/21 were broken down as follows in the trust's accounts:

Provision of IT and other services	£1.63 million
Increasing the use of technology in education	£822,000
Digital skills	£150,000
Research	£100,000
Miscellaneous	£77,000
Promoting volunteering	£1,000

Only beneficiaries of grants of £30,000 and above were listed in the accounts. Grants of under £30,000 were broken down as follows: 23 grants of between £10,000 and £29,999 (totalling £375,000); 164 grants of below £10,000 (totalling £148,000).

Beneficiaries included: Education Development Trust (£165,000); Enabling Enterprise (£102,000); Ada National College and STEM Learning (£100,000 each); Code Door (£80,000); UK Youth (£70,000); Purple Unicorn and Stop the Traffik (£46,000 each); Law Works (£35,000).

Applications

Apply in writing to the correspondent.

Sources of information

Accounts; annual report; Charity Commission record.

The Iceland Foods Charitable Foundation

General charitable purposes; dementia; sepsis; the environment; children

UK

£889,400 (2020/21)

CC number: 281943

Correspondent: The Trustees, Second Avenue, Deeside Industrial Park, Deeside, Flintshire CH5 2NW (tel: 01244 842885; email: ifcf@Iceland.co.uk)

Trustees: Tarsem Dhaliwal; Sir Malcolm Walker; Richard Walker; Paul Dhaliwal.

 www.ifcf.org.uk

 @icelandcharity

General information

As stated on its website, the Iceland Foods Charitable Foundation was established in 1973 with the mission, 'to make life better for people'. It is funded by the fundraising efforts of Iceland staff and customers, annual events and through the sale of single-use plastic bags in Iceland stores. The foundation raises and donates approximately £1 million each year.

According to its website, the foundation has four core focus areas:
- Dementia
- Environment
- Sepsis
- Children

Each year the foundation chooses to support one principle charity partner in each of these areas.

In addition to the core areas, the foundation also supports a range of other causes and organisations that have been nominated by Iceland employees.

Financial information

Year end	05/04/2021
Income	£365,500
Assets	£3,960,000
Grants to organisations	£889,400
No. of grants	13+

Further financial information

According to the 2020/21 accounts, grants totalled £889,400, of which £1,600 was given in 'donations to smaller charities'.

Beneficiaries included: Action for Children (£280,000); St John Ambulance and Surfers Against Sewage (£150,000 each); The UK Sepsis Trust (£65,500); NHS Charities Together (£37,600); DKMS Foundation (£10,000); Burnfoot Community (£2,000); EDEN Reforestation (£960).

Applications

Contact the correspondent for more information. At the time of writing (January 2022) the foundation's website stated that funding was fully committed for the financial year.

The website also notes:

> We receive a huge volume of requests from the areas around our 970+ stores and by focusing on our chosen partner charities we hope to make the best impact we can in those communities. We regret that we are therefore unable to consider requests for support from other good causes.

Sources of information

Accounts; annual report; Charity Commission record; funder's website.

Impact Funding Partners Ltd

Volunteering; loneliness and social isolation; social welfare; community engagement; health and well-being; support for women

Scotland

£9.79 million (2020/21)

OSCR number: SC035037

Correspondent: The Trustees, Robertson House, 152 Bath Street, Glasgow G2 4TB (tel: 01383 620780; email: info@impactfundingpartners.com)

Trustees: Daphne Biliouri-Grant; Sarah Shanahan; Jim Nicol; Joanna McLaughlin; Ailsa Bruce; Carlos Alba; Dalvir Johal.

 www.impactfundingpartners.com

 facebook.com/Impact-Funding-Partners-255493851220324

 @Impact_Funding

 @impact_funding

General information

Established in 1982, this charity was originally called the Unemployed Voluntary Action Fund (UVAF) and was managed under the auspices of the Carnegie UK Trust. In response to the economic and social challenges of the day, the initial Scotland-wide fund of £400,000 aimed to support volunteering opportunities for unemployed people, in health projects, social services and community development.

In 1990 UVAF became an independent charitable organisation. Later, as the scope of its funding expanded, the charity's name changed and in 2003 the Voluntary Action Fund (VAF) was reborn as a company limited by guarantee with charitable status. In 2019, the charity's name was changed once again to Impact Partners Funding Ltd.

The charity manages a number of programmes on behalf of the Scottish Government and other funders. At the time of writing (May 2022), these include:

- Volunteering Support Fund
- Well-being for Longer in Glasgow Fund
- Social Isolation and Loneliness Fund

We recommend checking the charity's helpful website for the most up-to-date information on open funds.

Financial information

Year end	31/03/2021
Income	£10,270,000
Assets	£780,100
Grants to organisations	£9,790,000

Further financial information

Only beneficiaries that received grants of over £100,000 were listed in the accounts. Grants of less than £100,000 totalled £8.07 million.

Beneficiaries included: South Lanarkshire and East Renfrewshire Women's Aid (£273,500); Glasgow Women's Aid (£243,800); Argyll and Bute Women's Aid (£230,200); East and Midlothian Women's Aid (£223,700); Perthshire Women's Aid (£165,000); Angus Women's Aid (£135,000); Monklands Women's Aid (£130,600); Barnardo's Scotland (£115,000); South Ayrshire Women's Aid (£102,400); Ross-shire Women's Aid (£101,200).

Exclusions

See the charity's website for details of any exclusions for each fund.

Applications

Application forms and guidance notes for open programmes are available on the charity's website. Grant programmes may open and close so potential applicants should check the website for the most recent updates.

Sources of information

Accounts; annual report; OSCR record; funder's website.

Impetus

Children and young people; education and training; employment

UK

£16.5 million (2020)

CC number: 1152262

Correspondent: The Trustees, 1st Floor, Golden Cross House, 8 Duncannon Street, London WC2N 4JF (tel: 07774 437 701 (10am–4pm Monday to Friday); email: info@impetus.org.uk)

Trustees: Hanneke Smits; Lisa Stone; Simon Turner; Bill Benjamin; Shani Zindel; Robert Ramsauer; Rohan Haldea; Filippo Cardini; Louis Elson; Charles Edwards; Natasha Porter; Vanessa Maydon.

 www.impetus.org.uk

 facebook.com/ImpetusPEF

 @ImpetusPEF

General information

Registered with the Charity Commission in 2013, Impetus (formerly Impetus – Private Equity Foundation) was formed from the merger of the Impetus Trust and Private Equity Foundation, bringing together 16 years of experience supporting charity sustainability, effectiveness and growth through its venture philanthropy model.

The charity's aim is to improve education and employment opportunities for disadvantaged young people. It achieves this by providing funding, expertise and pro bono support to charities with a similar focus.

According to its website, to be considered, a partner charity should have the following:

- A focus on improving the educational attainment or sustained employment of young people from economically disadvantaged backgrounds
- A leadership team and Board committed to improving and growing outcomes
- The potential for longer term sustainability and scale to reach more young people

Financial information

Year end	31/12/2020
Grants to organisations	£16,500,000

Further financial information

Impetus is the sole corporate trustee of The Youth Endowment Fund Charitable Trust (Charity Commission no. 1185413), which is dedicated to keeping young people safe from violence. Grants delivered through this trust are consolidated in Impetus' accounts.

During the year, grants paid to Youth Endowment Fund interventions totalled £13.2 million; grants paid to charity partners totalled £3.17 million; and grants paid to research organisations totalled £118,900. Only beneficiaries of grants over £50,000 were listed in the accounts. Grants of under £50,000 totalled £3.52 million.

Beneficiaries included: Comic Relief (£4 million); South London and Maudsley NHS Foundation Trust (£1.17 million); Lives Not Knives (£344,000); Family Support (£120,000); Essex Boys and Girls Clubs (£88,000); Nottingham City Council (72,400); Media Academy Cymru (£50,500).

Applications

Unsolicited applications are not accepted by Impetus. For more information on open funding rounds delivered by the Youth Endowment Fund Charitable Trust, see the trust's website.

Sources of information

Accounts; annual report; Charity Commission record; funder's website; Youth Endowment Fund (website).

The Indigo Trust

Technology-driven projects for social change in sub-Saharan Africa

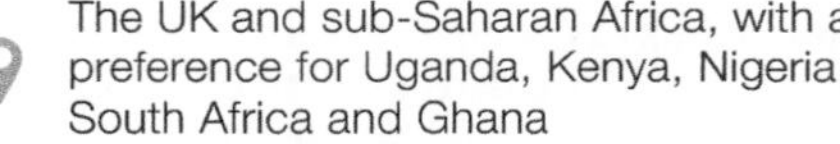

The UK and sub-Saharan Africa, with a preference for Uganda, Kenya, Nigeria, South Africa and Ghana

£1.91 million (2020/21)

CC number: 1075920

Correspondent: Louise Vickers, Personal Assistant, The Peak, 5 Wilton Road, London SW1V 1AP (tel: 020 7410 0330; email: indigo@sfct.org.uk)

Trustees: Dominic Flynn; Francesca Perrin; William Perrin; Sameer Padania; Sonia Sodha.

https://indigotrust.org.uk

facebook.com/IndigoTrust

@indigotrust

General information

This is one of the Sainsbury Family Charitable Trusts, which share a joint administration but work autonomously as independent legal entities. They have a common approach to grant-making and generally discourage applications from organisations not already in contact with the trust concerned, but some are open to unsolicited approaches.

The Indigo Trust funds organisations that use digital technologies to improve transparency and accountability in sub-Saharan Africa. On its website, the trust defines its mission as follows:

> The power of people and communities to effect change is heavily dependent upon the level of information that they can access. Information enables them to make informed decisions and hold authorities to account. We believe that mobile and web technologies have the power to transform how people access, share and create information.

Following a recent strategic review, international grants (usually from £10,000 to £20,000) are now almost solely made to:

- Projects and organisations that leverage the power of mobile and web technologies to foster active, informed citizens and accountable governments
- Civic tech communities and innovation hubs that use information communication technologies for positive social change

In addition to its international work, the trust also provides grants to support more open and effective philanthropy in the UK as well as grants to local community charities in London.

Financial information

Year end	05/04/2021
Income	£2,640,000
Assets	£12,010,000
Grants to organisations	£1,910,000
No. of grants	44

Beneficiaries included: 360Giving (£300,000); Rosa Fund (£200,000); Laws.Africa (£140,000); Access to Justice Foundation (£100,000); Friends, Families and Travellers (£75,000); The Angelou Centre (£50,000); DearSA NPC (£20,000); Hive Colab (£10,000); Icolyn Smith Foundation (£2,000).

Exclusions

Grants are not normally given to individuals. Grants are not made for educational fees or expeditions.

Applications

The trust's website states the following:

> Indigo is not currently accepting unsolicited proposals. Experience has taught us that an open application process is burdensome for both sides and rarely results in new grants being awarded.
>
> Through a combination of desk-based research, scoping visits, recommendations from partners and suggestions from grantees, we identify suitable partner organisations and projects to support. This approach allows us to directly target relevant and high-quality organisations, while reducing the burden associated with a high volume of unsuccessful, unsolicited proposals. We regularly review the process to identify potential improvements to the system.

Sources of information

Accounts; annual report; Charity Commission record; funder's website; guidelines for applicants.

The Worshipful Company of Information Technologists

 Education; digital skills; information technology; social welfare

UK

£151,700 (2020)

CC number: 1113488

Correspondent: Lindsay Wratten, Charity Co-ordinator, 39A Bartholomew Close, London EC1A 7JN (tel: 020 7600 1992; email: charity@wcit.org.uk)

Trustees: Bill Kennair; Elizabeth Sparrow; Gary Moore; Dr Stefan Fafinski; Richard Pone; Jonathan Soar; Bryan Parkinson; Augustus Machado.

 www.wcit.org.uk/apply_for_a_grant.html

 @WCITCharity

General information

The Worshipful Company of Information Technologists is the 100th livery company of the City of London. The charitable arm of the company, known as the WCIT Charity, was registered with the Charity Commission in 2006.

According to the charity's website, its aims are 'to unlock the power of IT for good through public education, promoting the effectiveness and efficiency of charities, donating funds and by providing access to technology professionals.'

The charity supports digital projects in four priority areas:

- Education
- Inclusion
- IT for charities
- Public understanding

Grants are typically for up to £15,000. All grants are restricted.

The charity also provides pro bono IT support for charities and social enterprises.

Eligibility

Eligible organisations include registered charities, educational organisations and organisations with a formal not-for profit constitution, such as CICs and CICs limited by shares. All projects must make use of IT.

Financial information

Year end	31/12/2020
Income	£315,900
Assets	£6,930,000
Grants to organisations	£151,700
No. of grants	9

Further financial information

Due to the impact of COVID-19, the charity had to temporarily suspend its discretionary grants programme in April 2020. Grants were still made to its annual strategic partners and major grantees. In the previous financial year (2019) the charity awarded grants totalling £445,300.

Only beneficiaries of grants of over £5,000 were listed in the 2020 accounts.

Beneficiaries included: Missing People (£60,000); Thames Reach (£22,100); Gresham College (£11,500); Lilian Baylis Technology School (£10,000); Lifelites (£7,100); AbilityNet and Hammersmith Academy (£5,000 each).

Exclusions

The charity does not support individuals, local authorities, councils or private companies. It will not fund: core costs; political/lobbying work; loans/debt repayments; work that has already been delivered; consultancy costs; work overseas; or projects that seek to build an endowment.

Applications

Online application forms can be accessed via the charity's online portal on its website. Alternatively, applications can be sent by post or email to the charity co-ordinator using a Word version of the form. Requirements for different grant amounts along with tips for making good applications can be found in the charity's guidelines on the website. Applications are considered four times a year, in February, May, September and November – see the charity's website for deadlines.

For information about pro bono support, contact the correspondent.

Sources of information

Accounts; annual report; Charity Commission record; funder's website; guidelines for applicants.

The Ingram Trust

General charitable purposes

UK and overseas, with some preference for Surrey

£693,000 (2020/21)

CC number: 1040194

Correspondent: The Trustees, 8th Floor, 6 New Street Square, London EC4A 3AQ (tel: 020 7842 2000; email: theingramtrust@rawlinson-hunter.com)

Trustees: Janet Ingram; Clare Maurice; Sally Ingram; Jonathan Ingram; Christopher Ingram.

General information

The Ingram Trust was established in 1994. According to its 2020/21 annual report, the grant-making policies of the trust are:

- To support specific projects which can include identifiable costs for special services or projects provided by the charity or equipment that is required.
- Generally, beneficiaries will be major national and international charities together with some local ones in the county of Surrey.
- The majority of grants will be made for periods of 3–4 years at a time.

Financial information

Year end	05/04/2021
Income	£153,400
Assets	£11,040,000
Grants to organisations	£693,000
No. of grants	33

Further financial information

Grants ranged from £5,000 to £60,000 during the year. Two COVID-19-specific grants were awarded to Age UK and British Exploring Society.

Beneficiaries included: WWF – UK (£60,000); The Royal National Theatre (£50,000); Shelter (£35,000); Alzheimer's Society (£20,000); Outward Bound Trust (£15,000); Princess Alice Hospice (£10,000); Cherry Trees (£5,000).

Exclusions

The trust does not support any of the following:

- Non-registered charities
- Individuals
- Charities specialising in overseas aid ('except those dedicated to encouraging self-help and providing more permanent solutions to problems', as stated in the accounts)
- Animal charities (except those concerned with wildlife conservation)

Applications

Apply in writing to the correspondent. The trustees consider grant applications from charities that they believe demonstrate concrete evidence of delivering public benefit.

Sources of information

Accounts; annual report; Charity Commission record.

The Inlight Trust

Religion

UK

£154,000 (2020/21)

CC number: 236782

Correspondent: Clare Pegden, Administrator, PO Box 2, Liss, Hampshire GU33 6YP (tel: 07970 540015; email: inlight.trust01@ntlworld.com)

Trustees: Judy Hayward; Sharon Knight; Jane Dunham; Shirley Vening; Stephen Collins; Paul Summerfield.

General information

This trust was established in 1957 and provides grants for religious purposes only, particularly the advancement and promotion of religion, on a non-denominational basis. The trustees also wish to promote spiritual health and well-being.

Financial information

Year end	31/03/2021
Income	£314,000
Assets	£7,210,000
Grants to organisations	£154,000
No. of grants	18

Further financial information

During 2020/21 the trust made grants totalling £154,000; however, in previous years grants have totalled over £300,000.

Beneficiaries included: St Clare West Essex Hospice Care Trust (£18,000); East Anglia Children's Hospice (£11,000); Dent Meditation Centre and Gaia House (£10,000 each); Prison Phoenix Trust (£7,000); Wesley House Cambridge (£5,000); Norwich Zen Buddhist Priory (£2,000).

Exclusions

According to our previous research, grants are not made for individuals, organisations that are not registered charities or general appeals from large national organisations. Grants are rarely made for church buildings.

Applications

Our previous research suggests that applications should be made in writing to the correspondent, including:

- Details of the need and the intended project to meet it
- An outline of the budget
- The most recently available annual accounts of your organisation
- A copy of your governing document or your entry on the Charity Commission register

The trustees meet four times a year.

Sources of information

Accounts; annual report; Charity Commission record.

The Inman Charity

General charitable purposes; medical causes; social welfare; physical and mental disability; armed forces

UK

£57,000 (2020)

CC number: 261366

Correspondent: The Trustees, BM Box 2831, London WC1N 3XX (tel: 020 7465 4300)

Trustees: Alan Walker; Belinda Strother; Michael Matthews; John Langdon; Inman Charity Trustees; Neil Winderath.

 www.inmancharity.org

General information

The charity supports a wide range of UK charities through its grant-making, with a particular interest in the following areas:

- Medical research
- Care of older people
- General welfare
- Hospices
- Deaf and blind individuals
- Care of people with physical and mental disabilities
- Armed forces

According to the website, the trustees aim to distribute £350,000 annually in grants.

Financial information

Year end	31/12/2020
Income	£128,900
Assets	£6,210,000
Grants to organisations	£57,000

Further financial information

The trustees did not meet during the year due to COVID-19 and therefore the only grants awarded were for ongoing annual commitments and no new grants were considered. As such, during the year the charity's grant total was much lower than its typical levels of giving (around £350,000 per year).

Beneficiaries included: Victor Inman Bursary Fund at Uppingham School (£25,000); Hospice UK (£10,000); Deafblind UK, FISH Neighbourhood Voluntary Care Scheme, Listening Books and Samaritans (£5,000 each).

Exclusions

The charity does not support: individuals; young children and infants; maintenance of local buildings (such as churches and village halls); animal welfare; wildlife and environmental conservation; religious charities.

Applications

Application guidelines are available to read on the charity's website.

Applications should be made in writing to the correspondent and should include:

- A letter confirming the registered charity number and the aims and objectives of your organisation
- Your latest annual reports and audited accounts
- The total amount required for the project
- Funding, if any, received to date
- Timeline of completion

Applications must be received by the end of February or August to be considered at the trustees' meetings in spring and autumn, respectively.

Only successful applicants will be contacted.

Sources of information

Accounts; annual report; Charity Commission record; funder's website.

Integrated Education Fund

Integrated education

Northern Ireland

£105,400 (2020/21)

CCNI number: NIC104886

Correspondent: Claire Carlin, Grants Officer, Forestview, Purdy's Lane, Belfast BT8 7AR (tel: 028 9069 4099; email: info@ief.org.uk or Claire@ief.org.uk)

Trustees: Mary Roulston; Kathleen O'Hare; Patricia Murtagh; Sorcha Diver; June Wilkinson; Peter Osborne; Richard Lemon; Gráinne Clarke; David Cooke; Jane Morrice; Ellen McVea; Barbara McAtamney; Michael McKernan; Brandon McMaster.

 www.ief.org.uk

 facebook.com/IntegratedEducationFund

 @IEFNI

 @intedfund

General information

This charity, which is known by the abbreviation IEF, was established in 1992 with funding provided by EU structural funds, the Department of Education Northern Ireland, the Nuffield Foundation and the Joseph Rowntree Charitable Trust. It provides funding to support the development and growth of integrated education in Northern Ireland. The charity's Charity Commission NI record defines integrated education as education that:

> brings together in each school, pupils, staff and governors from both the Protestant and Catholic traditions. The integrated school provides a learning environment where children and young people from these backgrounds, as well as those of other faiths and none, can learn with, from and about each other.

The charity receives funding from individuals, businesses and other grant-makers. The fund also acts as an intermediary body to administer grants and donations on behalf of outside funding bodies and individuals.

Grant-making programmes

The charity's website provides the following information:

> In order to support the growth in integrated school places to an initial 10% we will promote and manage grant programmes for:
>
> *Existing integrated schools* – we will provide capital enhancements to: aid growth, double enrolments and sixth form provision; create and support new pre-schools; and raise awareness.
>
> *Schools considering transforming* – IEF will financially assist schools that would like to, for example, implement an awareness campaign, using community audits to outline current local education provision and the potential for transformation to integrated status.
>
> *Funding for transformation* – related training for school staff, school governors, and parents will also be available.
>
> *Transformed integrated schools* – funding will be available to encourage and support the development of transformed integrated schools through grants for recurrent and capital costs which are not being met by the Department of Education.
>
> *Parent groups seeking integrated education provision* – funding will be provided to the groups to help with research, delivering information sessions and growing understanding of, and confidence in integrated education in their area.
>
> *Meaningful shared education led by integrated schools* – we will support integrated schools working and partnering with non-integrated schools to create deep and sustained contact aimed at developing mutual respect and understanding.

Bursaries and prizes are also available to individual students through the fund's Carson Awards.

Financial information

Year end	31/03/2021
Income	£1,050,000
Assets	£2,070,000
Grants to organisations	£105,400

Further financial information

Grants awarded in 2020/21 totalled £105,400; however, in previous years the charity has awarded grants totalling over £600,000. In its 2020/21 annual report, the charity stated the following: 'The COVID-19 pandemic has impacted on the life of pupils, parents and schools in an extreme way and consequently it has placed restrictions and limitations on some of our work.'

Beneficiaries included: Parental Engagement Campaign (£93,800); Trust Programme (£30,500); The Carson Awards Programme (£15,800).

Applications

Each grant-making programme has its own rounds and deadlines for applications – see the charity's website for eligibility and closing dates.

Sources of information

Accounts; annual report; Charity Commission for Northern Ireland record; funder's website.

International Bible Students Association

Overseas aid and Jehovah's Witnesses

Worldwide

£63.53 million (2020/21)

CC number: 216647

Correspondent: The Trustees, 1 Kingdom Way, West Hanningfield, Chelmsford CM2 8FW (tel: 020 8906 2211)

Trustees: Stephen Papps; Karl Snaith; Ivor Darby; Jonathan Manley; Stephen Symonds.

General information

The association was registered with the Charity Commission in 1964. According to its 2020/21 annual report:

> The object of the Association is to promote the Christian religion as practised by the body of Christians known as Jehovah's Witness, by supporting congregations of Jehovah's Witnesses and others in connection with their spiritual and material welfare in Britain and abroad within the charitable purposes of the Association. This is achieved by:
>
> - Providing serviced facilities to support religious activity
> - Arranging for venues to host conventions for Bible education
> - Financially assisting legal entities of Jehovah's Witnesses with similar aims and objectives, both foreign and domestic
> - Paying expenses for and taking care of living arrangements for members of the Worldwide Order of Special Full-Time Servants of Jehovah's Witnesses (the Order)

Financial information

Year end	31/08/2021
Income	£71,810,000
Assets	£154,240,000
Grants to organisations	£63,530,000

Beneficiaries included: A list of beneficiaries was not included within the accounts.

Applications

Apply in writing to the correspondent.

Sources of information

Accounts; annual report; Charity Commission record.

The Investindustrial Foundation

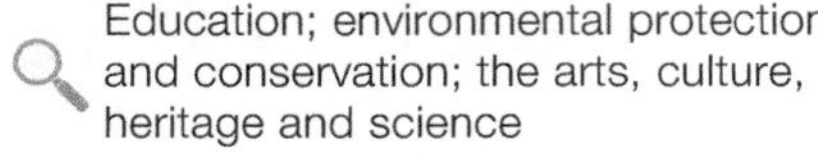

Education; environmental protection and conservation; the arts, culture, heritage and science

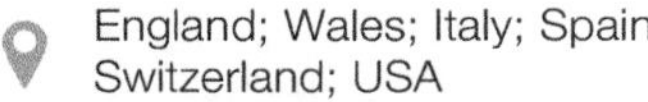

England; Wales; Italy; Spain; Switzerland; USA

£744,500 (2020/21)

CC number: 1169179

Correspondent: The Trustees, 16 Palace Street, London SW1E 5JD (tel: 020 7664 2121)

Trustees: Emanuele Bonomi; Rohan Maxwell; Natalie Ramsden; Oliver Dunn.

www.investindustrial.com/social-responsibility/our-foundation.html

General information

The Investindustrial Foundation was registered with the Charity Commission in 2016. According to its website, the foundation is primarily focused on the promotion of education, diversity, environmental protection and conservation, and the promotion of the arts, culture, heritage, and science.

Financial information

Year end	31/03/2021
Income	£744,400
Assets	£28,100
Grants to organisations	£744,500

Further financial information

Grants were broken down as follows: development of higher education (£531,700) and sustainability studies (£212,700).

Beneficiaries included: A list of beneficiaries was not available.

Applications

Apply in writing to the correspondent.

Sources of information

Accounts; annual report; Charity Commission record; funder's website.

Investream Charitable Trust

Jewish causes, including education, medical causes, community development and older people

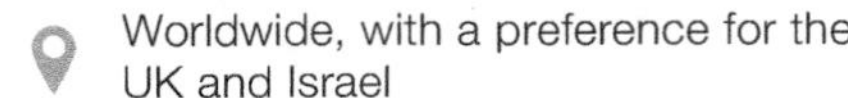

Worldwide, with a preference for the UK and Israel

£351,400 (2020/21)

CC number: 1097052

Correspondent: The Trustees, Investream Ltd, 1 Portland Place, London W1B 1PN (tel: 020 7486 2800)

Trustees: Mark Morris; Graham Morris.

General information

The trust was established in 2003 and makes grants for Jewish causes including education, medical causes, community development and older people.

Financial information

Year end	30/04/2021
Income	£312,100
Assets	£696,800
Grants to organisations	£351,400

Beneficiaries included: A list of beneficiaries was not available.

Applications

Apply in writing to the correspondent.

Sources of information

Accounts; annual report; Charity Commission record.

The Invigorate Charitable Trust

Social welfare; advancement of the Christian religion; citizenship and community development; arts and culture; human rights; children and young people; health and disability

UK and overseas

£349,600 (2020/21)

CC number: 1162752

Correspondent: Kate Aitchison, Trustee, 5th Floor, Central Square, 29 Wellington Street, Leeds, West Yorkshire LS1 4DL (tel: 0113 285 5000; email: kate.aitchison@rsmuk.com)

Trustees: Timothy Parr; Kate Aitchison.

General information

The Invigorate Charitable Trust was registered with the Charity Commission in July 2015 and makes grants to organisations for a wide range of purposes, including the following:

- Social welfare
- Advancement of the Christian religion (UK and overseas)
- Citizenship and community development
- Arts and culture
- Human rights
- Children and young people (UK and overseas)
- Health and disability

Financial information

Year end	05/04/2021
Income	£288,000
Assets	£139,100
Grants to organisations	£349,600

Further financial information

Grants were broken downs as follows:

Advancement of the Christian religion – UK	5	£116,800
Children and young people	9	£64,500
Citizenship and community development	7	£54,000
Health and disability	4	£25,500
Advancement of the Christian religion – overseas	2	£25,000
Social welfare	4	£24,000
Children and young people – overseas	1	£20,000
Human rights	2	£11,000
Arts and culture	1	£7,000
Other charitable purposes	2	£1,800

Beneficiaries included: A list of beneficiaries was not available.

Exclusions

The trust will not fund organisations in the following areas:

- Health or saving lives
- Amateur sport
- The environment
- Animal welfare
- Armed forces or emergency services

Applications

Apply in writing to the correspondent.

Sources of information

Accounts; annual report; Charity Commission record.

The Ireland Fund of Great Britain

Irish-related causes; education; community development; the arts and culture; peace and reconciliation

UK, with a preference for Northern Ireland, and the Republic of Ireland

£523,200 (2020/21)

CC number: 327889

Correspondent: Katie Jemmett, Director, Level 17, Dashwood House, 69 Old Broad Street, London EC2M 1QS (tel: 07597 665646; email: ifgb@irelandfunds.org)

Trustees: Seamus McGarry; Ruairi Conneely; Zach Webb; Rory Godson; Garrett Hayes; Eoin Bastible; Emily Bohill; Rachel Naughton; Declan Tiernan; Brian Dickie; Emer Finnan; Conor Hillery; John Feeney; Evelyn Bourke.

 https://irelandfunds.org/chapters/worldwide/great-britain

 facebook.com/TheIrelandFunds

 @TheIrelandFunds

 @theirelandfunds

General information

The Ireland Funds is a global philanthropic network established in 1976 to promote and support peace, culture, education and community development throughout the island of Ireland, and Irish-related causes around the world. The Ireland Funds has chapters in 12 countries, including Great Britain.

The Ireland Fund of Great Britain

Each year, The Ireland Fund of Great Britain supports charities, community groups and voluntary groups that promote well-being, community and culture across Great Britain, including those that support Irish communities.

According to its 2020/21 annual report, the objects of the charity are the relief of poverty, the advancement of education and the advancement of the arts in all of its spheres. It also supports peace and reconciliation projects that contribute to improved intercommunity relations in Northern Ireland.

The Ireland Funds

Two main grant programmes are delivered by The Ireland Funds to benefit organisations in the Republic of Ireland and Northern Ireland:

- Flagship grants for core funding, capacity building or programme costs for non-profit organisations working within one of the grant-maker's key areas. Grants range up to €/£100,000 over a two-year period
- Small grants of under €/£7,000 for smaller community organisations and for organisations that have not previously been supported by The Ireland Funds

The grant-maker's website has more information on the various grant programmes.

Financial information

Year end	31/03/2021
Income	£599,500
Assets	£217,300
Grants to organisations	£523,200

Further financial information

Grants to organisations were distributed as follows: community development (£301,200); education (£183,300); sharing and developing Irish culture (£38,800).

Beneficiaries included: Our Lady's Hospice and Care Services (£175,900); Blackrock College Development (£70,300); Social Entrepreneurs Ireland (£37,700); Irish Cultural Centre – Hammersmith (£22,000); Summerhill College Sligo (£10,000); Luton Irish Forum (£3,000); The Holy Child Killiney Building Appeal (£1,000); Dublin City University (£500).

Applications

Guidelines, exclusions and full information on the application process are announced on the website when individual programmes open.

Sources of information

Accounts; annual report; Charity Commission record; funder's website.

The J. Isaacs Charitable Trust

General charitable purposes, particularly young people, education, older people, community development and healthcare

 England and Wales

£819,600 (2020/21)

CC number: 1059865

Correspondent: The Trustees, JRJ Group, Mutual House, 70 Conduit Street, London W1S 2GF (tel: 020 7220 2305)

Trustees: Jeremy Isaacs: Joanne Isaacs; Helen Eastick; Vincent Isaacs.

General information

The charity was registered with the Charity Commission in 1996 and receives donations from Mr J. Isaacs alongside its investment income. According to its Charity Commission record, its objectives are:

- Care for children
- Education
- The well-being of older people
- Tolerance in our community
- Healthcare

Financial information

Year end	31/03/2021
Income	£860,400
Assets	£1,670,000
Grants to organisations	£819,600

Beneficiaries included: A list of beneficiaries was not available.

Applications

Apply in writing to the correspondent.

Sources of information

Charity Commission record.

The Isle of Anglesey Charitable Association (Cymdeithas Elusennol Ynys Mon)

General charitable purposes; community well-being and facilities; village hall running costs

 Isle of Anglesey

£787,400 (2019/20)

CC number: 1174536

Correspondent: Annwen Morgan, Trust Secretary and Chief Executive of Isle of Anglesey County Council, Cyngor Sir Ynys Mon, Swyddfeydd y Cyngor, Llangefni LL77 7TW (tel: 01248 750057)

Trustees: Gary Pritchard; Jeff Evans; Ieuan Williams; Dylan Rees; Kenneth Hughes; Alun Mummery; Meirion Jones; Vaughan Hughes; Carwyn Jones; Richard Griffiths; Glyn Haynes; Richard Dew; Aled Jones; Robin Williams; John Griffith; Llinos Huws; Dafydd Roberts; Bryan Owen; Peter Rogers; Alun Roberts; Dafydd Thomas; Margaret Roberts; Eric Jones; Richard Jones; Trefor Hughes; Robert Jones; Nicola Roberts; Arwel Roberts; Robert Parry; Gwilym Jones.

General information

The Isle of Anglesey Charitable Association, known informally as Y Gymdeithas, registered as a charitable incorporation in 2017. The charity is managed by 30 elected members of Isle of Anglesey County Council plus two independent elected trustees.

In 2019 the charity received the assets of the Isle of Anglesey Charitable Trust (Charity Commission no. 1000818), a trust formed in 1990 to manage a capital fund acquired by Shell (UK) Ltd after it ceased operating its oil reservoir in Amlwch.

Grant-making policy

The charity's 2019/20 annual report states:

> The charitable purposes of the Association are limited to the general public benefit of persons resident on the Island, including:-
>
> - The provision of amenities and facilities;
> - The preservation of buildings;
> - The conservation and protection of land;
> - The protection and safeguarding of the environment;
> - The sponsoring of publications and educational research projects.
>
> This is achieved by contributing towards spending on services provided for public benefit and by making grants to charitable and voluntary organisations.
>
> Grants are made from the annual investment income to charities, voluntary

organisations and other local bodies for projects on the Island of Anglesey.

The charity awards the following types of grant:

- Small grants of £8,000 or less
- Large grants of more than £8,000
- Grants for the annual running costs of village halls
- Small capital grants for community and sporting facilities

Grants are mainly one-off.

Financial information

Year end	30/09/2020
Income	£607,600
Assets	£19,570,000
Grants to organisations	£787,400
No. of grants	77

Further financial information

In 2019/20, the charity awarded 80 grants to 77 organisations. The grant total includes £85,000 awarded to 32 village halls for running costs.

Beneficiaries included: Mantar Mon Leader Scheme (£63,800); Anglesey Food Bank (£25,000); Llangoed Football Club (£20,700); Beaumaris Sea Scout Group (£8,000); Age Well (£5,000); Llandegfan Parish Hall (£2,500); Llanerchymedd Community Council (£1,100); Llangoed Knitting Group (£200).

Exclusions

Projects outside the Isle of Anglesey are not supported.

Applications

The charity invites applications for funding, usually once a year, through advertising in local papers. According to the charity's annual report for 2019/20, 'applications are by standard application form' – contact the correspondent for more information on the application process.

Sources of information

Accounts; annual report; Charity Commission record; Isle of Anglesey County Council (website).

The ITF Seafarers Trust

The welfare of seafarers, maritime workers and their families

Worldwide

£8.27 million (2020)

CC number: 281936

Correspondent: The Trustees, ITF House, 49–60 Borough Road, London SE1 1DR (email: info@seafarerstrust.org)

Trustees: Padraig Crumlin; Brian Orrell; Abdulgani Serang; Stephen Cotton; Jacqueline Smith; Dave Heindel.

 www.seafarerstrust.org

 facebook.com/ITFtrust

 @seafarers_trust

General information

This trust, established in 1981, makes grants to organisations that advance the well-being of maritime workers, seafarers and their families.

Grant-making information

The trust's website provides the following grants guidelines on its website:

> Who can apply?
>
> The Trust only makes grants to organisations that support the welfare of seafarers, maritime workers and their families. We do not make grants to individuals.
>
> The Trust accepts applications from:
>
> - Registered charities and non-profit organisations
> - Educational institutions (such as universities and colleges)
> - Trade unions
> - NGOs (non-governmental organisations)
>
> We make grants to organisations in any part of the world.
>
> **Your organisation must:**
>
> - Be able to show that the project will improve seafarers, maritime workers and/or their families' health and well-being irrespective of nationality, religion, race, language, gender or rank.
> - Have a constitution or a set of rules, which set out the aims of your organisation and how you work.
> - Have a bank account in the name of the organisation.
>
> **What types of grants are available?**
>
> - **Port based welfare:** The trust makes grants to support port based welfare projects such as developing ship visiting, outreach work, or projects to improve health, safety and wellbeing.
> - **Vehicles:** The trust makes grants for the purchase of vehicles such as mini-buses, vans and cars to support welfare organisations to transport seafarers and to undertake ship visiting.
> - **Research:** The trust accepts grant applications for research from organisations such as Universities and educational institutions. We will also consider funding for feasibility studies to see whether a research project or welfare project is possible.
> - **Welfare at sea and Welfare at home:** The trust provides grants for a variety of projects that support the welfare of seafarers while they are at sea or while they are at home. We also support projects that enhance the welfare of seafarers' families.
> - **Training and education/Conference and event/Publications:** The trust considers grant applications for training and education (scholarships and other training), conferences or for publications (books and leaflets) for or about seafarers and maritime workers.
> - **Operational support:** The trust provides a small number of grants to some organisations for operational support, supporting the general running costs of those organisations.

For further details see the trust's guidelines for applicants, which are available from its helpful website.

Financial information

Year end	31/12/2020
Income	£491,000
Assets	£42,000,000
Grants to organisations	£8,270,000

Beneficiaries included: All Japan Seamen's Union (£3.71 million); The Mission to Seafarers – London (£80,200); The Chirp Charitable Trust (£50,000); Queen Victoria Seamen's Rest (£2,500).

Exclusions

According to the trust's guidelines, the following are not likely to be supported:

- Retrospective costs for completed projects
- Deficits which have already been incurred
- Projects which promote particular religious beliefs
- Recurring costs
- Individuals

Applications

Applications have to be made online on the trust's website, where full criteria and guidelines are also available.

Sources of information

Accounts; annual report; Charity Commission record; funder's website; guidelines for applicants.

The J. J. Charitable Trust

Literacy, sustainable lifestyles and environmental projects in the UK and Africa

UK and overseas

£1.31 million (2020/21)

CC number: 1015792

Correspondent: Mrs K. Everett, Chief Operating Officer, The Peak, 5 Wilton Road, London SW1V 1AP (tel: 020 7410 0330; email: info@sfct.org.uk)

Trustees: Lucy Guard; John Sainsbury; Mark Sainsbury; Claudia Gonella.

 www.sfct.org.uk

General information

This is one of the Sainsbury Family Charitable Trusts, which share a joint administration but work autonomously as independent legal entities. They have a common approach to grant-making.

Established in 1992, The J. J. Charitable Trust funds registered charities, and grants are usually in the range of £5,000 to £200,000. The main areas of interest to the trust are:

- **Literacy** – helping to improve the effectiveness of literacy teaching in compulsory education for children with learning difficulties, such as dyslexia, and also for people who have previously offended or those at risk of offending
- **Social and cultural change towards more sustainable lifestyles** – finding creative approaches that visualise a sustainable future in positive ways, innovating economic models that support sustainable lifestyles, and the role of the media in communicating climate change and sustainability
- **Environmental projects in Africa** – particularly community-based agriculture projects promoting environmental sustainability

The trust is also committed to investing in forestry, microfinance in financially developing countries, renewable energy, clean technology infrastructures and social impact. It also works closely with the Ashden Trust and the Mark Leonard Trust on the Climate Change Collaboration, which supports projects seeking to reduce CO2 emissions quickly.

The trustees' objective is to support innovative schemes with seed-funding and development support, leading projects to achieve sustainability and successful replication.

Financial information

Year end	05/04/2021
Income	£673,800
Assets	£48,470,000
Grants to organisations	£1,310,000

Further financial information

During 2020/21, grants were distributed as follows:

The environment	£744,600
Literacy	£439,200
General	£130,000

Beneficiaries included: Purpose Disruptors (£550,800); Citizens UK (£55,000); Women's Aid Federation of England (£20,000); Schoolreaders (£10,000); British Dyslexia Association BDA (£9,800); Ready, Steady, Read (£5,000); The Commitment (£3,300).

Exclusions

Grants are not normally made to individuals. The trust will not fund educational fees or expeditions.

Applications

According to the 2020/21 annual report, unsolicited applications are discouraged and are unlikely to be successful unless they are closely aligned to the trust's areas of interest.

Funding enquiries can be submitted online. Generally, applications should be sent by post to The Sainsbury Family Charitable Trusts at the above address, or by email to proposals@sfct.org.uk. Details of what to include can be found on the website.

The website stresses that the vast majority of applications are unsuccessful. All applicants receive a standard acknowledgement letter. If your proposal is a candidate for support, you will hear from the trust within eight weeks of the acknowledgement.

Sources of information

Accounts; annual report; Charity Commission record; funder's website.

The Jabbs Foundation

Medical research; education; social welfare; community; crime prevention; research into the health of trees and forests

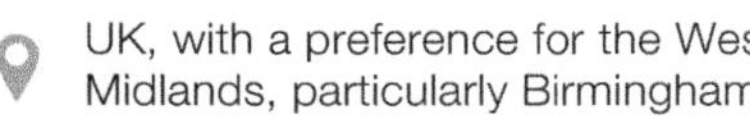

UK, with a preference for the West Midlands, particularly Birmingham

£1.71 million (2019/20)

CC number: 1128402

Correspondent: The Trustees, PO Box 16067, Birmingham, West Midlands B32 9GP (tel: 0121 428 2593; email: office@harborneoffice.co.uk)

Trustees: Robin Daniels; Alexander Wright; Ruth Keighley.

General information

The foundation was registered in 2009 for general charitable purposes. The objectives of the foundation set out in the trust deed are widely drawn and state that 'the objects are to advance for the public benefit any purpose which is exclusively charitable at law'.

According to its 2019/20 annual report, the foundation's trustees have to date focused on several areas of public benefit in making grants:

- Medical research.
- Education (including educational activities by arts organisations).
- Enhancing personal, family and community relationships in the West Midlands.
- Supporting vulnerable members of society and reducing the number of people involved in the criminal justice system.
- Research into the health of trees and forests and encouraging the planting of new trees where these offer educational opportunities.

The 2019/20 annual report states that projects that have a Birmingham connection are considered favourably.

Financial information

Year end	31/08/2020
Income	£769,500
Assets	£464,700
Grants to organisations	£1,710,000

Further financial information

Grants were broken down as follows in 2019/20:

Supporting vulnerable people and crime reduction	£1.48 million
Medical research	£95,200
Environmental research	£90,000
Education	£40,000

Only beneficiaries of grants of £50,000 and above were listed in the foundation's accounts. Grants of £50,000 or less totalled £171,200.

Beneficiaries included: Anawim (£606,600); The Trussell Trust (£250,000); University of Birmingham (£210,000); Heart of England Community Foundation (£100,000); University of Oxford (£95,200); Association of Applied Biologists (£90,000); Recre8now (£88,100).

Applications

The foundation's 2019/20 accounts state:

> The JABBS Foundation does not encourage speculative grant requests, but the trustees read all applications that are received [...] In the most part, new grant opportunities are highlighted by engagement with organisations and people who hold national or local influence in the priority areas. Where such opportunities are highlighted by trustees, a formal application is encouraged and reviewed in detail.

Sources of information

Accounts; annual report; Charity Commission record.

The Frank Jackson Foundation

Education; environmental research; general charitable purposes

South Africa and the UK, with a preference for Suffolk

£990,800 (2020/21)

CC number: 1007600

Correspondent: Lisa Mills, Administrator, 24 Taylor Way, Great Baddow, Chelmsford, Essex CM2 8ZG (email: frankjacksonfoundation@live.co.uk)

Trustees: Timothy Seymour; Tom Sheldon; David Tennant; Amanda Taylor; Mary-Anne Gribbon; Leila Brown.

www.frankjacksonfoundation.org.uk

General information

The Frank Jackson Foundation was established by the late Mr Frank Jackson MBE, a well-known businessman and philanthropist from Woodbridge in Suffolk.

The foundation's website states:

> The principal objectives of the Foundation, on which the majority of our funds are expended, are to benefit, through education, the disadvantaged and to support world-class research in institutions of higher learning. The Foundation supports a number of 'core' projects of this type. A secondary objective is to support, with smaller grants, a wider spectrum of causes which reflect the interests or expertise of the Trustees.

Education in the UK

According to its website, the foundation's strategy in the UK 'is to support education in its widest sense'. A proportion of the funding is expended in Suffolk and East Anglia, where Frank Jackson lived and worked. The foundation has a number of core partnerships in this area including the Island Trust, Cirdan Sailing Trust, Ellen MacArthur Cancer Trust and Green Light Trust.

Suffolk

According to the 2020/21 accounts, the foundation works in partnership with Suffolk Community Foundation, which distributes small grants on the foundation's behalf to community groups and charities in the county.

The environment

According to its website, the foundation 'supports research into the most pressing issues facing humanity and our planet, along with work to communicate research findings, bring about change and apply solutions.'

The foundation's largest core project in this area is its support of a number of senior academic posts in environmental research in partnership with the Environmental Change Institute at Oxford University (with funding channelled through Oriel College).

Education in South Africa

In this area the foundation funds teacher training, school fees for disadvantaged children, and education, employment and training projects.

Financial information

Year end	05/04/2021
Income	£497,500
Assets	£28,210,000
Grants to organisations	£990,800
No. of grants	35

Further financial information

Only beneficiaries that receive grants of over £10,000 were listed in the foundation's accounts. Grants of under £10,000 totalled £26,600. During 2020/21 the foundation awarded four smaller grants which reflected trustee interests.

Beneficiaries included: Oriel College Development Trust (£116,400); Physics Partners (£65,000); Suffolk Community Foundation (£60,000); Cirdan Sailing Trust (£25,000); Ellen MacArthur Cancer Trust (£15,000); Children on the Edge (£12,000); National Youth Ballet (£10,000).

Applications

The foundation's website states that it does not accept unsolicited applications and that the trustees 'prefer to actively seek out good causes which meet the foundation's aims'. The foundation does welcome enquiries if an organisation believes it meets the criteria. In this case, a short enquiry that summarises in a paragraph how your work meets the criteria should be emailed to the correspondent.

Sources of information

Accounts; annual report; Charity Commission record; funder's website.

The Jagclif Charitable Trust

General charitable purposes

UK and overseas

£5.55 million (2019/20)

CC number: 1163459

Correspondent: The Trustees, Marshall Wace Asset Management, George House, 131 Sloane Street, London, SW1X 9AT (tel: 020 7925 7723; email: jagclif@mwam.com)

Trustees: Duncan Eriksen; Ernesto Fragomeni; Claudia Wace; Ian Wace.

General information

The trust was registered with the Charity Commission in 2015 and supports general charitable purposes.

Financial information

Year end	30/06/2020
Income	£34,510,000
Assets	£25,290,000
Grants to organisations	£5,550,000

Beneficiaries included: The Eureka Charitable Trust (£1 million); Mail Force Charity (£750,000); Leon Foundation (£100,000); Sentebale (£50,000); The Sunshine Centre (£10,000); War Child (£200).

Applications

Apply in writing to the correspondent.

Sources of information

Charity Commission record.

The Karlsson Jativa Charitable Foundation

Music in the UK and Sweden; poverty, health and education in Latin America

UK; Sweden; Latin America (Peru, Bolivia, Ecuador and Colombia)

£1.21 million (2020)

CC number: 1168787

Correspondent: Claire Miller, 2nd Floor, 78–79 Pall Mall, London SW1Y 5ES (tel: 020 3931 5210; email: info@kjcf.org.uk)

Trustees: Erland Karlsson; Jeremy Arnold; Rose Karlsson; Martin Andersson; Annika Magnusson.

https://kjcf.org.uk

General information

The foundation, through its Signatur programme, aims to promote the advancement of music life in the UK. It makes around five grants a year in the field of music to other not-for-profit organisations. It awards grants to provide more people, especially young people, with access to music education and to improve opportunities for the public to enjoy high-quality music. The foundation also has a Swedish Signatur programme, which has the same aims as the UK programme.

The foundation's other main aim is the relief of poverty and the promotion of health and education in the Andean countries of Latin America. This is achieved through an annual donation to Latin American Children's Trust, a UK-registered charity.

The foundation's website states: 'Our philosophy is to fund partners who have the potential to deliver structural change over the long term improving the opportunities for those who otherwise might not be able to fulfil their potential.'

The foundation partners with registered charities, music schools, conservatories, orchestras, choirs and other music establishments, with preference given to well-established charities.

Financial information

Year end	31/12/2020
Income	£466,000
Assets	£30,850,000
Grants to organisations	£1,210,000
No. of grants	8

Further financial information

Grants awarded to seven UK-based organisations totalled £596,000, and one grant of £611,200 was made to a Swedish organisation.

Beneficiaries included: Signatur Foundation Sweden (£611,200); Latin American Children's Trust (£335,000);

Birmingham Conservatoire (£61,000); Aurora Orchestra and Noah's Ark Children's Hospice (£50,000 each); ORA Choir (£30,000); The Music Works (£20,000).

Applications

The trustees identify projects to be funded. Contact the foundation for further information.

Sources of information

Accounts; annual report; Charity Commission record; funder's website.

Jay Education Trust

Jewish causes

Worldwide

£489,200 (2020/21)

CC number: 1116458

Correspondent: The Trustees, 19A Oldhill Street, London N16 6LD (tel: 0161 798 1660)

Trustees: Aron Nezri; David Weis; Elimelech Bindinger; Rabbi Eli Schwartz.

General information

The trust was established in 2006. Its objects are as follows:

> the relief of poverty in the Jewish Community worldwide; the advancement of religious education according to the beliefs and values of the Jewish Faith worldwide and any charitable purpose at the discretion of the trustees for the benefit of the community.

Financial information

Year end	31/07/2021
Income	£1,290,000
Assets	£5,970,000
Grants to organisations	£489,200

Beneficiaries included: CML (£200,500); Edupoor Ltd (£24,000); Rise and Shine (£19,000); Bobov (£13,500); Wlodowa Charity and Rehabilitation Trust (£10,000); Merkaz Hatorah (£7,500); Tchabe Kollel (£3,000).

Applications

Apply in writing to the correspondent.

Sources of information

Accounts; Charity Commission record; annual report.

JD Foundation

Disadvantaged children and young people, including mental health and homelessness

UK

£397,700 (2020/21)

CC number: 1167090

Correspondent: Siobhan Mawdsley, Secretary, JD Sports Fashion, Edinburgh House, Hollins Brook Way, Bury BL9 8RR (tel: 0161 767 1000; email: thejdfoundation@jdplc.com)

Trustees: Daniel Finley; Siobhan Mawdsley; Traci Corrie; Julie Blomley; Nigel Keen; Neil Greenhalgh.

 www.jdplc.com/jd-foundation

 facebook.com/TheJDFoundation

 @JDFoundationUK

 @thejdfoundation

General information

The JD Foundation was founded in October 2015 by JD Sports Fashion plc. The JD Foundation receives 100% of the proceeds from carrier bag charges from JD Sports. This income is donated to Mountain Rescue and other charities working with young people in the UK that are chosen by JD employees. The foundation also receives financial contributions from employee fundraising.

In 2021 the foundation committed its support to 18 charity partners.

Financial information

Year end	31/01/2021
Income	£631,100
Assets	£263,500
Grants to organisations	£397,700

Beneficiaries included: Blueprint 4 All, Bolton Wanderers, Bright Futures, Buddies of the Birches, C.R.Y. (Cardiac Risk in the Young), HideOut, Kidscape, Manchester Youth Zone, Mountain Rescue England and Wales, Once Upon a Smile, Papyrus, Sacriston Youth Project, Salford Foundation, Scottish Mountain Rescue, Smiling Families, Sport 4 Life UK, The Wellspring, YoungMinds.

Applications

Support is provided to charity partners. Contact the foundation for further information.

Sources of information

Accounts; annual report; Charity Commission record; guidelines for applicants; funder's website; further information provided by the funder

The Jerusalem Trust

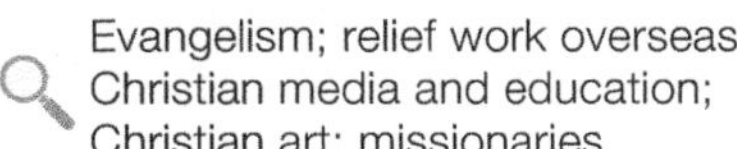

Evangelism; relief work overseas; Christian media and education; Christian art; missionaries

Worldwide

£3.39 million (2020/21)

CC number: 285696

Correspondent: The Trustees, The Peak, 5 Wilton Road, London SW1V 1AP (tel: 020 7410 0330; email: info@sfct.org.uk or proposals@sfct.org.uk)

Trustees: Lady Susan Sainsbury; The Rt Hon. Sir Timothy Sainsbury; Prof. Peter Frankopan; Melanie Townsend; David Wright; Mark Browning; Colin Harbidge.

 www.sfct.org.uk

General information

This is one of the Sainsbury Family Charitable Trusts, which share a joint administration but work autonomously as independent legal entities. They have a common approach to grant-making and generally discourage applications from organisations not already in contact with the trust concerned, but some are open to unsolicited approaches. Established in 1982, the objects of The Jerusalem Trust are to advance the Christian religion and promote Christian organisations, and to advance Christian education and learning.

The trust's website states that its priorities are:

Evangelism and Christian mission in the UK

- Christian projects that develop new ways of working with children and young people, including children who have little or no contact with the Church
- Support for Christian youth work
- Evangelistic projects, especially new and emerging evangelists
- Work with prisoners, ex-prisoners and their families

Christian education

- The development of Christian curriculum resource materials for schools in religious education and across the curriculum
- Support of religious education as a subject, both in curriculum development and teacher training
- Support, training and retention of Christian teachers in all subjects
- Adult lay Christian training and education
- Projects which encourage Christians in leadership in schools

Christian evangelism and relief work overseas

- Priority areas are anglophone sub-Saharan Africa, Ethiopia, Jordan, Syria, Lebanon, Egypt, Iraq and Iran
- Programmes that support theological training colleges
- Programmes that build the capacity of local churches through the training of the laity and clergy
- Translation of Christian books and materials
- The provision of aid to the persecuted church

Christian media

- Media projects promoting Christianity in the UK, North Africa and the Middle East
- Training and networking projects for Christians working in the media
- Creative use of digital media and the internet to promote Christianity
- Jerusalem Productions, which enters into co-productions with national broadcasters and runs the annual Jerusalem Awards for Christian radio and internet productions

Christian art

Commissions of works of art for places of worship.

It should be noted that while the trust does accept unsolicited applications, funding can only be provided for proposals that closely fit the trust's areas of interest. The trustees prefer to seek out organisations and projects to support.

Financial information

Year end	05/04/2021
Income	£3,080,000
Assets	£114,760,000
Grants to organisations	£3,390,000
No. of grants	140

Further financial information

Grants were awarded to 140 organisations and can be broken down as follows:

Evangelism and Christian mission in the UK	£1.56 million
Christian media	£1.19 million
Christian evangelism and relief work overseas	£437,600
Christian education	£200,000

Beneficiaries included: Alpha International (£160,000); Tearfund (£140,000); Catholic Agency for Overseas Development (£60,000); Middle East Media (£50,000); Passion Trust (£40,000); Saltmine Trust (£20,000); SAT-7 Trust (£10,000); Iraqi Christians in Need (£9,400).

Exclusions

The trustees do not normally make grants towards building or repair work for churches and grants are not normally made to individuals.

Applications

Apply using the online application form on the trust's website, which includes details of what to include. Alternatively you may submit a funding enquiry by post to The Sainsbury Family Charitable Trusts at the above address. Your enquiry should be no longer than two sides of A4 and provide the same information as the form.

Sources of information

Accounts; annual report; Charity Commission record; funder's website.

Jerwood Arts

The arts and culture

UK

£1.13 million (2020)

CC number: 1074036

Correspondent: John Opie, Deputy Director, 171 Union Street, Bankside, London SE1 0LN (tel: 020 7261 0279; email: jon@jerwoodarts.org)

Trustees: Katharine Goodison; Thomas Grieve; Rupert Tyler; Juliane Wharton; Lucy Ash; Catrin Griffiths; Miranda Thompson-Schwab.

 https://jerwoodarts.org

 facebook.com/jerwoodarts

 @Jerwoodarts

 @jerwoodarts

General information

History

Previously known as the Jerwood Charitable Foundation, this charity was established in 1998 with general charitable purposes. In 1999 it took over the administration of a number of initiatives of the Jerwood Foundation (the parent company), including the Jerwood Applied Arts Prize, Jerwood Choreography Award and Jerwood Painting Prize.

In 2005 the charity became completely independent after receiving the final endowment donation from the Jerwood Foundation. However, it retains close ties with all of the Jerwood family.

Today, the charity is registered under the name Jerwood Charity but goes by Jerwood Arts.

Aims

The current aims of the charity are to support the development of talented and dedicated artists, curators and producers in transitional stages of their careers. This support is delivered primarily through partnerships with outstanding arts organisations throughout the UK.

The charity's main objectives include:

- To support artists and arts producers, particularly in the early stages of their careers (usually within the first ten years of establishing their practice)
- To support the wider infrastructure of arts organisations and the arts sector
- To respond positively to those taking artistic risks
- To maintain an open, responsive strand of funding

Grant programmes

Open grant programmes are advertised on the charity's website as they arise. These programmes provide a variety of opportunities for early-career individuals through awards, fellowships, commissions, exhibitions and other opportunities delivered by arts organisations.

Depending on the programme, the charity may fund individuals, unincorporated groups, companies, limited companies or registered charities. Organisations funded have to be non-profit and have the arts as their core mission.

The charity's Development Programme Fund makes grants to organisations that can deliver transformational development opportunities for artists, curators and/or producers in their field. These opportunities should offer 'deep learning and tailor-made developmental support for individuals', as stated on the website.

At the time of writing (February 2022), the charity's website stated that funding opportunities were currently under review. It stated that the charity expects to unveil new funding opportunities that take into account the impact of COVID-19, equity, diversity and inclusion, and environmental sustainability.

See the website or sign up to the newsletter for updates.

Financial information

Year end	31/12/2020
Income	£1,570,000
Assets	£31,430,000
Grants to organisations	£1,130,000

Further financial information

Grants paid to organisations via the charity's Development Programme Fund totalled £1 million and the remaining grants were distributed via the charity's Gallery programme.

Beneficiaries included: Apples and Snakes – Jerwood Poetry in Performance (£71,200); FACT – Jerwood FACT Fellowships Programme (£63,500); Gate Theatre – Jerwood Young Designers (£50,000); Somerset House Trust – Sonic Terrains (£31,000); Pacitti Company (£12,500); London Symphony Orchestra (£5,000); OTO Projects UK Artists Residency Fund (£200).

Exclusions

According to the 2020 accounts, the following is not funded:

- Non-arts activities
- Retrospective costs
- Funding for buildings, core costs and equipment
- Costs of formal training, course fees, living costs and materials
- Feature films and short films
- Sponsorship of any kind

Applications

Information on applications is made available when funding rounds open. For enquiries, contact the correspondent or info@jerwoodarts.org. The charity's website also features a helpful FAQs page.

Sources of information

Accounts; annual report; Charity Commission record; funder's website.

Jewish Child's Day

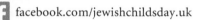

Jewish children who are disadvantaged, suffering or in need of special care

UK and overseas, particularly Israel

£783,900 (2020/21)

CC number: 209266

Correspondent: Adele Busse, Grants Manager, First Floor, Elscot House, Arcadia Avenue, London N3 2JU (tel: 020 8446 8804; email: adele.busse@jcd.uk.com)

Trustees: Virginia Campus; David Collins; Frankie Epstein; Gaby Lazarus; Joy Moss; Stephen Moss; Charles Spungin; Melvyn Orton; Gary Cohen.

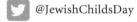

https://jcd.uk.com/grants

facebook.com/jewishchildsday.uk

@JewishChildsDay

General information

This charity was established in 1947 to support Jewish children across the world who had endured the decimation of their communities and displacement during the Second World War. Today, the charity exists to benefit Jewish children under the age of 18 who are living in difficult circumstances due to financial hardship, abuse, neglect, physical disabilities, learning challenges, educational barriers or emotional issues.

The trustees support registered charities running programmes which help these children, awarding grants for items of equipment or specific projects. All grants must directly benefit children (up to the age of 18). Grants have previously been made towards wheelchairs, educational equipment, therapy, rehabilitation programmes, after-school facilities, home teaching for housebound children, respite holidays and much more. Grants usually range from £2,500 to £5,000.

Financial information

Year end	30/06/2021
Income	£1,130,000
Assets	£2,100,000
Grants to organisations	£783,900
No. of grants	129

Further financial information

In 2020/21, 51 grants were awarded in the UK totalling £216,700, 69 grants totalling £527,800 were awarded in Israel and 9 other grants totalling £38,400 were made in other overseas countries.

Beneficiaries included: Ezra Umarpeh (£39,500); Hasmonean Charitable Trust (£10,000); Art Therapies and Teen Action (£5,000 each); Success Stories UK (£3,000); The London Reading Centre (£2,800); Blooming Blossoms (£1,100).

Exclusions

Grants are not made for the following:

- Individuals
- Young people aged 19 and above
- Projects where the majority of the costs are salaries (however, therapist salaries can be included as a major cost)
- Retrospective costs

Applications

Grants are awarded three times per year, in March, June and November. Applicants must email the correspondent for a link to an online application form. Include the name of your organisation and some details of your activities/project in the email.

Sources of information

Accounts; annual report; Charity Commission record; funder's website.

The Elton John AIDS Foundation

HIV/AIDS welfare and prevention

Worldwide

£11.19 million (2020)

CC number: 1017336

Correspondent: The Trustees, Work.Life Hammersmith, Kings House, 174 Hammersmith Road, London W6 7JP (tel: 020 7603 9996; email: admin@eltonjohnaidsfoundation.org)

Trustees: John Bergius; David Furnish; Dr Mark Dybul; Tracy Blackwell; Ilana Kloss; Ajaz Ahmed; Dr Eric Goosby; Thomas Moore; Samuel Segar; Sandra Lee; Emma Kane.

http://london.ejaf.org/grants

facebook.com/eltonjohnaidsfoundation

@ejaf

@ejaf

General information

The Elton John AIDS Foundation was established in 1993 to empower people infected, affected by or at risk of HIV/AIDS and to alleviate their physical, emotional and financial hardship, to enable them to improve their quality of life, live with dignity and exercise self-determination.

The foundation funds a range of services for those living with or affected by HIV/AIDS including education, peer support, medical care, income generation, counselling and testing. It supports operational research but not pure medical research. Particular emphasis is given to the most disadvantaged or high-risk groups, both nationally and internationally, and to community-driven programmes that place people living with HIV/AIDS at the centre of service provision.

In 2019, following the integration of the foundation's USA and UK operations, the foundation established a new global grant-making strategy. The foundation's five priorities for 2020–25 are:

- **Drugs:** tackling the criminalisation and discrimination that puts people who use drugs at elevated risk of HIV
- **LGBTQ+:** speaking out against homophobia, fear and stigma to change laws and policies that affect LGBTQ+ people, and improving access to testing, treatment and care
- **Young people in Africa:** addressing the needs of young people living with and at risk of HIV
- **USA:** tackling the discrimination that prevents access to treatment and care
- **Eastern Europe and Central Asia:** combatting the worsening of the HIV epidemic in the region through the RADIAN initiative

According to the foundation's website activities that can be funded include:

- Advocacy and policy work
- Testing new ways to reach vulnerable people with life-saving information
- Implementing better use of data to target and deliver HIV interventions
- Evidence gathering to support positive shifts in social, policy and legal norms
- New and more accessible ways for people at risk to get tested and access prevention services
- Reducing barriers and linking more people to high quality treatment and care
- Raising public awareness of, support for and engagement with people living with HIV

Financial information

Year end	31/12/2020
Income	£19,080,000
Assets	£10,330,000
Grants to organisations	£11,190,000

Beneficiaries included: ICAP (£2.04 million); Lambeth Borough Council (£880,000); Population Council (£751,000); Source of Hope (£407,100); John Hopkins University (£207,000).

Applications

Application information and guidelines vary for each programme – see the foundation's website for full details.

Sources of information

Accounts; annual report; Charity Commission record; funder's website.

John Lewis and Partners Foundation

Education and training; healthcare; community development; employment; the environment; international development

UK and overseas (particularly areas that support the John Lewis business)

£637,000 (2020/21)

CC number: 1118162

Correspondent: The Trustees, 171 Victoria Street, London SW1E 5NN (tel: 020 7592 5658; email: johnlewisfoundation@johnlewis.co.uk)

Trustees: Margaret Porteous; Paul Buchanan; Sarah Gillard; Simon Bishop; Christine Kasoulis; Johnathan Marsh; Nyika Brain; Andrew Hoad; Marija Rompani; Louise Stuart.

 www.johnlewisfoundation.org

General information

The John Lewis and Partners Foundation was established in 2007 to benefit communities in the UK and overseas within which the retailer John Lewis and Partners operates. The foundation supports a broad range of charitable causes; however, according to its website, the foundation's current focus is 'to support projects that promote training and skills and demonstrably lead to meaningful and sustainable employment'.

The following information is taken from the foundation's 2020/21 accounts:

> The Charity will make grants to fund projects that improve the well being of such communities. Potential projects may include, but are not limited to:
> - Funding the development of schools in areas where limited educational facilities are available;
> - Funding medical centres and health care initiatives in areas of deprivation;
> - Funding creches and other child care facilities to enable women with young children to work;
> - Funding training facilities to enable people with limited skills to improve their employability;
> - Funding community and recreational facilities in areas where few exist; and
> - Funding projects which help to protect the environment and improve biodiversity.
>
> Applications are welcome from the following groups or individuals:
> - John Lewis Partnership employees;
> - Supplier management committees;
> - Worker management committees; and
> - Independent charities and community groups

Financial information

Year end	31/01/2021
Income	£490,600
Assets	£762,500
Grants to organisations	£637,000

Further financial information

Grants totalled £637,000 during the year, of which £162,100 was COVID-19 funding awarded to the foundation's existing charity partners.

Alongside grants, the foundation also provided £37,200 worth of in-kind support. Donations of smartphones and laptops were donated to Business in the Community.

Beneficiaries included: Save the Children (£125,000); WaterAid (£100,000); Future Roots (£59,000); British Asian Trust (£41,800); The Baytree Centre (£25,000); Papworth Trust (£11,300); Care and Fair (£7,000).

Exclusions

The following information has been taken from the foundation's 2020/21 accounts:

> Grants will not be made to contribute towards elements of projects which might reasonably be considered 'core costs' including capital items, construction or refurbishment of buildings, development of computer programmes or educational materials, marketing and promotional activities, salaried positions, venue hire and other consumables.
>
> Projects which are ineligible for funding include:
> - Projects that do not offer benefit to communities who support the John Lewis and Partners business;
> - Projects that promote religious or political groups or activities that exclude any part of society;
> - Projects which seek to create an income stream or charge a fee to beneficiaries for access to it; and
> - Courses, conferences, festivals, expeditions, overseas travel, fundraising events, receptions, lectures, respite breaks or holidays
>
> The Trustees have also identified those organisations that are ineligible for funding, which include:
> - Pressure or campaign groups;
> - Endowment funds; and
> - Personal or company sponsorship

Applications

At the time of writing (January 2022), the foundation's website stated that the foundation was conducting a review of its giving and had therefore suspended all new funding. The application form and guidance pack were therefore temporarily unavailable. See the foundation's website for updates.

Sources of information

Accounts; annual report; Charity Commission record; funder's website.

The Joicey Trust

General charitable purposes

 Northumberland; Tyne and Wear; the eastern Scottish Borders

£216,900 (2020/21)

CC number: 244679

Correspondent: The Trustees, One Trinity, Broad Chare, Newcastle upon Tyne NE1 2HF (tel: 0191 279 9676; email: appeals@thejoiceytrust.org.uk)

Trustees: The Hon. Andrew Joicey; The Hon. Mrs K. J. Crosbie Dawson; The Rt Hon. Lady Joicey; The Rt Hon. The Lord Joicey.

 www.thejoiceytrust.org.uk

General information

The Joicey Trust provides grants to organisations in support of general charitable purposes. The trust will consider any applications from its main beneficial area which comprises the county of Northumberland, the old metropolitan county of Tyne and Wear, and the eastern Scottish Borders region. Grants are made for core funding or capital expenditure.

Financial information

Year end	05/04/2021
Income	£587,000
Assets	£8,260,000
Grants to organisations	£216,900
No. of grants	88

Further financial information

The trust awarded £216,900 in grants during the year; however, in previous years its grant-making exceeded £300,000.

Beneficiaries included: Greggs Foundation (£15,000); The Little Theatre (£5,000); Strathmore Road Methodist Church (£4,000); Northern Roots (£3,000); Percy Hedley Foundation (£2,500); Read for Good (£1,000); Wooler Fountain Restoration Group (£400).

Exclusions

Research and research costs within core funding applications. Charities not registered within the area of benefit and those whose gross incoming resources exceed £1 million.

Applications

Application forms can be obtained by completing a contact form on the trust's website. The trustees meet twice a year, usually in January/early February and late June/July. Applications should be submitted to the appeals secretary in time to allow for any queries to be resolved by 30 November or 31 May for consideration at the next trustees' meeting: early applications are therefore encouraged.

Sources of information

Accounts; annual report; Charity Commission record; funder's website.

The Jones 1986 Charitable Trust

Social welfare; disability; older people; children and young people

Primarily Nottinghamshire

£1.08 million (2020/21)

CC number: 327176

Correspondent: Charlene Truman, Trust Administrator, UHY Hacker Young LLP, 14 Park Row, Nottingham, Nottinghamshire NG1 6GR (tel: 0115 938 8762; email: c.truman@uhy-uk.com)

Trustees: John Pears; David Lindley; Richard Stanley.

 www.thejonescharitabletrust.org.uk

General information

The trust was established in 1986 with general charitable purposes. It primarily supports organisations in Nottinghamshire working in the following areas:

- Children and young people
- Older people
- People with disabilities
- Other charities or voluntary bodies

Financial information

Year end	05/04/2021
Income	£1,390,000
Assets	£50,670,000
Grants to organisations	£1,080,000
No. of grants	84

Beneficiaries included: REACH Learning Disability (£225,000); Nottingham Hospitals Charity (£103,000); Framework Knitters Museum (£85,500); Oasis Community Centre (£30,000); Headway UK (£12,000); Safer Living Foundation (£5,000); Riding for Smiles (£2,500); Rucksack Project – University of Nottingham Students' Union (£300)

Exclusions

Grants are not made to individuals, or for activities that are the responsibility of the local health authority, education authority or a similar body.

Applications

Application forms can be downloaded from the trust's website. The trustees meet quarterly each year, usually in January, April, July and October. Check the website for upcoming deadlines.

Sources of information

Accounts; annual report; Charity Commission record; funder's website.

The Muriel Jones Foundation

General charitable purposes

UK and overseas

£1.08 million (2020/21)

CC number: 1135107

Correspondent: The Trustees, c/o Ludlow Trust Co. Ltd, Tower Wharf, Cheese Lane, Bristol BS2 0JJ (tel: 0117 313 8200)

Trustees: Ludlow Trust Company Ltd; Richard Brindle; Katie Brindle.

General information

This foundation was established in 2010 with the aim to support general charitable purposes in the UK and abroad. Previous annual reports have shown a preference for environmental, welfare and human rights charities (note this is an observed trend and not an exclusively stated priority).

Financial information

Year end	28/02/2021
Income	£83,600
Assets	£4,360,000
Grants to organisations	£1,080,000
No. of grants	17

Further financial information

In 2020/21, the foundation awarded 23 grants to 17 organisations.

Beneficiaries included: Médecins Sans Frontières (£200,000); Animals Asia Foundation (£100,000); FareShare (£75,000); Bath Cats and Dogs Home (£50,000); Prada-Willi Syndrome Association UK (£25,000); Downside Up Ltd (£15,000); Celtic FC Foundation (£5,000); Clifton College Development Trust (£1,900).

Applications

Apply in writing to the correspondent.

Sources of information

Accounts; annual report; Charity Commission record.

The Jordan Charitable Foundation

Children and young people and education

Herefordshire

£6.82 million (2020)

CC number: 1051507

Correspondent: The Trustees, 8th Floor, 6 New Street Square, New Fetter Lane, London EC4A 3AQ (tel: 020 7842 2000; email: jordan@rawlinson-hunter.com)

Trustees: Christopher Bliss; Anthony Brierley; Sir George Russell; Nicholas Fry; Parkdove Ltd; Snowport Ltd.

General information

The Jordan Charitable Foundation was established in 1995.

The foundation's 2020 accounts state:

> Historically, the trustees' grant making policies have been guided by the intentions of the original Founders of the Foundation. Since inception, the Foundation has made substantial grants to local charities in the county of Herefordshire, in particular, charities operating within the city of Hereford.
>
> Following the death of the Founders, the trustees have begun to transition the objectives of the Foundation, with the new primary focus being education. The trustees' will remain conscious of the intentions of the Founders as the Foundation moves forward.
>
> The current mission statement for the Foundation is:
>
> To help young people with potential but poor prospects transform their lives by fostering their desire and confidence to learn, achieve and earn, in order to help transform our world for the better.
>
> To achieve this, the Foundation is looking to partner with a small number of charities and for the partnership's to be long term and ambitious.

Financial information

Year end	31/12/2020
Income	£3,530,000
Assets	£142,190,000
Grants to organisations	£6,820,000

Beneficiaries included: New Model Institute for Technology and Engineering (£3.09 million); IntoUniversity (£1.5 million); Wildfowl and Wetlands Trust (£1.44 million); Herefordshire Headway (£100,000); Angling Trust (£5,000).

Applications

Applications may be made in writing to the correspondent. The trustees meet four times a year.

Sources of information

Accounts; annual report; Charity Commission record.

The Joron Charitable Trust

General charitable purposes; education; medical research

UK

£920,000 (2020/21)

CC number: 1062547

Correspondent: The Trustees, c/o Ravensale Ltd, New Broadway, London W5 2XA (tel: 020 8908 4655; email: info@ravensale.com)

Trustees: Bruce Jarvis; John Jarvis; Sandra Jarvis; Juliet Jarvis.

General information

Established in 1997, The Joron Charitable Trust was founded by the Jarvis family. The family is involved in property investment and the manufacture of ballpoint pens.

The trust's policy is to make grants to charities which can demonstrate how the grant will be effectively used. The trust has a particular focus on medical and educational charities. It funds the development of educational programmes that teach social and communication skills, as well medical charities that support people with disabilities and terminal illness. The trust also funds medical research.

Financial information

Year end	31/03/2021
Income	£1,050,000
Assets	£340,200
Grants to organisations	£920,000
No. of grants	52

Beneficiaries included: The Gem Project (£370,000); The Wilderness Foundation (£70,000); Prostate Cancer (£30,000); Imperial Health Charity (£25,000); RSPCA and Shelter (£10,000 each); Magpas Air Ambulance (£5,000).

Applications

Apply in writing to the correspondent. There is no formal application procedure.

Sources of information

Accounts; annual report; Charity Commission record.

The Cyril and Eve Jumbo Charitable Trust

Children and young people; people with disabilities; medical research; literacy; homelessness; disaster relief; community support; social welfare

UK and overseas

£303,800 (2020/21)

CC number: 1097209

Correspondent: The Trustees, Mumbo Jumbo World, 48 Great Marlborough Street, London W1F 7BB (tel: 020 7437 0879; email: charity@mjw13.com)

Trustees: Geoffrey Margolis; Rafiq Hayat; Edward Engulu; Lorraine Margolis.

General information

The trust was set up in 2003 to support a range of charitable purposes.

The trust's website states:

> The Trust seeks to establish a relationship with the charities it supports, developing an ongoing working relationship over a timescale 3–5 years.
>
> We give preference to programmes which use education, transfer of knowledge or empathy as the mediums of change.
>
> We are less keen on capital projects.
>
> We prefer to support Adolescents and Post-Adolescents programmes in England and self sufficiency projects in the third world.
>
> We are motivated by HOPE and POSSIBILITY.

The trust has also previously made grants for people with disabilities, medical research, literacy, people experiencing homelessness, disaster relief, community support and social welfare.

Financial information

Year end	05/04/2021
Income	£251,800
Assets	£2,010,000
Grants to organisations	£303,800

Beneficiaries included: Action Against Cancer (£41,600); Jewish Care (£30,500); Send a Cow (£15,000); The Literacy Pirates Ltd (£7,500); The Selby Trust (£3,000); Grief Encounter (£1,500); Muswell Hill Soup Kitchen (£500).

Applications

Apply in writing to the correspondent. The 2020/21 annual accounts state:

> Applications can be submitted to the Trustees by charitable institutions and these applications are considered by the Trustees on a regular basis. Applications should be in writing and incorporate full details of the Charity and the course for which funding is requested.

Sources of information

Accounts; annual report; Charity Commission record; funder's website.

Kantor Charitable Foundation

General charitable purposes; the arts; health; education; the Jewish religion and culture

UK

£1.98 million (2020)

CC number: 1173550

Correspondent: The Trustees, c/o Withers LLP, Third Floor, 20 Old Bailey, London EC4M 7AN (tel: 020 7507 6000)

Trustee: Kantor Trustees.

General information

This foundation registered with the Charity Commission in June 2017. Currently, its funding priorities are the advancement of:

- Education
- Health
- Jewish religion and culture

In previous years, the foundation has also supported the advancement of the arts. Grants are primarily made in the UK. In recent times, the foundation has focused its support on longer-term grants and on providing sustainable funding.

Financial information

Year end	31/12/2020
Income	£375,600
Assets	-£2,870,000
Grants to organisations	£1,980,000
No. of grants	17

Beneficiaries included: The Thrombosis Research Institute (£1 million); The Prince's Foundation (£300,000); MS Society (£100,000); RNIB (£50,000); Kantor King Solomon High School (£25,000); Jewish Care (£18,000); University Jewish Chaplaincy (£5,000).

Applications

The foundation's 2020 accounts state: 'At this stage the Board does not invite unsolicited grant applications, rather relying on the Board's connections within the sector to bring relevant projects to the Foundation's attention.'

Sources of information

Accounts; annual report; Charity Commission record.

The Ian Karten Charitable Trust

Computer technology for people with severe physical, sensory or cognitive disabilities or mental health problems; higher education for students in challenging personal circumstances

UK; Republic of Ireland; Israel

£569,000 (2019/20)

CC number: 281721

Correspondent: Dawn Green, Karten Network Development Co-ordinator, International House, 64 Nile Street, London N1 7SR (tel: 07720 931477; email: dawn@karten-network.org.uk)

Trustees: Anthony Davis; Alexandra Moran; Sally Cooke; Edward Copisarow.

@kartennetwork

General information

The trust was initially established in 1980 by Ian Karten to support the Jewish community in the UK and Israel, and to provide scholarships for students studying at English and Israeli universities. Today, the trust continues to support disadvantaged students in partnership with universities. It also focuses on providing access to assistive technologies for people with disabilities.

Karten Centres

The trust has a network of Karten Centres, which provide access to adaptive computer technology for adults with physical, cognitive, sensory or learning disabilities or with mental health problems. The centres are typically established by and located in specialist colleges of further education or adult services host charities concerned with the provision of education, employment, health, rehabilitation and daily living services for such adults.

Existing centres can apply for up to £25,000 every three years for additional or upgraded equipment.

Scholarships and bursaries

The trust supports higher education by funding studentships for studies and research at universities in the UK and Israel and posts at Southampton University and Birkbeck College, University of Cambridge. Awards are mainly given via the educational institution.

Financial information

Year end	30/09/2020
Income	£410,500
Assets	£13,140,000
Grants to organisations	£569,000

Further financial information

Grants paid during the year totalled £586,000. New commitments made in the year consisted of grants to Karten Centres (£202,200) and educational grants, scholarships and bursaries (£130,400).

Beneficiaries included: Southampton University (£50,000); Motor Neurone Disease Association (£24,900); Treloar College (£18,600); Policy Connect (£10,000); British Friends of the Hebrew University (£2,000); The Anne Frank Educational Trust Ashkelon Foundation (£750).

Applications

Grants are no longer being made for new Karten Centres; however, existing centres can apply for additional or upgraded equipment using an application form available to download from the trust's website. The trustees meet every six months, in March and September, to review the accounts and to discuss any proposed donations, scholarships or bursaries.

Sources of information

Accounts; annual report; application form; Charity Commission record; funder's website.

The Kasner Charitable Trust

Jewish causes, particularly the relief of poverty, the advancement of education and the furtherance of Jewish faith

UK and overseas, with preference for Manchester, London and Israel

£5.38 million (2020/21)

CC number: 267510

Correspondent: Baruch Erlich, Trustee, 1A Gresham Gardens, London NW11 8NX (tel: 020 3637 2868)

Trustees: Baruch Erlich; Judith Erlich; David Winegarten.

General information

The trust was established in 1974 to fund organisations with a focus on Jewish causes in the UK and abroad, as chosen by the trustees in line with the principles set out by the founder of the trust, Josef Kasner.

According to the trust's annual report for 2020/21, when considering grants, the trustees pay attention 'to the organisational efficiency and reputation of the applicant and the ability to 'make a difference''.

In 2020/21 grants were made to organisations in the UK and Israel. The trust's annual report explains that grant recipients were involved in:

- Providing food and financial support to poor families
- Maintaining synagogues and places of communal religious services
- Jewish education at primary school and secondary school level
- Centres of advanced study and higher education
- Centres for children with special educational needs
- Medical advocacy
- Assisting couples experiencing infertility with treatment and support
- Development of 'immigrant' towns in Israel to benefit the welfare of their communities

The trust has a strong focus on Israel but receives many applications from organisations in the UK and aims to help them, especially where such organisations are not supported by larger grant-makers.

Financial information

Year end	31/03/2021
Income	£9,850,000
Assets	£9,890,000
Grants to organisations	£5,380,000

Further financial information

In 2020/21, grants were broken down as follows:

General charitable purposes	£1.82 million
The development of the land of Israel and its citizens	£1.33 million
Relief of poverty	£752,300
The advancement of education	£743,400
The furtherance of religion	£562,800
Medical advocacy and equipment	£164,600

Only beneficiaries of grants of £45,000 and above were listed in the accounts. Grants of under £45,000 totalled £221,200.

Beneficiaries included: UK Toremet Ltd (£2.86 million); JNF Charitable Trust (£545,000); Friends of the United Institutions of Arad (£450,000); Yad Eliezer Trust (£125,000); Dignity Organisation (£74,600); Yeshuas Chaim Synagogue (£62,200); Kehal Chasidei Wiznitz Ltd (£50,000).

Applications

Apply in writing to the correspondent.

Sources of information

Accounts; annual report; Charity Commission record.

Kavli Trust

Humanitarian work; medical research; culture

Norway; Sweden; Finland; UK; Asia; sub-Saharan Africa

£7.8 million (2021)

Correspondent: Inger Iversen, Chief Executive Officer, Kavlifondet, Postboks 7360, N-5020 Bergen, Norway (email: post@kavlifondet.no)

Trustees: Dag Opedal; Aksel Mjos; Solfrid Lind; Lise Hammergren; Erik Volden.

https://kavlifondet.no/en

facebook.com/Kavlifondet

@kavlifondet

@kavlifondet

General information

The Kavli Trust owns Norway's Kavli food group and distributes its profits to good causes. Kavli UK currently has over 200 employees across its three sites and makes a range of food products under its three brands: Primula, Castle MacLellan and St Helen's Farm. The trust aims to distribute around £8.2 million of funding each year. A proportion of the available funds is allocated each year for recipients nominated by the employees.

Causes supported

- Humanitarian work, particularly health projects for mothers and children, education, training and entrepreneurship (60%)
- Medical research, particularly on chronic fatigue syndrome (ME) and dementia (30%)

- Culture, with a particular focus on children, young people and older people (10%)

Geographical distribution of grants

According to the website, around 70% of grants go to the 'Kavli countries' of Norway, Sweden, Finland and the UK. The rest go to development projects in Asia and sub-Saharan Africa.

Grant type

Grants can be one-off or multi-year commitments.

Financial information

Year end	31/12/2021
Grants to organisations	£7,800,000
No. of grants	60+

Further financial information

The trust's website states: 'Kavli Trust allocated £7.8 million to more than 60 good causes in 2021, prioritising child and adolescent mental health and climate and responsible consumption and production.' Note: the financial figures have been converted from Norwegian Kroner using the exchange rate at the time of writing (May 2022).

Beneficiaries included: UK beneficiaries included: University of London (£700,000); Merse House – garden project (£60,000); Young People Count (£45,000); Children's Heart Unit Fund (£35,000); People's Pantry (£1,000); Sage Gateshead (£250).

Applications

The trust's website states:

> The Kavli Trust's general manager takes a proactive approach and largely identifies relevant projects, organisations and individuals herself. Projects can also receive support on the basis of an application, but this must then be specific, relevant, and clearly within the Kavli Trust's guidelines.
>
> What process is followed in deciding whether to support a project?
>
> After initial conversations and contacts which allow the general manager to collect basic information on the organisation and those involved, the applicant will be invited to submit a formal request to the board. The trustees may call on external experts to assess the project before they take a decision.

Sources of information

Annual report; funder's website.

The Emmanuel Kaye Foundation

General charitable purposes; medical research; penal reform; education; music; the performing arts; prevention of sexual exploitation; community development; social welfare

UK, with a preference for the north-east of Hampshire

£724,000 (2019/20)

CC number: 280281

Correspondent: The Trustees, PO Box 1579, Woking, Surrey GU21 9DS (tel: 07585 341626; email: finance@ekf.org.uk)

Trustees: John Forster; Louise Kaye; Eleanor Kaye; Madeleine Hawes; Anton Sternberg.

General information

The foundation was registered in 1980 and, according to its Charity Commission record, supports 'UK registered charities in social welfare, community development, education, arts and culture, healthcare and medical research, and activities in North East Hampshire'.

Grants are made to registered charities and charitable causes, with priority given to smaller charities without a national presence. Grants may be for core costs or specific project costs and range mostly between £5,000 and £30,000.

Financial information

Year end	31/07/2020
Income	£970,300
Assets	£4,470,000
Grants to organisations	£724,000
No. of grants	30

Further financial information

Grants were broken down as follows in 2019/20:

Educational support programmes	32%
Medical research	21%
Prevention of sexual exploitation	19%
Musical appreciation among young people	12%
The performing arts	8%
Penal reform	7%
Other	1%

Beneficiaries included: Parkinson's UK (£150,000); Lyric Hammersmith (£32,000); Rosa Fund (£30,000); Against Violence and Abuse (£25,000); Awards for Young Musicians (£20,000); Prison Reform Trust (£10,000); Cure Parkinson's (£5,000); Move into Well-being (£3,000).

Applications

The foundation's 2019/20 accounts state: 'The foundation does not accept unsolicited requests for grants or donations, focussing its support for registered charities principally, but not exclusively, where a relationship with trustees has been established.'

Sources of information

Accounts; annual report; Charity Commission record.

The Kay Kendall Leukaemia Fund

Research into leukaemia and patient care

UK

£2.67 million (2020/21)

CC number: 290772

Correspondent: The Trustees, The Peak, 5 Wilton Road, London SW1V 1AP (tel: 020 7410 0330; email: info@kklf.org.uk)

Trustees: Judith Portrait; Timothy Sainsbury; Charles Metcalfe.

 www.kklf.org.uk

General information

This is one of the Sainsbury Family Charitable Trusts, which share a joint administration but work autonomously as independent legal entities. They have a common approach to grant-making and generally discourage applications from organisations not already in contact with the trust concerned, but some are open to unsolicited approaches.

This charity was established in 1985 following the death of James Sainsbury in 1984. The charity provides funding for research into leukaemia and related diseases.

The charity also helps to support first-class clinicians and scientists who wish to pursue a career in haematological research by providing junior and intermediate-level fellowships, depending on the level of research already obtained.

The following types of support are available:

- **Project grants** – research grants are normally awarded for projects of up to three years' duration. Grants are usually awarded to give additional support to programmes already underway, with the aim being to further strengthen activities which are already of high quality. Requests for support for basic science programmes may be considered. Proposals which are closely related to the prevention, diagnosis or therapy of leukaemia and related diseases are particularly encouraged
- **Capital funding** – requests for capital grants for leukaemia research laboratories or for clinical facilities for leukaemia will be considered either alone or in conjunction with

proposals for the support of research and/or patient management. Capital requests must give a budget estimate of costs, together with a full justification

- **Equipment grants** – requests for single large items of equipment will be considered. Requests must give detailed cost estimates and a full scientific justification
- **Clinical care** – requests for clinical support must give full costing and a detailed explanation of how this support will enhance the existing service and/or research activities

Financial information

Year end	05/04/2021
Income	£113,000
Assets	£7,960,000
Grants to organisations	£2,670,000

Further financial information

Grants were broken down as follows:

Research grants	£1.2 million
Intermediate KKLF Fellowship	£688,000
Junior KKLF Fellowship	£601,300
Patient care	£307,500

Beneficiaries included: University of Leeds (£263,900); Cambridge Institute for Medical Research (£165,000); Beatson Institute for Cancer Research (£101,100); University Edinburgh (£85,600); The Royal Marsden Cancer Charity (£50,000); Sheffield Children's Hospital Charity (£20,000); Young Lives vs Cancer (£15,000).

Exclusions

Project grant applications submitted simultaneously to other funding bodies will not be accepted.

Applications

Application forms are available by contacting the charity's office and application guidelines can be found on the charity's website.

Sources of information

Annual report and accounts; Charity Commission record; funder's website.

The Kennedy Trust for Rheumatology Research

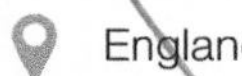

Research into rheumatic and related musculoskeletal diseases

England

£8.49 million (2019/20)

CC number: 260059

Correspondent: Zoe Montanaro, Grants and Office Manager, One Lyric Square, Hammersmith, London W6 0NB (tel: 020 8834 1562; email: z.montanaro@kennedytrust.org)

Trustees: Prof. Hill Gaston; Jennifer Johnson; Margaret Frost; Prof. Stephen Holgate; Prof. Andrew Cope; Edmund Buckley; Mark Dighero; Victoria White; Christopher Coombe; Prof. Michael Patton; Dr Paul Satchell; Richard Punt; Prof. Tracy Hussell.

 www.kennedytrust.org

General information

The trust was established in 1965 by Mathilda Kennedy (daughter of Michael Marks – the founder of Marks and Spencer) and her husband Terence Kennedy.

According to its website, the trust's mission is to 'provide support for basic and translational research into musculoskeletal and related inflammatory diseases, where [it] can make a clear difference and where other funding is not easily available'.

The trust focuses its grant-giving on the work of the Kennedy Institute of Rheumatology at the University of Oxford. In recent years the trust has expanded the scope of its funding, offering research fellowships and studentships as well as considering informal approaches from organisations in the fields of musculoskeletal and inflammatory disease research. See the trust's website for full details.

Financial information

Year end	30/09/2020
Income	£8,810,000
Assets	£276,280,000
Grants to organisations	£8,490,000

Further financial information

Grants were broken down as follows in the trust's 2019/20 accounts:

Fellowships	61%	£5.13 million
Studentships	18%	£1.5 million
Core facilities	6%	£505,000
Staff appointments	4%	£361,000
Director's Fund	4%	£300,000
Institute initiatives	3%	£286,000
COVID-19 support	3%	£285,000
Institute building	1%	£126,000

Beneficiaries included: The Kennedy Institute at Oxford (£3.93 million); University of Birmingham (£2.39 million); University of Edinburgh (£1.78 million); King's College London (£100,000); University of Manchester (£85,000).

Applications

Visit the trust's website for information on current funding initiatives. Regarding funding for additional projects, the website states, 'we consider informal approaches from, and offer support to, institutions only; we do not consider personal applications.'

Sources of information

Accounts; annual report; Charity Commission record; funder's website.

The Kennel Club Charitable Trust

Canine welfare and research into canine diseases

UK

£653,200 (2020)

CC number: 327802

Correspondent: The Trust Administrator, 10 Clarges Street, Piccadilly, London W1J 8AB (tel: 020 7518 6874; email: kcct@thekennelclub.org.uk)

Trustees: Michael Herrtage; The Revd William King; Dr Andrew Higgins; Jennifer Millard; Graham Hill; Rosemary Smart.

 www.kennelclubcharitabletrust.org

 facebook.com/TheKennelClubUK

 @TheKennelClubUK

 @thekennelclubuk

General information

Established in 1987, the trust provides funding for a wide range of activities and organisations supporting the health and welfare of all dogs. According to its website, the trust's objects are:

- To promote the advancement of education and science by furthering research into canine diseases and hereditary disorders of dogs.
- To promote the quality of life of human beings by promoting support dogs as therapeutic and practical aids to humans.
- To promote the relief and suffering of dogs that are in need of care and attention through welfare channels.

The trust will consider grant applications for science, welfare and education projects to benefit dogs.

Financial information

Year end	31/12/2020
Income	£899,200
Assets	£2,530,000
Grants to organisations	£653,200

Beneficiaries included: Royal Veterinary College (£93,800); PDSA (£21,900); Three Counties Dog Rescue and University of Birmingham (£3,000 each); West of England Cavalier King Charles Spaniel Club Welfare (£2,000).

Exclusions

The trust's website states that 'pure building costs or requests from organisations whose concern is not predominantly with the dog (e.g. general animal sanctuaries) are not supported.'

Applications

Application forms and further guidance can be found on the trust's website.

Sources of information

Accounts; annual report; Charity Commission record; funder's website.

The Kensington and Chelsea Foundation

Children and young people; skills and employment; isolation and loneliness; vulnerable older people experiencing fuel poverty

Kensington and Chelsea

£2.27 million (2020/21)

CC number: 1125940

Correspondent: The Trustees, 111–117 Lancaster Road, Ladbroke Grove, London W11 1QT (tel: 020 7229 5499; email: team@thekandcfoundation.com)

Trustees: Cynthia Dize; Lucinda Stafford-Deitsch; Jerome Raphaely; Martin Morgan; Clare Ferguson; Richard Briance; William Crone; Esma Dukali; Peter Winslow; Abdurahman Sayed; Abdi Aden.

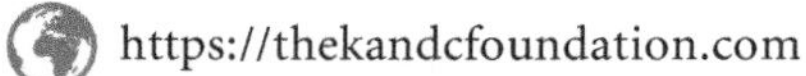

https://thekandcfoundation.com

facebook.com/kandcfoundation

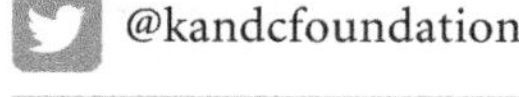

@kandcfoundation

General information

The foundation was established in 2008 by Jeremy Raphaely to address the inequalities that exist in the borough of Kensington and Chelsea.

Grant programmes

The foundation has a range of grant programmes:

- **Children and young people** – ensuring young people have the best chance to fulfil their potential
- **Skills and employment** – improving opportunities for local people to access employment through advice and training
- **Isolation and loneliness** – reducing isolation and loneliness in the borough and their negative effects on mental health
- **Grenfell Tower Development Fund** – established after the Grenfell Tower tragedy to support people in North Kensington

Financial information

Year end	31/03/2021
Income	£1,880,000
Assets	£988,100
Grants to organisations	£2,270,000
No. of grants	119

Further financial information

During the financial period, grants totalling £1.66 million were awarded to 67 local charities and community groups. In addition, £612,600 was awarded to 52 organisations through the Grenfell Community Development Fund.

Beneficiaries included: Age UK – Kensington and Chelsea (£120,000); Chelsea Theatre (£30,000); Earl's Court Youth Club (£15,000); Nova New Opportunities (£10,000); London Sports Trust (£9,900); African Women's Care (£2,500); Morley College (£500).

Applications

In the first instance, applicants should consult the foundation's website, which details what funding is currently available.

Sources of information

Accounts; annual report; Charity Commission record; funder's website.

The Kentown Wizard Foundation

Children and young people living with life-limiting conditions and disabilities, and their families

Worldwide, with a preference for the UK

£1.95 million (2020/21)

CC number: 1163956

Correspondent: The Trustees, Metro House Ltd, Unit 14–17, Metropolitan Business Park, Preston New Road, Blackpool FY3 9LT (tel: 01253 446923; email: enquiries@kentownwizard.org)

Trustees: David Bamber; Kenneth Townsley; Richard Ingle; Kathryn Graham.

www.kentownwizard.org

facebook.com/KentownWizard

@KentownWizard

@kentownwizard

General information

The foundation was established by Ken Townsley in 2015. Ken was a baggage handler at Blackpool Airport before going on to start Blackpool-based Gold Medal Travel, which he later sold to Thomas Cook for an estimated £87 million.

The foundation focuses on children and young people living with life-limiting conditions and disabilities, and their families. Grants are awarded to UK-registered charities selected by the foundation.

Financial information

Year end	31/03/2021
Income	£904,200
Assets	£81,060,000
Grants to organisations	£1,950,000

Beneficiaries included: Over the Wall (£800,000); Make-A-Wish Foundation UK (£550,000); Whizz-Kidz (£250,000); Dreams Come True (£200,000); Candlelighters (£16,000); Blackpool Tiggers (£6,000); Unique Kidz and Co. (£5,000).

Applications

According to its website, the foundation seeks out potential charity partners and therefore does not accept unsolicited applications.

Sources of information

Accounts; annual report; Charity Commission record; funder's website.

Keren Association Ltd

General charitable purposes; Jewish causes; education; religion; social welfare

UK and overseas

£10.75 million (2020/21)

CC number: 313119

Correspondent: The Trustees, 136 Clapton Common, London E5 9AG (tel: 020 8800 9677; email: mail@cohenarnold.com)

Trustees: A. Perlman; Mrs H. Weiss; Mr E. Englander; Mrs N. Weiss; J. Englander; S. Englander; J. Stern; Mr S. Englander; P. Englander.

General information

The charity was established in 1961 and supports the advancement of education and the provision of religious instruction and training in traditional Judaism. Assistance is also given to Jewish people who are in need.

Financial information

Year end	31/03/2021
Income	£3,000,000
Assets	£31,690,000
Grants to organisations	£10,750,000

Beneficiaries included: Friends of Mercaz Hatorah Belz Macnivka (£2 million); China Vechisda (£1.01 million); Mosdot Toras Aharon (£872,600); Mifalei Tzdokah V'chesed (£302,600); Zera Aharon Machnovka Belz Yerushalayim (£201,000); Synagogue D'Chasidei Belz (£140,800); Side by Side School Ltd (£50,000).

Applications

Contact the correspondent for further information. The annual report for 2020/21 states that 'the trustees consider all requests which they receive and make donations based on the level of funds available to charities whose purpose fall within the objects of the Charitable Company.'

Sources of information

Accounts; annual report; Charity Commission record.

E. and E. Kernkraut Charities Ltd

Education; the advancement of the Orthodox Jewish faith; general charitable purposes

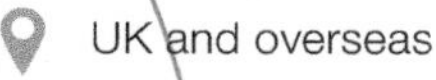
UK and overseas

£514,800 (2020/21)

CC number: 275636

Correspondent: The Trustees, The Knoll, Fountayne Road, London N16 7EA (tel: 020 8806 7947; email: mail@cohenarnold.com)

Trustees: Joseph Kernkraut; Jacob Kernkraut; Esther Kernkraut; Eli Kernkraut.

General information

The charity was established in 1973 and makes grants to support education, the advancement of the Orthodox Jewish faith and general charitable purposes.

Financial information

Year end	31/03/2021
Income	£504,000
Assets	£7,030,000
Grants to organisations	£514,800

Beneficiaries included: Vyoel Moshe Charitable Trust (£86,000); Yetev Lev London Jerusalem Trust (£52,000); Congregation Vyoel Moshe D'satmer Charitable Trust (£28,000); A T.I.M.E. Ltd (£20,000); Ben Amram Charitable Trust (£18,600); The Bais Rochel Dsatmar Charitable Trust (£15,000); Chevras Mo'oz Ladol (£10,000).

Applications

Apply in writing to the correspondent. Contact the correspondent for further information. According to the annual report for 2020/21, when making grants, the trustees 'use their personal knowledge of the relevant institutions, their representatives, operational efficiency and reputation'.

Sources of information

Accounts; annual report; Charity Commission record.

KFC Foundation

Children and young people (11 to 25 years old)

UK

£582,900 (2019/20)

CC number: 1163560

Correspondent: The Trustees, Orion Gate, Guilford Road, Woking GU22 7NJ (email: a contact form is available on the foundation's website)

Trustees: Akram Khan; Neil Morrison; Simon Coates; Paula McKenzie; Nichola Newman; James Fletcher.

www.kfc.co.uk/kfc-foundation

General information

The foundation provides grants to grassroots organisations that support young people in the UK to fulfil their potential by providing safe social spaces, mentoring and work or social skills. The foundation is focused on supporting young people in a position of social disadvantage (i.e. care leavers, those experiencing homelessness, young carers, young parents, young people at risk of or with experience of the criminal justice system).

The foundation has previously supported charities through partnerships with regional charities. However, these partnerships were concluded in May 2020 in order to move to a more locally focused community grants programme.

Community grants

The KFC Foundation provides grants to support grassroots organisations in the heart of its restaurants' communities.

Grants of up to £2,000 are made to registered charities, registered CICs, unincorporated clubs or associations or unregistered charities with a turnover of less than £300,000.

The following information has been taken from the foundation's website:

> The KFC Foundation welcomes funding applications from organisations which:
>
> - Benefit young people aged 11–25 years old.
> - Supports those in a position of social disadvantage (i.e. care leavers, those experiencing homelessness, young carers, young parents, young people at risk of or with experience of the criminal justice system).
> - Empower young people to fulfil their potential and build a positive future by providing spaces that allow young people to feel safe and secure, helping them to unlock talent, build life skills, provide mentoring and improve their chances to gain meaningful employment.
> - Are local to a KFC restaurant?
> - Will demonstrate positive results from their project within 12 months of our funding being received

Financial information

Year end	27/12/2020
Income	£869,200
Assets	£759,400
Grants to organisations	£582,900

Beneficiaries included: Comic Relief (£459,400); Young People First (£6,000); Childhood Trust, Include Youth and Positive Futures (£5,000 each).

Exclusions

According to the foundation's FAQs document, the following will not be funded:

- General fundraising
- Sponsorship appeals
- Political campaigns
- Promotion of religion
- Overseas travel
- Curricular activities occurring during the school day
- Research
- Loan repayments
- Vehicle purchase
- Medical equipment
- Major capital projects
- Work that fails to demonstrate a long-term impact or support
- Projects focusing on one-off events
- Generic youth work activities (i.e. work not tailored towards the foundation's priority groups)

Applications

Apply via the foundation's website.

Sources of information

Accounts; annual report; Charity Commission record; funder's website; guidelines for applicants.

Kidney Research UK

Kidney research

UK

£3.96 million (2020/21)

CC number: 252892

Correspondent: Research Grants Committee, Nene Hall, Peterborough Business Park, Lynch Wood, Peterborough, Cambridgeshire PE2 6FZ (tel: 0300 303 1100; email: enquiries@kidneyresearchuk.org)

Trustees: Dr Charles Tomson; Prof. Sunil Bhandari; Deirdre Jennings; Jill Norman; Adrian Akers; Prof. Jeremy Hughes; Dr Adnan Sharif; Prof. Elizabeth Lightstone; Dr David Hughes; Prof. Caroline Savage; Angela Watt; Ben Digby; Lisa Chan; Christopher Rolfe.

www.kidneyresearchuk.org

facebook.com/kidneyresearchuk

@kidney_research

@kidney_research_uk

General information

Kidney Research UK funds research with the aim of improving the understanding of kidney disease, its causes, treatment and management. It has a vision of lives free from kidney disease, which it looks to achieve by:

- Funding and delivering life-saving research into kidney diseases

- Improving treatments for people with kidney diseases and enhancing their quality of life
- Increasing awareness of kidney health and supporting the early diagnosis and prevention of kidney disease and damage

Research priorities

As outlined on the website, until 2030 Kidney Research UK's Research Strategy has the following three priorities:

- **Transforming treatments** – finding ways 'to make kidney transplants last longer, dialysis more tolerable, reduce the burden of treatment and monitoring, and improve quality of life for people living with kidney disease'
- **Multiple health conditions** – investigating 'how kidney disease is linked to other conditions that people commonly experience at the same time, including heart disease, diabetes and mental health problems'
- **Health inequalities** – highlighting 'why some groups of people are more at risk of kidney disease, and progress to kidney failure much faster' and pushing 'for greater diversity in kidney research, so that discoveries benefit everyone'

Alongside these priorities, the charity will also continue to fund research into rare, hereditary and paediatric kidney problems, acute kidney injury and the health complications that come with kidney disease.

Grants

The charity offers the following core annual research funding schemes:

- Research project grants and awards
- Innovation grants
- Training fellowships (clinical)
- Intermediate and senior (non-clinical) fellowships
- Training (clinical) fellowships
- Postdoctoral (non-clinical) fellowships
- PhD studentships (non-clinical)
- Allied health professional fellowships (clinical)
- Intercalated degree
- Jointly funded fellowships (these are listed on the website)

Check the charity's website for open funding rounds.

Eligibility

Grants are given to fund projects at universities, hospitals and other research institutions. All applicants must be resident in the UK and the project and work and/or employment must also take place in the UK.

Full eligibility criteria for each scheme can be found online and in the charity's Regulations and Conditions for Applicants document.

Financial information

Year end	31/03/2021
Income	£6,950,000
Assets	£9,780,000
Grants to organisations	£3,960,000

Further financial information

Grants paid during the year totalled £3.96 million. We were unable to determine the amounts given to organisations and individuals. As such, the grant total includes grants to individuals.

Beneficiaries included: A list of beneficiaries was not available.

Applications

At the time of writing (January 2022), the charity's website stated:

> - Our application process has changed – there will now be two phases, the first phase will be a shorter application, and those shortlisted will be invited to complete a more detailed application
> - Patients are much more involved in our grants review process than ever before – they now do a more comprehensive review from a patient perspective
>
> If you are thinking of applying, plan ahead by checking out our full programme of grant rounds coming up.

A grant application guide can be downloaded from the charity's website. Applications must be submitted through the online portal, which can be found on the charity's website. Paper application forms are not accepted for any grant types.

Sources of information

Accounts; annual report; Charity Commission record; funder's website; guidelines for applicants.

The Kildare Trust

General charitable purposes

Worcestershire

£1.33 million (2020/21)

CC number: 1148325

Correspondent: Louise Ruane, c/o Harrison Clark Rickerbys, 5 Deansway, Worcester, Worcestershire WR1 2JG (email: info@kildaretrust.org.uk)

Trustees: Martin Needham; Dawn Oliver; Ian Crockatt Smith; Anthony Champion; Geoffrey Probert.

General information

The Kildare Trust was established in 2012 and aims to provide financial support to charities in Worcestershire and the surrounding area.

Financial information

Year end	05/04/2021
Income	£22,600
Grants to organisations	£1,330,000

Further financial information

Full accounts were not available to view on the Charity Commission website due to the trust's low income. We have therefore estimated the trust's grant total based on its annual expenditure.

Beneficiaries included: A list of beneficiaries was not available. Previous beneficiaries include: Acorns Children's Hospice Trust and St Richard's Hospice (£20,000 each); Worcester Live Charitable Trust (£12,000); Macmillan Cancer Support (£10,000); St Mary's Church (£8,000); Age Concern and Happy Days (£5,000 each); PSP Association (£1,000).

Applications

Apply in writing to the correspondent.

Sources of information

Accounts; annual report; Charity Commission record.

The King Henry VIII Endowed Trust – Warwick

General charitable purposes

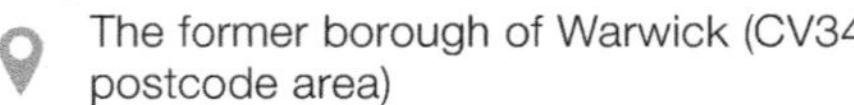

The former borough of Warwick (CV34 postcode area)

£1.45 million (2020)

CC number: 232862

Correspondent: Jonathan Wassall, 12 High Street, Warwick, Warwickshire CV34 4AP (tel: 01926 495533; email: jwassall@kinghenryviii.org.uk)

Trustees: John Edwards; Kathryn Parr; Neil Thurley; The Revd David Brown; Stephen Copley; Michael Peachey; Ian Furlong; Marie Ashe; Stephen Jobburn; Susan Grinnell; Stephen Cross.

 www.kinghenryviii.org.uk

General information

The trust was founded in 1545 following the reformation of the church by King Henry VIII and is one of the oldest grant-making charities in the UK.

The trust's website specifies that grants can be made for the following purposes, provided they are for the benefit of the inhabitants of the old borough of Warwick:

- The repair of historic buildings
- The relief of older people, those who are infirm and people in need
- The improvement of social welfare, recreation and leisure facilities
- The improvement of educational facilities
- Any other charitable purposes

Awards are made to both individual residents of the town and organisations benefitting such people. Assistance is also given to educational projects provided by organisations for Warwick Town LEA Schools (such requests should be submitted by the school). The geographical criterion is strict – it mostly covers the CV34 postcode district but there are exceptions (see the application guidelines available from the trust's website).

Financial information

Year end	31/12/2020
Income	£13,440,000
Assets	£66,410,000
Grants to organisations	£1,450,000

Further financial information

The trusts 2020 accounts state:

> During 2020 the Trust distributed a total of £1,454,931 to beneficiaries with £666,933 being distributed to the five Anglican churches in the town, £470,549 to the Warwick Independent Schools Foundation and £317,449 in discretionary grants to beneficiaries in the town of Warwick.

Beneficiaries included: Heathcote Parish Church (£60,000); Myton Hospice (£36,900); Citizens Advice – South Warwickshire (£10,000); Cruse Bereavement Care (£3,000); Heathcote Primary School (£2,000).

Applications

Application forms are available to download from the trust's website. They should be returned by post or email. Detailed grant guidelines are also available to view on the website. The trustees consider applications on a quarterly basis, usually in March, June, September and November. Check the website for current deadlines.

Sources of information

Accounts; annual report; Charity Commission record; funder's website.

The Mary Kinross Charitable Trust

Medical research; young people; penal affairs; health, including mental health; community development

UK

£838,700 (2020/21)

CC number: 212206

Correspondent: Fiona Adams, Trustee, 36 Grove Avenue, Moseley, Birmingham, West Midlands B13 9RY (email: marykinrossct@gmail.com)

Trustees: Elizabeth Shields; Fiona Adams; Dr Neil Cross; Gordon Hague; Elizabeth Barber.

General information

This trust, established in 1957, makes grants in the areas of medical research, young people, penal affairs, health (including mental health) and community development. Grants for young people tend to be made with crime prevention in mind.

The trust prefers to work mainly with a group of charities with which it develops a close connection, led by at least one of the trustees. It describes its grant policy in the 2020/21 annual report as follows:

> The Trustees wish to continue the policy of the Founders which was to use the Trust income to support a few carefully researched projects, rather than make many small grants. The fields of work chosen reflect the particular interests and knowledge of Trustees and at least one Trustee takes responsibility for ensuring the Trust's close involvement with organisations to which major grants are made.

Financial information

Year end	31/03/2021
Income	£941,300
Assets	£59,080,000
Grants to organisations	£838,700

Further financial information

Grants were awarded to 26 organisations and can be broken down as follows:

Medical research	£277,300
Young people	£201,400
Penal affairs	£128,000
Mental health	£80,000
Health	£77,000
Community development	£63,000
Miscellaneous	£12,000

Beneficiaries included: Royal College of Surgeons of England (£75,000); Guy's Head and Neck Cancer Unit (£57,300); University of Edinburgh Development Trust (£45,000); Margaret Carey Foundation (£30,000); Lucy Faithfull Foundation (£25,000); Depaul UK (£20,000); Restore Support Network (£10,000).

Exclusions

Individuals are not supported.

Applications

The majority of unsolicited applications are unsuccessful, as most new organisations are recommended by the trustees or the chair. However, should an organisation wish to submit an application, it must be done in writing. Telephone calls and emails are discouraged.

Sources of information

Accounts; annual report; Charity Commission record.

The Ernest Kleinwort Charitable Trust

Wildlife and environmental conservation (UK and international); charitable work in the county of Sussex (including care of older and young people, disability, general social welfare and hospices); reproductive health (international) – family planning work in Africa and Asia which has a clear impact on the environment

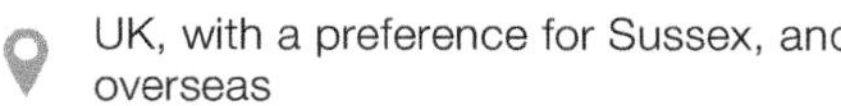
UK, with a preference for Sussex, and overseas

£1.66 million (2020/21)

CC number: 229665

Correspondent: Andrina Murrell, Administrator, EKCT, c/o Knill James, 1 Bell Lane, Lewes BN7 1JU (tel: 07960 057742; email: admin@ekct.org.uk)

Trustees: Marina Rose Kleinwort; Sir Richard Kleinwort; Alexander Hamilton Kleinwort; The Rt Hon. Edmund Christopher; Lord Chandos; Charlie Mayhew.

www.ekct.org.uk

General information

The trust was established in 1963 by Sir Ernest Kleinwort, who was the former chair of the merchant bank Kleinwort, Sons and Co.

The following information was taken from the trust's website:

> EKCT aims to 'make a difference'. The trustees will consider all applications that fall within the trust's area of activity from charities that are registered in the UK.
>
> **Principal support is given to charities working in the following areas:**
>
> 1 Charitable work in the County of Sussex
> 2 Wildlife and Environmental Conservation (UK and International)
> 3 Reproductive Health (International) – applications within this category will only be considered for family planning projects delivering in Africa and Asia, and preferably in areas where there is clear impact on the environment.
>
> **The trustees use the following programme areas to classify their grants:**
>
> - Care of older people
> - Disability
> - General Welfare
> - Hospices
> - Reproductive Health (International)
> - Wildlife and Environmental Conservation (UK and International)
> - Youth

Funding types

The trust's website states that

> Grants will be considered for start-up costs, core costs or for a specific project for which applicants have requested support. This could include a contribution

towards a building/refurbishment project, purchase of specialist equipment or other similar capital expenditure, or assistance with running costs.

The trust provides small grants (£3,000 and under), medium grants (£3,001–£10,000) and large grants (£10,001 and over).

Financial information

Year end	31/03/2021
Income	£611,900
Assets	£71,130,000
Grants to organisations	£1,660,000

Beneficiaries included: A list of beneficiaries was not available. Previous beneficiaries have included: Tusk (£168,000); St Catherine's Hospice (£130,000); Off The Fence Trust (£35,000); Galapagos Conservation Trust (£30,000); The Chaseley Trust (£15,000); The Sara Lee Trust (£10,000); Education Training Consortium Sussex (£8,000); Whizz-Kidz (£5,000); Bristol Natural History Consortium (£1,100); REACT (£500).

Exclusions

According to the trust's website, it will not consider funding for:

- Large national charities having substantial fund-raising potential, income from legacies and or endowment income.
- Organisations not registered as charities in the UK or those that have been registered for less than a year.
- Pre-school groups.
- Out of school play schemes including pre-school and holiday schemes.
- Charities not funded by any other charity.
- Very small and narrowly specialised activities.
- Local authorities.
- Individuals or charities applying on behalf of individuals.
- General requests for donations.
- Expeditions or overseas travel.
- 'Campaigning' organisations.
- Charities whose main aim is to raise funds for other charities with substantial cash reserves.
- Animal rescue or animal welfare organisations.
- International food security projects.
- Given the Trust's strong links with the county of Sussex, Trustees do not usually support proposals received from other regional **Wildlife Trusts**.
- Churches and places of worship outside of Cuckfield and Haywards Heath – please note; even within Cuckfield and Haywards Heath, grant opportunities for these purposes are extremely limited.
- **Charities with multiple branch offices in Sussex are requested to telephone or email for advice before making an application.**

Applications

Firstly, complete the eligibility questionnaire on the website. If you are eligible, application forms are available to be completed online on the trust's website. The trust is a paperless organisation. The trustees are unlikely to consider more than one application per year by any applicant.

Small grants: applications are accepted and considered throughout the year.

Medium grants: applications are accepted four times per year, during the following periods:

- 4 January to 11 February
- 18 April to 19 May
- 10 July to 20 August
- 9 October to 19 November

Large grants: applications are accepted twice per year, during the following periods:

- 4 January to 4 March
- 10 July to 10 September

Note that large grant applications are password protected. Contact admin@ekct.org.uk to discuss eligibility for a large grant.

Sources of information

Accounts; annual report; Charity Commission record; funder's website.

Sir James Knott Trust

General charitable purposes

Durham; Gateshead; Hartlepool; Newcastle upon Tyne; North Tyneside; Northumberland; South Tyneside

£1.71 million (2020/21)

CC number: 1001363

Correspondent: Ms J. Curry, Trust Secretary, Suite 103, First Floor, Broadacre House, Market Street East, Newcastle, Tyne and Wear NE1 6HQ (tel: 0191 432 8990; email: info@knott-trust.co.uk)

Trustees: John Cresswell; The Revd Fiona Sample; Ben Speke; Sir Walter Riddell.

www.knott-trust.co.uk

General information

This trust was founded and registered with the Charity Commission in 1990 to act as an independent grant-making charity. The aim of the trust is to improve the conditions for people living and working in the North East. Since 1990, the trust has made over 8,500 grants totalling over £27.8 million.

The trust supports a wide range of charitable causes, including:

- Arts and culture
- Community issues and events
- Conservation and the environment
- Education and training
- Public services
- Health and sport
- Heritage and historic buildings
- Housing, homelessness and hardship
- Maritime
- Service-related charities

Since 2019, the trust has preferred to offer multi-year grants, often £5,000 per year over three years, or sometimes £15,000 per year over three years. The trust makes grants for capital and project costs.

The trust funds charities, community groups and social enterprises. If your organisation does not fit into one of those categories, contact the trust before making an application.

Financial information

Year end	31/03/2021
Income	£1,960,000
Assets	£63,070,000
Grants to organisations	£1,710,000
No. of grants	222

Further financial information

The trust awarded 222 grants to organisations during the year. Only beneficiaries of grants of over £1,000 were listed in the accounts. Grants of under £1,000 totalled £41,400 (46 grants).

Analyses of grants by location and purpose were detailed in the accounts as follows:

Tyne and Wear	95	£781,100
North East general	47	£501,800
Northumberland	49	£251,200
County Durham and Hartlepool	31	£177,700

Health/sport and human services	80	£585,500
Education/training	22	£350,700
Historic buildings/heritage	24	£177,200
Service charities	16	£135,700
Public services	28	£126,400
Arts and culture	19	£117,500
Other	14	£108,000
Homelessness/housing/hardship	5	£52,500
Conservation/environmental	9	£37,300
Community issues/events	5	£21,000

Beneficiaries included: University of Sunderland Development Trust (£250,000); YMCA North Tyneside (£30,000); Wearside Women in Need (£15,000); Hartlepool Stage Society and Northumberland Wildlife Trust Ltd (£10,000 each); Just Finance Foundation (£5,000); Smile for Life Children's Charity (£3,500); Northern Ballet Ltd (£2,000).

Exclusions

The trust does not provide funds for:

- Individuals
- Research
- Activity which has already taken place or that takes place outside its area of benefit

Applications

Check the trust's website to see if you are eligible to apply. Applications can be made online via the website which also has details on how to apply, application deadlines and an FAQs page. The trust operates a rolling grants programme, so if you miss a deadline, your application will be considered at the following meeting.

Applications for small grants of £1,000 and under have an average turnaround of six weeks. For applications of £10,000 and above, the project will likely require a visit from a member of the trust's staff.

Sources of information

Accounts; annual report; Charity Commission record; funder's website.

Kollel and Co. Ltd

Jewish causes; relief of poverty; religious education; general charitable purposes

Worldwide

£1.7 million (2020/21)

CC number: 1077180

Correspondent: Simon Low, Trustee, 7 Overlea Road, London E5 9BG (tel: 020 8806 1570)

Trustees: Simon Low; Judith Weiss; Rachel Kalish.

General information

This charity was established in 1999 with the following objects: the advancement of education and religion in accordance with the doctrines of the Jewish religion; the relief of poverty; and general charitable purposes.

Donations are made to organisations providing a sound religious education in accordance with the doctrines and principles of traditional Judaism and to institutions set up to provide aid to Jewish people who are in need.

Financial information

Year end	31/01/2021
Income	£862,700
Assets	£4,590,000
Grants to organisations	£1,700,000

Beneficiaries included: Support the Charity Worker (£145,000); Edupoor Ltd (£108,000); Beis Aharon Trust (£80,000); Keren Chochmas Shlomo Trust (£65,000); Shir Chesed Beis Yisroel (£55,200); Friends of Beis Soroh Schneirer (£50,000).

Applications

Apply in writing to the correspondent.

Sources of information

Accounts; annual report; Charity Commission record.

Kolyom Trust Ltd

Judaism; Jewish religious education; the alleviation of poverty in the Jewish community

Worldwide

£3.47 million (2019/20)

CC number: 1112084

Correspondent: The Trustees, 134 Leicester Road, Salford, Greater Manchester M7 4GB (tel: 0161 740 1960; email: admin@kolyomtrust.org.uk)

Trustees: Michael Kaufman; Alan Klor; Victor Frankenhuis.

General information

The trust makes grants for the advancement and furtherance of the Jewish religion and Jewish religious education and to alleviate poverty in the Jewish community around the world.

Financial information

Year end	31/05/2020
Income	£3,460,000
Assets	£1,360,000
Grants to organisations	£3,470,000

Further financial information

Grants were broken down as follows:

Social welfare	£2.57 million
Education	£710,100
Religious grants	£194,300

Beneficiaries included: A list of beneficiaries was not available.

Applications

According to the trust's annual report 2019/20: 'The charity invites applications for funding through contacting local philanthropists to contribute towards projects that both the trustees and the philanthropists feel are appropriate for the charities objects.'

Sources of information

Accounts; annual report; Charity Commission record.

KPE4 Charitable Trust

Social welfare; education; health; community development; citizenship; the arts, culture, heritage and science; sport; recreational facilities; human rights, conflict resolution and reconciliation; racial harmony; equality and diversity; the environment, animal welfare

Edinburgh; Lothian; Fife

£1.22 million (2020/21)

OSCR number: SC047599

Correspondent: The Trustees, c/o Morton Fraser LLP, Quartermile Two, 2 Lister Square, Edinburgh EH3 9GL

General information

The trust makes grants for a variety of causes in Edinburgh, Fife and Lothian. According to its 2020/21 annual accounts, the trust will support the following:

1. the prevention or relief of poverty
2. the advancement of education
3. the advancement of health
4. the saving of lives
5. the advancement of citizenship or community development
6. the advancement of the arts, heritage, culture or science
7. the advancement of public participation in sport
8. the provision of recreational facilities or the organisation of recreational activities with the object of improving the conditions of life for the persons for whom the facilities are primarily intended
9. the advancement of human rights, conflict resolution or reconciliation
10. the promotion of racial harmony
11. the promotion of equality and diversity
12. the advancement of environmental protection or improvement
13. the relief of those in need by reason of age, ill-health, disability, financial hardship or other disadvantage
14. the advancement of animal welfare; and
15. any other purpose that may reasonably be regarded as analogous to any of the preceding purposes.

Financial information

Year end	05/04/2021
Income	£1,470,000
Assets	£1,990,000
Grants to organisations	£1,220,000

Beneficiaries included: Richmond's Hope (£50,000); School of Hard Knocks (£38,000); Bikes for Refugees (£17,400); Scottish Adoption (£4,800); Scottish Seabirds Centre (£500).

Applications

Apply in writing to the correspondent. The trustees meet four times per year.

Sources of information

Accounts; annual report; OSCR record.

The KPMG Foundation

Children and young people; education and training; social care; employment

UK

£1.15 million (2019/20)

CC number: 1086518

Correspondent: Judith McNeill, Chief Executive, 15 Canada Square, Canary Wharf, London E14 5GL (tel: 020 7311 4217; email: kpmgfoundation@kpmg.co.uk)

Trustees: Robin Cartwright; Peter Sherratt; Christine Gilbert; David Woodward; Rachel Hopcroft; Corrine Harms; David Bartram; Antony Cates.

 https://kpmgfoundation.org.uk/index.html

 @kpmg_foundation

General information

Established in 2001, the KPMG Foundation is the corporate charity of the audit, tax and advisory services company KPMG LLP.

According to its website, the foundation's aim is to support 'the most vulnerable children through their early years, including through 'whole family' approaches; in school and through adolescence'.

Grant-making policy

The foundation works with selected partners. Through grant-making, the trustees aim to improve outcomes in the following areas:

- Care of the most disadvantaged children and young people, in particular those in care or on the edge of care
- Unlocking the potential of the most disadvantaged children and young people, in particular, to improve: literacy and numeracy; life skills; life chances

An overview of some of the programmes supported by the foundation can be seen on its website.

Financial information

Year end	30/09/2020
Income	£914,000
Assets	£6,080,000
Grants to organisations	£1,150,000
No. of grants	17

Further financial information

During the year, the foundation awarded 17 grants to 14 organisations.

Beneficiaries included: Education Endowment Foundation (two grants totalling £262,000); Frontline and Reach Foundation (£100,000 each); Family Action (£65,500); Future First (£50,000); Enabling Enterprise (£49,600); School Home Support (£25,000).

Applications

The foundation proactively identifies organisations to support and therefore does not accept unsolicited applications; however, the foundation's website states the following:

> [...] if you share our purpose, priorities and approach, please contact us with a brief description of your work and a link to your own website. Where there is a strong alignment, we will respond.

Sources of information

Accounts; annual report; Charity Commission record; funder's website.

Kusuma Trust UK

Health and well-being; access to opportunities; community and the environment; research

India; Gibraltar; UK (primarily London)

£2.35 million (2020)

CC number: 1126983

Correspondent: The Trustees, 5th Floor, 55 New Oxford Street, London WC1A 1BS (tel: 020 7420 0650; email: info@kusumatrust.org)

Trustees: Dr Soma Pujari; Anurag Dikshit; Nitin Jain.

 www.kusumatrust.org

 @KusumaTrustUK

General information

Kusuma Trust UK was established in 2008 by Dr Soma Pujari and her husband, Anurag Dikshit, who both serve as trustees. The trust's 2020 annual accounts state:

> We are a family led philanthropic Trust created with the purpose of making grants to charities, organisations and initiatives for the benefit of society and the wider world.
>
> We believe that understanding challenges and applying creative and innovative solutions can achieve significant change. Communities themselves are best placed to understand what they need and very often require only a little help to make a big difference. For this reason we make grants that support research, innovation and creative solutions which are initiated by organisations and communities themselves. Where possible we prefer to give matched grants to encourage others to give and make our funding go further.
>
> We work with a range of grantees in our chosen priority areas. We are regularly in touch with other grant making bodies to share knowledge and experiences and keep up to date with the latest developments.
>
> As a family led trust we have the unique privilege of being able to look for opportunities to support novel ideas that may take longer to find support.
>
> **Strategic priorities**
>
> To identify organisations and initiatives led by motivated and committed people keen on exploring, delivering and consistently monitoring their impact in line with our current priority areas as listed below;
>
> **Health and Wellbeing:** Renovating, upgrading and expanding local health facilities and supporting advanced treatment and medical trials.
>
> **Access to Opportunities:** Supporting education opportunities for people from all walks of life including Special Educational Needs and supporting learning spaces and opportunities outside of formal settings.
>
> **Community and Environment:** Promoting green spaces and tackling the issue of air pollution in London.

Financial information

Year end	31/12/2020
Income	£3,670,000
Assets	£461,470,000
Grants to organisations	£2,350,000
No. of grants	61

Further financial information

The trust's accounts state: 'In 2020, we awarded 61 grants totalling over £2.3 million with £678,426 of this awarded in response to Covid.' Grants were broken down as follows: UK projects (£1.63 million); Gibraltar projects (£495,200); India projects (£217,400).

Beneficiaries included: UK grants included: University of Cambridge (£260,000); Chelsea and Westminster Hospital (£150,000); Global Action Plan (£30,000); Wetherby School (£22,200); Chefs in Schools (£20,000); In2scienceUK (£10,000); Give a Book (£5,000); Play for Progress (£2,500).

Applications

The trust's website states: 'We do not accept unsolicited applications for funding – instead we select our partnerships based on shared values and mutual interests: creating access to opportunities, improving health and well-being, and investing in our communities and environment.'

Sources of information

Accounts; annual report; Charity Commission record; funder's website.

The Kyte Charitable Trust

Jewish causes; sport; education; healthcare; children; international aid

UK

£119,500 (2020/21)

CC number: 1035886

Correspondent: The Trustees, First Floor, Nations House, 103 Wigmore Street, London W1U 1QS (tel: 020 7486 7700)

Trustees: David Kyte; James Kyte; Tracey Kyte; Ilana Kyte; Max Kyte.

General information

The trust was established in 1994 and supports general charitable purposes across the UK and overseas. In particular, grants are distributed within the following areas:

- Arts, culture and heritage
- Children
- Community support
- Education support
- Healthcare

- International aid
- Sport

Our previous research indicates that preference is given to Jewish charitable organisations.

Financial information

Year end	05/04/2021
Income	£137,500
Assets	£28,100
Grants to organisations	£119,500

Beneficiaries included: A list of beneficiaries was not available. Previous beneficiaries include: Maccabi London Brady Recreational Trust (£73,500); Jewish Care and UJIA (£25,000 each); Jewish Community Secondary School Trust (£22,500); Community Security Trust (£20,000); Chai Cancer Care (£7,200); ORT (£500).

Applications

Apply in writing to the correspondent.

Sources of information

Accounts; annual report; Charity Commission record.

Ladbrokes Coral Trust

General charitable purposes; healthcare; education; community projects; sports and recreation

UK

£364,600 (2020)

CC number: 1101804

Correspondent: The Trustees, c/o GVC Holdings plc, 3rd Floor, One New Change, London EC4M 9AF (tel: 020 3938 0000; email: charity@ladbrokescoral.com)

Trustees: Karen Thraves; Nick Batram; Jay Dossetter; Craig Watson; Simon O'Halloran; Steve Humphries; Simon Burnell.

General information

Ladbrokes Coral Trust was established in 2003. Formerly known as Ladbrokes in the Community Charitable Trust, the charity changed its name to Ladbrokes Coral Trust in May 2017, following the merger between Ladbrokes and certain businesses of Gala Coral Group Ltd. Its funding comes not from the Ladbrokes company, but via the fundraising efforts of the head office and shop staff and customers.

The trust's record on the Charity Commission's website states that support can be given to a range of causes 'with the overriding requirement being that the causes supported operate and serve the community in which the shops and businesses of Ladbrokes Coral group plc operate'.

According to the trust's annual report for 2020, grants are commonly given in the following categories:

- Health – principally research/treatment, hospice services and disability support
- Education – supporting the disabled/ disadvantaged and sports services in deprived areas or for disadvantaged persons
- Community – focusing on projects for the homeless and aged or social activity projects for those at risk

Financial information

Year end	31/12/2020
Income	£388,800
Assets	£221,700
Grants to organisations	£364,600

Further financial information

Grants awarded in 2020 were broken down as follows:

Medical causes	£256,700
Hospices and hospitals	£45,200
Various	£29,200
Social welfare	£24,400
The environment and animals	£9,200

Beneficiaries included: A list of beneficiaries was not available.

Applications

Apply in writing to the correspondent. The trust's Charity Commission record states that 'the Trustees meet every 4–6 weeks to consider grant requests from shop and head office fundraisers and registered charities.'

Sources of information

Accounts; annual report; Charity Commission record.

John Laing Charitable Trust

Community; disadvantaged young people; education; homelessness

UK and, occasionally, countries where John Laing Group plc operates

£2.55 million (2020)

CC number: 236852

Correspondent: Helen Parker, Trust Director, c/o Laing Family Trusts, 33 Bunns Lane, Mill Hill, London NW7 2DX (email: a contact form is available on the trust's website)

Trustees: Lynette Krige; Christopher Laing; Sir Martin Laing; Christopher Waples; Alexandra Gregory; Stewart Laing; Timothy Foster; Clare Underwood.

https://johnlaingcharitabletrust.com

General information

The trust was established in 1962 by John Laing Group plc, an infrastructure investor and asset management company. It was set up to support former and existing employees as well as for the benefit of the general public.

The work of the trust can be split into four separate areas:

- **Welfare** – support is given to former employees and their dependants in need
- **Charitable donations** – awarding grants to charitable organisations
- **Staff applications** - this includes a number of schemes for employees of John Laing Group plc to get involved in charitable work including a matched donation scheme
- **Named funds** – the trust has endowment funds with five UK community foundations to provide ongoing support to local charities

Areas of work

The trust's grant-making is focused on four main themes:

- Community
- Disadvantaged young people
- Education
- Homelessness

Types of funding

The trust's website states:

> The Trust funds charitable organisations who can demonstrate public benefit (and security over funding) including:
> - Project/Specific activity costs (typically £10,000 to £75,000)
> - Core funding (cover costs of running the organisation)
> - Capital projects (£250,000+) – We will only consider these from organisations whom the Trust have worked with in the past.
> - Single or Multi-year funding

There are also other four charities set up by the Laing family and administered at the same address – for more information see www.laingfamilytrusts.org.uk

Financial information

Year end	31/12/2020
Income	£1,870,000
Assets	£64,390,000
Grants to organisations	£2,550,000

Beneficiaries included: FareShare (£100,000); The Silver Line (£50,000); Peace4Kids (£47,800); ReadEasy and Safer London (£25,000 each); Orminston Families (£7,500).

Exclusions

According to its website the trust will not fund:

- Individuals (apart from current/ former John Laing employees)
- Organisations that do not fit with the trust's strategic priorities
- Organisations whose work is mainly focused on animal welfare
- Sponsorships
- Projects that do not benefit the public

Applications

At the time of writing (January 2022) the trust's website stated: 'Please note that applications to the Trust are currently closed. Until further notice, we only process invited applications.' Check the trust's website for further information.

Sources of information

Accounts; annual report; Charity Commission record; funder's website.

Maurice and Hilda Laing Charitable Trust

Social welfare and promotion of Christianity

Worldwide, with a preference for the UK and sub-Saharan Africa

£1.38 million (2020)

CC number: 1058109

Correspondent: Belgin Wingrove, Grants Manager, c/o Laing Family Trusts, 33 Bunns Lane, Mill Hill, London NW7 2DX (tel: 020 8238 8890; email: info@laingfamilytrusts.org.uk)

Trustees: Andrea Currie; Sir Ewan William Harper; Charles Laing; Stephen Ludlow; Simon Martle; Dr Paul Bosch.

 www.laingfamilytrusts.org.uk

General information

This trust was established in 1996 and is mainly concerned with the advancement of the Christian religion and relieving poverty, both in the UK and overseas. The trust is administered alongside The Beatrice Laing Trust, The Martin Laing Foundation and The Kirby Laing Foundation, with which it shares members of staff and office space; collectively they are known as the Laing Family Trusts.

Areas of giving

The following information has been taken from the trust's website:

> The Trustees' priority areas of giving are:
>
> 1 To advance Christian faith and values, with an emphasis on:
>   - making the Christian message relevant to all through innovative 'fresh expressions' of church
>   - projects which develop and affirm Christian faith
>   - resourcing theological training for ordained and lay ministry and pastoral support for those in ministry
>   - providing support for oppressed Christian communities overseas
>
> 2 To support organisations offering practical support to those in the U.K. who are disadvantaged, vulnerable and/or socially isolated with a particular emphasis on Christian organisations seeking to express their faith through practical action to help:
>   - prisoners and ex-offenders
>   - the homeless
>   - children and young people at risk
>   - refugees
>   - the elderly
>
> 3 Relief of poverty overseas, predominantly through Christian organisations working in the low income countries of Sub-Saharan Africa. We place emphasis on projects which seek to help:
>   - street children
>   - improve educational opportunities
>   - build sustainable livelihoods
>   - improve the lives of people with disabilities

Grants typically range between £5,000 and £25,000, although the trust has the capacity to make a small number of larger grants each year.

Financial information

Year end	31/12/2020
Income	£674,300
Assets	£24,590,000
Grants to organisations	£1,380,000

Further financial information

Grants were broken down as follows: religion (£863,200); social welfare (£245,000); overseas aid (£130,000).

Beneficiaries included: Ridley Hall (£645,700); Partners for Change Ethiopia (£35,000); Youthscape (£25,000); Workplace Matters (£15,000); Church Army and Crisis (£10,000 each); Bible Society (£5,000).

Exclusions

The trust's website states:

> **In general the Trusts only make grants to charities registered in the UK or to churches with exempt status.** Except in exceptional circumstances we do not make grants to:
>
> - Charities registered overseas
> - Umbrella, second tier or grant-making organisations
> - State maintained or independent schools (other than those for pupils with special educational needs)
> - Hospices (other than those with which the Trusts have a strong local connection)
> - NHS hospital trusts and other establishments offering medical care
> - Sports clubs
> - Individuals (whether for education, travel or medical purposes)
>
> In general the Trusts do not make grants to projects falling into the following categories:
>
> - Animal welfare
> - General appeals or circulars
> - Campaigning or lobbying activities
> - Feasibility studies and social research
> - Training of professionals (including attendance at conferences, courses etc)
> - Costs of staging one-off events such as festivals or conferences
> - Gap year projects, residentials and overseas exchange programmes
> - Summer activities for children/young people or after-school clubs
> - Core running costs of local organisations (rent, utilities, salaries etc)
> - Cancer research and cancer care
> - Cost of running national helplines
> - Salaries of church workers (children and family workers, youth workers, worship leaders, outreach workers etc)
> - Church restoration or repair* (including church roofs, spires, organs, bells, wall paintings etc)
>
> *Please see the Beatrice Laing Trust for guidance on the funding which is available for church building projects.

Applications

Apply in writing to the correspondent by post. Applicants are asked to download and complete an application cover sheet, which is available on completion of an eligibility quiz. Full details of what should be included in the application can be found on the trust's website.

Sources of information

Accounts; annual report; Charity Commission record; funder's website.

Christopher Laing Foundation

Young people; education; the environment; homelessness; disability

UK, with a preference for Hertfordshire and Oxfordshire

£620,000 (2020/21)

CC number: 278460

Correspondent: Vince Cheshire, TMF Global Services (UK) Ltd, 960 Capability Green, Luton, Bedfordshire LU1 3PE (tel: 01582 439200; email: claing_charity@tmf-group.com)

Trustees: John Keeble; Christopher Laing; Diana Laing; Michael Laing; Richard Haines; Carla Seale.

 www.christopherlaingfoundation.com

General information

The foundation was established in 1979 by Christopher Laing, a member of the Laing family, which has several charitable foundations.

Areas of work

Priority is given to organisations based in Hertfordshire and Oxfordshire working in the following areas:

- Reconstruction of communities following the COVID-19 pandemic
- Youth and education
- Homelessness
- Disabilities
- Environmental and conservation work

Grant programmes

The website states the following:

> The trustees make regular grants to certain charities with which the Foundation has historical connections. Larger grants vary in size according to the individual requirements of the applicant but are generally in the range of £1000–50000 per year. Many successful

applicants have gone on to receive continued support over many years.

Small grants programme

Grants of £500–£1,000 are made to registered charities, mainly in the Hertfordshire and Oxfordshire regions.

Financial information

Year end	05/04/2021
Income	£394,700
Assets	£12,070,000
Grants to organisations	£620,000

Further financial information

During 2020/21, grants were distributed as follows:

Social welfare	£385,000
Children and young people	£135,000
Charities Aid Foundation	£60,000
Culture and the environment	£40,000

Beneficiaries included: Oxfordshire Community Foundation (£150,000); The Lord's Taverners (£70,000); RNLI (£30,000); The Silver Line (£20,000); Action for ME (£10,000); The Henley Festival Trust (£5,000); Guilford Undetected Tumour Screening and Quest for Learning (£1,000 each).

Applications

Application forms can be downloaded from the foundation's website. Applications are considered regularly by the trustees and the application process is always open.

Sources of information

Accounts; annual report; Charity Commission record; funder's website.

The David Laing Foundation

General charitable purposes; arts and culture; social welfare; health; children and young people; religion; sport; overseas aid

Mainly Hertfordshire, Oxfordshire, Leicestershire and Northamptonshire with some UK-wide and worldwide grants

£186,200 (2020/21)

CC number: 278462

Correspondent: The Trustees, The Manor House, Grafton Underwood, Kettering, Northamptonshire NN14 3AA (tel: 01536 330404; email: david@david-laing.co.uk)

Trustees: Francis Barlow; David Laing; Stuart Lewis; David Laing.

General information

The foundation was registered with the Charity Commission in 1979 to provide funding for general charitable purposes. The trust particularly favours projects in the areas of young people, disability and the arts. It operates in Hertfordshire, Leicestershire, Northamptonshire and Oxfordshire.

The 2020/21 annual report states the following:

> Who knows where the future will lead us over the coming year, but trustees will look to support charities previously supported in order to ensure their ongoing viability as well as those where we can provide our help for cases of need.

Financial information

Year end	05/04/2021
Income	£220,600
Assets	£6,050,000
Grants to organisations	£186,200

Further financial information

In 2020/21 the foundation awarded grants totalling £186,200; however, its annual report states that the number of applications during the period was reduced due to the COVID-19 pandemic. In previous years, the foundation has awarded grants totalling over £300,000. Only beneficiaries that received grants of over £3,500 were listed in the accounts. Grants were broken down as follows:

Arts and culture	£97,500
Children and young people	£29,000
General charitable purposes	£23,900
Disability/disadvantage/health/medical causes	£20,500
Overseas aid	£9,000
Religion	£4,500
Social welfare/sports and recreation	£2,000

Beneficiaries included: Northamptonshire Community Foundation (£80,000); The Prince's Trust (£15,000); Northamptonshire Association of Youth Club (£12,500); The Living Room (£6,000); Fiori Musicals, Heart of Bucks and Nevill Holt Opera (£5,000 each); Cecily's Fund (£4,000).

Exclusions

No grants are given to individuals.

Applications

Apply in writing to the correspondent.

Sources of information

Accounts; annual report; Charity Commission record.

The Kirby Laing Foundation

General charitable purposes

UK and overseas, with a preference for Asia

£4.36 million (2020)

CC number: 264299

Correspondent: Elizabeth Harley, Trust Director, c/o Laing Family Trusts, 33 Bunns Lane, Mill Hill, London NW7 2DX (tel: 020 8238 8890; email: info@laingfamilytrusts.org.uk)

Trustees: The Revd Charles Burch; David Laing; Simon Webley; Dr Frederick Lewis.

 www.laingfamilytrusts.org.uk

General information

This foundation was established in 1972 by Sir Kirby Laing. It is one of four grant-making charities administered by the Laing Family Trusts along with The Beatrice Laing Trust (Charity Commission no. 211884), The Martin Laing Foundation (Charity Commission no. 278461) and The Maurice and Hilda Laing Charitable Trust (Charity Commission no. 1058109).

Areas of work

According to the foundation's website, the trustees' primary areas of interest are:

- the promotion of the evangelical Christian faith
- education and youth development, focused particularly on STEM education and vocational training in traditional crafts
- medical welfare and research, with a particular emphasis on dementia, stroke and neuro-degenerative diseases
- culture and the environment, focused on improving access for young people and the disabled, particularly to projects with a national focus/impact, and on encouraging young talent in opera and the performing arts
- overseas development projects, with a special interest in projects benefiting women and girls in low income countries in Asia

Grant-making policy

The foundation has a two-strand grants programme:

Small grants between £2,000 and £20,000 are awarded under the foundation's Open Grants programme. Unsolicited applications are accepted from organisations working in the foundation's areas of interest.

The foundation's Spend Down programme focuses on specific sub-themes identified within the broader areas of interest listed above. Applications for this type of funding are by invitation only. It is anticipated that charities selected for Spend Down funding will already have a working relationship with the foundation. Grants are typically made towards capital projects, programme development costs and endowment/capacity-building for future sustainability. A list of themes currently funded by the foundation can be seen on the website.

Financial information

Year end	31/12/2020
Income	£2,090,000
Assets	£2,930,000
Grants to organisations	£4,360,000
No. of grants	99

Further financial information

Grants were broken down as follows:

Culture and the environment	32	£2.33 million
Religion	24	£925,600
Health and medicine	23	£561,300
Children and young people (including education)	9	£410,200
Overseas aid	7	£73,000
Social welfare	4	£32,000
Charities Aid Foundation	1	£25,000

Beneficiaries included: Royal Albert Hall Trust (£650,000); Rock UK (£200,000); National Space Centre (£100,000); St Paul's Cathedral Foundation (£50,000); University of Gloucestershire (£30,000); Welsh National Opera (£10,000); Radley Foundation (£5,000); Fowey Community Bus (£2,000).

Exclusions

A list of exclusions can be found on the Laing Family Trust's website.

Applications

Applicants must first complete the eligibility quiz on the Laing Family Trusts' website. Once completed, an application cover sheet will be available to download. Applicants should complete the cover sheet and write a covering letter and a concise project proposal, about 3–4 pages in length. Full details of what information should be included in the application can be seen on the website. The application and a copy of your organisation's most recent annual report and accounts should be sent along with an SAE (no bigger than C5) to the foundation's postal address. Applications sent by email will not be accepted.

Sources of information

Accounts; annual report; Charity Commission record; funder's website.

The Martin Laing Foundation

Children and young people; culture and the environment; health and medicine; religion; social welfare; overseas development; older people

UK, with a preference for Norfolk, Essex and Hertfordshire; Malta

£298,900 (2020/21)

CC number: 278461

Correspondent: Becci McCormick, Grants Administrator, c/o Laing Family Trusts, 33 Bunns Lane, Mill Hill, London NW7 2DX (tel: 020 8238 8890; email: info@laingfamilytrusts.org.uk)

Trustees: Colin Fletcher; Nicholas Gregory; Lady Laing; Sir Martin Laing; Edward Laing; Alexandra Gregory.

 www.laingfamilytrusts.org.uk

General information

This foundation was established in 1979 by Sir Martin Laing, a grandson of Sir John Laing. It is one of the Laing Family Trusts, which seek to promote the Christian religion and alleviate poverty in the UK and overseas.

The foundation funds organisations and charities whose objectives are environmental and conservation based, and small community projects to benefit disadvantaged young people or older people. There is a preference for small charities in Norfolk, Essex and Hertfordshire. A small number of grants are also made to overseas projects in Malta, at the invitation of the founder only.

Funding types

A large proportion of the foundation's grants are one-off grants for capital purposes such as the purchase of equipment and vehicles or the extension, redevelopment or refurbishment of property. Most other grants are directed towards specific projects.

Financial information

Year end	05/04/2021
Income	£359,000
Assets	£12,660,000
Grants to organisations	£298,900

Further financial information

Grants were broken down as follows:

Overseas development	£83,900
Health and medicine	£60,000
Culture and the environment	£45,000
Children and young people	£40,000
Charities Aid Foundation	£25,000
Religion	£20,000
Social welfare	£15,000
The Reculver Trust	£10,000

Beneficiaries included: St John Ambulance (£20,000); University of East Anglia (£15,000); The Pushkin Trust (£10,000); Action for ME and the Wilderness Foundation (£5,000 each); The Inspire Foundation (£2,800).

Exclusions

The Laing Family Trusts' website states:

> Except in exceptional circumstances we do not make grants to:
> - Charities registered overseas
> - Umbrella, second tier or grant-making organisations
> - State maintained or independent schools (other than those for pupils with special educational needs)
> - Hospices (other than those with which the Laing Family Trusts have a strong local connection)
> - NHS hospital trusts and other establishments offering medical care
> - Sports clubs
> - Individuals (whether for education, travel or medical purposes)
>
> In general the Laing Family Trusts do not make grants to projects falling into the following categories:
> - Animal welfare
> - General appeals or circulars
> - Campaigning or lobbying activities
> - Feasibility studies and social research
> - Training of professionals (including attendance at conferences, courses etc)
> - Costs of staging one-off events such as festivals or conferences
> - Gap year projects, residentials and overseas exchange programmes
> - Summer activities for children/young people or after-school clubs
> - Core running costs of local organisations (rent, utilities, salaries etc)
> - Cancer research and cancer care
> - Cost of running national helplines
> - Salaries of church workers (children and family workers, youth workers, worship leaders, outreach workers etc)
> - Church restoration or repair* (including church roofs, spires, organs, bells, wall paintings etc)
>
> *Please see the Beatrice Laing Trust for guidance on the funding which is available for church building projects.

Applications

The Laing Family Trusts are administered and co-ordinated centrally; therefore, an application to one is considered for all funds.

Applications should be made by post providing a concise project proposal (three to four pages). Information on what should be included in the proposal can be found on the foundation's website.

Sources of information

Accounts; annual report; Charity Commission record; funder's website.

The Beatrice Laing Trust

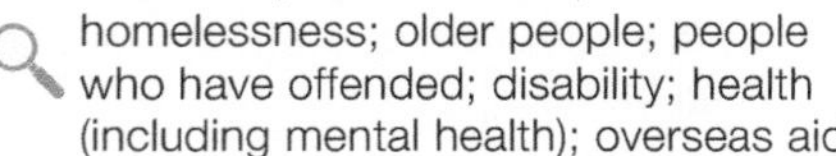

Churches; social welfare; homelessness; older people; people who have offended; disability; health (including mental health); overseas aid

UK and overseas

£2.55 million (2020/21)

CC number: 211884

Correspondent: Becci McCormick, Grants Administrator, c/o Laing Family Trusts, 33 Bunns Lane, Mill Hill, London NW7 2DX (tel: 020 8238 8890; email: info@laingfamilytrusts.org.uk)

Trustees: Paula Blacker; Alex Gregory; Christopher Laing; Charles Laing; Sir Martin Laing; David Laing.

 www.laingfamilytrusts.org.uk

General information

This trust was established in 1952 by Sir John Laing and his wife, Beatrice, both now deceased. The trust's main objects are the relief of poverty and the advancement of the evangelical Christian faith in the UK and abroad. It mainly concentrates on making small grants for the relief of poverty in its broadest sense.

The Beatrice Laing Trust is one of the Laing Family Trusts and administered alongside The Maurice and Hilda Laing Charitable Trust, The Martin Laing Foundation and The Kirby Laing Foundation, with which it shares members of staff and office space.

Areas of work

The trust's website states:

> The Trustees' priority areas of giving are:
>
> 1 To support new church building, extension or redevelopment projects, with a particular emphasis on churches using their physical resources to communicate Christian faith and respond to needs in their local community
>
> 2 To support organisations offering practical services to those who are disadvantaged and vulnerable, with a particular emphasis on Christian organisations seeking to express their faith through practical action to help:
>   - the homeless
>   - the elderly
>   - ex-offenders
>   - former Servicemen and women
>
> 3 To support organisations providing practical services to people with physical, mental and learning difficulties, predominately through:
>   - special schools seeking to make provision for those with increasingly complex needs
>   - support in the transition from childhood to adulthood and in accessing training and/or meaningful employment opportunities
>
> 4 To support small-scale overseas development projects aimed at building the capacity of local partners to provide long-term solutions to problems in the developing world, principally through Christian organisations working in the Anglophone countries of Sub-Saharan Africa and parts of Asia to:
>   - improve educational opportunities
>   - build sustainable livelihoods

Project types

The trust's website states:

> A significant percentage of the grants awarded are made on a one-off basis for capital purposes such as the purchase or construction of new premises, the extension, redevelopment or refurbishment of property, or the purchase of equipment and vehicles. Most other grants are directed towards specific projects which will meet a clearly defined and demonstrable need within the applicant charity's beneficiary/client group which cannot be met from statutory sources. Evidence of longer-term sustainability, potential for replicability and partnership working are important factors in the Trustees' decision-making.

Financial information

Year end	05/04/2021
Income	£2,340,000
Assets	£69,340,000
Grants to organisations	£2,550,000
No. of grants	276

Beneficiaries included: Greyfriars Church – Reading (£50,000); Extern Northern Ireland (£25,000); Step by Step (£10,000); TwentyTwenty (£5,000); Deafway (£3,000); Scottish Autism (£2,000).

Exclusions

The trust's website states:

> Except in exceptional circumstances we do not make grants to:
> - Charities registered overseas
> - Umbrella, second tier or grant-making organisations
> - State maintained or independent schools (other than those for pupils with special educational needs)
> - Hospices (other than those with which the Trusts have a strong local connection)
> - NHS hospital trusts and other establishments offering medical care
> - Sports clubs
> - Individuals (whether for education, travel or medical purposes)
>
> In general the Trusts do not make grants to projects falling into the following categories:
> - Animal welfare
> - General appeals or circulars
> - Campaigning or lobbying activities
> - Feasibility studies and social research
> - Training of professionals (including attendance at conferences, courses etc)
> - Costs of staging one-off events such as festivals or conferences
> - Gap year projects, residentials and overseas exchange programmes
> - Summer activities for children/young people or after-school clubs
> - Core running costs of local organisations (rent, utilities, salaries etc)
> - Cancer research and cancer care
> - Cost of running national helplines
> - Salaries of church workers (children and family workers, youth workers, worship leaders, outreach workers etc)
> - Church restoration or repair* (including church roofs, spires, organs, bells, wall paintings etc)
>
> *Please see the Beatrice Lang Trust funding page for guidance on the funding which is available for church building projects.

Applications

Information on the application process can be found on the trust's website. The website states:

> The Laing Family Trusts are run on a co-ordinated basis. This means that you do not need to make multiple applications to the individual Trusts; your application will automatically be directed to the most appropriate of the four Trusts.

Sources of information

Accounts; annual report; Charity Commission record; funder's website.

Lancashire Environmental Fund Ltd

The environment; conservation; local community

Lancashire (excluding the unitary authority districts of Blackpool and Blackburn). Projects must be located within ten miles of a landfill site

£993,200 (2020)

CC number: 1074983

Correspondent: Andy Rowett, The Fund Manager, The Barn, Berkeley Drive, Bamber Bridge, Preston, Lancashire PR5 6BY (tel: 01772 317247; email: general@lancsenvfund.org.uk)

Trustees: John Drury; Francis McGinty; Andrew Hughes; Shaun Turner.

www.lancsenvfund.org.uk

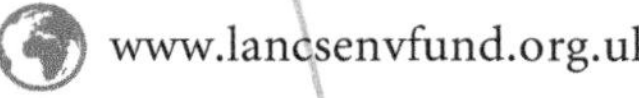

facebook.com/lancsenvfund

@LancsEnvFund

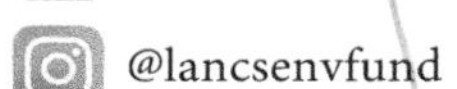

@lancsenvfund

General information

The Lancashire Environmental Fund (LEF) is a partnership between SUEZ Recycling and Recovery UK Ltd, Lancashire County Council, Community Futures and the Lancashire Wildlife Trust.

Since its creation in June 1998 the fund has distributed over £25 million of Landfill Communities Fund (LCF) grants to community and environmental projects which benefit the environment and people of Lancashire. The fund is supported financially by SUEZ Recycling and Recovery UK Ltd, Lancashire County Council and various third-party funders.

The fund awards grants to environmental projects which meet the criteria specified by the Landfill Tax Regulations 1996, these include:

- The maintenance of public amenities and parks, within ten miles of a landfill site, when the work benefits the natural social or built environment
- The provision, conservation, restoration or enhancement of a natural habitat and maintenance or recovery of a species

- The restoring and repair of buildings used for religious worship, or of architectural or historical interest that are within ten miles of a landfill site

The fund's website states that it has supported projects including 'improvements to community facilities, general environmental improvements, creation and management of habitats, improvements to parks, gardens, open spaces, play areas, recreational facilities, ponds, canals and rivers and natural biodiversity'.

There are three grant programmes to which community and environmental groups can apply.

- Green grants of up to £1,000
- Small grants of up to £15,000
- Main grants of up to £30,000

A full list of eligibility criteria and guidance notes for all grant programmes are available via the fund's website.

Financial information

Year end	31/12/2020
Income	£1,180,000
Assets	£1,120,000
Grants to organisations	£993,200
No. of grants	57

Further financial information

Grants paid during the year totalled £993,200. Grants were broken down as follows:

Community facility improvements	£542,200
Play areas and recreational facilities	£256,700
General environmental improvements	£159,100
Parks, gardens and open spaces	£74,000
Habitat creation and management	£60,000
Green grants	£7,200

Note: the sum of the grants in the table is higher than the grants total as it includes grants paid *and* committed during the year.

Beneficiaries included: Accrington Sea Cadets and Friends of Hurst Grange Park (£30,000 each); Heysham Cricket Club (£22,000); Bodies in Motion (£13,700); Grimsargh Wetlands Trust (£11,000); St Peter's Church and Community Centre – Haslingden (£5,900); Ribblesdale Wanderers Cricket and Bowling Club (£1,000); Byron Crescent Community Orchard (£700).

Exclusions

For a comprehensive list of exclusions, applicants are advised to refer to the guidance notes of the specific grants programme to which they intend to apply.

Applications

Guidance notes and application forms for each funding strand can be found on the fund's website. The trust's small and main grant programmes have a two-stage application process involving an expression of interest form and a full application form. All deadlines are posted on the website.

Sources of information

Accounts; annual report; Charity Commission record; funder's website; guidelines for applicants; Lancashire County Council (website).

The Lancashire Foundation

Children and young people, and social welfare

Worldwide, with a preference for the UK and Bermuda

£519,000 (2020)

CC number: 1149184

Correspondent: The Trustees, Lancashire Insurance Company (UK), Level 29, 20 Fenchurch Street, London EC3M 3BY (tel: 020 7264 4056)

Trustees: Derek Stapley; Louise Wells; Emma Grimes.

www.lancashiregroup.com/en/responsibility/lancashire-foundation.html

General information

This foundation is the corporate charity of the Lancashire group of insurance companies, which operates in Bermuda and London. The foundation receives its income through donations from the group and also holds over 141,000 shares in the company.

Areas of work

According to its website, the foundation is committed to meeting the needs of both its local and international communities and is 'particularly focused on helping young people and those severely disadvantaged in society'.

The foundation's annual report for 2020 states that it provides grants to organisations in the UK, Bermuda and other parts of the world whose work 'reflects and is aligned to the values and interests of the people and businesses within the Lancashire group of insurers'. Applications are also welcomed from members of staff on behalf of charities in which they have an interest of involvement.

Financial information

Year end	31/12/2020
Income	£624,600
Assets	£2,430,000
Grants to organisations	£519,000

Beneficiaries included: The Family Centre (£60,000); St Giles Trust (£40,000); Cancer Research UK (£25,000); FareShare (£12,500); Care for Children (£3,000).

Applications

The foundation makes grants predominantly through its key partnerships (which can be seen on the website) and by the recommendation of its employees. Contact the foundation for further information.

Sources of information

Accounts; annual report; Charity Commission record; funder's website.

Duchy of Lancaster Benevolent Fund

General charitable purposes; young people and education; people with disabilities; older people and people who are unwell; community; religious causes

Lancashire; Greater Manchester; Merseyside; elsewhere in the UK where the Duchy of Lancaster has historical links

£1.09 million (2020/21)

CC number: 1026752

Correspondent: The Secretary, 1 Lancaster Place, Strand, London WC2E 7ED (tel: 020 7269 1700; email: info@duchyoflancaster.co.uk)

Trustees: Chris Adcock; Lord Charles Shuttleworth; Warren Smith; Robert Miles; Sir Michael Stevens; Mark Blundell; Richard Snowden.

www.duchyoflancaster.co.uk

General information

The charity's Charity Commission records states that it aims 'to support charitable causes in the county palatine of Lancaster – the administrative counties of Lancashire, Greater Manchester and Merseyside – and elsewhere in the country where the Duchy has historical links (such as landed interests and the presentation of church livings)'. A wide range of charitable causes and organisations are supported each year.

Financial information

Year end	31/03/2021
Income	£1,060,000
Assets	£14,330,000
Grants to organisations	£1,090,000

Further financial information

Grants were broken down as follows:

Community help	£666,200
Youth and education	£183,200
Miscellaneous	£100,600
People with disabilities and older people	£90,100
Religious causes	£50,400

Beneficiaries included: Star Academies (£9,000); Francis House (£5,000); Autism Inclusive (£4,500); Cauldwell

Children and Whitechapel Centre (£2,000 each).

Applications

Apply in writing to the correspondent.

Sources of information

Accounts; annual report; Charity Commission record; funder's website.

Lancaster Foundation

Christianity; social welfare; health; children and young people

UK and Africa

£2.17 million (2020/21)

CC number: 1066850

Correspondent: The Trustees, Text House, 152 Bawdlands, Clitheroe, Lancashire BB7 2LA (tel: 01200 444404)

Trustees: Julie Broadhurst; Dr John Lancaster; Steven Lancaster; Rosemary Lancaster; Rosemary Lancaster.

General information

The Lancaster Foundation was established in 1997 by Dr John Lancaster, the founder of Ultraframe Ltd, which specialises in the design and manufacture of conservatory roofing systems based in Clitheroe, Lancashire. He remains one of the foundation's trustees, alongside other members of the Lancaster family.

The foundation's annual report for 2020/21 states, 'The Lancaster Foundation has been founded on Christian principles offering medical and practical support to the suffering, disadvantaged and marginalised people throughout the UK and Africa. Additionally, the foundation is committed to numerous ongoing local and national youth and community projects.'

Grants are awarded at the absolute discretion of the trustees, mainly to causes personally known to them. Unsolicited requests are not considered.

Financial information

Year end	31/03/2021
Income	£2,960,000
Assets	£61,320,000
Grants to organisations	£2,170,000
No. of grants	74

Beneficiaries included: Message Trust (£212,100); 24–7 Prayer (£105,000); Saltmine Trust (£96,000); Mission Aviation Fellowship (£50,000); Make Jesus Known (£20,000); Wren Bakery (£15,000); Bethany Project (£8,000); Charis Ministries (£1,000).

Applications

The trustees' annual report for 2020/21 states that: 'Although many applications are received, the administrative structure of the charity does not allow for the consideration of unsolicited requests for grant funding.'

Sources of information

Accounts; annual report; Charity Commission record.

LandAid Charitable Trust (LandAid)

Youth homelessness

UK

£1.87 million (2020/21)

CC number: 295157

Correspondent: Grants Team, St Albans House, 5th Floor, 57–59 Haymarket, London SW1Y 4QX (tel: 020 3102 7190; email: enquiries@landaid.org)

Trustees: Alistair Elliot; Susan Hickey; Melanie Leech; Mark Reynolds; Gillian Bowen; Scott Parsons; Suzanne Avery; David Erwin; Michael Slade; Daniel Hughes; Claire Milton; Andrew Gulliford; Robert Bould.

www.landaid.org

General information

LandAid is the charity of the property industry which works towards ending youth homelessness in the UK. Its key aims are:

- To provide accommodation and support for young people who have been homeless
- To profile youth homelessness within the property industry, especially where it can offer young people a platform to have their voices heard

According to the charity's website, support is given in two main ways:

- Supporting exceptional charities in the UK that are working towards homelessness by awarding grants for capital projects providing homes for young people
- Providing free professional property expertise and know-how to charity partners through a pro bono programme

Financial information

Year end	31/03/2021
Income	£2,840,000
Assets	£3,590,000
Grants to organisations	£1,870,000

Further financial information

Grants were awarded to 85 charities during the year.

Beneficiaries included: Lighthouse (£120,000); Depaul UK (£88,300); Blue Triangle Housing Association (£75,000); YMCA Humber (£57,000); Ovo Foundation Rock Trust (£40,800); St George's Crypt – Leeds (£28,000).

Applications

In the first instance, visit the LandAid website for full information of the charity's work. Open rounds of applications for funding are advertised online.

Sources of information

Accounts; annual report; Charity Commission record; funder's website.

The Allen Lane Foundation

Asylum seekers and refugees; Gypsy and Traveller communities; people who have offended; older people; people experiencing mental health problems; people experiencing violence or abuse

UK, excluding Greater London. Organisations with offices in London are eligible if the people who benefit from their work are not only in London

£634,700 (2020/21)

CC number: 248031

Correspondent: Gill Aconley, Grants Officer, 90 The Mount, York, North Yorkshire YO24 1AR (tel: 01904 613223; email: info@allenlane.org.uk or gill@allenlane.org.uk)

Trustees: Zoe Teale; Juliet Walker; Fredrica Teale; Margaret Hyde; Philip Walsh; Maurice Frankel; Justine Cadbury.

www.allenlane.org.uk

General information

The Allen Lane Foundation was set up in 1966 by the late Sir Allen Lane, founder of Penguin Books. The foundation has no connection now with the publishing company, but Sir Allen Lane's family are involved in the running of the foundation – two of his granddaughters are trustees.

Aims

The foundation has a focus on funding 'unpopular' causes. The foundation's website states that it aims to fund work which:

- will make a lasting difference to people's lives rather than simply alleviating the symptoms or current problems;
- is aimed at reducing isolation, stigma and discrimination, and;
- encourages or enables unpopular groups to share in the life of the whole community.

More recently, the foundation launched a new social cohesion programme that focusses on breaking down barriers and tensions between different groups of people. It funds work that builds a more cohesive and inclusive community for all. Note: at the time of writing (January 2022) the foundation's website stated this programme had been suspended until at least the summer of 2022.

Beneficiary groups

The foundation is interested in funding work which benefits people in the following groups, or generalist work which includes significant numbers from more than one such group:

- Asylum seekers and refugees
- The Gypsy and Traveller community
- Migrant communities
- People who have offended
- Older people
- People experiencing mental health problems
- People experiencing violence or abuse

The foundation focuses on work with adults, rather than children and young people.

Eligibility

Grants are only awarded to smaller organisations, including registered charities and also other organisations that are seeking funding for a charitable project, such as constituted voluntary groups and CICs.

The website states:

> If you work across a local area such as a village, estate or town, to be eligible you will need to have an income of less than around £100,000. At the other end of the spectrum, if you work across the whole of the UK you will need to have an income of less than around £250,000.

Types of grant

The foundation makes around 150 grants each year.

It will award grants for running and core costs, specific project costs or start-up funding.

The average grant size is around £5,000-£6,000. You can apply for funding to a maximum of £15,000, but this is generally only offered to larger organisations.

Funding can be awarded as a single grant or as grants split over two or three years.

Financial information

Year end	31/03/2021
Income	£635,700
Assets	£21,180,000
Grants to organisations	£634,700
No. of grants	131

Further financial information

Grants paid during the year totalled £634,700. The list of beneficiaries provided in the accounts refers to grants committed during the year. Overall 131 grants totalling £726,100 were committed in the following categories:

Older people	£180,600
Mental health	£132,900
People who have offended	£126,900
Refugees and asylum seekers	£121,700
Violence and abuse	£101,000
Migrant communities	£44,500
Social cohesion	£12,600
Travelling communities	£6,000

Of the grants committed, 94 were single grants, 33 were awarded over two years and 4 were awarded over three years.

From a total of 466 applications made to the foundation during the year, 335 were refused.

Beneficiaries included: Jericho Road Project (£12,000); Association for Post-Natal Illness (£10,000); Refugees Roots (£6,000); Vine Community Centre (£5,000); York Women's Counselling (£4,300); Open Hearts Open Borders (£2,000); HIMvisible (£1,000); Handcross Rosemary Club (£500).

Exclusions

Grants are not made towards work in Greater London. Organisations which have their offices in London are eligible provided the people who benefit from their work are not only in London. See the foundation's helpful website for a comprehensive list of exclusions.

Applications

The foundation has an online application system, which allows applicants to take an eligibility quiz. If a potential applicant is eligible to apply, they will be directed to the foundation's online application form. The foundation's website also states that applicants can contact the correspondent for any general enquiries. Applications can be submitted at any time and will be considered at the next trustee meeting (see website for meeting dates).

Enquiries relating to the foundation's social cohesion, migrant communities, people who have offended and older people programmes must be directed via email to: tim@allenlane.co.uk.

For enquiries relating to asylum seekers and refugees, Gypsies and Travellers, people with mental health problems or people experiencing violence or abuse, email gill@allenlane.org.uk.

For any other general enquiries, email info@allenlane.org.uk.

If you have previously received a grant, you will need to wait at least 12 months following the end of the grant period before applying again.

Full details and guidelines for applicants are available on the foundation's helpful website.

Sources of information

Accounts; annual report; Charity Commission record; funder's website.

The LankellyChase Foundation

Prevention of homelessness, substance abuse, violence and abuse; mental or physical disabilities; social welfare; women and girls; ethnic minorities

UK

£6.99 million (2020/21)

CC number: 1107583

Correspondent: The Trustees, Greenworks, Dog and Duck Yard, Princeton Street, London WC1R 4BH (tel: 020 3747 9930; email: enquiries@lankellychase.org.uk)

Trustees: Morag Burnett; Hilary Berg; Simon Tucker; Darren Murinas; Robin Tuddenham; Myron Kellner-Rogers; Amanda Hailes; Asif Afridi; Baljeet Sandhu; James Keenan; Marai Larasi.

 www.lankellychase.org.uk

 @lankellychase

 @lankellychase

General information

The LankellyChase Foundation was established in 2004 following the amalgamation of two grant-making trusts, the Lankelly Foundation and the Chase Charity. The foundation's mission is to bring about change that will transform the quality of life of people who face severe and multiple disadvantages, meaning the persistent clustering of severe social harms, particularly homelessness, substance misuse, mental and physical illness, extreme poverty, violence and abuse.

Grant-making policy

The foundation has moved away from traditional grant-making to working in partnership with selected organisations that match its charitable aims.

Note the following stated on the foundation's website:

> Currently, we aren't able to accept unsolicited funding applications.
>
> The community section [of the website] has a list of who, what and where we fund but in general, we support action that reveals, questions and dismantles or heals, reimagines and transforms systems of injustice and oppression.

Financial information

Year end	31/03/2021
Income	£2,700,000
Assets	£158,100,000
Grants to organisations	£6,990,000

Beneficiaries included: New Economy Organisers Network (£330,000); The Ballinger Trust (£110,000); Support and Action for Women's Network (£50,000); Mark Leonard Trust (£20,000); Centre for Knowledge Equity CIC (£10,000); Arts at the Old Fire Station (£5,000).

Applications

The foundation's website provides the following information:

> Even though we aren't able to accept unsolicited funding applications it still feels important to give a sense of how our funding process works.
>
> We don't have one catch-all funding process. Instead, we use a mixture of open call-outs, targeted commissions, devolved funding to specific places and lots of conversations through a variety of networks.

The foundation asks organisations interested in its work to keep up to date via its website and on Twitter. Organisations are welcome to email the foundation if they have any specific queries.

Sources of information

Accounts; annual report; Charity Commission record; funder's website.

The Lauffer Family Charitable Foundation

Jewish causes and general charitable purposes

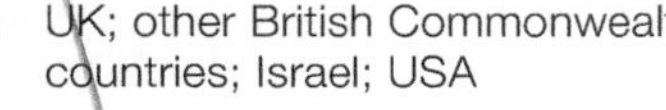

UK; other British Commonwealth countries; Israel; USA

£367,400 (2020/21)

CC number: 251115

Correspondent: Jonathan Lauffer, Trustee, 123 Hampstead Way, London NW11 7JN (tel: 020 7431 4200; email: jonathanlauffer13@gmail.com)

Trustees: Gideon Lauffer; Jonathan Lauffer; Robin Lauffer.

General information

The foundation was established to support general charitable purposes in the UK, Israel, the USA and any other territories forming part of the British Commonwealth. The majority of the foundation's beneficiaries are Jewish charities/organisations, but the foundation welcomes applications for general charitable purposes in any of the scheduled territories.

Financial information

Year end	31/03/2021
Income	£118,800
Assets	£4,900,000
Grants to organisations	£367,400
No. of grants	155

Further financial information

During 2020/21, grants were distributed as follows:

Welfare and care of children and families	£164,300
Education	£107,500
Religious activities	£53,600
Medical healthcare	£26,300
Recreation and culture	£14,600
Environment	£1,100

Only beneficiaries that received £1,000 or more were listed in the trust's accounts. Grants of under £1,000 were awarded to 49 organisations and totalled £15,500.

Beneficiaries included: Kehal Charedim Trust (£37,000 in four grants); Guy's Trust (£6,000 in two grants); Friends of Aetres Moshe (£6,000); Keren L'kiruv Yisroel (£5,000); JW3 Development (£2,000); Arts Therapies for Children and Holocaust Educational Trust (£1,000 each).

Applications

Apply in writing to the correspondent.

Sources of information

Accounts; annual report; Charity Commission record.

The Law Family Charitable Foundation

Education; health; social mobility; the environment; the arts

UK

£10.8 million (2020/21)

CC number: 1141997

Correspondent: The Trustees, c/o Caxton Europe Asset Management, Third Floor, 40 Berkeley Square, London W1J 5AL (tel: 020 7647 4057)

Trustees: Andrew Law; Zoe Law; Roger Sadewsky.

www.lawfamilycharitable foundation.org

General information

The Law Family Charitable Foundation was established in 2011 by Andrew and Zoë Law. Andrew is the Chair and Chief Executive Officer of Caxton Associates, a global macro hedge fund. Zoë has previously worked in the music and make-up industries and currently works as a photographer. She is best known for her Legends of British Industry exhibition at the National Portrait Gallery, London.

The foundation supports causes that are important to the founders. These include education, health, social mobility, the environment and the arts.

The foundation supports a number of charities that Andrew Law is a also trustee of, including Speakers for Schools and the Sutton Trust.

Financial information

Year end	04/04/2021
Income	£31,410,000
Assets	£56,420,000
Grants to organisations	£10,800,000

Beneficiaries included: University of Sheffield (£5.85 million); Policy Exchange (£175,000); The Sutton Trust (£30,000); Greenhouse Sport (£10,000); Maggie's at the Royal Marsden (£1,400).

Applications

Contact the foundation for further information.

Sources of information

Accounts; annual report; Charity Commission record; funder's website.

The Betty Lawes Foundation

General charitable purposes

UK and overseas

£543,500 (2020)

CC number: 274025

Correspondent: The Trustees, Volac International, 50 Fishers Lane, Orwell, Royston, Hertfordshire SG8 5QX (tel: 01223 208021)

Trustees: Margaret Lee; Patricia Neville; William Crane.

General information

The Betty Lawes Foundation was established in 1977 by Betty Lawes, founder of Volac International Ltd, a dairy products firm, through the donation of shares in the company. The foundation makes grants for general charitable purposes throughout the UK and overseas.

The foundation's Charity Commission record states that the foundation makes grants to organisations where its support 'will have a real and immediate impact'. There is a preference for smaller charities and 'specialised or local branches' of larger charities.

Financial information

Year end	31/12/2020
Income	£410,000
Assets	£27,990,000
Grants to organisations	£543,500
No. of grants	37

Beneficiaries included: National Emergencies Trust (£165,000); Jamie's Farm (£45,000); 1000 Hills Community Helpers (£25,900); The Prince's Trust (£12,500); Blue Smile (£8,000); Holy Trinity Church – Cambridge (£4,000); CALM (£2,000).

Applications

Unsolicited applications were not being accepted at the time of writing (January 2022). Contact the correspondent for further information.

Sources of information

Accounts; annual report; Charity Commission record.

The Richard Lawes Foundation

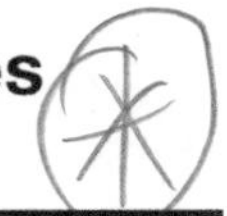

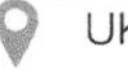 General charitable purposes

UK

£352,400 (2020/21)

CC number: 274042

Correspondent: Bobby Lawes, Trustee, Longhayes, Lowerdown, Bovey Tracey, Newton Abbot, Devon TQ13 9LF (tel: 07850 126351; email: Bobbylawes@aol.com)

Trustees: William Lawes; Dr Dorothea Lawes; Janet Withers; David Northcroft.

General information

The Richard Lawes Foundation was established in 1977, with the aim of making grants for general charitable purposes. Although all charitable organisations are considered, preference is given to registered charities and, in particular, small charities or local branches of larger charities. In the past, grants have been made to support areas such as medical research, bereavement support, mental health and young people.

The foundation's 2020/21 accounts note:

> The Trustees avoid supporting organisations of an overtly political nature, including those quasi-political secular organisations established for the promotion of a subjective opinion. They recommend appeals and organisations where it is felt that donations will have a real and immediate impact.

Financial information

Year end	05/04/2021
Income	£217,700
Assets	£9,170,000
Grants to organisations	£352,400

Beneficiaries included: A list of beneficiaries was not available.

Applications

At the time of writing (April 2022) the foundation's Charity Commission record stated that applications were not being considered.

Sources of information

Accounts; annual report; Charity Commission record.

The Lawson Trust CIO

The arts and heritage; education; the environment; health; social and economic disadvantage

Kent and Sussex

£401,500 (2020/21)

CC number: 1171822

Correspondent: The Trustees, PO Box 506, Ramsgate CT11 1DZ (email: enquiries@lawsontrust.co.uk)

Trustees: Philip Thomas; Sarah Hill; Michael Norrie; Jennifer Thomas; Robert Blundell; Antony Hooper; Sarah Playle.

 www.lawsontrust.org

General information

The trust, formerly known as Raymond and Blanche Lawson Charitable Trust, was re-registered as a CIO in 2017. The trust's five key funding priorities are:

- Arts and heritage
- Education
- Health
- Social and economic disadvantage
- The environment

There are three different funds originating from the trust: The Lawson Trust, The Lawson Endowment for Kent and The Lawson Endowment for Sussex.

The trust recently expanded its reach to national charities working with individuals and communities within Kent, having previously favoured smaller charities with specific projects or interventions. The trust provides single-payment grants to registered charities, including those registered as a company limited by guarantee and CIOs.

Financial information

Year end	31/03/2021
Income	£1,890,000
Assets	£21,610,000
Grants to organisations	£401,500

Beneficiaries included: Heart of Kent Hospice (£40,000); Safe Haven (£30,000); Serve On (£20,000); The Maypole Project (£10,000); The Girls' Network (£5,000); The Separated Child Foundation (£2,000); LUPUS UK (£1,000).

Exclusions

The trustees do not make grants for the following:

- Individuals
- Non-registered charities
- Overseas charities
- Political parties
- Causes promoting religion

Applications

Applicants based in Kent seeking funding of up to £5,000 can apply to the Lawson Endowment for Kent. Further information on this fund can be found on the Kent Community Foundation website.

The trust also has an endowment with Sussex Community Foundation. Applicants based in Sussex with an annual income of under £1 million can apply to the foundation for a grant via the community foundation's website.

National charities or charities outside the criteria for the two community foundations can apply via the trust's online application process. The average grant amount is £5,000.

Applicants should first complete the eligibility checker on the trust's website. Eligible organisations will then be provided with a link to the online application form. Applications can be made at any time. The trustees meet four times per year. Check the trust's website for meeting dates.

Sources of information

Accounts; annual report; Charity Commission record; funder's website.

The Leathersellers' Company Charitable Fund

 General charitable purposes

UK, particularly London

£3.02 million (2020/21)

CC number: 278072

Correspondent: David Santa-Olalla, Clerk to the Leathersellers' Company, 7 St Helen's Place, London EC3A 6AB (tel: 020 7330 1452; email: clerk@leathersellers.co.uk)

Trustees: Matthew Lawrence; The Leathersellers' Company.

 https://leathersellers.co.uk/charitablefund

 @charityleather

General information

This is the charity of The Leathersellers' Company, one of the ancient livery companies of the City of London. The charity supports UK-registered charities, including CIOs, and educational institutions across the UK. Grants typically focus on tackling deprivation and social problems, but a wide range of causes are supported. There is a preference for supporting the leather and hide trades and education in leather technology. The charity also awards educational grants to UK students taking a full-time undergraduate or postgraduate degree at a UK university.

There are two grant-making programmes for organisations and grants can be awarded as a single grant or a multi-year grant. Check the charity's website for current funding priorities.

Small Grants programme

The Small Grants programme is a fast-track grant assessment for one-off grants of up to £3,000 for UK-registered charities and CIOs. Applicants must: currently be supporting vulnerable people; be working in geographical areas of high deprivation in the UK; and have an annual income of under £200,000. Applicants can expect a result within a month of making an application.

Main Grants programme

The Main Grants programme awards multi-year grants for a period of up to four years and large one-off grants. Funding can be offered for special projects, capital grants and core costs such as salaries, rent and utilities. The value of the grant awarded varies according to the size of the charity, the total cost of the project and other funding that has been secured. Successful applications will typically have to pass through a four-stage process, which can take up to nine months.

Student grants

Individuals can apply for up to £5,000 per year for up to four years of study. Grants were only available for undergraduate students in the 2022/23 funding round.

Financial information

Year end	31/07/2021
Income	£1,660,000
Assets	£72,910,000
Grants to organisations	£3,020,000
No. of grants	364

Further financial information

Grants paid to organisations and individuals in 2020/21 were broken down as follows:

Education	37	£1.05 million
Domestic and sexual abuse	31	£343,000
Recreation	35	£287,000
Community support	53	£244,000
Disability	35	£234,000
Homelessness	33	£221,000
Health	26	£185,000
Advice	26	£168,000
Leather-associated grants	9	£141,000
Creative arts	20	£127,000
Employability	9	£92,000
Criminal justice and rehabilitation	10	£88,000
Food and essentials provision	20	£62,000
Services support and rehabilitation	7	£22,000
Heritage and the environment	13	£21,000

During the year, 364 grants totalling £3.02 million were made to organisations, of which 187 (totalling £656,000) were single-year grants and 177 (totalling £2.36 million) were multi-year grants.

Only beneficiaries of grants of £20,000 and above were listed in the 2020/21 accounts.

Beneficiaries included: Colfe's School (£420,000); Leathersellers' Federation of Schools (£174,000); University of Northampton (£40,000); Separated Child Foundation (£34,000); Be Free Young Caters (£27,000); My Sister's Place and The Bond Board (£20,000 each).

Exclusions

Grants are not awarded:

- For medical research
- For capital restoration projects for the sole purpose of conservation/heritage
- To hospices
- To CICs

Applications

Applications can be made using the online form on the charity's website during open funding periods. Applicants are advised to regularly check the charity's website for up-to-date information and deadlines.

Sources of information

Accounts; annual report; Charity Commission record; funder's website.

The William Leech Charity

General charitable purposes in the North East; the welfare of disadvantaged children in financially developing countries

North East England and overseas

£666,300 (2020/21)

CC number: 1186957

Correspondent: The Trustees, c/o Robson Laidler, Fernwood House, Fernwood Road, Jesmond, Newcastle upon Tyne, Tyne and Wear NE2 1TJ (tel: 0191 281 8191; email: enquiries@williamleechcharity.org.uk)

www.williamleechcharity.org.uk

General information

The charity was established by Sir William Leech in 1972 to support volunteers and charitable projects in the North East. William Leech began his working life as an apprentice before eventually going on to lead large-scale building operations to build affordable housing. He established three charities including the William Leech Charity. William Leech died in 1990 and has been awarded a knighthood for his charitable works.

Grants are made for general charitable purposes in line with the guidelines of the founder. According to its website, the charity distributes nearly £550,000 a year in grants for a range of causes.

Grant programmes

Main fund – grants are awarded to registered charities in the north-east of England. In some cases, the charity may provide an interest-free loan in place of a grant to charities that are faced with an unexpected crisis. Loans are repayable over five years and are usually for up to a maximum of £10,000 or 10% of the project.

The Lady Leech Fund – this fund was established in memory of Lady Ellen Leech in 1997. The fund's aim is to support charities with a North East connection that are assisting projects in less financially developed countries. Projects must focus on the welfare of disadvantaged children. Support may also be given towards major disasters anywhere in the world.

Volunteer support – support is given to volunteers at small registered charities for which at least two-thirds of the charitable work (excluding administration and fundraising) is done by volunteers.

Financial information

Year end	31/03/2021
Income	£18,760,000
Assets	£21,360,000
Grants to organisations	£666,300

Further financial information

The charity recently re-registered with the Charity Commission and its high income is due to an asset transfer of £18.27 million from the previous charity.

Beneficiaries included: Newcastle University (£348,700); Blood Bikes (£10,000); The Gateway Church (£3,000); Henry Dancer Days (£2,000); Northern Citrines Marching Band (£500).

Applications

Applications can be made online through the charity's website. The charity no longer accepts applications made by post.

Sources of information

Accounts; annual report; Charity Commission record; funder's website.

The Leeward Trust

Social welfare; education; health; citizenship and community development; arts, heritage, culture and science; recreational activities; human rights and conflict resolution; religious or racial harmony; equality and diversity; the environment; animal welfare

UK; India; Africa; South America

£350,500 (2020/21)

OSCR number: SC047870

Correspondent: The Trustees, c/o Gillespie Macandrew, 5 Atholl Crescent, Edinburgh EH3 8EJ

General information

The trust's objects are to provide grants and donations to groups/charities promoting the following purposes in the UK, India, Africa and South America:

- The prevention or relief of poverty
- The advancement of education
- The advancement of health
- The saving of lives
- The advancement of citizenship or community development
- The advancement of the arts, heritage, culture or science
- The provision of recreational facilities, or the organisation of recreational activities, with the object of improving the conditions of life for the persons for whom the facilities or activities are primarily intended
- The advancement of human rights, conflict resolution or reconciliation
- The promotion of religious or racial harmony
- The promotion of equality and diversity
- The advancement of environmental protection or improvement
- The relief of those in need by reason of age, ill health, disability, financial hardship or other disadvantage
- The advancement of animal welfare

Financial information

Year end	31/03/2021
Income	£360,000
Assets	£9,100
Grants to organisations	£350,500
No. of grants	50

Further financial information

During 2020/21, grants were distributed as follows:

Age, ill health, disability, financial hardship or other disadvantage	£133,600
Health	£53,800
Social welfare	£47,500
Environmental protection or improvement	£37,500
Education	£35,000
Religious or racial harmony	£11,700
Arts, heritage, culture or science	£11,500
Equality and diversity	£10,000
Human rights, conflict resolution and reconciliation	£7,500
Citizenship or community development	£2,500

Beneficiaries included: A list of beneficiaries was not available.

Applications

Apply in writing to the correspondent.

Sources of information

Accounts; annual report; OSCR record.

The Legal Education Foundation

Legal education and training; access to employment in the legal profession; public understanding of the law; the use of technology in legal education; research

UK

£8.72 million (2020/21)

CC number: 271297

Correspondent: Clare Johns, Foundation Accountant and Secretary, Suite 2, Ground Floor, River House, Broadford Park, Shalford, Guildford, Surrey GU4 8EP (tel: 020 3005 5695; email: clare.johns@thelef.org)

Trustees: Ailsa Beaton; Rupert Baron; Jonathan Freeman; Alison Pickup; Monica Risam; Vivek Luthra; Patricia Sloan; Rupen Shah; Hetan Shah; Alexander Temple.

http://thelegaleducationfoundation.org

@the_lef

General information

The origins of The Legal Education Foundation date back to the 1870s. Its purpose is 'to promote the advancement of legal education and the study of the law in all its branches', as stated on the foundation's website. The foundation does this by making grants to a wide variety of mostly charitable organisations working in different social, professional and academic settings and by commissioning research.

Grant-making (2020–25 strategy)

The foundation's 2020–25 strategy is delivered through three funding programmes, as described on its website:

Stronger Sector – 'This grants programme supports education, training and development aimed at addressing systemic gaps in skills in the social justice legal sector [...] It also includes the Justice First Fellowship.'

Fairer Systems – 'This grants programme supports work to increase people's capacity to understand the way laws are made and implemented. It has two linked areas of focus: the constitutional and legal implications of leaving the EU; and the growing use of automated decision-making by government.'

Smarter Justice – 'This programme seeks to strengthen a commitment to collecting and learning from robust evidence in the design and operation of the UK justice system.'

Further information on each programme is available on the foundation's website.

Grant types

According to the foundation's website, 'applications can include all costs related to achieving the hoped-for outcomes, including staffing, volunteer expenses, consultancy, travel, venue hire and a reasonable contribution to overheads.' The foundation mostly funds revenue costs, but can fund modest capital costs directly related to the work (but capital expenditure on building/vehicles will not be funded).

Eligibility

Applications to these main grant programmes are only accepted from legally constituted organisations undertaking charitable work in the UK. The majority of recipients are charities, but limited companies (including CICs) and private law firms can also be supported for non-profit making activities.

Additional support

As well as grant funding, the foundation supports grantees by offering advice on policy and strategy, and by convening meetings and conferences.

Financial information

Year end	30/06/2021
Income	£5,310,000
Assets	£289,300
Grants to organisations	£8,720,000

Further financial information

Grants were broken down as follows in 2020/21: Stronger Sector (£4.55 million); Fairer Systems (£1.06 million); Smarter Justice (£167,000).

Beneficiaries included: Justice First Fellowship (£1.78 million); The Access to Justice Foundation (£500,000); SafeLives (£230,000); Shelter Scotland (£196,000); Asylum Support Appeals Project (£136,000); London Legal Support Trust (£79,000); The Bureau of Investigative Journalism (£32,000); Advice UK (£26,000).

Exclusions

The foundation's website highlights areas it will not fund, including:

- Individuals
- Work outside the UK
- Funding that would directly replace or subsidise government, legal profession or university funding, including the costs of law clinics

- Capital expenditure on buildings and vehicles
- General fundraising appeals
- Projects related to commercial law
- Infrastructure for pro bono legal advice
- The provision of legal advice where it is not delivered as part of legal training
- Work that has already taken place

The foundation is unlikely to fund small-scale projects without the capacity for system influence. A full list of exclusions is available on the foundation's website.

Applications

Check the foundation's website for open funding rounds (there are two deadlines per year). A timetable of upcoming deadlines is available to view on the website.

Apply using an online application form on the foundation's website. If successful at the first stage, you will be invited to make a full application – you will be sent a personalised link to a second-stage form.

Sources of information

Accounts; annual report; Charity Commission record; funder's website.

Lempriere Pringle 2015

Regeneration and community development

Bishop Auckland and the surrounding areas

£20.67 million (2019/20)

CC number: 1161516

Correspondent: The Trustees, Ord House, Little Fencote, Northallerton, North Yorkshire DL7 0RR (tel: 01609 748284; email: ordhouse1@btinternet.com)

Trustees: Jonathan Ruffer; Dr Jane Ruffer; Ashe Windham; Harriet O'Rourke; Dr Norman Fraser; Elizabeth Booker; Richard Chartres.

General information

This charity was established in 2015 by philanthropist Jonathan Ruffer, co-founder of Ruffer Investment Management Ltd. The charity funds three Auckland Castle-based charities of which Jonathan Ruffer is a trustee – Auckland Castle Trust, Eleven Arches and The Zubaran Trust. The charity also funds the regeneration of Bishop Auckland and the surrounding areas through the awarding of grants to charitable organisations.

The charity's 2019/20 annual report states: 'A major proportion of the organisation's resources is allocated to various sister trusts based at Auckland Castle, with the underlying aim of stimulating regeneration in Bishop Auckland and surrounding areas.

Grants have also been made to a range of other charitable projects and initiatives in other areas.'

Financial information

Year end	31/03/2020
Income	£21,600,000
Assets	£18,900,000
Grants to organisations	£20,670,000

Beneficiaries included: The Auckland Project (£14.5 million); SHED (£3.5 million); Stockton Project (£121,600); First Fruit (£75,000); Japan Christian Link (£10,000).

Applications

The 2019/20 annual accounts state:

> The organisation is proactive in identifying projects, ministries, charities and individuals whose work relates to the organisation's objectives, but who generally are pursuing their causes without resorting to funding via professional fundraisers.

Contact the correspondent for further information before making an application to the charity.

Sources of information

Accounts; annual report; Charity Commission record.

The Mark Leonard Trust

Environmental causes, particularly sustainable agriculture, food and climate change; young people, particularly those at risk of offending

Worldwide, but mainly the UK

£915,800 (2020/21)

CC number: 1040323

Correspondent: Robert Bell, Director, The Peak, 5 Wilton Road, London SW1V 1AP (tel: 020 7410 0330; email: info@sfct.org.uk)

Trustees: Zivi Sainsbury; John Sainsbury; Mark Sainsbury.

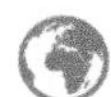 www.sfct.org.uk

General information

This is one of the Sainsbury Family Charitable Trusts, which share a joint administration but work autonomously as independent legal entities. They have a common approach to grant-making and generally discourage applications from organisations not already in contact with the trust concerned, but some are open to unsolicited approaches. According to the website, the trustees focuses their grant-making on the following areas:

- Sustainable agriculture and food; tackling climate change, energy efficiency and renewable energy
- Youth work that supports the rehabilitation of young people involved in anti-social or criminal activities and helps remove the barriers to social inclusion
- Refugees, especially unaccompanied minors
- Music and disability

Grants are made to support innovative schemes through seed-funding, with the aim of helping projects to achieve sustainability and successful replication.

The trust also works closely with some of the other Sainsbury Trusts on the Climate Change Collaboration, which supports projects seeking to accelerate progress towards a low-carbon society.

Financial information

Year end	05/04/2022
Income	£1,140,000
Assets	£21,620,000
Grants to organisations	£915,800

Beneficiaries included: Switchback (£92,000); Just for Kids Law (£50,000); Environmental Funders' Network (£40,000); On Road Media (£30,000); Global Legal Action Network GLAN (£27,000); C40 Cities Climate Leadership Group (£25,000); Uplift (£20,000).

Exclusions

Grants are not normally made to individuals.

Applications

Unsolicited applications are not accepted.

Sources of information

Accounts; annual report; Charity Commission record; funder's website.

The Leri Charitable Trust

General charitable purposes

UK, with a preference for Manchester and the London Borough of Brent

£549,300 (2020/21)

CC number: 1075107

Correspondent: Michael Reynolds, Administrator, c/o Edwin Coe LLP, 2 Stone Buildings, London WC2A 3TH (tel: 020 7691 4048; email: michael.reynolds@edwincoe.com)

Trustees: Alison Broadberry; Geoffrey Hellings; Leon Rosselson; Ruth Rosselson; John Ryan.

General information

The Leri Charitable Trust's 2020/21 annual report states that the charity supports the following causes:

- Empowering and facilitating the independence of those in need by reason of poverty, youth, age, ill-health, disability, financial hardship, or other disadvantage
- Advancing human rights, conflict resolution or reconciliation or the promotion of religious or racial harmony or equality and diversity
- Advancing education, the arts, culture, heritage and science
- Advancing community development and environmental protection and improvement
- Advancing and promoting health and the care of older people
- Supporting refugees and asylum seekers and raising awareness of issues affecting refugees and asylum seekers
- Promoting justice to Palestinians
- Promoting economic justice
- Supporting the projects of charitable organisations meeting these aims in the London Borough of Brent, Manchester and their immediate surrounds

Financial information

Year end	02/03/2021
Income	£305,400
Assets	£12,860,000
Grants to organisations	£549,300

Further financial information

The grant total was estimated using information available in the accounts.

Beneficiaries included: A list of beneficiaries was not available.

Applications

The trust does not accept unsolicited applications.

Sources of information

Accounts; annual report; Charity Commission record.

The Leverhulme Trust

Academic research

UK

£96.05 million (2020)

CC number: 1159154

Correspondent: Programme Correspondent, 1 Pemberton Row, London EC4A 3BG (tel: 020 7042 9888; email: grants@leverhulme.ac.uk)

Trustees: Niall Fitzgerald; Patrick Cescau; David Lewis; Leena Nair; Alan Jope; Christopher Saul; Doug Baillie; Steve Williams; Mhairi McEwan; Clive Butler; Rudy Markham; Prof. Keith Gull.

 www.leverhulme.ac.uk

 @LeverhulmeTrust

General information

This trust derives from the will of William Hesketh Lever, who left a proportion of his interest in Lever Brothers to benefit specific beneficiaries. A redefinition of the trust's objectives in 1983 led to the trust concentrating its attention solely on research and education. The trust offers research grants, fellowships and scholarships, project funding and prize awards.

Financial information

Year end	31/12/2020
Income	£93,770,000
Assets	£3,590,000
Grants to organisations	£96,050,000

Beneficiaries included: University of Oxford (£6.1 million); University of Edinburgh (£4.63 million); University of York (£963,000); University of Surrey (£510,000); University of Plymouth (£505,000).

Exclusions

The trust's website states:

> What kinds of research are not eligible for Leverhulme Trust funding?
>
> - Both because of the substantial funding available from other sources for applied medical research, and the Trust's priority to support investigations of a fundamental nature, we do not fund studies of disease, illness and disabilities in humans and animals, or research that is intended to inform clinical practice or the development of medical applications
> - Policy-driven research where the principal objective is to assemble an evidence base for immediate policy initiatives
>
> Proposals for the following are also ineligible for Leverhulme Trust support:
>
> - Research where advocacy is an explicit component
> - Research aimed principally at an immediate commercial application
> - Proposals in which the balance between assembling a data bank or database and the related subsequent research is heavily inclined to the former

Applications

The trust administers various grant programmes that open and close throughout the year. For full details on each programme, refer to the website.

Sources of information

Accounts; annual report; Charity Commission record; funder's website.

Lord Leverhulme's Charitable Trust

Health; community; education; the arts; animal welfare; the environment; places of worship

UK, with a strong preference for Cheshire, Merseyside and South Lancashire

£287,400 (2020/21)

CC number: 212431

Correspondent: The Trustees, Leverhulme Estate Office, Hesketh Grange, Manor Road, Thornton Hough, Wirral, Merseyside CH63 1JD (tel: 0151 336 4828; email: llctadmin@leverhulme.net)

Trustees: Anthony Hannay; Sir Algernon Heber-Percy; Henry Wilson.

General information

The trust was established in 1957 by the late Lord Leverhulme and supports general charitable purposes, in particular those organisations that have been chosen by the children and grandchildren of the settlor and other members of the Leverhulme family.

Financial information

Year end	05/04/2021
Income	£587,100
Assets	£41,080,000
Grants to organisations	£287,400

Further financial information

Only grants of over £20,000 are included in the list of beneficiaries.

Grants were distributed as follows:

Health	£102,800
Community	£96,300
Education	£38,400
The arts	£29,000
Religious establishments	£11,000
Animal welfare	£10,00
The environment	£0

Beneficiaries included: University of Liverpool (£100,000); Bolton School (£30,000); Warrington Youth Club (£25,000); Liverpool Heart and Chest Hospital (£20,000).

Applications

The trust states in its 2020/21 annual report:

> Priority is given [...] to applications from Cheshire, Merseyside and South Lancashire and the charities supported by the settlor in his lifetime. Others who do not meet those criteria should not apply without prior invitation but should, on a single sheet, state briefly their aims and apply fully only on being asked to do so. A handful of charities have heeded this warning and telephoned our administrator but the continuing volume of applications from charities which plainly do not meet the stated criteria suggests that many applicants do not concern themselves

with their target's policies. Generally, the trustees do not acknowledge receipt of applications or notify unsuccessful applicants in order to minimise management expense.

Sources of information

Accounts; annual report; Charity Commission record.

The Ralph Levy Charitable Company Ltd

General charitable purposes; education; medical causes; social welfare; the arts

UK and overseas

£396,300 (2020/21)

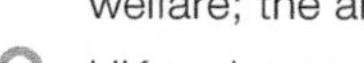

CC number: 200009

Correspondent: The Trustees, 116 Piccadilly, London W1J 7BJ (tel: 020 7408 9333; email: charity@ralphtrustees.co.uk)

Trustees: Daniel Levy; Stuart Levy; Christopher Andrews.

General information

The charity was established in 1961 with a settlement initially set up by Ralph Levy.

The charity's 2020/21 accounts state:

> The Memorandum and Articles of Association of the company permit the application of its income and assets towards any purpose recognised by law as charitable.
>
> The company (charity) does however give particular consideration to bodies with educational, welfare, medical and arts objectives, each grant application being reviewed by the trustees.

Financial information

Year end	05/04/2021
Income	£273,300
Grants to organisations	£396,300

Further financial information

Grants were broken down as follows:

Education	£158,800
Welfare	£141,700
Medical causes	£64,400
The arts	£31,400

Beneficiaries included: A list of beneficiaries was not available.

Applications

Apply in writing to the correspondent. The trustees meet monthly to discuss and approve grant applications.

Sources of information

Accounts; annual report; Charity Commission record.

Joseph Levy Foundation

Disadvantaged young people and cystic fibrosis

UK and Israel

£777,900 (2020/21)

CC number: 1165225

Correspondent: The Trustees, 1st Floor, 1 Bell Street, London NW1 5BY (tel: 020 7616 1200; email: info@jlf.org.uk)

Trustees: Jane Jason; James Jason; Melanie Levy; Claudia Giat; Katie Ellison; Mark Jason.

www.jlf.org.uk

General information

The Joseph Levy Foundation is a CIO established in January 2016 to take forward the work of the Joseph Levy Charitable Foundation (Charity Commission no. 245592). The Joseph Levy Charitable Foundation was established by the late Joseph Levy under a trust deed dated 5 April 1965. In March 2016 the two charities merged, and the merger was registered with the Charity Commission.

The following information has been taken from the foundation's website:

> From April 2021 to March 2022 we are concentrating our funding and resources on two main areas. During this period we will seek out charities to support and we will not consider any unsolicited applications
>
> **Youth Disadvantage**
>
> Joseph Levy passionately believed in the potential of all young people, some of whom face particular challenges due to ill-health, poverty or disability.
>
> **Who we will support:** Children and young people aged 16 to 25 who are experiencing loss and disadvantage as a result of the pandemic and its effects (e.g. on opportunities, education, etc.) in the UK and Israel. We will target those who are experiencing the greatest negative impact.
>
> **What we will fund:** Services and activities of a practical kind (e.g. mentoring, sport, etc.) that will support young people's mental health and wellbeing and provide opportunities for them to fulfil their potential – e.g. in relation to employment and education and during periods of transition. We will prioritise activities that prevent young people reaching crisis points. We will not fund specialist counselling or mental health therapeutic services.
>
> **How we will fund:** We will use a proactive approach to identify organisations that we would like to support and are hoping to award the first grants in July 2021. We anticipate that our grants will be in the region of £25,000 to £30,000 and we will generally offer core funding. The grants will be for one year only, although in some cases there may be the possibility of the funding relationship being extended beyond the end of the first year.
>
> **Cystic Fibrosis**
>
> The Cystic Fibrosis Trust was formed in 1964 with Joseph Levy's help and support. He served as Chairman for 20 years and the charity's success was ensured by his dedication.
>
> We continue to support two CF charities – specifically:
>
> - Cystic Fibrosis Trust
> - Cystic Fibrosis Holiday Fund

Check the foundation's website for the most up-to-date information.

Financial information

Year end	31/03/2021
Income	£896,900
Assets	£23,670,000
Grants to organisations	£777,900
No. of grants	36

Further financial information

In 2020/21, grants were distributed as follows:

Autism	£346,800
Cystic fibrosis	£197,600
COVID-19 emergency grants	£173,500
Small grants (up to and including £10,000)	£60,000

Beneficiaries included: Cystic Fibrosis Holiday Fund (£145,800); Ambitious about Autism (£49,700); Newark Youth London (£19,300); Manchester Refugee Support Network (£10,000); Team Up for Social Mobility (£6,800); World Jewish Relief (£3,000); Sport in Mind (£2,500); The Harington Scheme (£1,000).

Exclusions

Grants are not made to individuals.

Applications

Unsolicited applications are not generally accepted. The foundation's website states: 'Please note that JLF does not usually accept unsolicited grant applications. We search proactively for opportunities where funding could make a difference.'

Sources of information

Accounts; annual report; Charity Commission record; funder's website.

Bernard Lewis Family Charitable Trust

Child welfare; medical causes; older people; Jewish community support; education; general charitable purposes

UK

£1.41 million (2020)

CC number: 1125035

Correspondent: The Trustees, Chelsea House, Westgate, London W5 1DR (tel: 07730 091970)

Trustees: Caroline Grainge; Bernard Lewis; Leonard Lewis; Clive Lewis.

General information

The trust was established in 2008 and makes grants in the UK for general charitable purposes, with a particular interest in child welfare, medical causes, older people, education and support for Jewish communities. According to the trust's 2020 accounts, most grants are one-off, but occasionally multi-year grants are made over two to three years.

Financial information

Year end	31/12/2020
Income	£2,570,000
Assets	£9,060,000
Grants to organisations	£1,410,000
No. of grants	35

Further financial information

Grants were broken down as follows:

General charitable purposes	£890,900
Child welfare	£597,700
Medical causes	£372,500
Jewish community support	£158,300
Older people	£50,000

Beneficiaries included: Compassion of Dying (£250,000); Project 507 (two grants totalling £103,700); Jewish Care (£50,000); London Prisons Mission (£28,800); Donate4Refugees (£15,000); Pimlico Opera (£5,000); Care4Calais (£2,500).

Applications

The trust does not accept unsolicited applications.

Sources of information

Accounts; annual report; Charity Commission record; further information provided by the funder.

David and Ruth Lewis Family Charitable Trust

General charitable purposes; medical research; Jewish religious support; child and social care; older people; education

UK and overseas

£1.55 million (2020/21)

CC number: 259892

Correspondent: The Trustees, Chelsea House, Westgate, Ealing, London W5 1DR (tel: 020 8991 4502)

Trustees: Benjamin Lewis; Simon Lewis; Rachel Lewis.

General information

The trust was established in 1969 and originally aimed to serve for the charitable intentions of members of the families of David, Bernard, Geoffrey and Godfrey Lewis, and certain companies which they control. The trust makes grants to charitable organisations for a wide range of causes. Previously, support has been given in the following areas:

- Child and social care
- Medical research and support
- Support for older people
- General charitable purposes
- Education
- Tackling intolerance

Most grants are awarded as a single payment, although a few are committed over a period of two to three years. The annual report for 2020/21 states that 'certain medical research grants normally run for a period of three years'.

Financial information

Year end	31/05/2021
Income	£2,770,000
Assets	£25,060,000
Grants to organisations	£1,550,000

Further financial information

General charitable funding	£957,000
Child and social care	£392,500
Medical research and support	£78,600
Educational funding	£70,000
Support for older people	£50,000

Beneficiaries included: Campaign Against Antisemitism (£180,000); Orr Shalom (£107,900); Institute for Jewish Policy Research (£75,000); Keshet (£60,000); British Asian Trust, Community Security Trust and Jewish Care (£50,000 each)

Applications

Apply in writing to the correspondent.

Sources of information

Accounts; annual report; Charity Commission record.

The Linbury Trust

General charitable purposes; arts and culture; museums and galleries; heritage; education; social welfare; medical research; humanitarian aid overseas

UK and overseas, particularly Palestine and the Caribbean

£8.78 million (2020/21)

CC number: 287077

Correspondent: The Trustees, The Peak, 5 Wilton Road, London SW1V 1AP (tel: 020 7410 0330; email: linbury@sfct.org.uk)

Trustees: Sir Martin Jacomb; Richard Adams; John Sainsbury; Sarah Butler-Sloss; Lord Sainsbury of Preston Candover; Lady Anya Sainsbury; James Barnard; Hon. Mark Sainsbury.

 www.linburytrust.org.uk

 @TheLinburyTrust

General information

This trust is part of the Sainsbury Family Charitable Trust network. The trusts within this network share a joint administration but work autonomously as independent legal entities. They have a common approach to grant-making and generally discourage applications from organisations not already in contact with the trust concerned, but some are open to unsolicited approaches.

The Linbury Trust was established in 1983 and has traditionally been associated with arts. Nevertheless, in recent years about 65% of support has been allocated to other causes. Priority is given to charitable causes where the trustees have particular knowledge and experience. In past years the trust has supported major capital projects such as the Royal National Theatre and the Royal Opera House, as well as other museums and galleries. It also has a special interest in dance and dance education, Lady Sainsbury being the well-known ballerina Anya Linden.

Causes supported include:

Arts – particularly visual and performing arts. Grants are normally awarded to cultural institutions carrying out major capital projects. Funding is also available for acquisition costs.

Education – support for arts education, particularly in the fields of dance and visual arts. Funding is occasionally given for capital projects.

Museums and heritage – generally large museums with major development and capital projects.

The environment – support is given towards environmental causes including a long-standing relationship with Ashden Sustainable Solutions, which identifies and champion's projects using sustainable sources of energy.

Medical – historically the trust tended to support research into chronic fatigue syndrome/ME but has in recent years supported studies into paediatric issues with this condition. Recently the trust has funded a multi-year research project in Liverpool which will assess the feasibility of sub-retinal micro-surgery.

Social welfare – support is given to organisations working to improve the quality of life for older people and those living with dementia. The trustees also support charities that work with disadvantaged young people, particularly work with young people to reduce or prevent offending and homelessness. Recently the trustees have begun to support asylum seeker and migrant communities in the UK.

Overseas countries and humanitarian aid – organisations (particularly medical) working in Palestine and organisations that work in the Caribbean. The trust also provides emergency relief.

Financial information

Year end	05/04/2021
Income	£4,390,000
Assets	£138,780,000
Grants to organisations	£8,780,000
No. of grants	86

Further financial information

Grants were broken down as follows:

Culture	£5.91 million
COVID-19	£673,100
Education and young people	£592,100
Social welfare	£580.000
Overseas and emergency relief	£348,200
The environment	£307,000
Medical causes	£238,800
Older people	£130,800

Beneficiaries included: Royal College of Arts (£1.75 million); Courtauld Connects (£1.5 million); Ashmolean Museum (£1 million); Jumby Bay Fund (£189,700); Gainsborough's House Museum (£150,000); University of Winchester (£80,000); Local Solutions (£75,000); Culture Trust Luton (£50,000).

Exclusions

Our previous research suggests that the trust does not support individuals, educational fees or expeditions.

Applications

The trust's website states that it does not accept unsolicited applications, but rather identifies potential organisations 'through recommendation, partnership work and research'.

Sources of information

Accounts; annual report; Charity Commission record; funder's website.

The Linder Foundation

Medical research and education; hospices and respite care; young people; the environment; the arts

UK

£1.04 million (2020/21)

CC number: 267509

Correspondent: Elizabeth Fathi, The Clerk, c/o The Trust Partnership, 6 Trull Farm Buildings, Trull, Gloucestershire GL8 8SQ (tel: 020 3997 4444; email: admin@thelinderfoundation.org.uk)

https://thelinderfoundation.org.uk

General information

The foundation was established in 1974 by Enid Blanche Linder. It makes grants to UK-registered charities or charities with an exempt status. According to the website, the foundation seeks to maximise its impact by choosing to fund projects where it can be a major stakeholder within institutions. Grants typically range from £5,000 to £50,000.

Focus areas

According to the website, grants are divided into six areas (note, the funding focus within each area can change, so check the website for up-to-date information):

Medical research

Research into any branch of medicine is considered with a preference for those relating to surgery and translational research (using basic findings to create new therapies, procedures or diagnostics). In this area, the foundation often provides seed funding for innovative projects.

Medical electives (by invitation only)

Electives providing a unique opportunity for medical students to experience healthcare in an unfamiliar setting, typically providing assistance to ensure an elective in an overseas location where costs of travel are high.

Electives are awarded through invited university medical schools. Currently, these are Imperial College, Sheffield, Oxford, Glasgow, Queen Mary and Westfield, King's College and Swansea medical schools.

Hospices and respite care

Applications are welcomed from charitable institutions that focus on delivering palliative care for the chronically ill, terminally ill or seriously ill. Priority is given to those focusing on relieving pain or provision of emotional/ spiritual sustenance and temporary support to caregivers.

Young people

Applications are welcomed from projects that aim to improve outcomes for young people aged 12–24, particularly those who have experienced adverse childhood experiences and childhood trauma. Projects may involve education, intervention, mentoring or therapeutic activities. Particular consideration will be given to early intervention and rehabilitation projects designed to prevent offending or re-offending.

The environment

Support is given to research projects that aim to address the harmful effects of human activity on the environment. Projects may relate to biodiversity and/ or species preservation, terrestrial ecosystems or land use. Special interest is given to projects or charities centred around protecting and enhancing the natural world for the benefit of both humans and the wider environment.

The arts

The website states:

> The Linder family has a long history of supporting and championing the arts. Leslie Linder's decoding of Beatrix Potter's secret diary, and his subsequent bequests of her artwork to the Victoria and Albert Museum, made a significant contribution to the preservation of her extraordinary work

The foundation seeks to develop the potential of young people through music and theatre. It also supports the art of illustration.

Financial information

Year end	31/03/2021
Income	£654,500
Assets	£18,070,000
Grants to organisations	£1,040,000
No. of grants	39

Further financial information

During the year, the foundation awarded grants totalling £1.07 million. However, £33,300, which had been awarded to university medical schools to fund electives, was returned as students could not travel due to the COVID-19 pandemic. The grant total for 2020/21 was therefore £1.04 million.

A one-off grant of £500,000 was made to Mail Force Charity, a CIO set up by Daily Mail to supply laptops to children during the COVID-19 pandemic lockdown. The remaining grants were awarded in the following categories:

Medical research	8	£151,200
The arts	6	£136,500
Hospices and respite care	9	£104,000
The environment	8	£96,900
Young people	7	£82,300

Beneficiaries included: Mail Force Charity (£500,000); Royal College of Surgeons (£50,000); Anne Robson Trust and British Heart Foundation (£20,000 each); Bethany Christian Trust (£10,000); Purcell School of Young Musicians (£5,000); Westmoreland Red Squirrel Society (£1,000).

Exclusions

Grants are only made to UK-registered charities or exempt charities. The foundation does not typically fund projects outside the UK, even if the organisation is registered within UK. Applications are not accepted from individuals or for individual research or study. This includes gap year activities and sponsorship.

Applications

Applications can be made through the foundation's website when grant rounds are open (check the website for deadlines). Paper applications will not be accepted. Successful applicants or applicants who are required to provide additional information will be notified. Unsuccessful applicants will be notified but no feedback will be provided.

Sources of information

Accounts; annual report; Charity Commission record; funder's website.

Liverpool Charity and Voluntary Services (LCVS)

General charitable purposes; health; education; income stability; arts and culture

Merseyside

£738,300 (2020/21)

CC number: 223485

Correspondent: Grants Team, 151 Dale Street, Liverpool, Merseyside L2 2AH (tel: 0151 227 5177; email: grants@lcvs.org.uk)

Trustees: Sonia Bassey; Neil Sturmey; Henry Terefenko; Maxine Ennis; Susan Williams; Louise Scholes; Kenneth Perry; James Sloan; Dorcas Akeju; Michael Salla; Michael Thomas; John Price.

 www.lcvs.org.uk

General information

Liverpool Charity and Voluntary Services (more commonly known as LCVS) was founded in 1909, when the Lord Mayor of Liverpool called a meeting with Liverpool's network of charities to discuss creating a body that would encourage co-operation between organisations and with public authorities.

Today, LCVS' mission remains the same. According to the website, the charity aims 'to improve the well-being of individuals and communities in Liverpool through supporting and encouraging charitable giving and voluntary action and by bringing people, organisations and resources together'.

Grant programmes

LCVS' Community Impact Fund awards grants of up to £3,000 for projects that meet one or more of the four main priority areas:

- Health
- Education
- Income stability
- Arts and culture

Financial information

Year end	31/03/2021
Income	£2,830,000
Assets	£7,760,000
Grants to organisations	£738,300

Beneficiaries included: Violence Reduction Unit (£285,200); Play Partnership (£260,000); UW Giving (£119,200); Wirral Council MAMHS (£41,800); Pen Natal Grants (£19,200); Liverpool and Merseyside Charities Funds (£10,000); Ways to Well-being (£3,000).

Applications

Apply online via the charity's website.

Sources of information

Accounts; annual report; Charity Commission record; funder's website.

Jack Livingstone Charitable Trust

General charitable purposes and Jewish causes

UK and worldwide, with a preference for the Manchester area

£172,700 (2020/21)

CC number: 263473

Correspondent: The Trustees, Apsley Cottage, Vale Road, Bowdon, Altrincham, Cheshire WA14 3AF (tel: 0161 928 0760; email: 2taf56@gmail.com)

Trustees: Janice Livingstone; Terence Livingstone; Brian White.

General information

This trust registered with the Charity Commission in 1968. According to its 2020/21 accounts, the trust's aim is 'to utilise investment income in making donations to other charitable organisations'. It makes grants for general charitable purposes. In the past, support has been given to Jewish causes, the arts, animal welfare and health.

Financial information

Year end	05/04/2021
Income	£44,300
Assets	£2,060,000
Grants to organisations	£172,700

Further financial information

In 2020/21 the trust awarded grants totalling £172,700; however, in previous years its grant-making exceeded £300,000.

Only beneficiaries of grants of £1,000 and above were listed in the accounts. Grants of under £1,000 totalled £4,900.

Beneficiaries included: Manchester Art Gallery (£50,000); Federation Jewish Service (£10,000); Justifi (£7,500); Better World Charity (£5,000); The Lowry Centre Trust (£2,500); Hale Barns Club and Southport New Synagogue (£1,000 each).

Applications

Apply in writing to the correspondent.

Sources of information

Accounts; annual report; Charity Commission record.

The Ian and Natalie Livingstone Charitable Trust

Children and young people and disadvantage people

UK

£717,500 (2020/21)

CC number: 1149025

Correspondent: The Trustees, Blick Rothenberg Ltd, Palladium House, 1–4 Argyll Street, London W1F 7LD (tel: 020 7437 7666; email: email@blickrothenberg.com)

Trustees: Ian Livingstone; Natalie Livingstone; Mark Levitt.

General information

This trust was registered in September 2012 and its objectives are to support charities who work with children and disadvantaged groups. Charities are mostly supported on a recurrent basis.

The following is taken from the trust's 2020/21 annual accounts:

> It is the policy of the trustees to make grants to a wide range of charitable bodies, focusing on children and disadvantaged groups which are registered with the Charity Commission for England and Wales, or are exempt or excepted charities within the meaning of the Charities Act 2011. Grant applications of up to £250,000 will be considered and may be made towards revenue, capital or project expenditure.

Financial information

Year end	31/03/2021
Income	£660,500
Assets	-£42,900
Grants to organisations	£717,500

Beneficiaries included: Great Ormond Street Hospital Children's Charity (£400,000); Little Village (£190,000); Dalaid (£50,000); The Jagcliff Charitable Trust (£20,000); Highgate School (£5,000).

Applications

Apply in writing to the correspondent.

Sources of information

Accounts; annual report; Charity Commission record.

The Andrew Lloyd Webber Foundation

Heritage and performance art

UK

£1.25 million (2020)

CC number: 1015648

Correspondent: Sarah Miller, Director, Sydmonton Court Estate, Burghclere, Newbury, Berkshire RG20 9NJ (email: a contact form is available on the foundation's website)

Trustees: Louise Fennell; Philip Freedman; Lady Madeleine Webber; Mark Wordsworth; Dr Simon Thurley; Katherine Reardon; Emma Marsh.

www.andrewlloydwebberfoundation.com

facebook.com/The-Andrew-Lloyd-Webber-Foundation-112831905467918

@ALWFoundation

General information

The Andrew Lloyd Webber Foundation was registered with the Charity Commission in December 1992. Its objectives are 'to advance the arts, culture and heritage for the public benefit'.

Main grants scheme

Grants of up to £25,000 per year for three years are available for heritage and performance art through the main grants scheme. According to its website, in 2022 the foundation prioritised applications from:

- Organisations and projects increasing diversity in the arts and heritage by breaking down social, economic and geographical barriers, encouraging engagement and providing high quality training to young people aged under 25, e.g. youth theatres, youth orchestras, side-by-side music initiatives, music therapy groups, music in prisons, heritage skill training.
- Organisations and projects providing specialist training and work-place experience and apprenticeships for emerging artists and newly graduated professionals, e.g. theatre director schemes, actor mentoring and training, heritage building craft apprentices and training schemes, young composer schemes, writers' workshops.
- Organisations and projects unlocking access to high quality arts and heritage education and training for a significant number of people.

Victorian Theatres Small Repairs Fund

This fund provides capital funding grants of up to £15,000 for repairs and conservation projects in theatres built between 1837 and 1910.

Financial information

Year end	31/12/2020
Income	£334,900
Assets	£38,760,000
Grants to organisations	£1,250,000

Further financial information

The foundation also awarded £292,700 in scholarships.

Beneficiaries included: Music in Secondary Schools Trust (£1.05 million); Theatres Development Trust (£55,900); The Prince's Foundation (£12,000); Acting for Others (£5,900).

Exclusions

A full list of exclusions can be found on the foundation's website.

Applications

Applications can be made via the foundation's website.

Sources of information

Accounts; annual report; Charity Commission record; funder's website.

Lloyd's Charities Trust

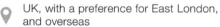

Disasters and emergencies; social welfare; education and training

UK, with a preference for East London, and overseas

£822,000 (2020)

CC number: 207232

Correspondent: The Trustees, Lloyd's Building, 1 Lime Street, London EC3M 7HA (tel: 020 7327 1000; email: responsiblebusiness@lloyds.com)

Trustees: Victoria Carter; David Ibeson; Andrew Brooks; Oliver Ferrari; Amy Bumstead; Mark Fidler; Caroline Klein; Claire O'Meara; Elizabeth Cabrera; Hannah-Polly Williams; Raza Hassan; Ola Jacob-Raji.

www.lloyds.com/about-lloyds/responsible-business/community-involvement/lloyds-charities-trust

General information

The charity was set up in 1953 and is the charitable arm of Lloyd's insurance market in London.

The trust's website states:

> As the Lloyd's market responds to emerging risks and the challenges that these pose to communities around the world, it becomes increasingly important that Lloyd's Charities Trust supports projects that aim to reduce the risk of devastation to the people who need it most. Through our charity partnerships, we work with organisations who help the most vulnerable groups with disaster risk reduction globally.
>
> Lloyd's Charities Trust also supports causes close to the hearts of our people in the Lloyd's market in London.
>
> Recognising the voluntary and fundraising efforts of individuals from across the market, we reward their chosen charities with unrestricted grants to help maintain stability and resilience in a changing world through an annual campaign.

Lloyd's Market Charity Awards

The awards are donations to charities supported by individuals from across the Lloyd's market. Donations are awarded to charities and CICs supported by individuals working in the market in recognition of their fundraising and voluntary work, and to charities that have given invaluable support to those in the market whose lives have been affected by difficult circumstances. In 2021, charities received £25,000 each and some grants were for COVID-19 recovery.

Lloyd's Community Programme

Through long-standing relationships with local delivery partners, this programme supports projects that tackle disadvantage. Grants are awarded to a small number of delivery partners each year to enable them to run projects. These projects provide volunteering opportunities to employees in the Lloyd's market.

Financial information

Year end	31/01/2020
Income	£1,410,000
Assets	£3,160,000
Grants to organisations	£822,000

Further financial information

Grants were awarded to organisations as follows:

Lloyd's Market Charity Awards	£534,000
Lloyd's Community Programme	£235,000
Habitat for Humanity*	£53,000

In addition, £108,000 was awarded to individuals through the Lloyd's Education Fund, which provides university bursaries to young people from schools in London.

*Since 2019 Lloyd's has partnered with Habitat for Humanity Great Britain to fund projects that build disaster-resilient communities in Malawi.

Lloyd's Market Charity Awards winners included: Bristol Metropolitan Orchestra, Hearing Dogs for Deaf People, Mental Health Innovations, Surrey Care Trust, The Miscarriage Association and The One Love Project (£25,000 each).

Applications

Applications for the Lloyd's Market Charity Awards can be made via the trust's website, where guidelines and application deadlines can also be found. Applicants must be permanent employees working in the Lloyd's market and must demonstrate direct and sustained personal engagement with their nominated charity during the past

12 months, for example as a volunteer, fundraiser, trustee or beneficiary of services provided.

Sources of information

Accounts; annual report; Charity Commission record; funder's website.

Lloyd's Patriotic Fund

Armed forces

England and Wales

£332,000 (2019/20)

CC number: 210173

Correspondent: Corporate Social Responsibility Manager, Lloyd's, One Lime Street, London EC3M 7HA (tel: 020 7327 5484; email: globalcommunityengagement@lloyds.com)

Trustees: Alexander Findlay; Richard Williams; Air Cdre Wendy Rothery; William Roscoe; Bruce Carnegie-Brown; Duncan Welham; Edward Butler; Caroline Sandeman-Allen; Michelle Alston; Neil Maidment.

 www.lloyds.com/lpf

General information

Established in 1803 following the Napoleonic Wars, the Lloyd's Patriotic Fund focuses on improving the transition to civilian life for veterans and their families. The fund provides long-term support to a number of partner organisations as well as smaller one-off grants of £10,000.

Financial information

Year end	30/06/2020
Income	£441,000
Assets	£3,440,000
Grants to organisations	£332,000
No. of grants	8

Beneficiaries included: Combat Stress and Regular Forces Employment Association (£110,000 each); SSAFA (£28,000); First Light Trust and Scotty's Little Soldiers (£20,000 each); Not Forgotten Association (£4,000).

Applications

Contact the correspondent for further information.

Sources of information

Accounts; annual report; Charity Commission record; funder's website.

Lloyd's Register Foundation

Improving public safety through engineering-related education, training and research

 Worldwide

£6.78 million (2020)

CC number: 1145988

Correspondent: Michelle Davies, Company Secretary, 71 Fenchurch Street, London EC3M 4BS (email: michelle.davies@lr.org)

Trustees: Sir Peter Gregson; Ishbel Macpherson; Andreas Sohmne-Pao; Rosemary Martin; Carol Sergeant; Thomas Andersen; Dame Una O'Brien; Lambros Varnavides.

 www.lrfoundation.org.uk

 @lr_foundation

General information

The Lloyd's Register Foundation was established in 2012. It is funded by its trading arm, Lloyd's Register Group Ltd, a professional services provider for the engineering and technology sectors.

According to its 2020 annual accounts, the mission of the foundation is:

> To secure for the benefit of the community high technical standards of design, manufacture, construction, maintenance, operation and performance for the purpose of enhancing the safety of life and property at sea, on land and in the air. The advancement of public education, including within the transportation industries and any other engineering and technological disciplines.

The foundation's small grants scheme will consider applications relating to the charitable mission of Lloyd's Register Foundation that support a range of activities including public engagement events or exhibitions, travel for research and conferences, organisation of meetings, and research expenses for pilot projects.

Financial information

Year end	31/12/2020
Income	£15,520,000
Assets	£327,600
Grants to organisations	£6,780,000

Beneficiaries included: Imperial College London (£550,000); Institute of Economics and Peace (£200,000); Shipwrights (£79,000); Nottingham Trent University (£41,000); Teesside University (£9,000).

Applications

Applications can be made via the foundation's grants portal.

Sources of information

Accounts; annual report; Charity Commission record; funder's website.

Lloyds Bank Foundation for England and Wales

Substance misuse; asylum seekers and refugees; care leavers; domestic abuse; people who are experiencing homelessness or are vulnerably housed; learning disabilities; mental health; offending, prison or community service; sexual abuse and exploitation; trafficking and modern slavery; young parents

England and Wales

£24.06 million (2020)

CC number: 327114

Correspondent: Grants Team, Pentagon House, 52–54 Southwark Street, London SE1 1UN (tel: 0370 411 1223; email: enquiries@lloydsbankfoundation.org.uk)

Trustees: Baroness Irene Fritchie; Catharine Cheetham; Joanna Harris; Neil Wooding; Dame Gillian Morgan; Gareth Oakley; Rebecca Shaw; Darren Knight; Kamran Mallick; Ruth Sutherland.

 www.lloydsbankfoundation.org.uk

 facebook.com/lloydsbankfoundation

 @LBFEW

General information

The foundation is principally funded from Lloyds Banking Group receiving a share of the group's profit under a deed of covenant.

Funding for complex social issues

According to its website, the foundation funds charities working on one of the following 11 complex social issues:

- Asylum seekers and refugees
- Care leavers
- Domestic and sexual abuse
- Homelessness/vulnerably housed people
- Learning disabilities
- Mental health
- Offending, prison or community service
- Sexual exploitation
- Substance misuse and/or gambling
- Trafficking and modern slavery
- Young parents

The foundation is looking to support small and medium-sized charities to recover and renew beyond the immediate crisis. In 2021 the foundation aimed to offer around 190 charities a two-year unrestricted grant of £50,000.

The foundation offers unrestricted funding, including for core costs, and tailored development support to help charities be more effective.

Funding for racial equity

The following information has been taken from the foundation's website:

> This year, at least 25% of the grants we make will go to charities led by-and-for Black, Asian and minority ethnic communities. Under our Racial Equity funding strand, we support charities where more than half of their Trustee Board self-identify as belonging to a Black, Asian or minority ethnic community.
>
> The scope of 'Minority Ethnic communities' includes those that have historically experienced marginalisation, racialisation, oppression and prejudice. Therefore, also in scope is work that benefits Jewish communities, Gypsy and Traveller communities and some migrant communities.

To be eligible, charities should support people from specific Black, Asian or minority ethnic communities to overcome any of the 11 complex social issues detailed above.

Financial information

Year end	31/12/2020
Income	£24,610,000
Assets	£32,700,000
Grants to organisations	£24,060,000

Beneficiaries included: A full list of beneficiaries can be found on the foundation's website. Previous examples include: Aurora New Dawn (£100,000); Asylum Link Merseyside (£83,600); Staffordshire Women's Aid (£81,700); The Mental Health Advocacy Scheme (£80,200); The Folkestone Rainbow Centre (£50,000).

Exclusions

The foundation's eligibility criteria document, available on its website, states:

> We do not provide funding for the following organisations:
>
> - Community Interest Companies, or any other organisations that are not charities or CIOs registered in England and Wales
> - Infrastructure or 'umbrella' organisations.
> - Organisations whose primary purpose is to give funds to individuals or other organisations. This means organisations using more than 50% of their annual expenditure as grants.
> - Hospitals, health authorities or hospices
> - Rescue services
> - Nurseries, pre-chools or playgroups
> - Schools, colleges or universities
> - Animal charities
> - Charities working predominantly outside England and Wales
> - Organisations that do not have a purpose/benefit beyond the promotion of religion

Applications

Applications can be made via the foundation's website. There is no closing date for applications. The foundation aims to give a decision within four months of receiving applications.

Sources of information

Accounts; annual report; Charity Commission record; funder's website.

Lloyds Bank Foundation for the Channel Islands

Health and disability; homelessness; drug and alcohol dependency; carers; disadvantage and discrimination; literacy; domestic violence; care leavers

Channel Islands

£970,000 (2020)

CC number: 327113

Correspondent: Johanna Le Poidevin, Executive Director, 1 Smith Street, St Peter Port, Guernsey GY1 4BD (tel: 01481 706360; email: jlepoidevin@lloydsbankfoundation.org.uk)

Trustees: John Henwood; Gavin Ferguson; Heather MacCallum; Tracey Johnson; Neil Fellows; Brian Heath; Alasdair Gardner; Philippa Stahelin; Poppy Murray.

www.lloydsbankfoundationci.org.uk

@lloydsbfci

General information

The foundation was set up by Lloyds Bank in 1986. The foundation derives its income almost entirely from Lloyds Banking Group but is an independent entity with policies determined by a board of trustees, which meets three times each year to agree on strategic priorities and to distribute funding. According to the foundation's website, grants are awarded 'to charities helping disadvantaged people play a fuller role in communities throughout the Channel Islands'.

Areas of work

According to its grant-giving guidelines, the foundation can fund:

> - **People with health issues or a disability** – We support charities which create opportunities for people with health issues or a disability to live and work independently.
> - **People experiencing homelessness –** We help charities which provide accommodation and support for people who are homeless, and support their return into society.
> - **People with dependency on alcohol or drugs** – We support charities providing education and rehabilitation for people who misuse alcohol and drugs.
> - **Carers** – We help charities providing support, training, and respite care.
> - **Challenging disadvantage and discrimination** – We help charities who challenge discrimination and stigma, and promote equality of opportunity for all.
> - **People with literacy problems** – We support learning programmes for people disadvantaged by poor education and literacy.
> - **People affected by domestic violence** – We support charities who help prevent and protect people from abusive relationships.
> - **People leaving institutional care to live independently** – We help charities providing support and accommodation for people who are getting back into society, maybe after leaving care or prison.

The foundation also supports the charitable sector through information and training.

Financial information

Year end	31/12/2020
Income	£890,800
Assets	£1,180,000
Grants to organisations	£970,000

Beneficiaries included: Sanctuary Trust (£55,400); Silkworth (£45,000); Autism Guernsey (£34,900); Guernsey Walking Football (£12,000); Relate Jersey (£4,100); Young Lives vs Cancer (£4,000).

Exclusions

According to the application guidelines, the following fall outside the funding criteria:

> - Organisations which are not registered charities.
> - Individual requests.
> - Sponsorship request.
> - International appeals.
> - Animal welfare.
> - Environmental charities.
> - Expeditions or overseas travel.
> - The promotion of religion.
>   We might not exclude charities which have a religious element, if their objectives demonstrate a wider benefit to people experiencing disadvantage.
> - Schools and colleges (except for projects that will benefit disadvantaged students and are clearly additional to statutory responsibilities).
> - Activities which are the responsibility of a statutory body or the islands' governments.
> - Activities which duplicates or overlaps a service already provided.
> - Applications for salaries which would apply to the applicant.

- Charities which have received one of our grants in the previous 12 months, or have received three years continuous funding.

Applications

Applications can be made via the foundation's website. Applicants are encouraged to discuss their project with the executive director before completing an application form.

Sources of information

Accounts; annual report; Charity Commission record; funder's website.

Localtrent Ltd

Advancement of the Orthodox Jewish faith and relief of poverty

UK, with some preference for Manchester

£272,400 (2020/21)

CC number: 326329

Correspondent: The Trustees, c/o Lopian Gross Barnett and Co., 1st Floor, Cloisters House, New Bailey Street, Manchester M3 5FS (tel: 0161 832 8721)

Trustees: Hyman Weiss; Mina Weiss; Philip Weiss; Zisel Weiss; Yocheved Weiss; Bernardin Weiss.

General information

The trust was established in 1982 for the distribution of funds to religious, educational and similar charities for the advancement of the Orthodox Jewish faith. The relief of poverty and hardship in the Jewish community is also assisted.

Financial information

Year end	31/03/2021
Income	£367,800
Assets	£1,170,000
Grants to organisations	£272,400

Further financial information

Grants to organisations were distributed as follows: relief of poverty of hardship and poverty in the Jewish community (£109,400); Orthodox Jewish education and religious studies (£89,000); advancement of religion and Orthodox Jewish faith (£74,000).

Beneficiaries included: Chasdei Yoni Charitable Trust (£50,900); Karen Chochmas Shlomo Trust (£25,000); Asser Bishvil Foundation (£21,000); Bsderech Kovoid (£20,000); Tchaba Kollel (£10,500); Bnos Yisroel School (£5,000).

Applications

Apply in writing to the correspondent. Contact the correspondent for further information.

Sources of information

Accounts; annual report; Charity Commission record.

The Locker Foundation

Jewish causes; health and disability; religious education

UK and overseas (Israel)

£649,600 (2020/21)

CC number: 264180

Correspondent: Malcolm Carter, Chair, 65 Flower Lane, Mill Hill, London NW7 2JN (tel: 07956 325198; email: thelockerfoundation@hotmail.com)

Trustees: Susannah Segal; Malcolm Carter.

General information

The trust was established in 1966 and mainly supports Jewish organisations. According to its 2020/21 annual report, the trustees 'target other charitable institutions whose activities principally relate to the welfare of the sick and disabled, and the teaching of religion, subject to being satisfied that such institutions are themselves registered charities'. This includes schools and places of worship.

Financial information

Year end	05/04/2021
Income	£770,000
Assets	£8,700,000
Grants to organisations	£649,600

Beneficiaries included: A list of beneficiaries was not available. Previous beneficiaries include: Magen David Adam UK (£112,100); Tikva Children's Home (£58,000); Chai Cancer Care (£50,000); Noa Girls (£25,000); Community Security Trust and Norwood Ravenswood (£20,000 each); World Jewish Relief (£15,000); Jewish Deaf Association (£9,900); Chicken Soup Shelter (£9,000); Birmingham Hebrew Congregation (£3,000); Kef Kids (£1,000); Matilda Marks Kennedy School (£500); United Synagogue (£200).

Applications

Apply in writing to the correspondent.

Sources of information

Accounts; annual report; Charity Commission record.

The Lockwood Charitable Foundation

General charitable purposes; health; education; culture and heritage; Christian causes

England and Wales

£125,000 (2020/21)

CC number: 1123272

Correspondent: The Trustees, The Tithe Barn, The Avenue, Compton, Guildford, Surrey GU3 1JW (tel: 01483 415480)

Trustees: Richard Lockwood; Lesley Lockwood; Dr Rebecca Lockwood.

General information

The foundation was established in 2008 and makes grants for general charitable purposes to registered organisations in the UK. It particularly focuses on:

- Helping to preserve public health by funding research projects to benefit people who are sick or terminally ill
- The advancement of education by providing equipment for schools, colleges and universities
- Financial support for museums, libraries and art galleries
- Organisations that seek to advance the Christian religion for the benefit of the public
- Other charitable purposes not provided by local authorities

Financial information

Year end	05/04/2021
Income	£303,300
Assets	£5,550,000
Grants to organisations	£125,000

Further financial information

In previous years grants have totalled around £400,000.

Beneficiaries included: James Place Charity (£100,000); Children's Trust CVMD (£15,000); Golf in Society and Help2Read (£5,000 each).

Applications

Apply in writing to the correspondent.

Sources of information

Accounts; annual report; Charity Commission record.

Loftus Charitable Trust

Jewish causes

UK

£1.08 million (2019/20)

CC number: 297664

Correspondent: The Trustees, 55 Blandford Street, Marylebone, London W1U 7HW (tel: 020 7604 5900; email: andrew@loftusfp.com)

Trustees: Andrew Loftus; Anthony Loftus; Richard Loftus.

General information

The trust was established in 1987 by Richard Ian Loftus. Its objects, as stated on its Charity Commission record, are the following:

- The advancement of the Jewish religion
- The advancement of Jewish education and the education of Jewish people
- Poverty relief among Jewish people who are on low incomes

Financial information

Year end	05/04/2020
Income	£423,500
Assets	£4,500,000
Grants to organisations	£1,080,000
No. of grants	178

Further financial information

Grants awarded in 2019/20 were broken down as follows:

Education	£693,700
Relief of poverty and ill health	£175,000
Other causes	£138,700
Religious organisations	£75,500

Only beneficiaries of grants of £10,000 and above were listed in the accounts.

Beneficiaries included: Kisharon (£410,000); Hasmonean High School (£100,000); Jewish School Network (£76,900); The Black Stork Charity (£50,000); Jewish Care (£30,500); Chai Cancer Care (£14,000); Neve Michael Charitable Trust (£10,000).

Applications

The trustees prefer to invite applications rather than consider unsolicited applications.

The trust's annual report for 2019/20 states:

> The trustees meet regularly to consider what grants they will make and to review any feedback they have received. Nominations for grants are elicited by formal and informal means. The trustees travel widely in the UK and abroad and use knowledge gained to support the objects of the Trust and to inform grant-making. Though the trustees make some grants with no formal application, they normally ask invited organisations to submit a formal application saying how the funds would be used and what would be achieved. The trustees have a policy, which is communicated to all beneficiaries, that they make grants with no guarantees of future funding.

Sources of information

Accounts; annual report; Charity Commission record.

London Catalyst

 Health; disability; social welfare

 Greater London, within the boundaries of the M25

(£) £303,700 (2020)

CC number: 1066739

Correspondent: The Trustees, 45 Westminster Bridge Road, London SE1 7JB (tel: 020 3828 4204; email: london.catalyst@peabody.org.uk)

Trustees: Andrew Davidson; Philippe Granger; Dr Sarah Divall; Mark Palframan; Emma Whitby; Danny Daly; Yasmin Hussain; Joan Major.

 www.londoncatalyst.org.uk

 @LondonCatalyst

General information

London Catalyst (formerly the Metropolitan Hospital-Sunday Fund) was established in 1873. Among its founders were Florence Nightingale, Elizabeth Garrett Anderson, Baroness Burdett-Coutts and William Henry Smith MP.

Since its creation, the charity has held an annual 'Hospital-Sunday' appeal to raise funds to provide food, clothing and other basic items to people leaving hospital and those living in the community who are in financial need.

Today, the charity makes grants to assist the work of charities, voluntary and community organisations, and social work and health agencies operating in Greater London (within the M25). The aim of its grant programmes is to:

- Improve health and well-being
- Help remove people from poverty
- Raise awareness of the work of the organisations it supports

Grant programmes

The charity's annual grants budget is £300,000 divided between three grant programmes:

Project grants – grants of £1,000 to £5,000 to support new initiatives and service developments targeted at people disadvantaged as a result of long-term ill health, disability and poverty.

Samaritan grants – a hardship fund available to frontline health, social work and advice agencies to offer assistance to people in an emergency.

Partners for Health – for projects which work in partnership with expert health agencies/providers to support people with long-term health conditions.

Financial information

Year end	31/12/2020
Income	£229,400
Assets	£14,190,000
Grants to organisations	£303,700
No. of grants	165

Further financial information

During the year project grants totalling £205,200 were allocated to 82 organisations. Samaritan grants totalling £97,800 were awarded to 83 organisations. These include grants for COVID-19 response and recovery. The charity's Partners for Health programme did not run during the year due to the pandemic.

Beneficiaries included: Birth Companions (£5,000); Lewisham Refugee Migrant Migrant Hub (£4,000); Made in Hackney (£3,000); Sport4health (£2,000); English for Action (£1,500); Ageing Well In Lewisham and Islington Boat Club (£1,000 each); Young and Inspired (£500).

Exclusions

The charity does not support individuals or general appeals.

Applications

Online application forms can be found on the charity's website along with full guidance and FAQs. The trustees usually meet four times a year, in February, May, September and November. Completed applications must be received at least four weeks in advance of meetings.

If you have an urgent application for a Samaritan grant, contact the office to discuss.

Sources of information

Accounts; annual report; Charity Commission record; funder's website.

London Freemasons' Charity

General charitable purposes; social welfare; education

 Greater London

(£) £1.42 million (2019/20)

CC number: 1081205

Correspondent: The Trustees, 60 Great Queen Street, PO Box 29055, London WC2B 5AZ (tel: 020 7539 2930; email: c.hunt@metgl.com)

Trustees: Marios Stylianides; Quentin Humberstone; Stratton Richey; Augustus Ullstein; Thomas Toumazis; Peter Jennings.

General information

The London Freemasons' charity, previously known as the Metropolitan Masonic Charity, seeks to address any general charitable needs in the area of London 'and in particular (but without restriction) the relief of need of poverty or distress or the advancement of education', as stated in the charity's 2019/20 annual report. The annual report notes that the charity's usual policy is to 'support small London charities for whom donations of between £2,000 and £10,000 [can make] a material difference'.

Financial information

Year end	30/09/2020
Income	£851,700
Assets	£2,160,000
Grants to organisations	£1,420,000
No. of grants	30

Further financial information

During the year, 30 grants were made to non-Masonic charities totalling £1.42 million.

Beneficiaries included: London Fire Brigade (£1.24 million); Masonic Almoners Fund (£27,600); Oral Health Foundation (£10,000); The Albany (£4,500); Brompton Cycles (£3,000); St John Ambulance (£1,500); British Red Cross (£500).

Exclusions

National charities are only supported if the grant will be used for work in London.

Applications

Apply in writing to the correspondent.

Sources of information

Accounts; annual report; Charity Commission record.

London Legal Support Trust (LLST)

Voluntary legal services

London and the Home Counties

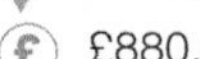

£880,000 (2020)

CC number: 1101906

Correspondent: Nezahat Cihan, Chief Executive Officer, National Pro Bono Centre, 48 Chancery Lane, London WC2A 1JF (tel: 020 7092 3974; email: info@llst.org.uk)

Trustees: Richard Dyton; Graham Huntley; Joy Julien; Marc Sosnow; Emma Turnbull; Amanda Illing; Rodger Pressland; Alistair Woodland; Katharine Pasfield; James Harper; Sarah McKeown; Sophie Hay; Candice Carboo-Ofulue; Conchita Anastasi; Joanna Vincent.

 https://londonlegalsupporttrust.org.uk

 facebook.com/LondonLegalSupportTrust

 @londonlegal

 @londonlegalsupporttrust

General information

The London Legal Support Trust (LLST) funds and supports the provision of free specialist legal advice services through law centres, advice agencies and Citizens Advice. The trust raises funds from fundraising events, including the London Legal Walk as well as ad hoc donations from law firms and chambers. The trust is part of a network of seven Legal Support Trusts across England and in Wales working with the Access to Justice Foundation to support pro bono and advice agencies, ensuring funds can be distributed where needed most throughout England and Wales.

Grant programmes

Small grants

At the time of writing (May 2022), the trust's website explained that its 2020 and 2021 small grant rounds were adapted to respond to the COVID-19 pandemic. It noted that plans for 2022 grants would be announced soon.

In previous years, the small grants programme has offered awards of up to £5,000 for pro bono surgeries, one-off capital costs, especially to improve sustainability, and the development of legal agencies where none currently exist. These awards typically form about 10–15% of the trust's total expenditure. Any charity that provides free legal advice in London and the South East can apply.

Centres of Excellence

About 80% of the trust's funding is directed through the Centres of Excellence programme which provides core funding, in-kind help and other support to organisations which have been providing free specialist legal advice (through employed staff providing casework and/or representation) for at least one year and whose service is based in and provided wholly or mostly to residents of London and the home counties.

In addition to financial support, the trust also offers any charity that provides free legal advice (including pro bono services) the opportunity to take part in LLST's events in order to raise funds for themselves. See the trust's website for more details.

Financial information

Year end	31/12/2020
Income	£1,340,000
Assets	£368,100
Grants to organisations	£880,000
No. of grants	121

Further financial information

Only beneficiaries of grants of £5,000 and above were listed in the accounts. Grants of under £5,000 totalled £104,300.

Beneficiaries included: Community Justice Fund (£67,000); Independent Workers' Union of Great Britain (£27,500); Working Families (£16,300); Law Centres Network (£13,000); Public Law Project (£10,000); Reading Refugee Support Group (£6,400); Toynbee Hall (£3,500); Migrants Organise (£1,800); Bridge the Gap (£530).

Exclusions

The trust's website states that it does not fund:

1. Any non-charitable activity
2. Organisations applying for general advice as opposed to specialist legal advice

Applications

See the trust's website for up-to-date details of how to apply.

Sources of information

Accounts; annual report; Charity Commission record; funder's website.

The London Marathon Charitable Trust Ltd

Sports, recreation and leisure activities

London

£4.43 million (2020)

CC number: 283813

Correspondent: The Trustees, Marathon House, 190 Great Dover Street, London SE1 4YB (email: info@lmct.org.uk)

Trustees: John Austin; Sir Rodney Walker; Charles Johnston; Alan Pascoe; Robert Rigby; Dawn Austwick; Gillian McKay; Clare Shepherd; Samantha Orde; Richard Henry; Terry Duddy; Lee Mason.

 www.lmct.org.uk

General information

The trust was established in 1981 to distribute the surplus income donated to the charity by its subsidiary, the London Marathon Ltd, which organises the annual London Marathon and other such events each year. Funds are used to award grants to organisations and projects that enable people to be physically active and challenge inequality of access to physical activity.

Note: the trust has no connection to the fundraising efforts of the individuals involved in the race.

The trust's website states that its current priorities are:

> to maintain and increase participation in physical activity by:
> - Improving facilities in our core area of London to encourage and support all members of the local community to become and remain physically active.
> - Supporting ambitious projects across the UK that will challenge inequality of access to physical activity and deliver the greatest possible impact for our target audiences: children and young people and groups we know are less likely to be active, such as women and girls, ethnically diverse communities, people from lower socio-economic groups, older people and people with a disability.
> - Reflecting the spirit of the London Marathon in our grantmaking.

Grant programmes

The trust's current grant programmes are:

Facilities Grants – supports London-based facility improvement projects that encourage the local community to become physically active.

Strategic Partnership Grants – supports UK projects that challenge inequality of access to physical activity. This programme is by invitation only and does not accept unsolicited applications.

Financial information

Year end	31/12/2020
Income	£23,370,000
Assets	£8,520,000
Grants to organisations	£4,430,000

Further financial information

Grants were broken down as follows: Strategic Partnership Grants (£2.67 million) and Facilities Grants (£1.76 million).

Beneficiaries included: Activity Alliance (£1 million); Phoenix Canoe Club Ltd (£250,000); Livability (£100,000); Claygate Primary School (£50,000); Welsh Harp Sailing Club (£8,000); Coin Street Centre Trust (£5,000).

Applications

Full details of application processes, funding guidelines, deadlines and FAQs can be found on the 'How to apply' page of the trust's website. At the time of writing (January 2022) the trust was not accepting any new applications to its grant programmes as a result of COVID-19 pandemic. Check the website for the latest information.

Sources of information

Accounts; annual report; Charity Commission record; funder's website.

Longleigh Foundation

Relief of people in need; provision of housing, amenities, facilities or services; skills and training to aid employment

England

£929,300 (2020/21)

CC number: 1169016

Correspondent: Charlotte Dicks, Grants Programme Manager, Stonewater Ltd, Suite C. Lancaster House, Grange Business Park, Enderby Road, Whetstone, Leicester, Leicestershire LE8 6EP (tel: 020 7164 6199; email: grants@longleigh.org)

Trustees: John Emerson; Elizabeth Morris; Ron Williamson; Anne Dokov; John Weguelin; Aisha Butera.

 www.longleigh.org

 @longleighfound

General information

The Longleigh Foundation was registered with the Charity Commission in 2016. It aims to relieve people in need, in particular through the provision of housing and associated services. The charity is supported and primarily funded through donations from Stonewater Ltd, a social housing provider operating across England.

The charity's website states:

> We provide funding for **registered, non-profit-distributing organisations** that are seeking to address the issues and challenges that are more prominent and prevalent to those who live in social housing and also in communities which have a significant amount of social housing.
>
> We also offer grants to fund **research** that furthers the understanding and potential solutions to the issues and challenges faced by people living in social housing and their communities.

The trustees have identified the following groups as priorities for grant funding: young people, older people, those affected by domestic abuse and people with disabilities. From April 2020 a new approach to funding commenced. The foundation will now issue calls for applications, the briefs for which will be published on the website.

Further to this, funding is provided to residents in Stonewater properties who are experiencing short-term hardship or crisis situations.

Financial information

Year end	30/06/2021
Income	£3,980,000
Assets	£7,700,000
Grants to organisations	£929,300

Beneficiaries included: A list of beneficiaries was not available. Previous beneficiaries include: Southampton Women's Refuge (£81,500); The Mustard Tree Foundation (£75,000); Lippy People Charitable Trust (£50,000); University of Stirling (£43,200); Justlife Foundation (£25,000); Bootcamp Project – Stonewater (£13,900).

Applications

The foundation puts out calls for applications with a specific brief. Applicants are then asked to send a short video with a response to the call and explain how the approach will help meet the foundation's current funding priorities. Check the website for further information.

Sources of information

Accounts; annual report; Charity Commission record.

The William and Katherine Longman Trust

General charitable purposes

UK

£575,500 (2020/21)

CC number: 800785

Correspondent: Karen Wall, Administrator, 28 Julian Road, Orpington, Kent BR6 6HU (tel: 07711 961788; email: karen@walltrustsupport.co.uk)

Trustees: William Harriman; Alan Bell.

General information

Established in 1988, the trust supports general charitable purposes by making grants to any registered charities in the UK.

Financial information

Year end	05/04/2021
Income	£18,300
Grants to organisations	£575,500

Further financial information

Full accounts were not available to view on the Charity Commission website. We have therefore estimated the trust's grant total based on its total expenditure.

Beneficiaries included: A list of beneficiaries was not available. Previous beneficiaries include: Mizpah Trust (£125,000); The Kel Trust (£80,000); Vanessa Grant Trust (£30,000); Chelsea Arts Club Trust (£25,000); Chelsea Festival and World Child Cancer Fund (£20,000 each); Hope Education Trust and RADA (£10,000 each); Action for ME (£5,000); The Children's Society (£4,500); Age Concern – Kensington and Chelsea (£3,500); RSPCA – Harmsworth Hospital (£3,000); St Mungo's (£2,500); Prisoners Abroad (£1,000).

Applications

Apply in writing to the correspondent. The trust's 2019/20 annual report states: 'The trustees' current policy is to consider all written appeals received but only successful applicants are notified of the trustees' decision.'

Sources of information

Charity Commission record; 2019/20 accounts and annual report.

The Lord's Taverners

Amateur sport, particularly cricket; provision of recreational facilities; sports for people with disabilities

UK

£1.11 million (2019/20)

CC number: 306054

Correspondent: Nicky Pemberton, Director of Programmes and Growth, 90 Chancery Lane, London WC2A 1EU (tel: 020 7025 0000; email: contact@lordstaverners.org)

Trustees: Richard White; Alistair Row; Mike Gatting; Ian Martin; Sandra Verkuyten; Caj Sohal; Tim Luckhurst; Gordon Kennedy; Suzanne Christopher; Julie Norris; Abeed Janmohamed.

 www.lordstaverners.org

 facebook.com/thelordstaverners

 @lordstaverners

 @lordstaverners

General information

The Lord's Taverners was founded in 1950 at the Tavern pub at Lord's Cricket Ground. At first, the money raised each year was given to the National Playing Fields Association (now the Fields in Trust) to fund artificial cricket pitches.

Today, the Lord's Taverners enables young people from disadvantaged backgrounds and those with disabilities to enjoy sport, and provides opportunities for young people to interact, play and train as well as to learn, have fun and make friends. The charity's mission is carried out by using specially adapted forms of cricket and other sports, including rugby, tennis, squash, basketball and boccia, as well as providing specialist equipment and minibuses. Grants are also made to organisations whose aims align with the charity's.

Grants have been awarded to organisations such as The Johnners Trust, which supports the development of young visually impaired cricketers, and Fields in Trust, which protects parks and green spaces. Grants have also been awarded to organisations including British Wheelchair Basketball, Great Britain Wheelchair Rugby and Boccia England to purchase sports wheelchairs.

Financial information

Year end	30/09/2020
Income	£4,740,000
Assets	£5,310,000
Grants to organisations	£1,110,000
No. of grants	73

Further financial information

During the year, charitable activities totalled £2.02 million, with 73 specific beneficiaries or organisations receiving grants of £1.11 million. The following breakdown was included in the accounts:

Cricket for people with disabilities and other disadvantaged individuals	£1.32 million
Minibuses	£956,000
Wheelchair and disability sports	£314,000
The Johnners Trust	£14,000

A full list of beneficiaries was not available.

Exclusions

See the charity's website for exclusion criteria for the relevant programmes and grants.

Applications

See the charity's website for up-to-date information on grants and programmes, or contact the correspondent for further information.

Sources of information

Accounts; annual report; Charity Commission record; funder's website.

The Lower Green Foundation

General charitable purposes

Worldwide

£516,200 (2020/21)

CC number: 1137862

Correspondent: The Trustees, The Lower Green Foundation, 28 Eaton Avenue, Matrix Office Park, Buckshaw Village, Chorley, Lancashire PR7 7NA (tel: 01772 299888; email: info@lowergreen.com)

Trustees: Laurence Billett; Marina Sajitz; Sinclair Beecham.

General information

This foundation was established in June 2010 to support general charitable purposes. It makes grants to both individuals and organisations. The annual report and accounts for 2020/21 state that in the future the trustees intend to focus on:

- Education for young people
- Youth apprenticeship schemes
- Medical research

Financial information

Year end	30/04/2021
Income	£375,100
Assets	£110,900
Grants to organisations	£516,200

Beneficiaries included: Pret Foundation (£300,000); Aldridge Foundation (£50,000); The Prince's Trust (£25,000); ACET UK (£20,000); Dream Children's Home (£15,300); The Pelican Trust (£10,000); The Lullaby Trust (£2,000).

Applications

Contact the foundation for more information.

Sources of information

Charity Commission record.

Robert Luff Foundation Ltd

Medical research

UK

£653,000 (2019/20)

CC number: 273810

Correspondent: Richard Price, Company Secretary, Waters Edge, Ferry Lane, Moulsford, Wallingford, Oxfordshire OX10 9JF (tel: 01491 652204; email: rpjprice@gmail.com)

Trustees: Melanie Condon; Richard Price; The Revd Matthew Tomlinson; Lady Ruth Bodey; Sir Paul Coleridge; Dr Helen Hughes.

General information

The foundation was established in 1966. The primary activity of the foundation is to award grants to other charitable institutions, with a strong preference for medical research.

Financial information

Year end	31/08/2020
Income	£806,700
Assets	£37,970,000
Grants to organisations	£653,000
No. of grants	10

Further financial information

In response to the COVID-19 pandemic, the foundation's trustees took the decision to only give donations to its long-term beneficiaries in 2019/20.

Beneficiaries included: Cystic Fibrosis Trust (£150,000); Bowel Disease Research Foundation (£80,000); Asthma UK (£60,000); International Spinal Research Trust (£40,000); Gordon Highlanders (£30,000); Autistica (£20,000).

Applications

While the foundation tends to support the same charities on an annual basis, several new beneficiaries are funded each year. Contact the correspondent for more information regarding the application process.

Sources of information

Accounts; annual report; Charity Commission record.

John Lyon's Charity

Children and young people up to the age of 25

The London boroughs of Barnet, Brent, Camden, City of London, City of Westminster, Ealing, Hammersmith and Fulham, Harrow and Kensington and Chelsea

£12.2 million (2020/21)

CC number: 237725

Correspondent: The Trustees, Griffin Lodge, 45A Cadogan Gardens, London SW3 2TB (tel: 020 7259 1700; email: info@jlc.london)

Trustee: Keepers and Governors of the Possessions, Revenues and Goods of the Free Grammar School of John Lyon.

 www.jlc.london

 @JohnLyonCharity

 @johnlyonscharity

General information

The history of John Lyon's Charity dates back to the 16th century when John Lyon donated his 48 acre Maida Vale farm as an endowment for the upkeep of two roads from London to Harrow and Kenton. In 1991 the charity was given discretion to use the revenue from the endowment to benefit the inhabitants of the London boroughs through which these roads passed. The charity is an independent branch of the larger Harrow Foundation, which also governs Harrow and the John Lyon schools.

The charity supports children and young people up to the age of 25 (or 30 for young people with special needs or disabilities).

Programme areas

The charity's grants are categorised into nine programme areas:

- Arts and science
- Children and families
- Education and learning
- Emotional well-being
- Special needs and disability
- Sports
- Training, apprenticeships and internships
- Youth clubs and activities for young people
- Issues affecting young people

Types of support

The charity provides the following types of support:

- Unrestricted/core funding
- Salary costs
- Direct project costs
- Apprenticeships
- Equipment
- Capacity building

Grant funds

The charity has a number of different funds to which organisations can apply, these are: the Main Grant Fund; Schools in Partnership Fund; Bursary Fund; the Small Grant Fund; the School Holiday Activity Fund; and the Capacity Building Fund. Guidelines, grant limits and applications processes differ depending on the fund applied to.

Home, school and community – £22 million funding strategy

As an extension of the charity's response to the COVID-19 pandemic, the charity has created a strategic plan to protect children and young people, with the core focus on home, school and community, as 'the three main points of reference in any child's life'. In March 2021, the charity announced it has ring-fenced £22 million from its endowment, to be spent over the next six years, to support children and young people. This funding will be in addition to its regular grant-giving of around £12 million each year.

According to its website, the charity will specifically look to support 'organisations by initiating collaborations, replicating successful initiatives and rehabilitating organisations, using this funding as a lifeline for many who are at risk of permanent closure'.

The first area it will address is the 'dramatic fall in the offer of creative opportunities in schools' by launching a new Cultural Capital Fund. The fund is designed to bring arts organisations and schools together. The charity will invite applications from both schools and arts institutions in London 'for projects that utilise the skills of the most experienced and high-quality practitioners, many of whom have been unable to work during the pandemic'.

More about the strategy can be found on the charity's website.

Financial information

Year end	31/03/2021
Income	£8,720,000
Assets	£391,700,000
Grants to organisations	£12,220,000

Further financial information

The charity awarded 240 grants during the year. Grants were broken down as follows:

Education and learning	£1.9 million
Youth clubs/activities	£1.7 million
Arts and science	£1.57 million
Bursaries	£1.5 million
Emotional well-being	£1.3 million
Special needs and disability	£1 million
Children and families	£870,000
Capacity building	£721,000
Sport	£683,000
Issues affecting young people	£605,000
Training	£204,000
Restricted grants	£61,000

Beneficiaries included: A list of beneficiaries was not available. Previous beneficiaries have included: Securing Success (£45,500); Belmont School (£40,000); Arts Depot (£30,000); National Youth Theatre (£25,000); The Listening Place (£14,000).

Exclusions

The charity's website specifies that grants are not made to:

- Individuals
- Organisations that do not have charitable status or those acting as a conduit
- National charities with no track record of delivery in the Charity's Beneficial Area
- Grant-giving organisations
- Not-for-profit organisations that are not registered charities
- Registered Social Landlords
- Schools that have not yet been inspected by Ofsted
- Hospitals, hospices or Clinical Commissioning Groups
- Registered charities that have applied on behalf of organisations that are not registered with the Charity Commission

Applications

Apply online via the charity's grants portal.

Sources of information

Accounts; annual report; Charity Commission record; funder's website; guidelines for applicants.

M. B. Foundation

Jewish causes; social welfare; religion and education

UK, with some preference for Greater Manchester

£860,700 (2019/20)

CC number: 222104

Correspondent: The Trustees, Fairways House, George Street, Prestwich, Manchester M25 9WS (tel: 0161 787 7898)

Trustees: Elazer Dresdner; The Revd Martin Stamler.

General information

The objects of the foundation are for the benefit of any such one or more charities as the trustees may select. In practice, the trustees award grants to organisations advancing the Jewish faith and education, and relieving poverty in the Jewish community.

Financial information

Year end	31/03/2020
Income	£941,200
Assets	£5,790,000
Grants to organisations	£860,700

Beneficiaries included: KBS (£325,300); Kalloh Care (£78,000); Toimchei

Shabbos (£37,500); Kolyom Trust Ltd (£37,200).

Applications

Apply in writing to the correspondent.

Sources of information

Accounts; annual report; Charity Commission record.

The M. K. Charitable Trust

Orthodox Jewish charities; education; religion; health and disability; relief of poverty

Worldwide, in practice mainly UK

£1.24 million (2020/21)

CC number: 260439

Correspondent: Simon Kaufman, Trustee, 50 Keswick Street, Gateshead, Tyne and Wear NE8 1TQ (tel: 0191 490 0140)

Trustees: A. Piller; David Katz; S. Kaufman.

General information

This trust was established in 1966 for general charitable purposes and applies its income for 'the provision and distribution of grants and donations to Orthodox Jewish charities', as stated in the trust's 2021 accounts. Support is given to educational and religious causes, health and disability and other needs. The trust's accounts state that grants are awarded to organisations that provide the following:

- Financial support to the poor
- Provision of basic necessities to the poor
- Relief of sickness and disabilities
- Jewish education and places of worship for the Jewish community

Financial information

Year end	05/04/2021
Income	£48,600
Assets	£342,200
Grants to organisations	£1,120,000

Further financial information

Only grants of over £25,000 were listed in the accounts. Grants of under £25,000 totalled £84,800. Included in the grant total are amounts totalling £692,500 paid to charities with which the trust has trustees in common.

Beneficiaries included: Five K Foundation, HP Charitable Trust and SK Charitable Trust (£135,000 each); Mendel Kaufman Memorial Trust (£120,000); Lingate Charitable Trust (£110,000).

Applications

Applications can be made in writing to the correspondent. The trust accepts applications for grants from representatives of Orthodox Jewish charities, which are reviewed by the trustees on a regular basis.

Sources of information

Accounts; annual report; Charity Commission record.

The R. S. Macdonald Charitable Trust

Neurological conditions; visual impairment; child welfare; animal welfare; medical research; RNLI lifeboats

Scotland

£1.75 million (2020/21)

OSCR number: SC012710

Correspondent: Katie Winwick, Grants and Relationship Manager, 21 Rutland Square, Edinburgh EH1 2BB (tel: 0131 228 4681; email: office@rsmacdonald.com)

Trustees: James Baird; John Paterson; Robert Ross; Fiona Patrick; Moira Easson; Frank Sullivan.

 www.rsmacdonald.com

 @rsmacdonaldct

 @rsmacdonaldct

General information

Established in 1978, this is the trust of the late R. S. Macdonald, whose family founded the famous whisky distillery Glenmorangie in 1893. The trust sold its shares in Glenmorangie in 2004 and then re-invested the proceeds, with a view to making more money available to charities.

The trust supports charities concerned with the following:

- Neurological conditions
- Visual impairment
- Child welfare
- Animal welfare
- Medical research into neurological conditions, visual impairment or sight loss
- RNLI lifeboats

The trust's website states:

> We provide around £2.5m in grants every year to charities working in Scotland. The Trust will consider applications for:
> - revenue or capital costs
> - project funding or core funding
> - one off awards (small and main grants)
> - multi-year awards for up to 3 years (main grants only)

The trust provides the following types of grants:

Small grants – awards of up to £15,000 can be applied for at any time of year. Multi-year applications are not considered under this programme.

Main grants – awards of over £15,000 with an average award of around £35,000. Multi-year grants are considered under this programme.

Medical research grants – research into neurological conditions, visual impairment or sight loss. Universities can apply for seedcorn or unrestricted funding for specific academics, research groups or centres. Charities can apply for specific research projects that have completed a peer review process.

Strategic grants – a small number of grants are provided to charities that have previously received funding from the trust.

The trust has an informative FAQs section on its website for more information on the grants.

Financial information

Year end	31/03/2021
Income	£1,780,000
Assets	£99,350,000
Grants to organisations	£1,750,000
No. of grants	57

Further financial information

Grants were broken down as follows:

Neurological conditions	22	£648,000
Tackling child abuse and neglect	19	£633,000
Medical research	7	£414,000
Animal welfare	4	£110,000
Visual impairment/sight loss	4	£95,000
RNLI	2	£50,000

Beneficiaries included: Back Up Trust; Dogs for Good; Headway Highland; Kirrie Connections; REACT; Wale Arts; The Yard.

Applications

Applications can be made through the trust's website. Small grant applications can be submitted at any time. The main grants programme has specific deadlines for each area of work. Check the website for the latest deadlines.

Sources of information

Accounts; annual report; OSCR record; funder's website.

The Mackintosh Foundation

Theatre and the performing arts; medical research; community projects; homelessness; the environment; social welfare

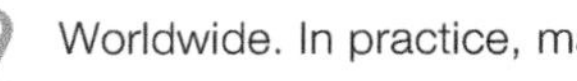

Worldwide. In practice, mainly UK

£1.1 million (2020/21)

CC number: 327751

Correspondent: Richard Knibb, General Secretary, 1 Bedford Square, London WC1B 3RB (tel: 020 7637 8866; email: info@camack.co.uk)

Trustees: Nicholas Allott; Sir Cameron Mackintosh; Nicholas Mackintosh;

Robert Noble; Bart Peerless; Thomas Schonberg; Richard Pappas; Alan Finch; Ms A. Paule Constable.

General information

The foundation was established in 1998 by Sir Cameron Mackintosh. It awards grants for a variety of purposes with a preference for the theatre and performing arts.

According to the 2020/21 annual report, the foundation particularly awards grants under the following categories:

- Financing education in the United Kingdom and abroad by making grants to schools' core costs and assisting the disadvantaged
- Funding the relief of poverty and those in hardship or distress In the United Kingdom and abroad
- Promoting and developing theatrical, musical and dramatic arts by a variety of means including education, theatre refurbishment/restoration programmes and the support of a broad range of theatre productions for the enjoyment and education of the public at large
- Funding medical research and the relief of sickness generally
- Providing grants to environmental projects aimed at the conservation, protection and enhancement of nature in the United Kingdom and elsewhere
- Funding community based projects where often a relatively small grant can make a big impact to many people both immediately and into the future.

The report also notes that the foundation also supports organisations working with people who are experiencing homelessness.

Financial information

Year end	31/03/2021
Income	£99,800
Assets	£14,280,000
Grants to organisations	£1,100,000
No. of grants	23

Further financial information

Grants were made in the following categories:

Theatre and performing arts	£971,400
Medical	£87,500
The environment	£31,700
Community projects	£16,300

Only beneficiaries of grants of £5,000 and above were listed in the accounts. Grants of under £5,000 totalled £9,500.

The accounts state that the foundation made fewer, larger donations during the year due to the impact of COVID-19 pandemic. In 2019/20, the foundation made 168 donations totalling £1.6 million.

Beneficiaries included: Theatre Development Trust (£625,900); Acting for Others (£177,400); NHS Charities Together (£88,300); The Royal Theatrical Fund (£25,000); Roundhouse Trust and Social Bite (£10,000 each); The National Student Drama Festival Ltd (£5,000).

Applications

Apply in writing to the correspondent, outlining details of the organisation and project for which funding is required and providing a breakdown of the costs involved. Supporting documentation should be kept to a minimum and an SAE enclosed if materials are to be returned.

Note the following stated in the latest annual report:

> In March 2020 because of the COVID pandemic, the Trustees took the decision to cease all normal donation making activities and stopped accepting any new applications in the short and medium term; the position remaining the same at the date of this report.

Sources of information

Accounts; annual report; Charity Commission record.

The MacRobert Trust 2019

Armed forces and emergency services; citizenship; children and young people; education and training; agriculture and horticulture; community; the arts; science and engineering

UK, mainly Scotland

£135,300 (2020/21)

OSCR number: SC049475

Correspondent: Alison Donaldson, Charity Manager, Cromar, Tarland, Aboyne, Aberdeenshire AB34 4UD (tel: 01339 881444; email: alison@themacroberttrust.org.uk)

Trustees: Sabrina Campbell; Charles Crole; Mr J. Fowlie; Group Capt. William Gibson; Prof. Gordon Masterton; Commodore Charles Stevenson; Jamie Montgomery; Dr Rebecca McCormick.

www.themacroberttrust.org.uk

General information

The MacRobert Trust is an amalgamation of four trusts established by Lady MacRobert in memory of her three sons, who were all killed as aviators – the eldest in a civil air accident in 1938 and the middle and youngest as officer pilots in the Royal Air Force on operational sorties in 1941.

This trust was established in 2001 when the assets of the no-longer-operating MacRobert Trusts, a collection of four charitable trusts and two holding companies, were merged into the new The MacRobert Trust 2019.

Applications for grants are welcomed from UK-registered charities, but note that preference is usually given to Scotland. The trust's current grant-making themes are:

- Armed forces and good citizenship
- Education and advancing professional excellence
- Local community and other MacRobert interests

More information on these themes can be found on the trust's website.

As well as grants, the trust offers non-monetary support, including an apprenticeship scheme run in partnership with Hospitality Apprenticeship North East. The MacRobert Trust Horticultural Training Scheme accepts up to six trainees each year.

Financial information

Year end	05/04/2021
Income	£3,350,000
Assets	£95,760,000
Grants to organisations	£135,300

Further financial information

In 2020/21 donations paid to organisations totalled £135,300 and were broken down as follows:

Tarland and the local area	£51,500
Children and young people	£40,000
Services and sea	£30,000
Education and training	£15,000
Awards and prizes	£4,800
Cancelled/returned donations	-£6,000

The trust was closed for a period in 2020/21 due to the COVID-19 pandemic. In previous years the trust has awarded grants totalling £837,500 (2019/20) and £525,000 (2018/19).

In addition to grants, the trust awarded non-monetary donations to organisations totalling £211,100 in 2020/21.

Beneficiaries included: Nuffield Farming Scholarship (£13,000); Horseback UK, Mid Deeside Community Trust, Poppy Scotland and Seafarers (£10,000 each); Finzean Community Association (£5,000); Dinnet Village Hall (£2,000); St Thomas' Church (£1,000); Scottish Crofting Federation (£500); Game and Wildlife Conservation Trust (£110).

Applications

The trust's website states: 'All award applications to the Trust must be via the online application portal. Hard copy and email applications will not be processed.' According to the trust's 2020/21 annual report, applications are reviewed and awarded bi-annually, typically in November and May.

Sources of information

Accounts; annual report; OSCR record; funder's website.

The Mactaggart Third Fund

General charitable purposes

UK and overseas

£333,100 (2020/21)

OSCR number: SC014285

Correspondent: The Trustees, 229 Fenwick Road, Giffnock, Glasgow G46 6JQ

Trustees: Alastair Mactaggart; Robert Gore; Fiona Mactaggart; Andrew Mactaggart; Sir John Mactaggart.

 www.mactaggartthirdfund.org

General information

The Mactaggart Third Fund is a grant-making charity with general charitable purposes established in 1968. Grants are made to charities working in the UK and overseas.

Financial information

Year end	30/04/2021
Income	£509,100
Assets	£20,830,000
Grants to organisations	£333,100

Beneficiaries included: Amazon Conservation (£13,800); Slough Immigration Aid Unit (£6,000); Angling for Youth Development (£3,000); Action on Hearing Loss and British Heart Foundation (£2,000 each); Strongbones Children's Charitable Trust (£500).

Applications

The fund does not accept unsolicited applications.

Sources of information

Accounts; annual report; OSCR record; funder's website.

The Mahoro Charitable Trust

General charitable purposes, with a preference for health and social welfare

UK

£452,000 (2020/21)

CC number: 1151200

Correspondent: The Trustees, Flat 25, Sir John Lyon House, 8 High Timber Street, London EC4V 3PA (tel: 01892 701847; email: mahorotrust@gmail.com)

Trustees: Holly Ellis; Jenny Ellis; Luke Ellis; Rory Ellis.

General information

Established in 2013, this trust makes grants to organisations with general charitable purposes. There appears to be a preference for supporting health and social welfare charities.

Financial information

Year end	05/04/2021
Income	£938,500
Assets	£2,080,000
Grants to organisations	£452,000

Beneficiaries included: Greenhouse and Sick Children's Trust (£100,000 each); FareShare – Sussex (£50,000); The Trinity Hospital (£15,000); Crawley Open House (£10,000); UK Reads (£5,000); Drama Express (£2,000).

Applications

Apply in writing to the correspondent.

Sources of information

Accounts; annual report; Charity Commission record.

Making a Difference Locally Ltd

General charitable purposes and community projects

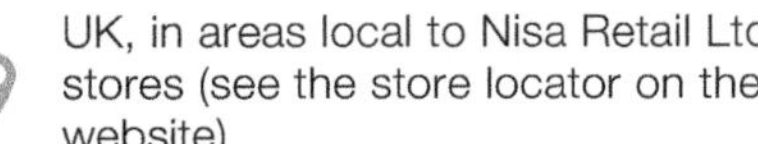

UK, in areas local to Nisa Retail Ltd stores (see the store locator on the website)

£1.06 million (2020/21)

CC number: 1123800

Correspondent: The Trustees, Waldo Way, Normanby Enterprise Park, Scunthorpe, North Lincolnshire DN15 9GE (tel: 01724 282028; email: makingadifference@nisaretail.com)

Trustees: Valerie Aston; Mohammed Aslam; Kathryn Marsden; John McNeill; David Stokes; Stephen Leach; Andrew Barber.

 www.nisalocally.co.uk/community

 facebook.com/MADLcharity

 @madlcharity

General information

Making a Difference Locally Ltd is the corporate charity of Nisa Retail Ltd, the groceries retailer.

The charity was established to allow the group's retail members to make donations to local charities and causes, such as local football teams, hospices and charities. Retailers and partners of Nisa raise funds through the sale of specific products in their stores and then choose a local beneficiary to receive the funds.

Eligibility

The charity's overall mission is to invest in building stronger local communities. Funding areas span health and well-being, education, employment, good food and nutrition, shelter and security. Its criteria for funding is outlined below:

- Requests must be local to a Nisa store (ideally within ten miles)
- Requests must be from a registered charity or good cause with a dedicated business bank account
- The registered charity or good cause must be transparent and accountable – this means that it must be able to confirm what any donation would be used for on request

There is no minimum or maximum turnover restrictions for the charity or cause.

Heart of the Community Awards

This initiative was launched in October 2020 and supports community projects with donations totalling £150,000 (£5,000 each). Nominations are accepted by Nisa partners via a dedicated website when funding rounds open (see www.nisalocally.co.uk/community/success-stories/heart-of-the-community-awards).

Check the website for future funding rounds.

Financial information

Year end	30/06/2021
Income	£1,200,000
Assets	£1,450,000
Grants to organisations	£1,060,000
No. of grants	1,725

Further financial information

Only beneficiaries receiving grants of over £10,000 were listed in the accounts. Grants ranged from £1.30 to £17,500.

Beneficiaries included: The Trussel Trust (£17,500).

Exclusions

The charity's website states that it will not make any donation to the following groups:

- Any group which is involved in the abuse of human rights;
- Any group which discriminates on the grounds of race, sexual orientation, religion, gender, disability or age;
- Any group which causes harm to animals for the purposes of either entertainment or sport;
- Any group which has as its main purpose the dissemination of political or religious information;
- Any group that will spend the funds directly in a Nisa partner's store;
- Any group that sends its funds out of the UK, even if it is a UK-registered charity.

Applications

Use the store locator on the Nisa website to contact your local store. Individual retailers can then submit a form to the charity's grants committee for approval.

Any enquiries should be sent via the contact form on the website.

Sources of information

Accounts; annual report; Charity Commission record; funder's website.

Man Group plc Charitable Trust

Literacy and numeracy

UK

£532,800 (2020)

CC number: 275386

Correspondent: The Trustees, Man Group plc, Riverbank House, 2 Swan Lane, London EC4R 3AD (email: charitable.trust@man.com)

Trustees: Carol Ward; Teun Johnston; Lydia Bosworth; Keith Haydon; Steven Desmyter; Christopher Pyper.

www.man.com/responsibility

General information

This trust, which was registered in 1978, is the corporate charity of the investment management firm Man Group plc. The trust is the vehicle for most of the company's charitable donations and operates as an independent charity.

The trust has two main aims: firstly, it looks to support organisations working to raise literacy and numeracy levels in the UK and, secondly, it looks to facilitate opportunities for Man Group employees to share their time and expertise for charitable causes. It works to achieve these aims by carrying out the following activities, which are outlined on the trust's web page:

- Providing grants via a two-stage application process, or through negotiated partnerships with selected charities.
- Tracking success by measuring impact, carefully monitoring all grants to ensure progress against agreed objectives.
- Providing volunteering opportunities to Man Group UK employees via the Trust's community volunteering programme, ManKind.
- Supporting Man Group UK employees' fundraising activity and charitable donations via the Trust's Sponsorship Matching and Give As You Earn schemes.

Funding criteria

The trust supports small to medium-sized charities registered in the UK whose work is focused on the promotion of literacy and/or numeracy. There is a document available to download from the website which sets out full criteria and guidelines for applying for support. It states that, in order to be eligible, a charity must:

- Have an annual income greater than £1 million and less than £10 million
- Raise levels of literacy and/or numeracy with evidence of an increase in attainment in one or both of these areas
- Have a significant impact; changing wider policy and practice or having the potential to be mainstreamed or replicate
- Have clear and measurable outcomes and benefits and use evidence of results to improve performance
- Lead to leverage of additional funding wherever possible

The document further explains that applicants must be able to show that their organisations are 'well run, with good governance and financial management' and that they 'have an ambitious approach to tackling social issues'. The trustees prefer to support activities that provide assistance directly to individuals, families and communities and also those that increase the capacity of organisations and individuals.

The trustees also consider the interest and involvement of Man Group employees and hold an interest in finding out about volunteering opportunities; however, no preference is given to organisations or projects that can offer such opportunities.

Grant-making

The document from the Man Group website explains that the trust is 'currently [January 2022], funding one-year grants of up to £50,000, but will consider longer-term support for applications that are deemed by trustees to have particular merit'. Grants are typically given to fund core costs (including salaries and overheads) and project costs.

Financial information

Year end	31/12/2020
Income	£600,800
Assets	£571,300
Grants to organisations	£532,800

Beneficiaries included: MyBnk and The Brilliant Club (£50,000 each); City Getaway (£45,000); NSPCC (£35,000); First Story and The Children's Literacy Charity (£25,000 each).

Exclusions

The trust's guidelines state:

> The Trust does not as a rule support, through its grants programme or its broader giving:
> - Large national charities
> - Charities which use external fundraising agencies
> - Charities primarily devoted to promoting religious beliefs
> - Endowment funds
> - Requests to directly replace statutory funding
> - Individual beneficiaries
> - General media campaigns or campaigning or advocacy work to influence policy debates
> - Applicants which have been successful during the last twelve months
> - Work which has already been completed
> - Capital projects and appeals
> - Sponsorship or funding towards marketing appeals or fundraising events
> - Organisations or projects whose primary purpose is political

Applications

In the first instance, see the trust's page on the Man Group website, where a document detailing eligibility criteria and guidelines on how to apply is available.

The document states that the trust has a two-stage application process. After reading the trust's eligibility criteria and exclusions, a brief expression of interest (not exceeding one side of A4) should be sent by email. Information on what should be included in the expression of interest can be found in the guidelines document on the trust's website.

Sources of information

Accounts; annual report; Charity Commission record; funder's website.

The Manoukian Charitable Foundation

General charitable purposes, with a preference for Armenian causes, medical research, the arts and culture, and education

UK and overseas

£568,800 (2020)

CC number: 1084065

Correspondent: Steven Press, Trustee, St Yeghiche's Armenian Church, 13B Cranley Gardens, London SW7 3BB (tel: 020 7341 4444)

Trustees: Tamar Manoukian; Steven Press; Dr Armen Sarkissian.

General information

The foundation was established in 2000 and is funded by the Manoukian family. According to its 2020 annual report, 'The objects of the Charity are the promotion of general charitable purposes; the Trustees give particular emphasis to projects with medical, educational or cultural aspects and those that relate to Armenian matters, although they consider applications for other charitable purposes.'

In previous years funding has typically been given in the following areas:

- Social services and relief
- Education and training
- Medical research and care
- Culture and the arts

The foundation will also consider providing assistance to projects that may be partly funded by others if this will enable the project to proceed.

Financial information

Year end	31/12/2020
Income	£737,500
Assets	£205,900
Grants to organisations	£510,800
No. of grants	9

Further financial information

The foundation's beneficiary list included grants for scholarships and to individuals (totalling £58,000).

Beneficiaries included: Action Innocence (£209,300); Chronic Care Centre (£82,600); Caring Foundation (£50,000); St Yeghiche Armenian Church Parish (£40,000); British Lebanese Association and Chain of Hope (£10,000 each).

Applications

The foundation's Charity Commission record states that it 'does not generally consider unsolicited requests for support but identifies potential donees through the personal experience and knowledge of the Trustees and their professional advisers'.

Sources of information

Accounts; annual report; Charity Commission record.

The Marchig Animal Welfare Trust

Animal welfare

Worldwide, with the exception of the USA and Canada

£1.21 million (2020)

CC number: 802133

Correspondent: The Trustees, Caledonian Exchange, 19A Canning Street, Edinburgh EH3 8HE (tel: 0033 (0)555 608055; email: applications@marchigtrust.org)

Trustees: Les Ward; Janice McLoughlin; Fraser Symon; Matthew Tickle.

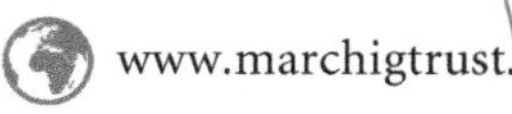
www.marchigtrust.org

General information

The Marchig Animal Welfare Trust was established in 1989 by the late Madam Jeanne Marchig of Geneva for nature and animals and in memory of her husband, the painter Giannino Marchig.

The objects of the charity are 'to protect animals and to promote and encourage practical work in preventing animal cruelty and the relief of animal suffering'.

Grants programme

The following information on grants has been taken from the trust's website:

> Since the Trust was founded it has supported a wide variety of projects including spay/neuter programmes, the search for alternatives to the use of animals in research, anti-poaching programmes, establishing veterinary hospitals, clinics and training programmes, a network of animal sanctuaries, as well as and in particular, assisting smaller groups committed to the cause of animal welfare. Special projects at a variety of sanctuaries and refuges have also been funded.
>
> There are no restrictions on the geographical area of the work (with the exception of the USA and Canada). All applications meeting the following criteria will be considered by the Trust:
>
> - Those encouraging initiatives designed to improve animal welfare.
> - Those promoting alternative methods to animal experimentation and their practical implementation.
> - Those promoting and encouraging practical work in alleviating suffering and preventing cruelty to animals.
> - Those groups who are registered charities or non-government organisations.

The trust also makes grants through The Jeanne Marchig Awards. These awards are given for 'practical work in the field of animal welfare and protection over a significant number of years, resulting in significant improvements that have made a real difference for animals either nationally or internationally'.

Financial information

Year end	31/12/2020
Income	£351,600
Assets	£14,600,000
Grants to organisations	£1,210,000

Further financial information

Only beneficiaries of grants of over £20,000 have been included. Grants of under £20,000 totalled £326,100.

Beneficiaries included: Worldwide Veterinary Service-UK (£662,400); Friendlicoes SECA and Wildlife SOS (£81,800 each); Soi Dog (£43,400); Help in Suffering (£19,200).

Applications

Application forms can be downloaded from the trust's website.

Sources of information

Accounts; annual report; Charity Commission record; funder's website; guidelines for applicants.

The Stella and Alexander Margulies Charitable Trust

Arts and culture; education; medical research; Jewish causes

UK and Israel

£610,200 (2020/21)

CC number: 220441

Correspondent: The Trustees, 27 Berkeley Square, London W1J 6EL (tel: 020 7343 7200; email: jill.tyrrell@timeproducts.co.uk)

Trustees: Marcus Marguiles; Alexander Sorkin; Martin Paisner; Leslie Michaels; Sir Stuart Lipton.

General information

The trust was established in 1962 and supports general charitable purposes, with a preference for Jewish organisations.

Financial information

Year end	05/04/2021
Income	£106,800
Assets	£10,790,000
Grants to organisations	£610,200

Beneficiaries included: Shaare Zedek UK (£358,400); Royal Opera House Foundation (£100,000); Wiener Library (£10,000); Western Marble Arch Synagogue (£1,800).

Applications

Apply in writing to the correspondent.

Sources of information

Accounts; annual report; Charity Commission record.

The Marsh Christian Trust

Social welfare; environmental and animal welfare; healthcare; education and training; literature, arts and heritage

UK

£353,700 (2020/21)

CC number: 284470

Correspondent: Annie McCarthy, Trust Manager, 4 Matthew Parker Street, London SW1H 9NP (tel: 020 7233 3112; email: mccarthy@bpmarsh.co.uk)

Trustees: Brian Marsh; Natalie Collings; Antonia Marsh; Charles Micklewright; Nicholas Carter.

 www.marshchristiantrust.org

 @marshawards

General information

The trust was established in 1981 and is founded on the Christian principles of helping others and caring for the natural world. The trust's support is inclusive of all organisations, regardless of faith.

Grants programme

The trust funds the following areas:

- Social welfare
- Environmental causes and animal welfare
- Healthcare
- Education and training
- Literature, arts and heritage

The trust's website states:

> The Trust focuses on providing funding which could help small organisations pay for various running costs, such as volunteer expenses, training days, equipment maintenance and other core outgoings.
>
> Our funding strategy is to provide long-term core funding for such costs, as we understand that many of the organisations we support depend on unrestricted income in order to meet their operating needs.
>
> Grants are unrestricted and range from £300 to £2,000, with new applications at the lower end of this scale.
>
> Applications are considered on the basis of the organisation's financial position, performance against charitable aims and objectives and the ratio of voluntary income against fundraising expenses.
>
> The Trust aims to build long-standing relationships with successful applicants and, subject to an annual review, continue its support over time.

Marsh Awards Scheme

The trust also maintains the Marsh Awards Scheme – to recognise individual and group achievements in the charity sector. The 2020/21 annual report notes that there are over 215 different programmes under this scheme and that details can be found on the website.

Financial information

Year end	05/04/2021
Income	£955,500
Assets	£17,070,000
Grants to organisations	£353,700

Further financial information

Grants were broken down as follows:

Social and welfare	£215,400
Arts and heritage	£60,500
The environment and animal welfare	£49,000
Healthcare and medical research	£18,900
Education and training	£9,900

Beneficiaries included: British Museum (£8,000); Human Trafficking Foundation (£5,000); Christians Against Poverty (£4,700); Connection at St Martin-in-the-Fields (£3,000); In Kind Direct (£2,000); Natural History Museum (£1,500); Mosaic Middle East (£1,000); New Life Community Counselling (£300); Society for the Protection of Ancient Buildings (£100).

Exclusions

The following are not funded by the trust:

- Individuals
- Churches
- Hospices or hospitals
- CICs
- Start-up costs
- Project costs
- Sponsorship

Applications

Apply in writing to the correspondent, there is no standard application form. The trust requires a cover letter and a full copy of the applicant's report and accounts. Applicants should demonstrate that they have understood the type of funding which the trust provides and illustrate how this would benefit their charity on a long-term basis.

There are no deadlines for applications. Further details of the application process can be found on the trust's website.

Sources of information

Accounts; annual report; Charity Commission record; funder's website.

Charity of John Marshall

Support for parsonage buildings throughout England and Wales; help with the upkeep of Anglican churches and cathedrals in Kent, Surrey and Lincolnshire (as the counties were defined in 1855); support for the parish of Christ Church in Southwark; awards for educational purposes to Marshall's Educational Foundation

England and Wales (for parsonage grants); Canterbury, Guildford, Lincoln, Rochester and Southwark (for church restoration grants)

£351,100 (2020)

CC number: 206780

Correspondent: Catherine de Cintra, Clerk to the Trustees, 66 Newcomen Street, London SE1 1YT (tel: 020 7407 2979; email: grantoffice@marshalls.org.uk)

 www.marshalls.org.uk

General information

This charity has a history dating back to 1631, when John Marshall, a baker in Southwark, left money in his will to be used for charitable purposes. Over the centuries, the charity's purposes have been adapted to suit changing needs. According to the 2020 annual report, it now has four primary purposes:

- to support as Patrons the parish church of Christ Church, Southwark
- to make grants for the support of parsonages to dioceses of the Church of England and the Church in Wales
- make restoration and repair grants to Anglican churches in the three counties of Kent, Surrey and Lincolnshire as those counties were defined in 1855
- 4% of the net income is made available to Marshall's Educational Foundation which makes grants for educational purposes in Stamford and Southwark.

The annual report also states:

> Each year, when approving the budget, the Trustees first decide how much to make available for the costs associated with Christ Church, Southwark. Then, after making adequate provision for the grant to Marshall's Educational Foundation, the Trustees decide how to split the available balance between grants for the support of parsonages and those for restoration of churches. In 2018 a pilot scheme was launched whereby the majority of the funds available were directed through the five dioceses that fall within the three historic counties set out in John Marshall's Will. [...] In 2020 this policy resulted in approximately 32% of the money available being awarded to parsonages and 68% to churches.

National Parsonage Grants programme

The charity makes grants to support parsonages of the Church of England and the Church in Wales. All grants are made through applications from the relevant Diocesan Parsonage Board. The website specifies:

> The Charity makes three different types of grant available to the Dioceses for the Support of Parsonages. The property must be a clergy house which is subject to The Repair of Benefice Buildings Measure 1972 within the Church of England or the Church in Wales (but including the Diocese of Sodor and Man which is not covered by this Act) and be occupied by a Rector, Vicar, Team Rector, Team Vicar or Priest-in-charge. This includes properties provided on a 'House for Duty' basis.

There are three types of grant available:

- **Grants for the purchase or improvement of a parsonage:** Dioceses that have indicated that they require a grant will be allocated funds, calculated on the number of parsonages, for the purchase or improvement of a parsonage.
- **Grants for the installation of burglar alarms in a parsonage:** In 1991, as a result of the rising levels of violence which were experienced by parish clergy, the Trustees offered to support the purchase and installation of burglar alarms in parsonages. Each grant is for

a maximum of £500 with a maximum of 50% of the cost of installation.
- **Grants for the installation of CCTV systems at a parsonage**: In 2001, the Trustees agreed to extend the above scheme to support the installation of CCTV systems in parsonages which were particularly at risk. Each grant is for up to £1,000 with a maximum of 50% of the cost of installation.

Church restoration grants

The website specifies:

> Grants are made to churches in the 5 dioceses connected to John Marshall, namely: Canterbury, Guildford, Lincoln, Rochester, Southwark.
>
> For technical reasons the parishes of North Woolwich and Staunton St Mary are also eligible.
>
> While grants are for building projects, Trustees want to support projects where the building works will benefit the mission and ministry of the church.
>
> The dioceses are well placed to advise where grants may best be directed in order to support the strategic priorities. Therefore when an application is received, the relevant diocese will be invited by Marshall's to supply a statement.

The website states that eligible repairs include:
- roof repairs
- tower repairs
- stonework
- church floors
- new heating and lighting*
- new toilets
- adaptations for disabled access
- reordering including kitchen facilities, as long as they are within the footprint of the church building
- sound systems
- rewiring
- mullions (not glazing)

> * The Trustees would like to encourage churches to consider installing heating systems based on renewable technologies (for example, air source heat pumps) or micro generation of electricity. An application for such a system is likely to be considered for the maximum possible grant.

Financial information

Year end	31/12/2020
Income	£1,220,000
Assets	£22,440,000
Grants to organisations	£351,100

Further financial information

During the year, church restoration grants totalled £156,000, parsonage grants totalled £90,200 and other grants totalled £105,000.

Beneficiaries included: St Mary and St John – Chatham (£37,000); Guildford Diocese (£17,000); Swansea Diocese (£11,100); St Peter's – Ash (£10,000); St Edith – Anwick (£5,000); Canterbury Diocese (£2,000); Monmouth Diocese (£800); Lichfield Diocese (£200).

Exclusions

Parsonage grants cannot be applied for by individual clergy or other denominations. Parsonage grants must be for building, purchasing, altering, dividing or modernising parsonages and *not* for repairs or non-consequential decorations. Any work carried out before 1 February in that year is not eligible for a grant.

For church restoration grants the church must be licensed for worship and not being considered for closure. The website states that ineligible repairs include:
- solely professional fees
- works outside the footprint of the church, including:
  - church halls
  - external meeting rooms and facilities
  - church grounds
  - boundary walls and fences
- redecoration including re-gilding
- bells
- organs
- clocks
- monuments
- brasses
- stained glass

Applications

Applications must be submitted through the charity's online portal. Applications for parsonages must be made through the relevant diocesan parsonage board. Applications for grants for burglar alarms and CCTV are open throughout the year. Applications for church restoration grants must give information on the project (description, cost and timings) and the importance of the proposed works, how they will benefit the mission and ministry of the church and how the project fits with the diocese's strategic aims. For church restoration grants, the grants committee meet three times per year to shortlist applications for the full board of trustees to approve.

The website also has a helpful page dedicated to other funding sources for church improvements.

Sources of information

Accounts; annual report; Charity Commission record; funder's website; guidelines for applicants.

John Martin's Charity

Religious activities; social welfare; education; health

Evesham and surrounding villages only

£198,900 (2020/21)

CC number: 527473

Correspondent: John Daniels, Clerk, 16 Queens Road, Evesham, Worcestershire WR11 4JN (tel: 01386 765440; email: enquiries@johnmartins.org.uk)

 www.johnmartins.org.uk

General information

The charity was created following the death of John Martin of Hampton, Worcestershire in 1714. His property was left for the benefit of local residents and over the years some of this property has been sold to generate income to enable the charity to carry out its objectives in accordance with his wishes. It was formally registered with the Charity Commission in 1981.

Aims and objectives

The overall aim of the charity is to benefit the residents of the town and neighbourhood of Evesham, Worcestershire. This is achieved through four specific aims, outlined within the annual report for 2020/21:
- **Religious support**: to assist the vicars in Hampton and Bengeworth and the three Parochial Church Councils within the town of Evesham
- **Relief in need**: to assist generally or individually, persons resident within the town of Evesham who are in conditions of need, hardship and distress
- **Promotion of education**: to promote education to persons residing within the town of Evesham and to provide benefits to schools in the town
- **Health and other charitable purposes**: to assist beneficiaries within the town of Evesham or within the immediate neighbourhood. The trustees mainly use this ability to support people with chronic health problems and other related health issues across a wider beneficial area

A great proportion of support is given to individuals directly, including helping pensioners by providing winter heating grants and making grants to assist people in education or training.

Organisations applying for a grant do not have to be based in Evesham, but must be able to provide evidence that Evesham residents are being assisted and that this local work forms the major (or a substantial) part of their purpose.

The trustees will consider requests for both capital items and general expenditure, including project costs.

The trustees also assist local charitable organisations by providing them with temporary meeting rooms without charge, together with the use of other office resources. According to the accounts, in 2020/21, this usage equated to 814 hours at an estimated value of £6,400.

Financial information

Year end	31/03/2021
Income	£684,600
Assets	£26,470,000
Grants to organisations	£198,900

Further financial information

In 2020/21, grants were awarded to organisations in the following categories:

Relief in need	£67,400
Religion	£58,600
Health and general charitable purposes	£42,200
Education	£30,700

In previous years the charity's grant-making exceeded £250,000.

Beneficiaries included: St Richard's Hospice (£30,000); Ourside Youth Association (£17,000); Yellow Scarf CIC (£7,000); St Egwin Roman Catholic Church (£5,000); Evesham Bowling Club (£2,000); Footsteps Worcestershire (£1,000); Smile Café (£500).

Applications

Application forms are available on the charity's website. Grants to organisations are considered once per quarter, approximately four weeks after the following application closing dates: 1 June, 1 September, 20 November and 1 March.

The receipt of the application will be acknowledged and you may be contacted in order to obtain further information. The clerk/trustees may also need to visit the applicant as part of the application process.

Sources of information

Accounts; annual report; Charity Commission record; funder's website; guidelines for applicants.

Masonic Charitable Foundation

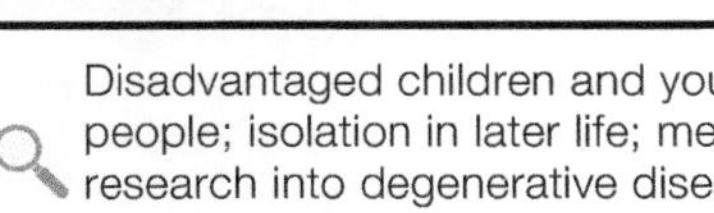

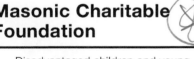

Disadvantaged children and young people; isolation in later life; medical research into degenerative diseases; hospice care; disaster relief

England and Wales

£12.56 million (2020/21)

CC number: 1164703

Correspondent: Grants Team, Freemasons Hall, 60 Great Queen Street, London WC2B 5AZ (tel: 020 3146 3337; email: charitygrants@mcf.org.uk)

Trustees: Sir Paul Williams; Antony Harvey; Timothy Dallas-Chapman; HHJ Richard Hone; Howard Sabin; Michael Heenan; David Watson; Christopher Head; John Boyington; Simon Duckworth; Charles Cunnington; Andrew Wauchope; Nigel Vaughan; Howard Wilson; Alan Graham; Sinead Brophy; Dr Simon Fellerman; Stephen Robinson.

 http://mcf.org.uk

 facebook.com/themcf

 @Masonic_Charity

General information

The Masonic Charitable Foundation was registered with the Charity Commission in December 2015 to bring together the work of four national Masonic charities: The Freemasons' Grand Charity; the Royal Masonic Trust for Girls and Boys; the Masonic Samaritan Fund; and the Royal Masonic Benevolent Institution.

The foundation provides support for Freemasons and their dependants and to a range of non-Masonic registered charities benefitting people in England, Wales and areas affected by natural disasters, both in the UK and overseas. The foundation's non-Masonic grant-making activities are outlined below.

The foundation has the following grant programmes:

Early years – grants to give children and young people from vulnerable families the best possible start in life.

Later life – grants to help reduce loneliness among older people.

Hospice care – funds are provided for core operating costs and bereavement support services.

The foundation also supports medical research and disaster relief. These grant programmes are for invited applicants only.

Financial information

Year end	31/03/2021
Income	£67,840,000
Assets	£413,930,000
Grants to organisations	£12,560,000
No. of grants	1,200

Beneficiaries included: Mind (£250,000); Young Minds (£85,000); Encephalitis Society (£60,000); Listening Ear – Merseyside (£52,200); The Peoples Kitchen (£20,000); Cornwall Air Ambulance (£1,000); Treetops Hospice Care (£250).

Exclusions

Each grants programme has its own exclusions. Consult the foundation's website for details.

Applications

Applications can be made through the foundation's website. Grants for medical research and disaster relief are for invited applicants only.

Sources of information

Accounts; annual report; Charity Commission record; funder's website.

Nancie Massey Charitable Trust

Medical research and care; the arts; education; the community

Scotland, particularly the City of Edinburgh

£275,200 (2020/21)

OSCR number: SC008977

Correspondent: The Trustees, c/o Chiene and Tait LLP, 61 Dublin Street, Edinburgh EH3 6NL

General information

The trust was established in 1989 to help organisations in Scotland, primarily in the area of City of Edinburgh. The trust's 2020/21 accounts state that the trust primarily assists in the following areas:

- Medical research and care
- The arts
- Education
- The community

Financial information

Year end	05/04/2021
Income	£262,800
Assets	£6,950,000
Grants to organisations	£275,200
No. of grants	74

Beneficiaries included: Tenovus Scotland (£19,600); Hearts and Minds Charity (£10,000); Dunedin School (£6,000); Age Scotland and Bethany Christian Trust (£5,000 each).

Exclusions

The trust does not make grants to individuals.

Applications

Apply in writing to the correspondent.

Sources of information

Accounts; annual report; OSCR record.

The Master Charitable Trust

General charitable purposes

UK and overseas

£43.53 million (2019/20)

CC number: 1139904

Correspondent: Hoare Trustees, 37 Fleet Street, London EC4P 4DQ (tel: 020 7353 4522)

Trustee: Hoare Trustees.

 www.hoaresbank.co.uk/master-charitable-trust

General information

The Master Charitable Trust was launched in 2011 and supports a wide variety of charitable activities undertaken by UK-registered charities both in the UK and abroad. It is a donor-advised fund, to encourage customers of C. Hoare banking in philanthropic activities. Donors can name their own giving fund and make an initial lump sum contribution through cash, shares or assets. Donors can also recommend UK charities and worldwide causes to the trust. The majority of grants awarded are for £100,000 and above.

Financial information

Year end	30/09/2020
Income	£87,900,000
Assets	£181,320,000
Grants to organisations	£43,530,000

Further financial information

Grants awarded in 2019/20 were broken down as follows:

Health and saving lives	£15.78 million
Education	£5.99 million
General charitable purposes	£5.03 million
The arts, culture, heritage or science	£4.74 million
Relief in need	£3.98 million
Relief of poverty	£3.78 million
Citizenship and community development	£1.78 million
Religion	£813,900
The environment	£788,000
Animal welfare	£473,100
Armed forces and emergency services	£218,500
Amateur sport	£108,900
Human rights, conflict resolution and equality and diversity	£51,000

Only beneficiaries of grants of £100,000 and above were listed in the accounts. Grants of above £100,000 totalled £37.07 million.

Beneficiaries included: NHS Charities Together (£5.25 million); Clink Charity (£2 million); Mailforce Charity CIO (£1 million); FareShare (£745,000); National Emergencies Trust (£500,000); Gloucester Cathedral (£250,000); Governors for Schools (£195,000); Zoological Society of London (£160,000); Machynlleth Tabernacle Trust (£100,000).

Applications

Apply in writing to the correspondent. Grantees are usually chosen at the donor's request.

Sources of information

Accounts; annual report, Charity Commission record; funder's website.

Material World Foundation

The arts; people with disabilities; social welfare

UK and overseas

£1.08 million (2020)

CC number: 266746

Correspondent: The Trustees, c/o Shipleys, 10 Orange Street, London WC2H 7DQ (tel: 020 7312 0000; email: advice@shipleys.com)

Trustees: Linda Arias; Dhani Harrison; Deborah Owen; Leslie Boss; Ken Roberts; Olivia Harrison.

 www.materialworldfoundation.com

General information

The foundation was established by George Harrison in 1973. According to its website, the foundation supports 'the exploration of alternate and diverse forms of artistic expression, life views and philosophies as well as a way to support established charities and people with special needs'.

Financial information

Year end	31/12/2022
Income	£741,600
Assets	£1,120,000
Grants to organisations	£1,080,000

Beneficiaries included: Macmillan Cancer Support (£139,000); Médecins Sans Frontières (£128,200); Community Organised Relief Effort (£81,300); Soulsville Foundation (£20,000); The Crossroads Antigua Foundation (£10,000); Siddhartha's intent (£800).

Applications

Apply in writing to the correspondent.

Sources of information

Accounts; annual report; Charity Commission record; funder's website.

Maudsley Charity

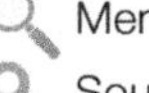

Mental health

South London

£3.68 million (2020/21)

CC number: 1175877

Correspondent: Grants Team, ORTUS Centre, 82–96 Grove Lane, London SE5 8SN (tel: 020 3696 9760; email: Rebecca.gray@maudsleycharity.org)

Trustees: David Barclay; Peter Baffoe; Daniel Acquah; Josephine Namusisi-Riley; Beatrice Butsana-Sita; David Bradley; Joshua Maisey; Nicola Byrne; Nigel Keen; Catherine Lee; Trevor Goode.

 https://maudsleycharity.org

 facebook.com/slamnhs

 @MaudsleyNHS

General information

Tracing its origins back to a charitable deed of gift in 1247, the Maudsley Charity today awards funds for hospital and community-based mental health projects. The Maudsley Charity works in partnership with South London and Maudsley NHS Foundation Trust and the Institute of Psychiatry, Psychology and Neuroscience at King's College London.

Grant programmes

The charity distributes grants through partnerships and open calls for funding. At the time of writing (May 2022) the charity had just announced two new priority areas: Living Well with Psychosis, which was set to launch in 2022, and Young People Most at Risk of Mental Illness, which will start disbursements in 2023.

Financial information

Year end	31/03/2021
Income	£4,470,000
Assets	£182,860,000
Grants to organisations	£3,680,000
No. of grants	74

Beneficiaries included: South London and Maudsley NHS Foundation Trust (£2.57 million in 55 grants); Kings College London (£308,000); Bethlem Gallery Projects Ltd (£243,000); Centre for Mental Health (£10,000).

Applications

See the charity's website for the latest information on open funding programmes.

Sources of information

Accounts; annual report; Charity Commission record; funder's website.

Mayfair Charities Ltd

The relief of poverty and Orthodox Jewish religion and education

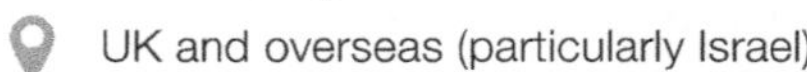

UK and overseas (particularly Israel)

£3.06 million (2020/21)

CC number: 255281

Correspondent: The Trustees, Freshwater Group of Companies, Freshwater House, 158–162 Shaftesbury Avenue, London WC2H 8HR (tel: 020 7836 1555)

Trustees: D. Davis; Solomon Freshwater; Benzion Freshwater; Richard Fischer.

General information

The charity was set up in 1968 and according to its 2020/21 annual report, it was 'established to support the activities of religious Jewish organisations recognised as charitable by English Law both in the United Kingdom and abroad, especially those in the field of education and relief of poverty'.

The charity supports a number of charities both in the UK and overseas, particularly in Israel. It appears to be a vehicle for the philanthropic activities of property investor Benzion Freshwater, which is closely connected with the management of some of the major beneficiary organisations.

Our previous research suggests that support for core or capital expenditure is usually given on a one-off basis.

Financial information

Year end	31/03/2021
Income	£5,290,000
Assets	£90,260,000
Grants to organisations	£3,060,000
No. of grants	225

Further financial information

During 2020/21, grants were distributed as follows: £2.99 million for the advancement of religion and education and £73,000 for the relief of poverty. Note: the grant total includes monetary donations of £2.7 million and non-monetary donations (the provision of facilities) totalling £400,000.

Beneficiaries included: Beth Jacob Grammar School for Girls Ltd (£1.8 million); Shaarei Orah Ltd (£75,000); BC Trust (£49,000); Kahal Chassidim Bobov (£37,000); Gateshead Talmudical College (£22,000); Marbeh Torah Trust (£11,000); Friends of Mercaz Hatorah Belz Macnivka (£10,000).

Applications

Apply in writing to the correspondent.

Sources of information

Accounts; annual Report; Charity Commission record.

Mayheights Ltd

Orthodox Jewish religion and general charitable purposes

Barnet; Hackney; Israel

£1.57 million (2020/21)

CC number: 1112291

Correspondent: The Trustees, 36 Gilda Crescent, London N16 6JP (tel: 020 8806 1234)

Trustees: Menashe Eichenstein; Rachel Low; Oscar Low.

General information

Mayheights Ltd was established in 1983. According to the charity's 2020/21 annual report, 'the objects of the charity are, the advancement of religion in accordance with the Orthodox Jewish Faith, the relief of poverty and for such other purposes as are recognised by English Law as charitable.'

Financial information

Year end	31/03/2021
Income	£1,560,000
Assets	£18,450,000
Grants to organisations	£1,570,000

Further financial information

In 2020/21, grants were broken down as follows:

The advancement of religion	£536,300
Religious education	£482,800
Relief of poverty	£317,800
General charitable purposes	£182,200
Social welfare	£47,500

Only beneficiaries of grants of £40,000 and above were listed in the charity's 2020/21 accounts. Grants of under £40,000 totalled £708,300.

Beneficiaries included: Hichal Aharon (£150,000); Mifal Torah (£100,000); Chasdei Ahron (£64,600); Nextgrant Ltd (£61,000); Tchabe Kollel Ltd (£50,000); Noam Halvovos (£40,000).

Applications

Apply in writing to the correspondent. The charity's 2020/21 annual report notes that while the charity does not actively invite applications, the trustees consider all requests received.

Sources of information

Accounts; annual report; Charity Commission record.

The Robert McAlpine Foundation

Children and young people; social welfare; older people; medical research; disability

UK

£645,600 (2020/21)

CC number: 226646

Correspondent: Appeals Manager, Eaton Court, Maylands Avenue, Hemel Hempstead, Hertfordshire HP2 7TR (tel: 0333 566 2069; email: foundation@srm.com)

Trustees: Adrian McAlpine; The Hon. David McAlpine; Cullum McAlpine; Gavin McAlpine.

 www.robertmcalpinefoundation.org

General information

Sir Robert McAlpine Ltd is a family-owned UK construction and civil engineering company. The foundation was established by the family of Sir Robert McAlpine and gives grants to support small charities situated throughout the UK that fall within specific categories, namely:

- Children with disabilities or life-limiting illnesses
- Social welfare
- Older people
- Young people
- Medical research

To be eligible, charities must meet the following criteria:

- Have a total income of less than £1 million per annum
- Be intending to use the funding for a UK-based project
- Work in one of the trust's areas of interest

The foundation's 2020/21 accounts state: 'The policy of the Trustees is to make grants to charitable institutions of amounts from £5,000 upwards in the specific categories of objectives which they support.'

Financial information

Year end	31/03/2021
Income	£678,500
Assets	£19,220,000
Grants to organisations	£645,600

Beneficiaries included: A list of beneficiaries was not available.

Exclusions

The foundation will not fund fundraising activities or support fundraising by established charities for a target sum.

Applications

Apply by post or via email to the correspondent. The foundation's website states that appeals should be 'no more than two A4 pages' and should outline:

- Who you are
- Your charity number
- What work your charity does
- Details of the specific project for which you require funding
- The amount of funding you are looking for
- Your contact details, together with website address if you have one

The foundation also asks that applicants enclose a copy of their most recent accounts. The trustees meet annually in November to approve grants – applications must be received no later than 31 August to be considered in the next meeting. The foundation is unable to accept any appeal requests by telephone.

Sources of information

Accounts; annual report; Charity Commission record; funder's website.

D. D. McPhail Charitable Settlement

Medical research; people with disabilities, particularly children; older people

UK

£320,100 (2020/21)

CC number: 267588

Correspondent: Katharine Moss, Executive Director, P. O. Box 78190, Wimbledon, London SW19 9QL (tel: 07523 440550; email: director.ddmcphail@gmail.com)

Trustees: Mary Meeks; Olivia Hancock; George Courcy-Wheeler; Helene Jelman; Jane Brake; Edward Coley; Ben Smith.

www.ddmcphailcharitablesettlement.co.uk

General information

The D. D. McPhail Charitable Settlement was established in 1973. It supports small and medium sized charities.

The charity's website states:

> The objective of a grant to a charity is to enable an investment and/or step change in its activities through a relatively large award, generally over a period of 2 to 4 years. Projects should be self sustaining following the conclusion of the grant. The trust deed specifies three key areas of preference in the UK around:
>
> - furtherance of medical research,
> - care of the disabled particularly disabled children, and
> - care of the aged and infirm

The trustees may also support other charitable activities in the UK at their discretion. In addition, the charity has a small grants programme via members of the UK Community Foundations network.

Financial information

Year end	05/04/2021
Income	£364,500
Assets	£10,630,000
Grants to organisations	£320,100

Beneficiaries included: Spitalfields Crypt Trust (£110,000); Helen Bamber Foundation (£80,000); Muscular Dystrophy UK (£12,500); Brixton Soup Kitchen (£9,000); South Liverpool Foodbank (£2,000).

Applications

The charity's website states:

> Trustees identify potential projects for assessment by the Executive Director. We are a small grant making charity with one part time worker. Please note that the Trustees make no commitment to respond to unsolicited applications.

Sources of information

Accounts; annual report; Charity Commission record; funder's website.

Medical Research Foundation

Medical research

UK and Africa

£1.53 million (2020/21)

CC number: 1138223

Correspondent: The Trustees, 99 Charterhouse Street, London EC1M 6HR (tel: 020 7250 8216; email: research@medicalresearchfoundation.org.uk)

Trustees: Prof. Moira Whyte; David Zahn; Prof. Nicholas Lemoine; Prof. Daniel Altmann; Susan Wilkinson; Richard Lackmann; Dr Hans Haitchi; Dr Patricia Kingori; Kristen Gallagher.

www.medicalresearchfoundation.org.uk

@medresfdn

General information

This is the foundation of the Medical Research Council (MRC), which has been accepting charitable donations and bequests since its inception in 1923. The foundation was launched in 2011, when the fund's previously held by the MRC's various medical research charities were transferred to the new charity.

According to the foundation's 2020/21 annual report, support is provided across four strategic research themes:

> **Increasing understanding** – Support for the discovery science that increases understanding of the processes underpinning all human health and disease.
>
> **Emerging research leaders** – Opportunities for the emerging research leaders who will address the biomedical research questions of the future and support for their cutting-edge research today.
>
> **High need, low research investment** – Support for research on the conditions and diseases that devastate lives, where there is unmet need for new research but a low research investment.
>
> **Changing policy and practice** – Support to disseminate research results beyond the scientific press to people and places that will influence healthcare policy and practice as well as personal life choices.

The foundation's website states:

> We provide support for research grants, infrastructure and equipment grants, fellowships and studentships, skill-sharing and collaborations, and the dissemination of research results. Unlike many other funding bodies, we are not restricted in having to support a particular disease area or institution.

Financial information

Year end	31/03/2021
Income	£3,310,000
Assets	£71,220,000
Grants to organisations	£1,530,000

Beneficiaries included: University of Bristol (£320,000 in two grants); University of Cardiff (£290,000); Imperial College London (£71,000); University of Edinburgh (£22,000); University of Lagos (£4,000).

Applications

Applications can be made via the foundation's website where details of open programmes and application deadlines can also be found.

Sources of information

Accounts; annual report; Charity Commission record; funder's website.

Medical Research Scotland

Medical research

Scotland

£2.37 million (2020/21)

OSCR number: SC014959

Correspondent: The Trustees, c/o Turcan Connell, Princes Exchange, 1 Earl Grey Street, Edinburgh EH3 9EE (tel: 0131 659 8800; email: enquiries@medicalresearchscotland.org.uk)

Trustees: Heather Wallace; Linda Duncan; Alasdair Gill; Fiona Gillespie; Andrea Nolan; Michael Roberts; Barry Rose; Jenny Woof.

www.medicalresearchscotland.org.uk

General information

Formerly known as the Scottish Hospital Endowments Research Trust, the charity's website states the following:

> Medical Research Scotland is Scotland's largest independent medical research charity committed to encouraging and supporting promising individuals at the start of their research careers, through the award of doctoral studentships but also through support for undergraduates and scientists returning after a career break.
>
> Our grants support research that aims to improve health in Scotland and globally in three ways: by improving the diagnosis, treatment or prevention of diseases; by understanding basic disease processes; and by the development of medical technologies.

Funding is provided in the following categories:

- PhD studentships – four years of funding for doctoral training programmes to be delivered by Scottish universities or research

institutions working in collaboration with an external partner organisation
- Daphne Jackson fellowships – two- to three-year part-time fellowships for scientists who wish to return to medical research after a career break of two years or more. The fellowships must take place at a Scottish university and involve a challenging research project addressing a question relating to human health or disease
- Undergraduate vacation scholarships – offer promising students hands-on experience or research related to human health or disease

Financial information

Year end	31/03/2021
Income	£1,670,000
Assets	£43,460,000
Grants to organisations	£2,370,000

Beneficiaries included: University of Strathclyde (£200,200 in seven grants); University of Edinburgh (£139,400 in nine grants); University of Glasgow (£124,900 in four grants); University of Aberdeen (£62,800 in two grants); University of Napier (£35,300); University of Stirling (£31,300); Scottish National Blood Transfusion Service (£19,800).

Applications

Detailed information regarding the foundation's grant programmes, guidance notes, deadlines for applications and more is available from the charity's website.

Sources of information

Accounts; annual report; OSCR record; funder's website.

The Medicash Foundation

Health and well-being

 North West England

£737,300 (2020)

CC number: 257636

Correspondent: Linda Traynor, Medicash Ltd, 1 Derby Square, Liverpool L2 1AB (tel: 0151 702 0334; email: linda.traynor@medicash.org)

Trustee: Medicash Health Benefits Ltd.

 www.medicash.org/charity

General information

In 2019, the foundation's name was changed from Medicash Charitable Trust to The Medicash Foundation. The foundation is the corporate charity of Medicash Health Benefits Ltd and receives a large proportion of its income from the company.

Grants are made to health-related charities in the North West. In the past, grants have been given for the following:
- Children's charities – including mental health and support for disadvantaged children
- Health and well-being projects
- People with disabilities
- Local hospitals, hospices and charities supporting people who are ill

Financial information

Year end	31/12/2020
Income	£718,500
Assets	£1,230,000
Grants to organisations	£737,300

Further financial information

Grants were distributed as follows:

Health and well-being	£245,000
Hospitals, hospices and charities supporting those with an illness	£178,000
Children's charities	£69,700
Disability	£26,700

Beneficiaries included: Inovus/AD Merchandise (£100,800); Clatterbridge Charity (£40,000); Feeding Britain (£18,000); Woodlands Hospice (£10,800); Liverpool Women's Charity (£9,300); Torus Foundation (£8,000); Woodwork to Wellness (£3,500); Tomorrow's Women Wirral (£600).

Applications

Application forms can be downloaded from the foundation's website.

Sources of information

Accounts; annual report; Charity Commission record; funder's website.

The Medlock Charitable Trust

General charitable purposes

 UK, with a preference for Bath and the Borough of Boston, Lincolnshire

£2.11 million (2020/21)

CC number: 326927

Correspondent: The Trustees, St George's Lodge, 33 Oldfield Road, Bath, Somerset BA2 3NE (tel: 01225 946226; email: office@medlockcharitabletrust.org)

Trustees: Jacqueline Medlock; David Medlock; Mark Goodman; Peter Medlock.

 https://medlockcharitabletrust.org

General information

The trust was established in 1985 to make grants to charities and universities in the UK. The trustees have a preference for funding projects in Somerset and Lincolnshire. The trust's 2020/21 accounts state that the trust prioritises Bath, Bristol and Boston in Lincolnshire. The trust particularly favours charities with volunteers.

Grants range up to £50,000, with the vast majority being between £5,000 and £15,000. The trust's website states:

> The projects we support usually fall within the following areas:
> - Education and training
> - Health and social care
> - Housing
> - Sports and recreation
> - Arts and culture
> - Environment and conservation
> - Community services
> - Employment

Financial information

Year end	31/07/2021
Income	£1,860,000
Assets	£41,830,000
Grants to organisations	£2,110,000
No. of grants	163

Further financial information

In 2020/21, the trust awarded 163 grants totalling £2.11 million, of which 135 were for £15,000 or less.

Beneficiaries included: The Research Institute for the Care of Older People (£125,000); Bath Recreation Ltd (£60,000); Peasedown Youth Partnership (£30,000); Centrepoint Outreach (£15,000); Buttle UK (£10,000); Venturers Trust (£5,000); Whitchurch Primary School (£2,000); The Dolphin Society (£1,000); The Rifles Benevolent Trust (£500).

Exclusions

The trust's website states:

> Grants will not be awarded for charitable projects being carried out overseas [...] We do not support individuals or animal charities. We do not sponsor competitions or events. We will not support educational institutions where only a privileged elite will benefit – we will however fund initiatives to further the education of those who need additional support.

Applications

Apply using the online application form on the trust's website. The trustees meet monthly to asses applications. The trust's website gives the following information:

> When assessing grant applications, we want charities to demonstrate the following points:
> - Why there is a need for their work, why it is not currently being met and how they plan to address it
> - The impact their work will have in terms of numbers of people helped and degree of improvement to those people's lives
> - What plans are in place to measure the qualitative and quantitative impact of the work
> - A forecast budget for the work to show short-term and long-term sustainability
> - The most recent annual report and accounts of the charity

- The number of volunteer days and pro bono services being given to the charity

Our online application form is designed to help applicants by ensuring they provide all the relevant information.

Sources of information

Accounts; annual report; Charity Commission record; funder's website.

The Meikle Foundation

General charitable purposes; children and young people; older people; medical causes; culture

Scotland, with a preference for the Fife and Aberdeen areas

£411,500 (2020/21)

OSCR number: SC009842

Correspondent: Sandra Graham, Administrator, Dentons UK and Middle East LLP, 1 George Square, Glasgow G2 1AL (tel: 0330 222 1765; email: sandra.graham@dentons.com)

 www.themeiklefoundation.com

General information

The foundation's website states:

> The Meikle Foundation began its existence in 1973 when the four Meikle sisters set up the Martin Connell Charitable Trust by a Deed of Trust. Following the passing of the last surviving sister, the Trust has been renamed from the Martin Connell Charitable Trust to The Meikle Foundation to reflect the family name of the four sisters.

The objectives of the foundation are widely drawn and cover a wider range of causes including medical, youth, older people and cultural. Grants are awarded predominately to charities based in Scotland or charities with a Scottish connection, with a particular emphasis on the Fife and Aberdeen areas. The trustees prefer to award small grants, typically of around £2,000, to causes where it will make a significant impact.

Financial information

Year end	05/04/2021
Income	£250,900
Assets	£10,330,000
Grants to organisations	£411,500

Beneficiaries included: Tenovus Scotland (£6,000); Erskine (£4,000); Leonard Cheshire Foundation (£3,000); Headway (£2,000); Fight for Sight (£1,000).

Applications

Apply in writing to the correspondent.

Sources of information

Accounts; annual report; OSCR record; funder's website.

The Melow Charitable Trust

Jewish causes and social welfare

UK and overseas

£919,200 (2020)

CC number: 275454

Correspondent: The Trustees, 21 Warwick Grove, London E5 9HX (tel: 020 8806 1549)

Trustees: Miriam Spitz; Esther Weiser.

General information

The trust was established in 1978 and makes grants to charitable organisations for the relief of poverty and the advancement of religion and religious education.

Financial information

Year end	31/12/2020
Income	£1,210,000
Assets	£12,290,000
Grants to organisations	£919,200

Beneficiaries included: Here 2 Help (£163,000); Tchabe Kollel Ltd (£102,200); The Rehabilitation Trust (£100,000); Start Upright (£30,000); Shaarei Chesed Trust (£150).

Applications

Apply in writing to the correspondent.

Sources of information

Accounts; annual report; Charity Commission record.

Menuchar Ltd

Orthodox Jewish faith and welfare

UK

£383,900 (2020/21)

CC number: 262782

Correspondent: Helena Bude, Secretary, Barry Flack and Co. Ltd, The Brentano Suite, Prospect House, 2 Athenaeum Road, London N20 9AE (tel: 020 8369 5170)

Trustees: Ruth Bude; Raphael Bude.

General information

The charity was set up in 1971 and its main objective is the advancement of religion in accordance with the Orthodox Jewish faith. Support may also be given for the relief of people in need.

Financial information

Year end	31/03/2021
Income	£250,000
Assets	£206,700
Grants to organisations	£383,900

Further financial information

Grants made to religious organisations in 2020/21 totalled £383,900.

Beneficiaries included: A list of beneficiaries was not available.

Applications

Apply in writing to the correspondent.

Sources of information

Accounts; annual report; Charity Commission record.

Mercaz Torah Vechesed Ltd

Orthodox Jewish faith, religious education and welfare

Worldwide, with a preference for Barnet, Hackney and Israel

£1.44 million (2020/21)

CC number: 1109212

Correspondent: Joseph Ostreicher, Trustee, 28 Braydon Road, London N16 6QB (tel: 020 8880 5366; email: umarpeh@gmail.com)

Trustees: Joseph Ostreicher; Mordche Rand.

General information

The charity was formed in 2005 for 'the advancement of the Orthodox Jewish faith, Orthodox Jewish religious education, and the relief of poverty and infirmity among members of the Orthodox Jewish community'.

Financial information

Year end	31/01/2021
Income	£1,510,000
Assets	£134,100
Grants to organisations	£1,440,000

Further financial information

Only beneficiaries of grants of £50,000 and above were listed in the accounts. Grants of under £50,000 totalled £218,800.

Beneficiaries included: Ohr Haganuz Maseh Rokeach (£663,200); Adnei Hakodesh (£309,000); Parshat Mordchai (£247,600).

Applications

Apply in writing to the correspondent.

Sources of information

Accounts; annual report; Charity Commission record.

The Brian Mercer Charitable Trust

Art in the North West; causes local to Blackburn; health and social welfare (UK and overseas)

UK (with a preference for Blackburn and the North West) and overseas

£895,800 (2020/21)

CC number: 1076925

Correspondent: The Trustees, c/o Beever and Struthers, Central Buildings, Richmond Terrace, Blackburn BB1 7AP (tel: 01254 686600; email: info@brianmercertrust.org)

Trustees: Roger Duckworth; Kenneth Merrill; Mary Clitheroe; Christine Clancy.

 www.brianmercertrust.org

General information

The trust was established in 1999 by Brian Mercer, an inventor and industrialist who invented a revolutionary process for the manufacture of plastic nets that became known as Netlon. The trust awards grants in the following areas:

- **Prevention and relief of human suffering** – to support interventions directed towards reducing poverty and ill health whether in the UK or overseas. Such interventions must be of proven best value or demonstrate the potential to become so
- **Art** – to encourage and support the development of promising young artists (working broadly in the field of visual arts), especially within the North West
- **Causes local to Blackburn, Lancashire** – to provide funding for well-designed, evidence-based interventions benefitting those living in the area of Blackburn, Lancashire

The trust welcomes applications for evaluation of previously unevaluated initiatives provided that these are consistent with one of the three funding categories, are methodologically robust and include an explanation of how the results will be used and disseminated.

The total value of all grants awarded annually is usually around £800,000. The proportion of funds allocated to the three causes is:

- 75% – prevention and relief of human suffering
- 15% – art
- 10% – causes local to Blackburn Lancashire

Financial information

Year end	05/04/2021
Income	£1,320,100
Assets	£36,870,000
Grants to organisations	£895,800

Beneficiaries included: Médecins Sans Frontières (£300,000); Against Malaria Foundation (£150,000); Blackburn with Darwen Borough Council (£120,000); Blackburn Youth Zone (£75,000); Legs4Africa (£30,000); Blackburn Food Bank (£20,000); Intercare (£10,000); Chifundo UK (£2,000).

Exclusions

The trust's website states that the trust does not make grants for:

- Charities based outside the UK and Ireland
- Individuals
- Medical research projects
- Interventions that discriminate on gender, religion, sexual orientation, disability, race, colour or ethnicity
- UK initiatives for specific local areas other than Blackburn, Lancashire

Applications

Application forms and deadlines can be found on the trust's website.

Sources of information

Accounts; annual report; Charity Commission record; funder's website.

The Mercers' Charitable Foundation

Education; children and young people; older people; housing and homelessness; refugees; community services; churches; families

UK, with a preference for London, Norfolk, Lincolnshire and the North East

£2.55 million (2020/21)

CC number: 326340

Correspondent: The Trustees, The Mercers' Company, 6 Frederick's Place, London EC2R 8AB (tel: 020 7776 7250; email: grants@mercers.co.uk)

Trustee: The Mercers' Company

 www.mercers.co.uk/philanthropy

General information

The Mercers' Company has several trusts, the main one being the Mercers' Charitable Foundation. The foundation was established in 1983 to make grants and donations for the benefit of a wide range of charitable purposes including welfare, education, the arts, heritage and religion.

The foundation seeks to support a range of organisations with the common theme of providing effective services and facilities to those in need and to strengthen communities. While continuing to support small grassroots organisations, the foundation has developed relationships with some much larger organisations, complementing work that is funded by statutory bodies.

Grants can be awarded as one-off awards or on a multi-year basis. Capital and core costs are supported.

Grant-making guidelines

The foundation supports the following purposes:

- **Young people and education** – particularly organisations that support families and children in their early years, schools and projects around citizenship and leadership. Only organisations in London are supported
- **Older people and housing** – particularly organisations supporting the resilience and emotional well-being and lifelong learning of older people in London and Norfolk
- **Church and communities** – particularly community projects and organisations in disadvantaged areas, community responses to supporting refuges and people experiencing homelessness, support for families facing poverty and carers. Areas of benefit include London, the North East, Norfolk and Lincolnshire

Financial information

Year end	31/03/2021
Income	£1,770,000
Assets	£17,610,000
Grants to organisations	£2,550,000

Beneficiaries included: Brentford Football Club Community Sports Trust (£110,000); Sandwell Academy (£75,000); Walsall Academy (£50,000); Abingdon School (£45,000); YMCA Lincolnshire (£30,000); InCommon Living (£25,000); Homelink Day Respite Care (£10,000); The Smallpeice Trust (£6,600); Guildhall School of Music and Drama (£6,000).

Exclusions

Exclusions include:

- Retrospective costs
- Newly established groups
- Individuals or students
- Work overseas
- Capital projects

Applications

All information (including guidelines and notes on exclusions) is available on the website. Note that only applications using the application form on the website are accepted.

Sources of information

Accounts; annual report; Charity Commission record; funder's website; further information from funder.

The Merchant Venturers' Charity

Social welfare; education; health; arts and culture; the environment

Greater Bristol area

£271,100 (2020)

CC number: 264302

Correspondent: Lisa Holyoake, The Old Court House, Church Street, Nailsworth, Stroud, Gloucestershire GL6 0BP (tel: 0117 973 8058; email: enquiries@merchantventurers.com)

Trustee: SMV Trustee Company Ltd.

 www.merchantventurers.com

General information

The trust was registered in 1972 and aims to enhance the quality of life for Bristol residents.

The trust's primary areas of support are:

- Social needs
- Young people
- Education
- Environmental causes
- Social enterprise
- Health care
- Culture and the arts
- Projects that will benefit Greater Bristol and its economic development

The charity awards grants of up to £5,000 in any 12-month period. Grants can be for capital equipment or ongoing revenue costs, but grants are unlikely to be made towards the cost of an existing salaried position.

Financial information

Year end	31/12/2020
Income	£390,800
Assets	£7,890,000
Grants to organisations	£271,100

Beneficiaries included: St Paul's Carnival CIC (£10,000); Healthy Holidays (£6,000); Supporting Family Change (£5,000); Strawberry Line Cafe (£4,700).

Exclusions

The charity's guidance for grant applicants states:

> We do not usually make grants for the following:
> - Individuals
> - General appeals (under this process; please contact enquiries@merchantventurers.com if you are fundraising for a specific project in the Greater Bristol area)
> - The direct replacement of statutory funding
> - Political groups or activities promoting political beliefs
> - The promotion of religious beliefs
> - Animal welfare
> - Arts projects with no community or charitable element
> - Sports projects with no community or charitable element
> - Medical research, equipment or treatment
> - Projects that take place before an application can be processed
> - Activities that raise funds for other organisations

Applications

Application forms and detailed guidelines are accessible on the charity's website. Once completed, they can be returned via email. The members of the charity committee meet four times a year, typically in January, April, July and October, to consider applications for funding.

Sources of information

Accounts; annual report; Charity Commission record; funder's website.

T. and J. Meyer Family Foundation Ltd

Education; health; conservation; overseas aid

Worldwide 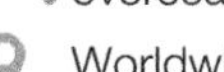

£1.11 million (2020)

CC number: 1087507

Correspondent: The Trustees, 5/6 Kendrick Mews, London SW7 3HG (tel: 020 7581 9900; email: info@tjmff.org)

Trustees: Jane Meyer; Edwin Falkman; Dr Della Drees.

General information

The foundation was set up in 2000 and is administered by the Meyer family. It focuses primarily on education, health and conservation in the UK and overseas.

Financial information

Year end	31/12/2020
Income	£863,800
Assets	£9,150,000
Grants to organisations	£1,110,000
No. of grants	15

Further financial information

Note: the grant total was converted from US dollars using the exchange rate at the time of writing (February 2022). Grants awarded in the UK totalled £213,200 (also converted from dollars).

Beneficiaries included: National Emergency Trust (£81,400); The Trussell Trust (£69,200); NHS Charities Together (£56,400); Chelsea and Westminster Hospital NHS Foundation Trust (£12,500); Advance Charity (£10,000).

Applications

The foundation does not accept unsolicited applications.

Sources of information

Accounts; annual report; Charity Commission record.

The Mickleham Trust

Social welfare; health and disability, particularly blindness; children and young people; people who have experienced abuse

UK, with a preference for Norfolk

£400,300 (2020/21)

CC number: 1048337

Correspondent: Phillip Norton, Trustee, c/o Hansells Solicitors and Financial Advisers, 13–14 The Close, Norwich, Norfolk NR1 4DS (tel: 01603 615731; email: philipnorton@hansells.co.uk)

Trustees: Philip Norton; The Revd Sheila Nunney; Anne Richardson.

General information

The trust was set up in 1995 and its main object, according to its 2020/21 annual report, is 'to provide relief for the abused and disadvantaged, particularly young people, and the blind'.

Financial information

Year end	31/03/2021
Income	£222,300
Assets	£5,710,000
Grants to organisations	£400,300
No. of grants	97

Further financial information

In 2020/21, grants were broken down as follows: support of disadvantaged people and people who have experienced abuse (£384,300); support of blind and partially sighted people (£18,000).

Beneficiaries included: Norfolk and Norwich University Hospital Dementia Support Workers (£43,000); Livability (£25,000); East Anglian Children's Hospice (£15,000); Home-Start (£7,000); Sense (£4,000); British Wireless for the Blind, Canine Partners and The Children's Society (£2,000 each); North Norfolk Community Transport (£1,000).

Applications

Apply in writing to the correspondent.

Sources of information

Accounts; annual report; Charity Commission record.

The Gerald Micklem Charitable Trust

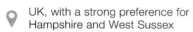

Adults and children with physical and learning disabilities; carers, especially young carers; the environment and wildlife; hospices; health; support for older people, including those with Alzheimer's or dementia

UK, with a strong preference for Hampshire and West Sussex

£329,400 (2020)

CC number: 802583

Correspondent: Susan Shone, Trustee, Bolinge Hill Farm, Buriton, Petersfield, Hampshire GU31 4NN (tel: 01730 264207; email: mail@geraldmicklemct.org.uk)

Trustees: Helen Ratcliffe; Joanna Scott-Dalgleish; Susan Shone.

 www.geraldmicklemct.org.uk

General information

The trust was established in November 1989 with a bequest left in the will of Gerald Micklem. According to the trust's website, it prefers to support UK charities working either on a national basis or specifically in Hampshire or West Sussex. Charities should also work in one of the fields listed below:

- Adults and children with physical disabilities
- Adults and children with learning disabilities
- Carers for the elderly and disabled, especially young carers
- Environment and wildlife
- Hospices for adults and children
- Medical conditions affecting both adults and children
- Support for the elderly, including those with Alzheimer's or dementia

Notably, the trust is unlikely to support the regional work of national charities in locations outside Hampshire or West Sussex or charities working only in other areas of the UK.

The trust's annual report for 2020 states that the trustees 'are prepared to fund core costs as well as capital projects, but are unlikely to provide initial funding for new established organisations'.

Financial information

Year end	31/12/2020
Income	£315,600
Assets	£2,640,000
Grants to organisations	£329,400

Beneficiaries included: Penny Brohn Cancer Care (£22,000); SeeAbility (£10,000); WheelPower (£7,500); RSPB (£6,500); New Forest Mencap (£4,100); Dystonia UK (£2,500).

Exclusions

The trust does not make grants to, or enter into sponsorship arrangements with, individuals. Grants are not made to organisations that are not UK-registered charities.

The website notes that the following areas fall outside the trust's current funding priorities:

- Churches
- Drug/alcohol abuse and counselling
- Disadvantaged children and young people
- Education/schools (excepting those for disabled children)
- Homelessness and housing
- Local community groups
- Medical research
- Mental health
- Museums, galleries and heritage
- Overseas aid
- Performing arts and cultural organisations

Applications

There is no formal application form and applications should be made in writing to the correspondent by post (*not* email). Applicants must also provide a copy of their latest annual report and accounts. Enquiries prior to any application may be made by email. The trustees usually consider awards early in the year; therefore, it asks for submissions to be sent as late as possible so that the information is up to date when considered. However, appeals are not carried forward and should be with the trustees by 31 December.

Sources of information

Accounts; annual report; Charity Commission record; funder's website.

Millennium Stadium Charitable Trust (Ymddiriedclaeth Elusennol Stadiwm Y Mileniwm)

Sport; the arts; community; the environment; young people

Wales

£454,600 (2019/20)

CC number: 1086596

Correspondent: Sarah Fox, Trust Administrator, c/o Fox SE Consultancy, Cardiff House, Cardiff Road, Vale of Glamorgan CF63 2AW (tel: 029 2002 2143; email: info@millenniumstadiumtrust.org.uk)

Trustees: Ian Davies; Russell Goodway; Gerallt Hughes; John Lloyd-Jones; Andrew Walker; John Rawlins; Cllr Peter Bradbury; David Hammond; Jonathan Day; David Young; Hywel Roberts; Momena Ali.

 www.millenniumstadiumtrust.org.uk

 facebook.com/Millennium-Stadium-Charitable-Trust-407704759357213

General information

The trust was established by an agreement between the Millennium Commission and the Millennium Stadium plc. Its income is generated through a levy on every ticket purchased for public events at the stadium.

Local and regional grants

Grants for both the local and regional grant programmes are made in four categories: the arts, community, the environment and sports. Refer to the trust's website for its priorities in these areas.

The maximum grant for regional projects is £7,500 and £2,500 for local grants.

Eligible organisations include charitable organisations, not-for-profit organisations, properly constituted voluntary organisations and voluntary groups working with local authorities.

The following information has been taken from the trust's website:

> **A regional project** is where the organisations usually have a remit to serve a region of Wales or a local authority area. This means that they are the only organisation providing that service within the county borough. Successful applicants in this category must demonstrate that their project is regional or local-authority wide.
>
> **A local project** is where the organisations usually have a remit to serve their local community or town. If there is more than one organisation providing a similar service in the local authority, the group should be considered local (i.e. if there is more than one tennis club in the local authority, then the tennis club will be considered a local organisation).
>
> Applicants are asked to note that bids must be classified by the organisation's geographical remit. It is the applicant's responsibility to determine and prove their classification.

Financial information

Year end	31/03/2020
Income	£520,100
Assets	£133,900
Grants to organisations	£454,600
No. of grants	125

Further financial information

In 2019/20, the trust awarded grants to 125 organisations. Grants were broken down as follows:

Community	£155,700
The arts	£139,300
The environment	£98,200
Sport	£61,400

Beneficiaries included: A list of beneficiaries was not available.

Exclusions

The trust does not support:

- Projects outside Wales
- Day-to-day running costs or salaries
- Projects that seek to re-distribute grant funds for the benefit of third-party organisations
- Payments of debts/overdrafts
- Retrospective requests
- Requests from individuals
- Payments to profit-making organisations
- Applications made solely in the name of a local authority

Applications

Application forms can be downloaded from the trust's website and must be completed in Word format and returned to applications@millenniumstadium trust.org.uk. The trustees meet twice per year to consider applications. Deadline dates can be found on the trust's website or Facebook page, along with full guidelines. Note: due to the impact of the COVID-19 pandemic, the trust cancelled its autumn 2020 regional grant round. Check the trust's website or social media for up-to-date information.

Sources of information

Accounts; annual report; Charity Commission record; funder's website; guidelines for applicants.

The Millichope Foundation

Arts and culture; heritage; conservation projects and the environment; disaster relief

Worldwide. Mainly UK, with a preference for Shropshire

£387,500 (2020/21)

CC number: 282357

Correspondent: Sarah Bury, Trustee, The Old Rectory, Tugford, Craven Arms, Shropshire SY7 9HS (tel: 01584 841234; email: sarah@millichope.com)

General information

The foundation makes donations in the UK in support of the arts, culture, conservation and heritage. Grants are made specifically within Shropshire for general charitable purposes. Worldwide conservation projects and disaster funds are also occasionally supported.

Financial information

Year end	07/01/2022
Income	£414,900
Assets	£7,840,000
Grants to organisations	£387,500
No. of grants	101

Beneficiaries included: Corvedale CofE Aided Primary School (£27,300); Brazilian Atlantic Rainforest Trust (£20,000); Fauna and Flora International (£10,000); Horatio's Garden (£5,000); Pentabus Theatre (£3,000); Marie Curie (£2,500); Shropshire Victim Support (£1,000); British Wireless for the Blind (£500).

Exclusions

The foundation does not support individuals.

Applications

Applications can be made in writing to the correspondent. The trustees meet several times a year to consider applications.

Sources of information

Accounts; annual report; Charity Commission record.

The Milne Family Foundation

Christianity; education; health; citizenship; community development; social welfare

UK, with a preference for Scotland; overseas

£1.55 million (2020)

OSCR number: SC046335

Correspondent: Julie Lowden, Secretary, Balmoral Park, Loirston, Aberdeen AB12 3GY

General information

The foundation was established in 2016 and receives the majority of its funding from Balmoral Group Holdings and its related companies. According to its 2020 annual report, its objects are:

- the advancement of religion and education through the promotion of the Christian gospel both in the UK and overseas
- the advancement of education, health and citizenship and community development
- the relief of poverty

The foundation makes grants to organisations and individuals.

Financial information

Year end	31/12/2020
Income	£1,950,000
Assets	£19,300
Grants to organisations	£1,550,000

Further financial information

During the year the foundation supported 55 organisations and individuals. Only organisations that received grants of over £5,000 were listed in the 2020 accounts. Grants of under £5,000 totalled £29,600.

Beneficiaries included: Kings Community Church (£750,000); Worldlink (£90,000); Sue Ryder (£55,000); Lessons 4 Life (£36,000); Bensham Gospel Hall (£27,000); Choices Aberdeen (£24,000); Seaton Community Church and The Gospel Outreach Trust (£12,000 each).

Applications

The foundation's 2020 accounts state that the trustees seek to identify projects that support the aims of the charity. Contact the correspondent for further information on applications.

Sources of information

Accounts; annual report; OSCR record.

The Clare Milne Trust

Disability

South West England, with a preference for Devon and Cornwall

£950,400 (2020)

CC number: 1191010

Correspondent: Emma Houlding, Secretary, Claypitts, Ladram Road, Otterton, Devon EX9 7HT (tel: 01395 270418; email: secretary@claremilnetrust.com)

www.claremilnetrust.com

General information

The trust (Charity Commission no. 1084733) was established in 2002 by Clare Milne, the granddaughter of the Winnie the Pooh author A. A. Milne, with funds derived from the sale of the copyright royalties from her grandfather's books. In December 2020 the trust re-registered with the Charity Commission as a CIO (Charity Commission no. 1191010).

The trust supports people living with disabilities in South West England, with preference for Devon and Cornwall. The trustees prefer to support registered charities (and sometimes CICs) which are small and well run, have strong support from volunteers and only a modest expenditure on fundraising and administration.

Grants typically range from £2,500 to £25,000. The trust does not normally consider applications for less than £2,500. Applicants in Devon and

Cornwall seeking grants of less than £2,500 are advised to apply to the Clare Milne funding programmes managed by the Devon Community Foundation and the Cornwall Community Foundation.

Help can be given to organisations providing services, facilities or equipment to people with disabilities. Previous grants have included building projects, provision of facilities for day care and activities (e.g. wheelchair dancing and sports), holidays, hospital transport and educational opportunities.

See the trust's grant-making policy available on its website for more information on what it will fund.

Financial information

Year end	31/12/2020
Income	£837,900
Grants to organisations	£950,400
No. of grants	70+

Further financial information

There was no figure for net assets in the trust's 2020 accounts, as it transferred all its funds during its re-registration as a CIO. According to the accounts, grants were made to over 70 organisations during the year.

Beneficiaries included: Helford River Children's Sailing Trust (£285,000); Exeter Deaf Academy (£155,000); Hospiscare (£20,000); Moorvision (£10,000); Spinal Injuries Association (£5,000); Foresight Gardening Enterprises (£3,000); Lewis Manning Hospice (£1,600); Drama Express (£500).

Exclusions

Individuals and national charities are not normally supported.

Applications

Application forms can be downloaded from the trust's website or requested from the correspondent. Forms should be submitted either by email (preferred) or post to the correspondent, along with a covering letter (on your letterhead), details regarding your proposal (up to two sides of A4) and a budget for the project. Applications are considered at trustee meetings, typically held four times a year. Check the trust's website for the latest information on application deadlines and detailed guidelines on how to apply.

Sources of information

Accounts; annual report; Charity Commission record; funder's website; further information provided by the funder; grant-making policy.

Mind

Mental health

England and Wales

£12.68 million (2020/21)

CC number: 219830

Correspondent: The Grants Team, Mind, 2 Redman Place, London E20 1JQ (tel: 020 8519 2122; email: info@mind.org.uk)

Trustees: Stephanie Spring; Valerie Harrison; Ian Ruddock; Emrys Elias; Alyson Scott; Anna Hughes; Cynthia Ko; Joanne Theodoulou; Rohan Kallicharan; Alex Jensen; Christer Stoyell; Shubulade Smith; Mandeep Rupra; Philippa Gluckich; Jonatan Wilderspin.

www.mind.org.uk

facebook.com/mindforbettermentalhealth

@mindcharity

@mindcharity

General information

Mind's mission is to provide advice and support to empower anyone experiencing a mental health problem. Mind campaigns to improve services, raise awareness and promote understanding of mental health.

Mind provides support and funding to a broad range of organisations to achieve five key strategic goals:

- **Goal A: Helping people to stay well** – work on public mental health and resilience and workplace well-being
- **Goal B: Giving people choice** – work on information services and peer support
- **Goal C: Improving services and support** – work on primary care, crisis care and strengthening funding, commissioning and service delivery
- **Goal D: Helping people take part in society equally** – work on home and community, welfare, work and rights, leadership and participation, and stigma and discrimination
- **Goal E: Making access to services equal for everyone** – work addressing inequalities faced by groups such as LGBTQ+ people, young Black men and those experiencing homelessness, substance misuse and the criminal justice system

Open funding programmes are advertised on the charity's website as they arise.

Local Minds

The charity acts as an umbrella organisation for around 125 local Minds, which are independent organisations that deliver mental health services in the local area. The Local Mind Grants Fund enables local Minds to set up the projects they know will make the biggest difference in their communities.

Financial information

Year end	31/03/2021
Income	£80,260,000
Assets	£35,970,000
Grants to organisations	£12,680,000

Further financial information

Grants were broken down as follows:

Service and support	£5.57 million
Equal access	£3.10 million
Social inclusion	£2.49 million
Helping people stay well	£1.26 million
Giving people choice	£306,000

Beneficiaries included: A detailed list of beneficiaries was not included in the accounts. Grantees that received grants greater than £5,000 included: Action on Addiction, African Caribbean Community Initiative, Bipolar UK, Gendered Intelligence, Peaceful Minds CIC, Refugee Radio, Swansea Carers Centre and Walking With The Wounded.

Exclusions

Exclusion criteria will differ between funding programmes – see the website for details.

Applications

Check the website for open funding programmes or contact the correspondent for further information. In addition to the correspondent's address listed here, local Mind organisations have their own correspondence addresses, which can be found online.

Sources of information

Accounts; annual report; funder's website; guidelines for applicants.

The Mittal Foundation

Education; young people; the arts; the prevention of poverty and malnutrition

UK; USA; India

£596,200 (2019)

CC number: 1146604

Correspondent: The Trustees, c/o Mittal Investments Ltd, Floor 3, Berkeley Square House, Berkeley Square, London W1J 6BU (tel: 020 7659 1033)

Trustees: Usha Mittal; Megha Mittal; Vanisha Bhatia; Aditya Mittal.

General information

Registered in March 2012, this foundation is one of the charitable endeavours of steel magnate Lakshmi Mittal and his wife Usha, who is a trustee. The foundation supports organisations that are focused on the advancement of education, the promotion of the arts, the prevention of poverty and malnutrition and the enhancement of the lives of young people. The foundation makes long-term commitments to a small number of organisations. It also awards a number of small grants to charities in the UK and USA each year.

Financial information

Year end	31/12/2019
Income	£2,020,000
Assets	£1,910,000
Grants to organisations	£596,200

Further financial information

The 2019 accounts were the latest available at the time of writing (May 2022).

Beneficiaries included: Boston Children's Hospital; Harvard University; The British Asian Trust (£138,400); The Prince's Trust; University of Pennsylvania.

Applications

The foundation does not accept unsolicited applications. The trustees research and use their personal contacts to identify suitable grantees.

Sources of information

Accounts; annual report; Charity Commission record.

The Monday Charitable Trust

Disadvantage, mainly in the fields of housing, education, social welfare and social mobility

UK

£5.79 million (2020/21)

CC number: 1174232

Correspondent: The Trustees, c/o BDB Pitmans, One Bartholomew Close, London EC1A 7BL (tel: 020 7783 3685)

Trustees: Douglas Blausten; Elspeth Lane; Sarah Baxter; Jonathan Brinsden; Andrew Johnston.

General information

The trust aims to improve the life chances of disadvantaged and often marginalised groups in the UK. Support is provided to UK-registered charities that work to tackle disadvantage, mainly in the fields of housing, education, welfare and social mobility.

The trust's 2020/21 accounts state:

> During 2020/21 the Trustees have continued to support charities that benefited the following:-
> - Hospices
> - Independent living for elderly and youth in general
> - Literacy in children
> - Those transitioning from rough sleeping
> - Supporting the homeless (with hot food)
> - Supporting young people with life skills and
> - Housing for those in need
> - Improving social mobility

Financial information

Year end	31/03/2021
Income	£4,920,000
Assets	£7,250,000
Grants to organisations	£5,790,000

Beneficiaries included: Construction Youth Trust (£900,000); Mental Health Foundation (£750,000); NHS Charities Together (£200,000); Family Lives (£100,000); Surrey Community Foundation (£50,000); Frimley Park Hospital (£25,000); The Forward Trust (£6,500).

Applications

Unsolicited applications are not accepted.

Sources of information

Accounts; annual report; Charity Commission record.

Moondance Foundation

Children; education; older people; the environment; health; social welfare; women

Wales

£15.84 million (2019/20)

CC number: 1139224

Correspondent: The Trustees, c/o Azets, Ty Derw, Lime Tree Court, Cardiff Gate Business Park, Cardiff CF23 8AB (email: moondancefoundation@gmail.com)

Trustees: Louisa Scadden; Diane Briere de L'Isle Engelhardt; Damien Englehardt; Adrian Engelhardt; Tara Briere de L'Isle Engelhardt; Henry Engelhardt; Shanna Briere de L'Isle Engelhardt.

 https://moondancefoundation.org.uk

General information

The foundation was established in 2010 by Henry Engelhardt, founder of Admiral Group and his wife Diane Briere de l'Isle.

Areas of work

The foundation's website states:

> Moondance's main focus is on organisations in Wales whose work falls into the following categories:
> - Children
> - Education
> - Elderly
> - Environment
> - Health
> - Relieving poverty
> - Women

Financial information

Year end	30/11/2020
Income	£43,510,000
Assets	£418,040,000
Grants to organisations	£15,840,000

Beneficiaries included: Plan International UK (£626,400); Hilltop Schools Inc. (£442,000); Surfers Against Sewerage (£30,000); YMCA Port Talbot (£20,000); Rowan Tree Cancer Care (£4,900).

Applications

Apply via the foundation's website.

Sources of information

Accounts; annual report; Charity Commission record.

The Henry Moore Foundation

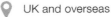

Fine arts, in particular sculpture; research and development; projects and exhibitions which expand the definition of sculpture

UK and overseas

£397,100 (2020/21)

CC number: 271370

Correspondent: Grants Committee, Dane Tree House, Perry Green, Much Hadham, Hertfordshire SG10 6EE (tel: 01279 843333; email: admin@henry-moore.org or enquiry form on the website)

Trustees: Celia Clear; Peter Wienand; Charles Asprey; William Edgerley; Prof. Antony Griffiths; Nigel Carrington; Pamela Raynor; Martin Barden; Courtney Martin; Ella Snell; Leonard Dunne; Lesley Sherratt.

 www.henry-moore.org

 facebook.com/henrymoorestudios

 @HenryMooreFDN

 @henrymoorestudios

General information

The foundation was established in 1977 by Henry Moore and his family to encourage the public appreciation of the visual arts.

The foundation aims to support innovative sculpture projects, create an imaginative programme of exhibitions and research worldwide, and preserve the legacy of Henry Moore.

Grants programme

Grants are made to organisations around the world. The foundation's website states the following:

> Henry Moore Grants continue Moore's legacy by supporting sculpture across historical, modern and contemporary

registers and seeking to fund research that expands the appreciation of sculpture.

Grants are awarded within the following categories:

New projects and commissions – grants of up to £20,000 are made towards exhibitions, exhibition catalogues and commissions that aim to encourage new thinking about sculpture.

Acquisitions and collections – support of up to £20,000 is given to museums and galleries wishing to acquire or conserve sculpture for their collections.

Research and development – support is given to both individuals and organisations to conduct extensive research into sculpture-based projects.

Long term – research grants of up to £20,000 are available to organisations that meet the criteria.

Conferences, lectures and publications – funding of up to £5,000 is given towards books, journals and conferences on the subject of sculpture.

Research fellowships – a small number of two-year postdoctoral research fellowships in the field of sculpture studies are supported by the foundation. At the time of writing (May 2022), the research fellowship programme was under review. Visit the website for any updates.

Further information for each category of grant is available on the foundation's website.

Financial information

Year end	31/03/2021
Income	£3,220,000
Assets	£122,240,000
Grants to organisations	£397,100
No. of grants	84

Beneficiaries included: South London Gallery (£50,000); Artists Support Award (£20,000); Hepworth Wakefield (£12,000); Compton Verney Art Gallery and Park (£10,600); ART UK, Philadelphia Museum of Art and Studio Voltaire (£10,000 each).

Exclusions

The foundation does not provide grants for revenue expenditure. No grant (or any part of grant) may be used to pay any fee or to provide any other benefit to any individual who is a trustee of the foundation. Applications from individuals are only accepted when applying for a small research grant.

Applications

Applications can be completed on the foundation's website. The grants committee considers applications four times a year. Check the website for further guidance and current deadlines.

Sources of information

Accounts; annual report; Charity Commission record; funder's website.

John Moores Foundation

 Tackling disadvantage

 Merseyside (including Skelmersdale, Halton and Ellesmere Port) and Northern Ireland

£553,600 (2020/21)

CC number: 253481

Correspondent: Phil Godfrey, Grants Director, 96 Bold Street, Liverpool, Merseyside L1 4HY (tel: 0151 707 6077; email: info@johnmooresfoundation.com)

 www.jmf.org.uk

 @JMF1964

General information

The foundation was established in 1964 and awards grants to community organisations undertaking charitable work. According to its website, the foundation's aim is to 'enable people who face barriers, as a result of social, educational, physical, economic, cultural, geographical or other disadvantage, to improve their social conditions and quality of life'.

Areas of work

The foundation's website states that it will fund organisations in Merseyside and Northern Ireland that support the following people:

- Those suffering from poverty and financial crisis
- Those in poor physical or mental health
- Black, Asian and minority ethnic people
- Refugees
- Women including girls
- Children and young people aged 5 to 25
- Those suffering discrimination
- Families needing support
- Homeless people
- Carers
- Adults with few or no educational qualifications

Eligibility criteria

According to its website, the foundation supports organisations and projects that are:

- Trying to build and strengthen communities
- Working in partnership with others
- Carrying out trust building initiatives
- Addressing previously unmet needs
- Providing advice and support
- Trying to change attitudes and broaden horizons

Priority is given to small, grassroots and volunteer-driven organisations. Grants can be given towards running costs, capacity building, volunteer training and out-of-pocket expenses, one-off projects and equipment (if part of a wider project).

Organisations that have received a grant from the foundation may also be offered additional support from a community groups development worker. This support can be given in areas such as fundraising, strategic planning and trustee development.

Financial information

Year end	06/09/2021
Income	£808,400
Assets	£30,750,000
Grants to organisations	£553,600
No. of grants	100

Further financial information

Grants paid in 2020/21 totalled £553,600. Grants made in Merseyside were broken down as follows:

Local community groups	15	£97,500
Grassroots social health initiatives	9	£70,400
Children and young people	7	£47,900
Refugees	6	£45,700
Black, Asian and minority ethnic organisations	8	£36,600
Equality and diversity	6	£32,000
Women and girls	5	£28,100
Relief of poverty	5	£28,100
Family support	5	£19,100
Carers	1	£15,000
People experiencing homelessness	2	£12,000
Joint-working and trust-building initiatives	1	£10,000

Grants made in Northern Ireland were broken down as follows:

Local community groups	16	£59,300
Grassroots social health initiatives	4	£16,000
Training for voluntary organisations	3	£11,500
Family support	2	£10,000
Women and girls	1	£5,000
Relief of poverty	2	£4,500
Equality and diversity	1	£3,000
Children and young people	1	£2,000

Beneficiaries included: Mencap Wirral (£30,000); In Another Place (£22,500); Knowsley Disability Concern (£15,000); Liverpool Bereavement Service (£10,000); Glencolin Residents Association and Jus Kidz (£5,000 each); Tuebrook Hope Group (£1,000); Stockbridge Disability Group (£150).

Exclusions

According to the foundation's website, as a general rule, it does not fund:

- Individuals
- Projects that are not substantially influenced by their target beneficiaries
- National organisations or groups based outside the Merseyside region even where some of the service users come from the area
- Statutory work

- Universities, colleges and schools or work done with children in school time
- Faith-based projects exclusively for members of that faith, or for the promotion of religion
- Capital building costs
- Festivals, carnivals and fêtes
- Medicine or medical equipment
- Holidays and expeditions
- Gifts, parties etc.
- Conferences
- Sport
- Vehicles
- Animal charities
- Arts and the creative industries
- Academic or medical research
- Veterans
- Uniformed groups (e.g. scouts, cadets, majorettes).
- Sponsorship, advertising or fund-raising events
- Counsellors not registered with BACP or UKCP

Applications

Applicants should first check their eligibility on the foundation's website. Following this, applicants should contact the foundation via email, letter or phone to obtain an online application form.

Sources of information

Accounts; annual report; Charity Commission record; funder's website.

The Steve Morgan Foundation

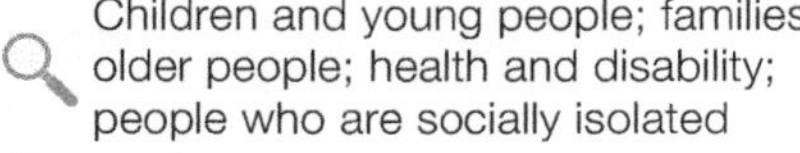

Children and young people; families; older people; health and disability; people who are socially isolated

North Wales, Merseyside and Cheshire

£25.68 million (2020/21)

CC number: 1087056

Correspondent: The Trustees, PO Box 3517, Chester CH1 9ET (email: hello@stevemorganfoundation.org.uk)

Trustees: Vincent Fairclough; Stephen Morgan; Rhiannon Walker; Ashley Lewis; Sally Morgan; Jonathan Masters; Brian Clark.

https://stevemorganfoundation.org.uk

facebook.com/Steve-Morgan-Foundation-106137272803911

@stevemorganfdn

@stevemorganfoundation

General information

The Steve Morgan Foundation was established in 2001 with an endowment of over £2 million from Stephen Morgan CBE, founder of Redrow plc.

Areas of work

The foundation's website states:

> All requests which would result in a positive effect on people's welfare or quality of life or improves opportunities and life choices, are considered.
>
> We are interested in receiving applications from organisations which help:
>
> - children and families
> - the elderly
> - those with disabilities
> - the socially isolated

Types of grant

Funding provided by the foundation typically falls into one of the following four categories:

- **Regional grants** – multi-year revenue grants for core funding, salaries and ongoing running costs
- **Major grants** – grants of over £100,000 including awards for capital costs
- **Enable** – funding for specialised disability equipment for people of all ages
- **Smiley Bus** – funding for both standard and wheelchair-accessible minibuses and other essential transport vehicles including bikes and vans

Financial information

Year end	31/03/2021
Income	£13,960,000
Assets	£304,660,000
Grants to organisations	£25,680,000

Beneficiaries included: Shine Right to Succeed (£1.97 million); Wirral Youth Zone (£200,000); Kim Inspire (£145,000); Cheshire Autism Practical Support (£103,500); Homebaked Bakery (£80,000); Healthbox CIC (£60,000); Maggie's Centre (£50,000).

Exclusions

Application guidelines and criteria for each funding programme can be found on the foundation's website.

Applications

For regional, major and Smiley Bus grants, applicants are requested to first check their eligibility against the criteria listed on the foundation's website. Eligible organisations are then asked to submit an expression of interest via email.

Sources of information

Accounts; annual report; Charity Commission record; funder's website.

Morgan Stanley International Foundation

Education and children's health

Europe; Middle East; Africa; local projects in Tower Hamlets and Glasgow

£963,300 (2020)

CC number: 1042671

Correspondent: The Trustees, Morgan Stanley and Co. International plc, 20 Bank Street, London E14 4AD (email: communityaffairslondon@morganstanley.com)

Trustees: Maryann McMahon; Hanns Siebold; Clare Woodman; Stephen Mavin; Sue Watts; Oliver Stuart; Graham Rogers; Piers Harris; Jamie Glynn; Norbert Fogarasi; Marco Gregotti; Aidan Armstrong; Sacha Anselm; Caroline Nicholls.

www.morganstanley.com/pub/content/msdotcom/en/about-us/giving-back/msif-guidelines.html

General information

The Morgan and Stanley International Foundation was registered with the Charity Commission in 1994, it is the corporate charity of Morgan Stanley and Co. International plc, a financial services corporation.

The foundation's goal is to make a sustainable impact on children's welfare in the communities in which it operates across Europe, the Middle East and Africa. According to its website, the foundation is primarily focused on providing funding in the following areas:

> **Children's Health** – The Foundation looks to invest in innovations and development in children's healthcare. Working with charitable organisations, hospitals and community based initiatives, the MSIF focuses on supporting young people. The MSIF strives to ensure that more children have access to quality healthcare to enable them to have a more meaningful life.
>
> **Education** – The MSIF aims to work with registered charities and state-funded schools which provide benefit to communities across EMEA. The MSIF works with organisations that increase access and opportunity for young people, supporting programmes that address academic achievement and employability skills, by inspiring talented but underserved young people

According to the 2020 annual report, the foundation makes grants through three different channels:

> - Direct charitable grants – Direct charitable grant applications are invited for the funding of projects in the EMEA region, and are reviewed at the

Trustees' meetings against specific grant objectives. Multi-year grants are monitored on an annual basis to ensure the grant criteria continue to be met
- Employee nominated charity partnerships – Employee nominated charity partnerships are voted for by Morgan Stanley employees, and the Foundation matches employee fundraising and donations up to a pre-determined amount.
- Employee matching grants recognise Morgan Stanley employees' fundraising and volunteering efforts in their local communities. The Foundation currently matches fundraising efforts by an employee for a charitable organisation up to a maximum of £500 per employee in one given year. In addition, grants in recognition of certain employees volunteering efforts are awarded of £500 per employee, to a charity of the employee's choice in one given year.

Financial information

Year end	31/12/2020
Income	£1,350,000
Assets	£2,800,000
Grants to organisations	£963,300

Beneficiaries included: Place2be – London (£173,900); PEEK – London (£88,100); Magic Breakfast – Glasgow and London (£31,100); Career Ready – London (£30,000); Glasgow Children's Hospital (£25,000).

Exclusions

According to its website, the foundation does not provide grants for any of the following:
- Organisations which are not registered as a non profit organisation with the appropriate regulatory agencies in their country (unless a state funded school).
- National or International charities which do not operate in the regions we are located.
- Grants will not be made to either political or religious organisations, "pressure groups" or individuals outside the Firm who are seeking sponsorship either for themselves (e.g. to help pay for education) or for onward transmission to a charitable organisation.
- Programmes that do not include opportunities for Morgan Stanley employee volunteer engagement.

Applications

The foundation's website gives the following details on making an initial approach for funding:

> The Morgan Stanley International Foundation takes a proactive approach to grant making and therefore does not accept unsolicited proposals. If you think your organisation is a match for the criteria set out below, send an email to communityaffairslondon@morganstanley.com with the following information:
> - Program description, including mission, goals and numbers served
> - Measurement strategies
> - Geographic scope
>
> Please note that due to the large number of quality proposals we receive, only applications that have been reviewed and are considered to fit within the MSIF priorities will be contacted directly.

Sources of information

Accounts; annual report; Charity Commission record; funder's website.

G. M. Morrison Charitable Trust

Medicine and health; social welfare; education and training; general charitable purposes

UK

£267,200 (2020/21)

CC number: 261380

Correspondent: The Trustees, c/o Currey and Co. LLP, 33 Queen Anne Street, London W1G 9HY (tel: 020 7802 2700; email: gen@curreyandco.co.uk)

Trustees: Jane Hunt; Elizabeth Morrison; Edward Perks.

General information

The trust makes grants to UK-registered charities that operate in the UK and abroad. Grants are awarded for a wide variety of causes, but mainly social welfare, medical causes, and education and training.

Financial information

Year end	05/04/2021
Income	£233,900
Assets	£15,360,000
Grants to organisations	£267,200
No. of grants	203

Further financial information

During 2020/21, grants were distributed as follows:

Medical and health	£114,100
Social welfare	£74,100
Others	£54,000
Education and training	£25,000

Beneficiaries included: Royal College of Surgeons (£3,300); Shelterbox (£3,200); Age UK (£2,100); University of Cambridge (£2,000); Alternatives to Violence Project (£1,700); Opera North (£1,600); Mental Health Foundation (£1,500); Migraine Trust (£1,000).

Exclusions

Support is not given for/to:
- Individuals
- Charities not registered in the UK
- Retrospective applications
- Schemes or activities which are generally regarded as the responsibility of statutory authorities
- Short-term projects or one-off capital grants (except for emergency appeals)
- Commercial or business activities

Applications

Apply in writing to the correspondent. The trust's 2020/21 annual report states:

> Beneficiaries of grants are normally selected on the basis of the personal knowledge and recommendation of a trustee. The Trust's grant making policy is however to support grant recipients on a long term recurring basis. The scope of its giving is determined only by the extent of its resources, and is not otherwise restricted. The trustees have decided that for the present, new applications for grants will only be considered in the most exceptional circumstances, any spare income will be allocated to increasing the grants made to charities currently receiving support. In the future this policy will of course be subject to periodic review. Applicants understanding this policy who nevertheless wish to apply for a grant should write to the charity's registered address.

Sources of information

Accounts; annual report; Charity Commission record.

The Morrisons Foundation

General charitable purposes; the arts and culture; health; education; social welfare; community

England; Wales; Scotland

£3.04 million (2020/21)

CC number: 1160224/SC045634

Correspondent: The Trustees, Hilmore House, Gain Lane, Bradford, West Yorkshire BD3 7DL (tel: 0845 611 5364; email: foundation.enquiries@morrisonsplc.co.uk)

Trustees: Kate Bratt-Farrar; Guy Mason; Jonathan Burke; David Scott; Andrew Clappen; Sarah Wilkinson; Zulfiqar Karim; Charles Jones.

www.morrisonsfoundation.com

General information

The Morrisons Foundation was established in 2014 and is fully funded by Wm Morrison Supermarkets plc, one of the biggest supermarket chains in the UK.

It supports registered charities that are making a difference in local communities across England, Scotland and Wales by awarding grants for charitable projects. Applications can be made for grants of up to £25,000 to fully fund projects that will help to improve people's lives. Occasionally, the foundation awards high-value grants to support larger projects and initiatives.

The foundation supports a wide range of causes including health care, social inclusion, mental health, arts and culture, education, armed forces, the environment, people with disabilities and so on.

The foundation also supports charities by matching the money raised by Morrison's employees for their chosen organisations.

Financial information

Year end	04/02/2021
Income	£3,690,000
Assets	£2,270,000
Grants to organisations	£3,040,000

Beneficiaries included: A list of beneficiaries was not available. Previous beneficiaries include: Ickle Pickles and The Children's Trust (£25,000 each); Dentaid (£20,000); Emmaus Oxford (£18,400); Lincolnshire Emergency Blood Bikes Service (£14,700); British Disabled Angling Association (£7,400); Pinpoint (£5,000); Disability Snowsport UK (£4,600).

Exclusions

According to the foundation's guidance for applicants, it will not generally consider the following:

- Staff costs, rent costs, utilities, administration costs or any other running costs;
- Support of ongoing services
- Grants, bursaries etc. to individuals;
- Expeditions, recreation or overseas travel;
- Fundraising events or grants to ongoing appeals;
- Work that is primarily the statutory responsibility of public agencies;
- Promotion of religious or political messaging;
- Part-funding or contributions towards projects or grants in excess of £25,000;
- Advertising, promotion or marketing of events or services;
- Part-funding or contributions towards projects or grants in excess of £25,000;
- Advertising, promotion or marketing of events or services;
- Overseas appeals;
- Conferences or seminars;
- Charities that are newly listed on the Charity Commission / OSCR, or whose accounts are overdue or filed late;
- Organisations that are not registered with the Charity Commission or OSCR;
- Equipment which will be retained by individuals rather than the charity;
- Animal charities, unless the objective is to improve the lives of vulnerable or disadvantaged individuals;
- Projects being delivered outside England, Scotland or Wales;
- Sports-based charities, unless the objective is to improve the lives of vulnerable or disadvantaged individuals;
- Projects which could harm the reputation of the Foundation.

Applications

Applications can be completed online through the foundation's website. Applications are accepted and reviewed on a continual basis. Applicants will be notified of a decision by telephone or email, even if the application is unsuccessful.

Sources of information

Accounts; annual report; Charity Commission record; funder's website; 2019/20 annual review.

The Mosawi Foundation

Children and young people; community development; education; healthcare and trauma relief; social welfare

UK, with a preference for Oxfordshire; overseas

£790,700 (2020/21)

CC number: 1157269

Correspondent: Ali Mosawi, Trustee, PO Box 4822, Henley on Thames, Oxfordshire RG9 1AY (email: ali@themosawifoundation.org)

www.themosawifoundation.org/index.php

General information

The foundation was formed in 2014 by Ali and May Mosawi. Ali is the chair and major shareholder of Al Hayat Scientific office in Baghdad. It is a distributor of pharmaceuticals throughout Iraq from major international companies.

The foundation provides support in the following areas:

- Young people and communities
- Nurturing talent
- Healthcare and trauma relief
- Outreach to marginalised people

Financial information

Year end	05/04/2021
Income	£863,800
Assets	£1,190,000
Grants to organisations	£790,900

Beneficiaries included: Glenwood Church (£103,600); Reading Rep (£70,000); Harpsden Cricket Club (£61,000); NOMAD (£28,000); Diamond Fund for Choristers (£25,000).

Applications

Apply in writing to the correspondent.

Sources of information

Accounts; annual report; Charity Commission record; funder's website.

Vyoel Moshe Charitable Trust

Orthodox Jewish education and social welfare within the Orthodox Jewish community

UK and overseas, including Israel, USA and Europe

£864,800 (2020/21)

CC number: 327054

Correspondent: The Trustees, 63A, Lampard Grove, London N16 6XA (tel: 07975 952011)

General information

The trust was established in 1986 to support general charitable purposes, including education, the advancement of religion and the provision of support to those in need. According to the latest accounts, organisations around the world can be 'assisted with financial grants over and above what is available to them locally'. Awards to individuals are given 'to financially deprived families, at Jewish holiday times and other special occasions'.

Financial information

Year end	31/01/2021
Income	£964,500
Assets	£99,300
Grants to organisations	£864,800

Further financial information

Grants for schools, higher education and other training courses totalled £551,800 and grants for the advancement of religion (including grants for synagogues, the preservation of cemeteries, and Jewish culture and heritage) totalled £15,000. Grants made to organisations for distribution to individuals and families in need totalled £298,000. We were unable to determine the portion of grants given in the UK.

Beneficiaries included: A list of beneficiaries was not available. Previous beneficiaries include: Mishkanos Haroyim, Mosdos Yetyev Lev Antwerp, Talmud Torah Tuv Yerushalaim, Talmud Tora Hamekoris Remoh, Toldos Aharon, Yeshivas Kol Aryeh and Yetev Lev Institutions (£25,000 each).

Applications

Applications can be made in writing to the correspondent. The accounts, however, state:

> In general, the trustees select the institutions to be supported according to their personal knowledge of the work of the institution. Individuals are referred to the charity by local rabbis. Any application is carefully considered and help given according to circumstances and funds then available.

Sources of information

Accounts; annual report; Charity Commission record.

The Alexander Mosley Charitable Trust

General charitable purposes; armed forces; international development; heritage; animal welfare; medical research

UK and overseas

£831,000 (2020/21)

CC number: 1142898

Correspondent: The Trustees, 10 New Square, Lincoln's Inn, London WC2A 3QG (tel: 020 7465 4300)

Trustees: Horatio Mortimer; Max Mosley; Emma Mosley; Max Mosley.

General information

The trust was established in 2011 and makes grants throughout the UK and overseas. The trust has previously supported the armed forces, international development, heritage, animal welfare and medical research.

The trust's 2020/21 annual accounts state:

> Applications from UK registered charities will be considered in priority to applications from unregistered charities. [...] The Charity will not normally support applications from large national charities i.e. those with an annual income in excess of £10 million or with >£100 million assets or charities dedicated to issues deemed by the Trustees to be already well-funded within the UK.

Financial information

Year end	05/04/2021
Income	£6,850,000
Assets	£12,760,000
Grants to organisations	£831,000

Beneficiaries included: Eastern Alliance for Safe and Sustainable Transport (£400,000); Imperial College of Science Technology and Medicine (£100,000); Justice (£50,000); Alive and Kicking (£15,000).

Exclusions

According to the annual report, the trust will not normally fund purposes for which statutory funding is available.

Applications

Apply in writing to the correspondent. The trustees will only reply to successful applicants.

Sources of information

Accounts; annual report; Charity Commission record.

Moto in the Community

Conservation of the environment; road safety education; community development

UK

£789,600 (2020)

CC number: 1111147

Correspondent: The Trustees, Moto in the Community Trust, Moto Hospitality Ltd, Toddington Service Area, Junction 12 M1 Southbound, Toddington, Bedfordshire LU5 6HR (tel: 01525 878500; email: motocharity@moto-way.co.uk)

Trustees: Gene MacDonald; Coral Brodie; Guy Latchem; Brynn Hewitt; Louise Hughes; Daniel Horsley; Stephen Rac; Peter Mould; James Gunn.

 www.moto-way.com/about-us/mitc-trust

 facebook.com/MotoHospitality

 @motoway

 @moto.way

General information

Established in 2005, Moto in the Community is the charitable arm of Moto Hospitality Ltd, the motorway services company. Moto service stations nationwide raise funds which are then distributed back into its local communities in three ways:

Community partners: each Moto service station has the opportunity to adopt a local community partner. Applications are welcome from charities and good causes within a 25-mile radius of a Moto site. Partners benefit from grants, volunteer support from Moto employees and publicity. There is no minimum or maximum grant amount.

Community schools: the charity also makes grants to local schools. Previous grants have been for sensory gardens, musical instruments and new sports equipment.

Charity of the Year: the charity has partnered with Help for Heroes since 2012, raising £2.9 million to date.

The trust also works in partnerships with Oxford University Press to donate books to schools.

Furthermore, the trust has a benevolent fund to support Moto employees and their families through times of hardship.

Financial information

Year end	31/12/2020
Income	£336,600
Assets	£173,600
Grants to organisations	£789,600

Beneficiaries included: Greggs Foundation Breakfast Clubs (£20,000); The Woodland Trust (£10,000); Wildfowl and Wetland Trust (£5,000); Pettteril Bank Community School (£1,000); Express and Star Bowls Club (£500); 2nd Brewood Scout Group (£600); Children's Bereavement Centre (£200).

Exclusions

The trust does not consider applications for religious or political projects. Grants outside the UK are only given in special circumstances.

Applications

The charity's website states:

> If you are interested in becoming a local community partner for a Moto site please email information on your charity to motocharity@moto-way.co.uk clearly stating which Moto service area you would like to apply to. Your application should give details of your short and long term objectives and ideas on how our staff can work with you. Local community partnerships run from 1st January to 31st December.

Note: at the time of writing (February 2022) the charity was not accepting new applications for community partnerships due to the COVID-19 pandemic. Check the charity's website for updates.

Sources of information

Accounts; annual report; Charity Commission record; funder's website.

Motor Neurone Disease Association

Scientific and medical research into motor neurone disease and support for individuals with motor neuron disease

 UK and overseas

 £3.0 million (2020)

CC number: 294354

Correspondent: Research Grants Team, Francis Crick House, 6 Summerhouse Road, Moulton Park Industrial Estate, Northampton, Northamptonshire NN3 6BJ (tel: 01604 611873; email: research.grants@mndassociation.org)

Trustees: Richard Coleman; Dr Nikhil Sharma; Dr Heather Smith; Janet Warren; Siobhan Rooney; Katy Styles; Andrew Cawdell; Catherine Knights; Vicky Paeschel; Devia Gurjar; Shaun Gee; Debra Martin; Elizabeth Ellis; Dr Usman Khan.

 www.mndassociation.org/research/for-researchers

 facebook.com/mndassociation

 @mndassoc

 @mndassoc

General information

Motor Neurone Disease Association (MNDA) works to support care, research and campaigning for people affected by Motor Neurone Disease (MND) in the UK. Its vision is 'a world free from MND'. The association awards grants for both research into the disease and organisations that provide care for people with MND.

Research grants

The MNDA's website explains that it only funds and supports 'scientific and medical research of the highest quality and relevance to MND' in the UK and overseas. Through its research strategy the association looks to support research into the causes and treatments of MND and, ultimately, into finding a cure for the disease.

There are a number of types of grants funded by MNDA, which are outlined on the website:

- PhD studentships
- Biomedical research projects
- Clinical research fellowships
- Non-clinical research fellowships
- Healthcare research projects
- Translational research projects

Eligibility information and guidelines for each of these grants types can be found on the website.

Financial information

Year end	31/12/2020
Income	£19,910,000
Assets	£15,010,000
Grants to organisations	£3,000,000

Further financial information

During the year grants for care and care centres totalled £2.5 million and research grants totalled £1.91 million. This includes grants made to individuals and organisations.

Beneficiaries included: University of Oxford (£842,000); Kings College London (£566,000); University of Sheffield (£232,000); Plymouth Primary Care (£105,000); Leeds Care Centre and University of St Andrews (£68,000 each); Marie Curie – Flemming (£48,000).

Exclusions

Programme-specific exclusions can be found on the website.

Applications

The application process varies according to the programme being applied to. Further information on each programme, including the application process, is available on the website.

Sources of information

Accounts; annual report; Charity Commission record; funder's website.

J. P. Moulton Charitable Foundation

Education and training; healthcare; medical research; clinical trials; counselling; social welfare

UK

 £1.31 million (2020)

CC number: 1109891

Correspondent: The Trustees, c/o Perscitus LLP, 10 Buckingham Street, London WC2N 6DF (tel: 020 3727 6601; email: Jon.Moulton@jonmoulton.gg)

 www.perscitusllp.com/moulton-charity-trust

General information

Established in 2004, this is the foundation of venture capitalist, Jon Moulton. The foundation's Charity Commission record explains that: 'The charity receives donations, particularly from net high worth individuals, and supports valid research plus funds appropriate charitable institutions.'

The 2020 annual report states that the primary purposes of the foundation are:

- to fund non-commercial clinical trials with the aim to make clinical advances and promote the relief of suffering
- to provide charitable donations for community service projects of any kind to promote education, training and counselling of disadvantaged persons
- to provide donations to hospitals, medical and care projects of any kind to assist with the general welfare of patients

Calls for funding are advertised on the website.

The 2020 annual report states that clinical trials funded in previous years 'have been conducted in a wide range of therapy areas and range from first in human to new uses for licenced drugs. [...] The charity has supported ground breaking research in diseases that struggle to obtain funding from other funders as they do not fulfil their funding criteria e.g. head and neck cancer.' It has also entered into joint ventures with other medical charities to help support larger trials.

Financial information

Year end	31/12/2020
Income	£1,020,000
Assets	£845,500
Grants to organisations	£1,310,000
No. of grants	8

Further financial information

During the year, all grants were awarded to medical research projects.

Beneficiaries included: University College London (£278,900); University of Manchester (£213,500); Institute of Cancer Research (£81,200); Newcastle University (£40,000); Royal Papworth Hospital NHS Foundation Trust (£10,000).

Applications

Details of how to apply can be found on the website.

Sources of information

Accounts; annual report; Charity Commission record; funder's website.

The Mulberry Trust

General charitable purposes, with a focus on family well-being; younger and older people; homelessness; health; debt relief; interfaith work

UK, with a preference for Essex

 £345,200 (2020/21)

CC number: 263296

Correspondent: The Trustees, c/o Farrer and Co., 65–66 Lincoln's Inn Fields, London WC2A 3LH (tel: 020 3375 7000; email: secretarialservices@farrer.co.uk)

General information

The trust was established in 1971 to support general charitable purposes. According to its 2020/21 annual report:

> The trust has a particular focus on parenting, children and the family, in order to strengthen family life and the general wellbeing of families from the very young to the very old; the elderly; the disadvantaged; homelessness; health; debt relief and counselling; and the promotion of interfaith work. The trust also supports education, research and the arts, provided that this contributes to the aims set out above. The trust also supports certain community and environmental organisations and areas of specific interest to individual trustees.

Grants typically range from £1,000 to £30,000. Grants go to a wide range of causes, with local and national organisations receiving funding. The majority of grants appear to go to regularly supported recipients.

Financial information

Year end	05/04/2021
Income	£1,170,000
Assets	£4,680,000
Grants to organisations	£345,200
No. of grants	51

Further financial information

Grants were made to 51 organisations in the following areas:

Mental health	8	£64,700
Education	13	£65,200
Community	6	£36,500
Homelessness	3	£35,000
Health	4	£30,000
Parenting, the family and children's work	2	£20,000
Debt relief and counselling	2	£18,500
Older people	4	£17,000
Relief of poverty	1	£15,300
COVID-19 grants	2	£15,000
Christianity	1	£10,000
Interfaith	1	£7,000
The arts	3	£6,000
Legal assistance	1	£4,000

Beneficiaries included: Pioneer Sailing Trust (£30,000); Harlow Parochial Church Council (£20,000); Chess Homeless (£15,000); Magic Lantern (£10,000); School Readers and St Clare Hospice (£5,000 each); Prisoners' Advice Service (£3,000); The Bugatti Trust (£1,000); Dr Edwin Doubleday Trust (£500).

Exclusions

Funding is not awarded to individuals.

Applications

The trust does not accept unsolicited applications.

Sources of information

Accounts; annual report; Charity Commission record.

The Frederick Mulder Foundation

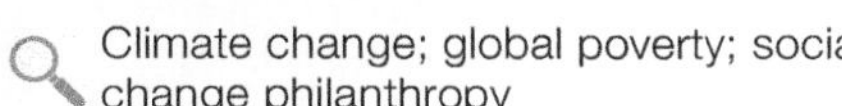

Climate change; global poverty; social change philanthropy

UK and overseas

£446,800 (2020/21)

CC number: 296019

Correspondent: Brynn Higgs, Director, 83 Belsize Park Gardens, London NW3 4NJ (tel: 07958 464373; email: brynn@frederickmulderfoundation.org.uk)

Trustees: Dr Frederick Mulder; Hannah Mulder; Robin Bowman.

 www.frederickmulderfoundation.org.uk

General information

Formerly known as the Prairie Trust, this foundation was founded in 1986 and takes the name of its settlor, Dr Frederick Mulder. Dr Mulder is a director of Frederick Mulder Ltd, a company specialising in European printmaking, and is also founder of The Funding Network, a giving circle of individuals who join together to fund social change projects.

The foundation's website states that it envisions 'a world which is fair, secure and environmentally sustainable, and in which the rights of future generations are respected in decisions taken today'.

Areas of support

Support is primarily directed towards organisations working in three main areas:

- The development of social change philanthropy
- The threat of climate change
- The persistence of global poverty

Financial information

Year end	31/03/2021
Income	£130,400
Assets	£5,880,000
Grants to organisations	£446,800

Beneficiaries included: Cyber Tracker (£64,700); Beaver Trust (£30,000); Cyber Tracker Conservation Trust (£24,100); Climate Bonds Initiative (£20,000); Give Directly (£10,000); Roddick Foundation/ Help Refugees (£8,000); SMK Foundation (£5,000); Samaj Serva Niketan (£2,500).

Applications

The foundation does not accept unsolicited applications or enquiries, but rather is proactive in identifying organisations and individuals within its areas of interest. The foundation's website states:

> We regret that as we are a small, proactive team, we do not accept unsolicited funding applications or enquiries and may not be able to reply to all correspondence.
>
> Our method is to identify individuals and organisations which fit within our areas of interest, enter into discussion with them, and if we believe there is an appropriate opportunity for us, invite them to apply for a grant.

Sources of information

Accounts; annual report; Charity Commission record; funder's website.

Edith Murphy Foundation

Social welfare; disability; older people; young people; animal welfare and research

UK, with a preference for Leicestershire and the East Midlands

£794,500 (2020/21)

CC number: 1026062

Correspondent: The Trustees, c/o Ludlow Trust Company Ltd, 1st Floor, Tower Wharf, Cheese Lane, Bristol BS2 0JJ (tel: 0117 457 2210; email: charitabletrusts@ludlowtrust.com)

Trustees: David Tams; Christopher Blakesley; Richard Adkinson; Dr Charlotte Blakesley; Julian Tams; Ludlow Trust Company Ltd.

 https://edithmurphy.co.uk

General information

The Edith Murphy Foundation established in 1993 by the late Edith Murphy in memory of her husband, Hugh Murphy. Following the death of Mrs Murphy in 2005, her will provided for the foundation to receive certain benefits including a proportion of the residue of her estate. The value of the benefits received the following year amounted to £28.2 million. A further £1.8 million was added in 2007. This has resulted in the level of grant-giving increasing substantially in recent years. Since its inception in 1993, the charity has supported over 650 organisations with grants totalling £17.5 million. The foundation supports organisations (predominantly, but not exclusively, registered charities) that assist people in need due to age, disability or financial or social circumstance, or that care for unwanted animals or carry out research.

The foundation's website states the following:

> The trustees have wide-ranging powers to make grants and are not restricted by geographic boundaries. In reality because of the number of applications received the trustees concentrate on national charities and local causes in Leicestershire and the East Midlands.

The value of grants made is normally between £500 and £5,000, although larger grants are made in some circumstances.

Financial information

Year end	31/03/2021
Income	£592,500
Assets	£37,200,000
Grants to organisations	£794,500

Further financial information

In 2020/21, grants were broken down as follows:

Welfare	£318,000
Children	£112,000
Research	£105,000
Heritage	£92,000
Education	£81,300
People with disabilities	£51,500
Animals	£34,700

Only organisations receiving grants of over £10,000 were listed as beneficiaries in the foundation's accounts.

Beneficiaries included: Leicestershire Cares (£50,000); Age UK (£30,000); Hope Against Cancer (£25,000); Healing Little Hearts (£20,000); Motor Neurone Disease Association (£15,000); The British Museum (£12,000); Galapagos Conservation Trust and Stroke Association (£10,000 each).

Exclusions

The foundation does not make grants to individuals.

Applications

Applications can be submitted online or by post. The foundation request that applicants provide the following information:

- The charity name
- The charity registration number
- What the grant will be used for
- Who will benefit
- The amount being requested with a breakdown of the costs being incurred
- Other fundraising activities and the amount raised to date

Non-registered charities will additionally be asked to complete a form to clarify their tax residency. The foundation's trustees meet four times a year to consider grant applications, usually in January, April, July and October.

Sources of information

Accounts; annual report; Charity Commission record; funder's website.

The John R. Murray Charitable Trust

Sport; citizenship and community development; arts, culture, heritage and science; health; social welfare; education

UK

£1.06 million (2020)

CC number: 1100199

Correspondent: The Trustees, 50 Albemarle Street, London W1S 4BD (tel: 020 7493 4361)

Trustees: Charles Murray; Virginia Murray; John Murray; Hallam Murray; John Murray.

General information

The John R. Murray Charitable Trust primarily awards grants to UK-registered charities in the following areas:

- Amateur sport
- Citizenship or community development
- The arts, culture, heritage and science
- Health and the saving of lives
- Relief of those in need
- Education

Financial information

Year end	31/12/2020
Income	£340,600
Assets	£30,520,000
Grants to organisations	£1,060,000

Beneficiaries included: David Parr House (£40,000); Young Lives vs Cancer (£15,000); Able Kidz and UK Antarctic Heritage Trust (£5,000 each); Edinburgh Young Carers and Seeing Dogs (£2,000 each).

Applications

The trustees do not consider unsolicited applications for grants.

Sources of information

Accounts; annual report; Charity Commission record.

Brian Murtagh Charitable Trust

Education and training for young adults and children with disabilities; social and financial disadvantage; sickness and trauma

UK and overseas

£327,100 (2020/21)

CC number: 1105099

Correspondent: The Trustees, 9 Hanson Drive, Fowey, Cornwall PL23 1ET (tel: 07759 367222; email: admin@brianmurtaghct.org.uk)

Trustees: Mary Noble; Brian Murtagh; Matthew Hahn; Anthony Michael Ryde; Benjamin Rencher.

www.brianmurtaghct.org.uk

General information

The trust was established in 2004. It makes grants to small charitable organisations with an income below £350,000 that support education and training for children and young people with physical and learning disabilities or who are experiencing social disadvantage or sickness or those who have experienced trauma.

Financial information

Year end	31/01/2021
Income	£341,000
Assets	£6,000,000
Grants to organisations	£327,100

Beneficiaries included: A list of beneficiaries was not available.

Exclusions

Applications for overseas capital projects are not accepted (but the trust will consider funding revenue costs).

Applications

Application forms are available from the trust's website. The trustee board meets four times a year in March, June, September and November, to consider applications.

Sources of information

Accounts; annual report; Charity Commission record; funder's website.

MW (HO) Foundation

Education; relief of poverty; advancement of the Orthodox Jewish faith

Worldwide, with a preference for Manchester

£275,900 (2019/20)

CC number: 1134919

Correspondent: The Trustees, 2nd Floor Parkgates, Bury New Road, Prestwich M25 0TL (tel: 0161 798 1660)

Trustees: Hilary Olsberg; David Olsberg.

General information

The foundation was registered with the Charity Commission in March 2010. It was initially known as the Meir Weisz Foundation and is closely linked with the MW (CL) Foundation, MW (GK) Foundation and MW (RH) Foundation and shares the same charitable objectives, as outlined in the foundation's latest annual report:

- to promote the education of people of all ages around the world in such ways as the charity trustees think fit, including awarding to such persons scholarships, maintenance allowances or grants; or by grants to charities or other organisations worldwide that provide education;
- the prevention or relief of poverty or financial hardship anywhere in the world by providing: grants or loans to individuals in need and/or charities, or other organisations working to prevent or relieve poverty or financial hardship;
- to advance the Orthodox Jewish religion worldwide for the benefit of the public in accordance with the principles of the Code of Jewish Law (Shulchan Aruch).

Financial information

Year end	30/11/2020
Income	£629,000
Assets	£2,530,000
Grants to organisations	£275,900

Beneficiaries included: A list of beneficiaries was not available.

Applications

Apply in writing to the correspondent.

Sources of information

Accounts; annual report; Charity Commission record.

MW (RH) Foundation

Education; relief of poverty; advancement of the Orthodox Jewish faith

Worldwide, with a preference for the UK

£388,700 (2019/20)

CC number: 1134918

Correspondent: The Trustees, 5 Park Hill, Bury Old Road, Prestwich, Greater Manchester M25 0FX (tel: 0161 737 7779)

Trustees: Rosalind Halpern; Jacob Halpern; Abraham Halpern.

General information

The foundation was registered with the Charity Commission in March 2010. It was initially known as the Deborah Weisz Foundation and is closely linked with the MW (CL) Foundation, MW (GK) Foundation and MW (HO) Foundation and shares the same charitable objectives. According to its 2019/20 annual report, the foundation's objects are:

- to promote the education of people of all ages around the world in such ways as the charity trustees think fit, including awarding to such persons scholarships, maintenance allowances or grants; or by grants to charities or other organisations worldwide that provide education;
- the prevention or relief of poverty or financial hardship anywhere in the world by providing: grants or loans to individuals in need and/or charities, or other organisations working to prevent or relieve poverty or financial hardship;
- to advance the Orthodox Jewish religion worldwide for the benefit of the public in accordance with the principles of the Code of Jewish Law (Shulchan Aruch).

Financial information

Year end	30/11/2020
Income	£1,250,000
Assets	£4,140,000
Grants to organisations	£388,700

Further financial information

Grants were broken down as follows:

Community grants	£162,400
Education grants	£103,500
Relief of poverty grants	£79,800
Religious grants	£31,500
Grants of under £1,000	£11,500

Beneficiaries included: A list of beneficiaries was not available.

Applications

Apply in writing to the correspondent.

Sources of information

Accounts; annual report; Charity Commission record.

The National Churches Trust

Repair, restoration and modernisation of Christian places of worship

UK; Channel Islands; Isle of Man and the Scilly Isles. Priority areas include: North East England, Northern Ireland and Wales

£1.62 million (2020)

CC number: 1119845

Correspondent: The Trustees, 7 Tufton Street, London SW1P 3QB (tel: 020 7222 0605; email: info@nationalchurchestrust.org)

Trustees: Richard Carr-Archer; Luke March; Sir Paul Britton; The Revd Lucy Winkett; Dr Stephen Sklaroff; Shirley Adams; Henry Stanford; Catherine McDonald; Catherine Pepinster.

 www.nationalchurchestrust.org/our-grants

 facebook.com/nationalchurchestrust

 @NatChurchTrust

 @nationalchurchestrust

General information

The National Churches Trust was launched in 2007 and promotes and supports buildings of historic, architectural and community value across the UK. The following information has been taken from the trust's website:

'The National Churches Trust exists to support church buildings from all Christian denominations, of all ages and listing status that are open and accessible across the United Kingdom.'

The National Churches Trust focuses its work over 2019–23 on three goals:

1 Preserving heritage
2 Promoting sustainability
3 Inspiring support

Grant programmes

The following grant programmes are relevant until 2023.

Foundation programme – grants of between £500 and £5,000 towards small, urgent maintenance and repair costs or small investigative works and required items costing up to £10,000.

Gateway programme – medium grants of between £3,000 and £10,000 for: project development and investigative work up to RIBA planning stage 1; strategic or capacity building projects; urgent and essential maintenance and repair projects costing between £10,000 and £100,000.

Cornerstone programme – large grants of £10,000 to £50,000 for structural repairs/maintenance issues costed over £100,000 or installation of kitchens and toilets over £30,000.

Preventative maintenance micro-grants programme – maintenance work costing up to £1,000. Grants are £500 maximum.

Funding is available for listed and unlisted churches, chapels and meeting houses, as long as they are open for regular public worship.

Financial information

Year end	31/12/2020
Income	£1,970,000
Assets	£5,330,000
Grants to organisations	£1,620,000

Beneficiaries included: Hull Minster (£40,000); Holy Trinity – Stapleton (£15,000); All Saints – Burythorpe (£7,000); Urban Crofters Church – Cardiff (£1,100); All Saints – Newton Heath (£900).

Exclusions

See the website's FAQ page for more information on exclusions.

Applications

Applications can be made through the trust's website. Each grants programme has a unique application form, as well as its own deadlines.

Sources of information

Accounts; annual report; Charity Commission record; funder's website.

The National Garden Scheme

Gardening and horticulture; nursing; healthcare

UK

£2.89 million (2020)

CC number: 1112664

Correspondent: Staff Team, East Wing Hatchlands Park, East Clandon, Guildford, Surrey GU4 7RT (tel: 01483 211535; email: hello@ngs.org.uk)

Trustees: Susan Phipps; Peter Clay; Richard Thompson; Susan Copeland; Rupert Tyler; Andrew Ratcliffe; Mark Porter; Maureen Kesteven; Atty Beor-Roberts; Alison Wright; Richard Barley; Susan Paynton; Vernon Sanderson; Arit Anderson.

 www.ngs.org.uk

General information

The National Gardens Scheme (NGS) was registered with the Charity Commission in 2005, but dates back to 1927, when it was founded by the Queen's Nursing Institute. The charity opens gardens to public visitors, through a network of volunteers, in order to raise money for charities – in particular, supporting charities that are focused on nursing and health care.

Main beneficiaries

The charity has a list of main beneficiary charities that it supports, which are nominated by the trustees and include:

- Macmillan Cancer Support
- Marie Curie
- Hospice UK
- Carers Trust
- The Queen's Nursing Institute
- Parkinson's UK

Gardens and health projects

Grants are made to fund gardens and health projects. Previous beneficiaries have included ABF The Soldiers' Charity, Horatio's Garden, Maggie's and Patchworking Garden.

Guest charities

The charity also supports a guest charity for between two and three years. In 2020 Mind completed its second year as guest charity. A new guest charity will not be appointed until 2022 at the earliest. Check the website for updates.

Community Gardens Awards

In 2011 the National Garden Scheme set up a bursary scheme in memory of Elspeth Thompson, a supporter of the NGS and a well-known gardener. The scheme has now been developed into the Community Gardens Awards, as the last of the original endowment was used up in 2019.

The awards provide funding to amateur gardeners from community groups in England and Wales to support the creation of gardens and similar projects, such as allotments, for the benefit of the local community. Grants do not normally exceed £5,000. A list of previous beneficiaries is available on the charity's website.

Supporting and training gardeners

The charity funds a variety of training and apprentice schemes for gardeners and those working in gardens and horticulture. In 2020 such payments were made to Garden Museum, National Botanic Garden – Wales, Perennial, Professional Gardeners' Trust and WRAGS (Work and Retrain as a Gardener Scheme).

Financial information

Year end	31/12/2020
Income	£1,630,000
Assets	£841,600
Grants to organisations	£2,890,000
No. of grants	19

Beneficiaries included: Hospice UK, Macmillan Cancer Support and Marie Curie (£425,000 each); Carers Trust (£345,000); Parkinson's UK (£157,500); Maggie's Centres (£100,000); Horatio's Garden (£75,000); National Botanic Garden Wales (£20,000); Garden Museum (£10,000).

Exclusions

See the website for exclusion criteria.

Applications

If contacting the charity, note that each county has its own contact – see website for more detail. Openings for the Community Gardens Awards are advertised on the charity's website along with an online application form. For information on other funding opportunities, see the charity's website.

Sources of information

Accounts; annual report; Charity Commission record; funder's website.

The National Lottery Community Fund

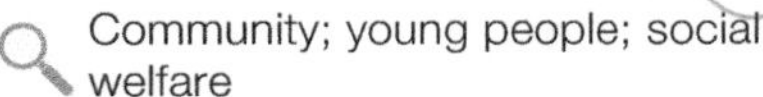

Community; young people; social welfare

 UK

 £509.15 million (2020/21)

Correspondent: The Grants Team, Apex House, 3 Embassy Drive, Edgbaston, Lirmingham B15 1TR (tel: 0345 410 2030; email: general.enquiries@tnlcommunityfund.org.uk)

 www.tnlcommunityfund.org.uk

 facebook.com/TNLCommunityFund

 @TNLComFund

 @TNLCommunityFund

General information

The National Lottery Community Fund, formerly known as the Big Lottery Fund, distributes money from the National Lottery to good causes as well as non-Lottery funding on behalf of public bodies, for example the Department for Education and the Office for Civil Society. It has established itself as a key funder of the voluntary sector and receives 40% of the total sums raised by the lottery which it distributes through grants to support community-focused projects. Since 2004 it has distributed over £10 billion in grants across the UK.

The organisation's website gives extensive information on the background of the funds, support available, application procedures and so on, which is subject to change. It would not be practicable to replicate all the details here and potential applicants are advised to study the organisation's helpful website to learn more about the funder.

Financial information

Year end	31/03/2021
Income	£1,035,420,000
Assets	£509,940,000
Grants to organisations	£509,150,000

Further financial information

In 2020/21, grants were distributed as follows:

England	£354.07 million
Scotland	£51.09 million
UK	£44.83 million
Wales	£31.26 million
Northern Ireland	£27,910 million

Beneficiaries included: Details of all previous grants made by the fund can be found on its website or on 360 Giving (see www.threesixtygiving.org).

Exclusions

There will be specific and detailed conditions for each separate programme – see the organisation's website for specific details on each programme.

Applications

Full details on current programmes, contacts, application forms and guidance are available on the National Lottery Community Fund website.

Sources of information

Accounts; annual report; funder's website.

The National Lottery Heritage Fund

 Heritage

UK

£315.42 million (2020/21)

Correspondent: The Trustees, Head Office, International House, 1 St Katharine's Way, London E1W 1UN (tel: 020 7591 6044; email: enquire@heritagefund.org.uk)

Trustees: Baroness Kay Andrews; Maria Adebowale-Schwarte; Dr Claire Feehily; Prof. David Stocker; Mukesh Sharma; Julian Glover; Taryn Nixon; Ray Macfarlane; Carol Pyrah.

General information

The National Lottery, which supports good causes like heritage, the arts, sport and charities, was established in 1994.

Responsibility for the UK-wide distribution of National Lottery proceeds allocated to heritage was given to the trustees of the National Heritage Memorial Fund (NHMF). The Lottery-distribution arm of NHMF became known as the Heritage Lottery Fund and was re-branded as The National Lottery Heritage Fund in 2019. Today it is a non-departmental public body accountable to Parliament via the Department for Culture, Media and Sport (DCMS).

Heritage funding is very wide ranging and the fund supports diverse projects with the criteria that they make a lasting difference for heritage, people and communities.

Grants

In February 2021, the fund re-opened its project funding for grants of up to £5 million. This marked a return to core business following the COVID-19 pandemic. As the fund builds back, its funding and expertise will support heritage organisations to 'adapt to fundamentally changed circumstances, to closely examine their existing business models and to develop new, creative and more resilient ways of operating', as stated on the fund's website.

Priorities up to the end of 2022–2023 financial year

The fund's website states:

> The impact of the coronavirus (COVID-19) pandemic means we will prioritise heritage projects that:
> - Promote inclusion and involve a wider range of people (a mandatory outcome)
> - Boost the local economy
> - Encourage skills development and job creation
> - Support wellbeing
> - Create better places to live, work and visit
> - Improve the resilience of organisations working in heritage

At the time of writing (May 2022), the fund was awarding three sizes of grants, each with separate guidelines and application details: £3,000 to £10,000, £10,000 to £250,000 and £250,000 to £5 million.

See the fund's website for more information on its grant programmes.

Financial information

Year end	31/03/2021
Income	£363,090,000
Assets	£349,570,000
Grants to organisations	£315,420,000

Further financial information

The grant total includes a UK-wide £50 million emergency fund, which supported almost 1,000 organisations during the COVID-19 pandemic.

Beneficiaries included: A list of beneficiaries was not available. Previous beneficiaries include: Canterbury Cathedral; Historic England; Hull City Council; Imperial War Museums; National Maritime Museum; The British Library.

Applications

All applications must be submitted via the fund's online application portal.

Sources of information

Accounts; annual report; funder's website.

The Nationwide Foundation

Community development; affordable housing; social welfare

UK

£1.32 million (2020/21)

CC number: 1065552

Correspondent: The Trustees, Nationwide House, Pipers Way, Swindon, Wiltshire SN38 2SN (tel: 0330 460 0709; email: enquiries@nationwidefoundation.org.uk)

 www.nationwidefoundation.org.uk

 @NationwideFdtn

General information

The Nationwide Foundation was established as an independent charity in 1997. It receives the majority of its funding from the Nationwide Building Society, which makes an annual lump sum donation of 0.25% of its pre-tax profit. According to its 2020/21 annual report, 'at its heart, the Nationwide Foundation seeks to tackle the root causes of social problems that lead to disadvantage, poverty, and inequality.' It aims to ensure that everyone in the UK has access to decent, affordable housing.

Grant programmes

The foundation provides support through three programmes:

Nurturing Ideas to Change the Housing System

This programme supports projects that are working to tackle systemic failings in the housing system. On its website, the foundation states that this programme funds the researching, testing, developing, piloting and evaluation of new ideas.

Backing Community-Led Housing

This programme aims to support the growth of community-led housing. The foundation's website clarifies that 'Community-led housing schemes come in a variety of forms, shapes and sizes. They can build new homes, create homes from empty properties, protect existing decent, affordable homes and provide homes of all types of tenure.'

This programme funds organisations that provide information, support, advice and technical expertise to help community-led housing schemes progress.

Transforming the Private Rented Sector

This programme aims to 'transform the private rented sector so that it provides homes for people in need that are more affordable, secure, accessible and are better quality', as stated on the foundation's website.

This programme supports projects that are working to build an understanding of life in the private rented sector, in particular for people who are vulnerable, disadvantaged or at risk of harm. It also supports a number of tenant's voice projects across the country.

Financial information

Year end	31/03/2021
Income	£2,280,000
Assets	£4,230,000
Grants to organisations	£1,320,000
No. of grants	28

Beneficiaries included: Wales Co-operative Centre (£225,100); Communities Housing Trust (£90,000); Affordable Housing Commission (£63,100); Citizens Advice (£43,800); Tenants Union (£25,300); University of Huddersfield (£10,500); Indigo House (£1,000).

Exclusions

The foundation will not consider funding for the following:

- The promotion of religion or politics
- Applications which do not comply with the foundation's funding criteria/guidelines

Applications

At the time of writing (April 2022) the foundation was focusing on its current partnerships and was not accepting new applications. Future invitations for new applicants will be advertised on the foundation's website.

Sources of information

Accounts; annual report; Charity Commission record; funder's website.

The NDL Foundation

General charitable purposes; education; medicine; the arts; women and children in financially developing countries

Worldwide

£314,300 (2020/21)

CC number: 1133508

Correspondent: The Trustees, 24 Chemin Des Moines, 1640 Rhode St Genese, Brussels, Belgium SW10 9LW (tel: 0322 358 1202; email: lucy@thendlfoundation.com)

Trustees: Laura Destribats; Sylviane Destribats; Diane Destribats; Nicolas Destribats; Claude Marion.

General information

The foundation was established in 2009 to support general charitable purposes. Support has been given to organisations working in the areas of education, medicine and the arts. Grants are made to UK-registered charities, although occasionally the foundation will support overseas not-for-profit organisations.

Financial information

Year end	05/04/2021
Income	£110,000
Assets	-£4,800
Grants to organisations	£314,300

Beneficiaries included: Don Bosco Bangalore Girls' School (£50,000); Chicken and Egg Pictures Inc. (£37,200); My Bnk (£30,000); KAA Intrepidus Trust (£29,500).

Applications

Apply in writing to the correspondent.

Sources of information

Accounts; annual report; Charity Commission record.

The Nepton Trust
The Clerk
20 Waltham Road
Woodford Green
Essex IG8 8DN.
poultersclerk@live.co.uk
(REDBRIDGE) - Poor + needy.

Near Neighbours

Community development and inter-community understanding

Birmingham; the Black Country; East London; East Midlands; Greater Manchester; Lancashire; Leicester; Luton; Nottingham; Peterborough; West London; West Yorkshire

£654,000 (2020)

CC number: 1142426

Correspondent: Local Near Neighbours Co-ordinator, The Foundry, 17 Oval Way, London SE11 5RR (tel: 020 3752 5651; email: hello@nearneighbours.org.uk)

Trustees: Richard Sudworth; Rachel Whittington; Susan Fcih; The Revd Malcolm Brown; The Revd Jessica Foster; The Revd Catherine Allison; Katherine Hodkinson; The Revd Rogers Govender.

www.near-neighbours.org.uk

facebook.com/nearneighbours

@nearneighbours

@nearneighbours

General information

Near Neighbours was established in 2011 and aims to bring people together in communities across the UK that are religiously and ethnically diverse so that they can collaborate together on community initiatives.

Small grants

The charity offers small grants of between £250 and £3,000 as seed funding for local groups and organisations who are working to bring together neighbours. Grants have been awarded for a variety of work, including environmental, social, cultural, artistic and sporting projects. Open funding rounds are advertised on the charity's website.

Community initiatives

The charity offers a number of other initiatives, including a leadership programme for young people, a network of community groups and spaces, and practical advice on fundraising and marketing for community groups. See the charity's website for details.

Financial information

Year end	31/12/2020
Income	£900,000
Assets	£96,000
Grants to organisations	£654,000

Further financial information

Grants were broken down as follows:

Building networks	£414,000
Small grants	£187,000
Public spaces	£19,000
Young leaders	£18,000
Faith leaders	£16,000

In 2020 the charity awarded 95 small grants in four focus areas:

- Marginalised women and girls
- Vulnerable young people
- Social divisions and tensions
- Combatting loneliness and promoting connectedness

Beneficiaries included: Thrive Together Birmingham (£47,000); St Philip's Centre – Leicester (£30,000); Transforming Notts Together – Nottingham (£11,000); Christian Muslim Forum (£8,000); Council of Christians and Jews (£4,000). **Beneficiaries of small grants included:** Kairos; ReflecTeen Hub; The Leicester Kids Covid Relief Family Cooking Project; Vanclaron CIC.

Exclusions

Consult the application guidelines for a full list of exclusions. These will become available on the charity's website when funding rounds open.

Applications

Full application details can be found on the charity's helpful website when funding rounds open. Join the charity's mailing list for notifications on openings. Near Neighbours runs local support hubs. Contact information for the local co-ordinators can be found on the website.

Sources of information

Accounts; annual report; Charity Commission record; funder's website.

Ner Foundation

The advancement of the Orthodox Jewish religion and education; the relief of poverty in the Jewish community

UK and Israel

£427,100 (2020/21)

CC number: 1104866

Correspondent: The Trustees, 309 Bury New Road, Salford, Manchester M7 2YN (tel: 0161 772 0099)

Trustees: Arnold Henry; Henry Neumann; Esther Henry.

General information

This foundation was registered with the Charity Commission in July 2004. According to its Charity Commission record, 'the objects of the foundation are the relief of poverty among the elderly or persons in need, hardship or distress in the Jewish Community; the advancement of the Orthodox Jewish Religion and the advancement of education according to the tenets of the Orthodox Jewish faith.'

Financial information

Year end	30/06/2021
Income	£371,400
Assets	£618,000
Grants to organisations	£427,100

Further financial information

Only beneficiaries receiving grants of over £1,000 were listed in the accounts. Grants of less than £1,000 totalled £22,700.

Beneficiaries included: T T T (£43,000); Kolyom Trust (£39,500); Choimel Dalim (£35,000); A. B. Foundation (£25,000); Friends of Gaon Yaakov (£15,000); Gefen Foundation (£6,900); Asos Chessed (£6,000).

Applications

Apply in writing to the correspondent.

Sources of information

Accounts; annual report; Charity Commission record.

Network for Social Change Charitable Trust

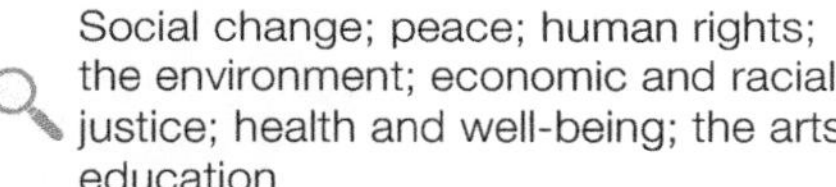

Social change; peace; human rights; the environment; economic and racial justice; health and well-being; the arts; education

UK and overseas

£1.19 million (2019/20)

CC number: 295237

Correspondent: The Trustees, BM 2063, London WC1N 3XX (tel: 01647 61106; email: thenetwork@gn.apc.org)

Trustees: Annie Schiff; Mark Tucker; Patricia Horrocks; Gillian Howarth; Roger Manser.

http://thenetworkforsocialchange.org.uk

General information

Network for Social Change Charitable Trust, formerly the Network Foundation, is a group of philanthropic individuals who have come together to fund projects that support progressive social change. Each year the trust awards around £1.5 million in grants to a variety of charitable and non-charitable projects, each sponsored by a member. The trust's website states:

> We look for projects that promote social change (broadly defined) and tend to favour projects which are innovative, highly leveraged, and/or difficult to fund (a category which may include core funding for an organisation). We like addressing the root causes of a problem, not the symptoms.
>
> Our funding is applied in the areas of: peace, human rights, arts and education, environment, health, economic and racial justice. We welcome projects led by people with lived experience of the issues they campaign about or the services they provide, including projects led or founded by people of colour.

Grants are usually of up to £30,000 but major and longer-term projects can also be funded with much higher donations. The trust will fund charities, CICs and social enterprises.

Financial information

Year end	31/08/2020
Income	£1,320,000
Assets	£166,400
Grants to organisations	£1,190,000

Further financial information

Only beneficiaries of grants of £10,000 and above were listed in the 2019/20 accounts.

Beneficiaries included: The Green Alliance Trust (£178,400); Oxford Research Group (£48,300); The Co-operative College (£28,700); The Poverty and Environment Trust (£20,000); Open Trust (£17,000); The Mindfulness Initiative (£14,200); Aegean Solidarity Network Team UK (£10,800).

Exclusions

Disaster appeals, building projects and direct contributions to political parties are not funded. Non-charitable projects are required to use the Network's money for non-violent and legal purposes only.

Applications

All applications to the trust must be sponsored by a member and unsolicited applications are not accepted. However, project summaries can be submitted on the trust's project noticeboard on its website. If a member is interested, they will get in touch. Visit the trust's website for further information.

Sources of information

Accounts; annual report; Charity Commission record; funder's website.

Newby Trust Ltd

Education; health; social welfare; medical research; children and young people

UK, with a preference for England

£439,600 (2020/21)

CC number: 227151

Correspondent: Annabel Grout, Company Secretary, PO Box 87, Petworth GU28 8BH (email: info@newby-trust.org.uk)

Trustees: Evelyn Montgomery; Anna Foxell; Ben Gooder; David Charlton; Duncan Reed; Dr Stephen Gooder; Antonia Gooder; Kate Callaghan; Katherine Bartholomew.

www.newby-trust.org.uk

General information

The Newby Trust was established in 1937 by Mr H. N. Smith, the industrialist who developed Smith & Nephew plc. The aim of the trust is 'to enable people to benefit from educational opportunities, to support excellence and to improve the quality of life and health in disadvantaged communities'.

Areas of work

The trust makes grants for the following purposes, details of which have been taken from its website:

> *Education*
>
> The current aims of the Trust's education programme are to enable people to benefit from educational opportunities and to support excellence. Within the over-arching aim, the Trust wishes
>
> 1 to enhance educational opportunities for children and young people through the funding of extra-curricular activities
> 2 to support the personal development of children who need extra help to enable them to benefit from education
> 3 to nurture ability and talent at all ages
>
> *Health*
>
> The broad objectives of the health category are to:
>
> 1 maintain and improve the mental health of children and young people
> 2 support the mental and physical health of older people
> 3 fund medical research
>
> *Social welfare*
>
> The aim of the social welfare category is to improve people's quality of life in disadvantaged communities. The Trust's broad objectives in this category are to:
>
> 1 provide small grants for short-term emergency relief
> 2 improve social support for disadvantaged groups
> 3 support cultural and physical activities to improve well-being

Special category

The trust also has an annual special category of grant. The special category for 2021/22 was the mental health of children and young people.

Types of grant

Grants are made for core costs, project funding, capital costs and salaries. Grants are usually between £2,000 and £10,000 and can be made for one, two or three years.

Financial information

Year end	05/04/2021
Income	£423,000
Assets	£25,500,000
Grants to organisations	£439,600

Further financial information

Grants were broken down as follows:

Welfare	£219,300
Education	£113,800
Health	£96,500
Miscellaneous	£10,000

Beneficiaries included: A list of beneficiaries was not available. Previous beneficiaries include: Yes Futures (£30,000); Empire Fighting Chance and The Wave Project (£20,000 each); Feeding Families, St Chad's Sanctuary and The Access Project (£10,000 each); Beyond the Horizon Charity, Freedom From Torture and White City Youth Theatre (£5,000 each); Riding for the Disabled (£1,000).

Exclusions

The trust's website states that it does not (normally) fund the following:

- Statutory bodies
- Large national charities enjoying widespread support
- Organisations not registered with the Charity Commission
- Exhibitions, conferences or events
- Individuals volunteering overseas
- The promotion of religion
- Work outside the UK
- Large capital appeals
- Endowment appeals

Applications

Only charities that are invited to apply will be eligible to apply, but charities – particularly those associated with the annual special category – are invited to make their activities known by email to the trust.

The trust's website states that:

> due to the number of enquiries received and limited staff time, the Trust regrets that it is only able respond to introductory emails if the Trust wishes to take the enquiry to the next stage.

The trust does not have an application form; applicants will receive a list of points to consider if invited to make a formal application.

Sources of information

Accounts; annual report; Charity Commission record; funder's website.

The Frances and Augustus Newman Foundation

Medical research projects and other medicine-related charitable causes

UK

£466,600 (2019/20)

CC number: 277964

Correspondent: Ben Haines, Administrator, c/o RSM, Hartwell House, 55–61 Victoria Street, Bristol BS1 6AD (tel: 0117 945 2000; email: ben.haines@rsmuk.com)

General information

The foundation aims to advance the work of medical professionals working in teaching hospitals and academic institutions, mostly (but not exclusively) by funding medical research projects, buildings and equipment. Projects submitted from major research centres are favoured, with grants awarded for between one and three years.

Financial information

Year end	31/03/2021
Income	£616,700
Assets	£17,210,000
Grants to organisations	£529,800
No. of grants	10

Beneficiaries included: University of Cambridge (£264,000); Royal College of Surgeons (£75,000); Stroke Association (£38,300); Care for Veterans (£20,000); Antibiotic Research UK (£15,000); Northamptonshire Rape Crisis (£10,000); DKMS Delete Blood Cancer (£2,000).

Applications

The annual report for 2020/21 states that

> [The trustees invite] applications for research grants from individuals. Applicants submit a summary of their proposals to the Trustees in a specific format; applications made in the correct format are reviewed against the research criteria established by the Trustees and the research objectives. Research posts are funded on an annual basis to undertake an agreed programme of research and continuation of the grants is subject to the annual assessment by the Trustees. The Trustees give substantial support to peer reviewed submissions from academic institutions. In respect of the limited number of other grants made, they favour projects submitted from major research centres. Grants made can be for one to three years.

Sources of information

Accounts; annual report; Charity Commission record.

Newpier Charity Ltd

Jewish causes; social welfare; education

UK and Israel

£480,200 (2019/20)

CC number: 293686

Correspondent: Mr C. Margulies, Secretary, 186 Lordship Road, London N16 5ES (tel: 020 8802 4449)

General information

The main objectives of the charity are the advancement of the Orthodox Jewish faith and the relief of poverty. The charity's 2019/20 annual report explains:

> The charity was set up to support the activities of religious Jewish organisations especially in the field of education. The trustees identify institutions and organisations which meet its criteria and regularly support a number of these institutions and organisations, which themselves are growing not only in England but also worldwide.
>
> The charity is also supportive of organisations which are solely committed to the relief of poverty. Such organisations assist needy Jewish families financially and also through the distribution of basic necessities.

Financial information

Year end	30/06/2020
Income	£561,600
Assets	-£1,270,000
Grants to organisations	£480,200

Beneficiaries included: A list of beneficiaries can be requested from the charity's secretary at a cost of £25.

Applications

Apply in writing to the correspondent. The trustees meet on a regular basis to consider applications.

Sources of information

Accounts; annual report; Charity Commission record.

The NFU Mutual Charitable Trust

Community development; education; social welfare; research focusing on initiatives that will have a significant impact on rural communities

UK, with a preference for rural areas

£1.11 million (2020)

CC number: 1073064

Correspondent: Jim Creechan, Secretary to the Trustees, Tiddington Road, Stratford-upon-Avon, Warwickshire CV37 7BJ (tel: 01789 204211; email: nfu_mutual_charitable_trust@nfumutual.co.uk)

www.nfumutual.co.uk/about-us/charitable-trust

General information

The NFU Mutual Charitable Trust was established in 1998 and is the corporate charity of the National Farmers Union Mutual Insurance Society Ltd (NFU

Mutual), one of the UK's leading insurers.

According to its website, the trust makes one-off grants to charities that work in the areas of agriculture, rural development and insurance. In particular those working to:

- Advance the education of the public by means of research and dissemination of information in relation to agriculture
- Advance the education of young people within rural areas
- Relieve poverty within rural areas
- Promote the benefit and social welfare of inhabitants of rural communities by associating together with the inhabitants and local authorities, voluntary and other organisations to advance education and leisure
- Promote research into agriculture associated activities
- Advance the education of the public by means of research and dissemination of information in relation to insurance provided that the charity may also promote, facilitate and support any such other purposes as are exclusively charitable according to the laws of England and Wales

The trustees are particularly interested in initiatives in the areas of education of young people in rural areas and relief of poverty within rural areas.

Grants can range from £1,000 to £50,000. The trust prefers to fund larger projects that will have a significant impact on the rural community.

Non-charitable organisations can also apply, but the funding request needs to be for charitable purposes.

Financial information

Year end	29/02/2020
Income	£963,400
Assets	£228,400
Grants to organisations	£1,110,000
No. of grants	21

Further financial information

During the year the trust made grants totalling £1.1 million to 21 organisations, of which £750,000 was focused on supporting COVID-19 response and recovery. Included in the grant total is £21,600 paid to universities to fund postgraduate bursaries.

Beneficiaries included: National Emergencies Trust (£250,000); Addington Fund and Farming Community Network (£105,000 each); Rural Support (£80,000); The Prince's Countryside Fund (£60,000); Royal Highland Educational Trust (£20,000); Farms for City Children (£10,000); Gareth Raw Rees Memorial Scholarship (£2,000).

Exclusions

The trust does not provide funding for university fees, salaries or overseas appeals. Generally, the trustees will not consider funding initiatives over multiple years.

Applications

Application forms are available from the trust's website and should be sent to the correspondent either via post or email.

The website states that applications should include details of the following:

- The project, initiative or organisation for which funding is sought
- An indication of the amount of the donation requested
- Any business plans
- Details of any other funding sought and or obtained
- Any recognition which would be given to the trust in recognition of its support
- Confirmation of whether or not the applicant is a registered charity

The trustees meet twice a year to consider applications. These meetings are currently held in June and November. Applications should be submitted by the 27th of the previous month.

Sources of information

Accounts; annual report; Charity Commission record; funder's website.

The Nineveh Charitable Trust

 Health and welfare of the general public; the environment; education; preservation of the countryside

UK

£605,000 (2020/21)

CC number: 256025

Correspondent: The Trustees, Park Farm, Frittenden Road, Ashford, Kent TN27 8LG (tel: 07710 998829; email: robert@ninevehtrust.org.uk)

 www.ninevehtrust.org.uk

 facebook.com/ninevehtrust

General information

The trust was established in 1968 by Marjorie and Thomas James, both of whom had strong interests in farming and the environment.

The trust supports a wide range of projects and activities with a strong focus on promoting a better understanding of the countryside as well as facilitating improved access, education and research.

According to the trust's website, its objects are:

- The health, welfare and education of the general public
- The study and appreciation of agriculture, silviculture, ecology and land management
- The study and appreciation of land and estate management that encourages conservation of the countryside

Grants are made to UK-registered charities and CICs. Individual applicants may be considered if the outcome benefits are clearly defined.

The trust will consider funding project and capital costs, as well as making grants for salaries. Matched funding is also available. Examples of successful grants can be found on the trust's website.

Financial information

Year end	05/04/2021
Income	£230,400
Assets	£10,170,000
Grants to organisations	£605,000

Beneficiaries included: Cancer Research (on behalf of the Francis Crick Institute Ltd) (£100,000); Armagh Social Farm CIC (£5,000); Andover Trees United (£4,200); Buckby Library and Hub (£3,500); Camelsdale Primary School PTA (£2,000); Broad Oak Primary School (£800).

Exclusions

The trust's website states that it is unlikely to provide funding for the following:

- Expeditions or personal educational needs without a wider benefit
- Animal sanctuaries and care
- Projects unrelated to the Trust's objects
- Organisations based outside the UK
- General appeals or mail-shots

Applications

Apply in writing to the correspondent. Three copies of the proposal should be sent to the correspondent along with an SAE. Applications should be no longer than two sides of A4. Four copies of the contact form, which is available to download from the trust's website, should be sent alongside the proposal. The trust suggests using a situation–target–proposal structure for applications.

The trust's website states that proposals should include the following information:

- How much you want.
- What the money is going to be used for (e.g. provide a breakdown).
- Methodologies (e.g. of a field study; how the data will be measured).
- Successful outcome indicators (e.g. please specify up to 3 measures that will demonstrate the success of your project)
- What the benefit will be, not only to your organisation but thinking about the wider world.
- How your target will support *our* aims

Background information such as websites and annual accounts should also be included.

Sources of information

Accounts; annual report; Charity Commission record; funder's website.

The Nisbet Trust

Community cohesion; disadvantaged young people; the arts; homelessness

Bristol; North Somerset; South Gloucestershire

£1.39 million (2020)

CC number: 1143496

Correspondent: Gemma Roberts, Administrator, 22 Clifton Road, Bristol BS8 1AQ (email: admin@nisbettrust.co.uk)

Trustees: Andrew Nisbet; Anne Nisbet; Joseph Nisbet; Emily Nisbet; Zoe Joyner; Henry Bothamley.

 www.nisbettrust.co.uk

General information

The trust was established in 2011 by the Nisbet Family and is primarily funded by Key West Holdings, which trades subsidiaries and commercial property. It makes single and multi-year grants for up to three years to charitable organisations in the Greater Bristol area. Support is provided to organisations working in the following areas:

- **Children and young people** – prioritising organisations and projects which support disadvantaged young people to gain skills and qualifications for employment
- **The arts** – supporting performance venues and groups
- **Prevention of homelessness** – including support for organisations that provide advice and guidance to people at risk of losing their homes
- **Community cohesion** – projects which support equality, diversity and social inclusion for high-need groups from all communities in Bristol

Three types of grant are available:

- Small – up to £5,000
- Medium – £5,001 to £30,000
- Large – over £30,000

Eligibility

Applicants must be a registered or exempt charity, not-for-profit social enterprise or CIC. CICs must have been established for at least three years, with an annual income of more than £50,000, which should include at least 25% from trading.

Financial information

Year end	31/12/2020
Grants to organisations	£1,390,000
No. of grants	49

Further financial information

In 2020, the trust paused its grant-making due to the COVID-19 pandemic. At the time of writing (February 2022), its grant-making had resumed.

Only beneficiaries of grants of over £5,000 were listed in the accounts. Grants of under £5,000 totalled £65,700. Grants were broken down as follows:

Children and young people	55%
Community cohesion	23%
Prevention of homelessness	9%
Other	7%
The arts	6%

Beneficiaries included: The Park Community Centre Ltd (£250,000); Creative Youth Network (£125,000); Royal West of England Academy (£50,000); Bristol Law Centre (£30,000); North Bristol Racism and Inequality (£20,000); Access Sports CIO and St Pauls Advice Centre (£10,000 each); Lawrence Weston Out of School Activity (£5,000).

Exclusions

The following are not eligible for support:

- Medical research
- Single-condition medical charities
- Individuals
- Animal welfare charities
- Sponsorship

CICs whose core business model is substantially grant-reliant are unlikely to be successful.

National charities applying for support for work in Bristol are less likely to be supported.

Applications

Application forms and guidance are available from the trust's website. Forms should be returned by email. The trustees meet quarterly to consider applications in January, April, July and October. Deadlines for applications are posted on the trust's website.

Sources of information

Accounts, annual report, Charity Commission record; funder's website.

NNS Foundation

Health and education

Worldwide, with a focus on the UK, USA, Egypt and the rest of Africa

£4.08 million (2020)

CC number: 1184159

Correspondent: The Trustees, Third Floor, 20 Old Bailey, London EC4 7AN (tel: 020 7597 6000)

Trustee: NNS Foundation Ltd.

General information

The foundation was established by Nassef Sawiris in 2018. Its 2020 annual accounts provide the following information on its grant-making strategy:

> Whilst maintaining flexibility, the Foundation's grant making strategy focuses on making grants of a meaningful size to fund educational and healthcare projects and programmes. The Foundation's strategy is to fund projects worldwide, but with a current focus on the UK, USA, Egypt and other countries in Africa.

Financial information

Year end	31/12/2020
Income	£4,344,000
Assets	£311,800
Grants to organisations	£4,080,000
No. of grants	5

Further financial information

Financial information has been converted from US dollars using the exchange rate at the time of writing (February 2022).

Beneficiaries included: Sawiris Foundation for Social Development (£3.92 million); African Mission Healthcare and Stanford University (£440,000 each); Egyptian Education Foundation (£372,300).

Applications

Unsolicited applications are not accepted. The foundation's 2020 annual accounts state:

> At this stage the Foundation does not invite unsolicited grant applications, rather relying on the Trustee's connections within the sector to bring relevant projects to the Foundation's attention.

Sources of information

Charity Commission record; accounts; annual report.

The Norman Family Charitable Trust

General charitable purposes

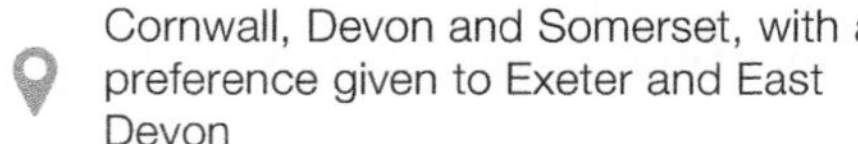

Cornwall, Devon and Somerset, with a preference given to Exeter and East Devon

£374,700 (2020/21)

CC number: 277616

Correspondent: Emma Le Poidevin, Grants Administrator, 14 Fore Street, Budleigh Salterton, Devon EX9 6NG (tel: 01395 446699; email: info@nfct.org)

Trustees: Catherine Houghton; Sarah Gillingham; Christopher Davis; William Tee; Liz Low; John Bain; Stephen Green.

 www.nfct.org

 facebook.com/normanfct

 @normantrust

General information

The trust was established in 1979 due to the success of a chain of cash and carry stores owned by the Norman family. Ken and Pat Norman, who started the cash and carry business, used some of the proceeds from the business to start the Norman Family Charitable Trust. The aim of the trust is to support worthy causes in South West England with the intention of repaying loyal customers who helped to make the Norman's business a success.

The trust's primary objective is to provide funding for registered charities, non-profits and voluntary organisations working in Somerset, Devon and Cornwall. Applications from Exeter and East Devon are prioritised. The trust does consider applications from national charities, but only if the proposed project with specifically benefit the South West.

Grants can be for capital items or for core costs such as staffing. Grants are typically for up to £10,000, but mostly less than £2,000.

Schools

In 2017/18, the trust reviewed its grant-making policy in order to fund schools in the Devon area, to benefit pupils and parents, as a result of government cuts and financial hardship being faced in the community. At the time of writing (January 2022) the website stated that the trust was continuing with this additional focus. Examples of applications encouraged could be to support the following: school libraries, minibuses, sports halls or equipment, outdoor play equipment, text books, music, drama, the arts and laboratory equipment.

Financial information

Year end	31/03/2021
Income	£447,400
Assets	£10,340,000
Grants to organisations	£374,700
No. of grants	241

Further financial information

During the year the trust received 328 applications and awarded 241 grants. Grants were awarded in the following categories:

Children	£94,800
Community projects	£66,600
Medical (including medical research)	£55,300
Homelessness and social welfare	£40,000
Blindness, deafness and physical disabilities	£25,800
Mental health and learning disabilities	£24,700
Animals, the environment and conservation	£20,900
Sport and leisure	£11,200
Employment, skills and training	£10,000
Older people	£9,800
Crime prevention, rehabilitation and addiction	£6,100
Armed forces and emergency services	£4,800
Young people	£4,800

Beneficiaries included: Wadebridge Foodbank (£10,000); Exmouth Community College (£5,300); Budleigh Relief In Need Charity and St Peter's Primary School (£3,000 each); TCR Radio Productions CIC (£2,000). A full list of beneficiaries was not available.

Exclusions

Grants are not made to individuals, organisations which use live animals for experimental or research purposes, or overseas organisations. The trust will not make grants for the maintenance or repair of religious buildings. National charities will only be supported for projects which will help the area of benefit.

Applications

Apply via the trust's website using an online form. You will have to complete an eligibility quiz before you can access the application form. See the trust's website for the latest information on applications and deadlines.

Sources of information

Accounts; annual report; Charity Commission record; funder's website.

Normanby Charitable Trust

Arts and culture; heritage; social welfare; disability; general charitable purposes

Mainly North Yorkshire and the North East

£173,100 (2020/21)

CC number: 252102

Correspondent: The Trustees, 52 Tite Street, London SW3 4JA (tel: 020 7352 3174; email: nct@normanby.org)

General information

The Normanby Charitable Trust makes grants to other charities and organisations for general charitable purposes. In previous years the trust has given for a wide range of causes including health, sport, heritage education and social welfare. The trust has also occasionally given grants for the preservation of religious and secular buildings of historical or architectural interest.

Priority is given to organisations based in North Yorkshire and the North East; however, grants are occasionally made to organisations outside the area of benefit.

Financial information

Year end	05/04/2021
Income	£183,000
Assets	£13,900,000
Grants to organisations	£173,100
No. of grants	35

Further financial information

In 2020/21 the trust awarded grants totalling £173,100; however, in previous years the trust's giving exceeded £300,000. In 2019/20 it awarded grants totalling £365,500 and £813,300 in 2018/19.

Beneficiaries included: Garden Museum (£23,800); Trinity Centre – Whitby (£18,500); Royal Academy of Arts (£10,000); The North York Moors Chamber Festival (£8,000); Cleveland Mountain Rescue (£3,000); Bipolar UK (£1,500); The Salvation Army (£1,000).

Exclusions

Grants to individuals are only made in exceptional circumstances.

Applications

Apply in writing to the correspondent. The trustees meet two to three times a year to award grants.

Sources of information

Accounts; annual report; Charity Commission record; National Churches Trust (website).

North Berwick Trust

Public recreational facilities and gardens; education; social welfare; sport; health; community development

North Berwick

£236,200 (2019/20)

OSCR number: SC048462

Correspondent: The Trustees, The Lighthouse, Heugh Road Industrial Estate, North Berwick, East Lothian, EH39 5PX (email: a contact form is available on the trust's website)

 www.northberwicktrust.co.uk

General information

The trust was established in 1973 and funds projects that benefit the residents of North Berwick.

The trust's website states:

> Through our grant-giving program, we support individuals and organisations in need living or operating within North Berwick. These include -
>
> - Supporting and enhancing recreational,

cultural and sporting activities and facilities
- Supporting and enhancing educational and lifelong learning opportunities
- Conserving and enhancing the historic and built environment of North Berwick

Financial information

Year end	31/03/2021
Income	£362,400
Assets	£16,080,000
Grants to organisations	£297,600

Beneficiaries included: North Berwick Youth Project (£30,000); Leuchie (£27,800); Herbspace (£12,500); Dirleton Playgroup (£3,000); North Berwick in Bloom (£1,000).

Applications

Application forms and deadlines can be found on the trust's website.

Sources of information

Accounts; annual report; OSCR record; funder's website.

North West Cancer Research

Cancer research

North West England and North Wales

£1.1 million (2019/20)

CC number: 519357

Correspondent: The Trustees, North West Cancer Research Centre, 200 London Road, Liverpool, Merseyside L3 9TA (tel: 0151 709 2919; email: info@nwcr.org)

Trustees: Francis Street; Nigel Lanceley; Catherine Jones; Catherine Bond; Hilary Atherton; Mark Haig; Philip Robertshaw; Stephen Claus; Michael Carter; Michael Ore; Philip Webster; Dr Sharvari Kothari-Short.

www.nwcr.org

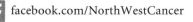

facebook.com/NorthWestCancer

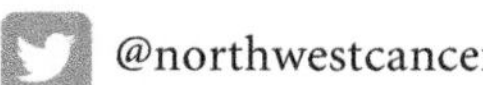
@northwestcancer

General information

North West Cancer Research is an independent research charity funding research for local people in North West England and North Wales. The charity prioritises research that has a direct impact on the people in the region and targets the cancers that are most prevalent. The charity invests in studies from 'bench to bedside' and will also support research into end of life care, as stated on its website.

Funded research is primarily carried out at the University of Liverpool, Lancaster University and Bangor University. Over 50 cancer research projects across the North West and North Wales are currently being funded.

According to its website, there are six key areas in which the charity will invest its resources:

- Researching the impact of cancer
- Researching the causes of cancer
- Clinical research – for improved diagnosis and treatment options
- Fundamental research – for improved understanding of how cells and cancers work
- Building the capacity for research
- Research for the future – ensuring the skills base in the region remains vibrant

Funding

Open calls

The charity advertises open calls on its website – there are several calls each year. Criteria and application guidance is made available on the charity's website. Researchers are encouraged to submit a research proposal and then an application which will be peer reviewed.

There are also numerous other funding options, such as studentships, project grants and equipment grants. Check the charity's website for current opportunities.

Financial information

Year end	30/09/2020
Income	£1,540,000
Assets	£3,230,000
Grants to organisations	£1,100,000

Further financial information

According to its 2019/20 accounts, the charity approved grants totalling £1.28 million during the year. However, this figure included £170,300 of support costs which we have deducted from the total.

Beneficiaries included: A list of beneficiaries was not available.

Exclusions

The charity generally does not fund buildings or direct clinical care. See the charity's website for the specific exclusion criteria of open calls.

Applications

Application guidance and deadlines are made available on the charity's website as open funding calls arise.

Sources of information

Accounts; annual report; Charity Commission record; funder's website.

The Northwick Trust

Conservation and the natural environment; social welfare; disability; young people and citizenship

UK and overseas

£469,000 (2020/21)

CC number: 285197

Correspondent: Peter McCarthy, Trustee, 13 Queensway, Wellingborough, Northamptonshire NN8 3RA (tel: 01933 222986; email: petermc1711@btinternet.com)

Trustees: Lady Rachel Willcocks; Anne Willcocks; Mary Morgan; Kate Willcocks; Xanthe Williams; Peter McCarthy; Andrew Laurie.

General information

The Northwick Trust registered with the Charity Commission in 1982 and supports general charitable purposes; including environmental sustainability and conservation, culture and heritage, social welfare, projects for people with disabilities, and projects encouraging young people to become more involved in their community. The trust supports registered charities in the UK and those operating overseas.

Financial information

Year end	31/03/2021
Income	£279,200
Assets	£12,080,000
Grants to organisations	£469,000

Beneficiaries included: Global Green Grants (£25,000); Cambridge Community Fund (£20,000); Cardinal Hume Centre (£15,000); Daylight Centre Wellingborough (£12,000); Calm (£10,000); Dove House Hospice (£8,000); Cogwheel (£5,000); Safe Passage (£2,000); Young Roots (£1,000).

Applications

Apply in writing to the correspondent.

Sources of information

Accounts, annual report, Charity Commission record.

Northwood Charitable Trust

General charitable purposes, particularly: the relief of poverty; education; health and mental health; community; heritage and culture

Dundee and Tayside

£4.37 million (2020/21)

OSCR number: SC014487

Correspondent: The Trustees, 22 Meadowside, Dundee DD1 1LN

www.dcthomson.co.uk/our-communities

General information

The Northwood Trust is connected to the D. C. Thomson Charitable Trust, D.C. Thomson and Co. Ltd and the Thomson family. It was established by Eric V. Thomson in 1972 and has received additional funding from other members of the family. The trust gives for general charitable purposes in Dundee and Tayside.

The D.C. Thomson and Co. Ltd website states the following about the trust:

> The Trust provides financial support to help enhance people's lives through a wide range of charitable organisations. Its main funding themes are addressing deprivation, poverty and inequality, advancing educational attainment, progressing physical and mental health and wellbeing and supporting community, heritage and cultural enrichment.

Financial information

Year end	05/04/2021
Income	£3,040,000
Assets	£110,710,000
Grants to organisations	£4,370,000

Beneficiaries included: Breakthrough Dundee (£463,200); Eden Trust (£125,000); Future Skills College (£50,000); Project Scotland (£20,000); Mercy Ships (£15,000).

Applications

The trust's 2020/21 accounts state: 'Unsolicited applications for donations are not encouraged and will not normally be acknowledged.'

Sources of information

Accounts; annual report; OSCR record.

The Norton Rose Fulbright Charitable Foundation

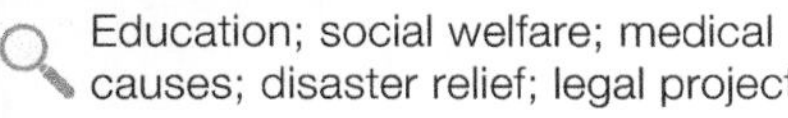
Education; social welfare; medical causes; disaster relief; legal projects

Worldwide

£419,300 (2020/21)

CC number: 1102142

Correspondent: The Trustees, c/o Norton Rose Fullbright, 3 More London Riverside, London SE1 2AQ (tel: 020 7283 6000)

Trustees: Patrick Farrell; Ffion Flockhart.

www.nortonrosefulbright.com/corporate-responsibility

General information

The Norton Rose Fulbright Charitable Foundation was established in 2004 and is funded by Norton Rose Fulbright LLP, an international law firm, and its employees.

The trust's principal activity is to make charitable donations. It supports a wide range of causes, notably medicine, education and social welfare. Many of the charities supported by the trust are nominated by employees of Norton Rose Fulbright. Funding is donated to charities alongside donations raised by the activities of Norton Rose Fulbright staff.

Financial information

Year end	30/04/2021
Income	£451,200
Assets	£21,800
Grants to organisations	£419,300

Beneficiaries included: Action for Children (£45,000); Child's i Foundation (£25,000); Advocates for International Development (£15,000); Barretstown (£10,000); Beanstalk (£5,000).

Applications

Apply in writing to the correspondent. Regarding the grant-making policy, the 2020/21 annual report states the following:

> In many cases, the charities we support are those we have supported in the past, but new charities are considered at Trustee meetings. The Trustees also meet on an ad hoc basis to consider specific urgent requests such as the support of major disaster relief appeals.

Sources of information

Accounts; annual report; Charity Commission record; funder's website.

Norwich Consolidated Charities

The provision of housing accommodation; social welfare; health; equality

Norwich

£660,700 (2020)

CC number: 1094602

Correspondent: David Hynes, CEO of Norwich Charitable Trusts, 1 Woolgate Court, St Benedicts Street, Norwich NR2 4AP (tel: 01603 621023; email: david.hynes@norwichcharitabletrusts.org.uk)

Trustees: David Fullman; Ashley Ford-McAllister; Vivien Thomas; Sally Button; Adam Giles; Laura McCartney-Gray; Jacqueline Hanlon; Eneida Mioshi; Philip Davies; John Garside; Boyd Taylor; Karen Davis; Michael Flynn; Jeanne Southgate.

www.norwichconsolidatedcharities.org.uk

@NorwichChTr

General information

Norwich Consolidated Charities is part of the Norwich Charitable Trusts, a group of three grant-making charities and one almshouse. The charity makes grants to both individuals and organisations. According to Norwich Charitable Trusts' website, preference is given to projects that fall into one of the following areas:

- Roofs and Support – Projects which make a significant contribution to the provision of housing accommodation for people who are in financial need and resident in the city of Norwich. This includes projects relating to the accommodation itself and projects providing support to those in need of, or living in, such accommodation.
- Money – Projects which make a significant contribution to the quality of life of people who are in financial need, financial hardship or financial distress and are resident in the city of Norwich. This includes projects directly addressing financial issues and projects providing respite from financial issues.
- Health – Projects which make a significant contribution to relieving the suffering or assisting the recovery of people who are in financial need, resident in the city of Norwich and are sick or convalescent. This does not include projects relating to the provision of private health care.
- Discrimination, Exclusion and 'Difference' – Projects which make a significant difference to improving the quality of life of people who are in financial need, resident in the city of Norwich and experiencing lack of equality of opportunity and /or discrimination as a result of being disabled or Deaf, or of identifying/being seen as identifying as being 'different' from the majority.

Financial information

Year end	31/12/2020
Income	£2,270,000
Assets	£37,870,000
Grants to organisations	£660,700

Beneficiaries included: Norfolk Community Law Service (£145,000); The Garage Trust (£50,000); Christians Against Poverty (£46,100); Leeway Domestic Violence and Abuse (£29,000); The Hamlet Centre (£13,000); Norfolk Accident Rescue Service (£9,000); AndAction Projects (£1,700).

Applications

Organisations that wish to apply should first contact the correspondent by email. A meeting will then be set up to discuss the potential application. After the meeting, organisations may then be invited to complete an application. Unsolicited applications will not be considered prior to a meeting.

Sources of information

Accounts; annual report; Charity Commission record; funder's website.

Norwich Town Close Estate Charity

Education; social welfare; general charitable purposes

Within a 20-mile radius of the Guildhall of the City of Norwich

£763,200 (2020/21)

CC number: 235678

Correspondent: The Trustees, 1 Woolgate Court, St Benedict's Street, Norwich, Norfolk NR2 4AP (tel: 01603 621023; email: david.hynes@norwichcharitabletrusts.org.uk)

Trustees: David Barber; Boyd Taylor; John Garside; David Fullman; Vivien Thomas; Owen Gibbs; Jacqueline Hanlon; Nigel Back; John Rushmer; Stuart Lamb; Melanie Kent; Philip Blanchflower; Cynthia Cooke; Michael Quinton; Jeanne Southgate; Elspeth Jones.

 www.norwichcharitabletrusts.org.uk

 @NorwichChTr

General information

Norwich Town Close Estate Charity is one of three trusts – sitting alongside Norwich Consolidated Charities and Anguish's Educational Foundation – which comprise the grant-giving arm of Norwich Charitable Trusts.

Norwich Town Close Estate Charity makes grants to individuals and organisations from the income generated in perpetuity from historic endowments – some dating back 400 years.

With respect to the types of organisations funded, the trust's 2020/21 annual report and accounts state that:

> These are largely organisations which, through their work, aim to promote the education of people who are in need of financial assistance or to provide facilities for recreation and leisure-time activities – in particular, but not exclusively, those related to the rich heritage and cultural life of our area of benefit.

Financial information

Year end	31/03/2021
Income	£1,060,000
Assets	£28,290,000
Grants to organisations	£763,200
No. of grants	55

Further financial information

During the year 55 grants were awarded to organisations, totalling £763,200. The average grant was £13,900.

Beneficiaries included: Soul Foundation (£75,000); Priscilla Bacon Norfolk Hospice (£60,000); Norwich Cathedral Choir (£30,000); The Garage (£25,000); The Forum Trust (£19,000); East Anglian Air Ambulance (£15,000); Young Norfolk Arts Trust (£7,000); Oak St Circus (£3,500); Bluebell Primary School (£500).

Applications

Apply in writing to the correspondent.

Sources of information

Accounts; annual report; Charity Commission record; funder's website.

The Norwood and Newton Settlement

Christian projects and churches

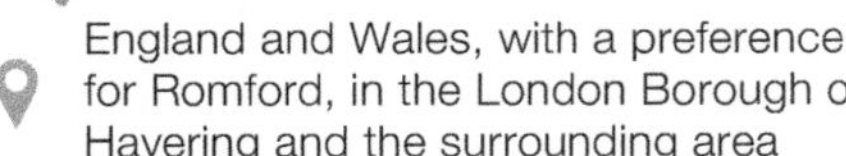

England and Wales, with a preference for Romford, in the London Borough of Havering and the surrounding area

£380,000 (2020/21)

CC number: 234964

Correspondent: The Trustees, 5 Convent Close, Upminster, London RM14 2FA (tel: 01708 226618; email: norwoodandnewton@btinternet.com or use the contact form on the charity's website)

Trustees: Stella Holland; Susan Bed; Alan Gray; Rodney Eborn; Trevor Marlow.

 http://norwoodandnewton.co.uk

General information

The charity was founded by Thomas England and his wife, who set up The Norwood and The Newton Settlement respectively in 1952 and 1960. The two charities were amalgamated in 1996 and support Methodist and other mainline Free Churches. Originally, the trust was set up to promote occupational education, social education and the Christian religion. At present, it mainly focuses on Christian activities.

According to the charity's website, it will support the following activities:

- Churches' new capital building schemes to include Church use (not solely for community use to provide a letting income).
- Church building schemes where there is a reasonable expectation of growth.
- Local Charities (Havering area) demonstrating Christian Values for capital schemes or clearly defined one-off capital projects.
- Havering based Christian Charities for projects to support and promote Christianity (small one-off grants only)

Financial information

Year end	31/03/2021
Income	£371,800
Assets	£11,390,000
Grants to organisations	£380,000

Beneficiaries included: Worcester Park Baptist Church – Surrey (£30,000); Christ Church Newham URC (£25,000); St Ives Methodist Church – Huntingdon (£15,000); Harold Hill Foodbank – Havering (£10,000); Ridgeway Evangelical Church – Chingford (£7,500); Didcot Baptist Church – Oxon (£5,000); Hemsworth Methodist Church – Pontefract (£2,000).

Exclusions

The charity's website states grants are not made for the following:

- Repairs and maintenance.
- Salaries and running costs.
- Equipment.
- Lottery funded or application being processed.
- Churches operating a policy of closed communion table.
- Individuals.
- Small schemes where the cost could be covered by the Church or Charity.
- Small schemes made up of individual elements that could be undertaken as and when funding is available.
- Small schemes that are purely to comply with Equalities Acts (e.g. ramps and WCs).
- Schemes where building work has already been completed.

Applications

Contact the charity, providing a brief outline of the project. The charity will then assess if the project meets the grant-making criteria and will send an application form to be completed.

Sources of information

Accounts; annual report; Charity Commission record; funder's website.

The Nuffield Foundation

Science, social science research and capacity development, particularly in the fields of education, welfare and justice

Predominantly in the UK

£10.36 million (2020)

CC number: 206601

Correspondent: Grants Team, 28 Bedford Square, London WC1B 3JS (tel: 020 7631 0566; email: info@nuffieldfoundation.org)

Trustees: Sir Keith Burnett; Prof. Ash Amin; Prof. Ann Phoenix; Prof. James Banks; The Hon, Sir Ernest Ryder; John Pullinger; Prof. Lorraine Dearden.

www.nuffieldfoundation.org

 facebook.com/nuffieldfoundation

 @nuffieldfound

General information

The Nuffield Foundation is an independent charity established in 1943 by William Morris, Lord Nuffield, the founder of Morris Motors.

In 2017 the foundation launched its five-year strategy for influencing social policy, shaping the research agenda and supporting new ideas. According to its website, the foundation's strategic goals are:

- Fund research that advances educational opportunity and social well-being across the United Kingdom.
- Improve the accessibility, use, and collection of the evidence and data necessary to understand the issues affecting people's life chances.
- Increase opportunities for young people – particularly those from disadvantaged backgrounds – to be active participants in a knowledge economy.
- Increase the profile and influence of our research portfolio.

Funding programmes

The foundation has several funds which open and close on a regular basis. These include:

- **Research, Development and Analysis Fund** – to advance educational opportunity and social well-being across the UK. Work funded is expected to improve the design and operation of social policy, especially in education, welfare and justice. Grant requests should be between £10,000 and £500,000, with most grants awarded being between £50,000 and £300,000, for projects between six months and three years in duration. Occasionally, proposals with larger budgets and longer timescales will be considered
- **Oliver Bird Fund** – research into musculoskeletal (MSK) conditions. The foundation has dedicated £12.5 million between 2019 and 2029 to this research fund

Visit the website for detailed information on each of the funds.

Financial information

Year end	31/12/2020
Income	£4,420,000
Grants to organisations	£10,360,000

Further financial information

Grants were broken down as follows:

Welfare	£3,230,000
Education	£2,950,000
Justice	£2,360,000
Strategic	£1,820,000

Beneficiaries included: Queen's University Belfast (£306,900); Centre for Evidence and Implementation Global (£299,400); University of Edinburgh (£160,000); Loughborough University (£93,700); University College London (£85,900); University of Sheffield (£12,000); Michael Sieff Foundation (£3,100).

Exclusions

For the Research, Development and Analysis Fund, the website lists the following areas which are not funded:

- Individuals without a formal employment or other relationship with the institution hosting the grant
- Projects led by individuals unaffiliated to any particular organisation
- Projects led by schools or further education colleges
- Projects led by undergraduates or Masters students
- PhD fees or projects where the main purpose is to support a PhD
- The establishment of academic posts
- Ongoing costs or the costs of 'rolling out' existing work or services
- 'Dissemination-only' projects, including campaigning work, which are not connected to our funded work
- Local charities, replacement for statutory funding, or local social services or social welfare provision
- Requests for financial help or educational fees from or on behalf of individuals
- Projects from individuals and institutions outside the UK, unless they are collaborative projects with a UK institution

Check the website for exclusion criteria of all the foundation's funds.

Applications

Applicants should firstly read the extensive 'Guide for applicants' for the relevant funding programme. The first stage is to submit an outline application, which will be considered and then the proposal may be shortlisted for consideration by trustees. In this case applicants will be asked to submit a full application. An application timetable of deadlines can be found on the foundation's website.

Sources of information

Accounts; annual report; Charity Commission record; funder's website; guidelines for applicants.

The Sir Peter O'Sullevan Charitable Trust

Animal welfare, especially horses; the racing industry; people with disabilities; children and young people

UK

£1.01 million (2020/21)

CC number: 1078889

Correspondent: Nigel Payne, Administrator, The Old School, Bolventor, Launceston, Cornwall PL15 7TS (tel: 07768 025265; email: nigel@earthsummit.demon.co.uk)

Trustees: Michael Dillon; Geoffrey Hughes; Nigel Payne; John McManus; Michael Kerr-Dineen; Sir Anthony McCoy; Dierdre Flood.

 www.thevoiceofracing.com

General information

This trust was established in 1999 by horse racing commentator Peter O'Sullevan in order to improve the welfare of retired, injured or ill-treated animals.

The trust's website states:

> In the main, applications to be submitted should be animal-related and most probably equine.
>
> However charities concentrating on young people, disabled or infirmed individuals or others associated with the racing industry are also welcomed.

The trust regularly supports six horse and animal welfare charities: Blue Cross, Brooke, Compassion in World Farming, World Horse Welfare, Racing Welfare and the British Thoroughbred Retraining Centre. Occasionally, it also supports other specific projects and causes, mainly but not exclusively related to horses or the racing industry. Currently the six charities named above receive £30,000 each per annum.

Financial information

Year end	30/04/2021
Income	£140,000
Assets	£4,050,000
Grants to organisations	£1,010,000

Beneficiaries included: Injured Jockeys Fund (£170,400); National Horseracing College (£30,000); Horse Sense Wirral (£10,000); Riding for the Disabled (£2,000).

Applications

Apply in writing to the correspondent. Further guidance is available on the trust's website. Applications need to be received by the last day of November each year and will be discussed in detail by the trustees to reach a decision by the end of January.

Sources of information

Accounts; annual report; Charity Commission record; funder's website.

Ocean Family Foundation

Marine conservation

Worldwide

£432,700 (2020/21)

CC number: 1174759

Correspondent: The Trustees, 3 Cadogan Gate, London SW1X 0AS (email: hello@oceanfamilyfoundation.org)

Trustees: Peter Dubens; David Till; Jessica Getty; Louise Creasey.

 www.oceanfamilyfoundation.org

General information

The foundation was established in 2017 and supports marine conservation projects worldwide.

The following information has been taken from the foundation's website:

> We seek out and donate to existing or start up marine and ocean orientated conservation projects. These are either projects out in the field or multimedia programmes. We choose projects that resonate with us in diverse global locations.
>
> Our emphasis is on having a direct connection with the projects we support. These are programmes that have a positive impact on marine life and ocean health; as well as research, education and reducing the use of plastics.

Financial information

Year end	28/02/2021
Income	£236,400
Assets	£91,300
Grants to organisations	£432,700

Beneficiaries included: A Plastic Free Planet Ltd (£100,000); The Africa Foundation (£87,000); Worldrise ONLUS (£62,900); Fundacion Save The Med (£44,800); Trash Hero World (£16,500).

Applications

Apply in writing to the correspondent. The foundation's website states that all funding proposals are welcomed.

Sources of information

Charity Commission record; funders website.

The Ofenheim Charitable Trust

General charitable purposes, particularly health, social welfare, the arts, animals and the environment

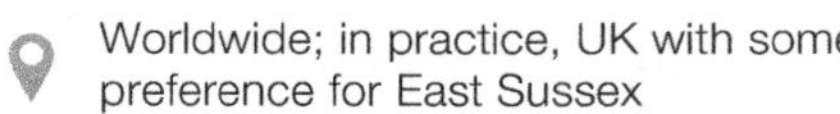
Worldwide; in practice, UK with some preference for East Sussex

£514,000 (2020/21)

CC number: 286525

Correspondent: The Trustees, c/o RSM UK Tax and Accounting Ltd, The Pinnacle, 170 Midsummer Boulevard, Milton Keynes, Buckinghamshire MK9 1BP (tel: 01908 687800)

Trustees: Fiona Byrd; Roger Clark; Dr Alexander Clark; Rory McLeod.

General information

Established in 1983 by Dr Angela Ofenheim, the trust provides regular support for a number of charities in East Sussex due to the founder's association with that area. Support is given for a range of purposes, particularly:

- The care and welfare of older people and children
- Hospices
- Medical research
- Music
- Education
- The arts
- Wildlife

One-off appeals may be considered if the trustees have some prior knowledge of the charity's work.

Financial information

Year end	31/03/2021
Income	£492,100
Assets	£18,190,000
Grants to organisations	£514,000
No. of grants	72

Beneficiaries included: Southern Thailand Elephant Foundation (£25,000); Barnardo's (£15,000); Scope (£12,000); St Wilfred's Hospice – Eastbourne (£10,000); Greater London Fund for the Blind and Save the Children Fund (£6,500 each); Holland Park Opera (£4,500); Songbird Survival (£3,500).

Exclusions

The trust does not make grants to individuals.

Applications

Apply in writing to the correspondent. Note: the trust tends to support the same organisations each year and prefers to support organisations of which the trustees have prior knowledge.

Sources of information

Accounts; annual report; Charity Commission record.

Oglesby Charitable Trust

General charitable purposes, particularly: the arts and culture; education; the environment; social welfare and health; medical aid and research

Mainly the north of England

£3.29 million (2019/20)

CC number: 1026669

Correspondent: Louise Magill, Trust Manager, Union, Albert Square, Manchester M2 6LW (tel: 0161 638 9200; email: welcome@oglesbycharitabletrust.org.uk)

Trustees: Jane Oglesby; Chris Oglesby; Jean Oglesby; Katharine Vokes; Kathryn Graham.

https://oglesbycharitabletrust.org.uk

General information

The Oglesby Charitable Trust was established in 1992 and has been active since the early 2000s. The trust is funded by annual contributions from Bruntwood Ltd, a company which is part of a group of North West England-based property investment companies owned by the founding trustees.

The trust make grants across five broad areas: the arts and culture; education; the environment; medical aid and research; and tackling social and health inequalities.

The trust makes grants ranging from under £1,000 to over £1 million. Grants can be one-off but the majority are multi-year. Funding proposals are considered by invitation only.

Grant holders can also access 'Funding Plus', a range of non-financial resources including access to advice, training, networking, signposting, complimentary meeting room hire and opportunities to advertise volunteer roles and opportunities to Bruntwood staff.

Financial information

Year end	30/09/2020
Income	£598,600
Assets	£3,130,000
Grants to organisations	£3,290,000
No. of grants	60

Further financial information

During the year the trust made 77 grants to 60 organisations, four of which were first-time grantees. Grants were broken down as follows:

Tackling social and health inequalities	£1.04 million
Medical aid and research	£740,000
Artistic development	£497,800
Environmental improvement	£464,900
Other	£358,400
Education	£189,900

Only beneficiaries of grants of over £33,000 were listed in the 2019/20 accounts.

Beneficiaries included: Royal Exchange Theatre (£300,000); Community Forest Trust (£250,000); University of Manchester (£210,000); Blood Cancer UK (two grants totalling £190,000); Safe Families for Children (£60,000); Manchester Museum (£33,000).

Exclusions

The following information is taken from the trust's website:

> Generally we do not consider applications from:
>
> - Non-registered charities – although we can support Community Interest Companies
> - Second tier organisations that exist to redistribute funds to other charities
> - Animal charities
> - Organisations that are active primarily outside the UK
> - Church and all building fabric appeals

- Charities for which the promotion of religion is their primary purpose

Equally, we rarely fund the following:

- Conferences
- Fundraising costs
- Expeditions
- General sports, unless for a specific, identified group
- Holidays
- Individuals
- Routine staff training
- Sponsorship and marketing appeals

Applications

The trust's website states:

> The Oglesby Charitable Trust is an invitation-only funder. A small team with a focused approach, we want to ensure that we use our resources, and those of others, effectively. This is why we limit the time and energy spent on preparing applications to those most likely to be successful.
>
> We find our grantees through our collective professional and personal networks. Each Trustee has an active role in one or more of our giving areas, and all those involved in decision-making have extensive experience of working with charitable and community organisations.

Sources of information

Accounts; annual report; Charity Commission record; funder's website.

The Hamish Ogston Foundation

Health; heritage; music

UK and worldwide

£6.37 million (2020/21)

CC number: 1185978

Correspondent: The Trustees, Dixon Wilson, 6th Floor, 22 Chancery Lane, London WC2A 1LS (tel: 020 3696 1447; email: office@hamishogstonfoundation.org)

Trustees: Hamish Ogston; Isabella Ogston.

 www.hamishogstonfoundation.org

 @HamishOgstonFdn

General information

This foundation was registered with the Charity Commission in October 2019.

The foundation is named after Hamish Ogston, a successful entrepreneur who has co-founded several different businesses throughout his career. These include Europe's first retail loyalty reward scheme, a tour operator and an international marketing service company, among others. Hamish Ogston has devoted a large portion of his life to philanthropy and, as a result of his work, been awarded a CBE for his services to business and the community in York.

His website states that Hamish's future philanthropic activity will be conducted through this foundation.

According to the application guidelines, the foundation seeks to 'invest in effective charities' by making grants of at least £1.5 million per request for causes relating to health (eliminating disparities in access to treatment), heritage (preservation of buildings and craftsmanship with historic value) and music (supporting the UK's great musical traditions through training programmes.) There are four key underlying principles the foundation aims to embody when selecting causes to support. These are:

- **Encouraging an entrepreneurial mindset:** constantly striving to create a 'best in class' philanthropy for all chosen projects
- **Maximising the benefit:** ensuring that no money is wasted and all donations are used cost-effectively to achieve an outcome
- **Addressing the north–south divide:** helping to re-balance the economic divide between the south of England and other parts of the UK (therefore preference will be given to projects outside the south of England)
- **Easy to measure outcomes:** outcomes should be easily monitored to ensure projects have a visible and lasting difference

Financial information

Year end	30/06/2021
Income	£11,630,000
Assets	£7,800,000
Grants to organisations	£6,370,000

Further financial information

Grants were broken down as follows: heritage (£5.55 million); music (£780,400); health (£31,700).

Beneficiaries included: Historic England Foundation (£4.32 million); Cathedral's Workshop Fellowship (£1.23 million); Diocese of Leeds Grant (£779,700); Venoms and Toxins 2021 (£16,700); Global Snakebite Initiative (£12,000).

Applications

Application forms can be downloaded from the foundation's website. Once completed, applications should be returned by email only. The foundation aims to respond within a week; however, the website does state that due to a high volume of applications, acknowledgements cannot be guaranteed in all circumstances.

Sources of information

Charity Commission record; funder's website; Hamish Ogston (website).

Oizer Charitable Trust

Jewish causes

 UK, with a preference for Greater Manchester

£342,200 (2020/21)

CC number: 1014399

Correspondent: The Trustees, 1st Floor, Cloister House, Riverside, New Bailey Street, Manchester M3 5FS (tel: 0161 832 8721)

Trustees: Joshua Halpern; Cindy Halpern.

General information

According to its 2020/21 annual report, the trust awards donations 'to a wide variety of charities within the Jewish community'.

Financial information

Year end	31/03/2021
Income	£332,700
Assets	£3,330,000
Grants to organisations	£342,200

Beneficiaries included: Chevras Mo'oz Ladal (£43,400); Teshivoh Tefilloh Tzedokoh (£26,900); Shaarei Orah Ltd (£20,500).

Applications

Contact the correspondent for further information. According to the trust's 2020/21 annual report: 'The trustees have identified a number of Orthodox Jewish charities which profess and teach the principles of traditional Judaism or which carry out activities which advance religion in accordance with the Orthodox Jewish faith. Grants are given on application to the trustees by these or similar charities.'

Sources of information

Accounts; annual report; Charity Commission record.

Old Possum's Practical Trust

 The arts; historical conservation; education and literacy; people who are disadvantaged; people with disabilities

UK

£306,000 (2020/21)

CC number: 328558

Correspondent: The Trustees, c/o RSM, The Pinnacle, 170 Midsummer Boulevard, Milton Keynes, Buckinghamshire MK9 1BP (tel: 01908 662255; email: generalenquiry@old-possums-practical-trust.org.uk)

Trustees: Judith Hooper; Deidre Simpson; Clare Reihill.

 www.old-possums-practical-trust.org.uk

General information

The trust's website states that it supports literary, artistic, musical and theatrical projects, with priority given to those which will have an impact on future literary work and that 'display enterprise in their artistic endeavour'. It was established in 1990 by Valerie Eliot, the widow of T. S. Eliot, from funds derived from the success of the musical *Cats* which was inspired by Eliot's *Old Possum's Book of Practical Cats.*

The trust's website states that:

> Priority is given to requests that display enterprise in artistic endeavour and demonstrate high sustainability and contextual impact. Particular interest is taken in those projects that will have an impact on future literary work.
>
> Special contributions made by the Trust to other related types of organisation reflect both the personal history of Old Possum's Practical Trust and the wishes of the Trustees. Support is more likely for those projects which best reflect the literary reputation and name of T. S. Eliot and the special interests of his late wife, Valerie Eliot.

Financial information

Year end	31/03/2021
Income	£144,600
Assets	£9,590,000
Grants to organisations	£306,000

Beneficiaries included: Kiran Society (£30,000); British Film Institute (£20,000); The Book Trade Charity (£10,000); Unicorn Theatre (£5,000); Refuge (£2,500).

Exclusions

According to the trust's website, grants are not usually made for/to:

- activities or projects already completed
- capital building projects
- personal training and education e.g. tuition or living costs for college or university
- projects outside the UK
- medical care or resources
- feasibility studies
- national charities having substantial amounts of potential funding likely from other sources

Applications

Applications can be made via the trust's website.

Sources of information

Accounts; annual report; Charity Commission record; funder's website.

Henry Oldfield Trust

 Promotion of entrepreneurship; homelessness and addiction; programmes which reduce offending and re-offending

 Kent and Medway

£1.62 million (2020/21)

CC number: 1156496

Correspondent: The Trustees, Doddington Place, Church Lane, Doddington, Sittingbourne, Kent ME9 0BB (tel: 01795 886385)

Trustees: Richard Oldfield; Leonora Philipps; Amicia Oldfield; Christopher Oldfield; Edward Oldfield; Baroness Jenkin.

General information

The trust was established in 2014 and, according to its Charity Commission record, aims to support 'programmes which reduce offending and re-offending, promote entrepreneurship among the young and disadvantaged, and tackle other challenges such as homelessness and addiction'. The trustees prefer to give grants to recognisable national charities and to local charities that are known to the trustees.

Financial information

Year end	31/03/2021
Income	£1,030,000
Assets	£15,760,000
Grants to organisations	£1,620,000

Beneficiaries included: Royal Marsden Cancer Charity (£175,000); University of Kent (£125,000); Murston All Saints Trust (£50,000); Speakers for Schools (£10,000); Guildhall School of Music (£9,300); Prisoners' Advice Service (£7,500); Greenbanks Care Trust (£2,000); Symi Music Festival (£500).

Applications

Apply in writing to the correspondent.

Sources of information

Accounts; annual report; Charity Commission record.

Orthopaedic Research UK

Medical research, in particular orthopaedic research; education and training; publishing

 UK

£488,500 (2020/21)

CC number: 1111657

Correspondent: Dr Arash Angadji, Chief Executive, Furlong House, 10A Chandos Street, London W1G 9DQ (tel: 020 7637 5789; email: info@oruk.org)

Trustees: Peter Harrison; Keith Tucker; Prof. Matteo Santin; Martin Gouldstone; Sarah Harkness; Adrian Downing; Dr Catherine Ball; Prof. Neil Rushton.

 www.oruk.org

 facebook.com/ORUKcharity

 @OR_UK

 @or_uk

General information

Orthopaedic Research UK (formerly known as the Furlong Research Charitable Foundation) was established in 1989 by the orthopaedic surgeon Ronald Furlong FRCS. The charity is dedicated to advancing orthopaedic knowledge by funding and publishing research, funding and organising education (predominantly workshops, training courses, lectures, seminars and symposia) and publishing and promoting publication in the field.

With respect to its grant-making policy, the charity's 2020/21 annual report and accounts states:

> We consider the support of grant applications that are within the scope of our charitable aims; that is to promote the advancement of orthopaedic research and education and, in particular, the encouragement of innovation and partnerships to advance bone, joint and muscle wellbeing in the UK.

The charity's website provides details on the availability and deadlines for research grants, with deadlines spaced throughout the year. At the time of writing (May 2022), the charity's website stated that the value of the charity's grants programme during 2021/22 would be £1 million.

The Ronald Furlong Fund

The fund was established in 2019 and aims to support UK-based start-ups with innovative and commercially viable ideas to solve the unmet needs of society around bone, joint and muscle well-being. Grants are of up to £100,000.

Financial information

Year end	31/03/2021
Income	£1,210,000
Assets	£29,490,000
Grants to organisations	£488,500
No. of grants	7

Beneficiaries included: Newcastle University (£165,000 in two grants); University College London (£95,600); University of Southampton (£75,000); Imperial College London (£50,000); University of Bristol (£46,800).

Applications

Specifics of the application process, deadlines and eligibility vary for research grants, research fellowships and start-up funding. Pre-submission enquiries are welcome. Full details can be found on the charity's website.

Sources of information

Accounts; annual report; Charity commission record; funder's website.

The O'Sullivan Family Charitable Trust

The care of people who have disabilities, especially children and young people, and genetic research

UK

£288,100 (2019/20)

CC number: 1123757

Correspondent: The Trustees, 36 Edge Street, London W8 7PN (tel: 020 7131 4000)

Trustees: Diana O'Sullivan; Finian O'Sullivan; Emily O'Sullivan; Sophie O'Sullivan; Tessa Cartwright.

General information

The trust was established in 2008 with a £5 million donation from Finian O'Sullivan, founder of Burren Energy, who reportedly made £67 million from the sale of the company in 2007.

According to its annual report, the trust's main objectives are:

> the advancement of health or the relief of those in need by reason of ill-health, disability, financial hardship or other disadvantage, in particular (without limitation) by 1 the provision of respite care for children and young adults affected by severe long-term disability and 2 the promotion of genetic research into the causes of such disability, and the dissemination of the useful results of such research and b the advancement of education or science, in particular (without limitation) in the field of long-term disability.

Financial information

Year end	30/06/2020
Income	£238,500
Assets	£4,980,000
Grants to organisations	£288,100

Beneficiaries included: The Playhouse Foundation (£94,100); Room to Read UK Ltd (£30,000); The Brickworks (£25,000); DEBRA (£15,000); Shepherds Down School Fund (£10,000); Whizz-Kidz (£5,000); Seenaryo (£2,000).

Applications

Apply in writing to the correspondent.

Sources of information

Accounts; annual report; Charity Commission record.

Ostro Fayre Share Foundation

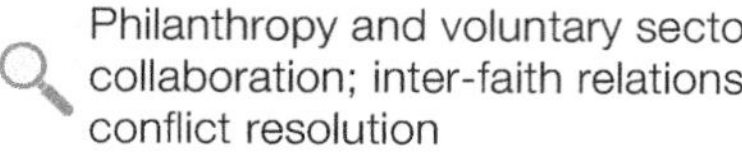
Philanthropy and voluntary sector collaboration; inter-faith relations; conflict resolution

UK and overseas, in particular Myanmar

£739,900 (2020)

CC number: 1090985

Correspondent: The Trustees, 77–79 Charlotte Street, London W1T 4PW (tel: 020 7569 9093; email: info@fayresharefoundation.org)

Trustees: Hetty Maher; Katy Ostro; Lyddon Simon; Maurice Ostro.

www.ostro.com/foundation

facebook.com/fayreshare.fdn?sk=wall

@fayresharefdn

General information

Entrepreneur Maurice Ostro established the Ostro Fayre Share Foundation in 2000. It was funded by the proceeds from the (sales of the) foundation endowed shares in Air Fayre plc. Today, the foundation supports organisations that are engaged with its priority causes, which comprise:

- Philanthropy
- Collaboration
- Interfaith relations
- Conflict resolution

Financial information

Year end	31/12/2020
Income	£936,400
Assets	£936,400
Grants to organisations	£739,900

Beneficiaries included: A list of beneficiaries was not available.

Applications

The Ostro Fayre Share Foundation does not accept unsolicited requests for funding. However, its website states that it may 'consider offers of partnership in its key priority areas: philanthropy, collaboration, interfaith relations, and conflict resolution'.

Sources of information

Accounts; annual report; Charity Commission record; funder's website.

The Ovo Charitable Foundation

Access to energy; youth poverty; climate action among young people

UK and overseas

£1.01 million (2020)

CC number: 1155954

Correspondent: Gabi Sethi, Head of Foundation, 1 Rivergate, Bristol BS1 6ED (tel: 0800 599 9440; email: hello@ovofoundation.org.uk)

Trustees: Gina Cicerone; Katherine Goldsmith; Phillip Kerry; Raman Bhatia.

www.ovofoundation.org.uk

General information

The foundation is the corporate charity of Ovo Energy, an energy supply company based in Bristol. It was established in 2014 and is funded by customer donations, which are then matched by the company. Ovo also covers the running costs of the foundation.

The foundation's website states that its vision is to 'give every child and young person a greener, fairer world to grow up in'.

The foundation has three main areas of work:

- Reducing poverty among young people
- Increasing energy access
- Empowering young people to take climate action

According to its 2020 annual report, the foundation is 'committed to funding projects that have potential to bring about long-term systemic change and can be scaled, wherever possible'.

Ovo Gives Back

As well as project-by-project partnerships, each year the foundation makes grants totalling at least £100,000 to local charities that help the communities that Ovo works in. Causes are nominated and voted for by Ovo employees and receive help from employees through volunteering and fundraising.

Financial information

Year end	31/12/2020
Income	£1,110,000
Assets	£1,570,000
Grants to organisations	£1,010,000
No. of grants	27+

Beneficiaries included: 1625 Independent People (£190,100); Energy Sparks (£107,000); Tales Toolkit (£80,000); Energy 4 Impact (£47,000); Action for Conservation (£27,500); Dunfermline Foodbank (£10,500); Youngminds (£8,300).

Applications

The foundation largely carries out its own research to identify projects to support. According to the website at the time of writing (February 2022), although the foundation is not currently accepting applications for grants, this might change so check the website for any updates.

The Ovo Gives Back grants are nominated and voted for by Ovo employees.

Sources of information

Accounts; annual report; Charity Commission record; funder's website.

Oxfordshire Historic Churches Trust (2016)

Major and minor repairs, restoration and modernisation of churches and chapels

Oxfordshire

£295,600 (2020/21)

CC number: 1168567

Correspondent: The Secretary, 4 Haslemere Gardens, Oxford, Oxfordshire OX2 8EL (tel: 01865 559305; email: secretary@ohct.org.uk)

Trustees: Giles Dessain; Hilary Hall; Cynthia Robinson; Michael Sibly; Dr Stephen Goss; Prof. Malcolm Airs; Richard Hughes; Dr Imogen Coldstream; Stephen Slack.

http://ohct.org.uk

facebook.com/OxfordshireHistoricChurchTrust

General information

The trust was founded in 2016, continuing the work of the Oxford Historic Churches Trust (which transferred its assets and liabilities to the new trust in April 2017). The trust gives grants for the preservation, repair and maintenance of churches, of any denomination, in Oxfordshire.

Grants also provide funding for protective measures such as the installation of roof alarms as well as helping make churches more widely accessible to people with disabilities.

Financial information

Year end	31/03/2021
Income	£2,880,000
Assets	£5,080,000
Grants to organisations	£295,600

Further financial information

During 2020/21, grants were distributed as follows: general purposes – major and minor repairs and restoration and the modernisation of facilities (£291,300); roof alarms (£4,300).

Beneficiaries included: St Michael and All Angels – Clifton Hampden (£22,000); St Margaret – Little Faringdon (£18,000); Holy Trinity – Headington Quarry (£11,000); All Saints – Middleton Stoney (£7,000); St Peter – Wolvercote (£4,000); St Thomas – Elsfield (£2,000); Church Recording Society (£250).

Exclusions

The trust will not consider applications for the following:

- Routine maintenance
- Work that has already started
- Removal or replacement of pews
- Liturgical re-ordering, such as nave altars and platforms
- Church or parish halls
- Car parks
- Buildings that are under 50 years old

Applications

Apply through the trust's website. Applications are considered three times a year – see the website for application deadlines.

Sources of information

Accounts; annual report; Charity Commission's record; funder's website.

The Doris Pacey Charitable Foundation

Jewish causes

UK

£817,500 (2020/21)

CC number: 1101724

Correspondent: The Trustees, c/o Charities Aid Foundation, 25 Kings Hill Avenue, Kings Hill, West Mailing, Kent ME19 4TA (tel: 0300 012 3701; email: paceyandbrynbergfoundations@cafonline.org)

Trustees: Ray Locke; Leslie Powell; Linda Courtney.

General information

The Doris Pacey Charitable Foundation was established in 2003 to make grants to organisations worldwide. It provides funding for large or specific projects with a focus on education, the arts and medical and social needs. The foundation has a preference for working with Jewish organisations.

Financial information

Year end	05/04/2021
Income	£66,800
Assets	£3,100,000
Grants to organisations	£817,500

Beneficiaries included: World Jewish Relief (£605,000); United Jewish Israel Appeal (£82,500); Jewish Women's Aid (£80,000) Shobana Jeyasingh Dance Company (£50,000).

Applications

Apply in writing to the correspondent.

Sources of information

Accounts; annual report; Charity Commission record.

The James Pantyfedwen Foundation (Ymddiriedolaeth James Pantyfedwen)

The advancement, encouragement and promotion of religion, education, the arts, agriculture and other charitable purposes for the benefit of Welsh people, primarily in Wales

Wales

£450,600 (2020/21)

CC number: 1069598

Correspondent: Gwenan Creunant, Executive Secretary, Pantyfedwen, 9 Market Street, Aberystwyth, Ceredigion SY23 1DL (tel: 01970 612806; email: post@jamespantyfedwen.cymru)

Trustees: Gwerfyl Jones; Dr Eurfyl Gwilym; Sian Jones; Alun Charles; Jane Aaron; Wyn Jones; Geraint Jones; Dr William Griffiths; David Lewis; The Revd Evans; Dr Eryn White; Ken Richards; Derec Morgan.

www.jamespantyfedwen.cymru

General information

The James Pantyfedwen Foundation began its operations on 1 April 1998. It is the successor of two former charitable trusts, both of which were set up by the late Sir D. J. James, whose aim was to create a permanent endowment to benefit the people of Wales. The foundation currently supports religion, education and culture in Wales by providing grants under three headings: church buildings, postgraduate students and Eisteddfodau.

Any local Eisteddfod in Wales can apply for a grant of up to £500 if it is a registered charity or if it is organised by a registered or exempt charity.

Grants for repairs and building improvements for churches (including vestries and halls) are available. To be eligible for a grant, churches must be in Wales, hold at least one service each Sunday, have a membership of at least 50 and be part of a wider denominational structure but registered as a charity.

Financial information

Year end	31/03/2021
Income	£504,100
Assets	£16,870,000
Grants to organisations	£450,600

Beneficiaries included: Bethel Community Church – Newport (£12,000); St Peter's Church – Rhoose (£10,000); St Mary the Virgin Church – Brynmawr (£4,000); St Cynwyd's Church (£2,000); Holy Trinity Church – Ystrad Mynach (£1,000).

Exclusions

The following requests from churches cannot be considered for support:

- Residential accommodation for example manses or chapel houses
- Cemeteries or outside work for churches
- The restoration and purchase of church organs

Additional eligibility criteria for students can be found on the foundation's websites.

Applications

Application forms and detailed guidelines can be downloaded from the foundation's website. The trustees meet three times a year to consider applications in March, July and November. Applications must be submitted at least a month before the date of a meeting. Detailed information about what should be included in your application can be found on the foundation's website.

Sources of information

Accounts; annual reports; charity Commission record; funder's website.

Parabola Foundation

General charitable purposes, with a particular focus on the arts, culture and music

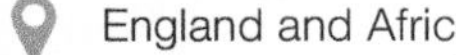

England and Africa

£617,000 (2020/21)

CC number: 1156008

Correspondent: The Trustees, Broadgate Tower, 20 Primrose Street, London EC2A 2EW (tel: 0191 500 8571)

Trustees: Deborah Jude; Anne Millican; Peter Millican.

General information

This foundation is the corporate charity of Parabola Land Ltd, a real estate and property development company. Trustee Peter Millican serves as a director of the company. Peter Millican has had a well-publicised involvement in the arts and was responsible for the development of Kings Place, a London concert venue and office space.

Parabola Foundation operates with general charitable purposes, although there is a particular focus on art, music and culture. Grants are made to UK-based organisations, with some awards made to organisations operating in Africa. The annual report for 2020/21 states:

> The objectives of the charity are to further charitable and cultural projects that will bring benefit to the public. It has been particularly keen to support music and the arts in a way that benefits the community.

The foundation gives regular support to a number of charities, such as Kings Place Music Foundation and Ruwenzori Sculpture Foundation. However, the foundation carefully evaluates all applications for funds based on merit.

Financial information

Year end	31/03/2021
Income	£863,000
Assets	£267,100
Grants to organisations	£617,000

Further financial information

Grants awarded in support of creative arts totalled £611,000, and other grants totalled £6,000. Only two grant amounts were listed in the accounts.

Beneficiaries included: Kings Place Music Foundation (£565,000); Ruwenzori Sculpture Foundation (£36,000); Edinburgh Leisure; Health In Mind; Grizedale Arts; People Know How; St Columbus Hospice.

Applications

Apply in writing to the correspondent.

Sources of information

Accounts; annual report; Charity Commission record; funder's website.

The Pargiter Trust

Older people and social inclusion

England and Guernsey

£525,000 (2020)

CC number: 1157779

Correspondent: David McManus, The Secretary, c/o AC Mole and Sons, Stafford House, Blackbrook Park Avenue, Taunton, Somerset TA1 2PX (tel: 07980 932716; email: admin@pargitertrust.org.uk)

Trustees: Suzanne Gardiner; Martyn Mogford; Victoria Westhorp; Mike Starkey; Louise Cook; Paul Metcalfe.

https://pargitertrust.org.uk

General information

The trust was established in 2005 by The Honourable Isobel Cooper-Heyman to support older people living in England and Guernsey. The trust's mission is to support disadvantaged older people (over the age of 65) to be independent, healthy and socially included. It achieves this by working with community foundations, charities and grassroots projects with similar objects.

The trust makes grants through seven community foundations in Surrey, Suffolk, Berkshire, Kent, Wiltshire, Guernsey and Tyne and Wear and Northumberland. In 2020 each community foundation received between £50,000 and £80,000.

Financial information

Year end	31/12/2020
Income	£725,900
Assets	£13,600,000
Grants to organisations	£525,000
No. of grants	84

Further financial information

The foundation made over 84 individual grants through seven community foundations.

Beneficiaries included: Community Foundation for Surrey, Kent Community Foundation and Suffolk Community Foundation (£80,000 each); Wiltshire Community Foundation (£50,000); Nesta T2C (£25,000).

Applications

Apply in writing to the correspondent. Most applications are received through one of the five community foundations the trust has a partnership with.

Sources of information

Accounts, annual report, Charity Commission record; funder's website.

Parkinson's UK

Research into Parkinson's disease

Mainly UK; occasionally the US

£4.51 million (2020)

CC number: 258197

Correspondent: The Trustees, 215 Vauxhall Bridge Road, London SW1V 1EJ (tel: 020 7963 3930; email: researchapplications@parkinsons.org.uk)

Trustees: Kyle Alexander; Matthew Durdy; Paresh Thakrar; Gary Shaughnessy; Dr Andrew Cavey; David Allan; Peter Miller; Helen Burston; Elaine Evans; Katrina Green; Ann McCallum.

www.parkinson's.org.uk

facebook.com/parkinsonsuk

@ParkinsonsUK

General information

The aim of Parkinson's UK is to find a cure for Parkinson's disease as well as improving the lives of everyone affected by it. Originally founded as the

Parkinson's Disease Society of the United Kingdom in 1969, the charity rebranded in 2010 and now operates under its trading name Parkinson's UK.

Research

While the charity's priority is to develop better treatments for Parkinson's and ultimately find a cure, research to improve quality of life is also supported. The following areas of research are supported by the charity:

- Balance and falls
- Stress and anxiety
- Uncontrollable movements
- Personalised treatments
- Dementia
- Mild thinking and memory problems
- Monitoring symptoms
- Sleep
- Dexterity
- Urinary problems

Funding programmes change periodically. All current funding streams can be seen on the website.

Other grant programmes

Grants are also made to various hospitals and health boards across the UK to improve services relating to Parkinson's care. During 2018, the charity launched its financial assistance programme for individuals. People affected by Parkinson's can apply for grants of up £1,500 towards costs such as specialist equipment, home adaptations and therapies. Funding rounds are advertised on the website.

Financial information

Year end	31/12/2020
Income	£36,320,000
Assets	£43,000,000
Grants to organisations	£4,510,000
No. of grants	24

Further financial information

During the year, research grants totalled £4.33 million. In addition, grants made to organisations for Parkinson's nurses and service improvements totalled £181,000. Donations made to individuals in the form of financial assistance grants totalled £89,000.

Only research grants of over £100,000 were listed in the accounts. Only Parkinson's nurses and service improvement grants over £50,000 were listed in the accounts.

Beneficiaries included: Neurolixis Inc (£784,000); University College London (four grants totalling £598,000); Newcastle University (two grants totalling £366,000); Northumbria Healthcare NHS Foundation Trust (£200,000); University of Bristol (£133,000); Barts Health NHS Trust (£83,000).

Exclusions

See the website for programme-specific exclusions.

Applications

Each grants programme has its own specific deadlines and application process. See the website for more information.

Sources of information

Accounts; annual report; Charity Commission record; funder's website.

Partners Global Foundation

General charitable purposes; education and training; health; arts, culture, heritage and science

UK and overseas

£4.06 million (2020/21)

CC number: 1177721

Correspondent: The Trustees, Floor 25, One Canada Square, Canary Wharf, London E14 5AB (tel: 07864 816313)

Trustees: Lonti Ebers; James Flatt; Ian Flatt.

General information

This foundation was registered with the Charity Commission in March 2018. According to its 2020 annual report, the foundation has refined its focus to:

- the support of art, culture, heritage, science and business; and
- the education of the general public and the education of children and young adults

Financial information

Year end	31/12/2020
Income	£548,000
Assets	£2,340,000
Grants to organisations	£4,060,000

Beneficiaries included: Museum of Modern Art – New York (£3.85 million); Tate Modern Art Gallery – London (£100,000); Bard College of Curatorial Studies – New York (£30,800); HRH Prince Charles Royal Drawing School (£15,000); Barbican Centre – London (£10,000); Camden Art Centre (£2,500); BRIC – New York (£1,900).

Applications

Apply in writing to the correspondent.

Sources of information

Accounts; annual report; Charity Commission record.

The JGW Patterson Foundation

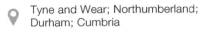

Research into cancer, arthritis and rheumatology; the purchase of equipment and caring services for the relief of such ilnesses

Tyne and Wear; Northumberland; Durham; Cumbria

£602,200 (2020/21)

CC number: 1094086

Correspondent: Pippa Aitken, Secretary, c/o Sintons LLP, The Cube, Arngrove Court, Barrack Road, Newcastle upon Tyne, Tyne and Wear NE4 6DB (tel: 0191 226 7878; email: info@jgwpattersonfoundation.co.uk)

Trustees: David Gold; James Dias; Prof. Alan Craft; Prof. Tim Cawston; Stephen Gilroy; Prof. David Young; Prof. Steven Clifford.

http://jgwpattersonfoundation.co.uk

General information

The foundation was established in 2002 with capital from the estate of the late John Patterson.

The foundation's website states:

> The main objectives of the Foundation are to fund research into, and purchase equipment and caring services for, the relief of cancer, arthritis and rheumatology in Tyne and Wear, Northumberland, Durham and Cumbria.
>
> The following areas are considered to be the most likely to be supported by the Foundation:
>
> - Pump Priming Research Projects
> - Fellowships and PhD Studentships
> - Bridging Funding
> - Special Purpose Grants
> - Charities and Hospices

Financial information

Year end	31/03/2021
Income	£967,200
Assets	£19,250,000
Grants to organisations	£602,200

Beneficiaries included: Newcastle University (£474,900); Durham University (£32,100); Marie Curie Hospice (£17,200); Butterwick Hospice Care (£15,000); Maggie's Newcastle (£10,000); Hospice at Home West Cumbria (£6,900); World Cancer Research Fund (£4,000).

Applications

Applications can be made through the foundation's website. The trustees meet quarterly in February, May, September and November. Completed applications for funding must be received at least one month prior to a quarterly meeting. Applications are usually then sent out for peer review and discussed again at the subsequent quarterly meeting of the trustees.

Sources of information

Accounts; annual report; Charity Commission record; funder's website.

David Pearlman Charitable Foundation

Social welfare; education; health; arts, culture and heritage; citizenship and community development; Jewish causes; general charitable purposes

 UK

£424,300 (2019/20)

CC number: 287009

Correspondent: Michael Goldberger, Secretary, New Burlington House, 1075 Finchley Road, London NW11 0PU (tel: 020 8731 0777)

Trustees: Michael Goldberger; Stuart Appleman; David Pearlman; Jonathan Hager; Mr H. Pearlman.

General information

Established in 1983, the foundation makes grants to charitable organisations for the following purposes:

- Social welfare
- Education
- Religion
- Health or the saving of lives
- Citizenship and community development
- The arts, culture, heritage and science
- General charitable purposes

Financial information

Year end	30/09/2020
Income	£2,180,000
Assets	£6,450,000
Grants to organisations	£424,300
No. of grants	20+

Further financial information

The foundation's 2019/20 accounts listed 20 beneficiaries – 'other grants' totalled £41,700.

Beneficiaries included: The National Youth Theatre (£60,000); The English Heritage Trust (£40,000); Support the Charity Worker (£30,000); The Cure Parkinson's Trust (£20,000); Care All Ltd (£15,000); Jewish Care and The Imperial War Museum (£10,000 each).

Applications

Apply in writing to the correspondent.

Sources of information

Accounts; annual report; Charity Commission record.

The Pears Family Charitable Foundation

Education, training and research; well-being; young people; supporting the voluntary sector; Jewish causes; health; social welfare; international development

 UK and overseas

£31.84 million (2020/21)

CC number: 1009195

Correspondent: The Trustees, 2 Old Brewery Mews, London NW3 1PZ (tel: 020 7433 3333; email: contact@pearsfoundation.org.uk)

Trustees: Sir Trevor Pears; Mark Pears; David Pears.

 www.pearsfoundation.org.uk

 @pearsfoundation

General information

The Pears Foundation is an independent family foundation rooted in Jewish values.

According to its 2020/21 annual accounts, the objects of the charity are to:

> create social benefit across a broad range of activities, based on the open nature of the founding trust deed. The Foundation promotes understanding of key issues through research and education programmes; drives engagement in social progress across the UK and globally, particularly in young people; and supports organisations focused on wellbeing for everyone.

In recent years the foundation awarded grants under the following categories:

- Special educational needs, disability and social welfare
- Holocaust education
- Health and mental health
- Care and support
- Youth social action
- Shared society
- International development
- Higher education
- Encouraging philanthropy
- Supporting the voluntary sector

The foundation supports the professional development of its grantees through the Pears Partners Professional Development Programme, which includes workshops and other non-financial support such as office space.

Financial information

Year end	31/03/2021
Income	£32,900,000
Assets	£27,750,000
Grants to organisations	£31,840,000

Beneficiaries included: A list of beneficiaries was not available. Previous beneficiaries include: Maudsley Charity (£5.5 million); University of Kent (£2 million); Hebrew University of Jerusalem (£1 million); Ambitious about Autism (£400,000); Marie Curie (£200,000); Olive Tree Initiative (£100,000); Young Minds (£80,000); Horatio's Garden (£50,000); The Royal Society of the Arts (£7,200); Dorset County Hospital Charity (£5,000).

Applications

Unsolicited applications are not accepted.

The annual report for 2019/20 states the following about the foundation's grant-making policy:

> We do not accept unsolicited applications which allows us to focus our time and resources on building strong partnerships with our grantees.
>
> We use research, reports, surveys and expert opinions to build and enhance our understanding of specific issues and challenges and enable us to direct funding most effectively. We have built a sizeable and diverse network of individuals and organisations who provide knowledge and expertise including existing grantees, other funders and community stakeholders.

Sources of information

Accounts; annual report; Charity Commission record; funder's website.

The Pebbles Trust

General charitable purposes; support for young people with talent; community

 Brighton and Hove

£412,600 (2020/21)

CC number: 1129132

Correspondent: James Arnell, Secretary, c/o New Quadrant Partners Ltd, 4th Floor, 5 Chancery Lane, London WC2A 1LG (tel: 020 7430 7159; email: charities@nqpltd.com)

Trustees: James Arnell; Louise Arnell; Louise Stoten.

 www.pebbletrust.org

 facebook.com/ThePebbleTrust

 @PebbleTrust

General information

The trust was established in 2009 and supports registered charities and talented young people in Brighton and Hove. Grants of between £500 and £5,000 are made to local organisations involved in community projects and work that supports disadvantaged people.

The trust supports individuals through talent grants of up to £500 to local young people to help develop their talents in sport, music, the performing arts and academia. It also offers bursaries to local young people who plan to put on an event at the Brighton Fringe.

Financial information

Year end	31/03/2021
Income	£250,600
Assets	£56,500
Grants to organisations	£412,600
No. of grants	19

Beneficiaries included: Martlets Hospice (£175,000); Brighton Festival Fringe (£171,700); South East Dance (£10,000); Moulsecoomb Forest Garden and Wildlife Project (£7,000); Brighton Parent infant Psychological Therapy (£5,000); Time to Talk Befriending (£3,000); Family Support Work (£2,000); Whitehawk Community Food Project (£1,800); Rockinghorse Children's Charity (£1,000).

Applications

Applications can be made in writing and will be considered if they include the following information:

- Aims and objectives of the charity
- Nature of appeal
- Total target if for a specific project
- Contributions received against the target
- Registered charity number
- Any other relevant factors

Applications can also be made online. Applications are accepted three times a year. Check the website for upcoming deadlines.

Sources of information

Accounts; annual report; Charity Commission record; funder's website.

The Dowager Countess Eleanor Peel Trust

Medical research; older people; social welfare

UK (medical grants); Lancashire; Cumbria, Greater Manchester, Cheshire and Merseyside (general grants)

£462,000 (2020/21)

CC number: 214684

Correspondent: The Secretary, c/o Hill Dickinson LLP, 50 Fountain Street, Manchester M2 2AS (tel: 0161 838 4977; email: secretary@peeltrust.com)

Trustees: Prof. Richard Ramsden; Julius Manduell; Michael Parkinson; Prof. Margaret Pearson; Prof. Colin Sibley; David Parkinson.

 www.peeltrust.com

General information

The Dowager Countess Eleanor Peel Trust was established by trust deed in 1951. The objects of the trust are for general charitable purposes but with a preference for medical charities, charities for older people and those who are disadvantaged.

General grants

Support is provided to charities supporting older people and assisting people who have 'fallen on evil days through no fault of their own'. Support is provided to charities operating in the trust's preferred locations of Lancashire, Cumbria, Greater Manchester, Cheshire and Merseyside. There is preference for small to medium-sized charities and supporting capital projects or project-related applications. Grants to disaster/ emergency appeals are considered on a case-by-case basis.

Medical grants

Medical grants are for sums up to a maximum of £25,000 and ordinarily are for areas such as pilot study costs or equipment.

The trust also funds fellowships in bio-medicine/health research.

Financial information

Year end	31/03/2021
Income	£571,300
Assets	£19,580,000
Grants to organisations	£462,000
No. of grants	48

Further financial information

Grants were broken down as follows:

Medical research	£175,500
People in need	£158,200
Other charitable purposes	£100,700
Older people	£10,000

Beneficiaries included: University of Manchester (£64,300); Lancaster University (£50,000); British Red Cross (£20,000); Bolton Deaf Society (£10,000); National Eye Research Centre (£8,500); Church in the Barn (£5,000); Bolton North CAP Centre (£3,000); Lancaster Royal Grammar School (£2,500); Heron Corn Mill/Beetham Trust (£1,500).

Exclusions

Grants are not made to charities primarily devoted to children and those that are under the control of central or local government.

Applications

Application forms are available on the trust website.

Sources of information

Accounts; annual report; Charity Commission record; funder's website.

People's Health Trust

Health and well-being; community; social welfare; tackling inequalities

England; Scotland; Wales

£3.53 million (2019/20)

CC number: 1125537

Correspondent: Grants Team, 2 Bath Place, Rivington Street, London EC2A 3DR (tel: 020 7749 9119; email: enquiries@peopleshealthtrust.org.uk)

Trustees: Barbara Simmonds; Paul Ballantyne; Prof. Elizabeth Dowler; Duncan Stephenson; Jacqueline Lodge; Thomas McIlravey; Leandra Box; Shavanah Taj; Jennifer Edwards.

www.peopleshealthtrust.org.uk

facebook.com/peopleshealthtrust

@Peoples_health

@peopleshealthtrust

General information

This trust is funded by the proceeds of 12 society lotteries, which operate through The Health Lottery. Since it launched in 2011, the trust has raised £122 million and has funded over 3,300 projects.

According to its website, the trust was set up to address health inequalities in England, Scotland and Wales. The trust funds work led by communities experiencing disadvantage, which addresses the underlying causes of health inequalities.

Grant programmes

The trust has three main funding programmes, which are described on its website as follows:

- **Active Communities** – grants of between £5,000 and £40,000 for local projects lasting up to two years. The programme is open in different parts of the country at different times
- **Local Conversations** – an approach which involves working together with the residents of a neighbourhood to determine how they would like to use the money raised through their local society lottery
- **Local People** – a programme through which several larger charities are funded, all of which work locally with residents to co-produce projects

The only funding programme that accepts applications is Active Communities. This programme is for community groups and not-for-profit organisations with an income of less than £350,000 a year or an average of

£350,000 over the last two years. The trust's website states:

> We're looking for small and local projects, genuinely designed and run by local people. [...] We support two types of project: neighbourhood-based projects (based in a small local area) and communities of interest (a group with shared identity or experiences).

For information on what funding is currently available in your area, refer to the trust's website.

Financial information

Year end	30/09/2020
Income	£5,920,000
Assets	£8,930,000
Grants to organisations	£3,530,000
No. of grants	158

Further financial information

Grants were distributed as follows:

Active Communities	£2.22 million
Local Conversations	£881,500
Local People	£386,300
Strategic Funding Programme	£28,900
Research	£8,100

Beneficiaries included: Mount Pleasant Road Community Group (£40,000); Leeds Muslim Youth Forum (£33,600); Aaina Community Hub (£20,100); Rewild Play (£14,100); Entrust Care Partnership CIC (£12,200); Cynon Valley Museum Trust (£5,200).

Exclusions

See the trust's website for full eligibility criteria.

Applications

Grant rounds are divided into regional schemes. In the first instance, check if funding is available in your area. If your project is neighbourhood based, you can complete a stage-one application form on the trust's website. If your project is for a community of interest (defined in the application guidance as 'a group of people who have a shared identity or experiences, and wish to come together to address specific issues that are important to them' – see the guidance for further detail), contact the trust to request an application form. If your application proceeds to stage two (applicants will be notified within ten working days), a second application form will need to be completed.

Sources of information

Accounts; annual report; Charity Commission record; funder's website.

People's Postcode Trust

Mental well-being; participation in arts and sports; social welfare; disadvantaged people; biodiversity and green space; climate emergency and sustainability; access to outdoors

Scotland

£2.42 million (2020)

OSCR number: SC040387

Correspondent: The Trustees, 28 Charlotte Square, Edinburgh EH2 4ET (tel: 0131 322 9377; email: info@postcodetrust.org.uk)

 www.postcodetrust.org.uk

 facebook.com/peoplespostcodetrust

 @PostcodeTrust

General information

This trust is funded by the income from the People's Postcode Lottery.

Community Grants Programme

According to the trust's Funding Guide 2022, the trust provides funding for smaller charities and good causes in Scotland under the following themes:

- Improving mental well-being
- Enabling community participation in the arts
- Preventing or reducing the impact of poverty
- Supporting marginalised groups and promoting equality
- Improving biodiversity and green spaces
- Enabling participation in physical activity
- Responding to the climate emergency and promoting sustainability
- Increasing community access to outdoor space

Grants, ranging from £500 to £20,000, are available to organisations with an annual income of less than £1 million (although preference is given to organisations with an income of under £500,000). Registered charities, CICs and charitable community benefit societies can apply for between £500 and £25,000, while companies limited by guarantee and community groups not formally registered as a charity can apply for between £500 and £2,500.

This programme offers project funding (including running costs related to project delivery such as staff and utilities) or unrestricted funding.

Other funding

- **Magic Little Grants** the programme gives smaller charities and community groups the chance to apply for a £500 grant to deliver projects across the UK. The application process is administered entirely by Localgiving
- **The Local School Nature Grants Programme** is open to schools for nature equipment and training. The programme is entirely administered by Learning through Landscapes

Financial information

Year end	31/12/2020
Income	£7,960,000
Assets	£306,500
Grants to organisations	£2,420,000
No. of grants	176

Further financial information

During the year, 176 projects were funded by the Community Grants Programme. These grants were made across the following areas and themes:

England	145	£2.03 million
Scotland	17	£241,300
Wales	14	£153,600

Preventing poverty	90	£1.28 million
Promoting human rights	32	£494,600
Combatting discrimination	54	£643,900

A full list of beneficiaries can be found on the trust's website.

Beneficiaries included: LGBT Healthy Living Centre (£19,000); Govanhill Baths Community Trust (£18,200); Carers of East Lothian (£15,200); HIV Scotland (£14,600); Pregnancy Counselling and Care (Scotland) (£13,400); Stellar Quines (£10,300).

Exclusions

A comprehensive list of exclusions with respect to activities and recipients can be found in the trust's funding guide on its website. Example exclusions include:

- Individuals
- Activities taking place outside Scotland, or foreign travel
- Statutory bodies that the state has an obligation to fund
- Nurseries, schools, PTAs, colleges and universities (see Learning Through Landscapes and Magic Little Grants)
- Organisations with annual income over £1 million
- Political parties or party-political activities
- For unrestricted funding, organisations that work overseas/ internationally

Applications

Funding rounds open each month and close when either the maximum number applications have been submitted or by the dates found on the trust's website. An online application form becomes available on the trust's website when funding rounds open. Full details, including guidance notes and deadlines, are available from the trust's website.

Sources of information

Accounts; annual report; OSCR record; funder's website; guidelines for applicants.

Dina Perelman Trust Ltd

Orthodox Jewish faith and general charitable purposes

UK and overseas

£836,700 (2020/21)

CC number: 274165

Correspondent: The Trustees, 39 Overlea Road, London E5 9BG (tel: 020 8809 2345)

Trustees: Asher Perelman; Jonah Perelman; Sara Perelman.

General information

This trust registered with the Charity Commission in 1977 and supports the advancement of the Orthodox Jewish faith through its grant-making. The trust's 2020/21 accounts state:

> The Trustees are approached for donations by a wide variety of charitable institutions operating all over England and the rest of the world. The trustees consider all requests which they receive and make donations based on level of funds available.

Financial information

Year end	31/03/2021
Income	£1,100,000
Assets	£9,800,000
Grants to organisations	£836,700

Further financial information

During 2020/21, grants were distributed as follows:

Advancement of education	£627,300
Advancement of religion	£102,500
Advancement of health and saving lives	£50,700
Prevention or relief of poverty	£39,200
Advancement of community development	£13,900
Grants to other grant-making charity	£3,100

Only beneficiaries receiving grants of over £15,000 were listed in the trust's accounts. Grants of under £15,000 totalled £161,200.

Beneficiaries included: The Friends of Alexander Institutions Trust (£464,500); Friends of Mercaz Hatorah Belz Macnivka (£37,000); British Friends of Mishan L'Choleh (£36,000); Beis Aharon Trust Ltd (£28,200); Ma'at Min Ha'Ohr (£18,000); Mosdos Hatorah Pnei Menachem Ltd (£17,300); Chofetz Chaim Trust Foundation (£17,100).

Applications

Apply in writing to correspondent.

Sources of information

Accounts; annual report; Charity Commission record.

The Performing Right Society Foundation

Music

UK

£1.96 million (2020)

CC number: 1080837

Correspondent: Fiona Harvey, Secretary, 41 Streatham High Road, Streatham, London SW16 1ER (tel: 020 3741 4233; email: info@prsfoundation.com)

Trustees: Richard King; Mark Poole; Caroline Norbury; Chris Butler; Susannah Simons; Lorna Clarke; Michelle Escoffery; Christine Geissmar; Nitin Sawhney.

 www.prsfoundation.com

 facebook.com/PRSforMusicFoundation

 @PRSFoundation

 @prsfoundation

General information

The PRS Foundation is an independent charitable foundation established in 2000 by the UK's largest collection society, PRS for Music Ltd, from which it receives an annual donation of £3 million.

The foundation is currently the UK's largest independent funder of new music of any genre. The principle objectives of the foundation are to support, sustain and further the creation and performance of new music and to educate the public in order to augment its appreciation in the UK. The foundation awards grants and works in strategic partnerships with like-minded organisations.

Grant programmes

The foundation awards grants under a variety of themes, which are listed on its website. Of these, four are available for charities and not-for-profit organisations:

The Open Fund

This fund supports new music projects across all genres led by promoters, talent development organisations, venues, curators and large performance groups (which includes orchestras, choirs, jazz bands or folk groups with 12 or more performers). Projects must involve the creation, performance and promotion of new music and enable songwriters, composers, solo artist, bands and performers of all backgrounds to develop creatively and professionally. Grants are available for up to £10,000 and can be provided to support the creation, performance, touring, recording, marketing and commissioning of new music by UK-based creators, community projects, residencies and live programmes. This fund prioritises not-for-profit organisations and tends not to support organisations limited by shares.

At the time of writing (February 2022), the foundation had adapted the fund to be more flexible in response to the COVID-19 pandemic. See the website for details.

Beyond Borders

Grants of up to £15,000 are available to organisations working with partners based in the UK or Ireland that want to co-commission or tour new music across the UK. Funding is available for projects that include new commissions, recordings and repeat performances of music written in the past five years. Support is given to around eight to ten projects per year.

Resonate

Grants of up to £10,000 are available to orchestras that commit to exploring contemporary UK repertoire as part of a season/tour and longer-term audience development programmes. The programme supports projects that benefit audiences, composers and players in the UK and overseas.

New Music Biennial

Grants are available to organisations which are developing local and regional audiences for new music. The aim of the programme is to reach new audiences for contemporary music and encourage ideas for short works (no longer than 15 minutes) which could be performed in a range of settings.

Full details of the foundation's grant schemes, including grant-making priorities and application forms, are available on the website.

Financial information

Year end	31/12/2020
Income	£4,120,000
Assets	£1,090,000
Grants to organisations	£1,960,000
No. of grants	180

Beneficiaries included: Apples and Snakes; Chamber Music Scotland; Horniman Museum and Gardens; Dante or Die Theatre; Kings Place Music Foundation; National Youth Orchestra of Great Britain; Presteigne Festival; The Belfast Ensemble; The Old Vic Theatre Trust 2000.

Exclusions

See the relevant funding programme on the website for exclusion criteria.

Applications

Apply via the foundation's website where full guidelines for each programme are available. Deadlines for applications vary from programme to programme. The website notes that the trust cannot offer specific telephone or email support prior to stage-one applications due to the high number of applications.

Note: organisations can only apply once per calendar year to the Open Fund.

Sources of information

Accounts; annual report; Charity Commission record; funder's website.

B. E. Perl Charitable Trust

Jewish causes and general charitable purposes

Barnet; Brent; Hertfordshire

£83,100 (2020/21)

CC number: 282847

Correspondent: The Trustees, Foframe House, 35/37 Brent Street, Hendon, London NW4 2EF (tel: 020 3411 2001)

Trustees: Rachel Jeidel; Dr Shoshanna Perl; Joseph Perl; Mr J. Perl; Benjamin Perl; Naomi Tsorotzkin.

General information

The trust's main focus is the advancement of education in and the religion of the Orthodox Jewish faith. Grants are made to Jewish schools, other educational organisations and other charities. Several of the trustees are also trustees for other Orthodox Jewish educational charities.

Note the following statement taken from the 2020/21 annual report and accounts:

> The Trustees have considered and approved plans for the establishment of a major educational project in the UK. It is anticipated that the cost of this project will be in excess of £5,000,000. During the year an amount of £500,000 (2020: £500,000) was transferred to the Educational Reserve in order to fund this project. Following the transfer this year, the funds have been raised.

Financial information

Year end	31/03/2021
Income	£2,500,000
Assets	£28,070,000
Grants to organisations	£83,100

Further financial information

During 2020/21 grants totalled £83,100; however, in previous years the trust has made grants totalling over £300,000. Grants were distributed as follows:

Relief of poverty and illness	£43,000
Educational purposes	£36,700
General purposes	£3,400

Beneficiaries included: Interlink Foundation (£20,000); Achisomoch Aid Company Ltd (£15,500); BFO Igud Hakollelim and Kisharon (£15,000 each); Beit Halochem (£10,000).

Applications

Apply in writing to the correspondent.

Sources of information

Accounts; annual report; Charity Commission record.

The Persimmon Charitable Foundation

General charitable purposes; community and economic development; the environment; education; young people; sport; the arts and culture; health; social welfare

Areas of company presence in England, Scotland and Wales

£1.84 million (2020)

CC number: 1163608

Correspondent: The Trustees, Persimmon plc, Persimmon House, Fulford, York, North Yorkshire YO19 4FE (tel: 01904 642199; email: contact@persimmonhomes.com)

Trustees: Mike Killoran; Roger Devlin; Joanna Place; Dean Finch.

 www.persimmonhomes.com/charity

General information

Established in 2015, this foundation is the corporate charity of Persimmon plc, a large housebuilding company. The foundation receives its income from independent financial advisers (IFAs) and the Persimmon group. The IFAs that make donations are those companies or firms who give advice on mortgage products to customers of the group.

Funding

The foundation makes grants to charities, particularly small local charities and community groups, to promote urban regeneration in areas of economic and social deprivation. The trustees' aim is to improve local communities in the UK by improving health, relieving poverty, advancing amateur sport, improving the local environment and supporting the arts and culture.

There are two programmes, the Community Champions campaign, which supports grassroots groups and charities, and the Building Futures campaign, which supports children's health, sport, education and the arts. The Persimmon Group matches donations made by the foundation under the Community Champions campaign.

Community Champions: organisations can apply for funding of up to £1,000 to match funding they have raised themselves to support local charitable purposes. Two organisations per operating business (of which there are 31) are selected each month to receive funding.

Building Futures: launched in 2019, in partnership with the British Olympic Association, the £1 million scheme supports projects for young people under 18 across three categories: education and the arts, sport and health. In each of the three categories, awards of £100,000, £50,000 and £20,000 are made. There are also smaller awards of £5,000 and £1,000 available to shortlisted projects.

Eligibility

The foundation will support a range of organisations, including charities, sports groups, Scouts and Brownies, hospices, foodbanks, theatres and art projects.

Financial information

Year end	31/12/2020
Income	£1,890,000
Assets	£85,100
Grants to organisations	£1,840,000

Further financial information

Beneficiaries of Building Futures funding included: Northampton Swimming Club (£100,000); Newbury's KD Gymnastics (£50,000); Afan Lido Ladies and Girls' FC (£20,000).

Community Champions grants included: North East Ambulance Service and Rushwick Cricket Club (£1,000 each); Wetwheels Yorkshire (£850); Droitwich Community Transport (£780); Chalke Valley Sports Centre (£700); The Brigitte Trust (£500).

Beneficiaries of Building Futures funding in 2020 and 2021 can be found on the foundation's website.

Applications

Community Champions

Applicants need to complete an online form. Included in your application the foundation needs to know how much you have already raised and how much money you need. Applications are accepted each month; charities and groups that were previously unsuccessful can apply again.

The trustees prefer to support local charities. Go to www.persimmonhomes.com/contact to find your nearest Persimmon office.

Building Futures
Contact the correspondent for further information on applications.

Sources of information

Accounts; annual report; Charity Commission record; funder's website.

The Jack Petchey Foundation

Young people aged 11–25

London and Essex

£5.55 million (2020)

CC number: 1176221

Correspondent: Grants Team, Dockmaster's House, 1 Hertsmere Road, London E14 8JJ (tel: 020 8252 8000; email: mail@jackpetcheyfoundation.org.uk)

Trustees: Ronald Mills; Amanda Galanopoulos; Robert McArthur; Lewis Hooper; Mattew Rantell; Raymond Henry; Sonia Sinclair.

www.jackpetcheyfoundation.org.uk

facebook.com/JackPetcheyFoundation

@JPFoundation

@jackpetcheyfoundation

General information

This foundation was established in 1999 by Jack Petchey and gives grants to programmes and projects that benefit young people aged 11–25 by enabling young people to achieve their potential by inspiring, investing in and developing activities that increase their personal, social, emotional and physical development. In the UK, the foundation benefits all London boroughs and Essex.

Grant programmes

Open grants

The foundation periodically offers grant opportunities to organisations that are part of its Achievement Award scheme to provide further opportunities for young people across London and Essex.

Achievement Award scheme

The scheme is run in schools, colleges and clubs throughout London and Essex, and contributes over £3.5 million annually to youth organisations. The scheme is a reward and recognition initiative which enables schools and clubs to celebrate the achievements of young people and receive additional funding for the organisation.

Each month participating youth clubs, schools, colleges and registered charities select one young person to receive an achievement award. The month's winner receives a framed certificate and a cheque for £250 (payable to the organisation) to be spent on a school, club or community project of the recipient's choice.

Leader Award

Young people in organisations that are participating in the Achievement Award scheme can nominate an adult to honour the dedication of exemplary staff and volunteers. The award-winning organisations will then be offered the opportunity to apply for a small grant of up to £1,000 once a year for the organisation.

Leader Award Grant

Organisations that are running the Achievement Awards effectively can apply for up to £1,000 to enhance their work with young people once a year. Organisations are eligible for a Leader Award Grant if they have applied for and received a Leader Award within the past six months.

Educational visits

Organisations participating in the Achievement Award scheme can apply for two grants per year of up to £10 per head and a maximum of £300 per trip for educational visits.

Individual grants for volunteering

The foundation will consider sponsoring young people (11–25 years old) who live in London and Essex and are undertaking voluntary projects with a UK-based organisation. The usual support from the foundation will be £400 (maximum of 50% of the costs). An application form is available from the foundation's website.

Partnership programmes

The foundation funds and works in partnership with several organisations to deliver programmes. Details of all partnerships can be found on the website.

Internship programme

The foundation provides funding to charities to employ an intern for a year. The programme includes up to 90% funding towards the intern's salary, a training bursary for each intern, six professional development workshops and mentoring to help interns improve their skills.

These funds may change and others may be added so potential applicants should always check the foundation's website.

Financial information

Year end	31/12/2020
Income	£7,490,000
Assets	£3,430,000
Grants to organisations	£5,550,000

Beneficiaries included: Speakers Trust (£623,700); Essex Boys and Girls Clubs (£56,000); Intermission (£19,700); Salmon Youth Centre (£19,400); Thurrock Young Carers (£5,000).

Applications

Applications can be made via the foundation's website. See the website for the eligibility criteria of the relevant programme.

Sources of information

Accounts; annual report; Charity Commission record; funder's website.

Petplan Charitable Trust

The welfare of dogs, cats, horses or rabbits; veterinary research and education

UK and overseas

£1.14 million (2020)

CC number: 1032907

Correspondent: Catherine Bourg, Trust Administrator, Great West House (GW2), Great West Road, Brentford, Middlesex TW8 9EG (email: info@petplancharitabletrust.org.uk)

Trustees: Clarissa Baldwin; John Bower; Ted Bvetmed; David Simpson; Kathryn Willis; Peter Laurie; Jamie Crittall; Gary Davess; Lord Prof. Lord Trees; Alan Farkas; Irene Santos.

https://petplancharitabletrust.org.uk

facebook.com/PetplanCharitableTrust

@petplan_charitable_trust

General information

The trust was established in 1994 by pet insurance company Petplan Ltd, a subsidiary company of Allianz Insurance plc, to provide funds to promote the health and welfare of dogs, cats, horses and rabbits. Petplan gives its policy holders the option of making a small annual donation to the trust, which they are able to increase from the suggested £2 per year if they wish.

The trust has two active grant rounds each year.

Scientific grants

The trust awards two types of scientific grants:

- Full grants for in-depth research, tenable for up to three years
- Pump priming/pilot grants of up to £10,000 to fund initial research over a period of no more than one year

Welfare grants

According to the trust's terms and conditions document, applicants must have registered charity status and must demonstrate a direct benefit to a species supported by Petplan (i.e. dogs, cats horses or rabbits). Grants to human charities may be considered when it can be clearly demonstrated that the grant will enhance/give support to the animals' best interests.

Welfare grants can include items such as neutering, kennelling and veterinary costs and animal housing and repairs, but not general overheads. Requests for funding for education in animal welfare will also be considered.

Check the website for up-to-date guidance.

Financial information

Year end	31/12/2020
Income	£986,900
Assets	-£95,300
Grants to organisations	£1,140,000

Further financial information

Grants were broken down as follows: scientific grants (£601,300); special grants (£288,500); welfare and education grants (£248,800).

Beneficiaries included: ADCH Emergency Fund (£150,000); Lead Up International (£111,500); Birmingham Dogs Home (£25,000); Dogs Trust (£19,000); Our Special Friends (£5,000); Rain Rescue (£500).

Applications

Application forms, eligibility criteria, full terms and conditions, and the dates for application rounds for each grants programme are available via the trust's website.

Sources of information

Accounts; annual report; Charity Commission record; funder's website; guidelines for applicants.

The Pets at Home Foundation

Animal welfare

UK

£2.58 million (2020/21)

CC number: 1104152

Correspondent: The Charity Team, c/o Pets at Home, Chester House, Epsom Avenue, Stanley Green Trading Estate, Handforth, Cheshire SK9 3DF (tel: 0161 486 6688; email: info@petsathomefoundation.co.uk)

Trustees: Louise Stonier; George Lingwood; Jill Shields; Dan Laurence; Adrian Bates; Andrew Bickerton; Claire Gavin; Dr Catriona Curtis.

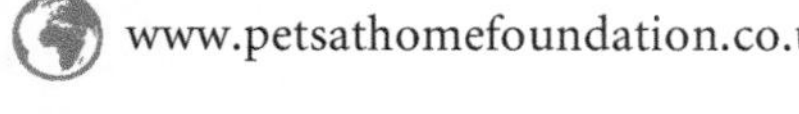

www.petsathomefoundation.co.uk

facebook.com/PetsAtHomeFoundation

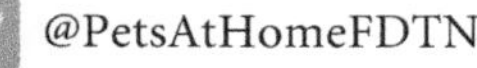

@PetsAtHomeFDTN

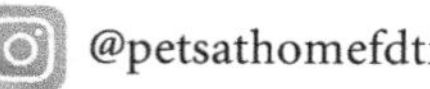

@petsathomefdtn

General information

The Pets at Home Foundation (formerly known as Support Adoption for Pets) was established in 2006 by Pets at Home, a pet supplies retailer.

Rescue Centres

According to the foundation's website, it provides funding to organisations whose main activity is the rescue and rehoming of UK pets.

Grants range from £250 upwards and can be used to fund the following:

- Vet bills
- Boarding fees
- Trap and neuter schemes for feral or stray cats
- Food
- Equipment
- Vehicles
- Building work

Helping People Through Pets

The foundation will also support organisations providing temporary or ongoing assistance to ensure pets can remain with their owners, or organisations changing the lives of children and adults through the provision of animal-based activities and practical assistance. These grants typically range from £250 to £50,000 and can be used to fund:

- Building work
- Vehicles
- Equipment
- Vet bills
- Salaries
- New initiatives directly involving pets and people

For full eligibility criteria see the foundation's guidelines on its website.

Charity of the Year

The foundation also runs a Charity of the Year scheme, supporting rescue centres that are local to Pets at Home stores. Rescue centres interested in learning more about the scheme are encouraged to contact the foundation.

Financial information

Year end	25/03/2021
Income	£4,090,000
Assets	£3,570,000
Grants to organisations	£2,580,000

Beneficiaries included: RSPCA (£434,700); Cats Protection (£191,000); Greyhound Trust (£51,500); Blue Cross (£22,800); Horse Sense Wirral (£15,000); Small Pet Rescue Centre (£12,300); Lluest Horse and Pony Trust (£11,000). Lincs Ark (£10,000).

Exclusions

The foundation will not fund:

- Salaries, uniforms or expenses
- The cost of leasing a vehicle, road tax, insurance or petrol costs
- The purchase of land or buildings
- Any costs associated with a charity shop
- Fundraising costs such as marketing materials

Applications

Prospective applicants should first check the grant criteria to confirm their eligibility and then complete the online request for an application form. The foundation's website notes that a virtual or in person visit may be requested. There are no deadlines for Rescue Centres grants. Applications for Helping People Through Pets grants are considered three times a year; contact the foundation for information on timescales.

Sources of information

Accounts; annual report; Charity Commission record; funder's website; guidelines for applicants.

The Phillips and Rubens Charitable Trust

General charitable purposes; social welfare; homelessness; disability; health; medical research; the arts; older people; Jewish causes

UK

£281,000 (2020/21)

CC number: 260378

Correspondent: The Trustees, 67–69 George Street, London W1U 8LT (tel: 020 7487 5757; email: psphillips@aol.com)

Trustees: Carolyn Mishon; Martin Paisner; Ruth Phillips; Michael Phillips; Gary Phillips; Paul Phillips.

General information

The trust's 2020/21 annual report states:

> The trustees receive applications for donations from a wide variety of charitable institutions including those engaged in medical and ancillary services (including medical research), education, helping the disabled and old aged, relieving poverty, providing sheltered accommodation, developing the arts etc. The trustees consider all requests which they receive and make such donations as they feel appropriate.

In practice, most of the charities supported are Jewish organisations.

Financial information

Year end	05/04/2021
Income	£426,600
Assets	£13,190,000
Grants to organisations	£281,000

Beneficiaries included: The Phillips Family Charitable Trust (£100,000); The Jewish Book Trust (£14,000); St John's Hospice (£10,000); Lionel Rosenfeld Testimonial Fund and Work Avenue (£5,000 each); Cystic Fibrosis Trust (£3,000); Jewish Leadership Council and RAF Museum (£2,500 each).

Applications

Apply in writing to the correspondent.

Sources of information

Accounts; annual report; Charity Commission record.

The Pilgrim Trust

 Women's mental health and the preservation of buildings and heritage

UK

£2.91 million (2020)

CC number: 206602

Correspondent: The Trustees, 3rd Floor, Ebury Gate, 23 Lower Belgrave Street, London SW1W 0NR (tel: 020 7834 6510; email: info@thepilgrimtrust.org.uk)

Trustees: Sir Mark Jones; Sarah Staniforth; Caroline Butler; David Barrie; Joan Winterkorn; Atulkumar Patel; Marie Staunton; Alexander Sturgis; Alice Weston; Cullagh Warnock; Matthew Ridley; Asif Afridi.

 www.thepilgrimtrust.org.uk

General information

The Pilgrim Trust was founded in 1930 by the American philanthropist Edward Stephen Harkness. According to the website, it was Harkness's wish that his gift be given in grants for some of Britain's 'more urgent needs' and to 'promote her future well-being'. The first trustees decided that the trust should assist with social welfare projects, preservation (of buildings and countryside) and the promotion of art and learning. This has remained the focus of The Pilgrim Trust and the current Board of Trustees follow Harkness's guidelines. The trustees regularly discuss and review the grant focuses.

The trust aims to distribute at least £2 million a year with 60% directed towards preservation and conservation and 40% towards social welfare.

There are two grant schemes:

- **Main Grant Fund**: approximately 90% of the annual grant budget is allocated to this scheme, for grants of over £5,000
- **Small Grant Fund**: the remainder of the grants budget is distributed through this scheme in grants of £5,000 or less

The following is taken from a funding guideline document, available in full on the trust's website, with the main points reproduced here:

Preservation and scholarship fund

- Preservation of and repairs to historic buildings and architectural features. Special consideration is given to projects that give new use to buildings which are at risk and of outstanding importance
- Conservation of works of art, books, significant ephemera, museum objects and records held in museums, galleries, specialist archives and repositories
- Promotion of knowledge through academic research and its dissemination, including cataloguing within museums, galleries and libraries and institutions where historic, scientific or archaeological records are preserved
- Cataloguing of manuscripts is funded through the National Manuscripts Conservation Trust (see www.nmct.co.uk)
- Maintenance and repair of places of worship, including historic churches, chapels and meeting houses across the UK through Preventative Maintenance Micro Grants and Foundation Grants for Maintenance – note that both grants are administered by the National Churches Trust and should be applied for through that organisation

Eligibility

Grants are available to UK-registered charities including exempt charities, recognised public bodies and registered Friendly Societies for revenue costs, project costs and costs of initial exploratory work for organisations seeking to rescue important buildings and monuments. Capital costs can be funded under the theme of preservation and scholarship as long as the total capital costs is less than £5 million. All work/projects must be UK based.

Young Women and Mental Health PLUS

In summer 2021, the trust launched a new funding programme called Young Women and Mental Health PLUS to replace its previous Social Welfare fund. Running between 2021 and 2026, the fund will support access to mental health services for women aged 16–25. The trust is making available £5 million over five years.

In its first year (2021), which is seen as a pilot, the programme was open to charities in Greater Manchester and Northern Ireland. Charities could apply for between £60,000 and £90,000, spread over three years. Grants were for project delivery costs as well as core costs.

New funding rounds are announced on the trust's website and social media. The website states that the next funding round will be open to organisations working in the north-west and north-east of England and Northern Ireland.

The funding guidelines state:

> We want to support organisations delivering high quality services specifically designed to respond to the needs of young women experiencing mental health difficulties. We particularly welcome applications from organisations leading the way in good practice or innovation relating to age and gender informed approaches to mental health provision. We will prioritise those that work collaboratively with partners to extend their impact and share expertise.

The trust will consider funding projects where at least 80% of the participants of the work fall within the 16–25 age band.

Eligibility

Funding is available for registered an exempt UK charities with an annual income between £100,000 and £1 million (based on the average of the last three years to allow for fluctuations caused by the COVID-19 pandemic). Charities must have been in operation for a minimum of three years.

See the trust's website for full information on its grant-making.

Financial information

Year end	31/12/2020
Income	£1,330,000
Assets	£77,280,000
Grants to organisations	£2,910,000
No. of grants	106

Further financial information

Grants were broken down as follows: preservation and scholarship (£1.88 million) and social welfare (£1.02 million).

During the year, 270 stage-one applications were received, of which 141 were successful. Of the stage-two applications received, 106 were successful.

Beneficiaries included: The National Archives (£300,000); National Churches Trust (£260,000); Cathedral Church of St Peter in Exeter (£60,000); Northumberland Domestic Abuse Services Ltd (£55,000); A Way Out (£45,000); British Refugee Council (£20,000); Aberlour Child Care Trust (£15,000); Elpis Trust (£5,000).

Exclusions

According to the trust's website and funding guidelines, grants are not made to:

- Individuals
- Non-UK-registered charities or charities registered in the Channel Islands or the Isle of Man

- CICs and social enterprises (unless they are registered charities)
- Projects based outside the UK

The following programme-specific exclusions apply:

Preservation and scholarship fund

- Projects where the work has already been completed or where contracts have already been awarded
- Projects with a capital cost of over £5 million are not normally considered
- Projects where the activities are considered to be primarily the responsibility of central or local government
- General appeals or circulars
- Projects for the commissioning of new works of art
- Organisations seeking publishing production costs
- Projects seeking to develop new facilities within a church or the re-ordering of churches or places of worship for wider community use
- Arts and drama projects – unless they clearly link to the trust's priorities
- One-off short-term interventions
- Youth or sports clubs, travel or adventure projects, community centres or children's play groups
- Organisations seeking funding for trips abroad
- Organisations seeking educational funding, such as assistance to individuals for degree or post-degree work or school, university or college development programmes
- One-off events such as exhibitions, festivals, seminars, conferences or theatrical and musical productions

Young Women and Mental Health PLUS

- Retrospective costs
- Building work or capital costs associated with buildings
- Work which is a statutory responsibility
- Activities promoting religious beliefs
- One-off activities and events
- Unrestricted funding

Applications

Applications to the Preservation and Scholarship fund can be made using the trust's two-stage online form, available through the trust's online application portal. There are no deadlines; applications are considered at quarterly trustee meetings. The trust welcomes informal contact prior to an application via phone or email.

To apply for the Women and Mental Health PLUS programme, applicants must book a conversation with the trust's grants manager when funding rounds are open. See the website for up-to-date deadlines and guidelines.

All applicants should read the application guidelines available on the website in full before applying. There is also a useful FAQs section.

Sources of information

Accounts; annual report; Charity Commission record; funder's website; guidelines for applicants.

Cecil Pilkington Charitable Trust

General charitable purposes; the environment; medical causes; the arts; education; social welfare

UK

£376,000 (2019/20)

CC number: 249997

Correspondent: The Trustees, Duncan Sheard Glass, Castle Chambers, 43 Castle Street, Liverpool, Merseyside L2 9TL (tel: 0151 243 1200)

Trustees: Arnold Pilkington; Mark Feeny; Dr Vanessa Pilkington; Heloise Pilkington.

General information

The Cecil Pilkington Charitable Trust was established in 1966. It makes grants for a wide range of charitable purposes, including the environment, social welfare, education, the arts and medical causes.

Financial information

Year end	05/10/2020
Income	£325,600
Assets	£23,950,000
Grants to organisations	£376,000

Further financial information

Grants were broken down as follows:

Welfare	£263,000
Medical causes	£73,000
Arts	£20,000
Education	£20,000

Beneficiaries included: Willowbrook Hospice (£10,000); Alzheimer's Research UK, National Museum Liverpool, RSPB and Soil Association (£5,000 each).

Applications

Apply in writing to the correspondent.

Sources of information

Accounts; annual report; Charity Commission record.

Pilkington Charities Fund

Helping people affected by poverty, old age or ill health

UK, with a strong preference for Merseyside

£365,500 (2019/20)

CC number: 225911

Correspondent: The Trustees, Rathbones Investment Management, Port of Liverpool Building, Pier Head, Liverpool, Merseyside L3 1NW (tel: 0151 236 6666; email: trustadminliverpool@rathbones.com)

Trustees: Neil Jones; Philip Pilkington; Eleanor Jones.

http://pilkingtoncharitiesfund.org.uk

General information

This charity was established in 1950 to assist employees or former employees of Pilkington plc and its associated companies. It now supports registered charities helping people affected by poverty, old age or ill health. While the charity will consider applications from national charities working in these fields, priority is given to specific projects undertaken in the Merseyside area. In exceptional circumstances, the charity may consider applications from outside the UK or longer-term funding where a project requires a two- or three-year commitment.

The minimum grant size is £1,000, with most grants ranging from £1,000 to £6,000. Grants are made for core costs, capital costs and project costs.

The charity will support charities, social enterprises, CICs and non-profits, as long as they are registered with one of the national regulatory bodies within the UK.

Financial information

Year end	30/06/2020
Income	£644,200
Assets	£23,590,000
Grants to organisations	£365,500
No. of grants	65

Beneficiaries included: C. and A. Pilkington Trust Fund (£70,000); Macmillan Cancer Support (£15,000); Barnardo's and Wellbeing of Women (£10,000 each); Child Brain Injury Trust (£5,000); Combat Stress and Respite Association (£3,000 each); Spinal Injuries Association (£2,000); Fallen Angels Dance Theatre (£1,000).

Exclusions

The charity will not consider grant applications from individuals or non-profits, social enterprises or CICs that are not registered charities. Work outside the UK will only be funded in exceptional circumstances.

Applications

Apply by post or email to the correspondent. The charity's helpful website states:

> Charities can apply for a grant at any time. The Trustees meet twice a year, with deadlines for applications on 1st May and 1st October. Urgent applications may be considered separately: please highlight and explain the need for urgency in your covering letter.

Applications should include:

- A concise explanation of the reasons for the request and the expect outcomes
- A request for a specific sum of money
- For national charities – how the work will specifically benefit the region of Merseyside
- Details relating to budgets, costs and other sources of funding received (where relevant)

Sources of information

Accounts; annual report; Charity Commission record; funder's website.

The Austin and Hope Pilkington Trust

The arts; young people; BAME communities

UK

£327,200 (2020)

CC number: 255274

Correspondent: The Trustees, Rathbones, Port of Liverpool Building, Pier Head, Liverpool, Merseyside L3 1NW (email: admin@austin-hope-pilkington.org.uk)

Trustees: Debbie Nelson; Penny Badowska; Eleanor Stride; Harry Shankar.

www.austin-hope-pilkington.org.uk

General information

The trust focuses on supporting a different funding priority each year. In 2021 it supported people experiencing homelessness, refugees and asylum seekers. The following information about the trust's 2022 priorities has been taken from its website:

> **The Arts: People in the early stages of their career**
>
> We are prioritising projects supporting performers and creatives
>
> **The Arts: BAME communities**
>
> - BAME performers
> - outreach projects within BAME communities
> - initiatives to increase participation with BAME communities

Financial information

Year end	31/12/2020
Income	£210,200
Assets	£11,220,000
Grants to organisations	£327,200

Beneficiaries included: Deafblind UK, FareShare and Manchester City Galleries Trust (£5,000 each); Hourglass (£3,000); The Apple Trust, Listening Books and Spitalfields Music (£1,000 each).

Exclusions

According to its website, the foundation will not fund:

- Capital appeals, including equipment
- Charities involved with religion (including repair of Church fabric)
- Charities involved with animals (welfare and conservation)
- Holidays, including respite holidays
- Individual hospices (national organisations can apply)
- Individuals, including individuals embarking on a trip overseas with a charitable organisation
- Minibuses or other Vehicles
- Overseas projects
- Schools, including activities
- Scouts, Guides, Cubs, Brownies
- Sea Cadets
- Shopmobility
- Students
- Village Halls

Applications

Apply via the trust's website.

Sources of information

Accounts; annual report; Charity Commission record; funder's website.

PIMCO Foundation Europe

Education; homelessness; overseas aid; the environment; children; arts, culture and heritage; disability

London

£820,300 (2020)

CC number: 1139109

Correspondent: Carolina Leite, Senior Associate, 11 Baker Street, London W1U 3AH (tel: 020 7872 1300; email: carolina.leite@uk.pimco.com)

Trustees: Thomas Rice; Vishalakshi Ananthanarayanan; Ryan Blute; Craig Dawson; Ketishweran Pothalingam.

www.pimco.co.uk/en-gb/our-firm/purpose/foundation

General information

The foundation is the charitable arm of PIMCO, a global investment management firm. The foundation receives its funding from investments, donations from trustees/directors, employee fundraising and donations from the company.

According to its website, the foundation's global focus areas are hunger and gender equality, while the trust's UK local grants programme currently focuses on homelessness and rough sleeping, particularly in Westminster, where the firm is located.

The foundation also matches funds raised by PIMCO employees.

Financial information

Year end	31/12/2020
Income	£1,080,000
Assets	£5,860,000
Grants to organisations	£820,300
No. of grants	107

Further financial information

Grants were broken down as follows:

Homelessness	£181,400
Education	£180,600
The environment	£165,900
Overseas aid	£160,900
Health	£126,300
Children	£10,600
Culture	£1,200
Disability	£360

We were unable to determine the portion of grants awarded in the UK.

Beneficiaries included: MyBnk (£133,500); House of St Barnabas (£108,700); FareShare (£103,500); British Red Cross (£80,000); Passage 2000 (£70,000); Action for Stammering Children (£69,500).

Exclusions

Our previous research found that the foundation does not support the following:

- Individuals
- Scholarships or tuition assistance
- University/school endowments
- Religious organisations for religious purposes, election campaigns or general fundraising drives
- Social, labour, alumni or fraternal organisations
- Professional or amateur sports organisations and teams, or athletic events and programmes
- Political organisations
- One-off fundraising events
- Political organisations
- Emergency funding
- Loans, debt reduction or operating expenditure
- Capital expenditure
- Foundations, pass-through or other grant-making organisations
- Organisations that discriminate against certain groups or individuals in the delivery or programmes and services on the basis of race, religion, sex, sexual orientation, gender, age, marital status, military or veteran status, disability or medical condition

Applications

The foundation does not accept applications for its hunger and gender equality programmes. Contact the correspondent for further information on the foundation's UK local grants programme. At the time of writing (February 2022) applications were closed – check the foundation's website for updates.

Sources of information

Accounts; annual report; Charity Commission record; funder's website.

Thomas Pockington Trust

 Research into sight loss and support for people with sight loss

UK

£1.91 million (2020/21)

CC number: 1113729

Correspondent: The Trustees, Pocklington Hub, 3 Queen Square, London WC1N 3AR (tel: 020 8995 0880; email: info@pocklington-trust.org.uk)

Trustees: Alastair Chapman; Mervyn Williamson; Jenny Pearce; Philip Longworth; Matt Wadsworth; Graham Findlay; Rashmikant Mehta; Judith Potts; Helen Mitchell; Robert Holl; Simon Curtis.

 www.pocklington-trust.org.uk

 facebook.com/Thomas-Pocklington-Trust-141381932556445

 @TPTgeneral

 @thomas_pocklington_trust

General information

Thomas Pocklington Trust (TPT) provides grants for a broad range of projects that support blind and partially sighted people across the UK. The trust has the following priority funding themes:

- **Education:** projects that enable blind and partially sighted children and young people to enter education
- **Employment:** projects that create employment opportunities for blind and partially sighted people
- **Engagement:** projects that facilitate the voice and encourage self-determination of blind and partially sighted people
- **Collaboration and sustainability:** projects that promote positive change to improve the sustainability of the sight loss sector. Transformative activities that require an investment to make that change happen will be considered. This includes developing organisations' technological capabilities, feasibility studies, restructuring reviews, partnership working (including resource sharing) and integrations and mergers

TPT also funds research and technology projects that support the key funding themes.

As well as its regular funding rounds, the trust awards grants to 'close partners' which have similar objectives to the trust. These are currently: London Vision, Visionary, Metro Blind Sport and Sight Support West of England.

Financial information

Year end	31/03/2021
Income	£5,220,000
Assets	£169,070,000
Grants to organisations	£1,910,000
No. of grants	68

Further financial information

In the 2020/21 accounts, grants were broken down as follows: 'meeting needs' (support for local, regional and national service provisions for individuals with impaired vision) (£1.8 million) and 'understanding needs' (research grants) (£102,000). Included in the 'meeting needs' grant total are 56 COVID-19 emergency grants totalling £504,000.

The charity also provides administration support to a number of charities. The value of this support in 2020/21 was £155,000.

Beneficiaries included: London Vision (£429,000); Visionary (£284,000); Focus (£70,000); Sense (£38,000); Birmingham Vision (£17,000); Alstrom Syndrome UK, Dorset Blind Association and Yorkshire Coast Sight Support (£10,000 each); Angel Eyes NI (£6,000); Centre of Sign-Sight-Sound (£2,000).

Applications

Grant application forms are made available on the trust's website when funding rounds are open (check the website or the trust's social media for updates). Applicants should first send an email to research@pocklington-trust.org.uk, detailing their project goals and how they will achieve them in two or three brief paragraphs. A draft proposal may be requested either in short or full version.

Sources of information

Accounts; annual report; Charity Commission record; funder's website.

Polden-Puckham Charitable Foundation

Peace and security and environmental sustainability

UK and overseas

£754,700 (2020/21)

CC number: 1003024

Correspondent: C. Oliver, Trust Secretary, BM PPCF, London, Greater London WC1N 3XX (tel: 020 7193 7364; email: ppcf@polden-puckham.org.uk)

Trustees: Jonathan Gillett; Angela Seay; Dorothy Ball; Simon Fisher; Stephen Pittam.

 www.polden-puckham.org.uk

General information

The Polden-Puckham Charitable Foundation is a grant-making charity with Quaker roots. The trust's 2020/21 annual report and accounts state that the trust:

> aims to support projects that change values and attitudes within our main areas of focus that promote equity and social justice, and that develop radical alternative to current economic and social structures.

The foundation's website notes the following:

> We plan to 'spend down' our endowment over a seven year period, beginning in 2021 and winding up by 2028. This means we will be making fewer, larger grants. We will support work in our existing funding areas of Peace and Sustainable Security and Environmental Sustainability, with a particular focus on the intersection between the two.
>
> **Peace and Sustainable Security**
> We will support work that addresses the underlying causes of violent conflict, develops ways to prevent and resolve conflict and promotes human security.
>
> **Environmental Sustainability**
> We will support work that addresses the pressures and conditions that contribute to climate change and global environmental breakdown.

In 2019, the trust became a signatory to the Funder Commitment on Climate Change.

The foundation's website states that it supports UK-registered charities and non-governmental organisations. In particular, small charitable organisations:

> We usually support organisations for whom this would represent between 4% and 50% of their annual income (organisations with an annual income of between £10,000 and £500,000 approximately).

It considers supporting organisations that are not UK-registered charities on the condition they can evidence that a UK-registered charity is able to receive funds on their behalf and that their work is charitable and international in focus.

Grants are usually between £50,000 and £150,000 per year, typically for up to three years.

Financial information

Year end	05/04/2021
Income	£282,700
Assets	£15,390,000
Grants to organisations	£754,700
No. of grants	58

Beneficiaries included: Power for People (£30,000); Promoting Economic Pluralism (£20,000); Women's Environmental Network (£14,400); Drone Wars UK (£10,000); This Is Rubbish (£8,000); Climate Coalition (£6,000); Peace Direct (£5,000).

Exclusions

According to the foundation's website, the following will not be considered for funding:

- organisations that are very large
- organisations that are outside UK (unless they are doing work of international focus)
- work outside the UK (unless it is of international focus)
- grants to individuals
- travel bursaries (including overseas placements and expeditions)
- study
- academic research
- capital projects (e.g. building projects or purchase of nature reserves)
- community or local practical projects (unless they have potential for influencing UK national policy and can be scaled up at pace.)
- youth work, youth training and youth camps
- environmental/ecological conservation
- international agencies and overseas appeals
- general appeals
- human rights work (except where it relates to peace and environmental sustainability)
- community mediation, criminal or restorative justice work

Applications

Applications can be made via the trust's online form. Applicants should first read the funding guidelines and may wish to complete the eligibility survey, both found on the foundation's website. The foundation advises new applicants to get in touch with the trust secretary to informally discuss the project before making a formal application; rejected applicants can only reapply after 12 months.

Applications are generally acknowledged by email within two weeks of receipt, or one week after the deadline. If an acknowledgement is not received within this timeframe, applicants should contact the foundation.

The trustees usually meet to discuss applications twice a year, in spring and autumn. Deadlines for applications are posted on the foundations website.

Sources of information

Accounts; annual report; Charity Commission record; funder's website.

The Institute for Policy Research

Policy research; social science; management studies; economic policy

UK

£249,500 (2019/20)

CC number: 285143

Correspondent: The Trustees, Flat 38, Charleston Court, 61 West Cliff Road, Broadstairs, Kent CT10 1RY (tel: 07815 502279; email: peter.orbelljones@yahoo.com)

Trustees: Simon Webley; Eric Koops; Anthony Speaight; Jennifer Nicholson.

General information

The institute was registered with the Charity Commission in 1982 and funds research studies, conferences and seminars which promote the education of the public in major social sciences, management studies and economic policy studies.

Grants are made to organisations to fund specific policy studies, conferences and lectures. The purpose of these studies must be to enhance public discussion of issues in the economic, industrial, social and foreign policy fields. The institute expects any findings to be published and made publicly available.

Financial information

Year end	30/09/2020
Income	£317,500
Assets	£454,200
Grants to organisations	£249,500
No. of grants	14

Further financial information

In previous years, the charity's grant total has typically been over £400,000.

Beneficiaries included: Tax Payers' Alliance (£117,500); Centre for Policy Studies (£50,000); Open Europe and Politeia (£40,000); The Bruges Group (£2,000).

Applications

Apply in writing to the correspondent.

Sources of information

Accounts; annual report; Charity Commission record.

The Polonsky Foundation

Cultural heritage and digitisation; humanities/social science education and research; innovation and excellence in the performing arts

UK; Israel; USA; France; Italy

£2.02 million (2020/21)

CC number: 291143

Correspondent: The Trustees, 8 Park Crescent, London W1B 1PG (tel: 020 7436 1997)

Trustees: Dr Leonard Polonsky; Dr Georgette Bennett; Marc Polonsky; Hannah Whitney; Joshua-Marc Tanenbaum.

 https://polonskyfoundation.org

General information

Established in 1985, this is the foundation of Dr Leonard Polonsky, founder and president of Hansard Global plc, a global financial services company based in the Isle of Man and listed on the London Stock Exchange.

The foundation supports three main areas:

- **Cultural heritage and digitisation** – supporting major libraries and museums in digitising and displaying their collections
- **Humanities education and research** – supporting research and educational initiatives in the humanities at significant academic institutions to inspire young people
- **Excellence and innovation in the arts** – supporting artistic heritage, the development of new creative work at performing arts organisations and the nurturing of young performers

Financial information

Year end	31/03/2021
Income	£399,800
Grants to organisations	£2,020,000

Beneficiaries included: The Van Leer Jerusalem Institute (£550,500); Friends of Bezalel Academy of Arts (£399,200); The Hebrew University of Jerusalem (£90,200); Royal National Theatre (£40,100); Biblioteca Nazionale Centrale Rome (£18,700); American Friends of Tel Aviv University (£15,000).

Applications

According to the website, the foundation 'generates its own projects and generally does not respond to unsolicited communications'.

Sources of information

Accounts; annual report; Charity Commission record.

The Portal Trust

Education

Camden; Greenwich; Hackney; Hammersmith and Fulham; Islington; Kensington and Chelsea; Lambeth; Lewisham; Newham; Southwark; Tower Hamlets; Wandsworth; Westminster; the City of London

£1.36 million (2020/21)

CC number: 312425

Correspondent: Megan Falck, Grants Manager, 31 Jewry Street, London EC3N 2EY (tel: 020 7480 5884; email: contactus@sirjohncass.org)

Trustees: Cllr Denise Jones; John Hall; David Hogben; Hon. Brian Barker; The Revd Trevor Critchlow; The Revd Laura Jorgensen; Jenny Moseley; Sophie Fernandes; Helen Folorunso; Sarwar Zaman; Ratidzo Agnes Starkey; Fancy Sinantha.

 http://sirjohncassfoundation.com

 @sjcfgrants

General information

The foundation is one of the largest educational charities benefitting children and young people in inner London. The following information is taken from the foundation's website:

> We champion and support the education of children and young people in London who come from low income or disadvantaged backgrounds.
>
> We do this by providing grants to charitable organisations and educational establishments working with children and young people who meet our criteria. We also support individuals directly through bursaries and scholarships.

Grants to organisations

The foundation will only consider proposals from schools and organisations that benefit children or young people under the age of 25, who are:

- Permanent residents of the inner London boroughs listed in the beneficial area
- From a low income background
- From disadvantaged backgrounds or areas of high deprivation

Priorities

The foundation has four areas of focus for grant giving, which are as follows:

- Widening participation in further and higher education
- Truancy, exclusion and behaviour management
- Prisoner education
- New initiatives

Within each of these priorities the charity has specific aims, objectives and priority areas. Interested applicants should visit the foundation's website for full information regarding each grants programme.

In 2021 the trust changed its name from the Sir John Cass's Foundation to The Portal Trust due to Sir John Cass's links with the slave trade.

Financial information

Year end	31/03/2021
Income	£7,940,000
Assets	£263,990,000
Grants to organisations	£1,360,000

Beneficiaries included: London College of Fashion (£200,000); Hampshire County Council (£95,000); Stepney All Saints Church of England Secondary School (£72,400); The Share Foundation (£54,000); Lyric Theatre Hammersmith (£30,000); The Old Vic Theatre Trust (£25,000); National Youth Theatre of Great Britain (£20,000); Queen Mary University of London (£15,000); Bush Theatre (£10,000); Finding Rhythms (£5,000).

Exclusions

The foundation's website states the following:

> **What we will not normally fund (for external organisations):**
>
> - Projects that do not meet a Foundation priority
> - Supplementary schools or mother tongue teaching
> - Youth and community groups, or projects taking place in these settings
> - General fund-raising campaigns or appeals
> - Costs for equipment or salaries that are the statutory responsibility of education authorities
> - Costs to substitute for the withdrawal or reduction of statutory funding
> - Costs for work or activities that have already taken place prior to the grant application
> - Costs already covered by core funding or other grants
> - Capital costs, that are exclusively for the purchase, repair or furnishing of buildings, purchase of vehicles, computers, sports equipment or improvements to school grounds.

Applications

The foundation operates a two-stage application process – an initial enquiry and a full application stage.

The grants committee meets in March, June and October each year. Typically, within six months from receipt of a full application, a decision is made. Unsuccessful applicants may reapply after 12 months.

Sources of information

Accounts; annual report; Charity Commission record; funder's website.

Postcode Community Trust

Mental well-being; participation in arts and sports; social welfare; disadvantaged people; biodiversity and green space; climate emergency and sustainability; access to outdoors

 Wales

£1.99 million (2020)

OSCR number: SC044772

Correspondent: The Trustees, 28 Charlotte Square, Edinburgh EH2 4ET (tel: 0131 322 9399; email: info@postcodecommunitytrust.org.uk)

Trustees: Rob Flett; David Sharrod; Gareth Hill.

 www.postcodecommunitytrust.org.uk

 facebook.com/postcodecommunitytrust

General information

Postcode Community Trust is a grant-giving body funded by players of People's Postcode Lottery.

Community Grants Programme

According to the trust's Funding Guide 2022, the trust provides funding for smaller charities and good causes in Wales under the following themes:

- Improving mental well-being
- Enabling community participation in the arts
- Preventing or reducing the impact of poverty
- Supporting marginalised groups and promoting equality
- Improving biodiversity and green spaces
- Enabling participation in physical activity
- Responding to the climate emergency and promoting sustainability
- Increasing community access to outdoor space

Grants, ranging from £500 to £20,000, are available to organisations with an annual income of less than £1 million (although preference is given to organisations with an income of under £500,000). Registered charities, CICs and charitable community benefit societies can apply for between £500 and £25,000, while companies limited by guarantee and community groups not formally registered as a charity can apply for between £500 and £2,500.

This programme offers project funding (including running costs related to project delivery such as staff and utilities) or unrestricted funding.

Other funding

- **Magic Little Grants:** the programme gives smaller charities and community groups the chance to apply for a £500 grant to deliver projects across the UK. The application process is administered entirely by Localgiving
- **The Local School Nature Grants Programme:** is open to schools for nature equipment and training. The programme is entirely administered by Learning through Landscapes

Financial information

Year end	31/12/2020
Income	£8,120,000
Assets	£333,600
Grants to organisations	£1,990,000
No. of grants	201

Further financial information

During the year, 201 projects were funded by the community grants programme. These grants were made across the following areas and themes:

England	171	£1.68 million
Scotland	16	£241,300
Wales	14	£128,300

Community health and well-being	98	£1.05 million
Arts and physical recreation	64	£534,100
Reducing isolation	39	£412,500

A full list of beneficiaries can be found on the trust's website.

Beneficiaries included: Butterfly Conservation (£20,000); CleanupUK (£16,700); Darnhill Festival Association (£14,900); Grand Union Arts CIO (£12,300); Crossroads Community Hub (£8,400); Ruperra Conservation Trust (£5,500); Brandon in Bloom (£2,000); The Penstone Village Glade Community Association (£730).

Exclusions

A comprehensive list of exclusions with respect to activities and recipients can be found in the trust's funding guide on its website. Example exclusions include:

- Individuals
- Activities taking place outside Wales, or foreign travel
- Statutory bodies that the state has an obligation to fund
- Nurseries, schools, PTAs, colleges and universities (see Learning Through Landscapes and Magic Little Grants)
- Organisations with annual income over £1 million
- Political parties or party-political activities
- For unrestricted funding, organisations that work overseas/internationally

Applications

Funding rounds open each month and close when either the maximum number applications have been submitted or by the dates found on the trust's website. An online application form becomes available on the trust's website when funding rounds open. Full details, including guidance notes and deadlines, are available from the trust's website.

Sources of information

Accounts; annual report; OSCR record; funder's website; guidelines for applicants.

Postcode Local Trust

Mental well-being; participation in arts and sports; social welfare; disadvantaged people; biodiversity and green space; climate emergency and sustainability; access to outdoors

West Midlands and the South West

£2.47 million (2020)

OSCR number: SC045504

Correspondent: The Trustees, 28 Charlotte Square, Edinburgh EH2 4ET (tel: 0131 322 9388; email: info@postcodelocaltrust.org.uk)

 www.postcodelocaltrust.org.uk

 facebook.com/postcodelocaltrust

General information

The Postcode Local Trust is a grant-giving body funded by players of People's Postcode Lottery.

Community Grants Programme

According to the trust's Funding Guide 2022, the trust provides funding for smaller charities and good causes in the West Midlands and the South West under the following themes:

- Improving mental well-being
- Enabling community participation in the arts
- Preventing or reducing the impact of poverty
- Supporting marginalised groups and promoting equality
- Improving biodiversity and green spaces
- Enabling participation in physical activity
- Responding to the climate emergency and promoting sustainability
- Increasing community access to outdoor space

Grants, ranging from £500 to £20,000, are available to organisations with an annual income of less than £1 million (although preference is given to organisations with an income of under £500,000). Registered charities, CICs and charitable community benefit societies can apply for between £500 and £25,000, while companies limited by guarantee and community groups not formally registered as a charity can apply for between £500 and £2,500.

This programme offers project funding (including running costs related to project delivery such as staff and utilities) or unrestricted funding.

Other funding

- **Magic Little Grants:** the programme gives smaller charities and community groups the chance to apply for a £500 grant to deliver projects across the UK. The application process is administered entirely by Localgiving
- **The Local School Nature Grants Programme:** is open to schools for nature equipment and training. The programme is entirely administered by Learning through Landscapes

Financial information

Year end	31/12/2020
Income	£7,980,000
Assets	£267,000
Grants to organisations	£2,470,000

Further financial information

Grants were broken down as follows: community grants (£1.77 million); Learning Through Landscapes (£550,000); Bulldog Trust (£150,000). A full list of beneficiaries can be found on the trust's website.

Beneficiaries included: Young Epilepsy (£20,000); Woodlarks Campsite Trust (£15,900); Treverbyn Community Hall (£4,000); Tide Plymouth (£2,000).

Exclusions

A comprehensive list of exclusions with respect to activities and recipients can be found in the trust's funding guide on its website. Example exclusions include:

- Individuals
- Activities taking place outside the beneficial area, or foreign travel
- Statutory bodies that the state has an obligation to fund
- Nurseries, schools, PTAs, colleges and universities (see Learning Through Landscapes and Magic Little Grants)
- Organisations with annual income over £1 million
- Political parties or party-political activities
- For unrestricted funding, organisations that work overseas/internationally

Applications

Funding rounds open each month and close when either the maximum number applications have been submitted or by the dates found on the trust's website. An online application form becomes available on the trust's website when funding rounds open. Full details, including guidance notes and deadlines, are available from the trust's website.

Sources of information

Accounts; annual report; OSCR record; funder's website; guidelines for applicants.

Postcode Society Trust

Mental well-being; participation in arts and sports; social welfare; disadvantaged people; biodiversity and green space; climate emergency and sustainability; access to outdoors

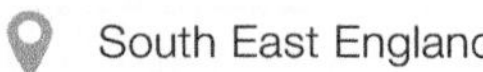

South East England

£3.81 million (2020)

OSCR number: SC044911

Correspondent: The Trustees, 28 Charlotte Square, Edinburgh EH2 4ET (tel: 0131 322 9430; email: info@postcodesocietytrust.org.uk)

Trustees: Michael Pratt; Judith Hills; Francis Fletcher.

www.postcodesocietytrust.org.uk

General information

The Postcode Society Trust (formerly the Postcode Dream Trust, up to November 2020) is funded entirely by the players of the People's Postcode Lottery's.

The trust previously delivered the Dream Fund, which awarded large grants to partnerships of charities delivering join projects. Following a change of focus, since 2021 the trust has delivered a Community Grants Programme instead.

Community Grants Programme

According to the trust's Funding Guide 2022, the trust provides funding for smaller charities and good causes in the South East England under the following themes:

- Improving mental well-being
- Enabling community participation in the arts
- Preventing or reducing the impact of poverty
- Supporting marginalised groups and promoting equality
- Improving biodiversity and green spaces
- Enabling participation in physical activity
- Responding to the climate emergency and promoting sustainability
- Increasing community access to outdoor space

Grants, ranging from £500 to £20,000, are available to organisations with an annual income of less than £1 million (although preference is given to organisations with an income of under £500,000). Registered charities, CICs and charitable community benefit societies can apply for between £500 and £25,000, while companies limited by guarantee and community groups not formally registered as a charity can apply for between £500 and £2,500.

This programme offers project funding (including running costs related to project delivery such as staff and utilities) or unrestricted funding.

Other funding

- **Magic Little Grants:** the programme gives smaller charities and community groups the chance to apply for a £500 grant to deliver projects across the UK. The application process is administered entirely by Localgiving
- **The Local School Nature Grants Programme:** is open to schools for nature equipment and training. The programme is entirely administered by Learning through Landscapes

Financial information

Year end	31/12/2020
Income	£6,250,000
Assets	-£209
Grants to organisations	£3,810,000
No. of grants	3

Further financial information

The trust made three donations to Dream Fund projects in 2020: Children 1st (£1.5 million); Zoological Society of London (£1.18 million); and Kent Wildlife Trust (£1.25 million). The list of beneficiaries provided in this entry includes grants awarded in 2021 from the Community Grants Programme, taken from the trust's website.

Beneficiaries included: Children 1st (£1.5 million); Home-Start East Sussex (£20,000); Natural Enterprise Ltd (£17,100); The Purple Elephant Project (£14,300); The Dot Collective (£7,800); The Otakar Kraus Music Trust (£6,600); Lacey Green and Loosley Row Tennis Club (£2,000).

Exclusions

A comprehensive list of exclusions with respect to activities and recipients can be found in the trust's funding guide on its website. Example exclusions include:

- Individuals
- Activities taking place outside the beneficial area, or foreign travel
- Statutory bodies that the state has an obligation to fund
- Nurseries, schools, PTAs, colleges and universities (see Learning Through Landscapes and Magic Little Grants)
- Organisations with annual income over £1 million
- Political parties or party-political activities
- For unrestricted funding, organisations that work overseas/ internationally

Applications

Funding rounds open each month and close when either the maximum number applications have been submitted or by the dates found on the trust's website. An online application form becomes available on the trust's website when funding rounds open. Full details, including guidance notes and deadlines, are available from the trust's website.

Sources of information

Accounts; annual report; OSCR record; funder's website; guidelines for applicants.

David and Elaine Potter Foundation

Education; civil society; social research; the arts

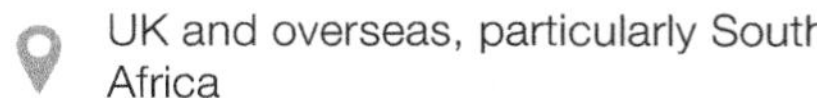

UK and overseas, particularly South Africa

£901,300 (2020)

CC number: 1078217

Correspondent: The Trustees, 6 Hamilton Close, London NW8 8QY (tel: 020 3915 9283; email: info@potterfoundation.com)

Trustees: Michael Langley; Dr Elaine Potter; Dr David Potter; Samuel Potter; Michael Polonsky.

www.potterfoundation.com

General information

The foundation was established in 1999. Its website states that its purpose is to 'support projects promoting reason, accountability and education that will improve understanding, human rights, good governance and a stronger civil society'.

Its main areas of focus are education and civil society. Grants are made by invitation only.

Education

Funding is given to projects that work on improving policy, improved practices and techniques and sustainability. Preference is given to education in support of economic and social well-being in the UK and historically in South Africa. Grants made to UK organisations are focused on technical/ vocational education, out of school/after school mentoring, life skills, employability and the development of young leaders.

The foundation will fund pilot projects, especially those that could influence policy and those that explore the role of new technology in education.

Civil society

The foundation's primary focus is on transparency, accountability, anti-corruption and good governance, with further interests in work that looks at the impact of drones on human rights work, investigative journalism, the rule of law, democracy and inequality.

Grants are made to UK-based organisations that look at these issues in a global context, for example, which are cross-border or not limited to a specific geographic area.

Non-strategic
Outside the core grant themes above, the foundation also supports causes of personal interest to the Potter family, including the arts. The foundation supports a number of London-based theatres.

Grants can be made for up to a maximum of three years and the foundation is willing to enter into joint funding agreements with other grant-makers.

Financial information

Year end	31/12/2020
Income	£308,300
Assets	£16,470,000
Grants to organisations	£901,300
No. of grants	22

Further financial information

Grants were broken down as follows:

Civil society	£420,000
Education	£346,300
The arts	£110,000
Non-strategic	£25,000

Beneficiaries included: Trust for the Bureau of Investigative Journalism (£150,000); IntoUniversity (£100,000); University of Cape Town (£106,900); Philharmonia (£50,000); Spotlight on Corruption (£20,000); Almeida Theatre and Ethical Journalism Network (£10,000 each).

Exclusions

The foundation does not provide support for/to the following:

- Individuals, including bursaries for individual schoolchildren or undergraduate education
- CICs
- Retrospective costs
- Full economic costs for universities
- Political organisations
- Clinical trials
- Religious organisations that only work for the benefit of members of their own religion
- Non-profit companies
- Capital works
- Building or rebuilding schools
- Individual schools or school projects
- School equipment
- Scaling up projects
- Civic education/citizenship education programmes

Applications

Applications are by invitation only, unsolicited applications are not accepted. The website notes that organisations that believe their work may align with the foundation's focuses should contact the foundation by email to discuss potential eligibility. The foundation asks that no written correspondence be sent.

Sources of information

Accounts; annual report; Charity Commission record; funder's website.

The Pret Foundation

Homelessness; social welfare; food poverty; education, training and employment

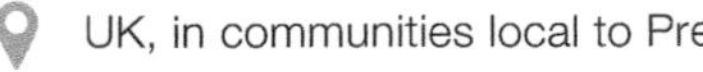

UK, in communities local to Pret shops

£730,200 (2019)

CC number: 1050195

Correspondent: The Trustees, 10 Bressenden Place, London SW1E 5DH (tel: 07584 213354; email: pretfoundation.donations@pret.com)

Trustees: Clive Schlee; Andrea Wareham; Valerie Cuminet; Pano Christou; Dilys Winterkorn; Dulcie McDermott.

www.pret.co.uk/en-GB/the-pret-foundation

General information

The Pret Foundation, formerly known as Pret Foundation Trust, was founded in 1995 and its aim is the alleviation of poverty, hunger and homelessness. It does this in four main ways:

- Delivering surplus foods from its shops to hostels and charities supporting people experiencing homelessness
- Supporting smaller charities working with people who are experiencing homelessness and poverty
- Running the Rising Stars Initiative, which helps vulnerable people off the streets and into work, and the Shooting Stars Initiative, which offers Rising Stars graduates a seven-month career development programme
- In partnership with West London Mission, the foundation also established 'The Pret House at St Luke's', a 13-bedroom annex in Kennington providing shelter for current or graduated Rising and Shooting Stars who work in Pret shops nearby

Financial information

Year end	31/12/2019
Income	£2,010,000
Assets	£517,400
Grants to organisations	£730,200

Further financial information

The 2019 accounts were the latest available at the time of writing (June 2022).

Beneficiaries included: Olallo (£40,000); Off the Fence Trust (£24,800); Shelter from the Storm (£20,900); Harrow Law Centre (£14,800); C4WS (£12,000); Notre Dame Refugee Centre (£6,500); Wycome Homeless Projects (£5,000).

Applications

Apply in writing to the correspondent.

Sources of information

Accounts; annual report; Charity Commission record; funder's website.

Sir John Priestman Charity Trust

Social welfare; older people; children and young people; upkeep of Church of England institutions, including the purchase of organs

Sunderland; County Durham; churches in the County of York

£391,200 (2020)

CC number: 209397

Correspondent: The Trustees, 47 John Street, Sunderland, Tyne and Wear SR1 1QU (tel: 0191 567 4857)

Trustees: Peter Taylor; Timothy Norton; Thomas Greenwell; Jean Majer; Frank Nicholson.

General information

The trust was established in 1931 by Sir John Preistman for general charitable purposes and social welfare in the regions of County Durham and Sunderland. The charity makes grants to charitable organisations operating in these areas that work in poverty relief, to aid older people, to assist young people going to university, to maintain hospitals and convalescent homes and to benefit young people. The charity also works to benefit members of the Church of England in this region, as well as in York, by maintaining and furnishing churches, mission halls and schools and through offering assistance to ministers who have worked in this area and are in need.

According to the charity's 2020 annual report:

> The trustees support a number of charities by way of regular annual grants, but otherwise the trustees aim where possible to award grants for specific projects as opposed to general running costs. In this way the trustees aim to assist charities to achieve particular objectives such as acquiring or replacing essential equipment or extending the scope of the benefits which they provide. In making grants the trustees are particularly concerned to establish that projects are viable. Accordingly grants are awarded subject to such conditions as to funding or otherwise as the trustees consider appropriate and payment is deferred until the conditions are satisfied. If these cannot be fulfilled the grant is cancelled.

Grants are awarded to churches in the Church of England for 'building, restoring, altering, enlarging, maintaining and furnishing (including provision of organs)' and the trustees 'recognise the challenges faced by parishes, often in deprived areas, in maintaining historic church buildings which often fulfil a vital role in the wider community'.

Financial information

Year end	31/12/2020
Income	£391,100
Assets	£14,170,000
Grants to organisations	£391,200

Beneficiaries included: Durham Association of Boys and Girls Clubs (£7,500); Alice House Hospice (£5,700); Age UK Sunderland (£4,000); Blue Watch Youth Centre (£1,500); Clowns in the Sky (£800).

Applications

Apply in writing to the correspondent. The trustees meet on a quarterly basis to consider applications and award grants.

Sources of information

Accounts; annual report; Charity Commission record.

The Prince of Wales's Charitable Foundation

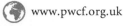

Heritage and conservation; education; health and well-being; social inclusion; the environment; the countryside

UK

£4.49 million (2020/21)

CC number: 1127255

Correspondent: Small Grant Committee, 105 Victoria Street, London SW1E 6QT (email: a contact form is available on the foundation's website)

 www.pwcf.org.uk

 @theprincesfund

 @theprincesfund

General information

The Prince of Wales's Charitable Foundation was established in 1979 with aim of transforming lives and building sustainable communities. It is funded through profits from sales of 'Waitrose Duchy Organic' and Highgrove products, as well as from tours of the Gardens at Highgrove.

The foundation provides support within the following core funding themes:

- Heritage and conservation
- Education
- Health and well-being
- Social inclusion
- The environment
- The countryside

The foundation is particularly interested in funding projects in deprived communities across the UK.

The foundation's small grants programme provides single or multi-year grants up to a maximum value of £5,000 and £15,000 respectively. Larger grants are made through the foundation's major grants programme which is not open to applications.

Financial information

Year end	31/03/2021
Income	£10,350,000
Assets	£11,030,000
Grants to organisations	£4,490,000

Beneficiaries included: Erskine Hospital; In Kind Direct; PIPS Suicide Prevention; Soil Association; Trees for Cities; Woodland Heritage.

Exclusions

According to the foundation's website, grants will not be made to:

- Individuals
- Public bodies
- Organisations that mainly distribute grants to other organisations
- Organisations that are looking to support similar projects delivered by the Prince of Wales's core charities – Prince's Foundation and The Prince's Trust.
- Organisations with political associations or interests
- Cover capital expenditure with the exception of community-based heritage conservation and restoration projects.

Applications

For the small grants programme, an online application form and further guidance is available from the foundation's website. Applications can be submitted at any time. The committee meets four times a year, usually in February, May, July and October; applications should reach the committee a month before the next meeting.

Applications to the major grants programme can be made by invitation only therefore it is not open to unsolicited applications.

Sources of information

Accounts; annual report; Charity Commission record; funder's website.

The Prince's Countryside Fund

 Rural communities

UK

£465,200 (2020/21)

CC number: 1136077

Correspondent: Liv Dryden, Senior Grants Officer, 137 Shepherdess Walk, London N1 7RQ (email: odryden@countrysidefund.org.uk)

 www.princescountrysidefund.org.uk

 facebook.com/countrysidefund

 @countrysidefund

General information

The fund was established in 2010 by HRH The Prince of Wales in response to concerns regarding the future of farming and rural communities in the UK. According to its 2020/21 annual report, the charity's three goals are:

- To improve the prospects of viability for family farm businesses
- To support aid delivery in emergencies and build resilience
- To sustain rural communities and drive economic vibrancy

Supporting Rural Communities

The programme provides grants of up to £25,000 over two years for projects that have a lasting impact on rural communities in the UK. The charity is particularly interested in applications from groups and organisations with projects in hamlets, villages and small market towns.

According to the programme's guidance document, successful projects will achieve one or more of the following aims:

- Support people to resolve existing and emerging community issues, circumstances, and priorities in their locality
- Build rural community resilience
- Develop innovative and replicable projects
- Enable leadership and community planning
- Improve the economic or social resilience of a rural community
- Reduce isolation for people living in rural areas through improving service provision
- Create a self-sufficient rural community fit for the future

Financial information

Year end	31/03/2021
Income	£1,580,000
Assets	£1,490,000
Grants to organisations	£465,200

Beneficiaries included: The Farming Life Centre (£10,000); Mull and Iona Community Trust (£9,000); Rural Housing Association (£8,000); Countrymen UK (£5,000); Herefordshire Rural Hub (£3,400).

Applications

Applications should be made online through the fund's website. Check the website for updates on when the next funding round will open.

Sources of information

Accounts; annual report; Charity Commission record; eligibility and guidance document 2019; funder's website.

The Privy Purse Charitable Trust

General charitable purposes; ecclesiastical causes; national and international disasters

UK and overseas

£656,200 (2020/21)

CC number: 296079

Correspondent: The Trustees, Privy Purse Office, Buckingham Palace, London SW1A 1AA (tel: 020 7930 4832; email: mike.stevens@royal.uk)

Trustees: Sir Michael Stevens; Sir Edward Young; Jane Graham.

General information

This trust was established in 1987 to support a wide range of causes. In particular, grants are given to charities of which The Queen is patron and to ecclesiastical organisations associated with The Queen. Support is also given towards national and international disasters.

Financial information

Year end	31/03/2021
Income	£98,400
Assets	£5,220,000
Grants to organisations	£656,200
No. of grants	342

Further financial information

During the year, The Privy Purse Charitable Trust made 342 grants to organisations. Grants were broken down as follows:

The environment	£39,400
Children and young people	£24,000
Armed forces	£22,300
Trades and professions	£21,000
Hospices and hospitals	£20,600
Other	£17,600
Sport	£16,900
Medical welfare	£15,300
Restoration of cathedrals and churches	£14,500
Disability	£11,600
Cultural causes	£11,300
Animals	£10,200
Social welfare	£9,700
Medical research	£6,000
Royal almonry	£6,000
Family welfare	£4,300
Voluntary services	£3,300
Overseas aid	£1,500

Beneficiaries included: City of London School (£142,000); Sandringham Group of Parishes (£61,900); Chapel Royal – Hampton Court Palace (£50,600); Chapel Royal – St James's Palace (£30,000); Game and Wildlife Conservation Trust (£27,400); Chapel Royal – Windsor Great Park (£26,700).

Applications

The trust does not accept unsolicited applications and only awards grants to charities of which the Queen is patron.

Sources of information

Accounts; annual report; Charity Commission record.

The Progress Foundation

Work that helps young people become fully involved with society, particularly through education, assistance with finding work or involvement with social enterprise

UK, with a strong preference for Greater London

£278,000 (2020/21)

CC number: 1123219

Correspondent: The Trustees, c/o New Quadrant Partners Ltd, 5 Chancery Lane, London WC2A 1LG (email: a contact form is available on the foundation's website)

Trustees: Roger Pilgrim; Nadine Majaro; Nigel Hamway.

 www.progressuk.org

General information

The foundation was established in 2008. Its website states that grant-making is focused on the following:

- Organisations working with young people, normally in the age range 14–21, though we will also look at projects helping younger children or young people up to age 25
- Organisations which help young people to become fully involved with society, particularly through education, assistance with finding work or involvement with social enterprise
- Organisations working primarily within Greater London

The maximum grant is £25,000 and awards are typically between £10,000 and £15,000. Grants will not be given to the same project for more than three years.

Financial information

Year end	31/03/2021
Income	£132,300
Assets	£2,510,000
Grants to organisations	£278,000

Beneficiaries included: Reachout and Refugee Council (£40,000 each); Redthread (£20,000); Social Enterprise Academy (£18,500); Vauxhall City Farm (£10,000); The Garden Classroom (£3,000).

Exclusions

The foundation does not give grants to individuals, medical charities or to organisations that promote a particular religious belief unless the work is not for religious purposes and clearly fits the guidelines. Typically, large and established charities will not be supported; however, the foundation will occasionally consider applications where such charities apply for new or innovative projects. The foundation will not provide support that replaces or subsidises statutory funding.

Applications

Application forms and details of application deadlines are available on the foundation's website.

Sources of information

Accounts; annual report; Charity Commission record; funder's website.

Prostate Cancer UK

Prostate cancer research; education; training; campaigning

UK

£5.8 million (2020/21)

CC number: 1005541

Correspondent: The Research Team, Fourth Floor, The Counting House, 53 Tooley Street, London SE1 2QN (tel: 020 3310 7000; email: research@prostatecanceruk.org)

Trustees: Prof. Jonathan Waxman; Michael Tye; Prof. Sara Faithful; Simon Hammett; Andrew Mitchell; Prof. Martin Cbefmedsci; Charles Packshaw; Marion Leslie; Prof. David Neal; Lynne Robb; Simon Peck; Cristian Cussen; Samia Qadhi; Henry Obi; Prof. Richard Neal; Dr Nicholas Hicks; Prof. Paul Stewart.

www.prostatecanceruk.org

 facebook.com/prostatecanceruk

 @prostateuk

General information

Prostate Cancer UK was established in 1991 with the aim of improving the care and welfare of those affected by prostate cancer, increasing investment in research, and raising public and political awareness of the disease. The trust's grant-making focuses on research.

According to the trust's 2020/21 annual report and accounts, a new research strategy was set out for 2020 which focuses on:

- Better diagnosis
- Better treatments
- Smarter data

Information on current and upcoming funding calls can be found on the charity's website. At the time of writing (May 2022) upcoming calls included:

Transformational Impact Awards – support for larger-scale research investments which aim to tackle the biggest challenges in prostate cancer, covering high-quality discovery science, through to translation and clinical research.

Research Innovation Awards – funding for bold, innovative and game-changing investigator-led research.

Financial information

Year end	31/03/2021
Income	£27,870,000
Assets	£25,960,000
Grants to organisations	£5,800,000

Beneficiaries included: The Institute of Cancer Research (£1.31 million); Newcastle University (£670,000); University of Cambridge (£300,000); University of East Anglia (£77,000).

Applications

Applications can be made online using the charity's grant management system. Each grant-making programme has its own guidelines and deadline dates; applicants should check the charity's helpful website for further information.

Sources of information

Accounts; annual report; Charity Commission record; funder's website.

The Prudence Trust

Mental health

UK

£434,000 (2020)

CC number: 1187700

Correspondent: The Trustees, The Prudence Trust, 16 Berkeley Street, London W1J 8DZ (email: info@theprudencetrust.org)

Trustee: The Prudence Trust Company Ltd.

 https://theprudencetrust.org

General information

The trust supports research and services which address both preventative and curable mental health treatments and therapies, with a specific focus on social interventions, such as creativity and the arts. Support is focused on young people aged between 11 and 25 from disadvantaged groups – those who face greater difficulty in accessing support when they need it.

Grants usually range from £30,000 to £500,000 and can be made for programme costs, salaries, equipment and core costs.

Financial information

Year end	31/12/2020
Income	£116,400,000
Assets	£120,640,000
Grants to organisations	£434,000

Further financial information

Grants were distributed as follows:

Mental health	£200,000
General purposes	£154,000
Disadvantage	£50,000
Arts	£30,000

Beneficiaries included: A list of beneficiaries was not available.

Applications

Apply via the foundation's website, where information on open funding opportunities can also be found.

Sources of information

Accounts; annual report; Charity Commission record; funder's website.

The PwC Foundation

Social inclusion through employability and education; mental health and healthcare; general charitable purposes

UK

£1.26 million (2019/20)

CC number: 1144124

Correspondent: Community Engagement Team, PriceWaterhouseCoopers, 1 Embankment Place, London WC2N 6RH (tel: 07764 902846; email: uk_pwcfoundation@pwc.com)

Trustees: Kevin Ellis; David Adair; Zelf Hussain; Kalee Talvitie-Brown; David Walters; Emma Cox.

 www.pwc.co.uk/corporate-sustainability/the-pwc-foundation.jhtml

General information

The PwC Foundation was established in 2011 and is the corporate charity of PriceWaterhouseCoopers LLP (PwC).

The objectives of the foundation are to promote sustainable development and social inclusion and environmental awareness for public benefit. Grants are made under the following themes:

- Social inclusion through employability
- Social inclusion through education
- Healthcare
- Environmental and other general charitable purposes

The foundation is also the company's vehicle for providing matched funding, whereby the foundation matches an individual's fundraising to a maximum of £250 per person, per year.

Grants can be made to registered charities, CICs and social enterprises.

Financial information

Year end	03/06/2020
Income	£1,760,000
Assets	£860,900
Grants to organisations	£1,260,000

Further financial information

Grants were broken down as follows:

Employability	£553,500
Healthcare	£369,200
The environment	£140,300
Matched-giving programme	£120,500
Education	£53,900

Beneficiaries included: Wellbeing of Woman (£136,400); School for Social Entrepreneurs (£104,500); Samaritans (£97,000); The World's Big Sleep Out Trust (£54,000); Teach First (£36,000); National Literacy Trust (£14,900); Mind – The National Association for Mental Health (£6,200); Barnardo's Northern Ireland (£40).

Exclusions

The foundation will not fund political organisations, lobbying groups, animal rights groups or religious bodies.

Applications

The foundation's 2019/20 accounts state:

> There is no current requirement for a formal open grant application process. The Steering Committee and trustees can independently identify recipients for funding who meet the charitable objectives of the Foundation. Recipients are approved by the trustees.

Sources of information

Accounts; annual report; Charity Commission record; funder's website.

Mr and Mrs J. A. Pye's Charitable Settlement

General charitable purposes, particularly the environment, adult and children's health, youth organisations, education and heritage

UK, with a strong preference for Oxfordshire

£478,300 (2020)

CC number: 242677

Correspondent: Lucy McCallum-Toppin, Grants Manager, Springfield, Farringdon Road, Southmoor, Oxfordshire OX13 5BG (tel: 07775 882715; email: pyecharitablesettlement@gmail.com)

Trustees: Patrick Mulcare; Graham Flint; Valerie Buzzard.

 www.pyecharitablesettlement.org

General information

The charity was established in 1965, at a time when the charity's primary asset was a shareholding in the Pye building company. Today, the trustees no longer hold shares in the company but focus much of their grant-making in the areas in which the company operated. Applications are welcomed from charities based in, or charitable causes relating to, the county of Oxfordshire and surrounding areas. Grants can be made across the UK in theory, but the charity has a strong preference for Oxfordshire.

Areas of work

According to the charity's 2020 accounts, the types of causes typically supported are:

- Environmental – particularly organic farming matters, conservation and health-related matters such as pollution research and some wildlife protection
- Education – relating to nursery, primary, secondary or higher
- Adult health and care – particularly post-natal depressions, schizophrenia, mental health and research into the main causes of early death
- Children's health and care – physical, mental and learning disabilities, respite breaks, etc.
- Youth organisations – particularly projects encouraging self-reliance or dealing with social deprivation
- Heritage and the arts

Financial information

Year end	31/12/2020
Income	£685,100
Assets	£14,550,000
Grants to organisations	£478,300
No. of grants	118

Beneficiaries included: Music at Oxford (£100,000); Magdalen College School (£30,000); Pegasus Theatre (£10,000); Oxfordshire Scouts (£5,000); Earth Trust (£2,500); Maggie's Oxford (£2,000); Footsteps Foundation and The Big Issue (£1,000 each); Oxford Preservation Trust (£600).

Exclusions

Applications will not be considered from/for:

- Individuals
- Organisations that are not registered charities
- Animal welfare
- The promotion of religion

Applications

All applications should be sent to the administrative office. The trustees meet quarterly to consider grant applications.

While there is no application form, the following information is required, as listed on the charity's website:

> - The registered charity number or evidence of an organisation's tax exempt status;
> - Brief description of the activities of the charity;
> - The names of the Trustees and chief officers [NB more important than Patrons];
> - Details of the purpose of the application and where funds will be put to use;
> - Details of the public benefit that will arise if your application is successful;
> - Details of the funds already raised and the proposals for how remaining funds are to be raised;
> - The latest Trustees' report and full audited or independently examined accounts (which must comply with Charity Commission guidelines and requirements);
> - A covering letter with a brief description of the charity in one paragraph and a brief paragraph of the purpose of the application. We ask that you include the charities turnover and reserves in this letter also;
> - **Details of full name of the bank account, sort code, and number into which any grant should be paid;**
> - The charity's email address.
> - **All application information is preferred by email with word documents attached**

Applicants may apply via email.

Sources of information

Accounts; annual report; Charity Commission record; funder's website.

QBE European Operations Foundation

Education and work; healthcare; community-based projects; climate resilience; inclusion

UK and Europe

£956,200 (2020)

CC number: 1143828

Correspondent: Sophie Wraith-Lee, Foundation Adviser, QBE Insurance, 30 Fenchurch Street, London EC3M 3BD (tel: 01245 343253; email: QBEFoundationEO@uk.qbe.com)

Trustees: Grant Clemence; Beth McLeod; Alexandra Smith; Benjamin McBean; Philippe Gueret; Naintara Agarwal.

 https://qbeeurope.com/sustainability/qbe-foundation

General information

The QBE European Operations Foundation, the charitable foundation of global business insurance company QBE, was registered with the Charity Commission in 2011.

The foundation's website gives the following summary of its activities:

> Through our efforts with like-minded charities we seek to build strong, sustainable, and inclusive communities that have a positive impact for people, our customers, and broker partners.
>
> We support charities in a variety of ways, from matching employee fundraising efforts, encouraging employee volunteering and providing grants to charities that align with Climate Resilience and Inclusion.

The foundation also supports areas including homelessness, healthcare and mental health, and education and work opportunities. At the time of writing (February 2022), the foundation's main charity partners were Crisis and Mind.

The foundation matches QBE employee fundraising up to £10,000 per employee and matches payroll giving up to £12,000 per employee.

Financial information

Year end	31/12/2020
Income	£960,000
Assets	£8,000
Grants to organisations	£956,200
No. of grants	32+

Further financial information

During the year, the foundation awarded general grants totalling £880,400. Grants made matching employees' donations totalled £42,700 and grants made matching employees' payroll donations totalled £33,100. The majority of grants made during the year were for UK-based organisations.

Beneficiaries included: Crisis UK (£130,900); Mind (£129,300); British Red Cross Society (£70,300); Alzheimer's Society (£21,900); FareShare (£10,600); Age UK and StepChange (£10,000 each); Autism Parents Together (£1,400); National Rheumatoid Arthritis Society (£120).

Exclusions

According to the foundation's 2020 accounts, it does not fund the following:

- Non-registered charities
- Political, local authority, union-affiliated and religious organisations
- Schools and associated parent–teacher organisations
- Animal welfare charities (not including those whose objectives are to support people)
- Charities whose beneficiaries are predominantly outside the foundation's operating areas
- Salaries

Applications

The foundation no longer accepts applications directly from charities. QBE employees nominate charities for grants. Employees involved with a specific charity can request a grant application form from the QBE EO Foundation Adviser. See the website for deadlines.

Sources of information

Accounts; annual report; Charity Commission record; funder's website.

Quadrature Climate Foundation

Climate change

Worldwide

£54.06 million (2020/21)

CC number: 1187301

Correspondent: The Trustees, The Leadenhall Building, Leadenhall Street, London EC3V 41B (email: contact@qc.foundation)

Trustees: Jennifer Hooke; Suneil Setiya; Greg Skinner; Neil Cosgrove.

https://quadrature.ai/foundation

General information

The foundation was established by Quadrature Capital Ltd in 2019 and receives a proportion of the company's annual profits to fund work that combats climate change.

The foundation's website states:

> We are focused on helping get global emissions of greenhouse gases onto a rapidly declining pathway. We support work on the main sources of the problem, and are happy funding a wide range of ideas and ways of working that can trigger positive change.

Financial information

Year end	30/06/2021
Income	£60,260,000
Assets	£7,880,000
Grants to organisations	£54,060,000

Beneficiaries included: Stitching SED Fund (£5.29 million); Winward Fund (£2.45 million); Canopy Planet Society (£1 million); Count Us In (£800,000).

Applications

Unsolicited applications are not accepted. The foundation's website states:

> Whilst we are interested in connecting with partners and learning more about what others are doing, at this time we are only able to accept proposals by invite only.

Sources of information

Accounts; annual report; Charity Commission record; funder's website.

Queen Mary's Roehampton Trust

People who have a disability as a result of service in the armed forces, and their dependants; medical or surgical research associated with this group

UK

£370,000 (2020/21)

CC number: 211715

Correspondent: Col. S. Rowland-Jones, Clerk to the Trustees, 2 Sovereign Close, Quidhampton, Salisbury, Wiltshire SP2 9ES (tel: 01722 501413; email: qmrt@hotmail.co.uk)

Trustees: Col. Paul Cummings; Colin Green; James MacNamara; Sir Barry Thornton; Anne Child; Dr Rakesh Bhabutta; Miranda Thompson-Schwab; Heather Betts; Harvey Tilley; Air Cdre Barbara Cooper; Ian Nicoll; Alison Wyman; Benjamin Marshall.

General information

The trust was established for the assistance of people who served in either the armed forces, the mercantile marine service or in any Service established under the Civil Defence Acts 1937 and 1939 and who suffered a disability in that Service. Support is extended to the dependants of such people.

The trust makes grants to charities and other organisations whose objects include the reception, accommodation, treatment or after-care of people relevant to the charity's objects. Grants may also be made in aid of medical or surgical research, with particular regard to the needs of people with disabilities who served in the armed forces.

Financial information

Year end	31/03/2021
Income	£371,400
Assets	£14,450,000
Grants to organisations	£370,000
No. of grants	28

Beneficiaries included: Erskine Hospital (£25,000); Broughton House (£20,000); Royal British Legion Industries (£15,000); Canine Partners (£10,000); Chaseley Trust (£8,000); Turn to Starboard (£6,000); Holidays for Heroes Jersey (£4,000).

Applications

Apply in writing to the correspondent.

Sources of information

Accounts; annual report; Charity Commission record.

The Quilter Foundation

Young people; young carers; education; employment; health and well-being

UK and the Isle of Man

£487,500 (2020)

CC number: 1175555

Correspondent: The Trustees, c/o Quilter plc, Senator House, 85 Queen Victoria Street, London EC4V 4AB (tel: 020 7778 9614; email: responsiblebusiness@quilter.com)

Trustees: Timothy Childe; Philippa Foster Back; Jane Goodland; Matthew Burton; Paul Feeney.

www.quilter.com/responsible-business/the-quilter-foundation

General information

The foundation was established in 2018 by Quilter plc, a wealth management company. It provides funding to selected charity partners that support young people in three areas: financial education and empowerment; sustainable employment; raising awareness of young carers and supporting their health and well-being. Since launching in 2018, the foundation has awarded £2.2 million to charity partners, often through multi-year commitments.

Financial information

Year end	31/12/2020
Income	£801,700
Assets	£8,950,000
Grants to organisations	£487,500
No. of grants	4

Further financial information

During the year grants made in support of young carers totalled £203,100 and grants made in support of financial education totalled £40,000. In addition, a grant of £244,500 was awarded to the Disasters Emergency Committee.

Beneficiaries included: Disasters Emergency Committee (£244,500); Carers Trust (£183,100); Savings Alliance (£40,000); Crossroads Care (£20,000).

Exclusions

The foundation does not provide funding to political, religious or profit-making organisations.

Applications

The foundation makes grants to selected charity partners. Contact the correspondent for further information.

Sources of information

Annual report and accounts; Charity Commission record; Quilter plc's Responsible Business Report 2020.

Rachel Charitable Trust

General charitable purposes; the advancement of religion and religious education; the relief of poverty

Worldwide

£2.44 million (2020/21)

CC number: 276441

Correspondent: Robert Chalk, Charity Secretary, 30 Market Place, London W1W 8AP (tel: 020 7846 3036)

General information

This trust was established in 1978 for general charitable purposes and focuses on the relief of poverty and the advancement of religion and religious education. Our research indicates that, in practice, the trust gives mainly to Jewish organisations.

Financial information

Year end	30/06/2021
Income	£5,680,600
Assets	£20,480,000
Grants to organisations	£2,440,000

Further financial information

Only beneficiaries receiving grants of £200,000 or more were listed in the trust's accounts. Grants of under £200,000 totalled £1.51 million.

Beneficiaries included: The Kemach Foundation (£698,600); The Rosin Sadagora Trust (£230,000).

Applications

Apply in writing to the correspondent.

Sources of information

Accounts; annual report; Charity Commission record.

The Racing Foundation

Welfare of members of the horseracing industry; education and training connected with the horseracing industry; racehorse welfare; equine science research

UK

£3.47 million (2020)

CC number: 1145297

Correspondent: Tansy Challis, Grants Manager, 75 High Holborn, London WC1V 6LS (tel: 07741 035907; email: tansy.challis@racingfoundation.co.uk)

 www.racingfoundation.co.uk

 @RacingGrants

General information

The foundation was established in 2012. The Racing Foundation received an endowment of £78 million from the net proceeds of the UK government's sale of the Horserace Totalisator Board ('Tote') and aims to use these funds to achieve a lasting legacy for the sport of horseracing.

Focus areas

The foundation's website states that it will make grants for the following purposes:

- **Social welfare** – projects that improve the health, welfare or the rehabilitation of members of the horseracing industry; or community development work in areas connected to the industry
- **Education, training and participation** – the promotion of education and training connected with the horseracing and thoroughbred breeding industry
- **Thoroughbred horse welfare** – organisations working to improve the welfare of current or former thoroughbred racehorses and veterinary research into the thoroughbred horse that will benefit both the breed and the sport
- **Sustainability and emerging issues** – activities and projects focusing on environmental awareness and sustainability to increase understanding and cultivate an industry response. Projects that respond to emerging issues being faced by the racing and breeding industries

Grant types

There are three types of grants available:

- **Small grants** of up to £20,000, typically for items of equipment (but not basic stable management equipment)
- **Open grants** from £20,000 upwards
- **Equine science research grants** – see the website as this is broadly defined and administered by another organisation

Grants can be made for project costs (either research or capital), core costs, equipment, innovative or risky projects and matched funding. The foundation will fund multi-year projects up to three years and will occasionally grant loans for capital projects.

Financial information

Year end	31/12/2020
Income	£2,120,000
Assets	£91,780,000
Grants to organisations	£3,470,000
No. of grants	33

Further financial information

Grants were broken down as follows:

Education, training and participation	£1.84 million
Social welfare	£1.07 million
Thoroughbred horse welfare	£533,000
Heritage and culture	£21,000

The grant total includes £1.9 million awarded for COVID-19 response and recovery.

Beneficiaries included: Pony Racing Authority (£905,000); Professional Jockeys Association (£603,000); Liverpool John Moores University (£120,000); British Racing School (£85,000); Urban Equestrian Academy (£38,000); National Horseracing Museum (£21,000); Injured Jockeys Fund (£5,000).

Exclusions

The foundation's website states that no grants are made for:

- Work that does not deliver benefits associated with the UK horseracing and Thoroughbred breeding industry.
- Grants to individuals or to causes that will benefit one person.
- Long-term grants towards staffing costs primarily associated with fundraising.
- The promotion of religion.
- Work that addresses gambling addiction (unless specifically focussed on participants within the horseracing and Thoroughbred breeding industry).
- Retrospective funding, meaning support for work that has already taken place.
- Work that does not have a charitable purpose.

Applications

For all grants applications, apart from those for equine science research, there is a three-stage process. There are three funding rounds each year. Applicants should submit a first-stage application using the online form, providing basic details about their organisation. Guidelines, along with dates of application deadlines, are available on the foundation's website. Applicants are encouraged to contact the grants manager for further advice and guidance before submitting an application.

For equine science research applications, the foundation's website requests applicants register as a user of the Horserace Betting Levy Board's equine grants system. Once registered, applicants will be able to build and submit a grant application form. To ensure that your application is considered for Racing Foundation funding you will need to mark the relevant box on the application summary. A link for the online application system along with application deadline dates and further guidance can be found on the foundation's website. For further information, contact Annie Dodd, Grants Manager at the Horserace Betting Levy Board on 020 7333 0043 ext. 873 or email equine.grants@hblb.org.uk.

Sources of information

Accounts; annual report; Charity Commission record; funder's website.

The Radcliffe Trust

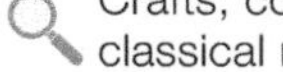 Crafts; conservation; chamber and classical music

 UK

£489,000 (2020/21)

CC number: 209212

Correspondent: The Administrator, 6 Trull Farm Buildings, Trull, Tetbury, Gloucestershire GL8 8SQ (tel: 01285 841900; email: radcliffe@thetrustpartnership.com)

Trustees: Sir Christopher Butcher; Hon. Felix Warnock; Timothy Wilson; Ellen Schroder; Richard Morrison; Margaret Casely-Hayford; Melanie Howse; David Whelton; Countess Howe.

 www.theradcliffetrust.org

General information

The Radcliffe Trust was established in 1714 as a charitable trust under the will of Dr John Radcliffe, the most eminent physician of his day. The will provided for a permanent endowment, the income from which is used exclusively for charitable purposes.

The following information is taken from the trust's website:

> By his will, Dr. Radcliffe directed his trustees to spend £40,000 on building a library, and today the Radcliffe Camera is one of Oxford's architectural glories. The trustees subsequently built two other important Oxford landmarks, the Radcliffe Observatory and the Radcliffe Infirmary, precursor of the modern John Radcliffe Hospital. In 1970 the agricultural holdings which Dr. Radcliffe had bought in 1713 were acquired to become the new town of Milton Keynes, leaving the trustees with a substantial endowment and increased income.
>
> Today, The Radcliffe Trust continues his charitable bequest through the support of Music and Heritage and Crafts.
>
> **Music**
>
> The Radcliffe Trust supports classical music performance and training, especially chamber music, composition and music education. Particular interests within music education are music for children and adults with special needs, youth orchestras and projects at secondary and higher levels, including academic research. The Trustees respond to applications and also initiate their own projects.
>
> **Heritage and crafts**
>
> The Radcliffe Trust supports the development and practice of the skills, knowledge and experience that underpin the UK's heritage and crafts sector. This includes support for emerging craftspeople of high quality, craft and conservation projects and training, projects demonstrating creative outcomes by designer-makers, projects with potential for capacity building within the sector, and some special needs projects focusing on the therapeutic benefits of skills development.

All grants are generally in the region of £2,500 to £7,500. Funding is for project costs (including training opportunities), and the trust will consider the inclusion of a proportionate but limited share of an organisation's overheads relating to the project. The trust accepts applications from charities, CICs, CIOs and other not-for-profit organisations.

Financial information

Year end	31/03/2021
Income	£558,600
Assets	£22,170,000
Grants to organisations	£489,000
No. of grants	93

Further financial information

Grants paid in 2020/21 totalled £489,000 and were broken down as follows in the trust's accounts:

Heritage and crafts	£234,700
Music	£224,700
Tercentenary and trustee-initiated grants	£27,500
Miscellaneous	£2,100

Beneficiaries included: Crafts Council (£75,000); Church Buildings Council (£20,000); Coventry City of Culture Trust (£10,000); Multiphonic Arts (£5,000); Key Changes Music Therapy (£3,000); Benedetti Foundation (£2,000); Ash Lea School (£1,000); Barts Charity (£600).

Exclusions

In general, the trust does not support:

- Individuals
- Retrospective appeals
- General appeals or endowment funds
- Mainstream schools

See the trust's website for scheme-specific exclusions.

Applications

Applications can only be submitted using the trust's online application form. See the trust's website for further details of its schemes.

Deadlines for applications to both the Music and Heritage and crafts schemes are as follows:

- **For consideration by the trustees in June**: the deadline is 31 January
- **For consideration by the trustees in December**: the deadline is 31 July

Sources of information

Accounts; annual report; Charity Commission record; funder's website.

The Bishop Radford Trust

Christian ministry and church projects

UK and overseas

£489,300 (2020/21)

CC number: 1113562

Correspondent: Suzannah O'Brien, Trustee, Devonshire House, 1 Devonshire Street, London W1W 5DR (tel: 020 7304 2000; email: enquiries@bishopradfordtrust.org.uk)

Trustees: Lord Stephen Green; Lady Janian Green; Suzannah O'Brien; Dr Ruth Dare.

 http://bishopradfordtrust.org.uk

General information

The Bishop Radford Trust was registered with the Charity Commission in 2006 to help promote the work of the Christian church in line with the doctrines and principles of the Church of England. According to the trust's 2020/21 annual report, it will support:

- Church related projects promoting charitable purposes
- The education of priests, future priests and church workers
- Other support for church ministry

Grants are only made to churches and UK-registered charities, with a relatively even split between UK and overseas giving. According to its 2020/21 annual report, the trust operates a three-tier giving system:

- Low-level grants are typically one-off donations of under £2,000
- Mid-level grants are typically of between £5,000 and £10,000 and focused on organisations that connect the trust to the Christian community
- High-level grants are typically recurrent grants towards multi-year objectives, awarded to partner organisations with whom a 'funder plus' relationship is developed

The majority of the trust's grants are low-level, with smaller numbers of mid- and high-level grants.

Financial information

Year end	31/03/2021
Income	£1,110,000
Assets	£21,920,000
Grants to organisations	£489,300
No. of grants	43

Further financial information

In 2020/21, the trust received 206 applications and awarded 43 grants, of which 22 were 'low level' grants. Grants were broken down as follows:

	Church-related projects	Support of church ministry	Total
UK	£95,000	£138,500	£233,500
International	£130,000	£125,800	£255,800

Beneficiaries included: The Friends of the Archbishop of Canterbury's Anglican Communion Fund (£130,000); Bible Reading Fellowship (£70,000); Exeter College Chaplaincy (£38,200); Transforming Lives for Good (£10,000); Purple Shoots (£5,000); The Mustard Tree Foundation (£2,300); Highway Hope (£1,000); Latin Link UK (£500).

Exclusions

According to the trust's website, it will not support:

- Charities that are not registered in the UK
- Building or capital projects
- Individuals
- Campaigns or lobbying
- Retrospective funding
- Charities that do not have Christian ministry in their charitable objectives

The trust's website also details the following as reasons for applications being refused:

- When giving to projects based overseas we tend to give through larger, more established Christian UK registered charities, or through charities where we have a personal connection, recognising that due diligence is more challenging with these donations.
- For grants awards within the UK, Trustees tend to give to smaller charities where our contribution makes a significant difference.
- We prefer to support projects where the apparent need is great and the potential scale of the impact is substantial.
- We don't often support individuals however we recognise that a contribution to core running costs is valuable.
- Advocacy work/campaigning and lobbying related work are not usually supported.
- We sometimes support pilot tests, but we prefer to focus on projects that have a track record.
- We don't have sufficient resources to fund all requests. We favour projects which spark interest and passion. As a general rule, if we cannot award funds ourselves, we do try to help to redirect grantees.

Applications

Applicants must check their eligibility using the eligibility quiz on the trust's website before making an application using the trust's online form.

Sources of information

Accounts; annual report; Charity Commission record; funder's website.

The Randal Charitable Foundation

Health; mental health; social disadvantage; addiction; education

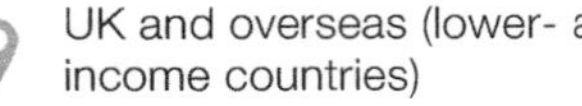

UK and overseas (lower- and middle-income countries)

£829,500 (2021)

CC number: 1176129

Correspondent: The Trustees, 5 Pavilion Way, Loughborough, Leicestershire LE11 5GW (tel: 01509 217705; email: grants@randalfoundation.org.uk)

Trustees: Dr Nik Kotecha; Moni Kotecha; Yanyan Huang; Matthew Thompson; Christopher Hobson.

 www.randalfoundation.org.uk

General information

The foundation was established in 2017 and receives a large proportion of its income from Morningside Pharmaceuticals Ltd.

The foundation supports the following causes in the UK and overseas:

- Health
- Mental health
- Poverty
- Social disadvantage
- Addiction
- Education

The foundation currently provides grants to UK-based registered charities or organisations. It welcomes applications for smaller grants (over £3,000) as well as large-scale funding. The foundation funds one-off causes as well as multi-year projects. Occasionally, it may also provide general funding for charities/causes on a specific case by case basis.

Financial information

Year end	31/12/2021
Income	£3,050,000
Assets	£9,730,000
Grants to organisations	£829,500
No. of grants	42

Further financial information

During the year, grants paid totalled £829,500 and an additional £60,000 of grants were approved but not paid. Grants paid to 19 UK-based projects totalled £354,700. The remaining grants were for work outside the UK.

Beneficiaries included: Mental Health Innovations (£50,000); Centre for Social Justice (£40,000); The Forward Trust (£31,500); Shama Women's Centre (£16,000); Home From Hospital Care (£10,000); Hot Line Meals Service and Tiny Tim's (£5,000 each).

Applications

The foundation's website states that to begin the application process, applicants must first make an enquiry to the foundation (by email, post or via the online contact form) including details such as:

- Name, contact details and registered charity or company number (if applicable)
- An overview of the organisation's objectives and focus
- The organisation's area of operation (this may be different to the registered address)
- The specific cause/project the funding is for
- Total funding required in UK pounds (£)
- Please state if the enquiry is time sensitive

For full details of what to include, see the foundation's website. If the trustees wish to progress an enquiry, the applicant will be asked to send additional information or complete an application form.

Sources of information

Accounts; annual report; Charity Commission record; funder's website.

The Rank Foundation Ltd

Christian communication; young people; education; older people; general charitable purposes

 UK

£7.33 million (2020/21)

CC number: 276976

Correspondent: The Trustees, 12 Warwick Square, London SW1V 2AA (email: contactus@rankfoundation.com)

Trustees: Nicholas Buxton; Jason Chaffer; Deputy Fitzpatrick; Joey Newton; Johanna Ropner; Daniel Simon; William Wyatt; Andrew Fleming; Lindsey Clay; Joel Davis; Stuart Cowen.

 www.rankfoundation.com

 facebook.com/TheRankFoundation

 @RankFoundation

General information

The foundation was established in 1953 by the late Lord and Lady Rank (the founders). It was one of a number established by the founders at that time and to which they gifted their controlling interest in The Rank Group plc (formerly The Rank Organisation plc), best known as a film production company. The Rank trusts and foundations all share a Christian ethos.

According to the foundation's website:

> Our mission is to improve the lives of people and their communities, across the UK, and we look to do this by:
> - encouraging and developing leadership
> - promoting enterprise and innovation
> - supporting disadvantaged young people and those frail or lonely through old age or disability
> - promoting the understanding of Christianity from a perspective that respects those of all faiths and those of none

Pebble grants

The following information has been taken from the foundation's website:

> Pebbles is our small funding stream for UK registered charities and recognised churches which are raising money for projects where the total cost is less than £150,000. This money can be spent on **short breaks** (such as an annual respite break or holiday for disadvantaged young people), **equipment** (such as white goods), or **capital costs** (refurbishment or minor building work).
>
> Pebble grant applications are processed on a quarterly basis. It can take up to 4 months for a decision and payment to be made. Grants are awarded on a discretionary basis; the Rank Foundation's contribution ranges from £250 up to and including £4,000, depending on the total cost of the project.

Financial information

Year end	31/01/2020
Income	£7,510,000
Assets	£275,260,000
Grants to organisations	£7,330,000

Further financial information

In 2020/21, the Pebbles grants programme funded 274 organisations with an average grant of £1,365.

Beneficiaries included: Venture Trust (£25,000); Making the Leap (£20,000); First Give (£15,000); Dementia Adventure (£10,000); Dundee Comics Creative Space (£3,000); Family Links (£750).

Applications

Apply via the foundation's website.

Sources of information

Accounts; annual report; Charity Commission record; funder's website.

The Joseph Rank Trust

Improvement of church properties and use of Christian approach to the educational and practical needs of people of all ages

UK; Republic of Ireland; Channel Islands

£2.6 million (2020)

CC number: 1093844

Correspondent: Dr John Higgs, Secretary, Worth Corner, Turners Hill Road, Crawley, West Sussex RH10 7SL (tel: 01293 873947; email: secretary@ranktrust.org)

Trustees: Gay Moon; Colin Rank; James Rank; Tony Reddall; Sue Warner; The Revd John Irvine; The Revd Darren Holland; The Revd Carole Holmes; Joseph Jennings.

 www.ranktrust.org

 @josephranktrust

General information

The Joseph Rank Trust is an independent Christian grant-maker which works with all Christian denominations in the UK. The trust was established in 2002 for the advancement of the Christian faith and represents an amalgamation of a number of charities established by the late Joseph Rank, or members of his family, during the period from 1918 to 1942.

The trust's two main areas of interest are:

- Projects that demonstrate a Christian approach to the practical, educational and spiritual needs of people of all ages
- The adaptation of church properties with a view to providing improved facilities for use by the church and its work in the community in which it is based

The trust provides one-off grants for capital expenditure or three-year grants for core costs or project funding.

Financial information

Year end	31/12/2020
Income	£2,880,000
Assets	£88,090,000
Grants to organisations	£2,600,000

Beneficiaries included: The Trussell Trust (£200,000); Church Revitalisation Trust (£45,000); Hope Church – Ipswich (£35,000); Hull Lighthouse Project and The Souster Youth Trust (£30,000 each); Grace Church – Salisbury (£15,000).

Exclusions

A full list of exclusions can be found on the trust's website.

Applications

Refer to the funder's website for information on how to make an application.

Sources of information

Accounts; annual report; Charity Commission record; funder's website.

The Eleanor Rathbone Charitable Trust

Women; deprivation; social exclusion; unpopular causes

UK, with the major allocation for Merseyside; international projects (sub-Saharan Africa, the Indian Sub-Continent, Afghanistan and Palestine)

£356,600 (2020/21)

CC number: 233241

Correspondent: The Trustees, 546 Warrington Road, Rainhill, Prescot, Merseyside L35 4LZ (tel: 07837 656314; email: eleanorrathbonetrust@gmail.com)

Trustees: William Rathbone; Jenny Rathbone; Andrew Rathbone; Lady Angela Morgan; Mark Rathbone; Joan Bonenfant.

 www.eleanorrathbonetrust.org.uk

General information

Eleanor Rathbone was the first woman to be elected to Liverpool City Council, representing Granby from 1909 to 1934. In 1929 she was elected as an independent MP and campaigned for social reform, particularly on issues affecting women, human rights and refugees. This charitable trust was established in 1947 with money left by Eleanor following her death in 1946.

The trust's website states that it concentrates its support on the following causes:

- Charities and charitable projects focused on Merseyside
- Charities benefitting women and unpopular and neglected causes, but avoiding those with a sectarian interest

Most donations are one-off, although requests for two- or three-year grants will be considered. Applications are considered only from small to medium-sized charities.

Areas of work

According to the trust's website, its current priorities are as follows:

> - **1. Merseyside –** Charities and charitable projects that meet our priorities and are based in, and/or delivered in Merseyside, particularly the more deprived areas of the county.
> - **2. Holiday Fund –** We hold a small holiday fund providing small grants for holidays and outings. This is restricted to charities helping disadvantaged children and adults from Merseyside.
> - **3. National –** Charities and charitable projects that meet our priorities, but only those that have a nationwide scope or remit – or whose work is not specific to any geographical area. We do not offer grants to local charities outside of Merseyside.

- **4. International –** We consider projects delivered in Sub-Saharan Africa, Afghanistan, Bangladesh and projects in Palestine, or supporting Palestinian refugees. Projects must be sponsored and monitored by a UK registered charity. In addition, projects must meet one or more of the following criteria:
  - They will benefit women or orphaned children.
  - They will demonstrate local involvement in scoping and delivery, except where skills required are not currently available e.g. eye surgeons in remote rural areas.
  - They will aim to repair the damage in countries recently ravaged by international or civil war.
  - They will deliver clean water and sanitation.

Grants are made in the range of £1,000 to £3,000 for national and international grants, and up to £5,000 for Merseyside grants. In exceptional cases grants may be higher.

Financial information

Year end	05/04/2021
Income	£288,000
Assets	£11,460,000
Grants to organisations	£365,600

Further financial information

Grants were broken down as follows:

Merseyside	70	£227,500
International	54	£60,000
National	26	£59,000
Holidays (Merseyside)	3	£10,100

Beneficiaries included: Liverpool Charity and Voluntary Services (£20,000); Action on Addiction (£5,000); Arts 4 Dementia (£3,000); Bipolar UK (£2,000); Alive and Kicking (£1,000).

Exclusions

The following will not be funded:

- Any activity which relieves a statutory authority from its obligations
- Individuals
- Medical research
- Gap year projects
- Organisations whose primary purpose is the promotion of a religion, church or sectarian interest

Applications

Apply using the online form available on the website. In addition, supporting documents (listed on the website) must be sent as an email attachment. Applications are accepted at any time and are considered at trustee meetings, held three times a year.

Sources of information

Accounts; annual report; Charity Commission record; funder's website.

Elizabeth Rathbone Charity

 Education; health; social welfare; the arts; people who are disadvantaged; community projects

 Merseyside

£ £356,600 (2020/21)

CC number: 233240

Correspondent: Liese Van Alwon, Administrator, 546 Warrington Road, Rainhill, Prescot, Merseyside L35 4LZ (tel: 07837 656314; email: elrathbonetrust@gmail.com)

Trustees: Lady Angela Morgan; Andrew Rathbone; William Rathbone; Mark Rathbone; Jenny Rathbone; Joan Bonenfant.

 www.elizabethrathbonetrust.org

General information

The charity has a special interest in funding projects that support disadvantaged women, young people and communities. There is a strong preference for Merseyside with local beneficiaries receiving the majority of funding.

The website states that applications are welcomed from charities and community organisations that have the following aims:

- To alleviate poverty by education
- To advance the interests of women
- To help the less able
- To support certain medical fields
- To support the arts
- To help the disadvantaged through community projects

Financial information

Year end	30/04/2021
Income	£288,000
Assets	£11,460,000
Grants to organisations	£356,600

Beneficiaries included: Liverpool Charity and Voluntary Service (£20,000); Action on Addiction (£5,000); Woodlands Hospice (£4,000); Read for Good (£3,000); Bipolar UK (£2,000); Give a Book (£1,000).

Exclusions

The following will not normally be supported:

- Applicants from outside Merseyside
- Individuals
- Any form of sponsorship
- Political organisations
- Pressure groups
- Feasibility studies
- Annual applications

Applications

Application forms can be downloaded from the charity's website.

Sources of information

Accounts; annual report; Charity Commission record; funder's website.

The Sigrid Rausing Trust

 Human rights and social justice; the arts; environmental conservation

Worldwide

£ £32.08 million (2020)

CC number: 1046769

Correspondent: The Trustees, 12 Penzance Place, London W11 4PA (email: info@srtrust.org)

Trustees: Sigrid Rausing; Andrew Puddephatt; Chris Stone; Sir Jeffrey Jowell; Hosh Ibrahim; Ruth Rogers; Joshua Mailman; Geoffrey Budlender; Mabel Oranje.

 www.sigrid-rausing-trust.org

 @SRausingTrust

General information

The Sigrid Rausing Trust was set up in 1995 by Swedish philanthropist, anthropologist and publisher Sigrid Rausing and takes as its guiding framework the United Nations' Universal Declaration of Human Rights. Its vision is 'A world where the principles of the Universal Declaration of Human Rights are implemented and respected and where all people can enjoy their rights in harmony with each other and with the environment.'

The trust made its first grants in 1996 for work that promotes international human rights. It was originally called the Ruben and Elisabeth Rausing Trust after Sigrid's grandparents. In 2003 the trust was renamed the Sigrid Rausing Trust to identify its work more closely with the aims and ideals of Sigrid Rausing herself.

Areas of support

The trust currently has ten grant programmes:

- Strengthening the human rights field
- Detention, torture and death penalty
- Defending civic space
- Transitional justice
- Women's rights
- LGBTQ+ rights
- Xenophobia and intolerance
- Transparency and accountability
- Arts
- Conservation

The trust has five main principles which guide its grant-making:

- The essential role of core funding
- Good and effective leadership
- Flexibility and responsiveness to needs and opportunities
- The value of clarity and brevity in applications and reports
- Long-term relationships with grantees

In addition, a Small Grants Fund allows individual trustees to nominate organisations for support.

Types of grant

The trust's grants are mostly for core costs or for funding specific projects. The trust typically makes a one-year initial grant followed by several cycles of three-year grants. There is no minimum or maximum level for a grant but the trust will not normally support more than 25% of the budget of an organisation or a project.

If one of the grantees is faced with a genuine emergency or unexpected opportunity, they can contact their programme officer to ask if an emergency grant can be arranged.

Financial information

Year end	31/12/2020
Income	£33,130,000
Assets	£1,760,000
Grants to organisations	£32,080,000

Beneficiaries included: A list of beneficiaries was not available. Previous beneficiaries include: Fundación de Antropología Forense de Guatemala (£100,000); Women's Legal Aid Centre (£90,000); Civitas Maxima (£75,000); Safe Passage (£70,000); Campaign Against Homophobia – KPH (£50,000); Above Ground (£45,000); René Cassin (£30,000); Team Domenica (£25,000); Caine Prize for African Writing (£10,000).

Applications

The trust does not accept unsolicited applications for funding, but rather invites applications from organisations that it has proactively identified. However, the trust's website states:

> If you wish to let us know about the work of your organisation, please write to research@srtrust.org. The programme staff review all emails regularly. From time to time programme directors will look for new organisations in particular areas. When they do, details will be posted on our application process page.

Sources of information

Accounts; annual report; Charity Commission record; funder's website.

The Rayne Foundation

The arts; health and well-being; mental health; carers; older people; refugees and asylum seekers; relationships between Jews and Arabs

UK

£6.27 million (2019/20)

CC number: 1179912

Correspondent: Morin Carew, Grants Administrator, 3 Bromley Place, London W1T 6DB (tel: 020 7487 9657; email: info@raynefoundation.org.uk)

Trustees: Lady Hilary Browne-Wilkinson; Lady Jane Rayne; Sir Prof. Anthony Taylor; Sir Emyr Parry; Baroness Julia Neuberger; The Hon. Robert Rayne; The Hon. Natasha Rayne; The Hon. Nicholas Oxon.

www.raynefoundation.org.uk

General information

The Rayne Foundation was founded in 1962 by Lord Rayne who chaired or was on the board of numerous arts, education, medical and social welfare organisations. The mission of the foundation is to build bridges that connect people and communities.

Areas of work – UK

The foundation's website states:

> We will consider applications in the fields of arts, health and wellbeing, education in its widest sense, and those that cover social issues. Our focus is to connect communities, building bridges between marginalised groups and mainstream society, and to enable individuals to reach their full potential. Within these broad criteria, we have a number of areas of special interest:
>
> - Young people's improved mental health
> - Arts as a tool to achieve social change
> - Improved quality of life for carers and for older people

Areas of work – Israel

The foundation's website states:

> Our work is focused on:
>
> - The strengthening of relationships between Jews and Arabs
> - The wellbeing of refugees and asylum seekers
> - Improved mental health

Grants are made through the foundation's sister organisation, The Rayne Trust (Charity Commission no. 207392).

Types of grant

Salaries and project costs (including a reasonable contribution to overheads or on-costs) for up to three years will be considered. The trustees will consider grants towards an organisation's core costs but only tend to award these when an organisation is making a step-change in the way that it works or tackles a particular issue, and where a core grant will provide greater flexibility during the transition period.

Grants typically fall between £10,000 and £20,000 per year for up to three years. The foundation prefers to fund alongside others as they are unlikely to fund a project in full.

Financial information

Year end	30/11/2020
Income	£2,230,000
Assets	£93,350,000
Grants to organisations	£6,270,000

Beneficiaries included: Jewish Care (£335,000); Age Exchange (£49,000); Cardboard Citizens (£30,000); Enabling Enterprise and National Care Forum (£10,000 each).

Exclusions

The foundation's application guidelines state:

> **We do not consider applications:**
>
> - For work that has already taken place
> - For repayment of debts
> - For endowments
> - For one-off events (including performances, festivals, conferences, holidays, respite breaks and trips)
> - For feasibility studies or research
> - For capital appeals
> - For awareness raising campaigns and lobbying
> - From organisations whose levels of free reserves are higher than 75% of annual expenditure.
> - From individuals
> - From those who have been rejected in the last 12 months
> - From organisations already in receipt of an active grant
> - General appeals

Applications

Application forms and guidelines can be downloaded from the foundation's website.

Sources of information

Accounts; annual report; Charity Commission record; funder's website.

The Rayne Trust

Jewish organisations; mental health; disadvantaged people; the arts; education; understanding between cultures; social cohesion

UK and Israel

£562,500 (2020/21)

CC number: 207392

Correspondent: The Trustees, 3 Bromley Place, London W1T 6DB (tel: 020 7487 9650; email: info@raynefoundation.org.uk)

Trustees: Lady Jane Rayne; The Hon. Robert Rayne; The Hon. Tamara Wood; Damian Rayne.

 www.raynefoundation.org.uk/grants/isr/current/guidelines

General information

The Rayne Trust is the sister organisation of the Rayne Foundation, founded by Lord Rayne. The overarching theme of the two organisations is social cohesion; however, the Rayne Trust is particularly focused on Jewish causes in the UK and Israel.

According to the trust's website, the trustees are interested in funding work which is 'untried, tests new approaches, but has clear objectives'. The trustees 'favour new work which could change the way social issues are tackled in our society and which could have lessons for others beyond the funded organisation'.

The work of the trust is primarily focused on strengthening relationships between Jews and Arabs, and improving mental health. However, the 2020/21 accounts show that in the UK the trust also funds the arts, education and social welfare with the aim of supporting the most vulnerable in society and increasing tolerance and understanding between communities.

Organisations and projects that are considered

The trustees look for all of the following characteristics in the organisations and projects that they fund:

- Wider than local application and awareness of the bigger picture
- Real expertise and sector knowledge
- Commitment to demonstrating results and sharing learning
- Strong leadership, management and track record

See the website for full and helpful detailed information.

The trustees fund charitable and not-for-profit organisations, targeting funding towards unpopular issues and organisations. Large, national organisations are unlikely to receive support unless they are the only organisation in a position to tackle a particular problem.

Salaries and project costs (including a reasonable contribution to overheads or on-costs) for up to three years can be considered.

Grants typically range between £10,000 and £20,000 per year for up to three years. The trustees prefer to contribute alongside other funders as they will not donate more than 50% of the funding required.

All financial information should be submitted in pound sterling (£). The Hebrew Audited Accounts need to be included with the application.

Financial information

Year end	31/03/2021
Income	£675,500
Assets	£33,490,000
Grants to organisations	£562,500

Further financial information

Grants totalling £1.09 million were awarded to 58 organisations during the year (18 in Israel and 40 in the UK). Grants to UK organisations amounted to £562,500.

Beneficiaries included: Jewish Care (£165,000); Desert Stars Association (Kohvey Hamidbar) (£100,000); aChord: Social Psychology for Social Change (£80,000); SHIFT (£75,000); Sikkuy – Association for the Advancement of Civic Society (£50,000); The Wiener Holocaust Library (£30,000); Migration Museum Project (£10,000); Norwood (£5,000).

Exclusions

Grants are not made to/for:

- Individuals
- Retrospective costs
- Repayment of debts
- Organisations which have had a grant in the last year
- General appeals
- Endowments
- Capital appeals
- One-off events
- Awareness-raising campaigns and lobbying
- Feasibility studies or research

Organisations with more than nine months' running costs in unrestricted reserves are less likely to receive support. Organisations with small reserves or an overall deficit will need to convince the trustees that their organisation is viable and they are taking action to increase reserves. This is used as a measure of financial health.

Applications

Stage one application forms can be downloaded from the trust's website and should be returned to israelapplications@raynetrust.org. If successful, in stage two you will have an opportunity to offer a more fully developed and formal proposal.

Sources of information

Accounts; annual report; Charity Commission record; funder's website.

The Sir James Reckitt Charity

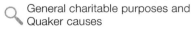

General charitable purposes and Quaker causes

Hull and the East Riding of Yorkshire; UK (Quaker causes)

£1.18 million (2020)

CC number: 225356

Correspondent: Kelly Sykes-Moody, 4 Summergangs Drive, Thorngumbald, Hull HU12 9PW (tel: 07507 340121; email: a contact form is available on the charity's website)

Trustees: Rebecca Holt; William Upton; Edward Upton; Simon Upton; Caroline Jennings; Ondine Upton; Philip Holt; Charles Maxted; James Atherton; Robin Upton; Nicholas Watts; Michelle Fisher; Sarah Craven; Oliver Jennings; Simon Upton.

 www.thesirjamesreckittcharity.org.uk

General information

Established in 1921, the charity is named after the late Sir James Reckitt. He was the former chair of Reckitt and Sons Ltd, a manufacturer of many well-known household products such as Dettol and Brasso. He was a champion for Hull and the East Riding of Yorkshire, campaigning to bring public libraries to the area and when unsuccessful, using his own funds to build a library. Reckitt also established a substantial garden village in the city.

Grant-making policy

The charity supports charitable organisations in Hull and the East Riding of Yorkshire as well as causes associated with the Society of Friends (Quakers) throughout the UK. Grants can be made for:

- Start-up and core costs
- The purchase of equipment and materials
- Building improvements
- Training costs
- Project development costs

Grants are also made to local individuals in need through organisations.

Financial information

Year end	31/12/2020
Income	£1,580,000
Assets	£53,010,000
Grants to organisations	£1,180,000

Further financial information

Grants were broken down as follows:

Social work	£667,600
Education	£243,400
Religion	£129,500
Medical	£100,500
Youth	£54,900
Children	£51,500
Older people	£17,500
The environment	£9,000

Beneficiaries included: Woodbrooke Quaker Study Centre (£50,000); The University of Hull (£30,000); Age UK – Hull (£10,000); Save the Children Fund (£8,000); Farm Africa (£5,500); Anthony Nolan and East Hull Foodbank (£2,000 each).

Applications

Apply via the charity's website.

Sources of information

Accounts; annual report; Charity Commission record; funder's website.

The Reece Foundation

Development of maths, science and engineering skills; STEM employment opportunities

UK, with a strong preference for North East England including Northumberland, Tyne and Wear and County Durham

£1.29 million (2020)

CC number: 1121325

Correspondent: The Trustees, Armstrong Works, Scotswood Road, Newcastle upon Tyne, Tyne and Wear NE15 6UX (tel: 0191 234 8700; email: enquiries@reece-foundation.org)

Trustees: Simon Gilroy; Eric Morgan; John Reece; Anne Reece; Prof. David Sandbach.

 www.reece-foundation.org

 @reecestem

General information

The foundation was established in 2007 by engineer and businessman John Reece. The aim of the foundation is to improve the long-term and sustainable prosperity of the North East, primarily through the promotion of engineering and manufacturing. There is a particular focus on the improvement of education in engineering and related scientific and mathematical subjects, training in engineering skills and the development of employment opportunities. The foundation may occasionally support other causes which the trustees feel are beneficial to the area or the country.

Funding is currently focused on projects and groups based in the North East, including Northumberland, Tyne and Wear and County Durham. Projects with a national or wider area of focus may also be considered.

Financial information

Year end	31/12/2020
Income	£1,520,000
Assets	£33,350,000
Grants to organisations	£1,290,000

Beneficiaries included: Northumberland National Park (£250,000); Calvert Trust (£200,000); Teen Tech (£36,000); Kielder Observatory (£25,000); The Sill (£20,000); Centre for Life (£10,000).

Applications

Application forms are available to download from the foundation's website. Forms should be returned by post or email (applications@reece-foundation.org). Applications can be made at any time and are considered at quarterly meetings. Be aware that a decision may take up to six months.

Sources of information

Accounts; annual report; Charity Commission record; funder's website.

Richard Reeve's Foundation

Education and training for children and young people

Camden, City of London and Islington

£657,900 (2020/21)

CC number: 1136337

Correspondent: Suzanna Nagle, Clerk and Company Secretary, 20–22 Wenlock Road, London N1 7GU (tel: 020 8323 2662; email: clerk@richardreevesfoundation.org.uk)

Trustees: Michael Hudson; Mark Jessett; Gerald Rothwell; Charlotte Hilton; Jo Emmerson; Benjamin Monaghan; Alistair Wilson; Tracey Shackle; Elizabeth Gallagher.

 www.richardreevesfoundation.org.uk

General information

The Richard Reeve's Foundation was first established in 1706 following the death of Richard Reeve, a Merchant Taylor who had no immediate family. He left his estate in trust to help educate children in the parish of St Sepulchre. The foundation now makes grants to local organisations, charities and schools towards the education and training of disadvantaged children and young people (up to the age of 25) who live in the City of London, Camden or Islington.

The foundation's website states:

> Projects are usually funded for up to three years to increase their impact. We are flexible in our approach to these issues. We look for projects that are exciting, innovative and attractive to the people we most want to help.
>
> The Foundation's current focus is:
>
> - Raising Literacy and Numeracy among early years and primary school students
> - Aiding young people's progression into work through:
>   - supporting improved Careers Education and Guidance in secondary schools
>   - enabling increased opportunities for young people, aged 16–24, to 'earn while they learn'.
>
> Sometimes we fund other work related to our general aims of education and care of young people under 25. Please ask the Clerk for advice if you would like to submit an application that does not meet the above priorities.

In addition to our 2 main areas of strategic focus, the Foundation provides:

- Support to projects which assist young people under 25 from disadvantaged backgrounds who wish to study music
- Maintenance grants to college students aged 16–24 attending colleges within our area of benefit
- Maintenance grants to City University NHS students under the age of 40
- An annual grant to Christ's Hospital school in Horsham, West Sussex.

The foundation is happy to consider projects of any size, and will support projects for up to three years, or five years in exceptional circumstances.

Financial information

Year end	30/06/2021
Income	£1,230,000
Assets	£50,250,000
Grants to organisations	£657,900

Beneficiaries included: London Borough of Islington (£125,000); Camden Learning (£120,263); Drayton Park Primary School (£35,600); Ambler Primary School (£20,500); New North Academy (£19,600); Highbury Quadrant (£14,000); Rotherfield Primary School (£9,300); London Borough of Islington (library) (£1,000).

Exclusions

The foundation does not directly fund individuals.

Applications

The website states:

> Please contact us with an outline of any proposed project and discuss it with the clerk in the first instance. We will advise of the application process at that stage.

Check the website for up-to-date information on applications.

Sources of information

Accounts; annual report; Charity Commission record; funder's website.

Rentrust Foundation Ltd

Education; relief of poverty; social welfare; Jewish causes

 UK

£276,000 (2020/21)

CC number: 1163817

Correspondent: The Trustees, 5 Windus Road, London N16 6UT (tel: 020 3137 9885; email: cf@nuenterprise.co.uk)

Trustees: Esther Wosner; Pessi Eisenbach; Chavi Simon.

General information

The foundation was established in 2014 and, according to its 2020/21 accounts, its objects are:

- The advancement of education
- The relief of poverty, illness and frailty

- The advancement of such other objects as the directors of the Company may from time to time determine that are for the benefit of the public and are charitable according to the Law of England and Wales

Financial information

Year end	31/07/2021
Income	£118,800
Assets	-£161,700
Grants to organisations	£276,000

Further financial information

The foundation's 2020/21 accounts state that all grants made during the year were for 'the purposes of either the advancement of education and Jewish religion or the alleviation of poverty'. Only beneficiaries of grants of £10,000 and above were listed. Grants of under £10,000 totalled £104,400.

Beneficiaries included: United Talrnudical Associates Ltd (£65,000); Chasdei Aharon Ltd (£40,000); Toldos Aharon Trust Ltd (£25,000); The Beth Hamedrash Satmar Trust (£10,000).

Applications

Apply in writing to the correspondent. The foundation's 2020/21 accounts state that the foundation 'accepts applications for grants from representatives of various charities, which are reviewed by the trustees on a regular basis'.

Sources of information

Accounts; annual report; Charity Commission record.

Reuben Foundation

Healthcare; education; community; culture

UK and overseas (particularly Israel)

£35.88 million (2020)

CC number: 1094130

Correspondent: The Trustees, 4th Floor, Millbank Tower, 21–24 Millbank, London SW1P 4PQ (tel: 020 7802 5000; email: contact@reubenfoundation.com)

www.reubenfoundation.com

General information

This foundation was established in 2002 as an outlet for the charitable giving of billionaire property investors David and Simon Reuben. The foundation was endowed by the brothers with a donation of $100 million (£54.1 million), with the income generated to be given to a range of charitable causes. The foundation supports healthcare, education community and culture. However, grants are mainly made for educational and healthcare purposes.

The foundation supports a number of scholarship initiatives including the Reuben Scholarship Programme, which was launched in 2012 in partnership with the University of Oxford, University of Cambridge, University College London and ARK Schools.

Financial information

Year end	31/12/2020
Income	£7,760,000
Assets	£12,890,000
Grants to organisations	£35,880,000

Beneficiaries included: University of Oxford (£30 million); Illuminated River Foundation (£1.5 million); ARK Schools (£225,000); Great Ormond Street Hospital (£35,000); Centrepoint (£25,000).

Applications

The foundation's website states that applications for grants are made by invitation only.

Sources of information

Accounts; annual report; Charity Commission record; funder's website.

The Revere Charitable Trust

Medical research; the environment; arts and culture; animal welfare; children and young people with disabilities

UK

£690,200 (2020/21)

CC number: 1117369

Correspondent: Teifion Evans, Trustee, 9 Hillside Close, Heddington, Calne, Wiltshire SN11 0PZ (tel: 01380 859198; email: teifion@tevans.plus.com)

General information

The trust was registered with the Charity Commission in 2006. The trust makes grants to organisations to support the following:

- Hospices
- Children with disabilities
- Asthma and cancer research
- Other medical organisations, both national and international
- Environmental and cultural projects
- Animal welfare
- Youth groups

Financial information

Year end	05/04/2021
Income	£398,700
Assets	£7,440,000
Grants to organisations	£690,200

Beneficiaries included: Tadworth's Children's Trust and Alzheimer's Research (£125,000 each); Woodlands Trust (£40,200); Stroke Association (£10,000); The Royal Horticultural Society and Young Lives vs Cancer (£5,000 each); LINK Transport Services (£2,500).

Applications

Apply in writing to the correspondent.

Sources of information

Accounts; annual report; Charity Commission record.

The Clive Richards Foundation

General charitable purposes, although there is a preference for community, education, healthcare, heritage, military, the arts and religion

Within a 100-mile radius of the centre of Hereford city (see the website for a map); Africa; India

£561,800 (2020/21)

CC number: 327155

Correspondent: The Administrator (Caren), Lower Hope Estate, Ullingswick, Hereford, Herefordshire HR1 3JF (tel: 01432 820557; email: admin@csrcharity.com)

http://csrcharity.com

General information

Formerly known as The Clive and Sylvia Richards Charity Ltd, this charity was established in May 1986 by Sylvia Richards and her husband Clive. Following Clive's death in 2021, the charity was renamed in his honour. Sylvia continues to donate the vast majority of the charity's income, which is used to make grants to a wide range of organisations. The charity donates between £500,000 and £1.5 million each year.

Grant-making

The charity focuses its support on healthcare and medical causes, education (including overseas education), community, heritage and military, the arts and religious institutions.

The website explains that the charity 'will provide support to charity organisations where we seek to be a catalyst to unlock other funding sources for good causes and ensure sustainability and transformational change'. The trustees prefer to focus on smaller charities or projects that probably would not happen if not for the charity's help.

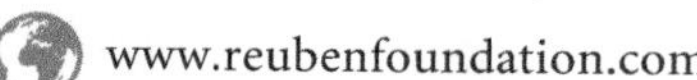

There is an upper limit of £100,000 in any one year to any one charity.

The charity's website states that, while historically the emphasis of funding has centred on the West Midlands with a focus on Herefordshire, in recent years grants have been given within a broader geographic region – a 100-mile radius from the centre of Hereford now comprises the beneficial area.

The guidelines state: 'We will only support overseas applications from English speaking countries restricted to Africa and India, and they must have a UK based representative/contact.'

Individuals who are seeking to further their education can also be supported with bursaries and UK-based research grants. Individuals are supported via educational institutions, not directly.

Financial information

Year end	31/03/2021
Income	£425,800
Grants to organisations	£561,800

Further financial information

Grants were awarded in the following categories:

Medical, health and well-being	£380,900
Education	£50,200
Arts, culture and heritage	£44,900
Community and general charitable purposes	£40,100
Religion	£25,500
Other	£20,300

Only beneficiaries of grants of £50,000 and above were listed in the accounts (two grants).

Beneficiaries included: Cobalt Health (£225,000); Childhood Eye Cancer Trust (£50,000).

Previous beneficiaries have included: Queen Elizabeth High School (£150,000); Sir Thomas Rich's School (£70,000); Bristol Aero Collection Trust (£50,000).

Exclusions

The charity does not usually fund the following:

- National charities
- Operating costs (i.e. revenue costs)
- Salaries

Activities that are/were the responsibility of a statutory organisation are not eligible.

Overseas applications must have a UK sponsor, preferably one that is known to the trustees.

Applications

An initial enquiry form can be found on the website which includes an eligibility quiz. Once your eligibility has been confirmed, the charity will send a relevant application form. Applications can be submitted at any time. Full guidelines can be found on the website.

Sources of information

Accounts; annual report; Charity Commission record; funder's website.

Richmond Parish Lands Charity

General charitable purposes; education; sport and recreation; health; community services; younger and older people; social welfare

Richmond; Ham; Sheen; Mortlake; and Barnes (the SW13, SW14, TW9 and TW10 postcode areas)

£2.14 million (2020/21)

CC number: 200069

Correspondent: Eleanor Rees, Grants Manager, Vestry House, 21 Paradise Road, Richmond, Surrey TW9 1SA (tel: 020 8948 5701; email: grants@rplc.org.uk)

Trustees: Peter Buckwell; Owen Carew-Jones; Paul Lawrence; Jerome Misso; Carol Fletcher; Joanna Nakielny; Chris Phillips; Cllr Richard Pyne; Ruth Scott; Claire O'Donnell; Duncan Richford; Stephen Speak.

 www.rplc.org.uk

 @RPLC1786

General information

Established in 1786 by a gift of land from King George III and Queen Charlotte, the Richmond Parish Lands Charity supports a wide range of causes in the beneficial area comprised of the TW9, TW10, SW13 and SW14 postcode districts.

The charity's 2020/21 annual report describes its objectives as:

- The support of the elderly and those in need
- The care of people suffering ill health or hardship
- The provision of recreational facilities and support for leisure activities
- The promotion of education and helping people to undertake courses and training
- Any other charitable purposes for the benefit of the local community

The trustees carry out these objectives through the provision of charitable housing, education support and grant-making. Some organisations are supported on a regular basis through grants for their core operational costs, while others are offered funds to assist with project-related activities or salaries. Individuals are given assistance with education courses and costs, winter fuel payments or help in times of crisis.

According to the charity's website, the following grant categories are available:

- Project grants of under £15,000
- Project grants of over £15,000

Project funding is given to one-off projects or multi-year specific needs such as salaries. Check the website for up-to-date information on current grants.

Eligible organisations include: registered charities; start-ups with a charitable purpose; CICs and CIOs; sports associations and other properly constituted not-for-profit organisations. Organisations must be working in the area of benefit.

Financial information

Year end	30/06/2021
Income	£3,240,000
Assets	£115,490,000
Grants to organisations	£2,140,000
No. of grants	110

Further financial information

Grants to organisations were broken down as follows:

Projects	£886,000
COVID-19 grants	£618,500
Regularly funded organisations	£419,700
Child support (grants to schools)	£113,800
Other	£106,300

Grants to individuals totalled £199,700.

Beneficiaries included: Achieving for Children (£119,500); Citizens Advice Richmond (£55,600); Barnes Community Arts Centre (£20,000); Beautifully Made Foundation (£13,800); Darell Primary School (£5,900); Pensford Tennis Club (£2,000); Windham Nursery (£1,100); Westerley Ware Association (£250).

Exclusions

Private companies are not eligible to apply.

Applications

There are separate online application forms for the various types of grants, all of which can be found on the charity's helpful website. The charity welcomes enquiries to discuss ideas for applications. The trustees consider applications at quarterly meetings. If you wish to be considered for regular core funding, contact the correspondent. An online contact form is also available on the charity's website.

Sources of information

Accounts; annual report; Charity Commission record; funder's website.

Ridgesave Ltd

The advancement of the Jewish religion; education; social welfare

UK and overseas

£1.26 million (2020/21)

CC number: 288020

Correspondent: The Trustees, 141B Upper Clapton Road, London E5 9DB (tel: 020 8806 4271; email: mail@cohenarnold.com)

Trustees: E. Englander; Zelda Weiss; Joseph Weiss; Aaron Hoffman; Menachem Reichman.

General information

Ridgesave Ltd was registered with the Charity Commission in 1983.

The charity is largely focused on supporting the charitable activities of organisations, both in the UK and abroad, that teach the principles of Orthodox Judaism as well as providing support to people in need.

Financial information

Year end	31/03/2021
Income	£1,330,000
Assets	£650,300
Grants to organisations	£1,260,000

Beneficiaries included: Keren Association (£400,000); Kolel Belz Machnovkeh (£157,500); Friends of Mercaz Hatorah Belz Macnivka (£142,700); Beis Aharon Trust (£141,300); Kollel Mishkon Yakov (£139,700); Achisomoch Aid Company Ltd (£88,000); Keren Ezra Mimtzika (£61,000).

Applications

Apply in writing to the correspondent.

Sources of information

Accounts; annual report; Charity Commission record.

Rigby Foundation

General charitable purposes; health and saving of lives; education; arts, culture and heritage; social welfare; armed forces

UK

£467,200 (2020/21)

CC number: 1011259

Correspondent: The Trustees, Bridgeway House, Bridgeway, Stratford-Upon-Avon, Warwickshire CV37 6YX (tel: 01789 610000)

Trustees: Sir Peter Rigby; Patricia Rigby; Steven Rigby; James Rigby.

General information

The foundation was established in 1992 and supports a wide variety of charitable purposes. According to the foundation's 2020/21 annual report, organisations supported during the year had the following charitable purposes:

- the advancement of health or the saving of lives;
- the advancement of education;
- the advancement of the arts, culture and heritage; and
- the relief of these in need, by reason of ill health and/or disability, financial hardship or other disadvantage.

The annual report further states with respect to the foundation's grant-making:

> Grants are issued at the discretion of the trustees and there are no set rules or procedures. The Rigby Foundation has historically made donations to other charities or organisations which served charitable purposes, including the provision of benefits to third parties.

Grants made by the charity are typically under £30,000, with a few larger grants each year.

Financial information

Year end	05/04/2021
Income	£645,300
Assets	£3,530,000
Grants to organisations	£467,200

Beneficiaries included: South Warwickshire NHS Foundation Trust (£150,000); The Prince's Trust (£100,000); Place2be (£83,200); Coventry City of Culture Trust and The Shakespeare Hospice (£20,000 each); Coventry Cathedral, 84 Squadron and Teach First (£10,000 each); Smiling Faces (£1,000); Coventry Cyrenians (£500); SSAFA, the Armed Forces charity (£200).

Applications

Apply in writing to the correspondent.

Sources of information

Accounts; annual report; Charity Commission record.

The River Farm Foundation

General charitable purposes; health; education; community development; children; homelessness; disadvantaged groups

UK and overseas

£728,400 (2020/21)

CC number: 1113109

Correspondent: Deborah Fisher, Trustee, Unit 4 Hill Farm, Kirby Road, Kirby Bedon, Norwich, Norfolk NR14 7DU (tel: 01508 480100; email: info@fisherlegal.co.uk)

Trustees: Mark Haworth; Nigel Langstaff; Deborah Fisher.

General information

The foundation was established in 2006 with an initial donation from Sloane Robinson Investment Services Ltd. It makes grants to charities for general charitable purposes, in particular in the areas of health and welfare, education, and community development. The foundation's 2020/21 accounts state:

> The Trustees intend to continue making grants to other charities, using funds they are holding. In particular, they continue to develop and forge new links with previous recipients, academic institutions, museums and charities providing support to children, the homeless and other disadvantaged groups.

Financial information

Year end	05/04/2021
Income	£763,000
Assets	£64,380,000
Grants to organisations	£728,400

Further financial information

Grants were broken down as follows:

Community development	£253,000
Education	£248,700
Health and welfare	£210,200
The environment and heritage	£16,500

Beneficiaries included: Busoga Trust (£253,000); The Trussell Trust (£100,000); The King's School Worcester (£91,000); St Edmund Hall (£50,000); Centrepoint Soho (£28,600); Acorns Children's Hospice Trust (£20,000); Royal British Legion (£6,600).

Applications

Apply in writing to the correspondent.

Sources of information

Accounts; annual report; Charity Commission record.

The Roan Charitable Trust

General charitable purposes; social welfare; medical research; overseas aid; education; animal welfare

UK and overseas

£491,800 (2020/21)

CC number: 1122851

Correspondent: The Trustees, c/o Solid Management Ltd, PO Box 2696, Woodford Green, London IG8 1UF (tel: 07771 711188; email: jeff@solidmanagement.co.uk)

Trustees: Amelia Harris; Susan Swete; Lady Margaret Jarvis; Trevor Swete.

General information

The trust was established in 2008 and supports general charitable purposes, including education, medical research, social welfare, overseas aid and education.

Financial information

Year end	31/03/2021
Income	£214,100
Assets	£8,620,000
Grants to organisations	£491,800
No. of grants	23

Beneficiaries included: Cancer Research UK (£100,000); The Royal National Institute of Blind People (£75,000); REACT (£40,700); Jewish Care (£25,000); British Heart Foundation (£10,000); Haven House Foundation (£5,000).

Applications

Apply in writing to the correspondent. The trust's 2020/21 accounts state: 'There is no formal grant application procedure. The trustees retain the services of a charitable grants advisor and take account of the advice when deciding on grants.'

Sources of information

Accounts; annual report; Charity Commission record.

The Robertson Trust

Poverty and trauma; emotional well-being and relationships; financial well-being; education and employment pathways

Scotland

£23.82 million (2020/21)

OSCR number: SC002970

Correspondent: The Trustees, Robertson House, 152 Bath Street, Glasgow G2 4TB (tel: 0141 353 7300; email: funding@therobertsontrust.org.uk)

Trustees: Mark Batho; Andrew Walls; Campbell Robb; Donald Workman; Edel Harris; Fiona Larg; Garry Coutts; Gerry McLaughlin; Heather Lamont; John Loughton; Judy Cromarty; Ligia Teixeira; Lorne Crerar; Prof. Morag Treanor.

 www.therobertsontrust.org.uk

 @robertsontrust

General information

The trust was established in 1961 by the Robertson sisters, who inherited a controlling interest in companies in the Scotch Whiskey Industry (now the Edrington Group) from their father and wished to ensure the dividend income from the shares would be given to charitable purposes.

Funding strategy 2020–30

Currently, the trust's funding is aimed at constituted community groups and registered charities that are working to alleviate poverty and trauma in Scotland and have an annual income of under £2 million.

The trust has three funding strands:

- **Financial security** – work which helps people who are struggling with day-to-day costs and/or creates access to advice, support and advocacy around welfare, debt, income maximisation, housing and employment advice, or improves access to quality childcare
- **Emotional well-being and relationships** – work which supports the emotional and relational needs of people and families
- **Educational and work pathways** – work which equips people for the future by supporting learning and skills

Within these three strands there are several key areas that the trust is keen to fund. See the website for details.

Overall, the trust is particularly interested in funding organisations that work with the following groups of people who are more likely to experience poverty or trauma:

- Certain family groups (larger families, single parents, those with care-experienced children)
- Women
- People with a disability
- People from a BAME background
- Asylum seekers and refugees
- People experiencing severe and multiple disadvantage
- People living in certain geographical locations (particularly remote and rural ones)
- Older people
- Young people under 25

According to its website, the trust also has preference for organisations that apply the following approaches to their work:

Community: organisations that place communities at the centre of their work and aim to build resilience within communities to tackle issues associated with poverty or trauma

Relationships and rights: organisations which take a relational approach to their work and focus on the key principles of fairness, dignity and respect and recognise the impacts that poverty and trauma can have on people's lives.

Collaboration: organisations that work with others to deliver services or to change how services are delivered for people facing poverty, trauma or both.

Grants

The trust offers both revenue (unrestricted and restricted) and capital funding. Current grant types and criteria are listed on the website. At the time of writing (May 2022) these included: Wee Grants, Small Grants, Large Grants, Community Vehicle Grants and Community Building Grants.

The trust's website features a 'funding checker', where you can check your eligibility.

Financial information

Year end	31/03/2021
Income	£7,480,000
Assets	£781,300
Grants to organisations	£23,820,000

Beneficiaries included: The trust publishes a full list of grants it has awarded to organisations on its website. Some recent beneficiaries (grants awarded in 2022) include: Glasgow Council on Alcohol (£120,000); St Andrew's Children's Society (£108,000); South Seeds (£48,000); Childcare in the Community (£10,000); Govanhill Baths Community Trust (£1,000).

Exclusions

Funding is aimed at organisations with an annual income under £2 million. However, each of the grant types have their own eligibility criteria which specify the organisation types and annual income levels that can apply. Consult the trust's website for full exclusion criteria.

Applications

Applications can be made through the trust's website where you can find guidance. According to the website, 'there are no set closing dates, so you're welcome to apply anytime.'

Sources of information

Accounts; annual report; OSCR record; funder's website.

Sloane Robinson Foundation

Education and training

England and Wales

£547,300 (2020/21)

CC number: 1068286

Correspondent: The Trustees, c/o FisherLegal LLP, Unit 4 Hill Farm, Kirby Road, Kirby Bedon, Norwich, Norfolk NR17 7DU (tel: 01508 480100; email: info@fisherlegal.co.uk)

Trustees: George Robinson; Hugh Sloane; Deborah Fisher.

General information

The principal objective of the foundation is the advancement of education. The foundation maintains long-term relationships with academic organisations in order to establish scholarships and bursary schemes for overseas students to study in the UK, for British students to study abroad, and generally to provide opportunities for education which would not otherwise be possible.

Financial information

Year end	28/02/2021
Grants to organisations	£547,300
No. of grants	9

Beneficiaries included: Lincoln College, Oxford (£147,900); Karta Initiative (£100,000); United World Schools (£46,700); RSPB (£17,800); Veerni Foundation (£9,600); Future Hope UK (£5,000); Eagle Height Academy (£550).

Exclusions

The foundation has previously stated that grants are not awarded for:

- Undergraduate-level study
- Fellowships and professorships at universities and places of higher education for both teaching and research
- Religion, social sciences and languages
- Funding of overseas programmes should be focused on the studies in which the country concerned offers better courses (e.g. Chinese history in China)
- Only in exceptional circumstances funding will be provided for the provision of sporting facilities

Applications

Apply in writing to the correspondent. To avoid increased administrative costs, only successful candidates will be notified of the outcome of their application.

Sources of information

Accounts; annual report; Charity Commission record.

Rockcliffe Charitable Trust

General charitable purposes, including health and social welfare

UK

£398,300 (2020/21)

CC number: 274117

Correspondent: The Trustees, c/o Matheson and Co. Ltd, Scottish Provident Building, 3 Lombard Street, London EC3V 9AQ (tel: 020 7816 8137)

Trustees: Emma Keswick; Simon Keswick; Nicholas Goodson.

General information

The trust was established in 1977 to support general charitable purposes in the UK. The trust's 2020/21 annual report and accounts state that:

> The income shall be applied by the trustees in the payment of donations or subscriptions to such charitable institution or institutions for all or any of the charitable purposes as the trustees may, in their absolute discretion from time to time, think fit and determine.

Financial information

Year end	05/04/2021
Income	£375,300
Assets	£13,450,000
Grants to organisations	£398,300

Beneficiaries included: Imperial College London (£120,000); Oxford Hospitals Charity (£50,000); The Mary Hare Foundation (£10,000); Duchenne UK (£5,000); Rare Breeds Survival Trust (£1,000).

Exclusions

The trust does not make grants to individuals.

Applications

Apply in writing to the correspondent. The 2020/21 annual report and accounts state that 'grant applications are reviewed by the trustees on a regular basis.'

Sources of information

Accounts; annual report; Charity Commission record.

The Roddick Foundation

Arts and culture; the environment; human rights; health; social justice; education; the media; humanitarian aid

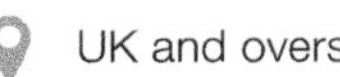

UK and overseas

£1.3 million (2020/21)

CC number: 1061372

Correspondent: Karen Smith, The Roddick Foundation, PO Box 838, Chichester PO19 9XP (email: karen@theroddickfoundation.org)

Trustees: Justine Roddick; Samantha Roddick; Tina Schlieske.

www.theroddickfoundation.org

General information

The Roddick Foundation was established in 1997 by the late Dame Anita Roddick, founder of the Body Shop. On its website the foundation describes itself as a 'family-run, independent and progressive organisation dedicated to the support of visionary organisations and individuals who show leadership and results in making this a more just and kind world'.

The foundation states that it favours applications from 'people and groups who show exceptional creativity, entrepreneurial spirit, and courage' as well as those who can 'affect social change on a measurable scale'. The foundation generally provides funds for arts and culture; protecting the environment; securing human rights; medicine and health; and social rights, and notes that it is open to collaborations with other foundations and philanthropic organisations.

Financial information

Year end	31/03/2021
Income	£242,300
Assets	£18,030,000
Grants to organisations	£1,300,000
No. of grants	46

Further financial information

Grants awarded during the year can be broken down as follows:

Poverty/social justice	£411,500
Human rights	£314,800
The environment	£269,900
Arts and culture	£130,000
Medical/health	£117,000
Educational and media	£60,000

Beneficiaries included: A Team Foundation (£100,000); Good Chance Theatre (£50,000); Everydoctor (£43,000); Death Penalty Project (£20,000); Freedom Archives (£7,700).

Exclusions

The foundation does not accept applications from individuals. The foundation has previously stated that it would not consider funding any of the following:

- Projects related to sport
- Fundraising events or conferences
- Sponsorship of any kind

Applications

The foundation does not accept unsolicited applications.

Sources of information

Accounts; annual report; Charity Commission record; funder's website.

The Gerald and Gail Ronson Family Foundation

General charitable purposes, with particular interests in: Jewish causes; education; arts and culture; community; medical work; social welfare; security

UK; Israel; USA

£5.81 million (2020)

CC number: 1111728

Correspondent: Jeremy Trent, Secretary, c/o H. W. Fisher and Co., Acre House, 11–15 William Road, London NW1 3ER (tel: 020 7388 7000; email: jtrent@hwfisher.co.uk)

Trustees: Alan Goldman; Jonathan Goldstein; Gerald Ronson; Lisa Althasen; Dame Gail Ronson; Nicole Allalouf; Marc Zilkha; Jeffrey Shear; Ian Rosenblatt; Amanda Ronson; Hayley Ronson.

https://ronsonfoundation.org

General information

The foundation was registered with the Charity Commission in 2005. It is the foundation of businessman and philanthropist Gerald Ronson, chief executive of Heron International, a UK-based property developer. The trustees make donations to registered charitable organisations undertaking a wide range of charitable activities, with a particular preference for Jewish causes, education, community, security, health and disability, arts and culture, and welfare.

The foundation's 2020 accounts specify: 'The Foundation supports capital projects including children's hospices, medical and research facilities and schools. Grants have been given for Holocaust education, universities, help for those in need to seek employment, retirement homes and youth programmes. [...] While maintaining their discretion, the Trustees currently award grants to charities in the United Kingdom, Israel and the United States.'

Financial information

Year end	31/12/2020
Income	£546,700
Assets	£217,140,000
Grants to organisations	£5,810,000

Further financial information

Grants paid during the year totalled £5.81 million. We were unable to determine the proportion of grants made in the UK.

Beneficiaries included: Kfar Silver Youth Village (£2.08 million); Jewish Homes Emergency Appeal (£250,000); Royal Free Hospital Charity (£100,000); The Work Avenue Foundation (£25,000); Central School of Ballet Charitable Trust Ltd (£8,000); British Friends of the Art Museums of Israel (£5,000); The London Soup Kitchen (£1,000).

Applications

Applications for funding can be made on the foundation's website. According to its 2020 accounts, 'the Foundation makes grants on a monthly basis. All requests for donations are approved by the Trustees via e-mail. The Trustees meet quarterly to discuss new applications which have been previously reviewed and shortlisted once the foundation's criteria have been met.'

Sources of information

Accounts; annual report; Charity Commission record; funder's website.

Mrs L. D. Rope's Third Charitable Settlement

Education; religion; relief of poverty; general charitable purposes

UK and overseas, with a particular interest in East Suffolk

£606,700 (2020/21)

CC number: 290533

Correspondent: The Trustees, Lucy House, St William Court, Kesgrave, Ipswich, Suffolk IP5 2QP (tel: 01473 333288; email: ropetrust@lucyhouse.org.uk)

General information

The charity takes the name of Lucy Rope, who died in 2003 aged 96. Mrs Rope engaged in many charitable endeavours throughout her life. The charity, administered by her son Crispin, is based near Ipswich, and takes a keen interest in helping people from its local area and works closely with local organisations. A smaller proportion of grants are also awarded to UK-based organisations for work overseas.

According to the charity's 2020/21 annual report, grants are awarded to organisations if they are:

- In the Primary Area and are providing essential services to individuals locally and who have the greatest need of help
- Helping people who struggle to live on very little income, including the homeless
- Helping people who live in deprived inner-city and rural areas of the UK, particularly young people who lack the opportunities that may be available elsewhere
- Helping to support family life
- Helping disabled people
- Helping certain types of Roman Catholic charities and ecumenical projects which are in accordance with the Founder's Wishes

In addition to making grants to organisations, the charity also makes grants to individuals for welfare purposes, with a preference for those living in East Sussex.

Financial information

Year end	05/04/2021
Income	£1,460,000
Assets	£73,780,000
Grants to organisations	£606,700
No. of grants	155

Further financial information

Grants were broken down as follows: other charitable causes (£327,300); relief of poverty (£216,600); advancement of education (£62,800).

Beneficiaries included: Ormiston Families (£30,000); Felixstowe and District Citizens Advice (£26,000); Level Two Youth Project (£24,000); Museum of East Anglian Life (£15,000); Raedwald Trust (£11,400); Westbourne High School (£10,400).

Exclusions

The following categories of unsolicited applications will not be successful:

- Overseas projects
- National charities
- Buildings
- Medical research/healthcare (outside the beneficial area)
- Schools (outside the beneficial area)
- Environmental charities and animal welfare
- The arts
- Matched funding
- Repayment of debts for individuals

Applications

Send a concise letter (preferably one side of A4) explaining the main details of your request. Always send your most recent accounts and a budgeted breakdown of the sum you are looking to raise. The trustees will also need to know whether you have applied to other funding sources and whether you have been successful elsewhere. Your application should say who your trustees are and include a daytime telephone number.

Sources of information

Accounts; annual report; Charity Commission record.

Rosa Fund

Initiatives that benefit women and girls in the UK

UK

£1.69 million (2020/21)

CC number: 1124856

Correspondent: The Trustees, 4th Floor, United House, North Road, London N7 9DP (tel: 020 7697 3466; email: info@rosauk.org)

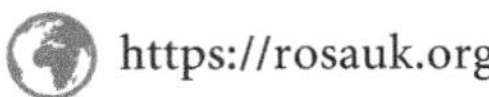

https://rosauk.org

facebook.com/RosaUK

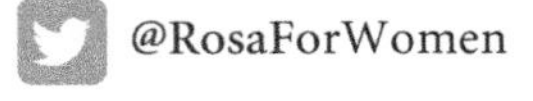

@RosaForWomen

@rosaforwomen

General information

This charity was established in 2008 and is named after three figures renowned for their commitment to gender equality:

Rosa Luxemburg, Rosa May Billinghurst and Rosa Parks. The charity's website describes Rosa as a grant-making charity that funds grassroots women's organisations working to make the UK a fairer, safer place for women and girls.

Rosa's work is underpinned by four pillars:

- Leadership and representation
- Safety
- Health and well-being
- Economic justice

Grant programmes

The charity has several different programmes, which open and close during the year. See the charity's website for the latest information on these programmes.

Financial information

Year end	31/03/2021
Income	£4,480,000
Assets	£3,300,000
Grants to organisations	£1,690,000

Beneficiaries included: Fawcett Society (£69,600); Agenda and Welsh Women's Aid (£40,000 each); Centre for Women's Justice (£14,600); Deaf Ethnic Women's Association, Girls Friendly Society and Women's Budget Group (£5,000 each); Devon Rape Crisis and Sexual Abuse Services (£3,100 each).

Exclusions

Applicants should consult the guidance document, found on each funding programme's web page, for a detailed list of funding exclusions.

Applications

Consult the charity's website for information on open programmes. Applications can be made through the charity's online application form before the specific deadline for each programme.

Sources of information

Accounts; annual report; Charity Commission record; funder's website.

The Rose Animal Welfare Trust CIO

 Animal welfare

 UK, with a preference for Yorkshire and the Humber

£303,000 (2019/20)

CC number: 1169516

Correspondent: The Trustees, Triune Court, Monks Cross Drive, Huntington, York, North Yorkshire YO1 7PR (tel: 01274 593779; email: npshaw63@gmail.com)

Trustees: Antoinette Tomkinson; Nigel Shaw; Elizabeth Webb.

General information

According to its 2019/20 annual report, the primary objective of the trust is 'the promotion of human behaviour and relieving suffering of domestic and wild animals'.

Financial information

Year end	31/10/2020
Income	£18,600
Assets	£636,600
Grants to organisations	£303,000

Beneficiaries included: Hull Animal Welfare Trust (£15,000); Battersea Dogs and Cats Home, Blue Cross for Pets and Cats Protection (£10,000 each); Four Paws (£5,000); Good Life Dog Rescue (£3,000).

Applications

Apply in writing to the correspondent. Grants are made each year in May and November.

Sources of information

Accounts; annual report; Charity Commission record.

The Rose Foundation

 General charitable purposes and grants towards building projects

 London

£972,600 (2019/20)

CC number: 1167144

Correspondent: Martin Rose, Trustee, 28 Crawford Street, London W1H 1LN (tel: 020 7262 1155)

Trustees: Martin Rose; Alan Rose; John Rose; Paul Rose.

 www.rosefoundation.co.uk

General information

The foundation was established in 1978 to support London-based charities requiring assistance for their building projects.

What is funded

The foundation provides financial assistance and advice to registered charities and exempt bodies undertaking building projects that cost less than £200,000 in the London area. Donations are usually of between £5,000 and £10,000.

Types of building projects

The foundation defines a building project as 'anything involving the use of builders'. This includes refurbishment, repairs, creating disability access, adaptations, extensions, landscaping, redecoration and meeting health and safety requirements.

Financial information

Year end	31/10/2020
Income	£1,240,000
Assets	£30,010,000
Grants to organisations	£972,600

Beneficiaries included: St John Ambulance (£593,000); Antenatal Results and Choices (£45,000); Fred Hollows Foundation (£17,800); The Variety Club (£11,300); The English Heritage Trust (£2,500).

Applications

Applications should be made in writing to the correspondent including details of the organisation and the registered charity number, together with the nature and probable approximate cost of the scheme and its anticipated start and completion dates. Further information can be found on the foundation's website.

Sources of information

Accounts; annual report; Charity Commission record; funder's website.

The Cecil Rosen Foundation

Jewish causes; health; education; care; social welfare; religion

 UK and Israel

£392,700 (2020/21)

CC number: 247425

Correspondent: The Trustees, 35 Langstone Way, Mill Hill East, London NW7 1GT (tel: 020 8346 8940; email: contact@cecilrosenfoundation.org)

Trustees: Malcolm Ozin; John Hart; Peter Silverman; Simon Lever.

General information

Established in 1966, this foundation's Charity Commission record states that it supports a number of Jewish organisations and organisations working with people who are blind or have a disability. The 2020/21 annual report states that the foundation supports causes in the areas of health, education, care, social welfare and religion.

The foundation makes long-term commitments to a small number of charities but also considers new applications.

Financial information

Year end	05/04/2021
Income	£473,200
Assets	£6,720,000
Grants to organisations	£392,700

Beneficiaries included: Previous beneficiaries include: Alma Primary School; British Heart Foundation; Cancer Research UK; Great Ormond

Street Hospital; Heart Cells Foundation; Jewish Deaf Society; National Institute for the Blind; Yesodeh Hatorah Primary School.

Applications

Apply in writing to the correspondent. The 2020/21 annual report states:

> The Trustees consider all applications received and give special attention to those which were originally chosen by the Settlor, Cecil Rosen.

Sources of information

Accounts; annual report; Charity Commission record.

Rosetrees Trust

Medical research

UK

£5.90 million (2020/21)

CC number: 298582

Correspondent: Ann Berger, Chief Executive, Regents Mead Group, Russell House, 140 High Street, Edgware, Middlesex HA8 7LW (tel: 020 8952 1414; email: info@rosetreestrust.co.uk)

Trustee: Rosetrees.

www.rosetreestrust.co.uk

General information

The Teresa Rosenbaum Golden Charitable Trust, known as the Rosetrees Trust, was registered in 1988 initially to fund social care programmes but later re-focused towards supporting medical research. In 2009/10 a transfer of assets from the settlors' estate to the trust amounted to around £30 million. Richard Ross is the settlors' son and a well-known philanthropist.

The trust's website states that:

> The aim is to improve the health and wellbeing of society. 400 projects are supported, from seedcorn 'out of the box' research ideas to large awards, many with co-funders. The focus is on testing new ideas across the spectrum of medical research to bring the earliest patient benefit.

Several different grant programmes are offered by the trust. Comprehensive details can be found on the trust's website and the following provides a brief overview:

- **Seedcorn grants** seek to provide a starting point for innovative and novel research into prevention, diagnosis and treatment through the provision of £10,000 over 12–18 months (or up to £15,000 over 18 months for clinical studies requiring patient recruitment)
- **Interdisciplinary awards** seek to encourage innovative research with collaboration between discipline areas through the provision of up to £300,000 over three years
- **PhD Plus awards** seek to enable students carry out additional studies to improve their research through grants of up to £2,100 per calendar month for 6–12 months
- **Project grants** seek to foster the clinical translation of research projects through small (£30,000 per annum) or large (£80,000 per annum) grants

The trust is also happy to work and share expertise with co-donors.

Financial information

Year end	31/03/2021
Income	£7,460,000
Assets	£35,080,000
Grants to organisations	£5,900,000

Beneficiaries included: UCL8 Royal Free (£1.42 million); Imperial College London (£622,000); University of Oxford (£509,300); Queen Mary University of London (£358,100); Imperial College London (£178,300); University of Southampton (£62,300).

Exclusions

Detailed eligibility criteria can be found on the trust's website for each funding programme.

Applications

Application forms and guidelines for each grants programme are available to download from the website. Refer to the website for the dates of application rounds.

Sources of information

Accounts; annual report; Charity Commission record; funder's website.

The Ross Foundation

Children and young people, including in the areas of education, sport, heritage and the arts

UK

£514,300 (2020/21)

CC number: 1121871

Correspondent: Joanne Hoareau, Operations Manager, 10 St James's Place, London SW1A 1NP (tel: 020 7534 1551; email: joanne@rossfoundation.com)

Trustees: Mark Bolland; Anita Bott; David Ross; Marcia Mercier; Lady Caroline Ryder; Ottilie Windsor; Henry Carling; Carl Ross.

www.davidrossfoundation.co.uk

facebook.com/davidpeterjohnross

@davidrosspr

General information

The Ross Foundation, previously known as The David Ross Foundation, was registered with the Charity Commission in 2007. The foundation's belief is that every child and young person has passions and talents, and so it supports a range of educational opportunities for young people to explore these talents.

Areas of support

The foundation has four key areas of interest, details of which have been taken from its website:

> **Education:** The Ross Foundation is the sponsor of the David Ross Education Trust. The David Ross Education Trust is developing a network of unique and diverse schools and academies. There are currently 33 within the Trust group.
>
> **Sport:** Key priorities are to increase the number of students participating in quality sport, to encourage and deliver quality sports competition opportunities and to provide pathways and support for talented individuals to participate and succeed in elite sport.
>
> **The arts:** The Ross Foundation is a passionate supporter of projects that work towards providing greater access to the arts. The Foundation supports a number of organisations and schemes across a range of artistic fields, from music to theatre and the visual arts and is the major sponsor of Nevill Holt Opera.
>
> **Heritage:** Though a national charity, many of the Foundation's activities are concentrated on the areas that David cares deeply about; areas where he is from and now lives. That is why every decision made and project supported must have a lasting impact and make a real difference to the communities that they serve.

Financial information

Year end	31/03/2021
Income	£17,800
Grants to organisations	£514,300

Further financial information

The foundation was not required to file accounts for the 2020/21 financial year due to its low income. We have therefore estimated the foundation's grant total based on previous financial information available. In previous years the foundation's grant expenditure totalled between 85% and 90% of its total expenditure.

Beneficiaries included: A list of beneficiaries was not available. Previous beneficiaries include: Nottingham University (£300,000); British Paralympic Association (£50,000); Action for Addiction (£5,000); National Youth Orchestra (£250); Cancer Research UK (£100).

Applications

Apply in writing to the correspondent. The foundation's website states that applications should outline: the project's purpose and activities; the budget, fundraising strategy and grant request;

the beneficiaries of the project; and the sustainability and legacy of the project.

Sources of information

Accounts; annual report; Charity Commission record; funder's website.

The Rothermere Foundation

General charitable purposes; education; medical research; the arts; religion; sport; children's charities

UK

£378,400 (2019/20)

CC number: 314125

Correspondent: Vyvyan Harmsworth, Trustee, Beech Court, Canterbury Road, Challock, Ashford, Kent TN25 4DJ (tel: 01233 740641)

Trustees: Vyvyan Harmsworth; The Rt Hon. Viscount Rothermere; The Viscountess Rothermere; Gilbert Holbourn.

General information

The foundation was established in 1956 to deliver Rothermere Scholarships, which enable post-PhD graduates from the Memorial University of Newfoundland to undertake further periods of study in the UK. The foundation also makes grants for general charitable purposes, including the arts, children and young people, religion, sport, education and medical research.

Financial information

Year end	30/09/2020
Income	£1,170,000
Assets	£36,450,000
Grants to organisations	£378,400

Further financial information

Grants paid during the year totalled £378,400, and an additional £15,000 was committed. Grants were broken down as follows:

General charitable purposes	£225,100
Educational and children's charities	£156,300
Medical research	£6,000
The arts and sport	£6,000

In 2018/19, the foundation made a substantial grant of £1 million to The Imperial War Museum Foundation, but its grant-making returned to normal levels in 2019/20.

Beneficiaries included: Mail Force Charity CIO (£150,000); St Peter's College Oxford (£100,000); University of Oxford Charitable Trust (£30,000); Game Alliance Ltd (£10,000); Horatio's Garden, Wellbeing of Women and World Horse Welfare (£5,000 each); Cherubim Music Trust (£1,000); Stars Appeal (£100).

Applications

Apply in writing to the correspondent. The trustees meet twice a year to consider grant applications.

Sources of information

Accounts; annual report; Charity Commission record.

The Eranda Rothschild Foundation

Education; medical research; the arts; social welfare

UK and overseas. For charities working locally, priority is given to those in Buckinghamshire and Bedfordshire

£838,200 (2020/21)

CC number: 255650

Correspondent: The Secretary, PO Box 6226, Leighton Buzzard, Bedfordshire LU7 0XF (tel: 01296 689157; email: secretary@erandarothschild.org)

Trustees: Sir Evelyn de Rothschild; Anthony de Rothschild; Lady de Rothschild; Jessica Rothschild; Sir John Peace; Benjamin Elliot.

 www.erandarothschild.org

General information

Established in 1967, this is one of the charitable foundations of the de Rothschild finance and banking family.

The foundation supports registered charities working in the fields of medical research, education and the arts. Social welfare is also supported, particularly if it is work that is known to the trustees.

The following information has been taken from the foundation's website:

Education

> We consider applications from universities and other charities to support young professionals in fields including medicine, science and business. We support disadvantaged young people and apprenticeships.

Medical research

> We support original research and the continuation of existing research. Welfare is also considered under the medical theme and here the priority is to support work well known to the Trustees.

The arts

> We support the education and outreach work of arts charities and prioritise work which is well known to the Foundation.

Financial information

Year end	05/04/2021
Income	£4,450,000
Assets	£542,500
Grants to organisations	£838,200
No. of grants	27

Further financial information

Grants were broken down as follows: education (£838,200); health, welfare and medical research (£100,200); the arts (£154,800). In previous years, the foundation has awarded grants totalling upwards of £3 million.

A list of recent beneficiaries can be requested from the correspondent.

Beneficiaries included: A list of beneficiaries was not available. Previous beneficiaries include: Alzheimer's Society; Dyslexia Scotland; Elton John AIDS Foundation; Give a Book; Jewish Care; Lowry Centre Trust; Pace Centre; Philharmonic Orchestra; Teach First.

Exclusions

The foundation does not make donations to individuals or to organisations that are not registered charities. The foundation does not support capital appeals unless they are of personal significance to the trustees.

Applications

The trustees prefer applications to be made using the online form on the foundation's website. Applications are considered at meetings held three times a year, usually in February/March, June/July and October/November. Charities should make only one application per year. Online applications are acknowledged automatically and every applicant will be notified of the trustees' decision (this may take several months). The foundation's website notes that it always receives more applications than it is able to fund.

Sources of information

Accounts; annual report; Charity Commission record; funder's website.

The Rothschild Foundation

The arts and humanities; heritage; education; the environment; social welfare

UK, with a preference for the area within ten miles of the Waddesdon Estate in Buckinghamshire

£8.5 million (2020/21)

CC number: 1138145

Correspondent: Ellie Stout, Head of Grants, Windmill Hill, Silk Street, Waddesdon, Buckinghamshire HP18 0JZ (tel: 01296 653208; email: grants@rothschildfoundation.org.uk or info@rothschildfoundation.org.uk)

Trustees: Lord Rothschild; The Hon. Emily Freeman-Attwood; Peter Troughton; The Hon. Janet De Botton; The Hon. Hannah Rothschild; Lord David Ogilvy; Francesco Goedhuis; S.J.P. Trust Corporation Ltd.

 https://rothschildfoundation.org.uk

 facebook.com/therothschildfoundation

General information

The Rothschild Foundation was established by Lord (Jacob) Rothschild to maintain and promote Waddesdon Manor and to further the Rothschild family's charitable aims. Assets are derived from a number of charitable trusts inherited or created by Lord Rothschild, which were merged in 2010. The foundation's grant-making work focuses on several key policy areas, including the arts and heritage, the environment, education and social welfare.

Although much of the foundation's funding is proactive and closed to unsolicited applications, the charity also operates some grant programmes which are open to applications from charities that meet the eligibility criteria.

All these programmes are largely focused on Buckinghamshire, this being the foundation's home county.

Schools Access Fund

The aim of this fund is to 'enhance creative learning and enrich how schools teach the arts curriculum'. Applications are encouraged for all key stages, as well as preschools and colleges, and should be submitted by a school, PTA or charity connected to the school. Visit the foundation's website for details of opening and closing dates for applications.

Local and Community Grants programme

The Local and Community Grants programme provides small grants of up to £5,000 to organisations in the area around Waddesdon working in the broad field of social welfare. Small and medium-sized charities and CICs are generally prioritised for funding. Grants are awarded for core costs, projects and organisational development.

Further details on each grants programme are available on the foundation's website.

The foundation primarily focuses on funding registered charities or organisations with charitable status. CICs which are limited by guarantee may apply following confirmation from the grants manager.

Strategic Fund

This fund supports organisations that share similar priorities and interests in bringing about positive changes for Buckinghamshire. Priorities include building a sustainable food system and increasing cultural activity and opportunities for young people. The fund offers grants of up to £100,000 and is open throughout the year.

Financial information

Year end	28/02/2021
Income	£37,680,000
Assets	£764,390,000
Grants to organisations	£8,520,000
No. of grants	8,497

Beneficiaries included: Trent Park Museum Trust (£100,000); Wildlife Trust (£92,000); Sustainable Food Trust (£90,000); Roche Court Educational Trust (£62,000); Thames Valley Partnership (£60,000); Wycombe and District Citizens Advice (£50,000).

Exclusions

The foundation does not make grants for/to the following:

- Individuals
- Major capital projects
- Medical equipment and research
- Academic research and bursaries
- Animal charities
- Projects outside the UK
- Projects promoting religion
- Overseas travel
- Expeditions
- Adventure and residential courses

Only charities and organisations with charitable status are supported.

Applications

Application processes may vary depending on the programme being applied to. Check the website for open programmes and relevant application details.

Should applicants require support or advice, enquiries should be submitted to grants@rothschildfoundation.org.uk with the relevant programme name in the subject heading.

Sources of information

Accounts; annual report; Charity Commission record; funder's website.

Rothschild Foundation (Hanadiv) Europe

Jewish causes; religious education; scholarship and research; culture and heritage

Europe and Israel

£5.49 million (2020)

CC number: 1083262

Correspondent: Grant Programmes Manager, 15 St James's Place, London SW1A 1NP (tel: 01296 658778; email: info@rothschildfoundation.eu)

 www.rothschildfoundation.eu

General information

Rothschild Foundation (Hanadiv) Europe is one of the philanthropic charities supported by the Rothschild family and supports initiatives across Europe, continuing the family's commitment to the Jewish community.

The foundation's website states that its aim is:

> to ensure that Jewish communal life and cultural heritage are sustained for future generations. Our grants assist organisations, institutions and individuals who share our vision for the dynamic role Jewish culture and heritage have to play in contemporary society. We support archives, libraries, museums, universities and Jewish communal organisations and we also initiate our own projects which are designed to enhance the fields we support.

The foundation welcomes applications from any organisation or institution active in Europe that qualifies as charitable under UK charity law.

Comprehensive details can be found on the foundation's website for each funding programme. The following offers a brief overview of the programmes administered:

- **Academic Jewish Studies:** includes funding for doctoral, postdoctoral and teaching fellowships, with the aim of developing future Jewish Studies scholars, in addition to funding for the establishment of research consortia, teaching networks and scholarships for language studies students
- **Archives and Libraries:** for archives and libraries relating to Jewish studies and Jewish history. This includes the following programmes:
  - Professional development language grant
  - Conservation and preservation
  - Inventories and cataloguing
  - Professional training
  - Digital resource creation and digital humanities
- **Museums:** available to European museums for projects relating to the preservation, documentation, and dissemination of Jewish heritage. The grants aim to support several aspects of projects including – but not limited to – collection management, exhibition support and professional training

- **Jewish Communal Life (formerly Jewish Education):** this funding programme seeks 'to ensure Jewish communities are equipped to engage more Jews with Jewish life and learning', as stated on the website. This can include professional development, community engagement and education of local Jewish heritage

Financial information

Year end	31/12/2020
Income	£42,400
Assets	£135,220,000
Grants to organisations	£5,490,000
No. of grants	43+

Further financial information

Note: the grant total includes grants made in the UK and Europe. It also includes £1.4 million of COVID-19 response and recovery grants. Grants were broken down as follows:

Culture and heritage	£1.69 million
Community welfare	£1.61 million
Academic Jewish studies	£1.04 million
Education and research	£647,800
National Library of Israel	£500,000

Only beneficiaries of grants of over £50,000 were listed in the accounts (43 grants).

Beneficiaries included: Gesher L'Europa (£390,000); Jewish Care (£250,000); National Library (£110,000); Oxford Centre for Hebrew and Jewish Studies (£106,400); Imperial War Museum (£75,000); Jewish Women's Aid and University of London (£50,000 each).

Exclusions

The foundation does not fund any of the following:

- Ongoing costs of schools and synagogues
- Retrospective costs
- Building of new museums or communal institutions
- Restoration of Jewish built heritage
- Artistic projects in the fine arts, the performing arts, film production, creative writing
- Publication of books, including the translation of academic works
- Individuals (except for Professional Development Language Grants and certain grants within the Academic Jewish Studies programme)
- Previously refused applications without substantial changes

Further programme-specific restrictions may also apply. Check the website for full details.

Applications

Refer to the website for application forms, deadlines and guidance for each programme. Contact details for each grants programme manager are also provided. Applications must be submitted via the online application process.

Sources of information

Accounts; annual report; Charity Commission record; funder's website.

The Roughley Charitable Trust

Community projects; special needs; young people; older people; social welfare; disability; health and well-being; education; arts and leisure; heritage; the environment

Birmingham and overseas

£225,000 (2020/21)

CC number: 264037

Correspondent: Adam Wilkins, 562 Kenilworth Road, Balsall Common, Coventry CV7 7RZ (email: correspondent@roughleytrust.org.uk)

www.roughleytrust.org.uk

General information

The trust makes grants to registered charities based in Birmingham and overseas for a wide range of causes. Priority tends to be given to small or medium-sized organisations.

Grant programmes

Larger grants

The trust awards grants to a small number of Birmingham registered charities of which one or more of the trustees have a special knowledge.

Smaller grants

The trust's website states:

> Applications from local Birmingham charities working inside the city boundary will be accepted. In some cases trustees will accept applications from charities working near to the Birmingham boundary if the majority of their clients are in Birmingham.

Charities must have an annual turnover of less than £1 million and work within one of the following areas (taken from the website):

- Area-based community work such as church-based community projects
- Work with special needs including the following: childhood and youth, old age, death and bereavement, homelessness, disability, prison, addiction, victim support and other special needs
- Health and well being, including syndrome support groups, counselling, bereavement support, complementary health and mental health initiatives
- Education
- Arts and leisure, including theatre in education groups, museums and arts centres
- Heritage
- Environment: environmental improvement projects, and green projects generally are particularly welcome

National and overseas grants

The trust offers regular support to a small number of development charities working overseas. (The trust does not accept unsolicited applications from overseas charities.) In addition, the trust may also provide funding to some individual charities that are based outside Birmingham but which have a Birmingham branch that is a registered charity.

Since November 2015, the trust has also awarded grants from funds gifted by the AW60 Trust. The Roughley Charitable Trust also funds up to five students for gap year travel each year.

Financial information

Year end	05/04/2021
Income	£229,000
Assets	£7,840,000
Grants to organisations	£225,000

Further financial information

In 2020/21 grants were broken down as follows: international grants (£90,000); Birmingham area larger grants (£90,000); Birmingham area smaller grants (£45,000).

Birmingham smaller grants were broken down as follows:

Special needs	£17,000
AW60 grants	£10,000
Church-based community projects	£6,000
Community and youth work	£5,000
Refugees and asylum seekers	£3,000
The arts	£2,000
The environment	£2,000

Beneficiaries included: Hope Projects West Midlands (£38,000); Appropriate Technology Asia (£25,000); The Wildlife Trust for Birmingham and the Black Country (£12,000); Restore Birmingham Churches Together (£5,000); Bethel Heath and Healing (£3,000); Sports for Life (£2,000).

Exclusions

Grants are not accepted from:

- Birmingham-based medical charities
- Church fabric appeals
- CICs
- Social enterprises
- Church-based projects which are essentially about the teaching of religion
- Animal charities

A Birmingham branch of a national charity cannot be funded unless the branch has its own charity number and accounts.

Applications for projects in Sandwell, Solihull, Wolverhampton and Walsall are not normally accepted.

Applications

Applications should be made using the form available to download from the trust's website, where the trust's criteria and guidelines are also available. Application forms should be returned to the trust by email, along with a signed letter on headed paper, two or three photographs which give a good idea of what the project is about, and any other supporting material (in moderation). Your latest accounts should only be sent if they are not available to view on the Charity Commission website. For more information, including details of key dates for applications, refer to the trust's website.

Note: unsolicited applications are only accepted from charities based in Birmingham.

Sources of information

Accounts; annual report; Charity Commission record; funder's website; further information provided by the funder.

Rowanville Ltd

The advancement of the Orthodox Jewish faith

UK and overseas (particularly Israel)

£970,100 (2019/20)

CC number: 267278

Correspondent: The Trustees, 8 Highfield Gardens, London NW11 9HB (tel: 020 8458 9266)

Trustees: Joseph Pearlman; Ruth Pearlman; Allan Becker.

General information

The objectives of this charity are to advance religion in accordance with the Orthodox Jewish faith. The charity provides grants to charitable institutions and its charitable subsidiary provides a Jewish faith school with accommodation free of charge, in addition to providing budgetary assistance to the school.

Financial information

Year end	30/06/2020
Income	£1,210,000
Assets	£10,620,000
Grants to organisations	£970,100

Beneficiaries included: Ader Charitable Trust and Mercaz Chasidei Wiznitz Trust (£50,000 each); Friends of Eidah Chareidis Orthodox Council of Jerusalem (£44,000); Friends of Nachalas Bnei Shimon and Start Upright (£40,000 each).

Applications

Contact the correspondent for further information.

Sources of information

Accounts; annual report; Charity Commission record.

The Rowlands Trust

General charitable purposes; armed forces; music and the arts; health and social welfare; older people; disability; the environment; church buildings; research, education and training, particularly medical and scientific research

Primarily the West Midlands and South Midlands, including Birmingham, Gloucestershire, Herefordshire, Shropshire, Warwickshire and Worcestershire

£377,200 (2020)

CC number: 1062148

Correspondent: Louise Ruane, Administrator, c/o Bishop Fleming LLP, 1–4 College Yard, Worcester, Worcestershire WR1 2LB (tel: 07812 743485; email: louise.ruane@therowlandstrust.org.uk)

Trustees: Gary Barber; Diana Crabtree; Ian Smith; Rebecca Widdowson; Patrick Wrixon.

General information

The Rowlands Trust was established in 1996 following the death of Herbert Roy Rowlands. The trust primarily supports projects in the West Midlands and the South Midlands, including Hereford and Worcester, Gloucester, Shropshire and Birmingham. Grants are given for general charitable purposes, particularly in the following areas:

- Research, education, and training in the broadest sense with special regard to medical and scientific research
- Older people
- People with disabilities
- Health and social welfare
- The Services
- Music and the arts
- The environment
- The maintenance and restoration of Anglican church buildings

The trust makes grants for capital and project costs.

Financial information

Year end	31/12/2020
Income	£114,600
Assets	£2,660,000
Grants to organisations	£377,200
No. of grants	118

Further financial information

Grants paid during the year totalled £377,200. Grants were distributed as follows:

Welfare and older people	£184,600
Research, education and training (including medical research)	£77,700
Church buildings	£56,500
Music and the arts	£37,100
The environment	£21,300

Beneficiaries included: University of Birmingham – prostate cancer research (£41,900); Lapal Canal Trust and Worcester Cathedral (£10,000 each); National Trust (£5,000); St Richard's Hospice (£3,000); Sandwell African Women Association (£2,000); British Dyslexics UK (£1,000); Kington and District Museum (£250).

Exclusions

The trust does not fund core costs or projects which are eligible for state funding. It was previously understood that animal charities and individuals are not eligible for a grant.

Applications

Application forms are available from the correspondent and are the preferred means by which to apply. The trustees meet to consider grants four times a year.

Sources of information

Accounts; annual report; Charity Commission record.

The Joseph Rowntree Charitable Trust

Equalities, rights and justice; power and accountability; peace and security; Northern Ireland

UK and overseas

£10.47 million (2020)

CC number: 210037

Correspondent: The Trustees, The Garden House, Water End, York, North Yorkshire YO30 6WQ (tel: 01904 627810; email: enquiries@jrct.org.uk)

Trustees: Helen Carmichael; Susan Seymour; Hannah Torkington; Jennifer Amery; Linda Batten; John Fitzgerald; Huw Davies; David Newton; Janet Slade; Nicholas Burton.

www.jrct.org.uk

@jrctinfo

General information

The Joseph Rowntree Charitable Trust (JRCT) was established in 1904 for general charitable purposes and benefits people and organisations mainly within Britain. Outside Britain, the trust makes grants for work towards peace, justice and reconciliation in both jurisdictions of the island of Ireland and, increasingly, in relation to influencing the policies of the European Union.

This is a Quaker trust and the value base of the trustees, as of the founder Joseph Rowntree (1836–1925), reflects the religious convictions of the Society of Friends. In the original founding trust deed of 1904 (from which the present deed is derived) Joseph Rowntree gave the trustees power to spend the trust fund and its income on any object which is legally charitable. In a memorandum written at the same time, which is not part of the trust deed and therefore not binding, he expressed a clear vision of how he hoped the fund would be used, while urging that 'none of the objects which I have enumerated, and which under present social conditions appear to me to be of paramount importance, should be pursued after it has ceased to be vital and pressing'.

Grant-making programmes

The trust's current programme areas are:

- **Peace and Security**, particularly:
  1. Challenging militarism
  2. Scrutiny of counter-terrorism measures in the context of human rights and peacebuilding
  3. Building support for alternative approaches to defence and security
  4. Responding to the dual harms of COVID-19 and systemic racism
- **Power and Accountability,** particularly:
  1. Strengthening corporate accountability
  2. Strengthening democratic accountability
  3. Encouraging responsible media
  4. Responding to the dual harms of COVID-19 and systemic racism
- **Rights and Justice**, particularly:
  1. Protection and promotion of equality and human rights and their enforcement in the UK
  2. Promoting rights and justice for minorities who face the most severe forms of racism
  3. Promotion of rights and justice for refugees and other migrants by identifying and tackling structures and systems that may deny them their rights
  4. Responding to the dual harms of COVID-19 and systemic racism
- **Sustainable Future**, particularly:
  1. Better economies
  2. Beyond consumerism
  3. New voices
  4. Responding to the dual harms of COVID-19 and systemic racism
- **Northern Ireland**, particularly:
  1. Strengthening human rights and equality
  2. Supporting inclusive, non-sectarian and participatory politics
  3. Supporting processes of demilitarisation
  4. Dealing with the past
  5. Dealing with the dual harms of COVID-19 and systemic racism

Detailed guidelines for each of these funding priorities can be found on the website.

Financial information

Year end	31/12/2020
Income	£1,630,000
Assets	£296,340,000
Grants to organisations	£10,470,000

Beneficiaries included: Action on Armed Violence (£170,000); Full Fact (£150,000); Crisis Action (£105,000); MayDay Rooms (£23,200); Thirty Percy Foundation (£15,000); Menwith Hill Accountability Campaign (£7,500).

Exclusions

The trust does not make grants for work that is party political, commercial in nature or otherwise intended for private benefit. See the trust's website for a full list of exclusions.

Applications

Apply via the trust's website, where application deadlines can also be found.

Sources of information

Accounts; annual report; Charity Commission record; funder's website.

The Joseph Rowntree Foundation

Research and policy work related to solving poverty

UK

£4.82 million (2020)

CC number: 1184957

Correspondent: The Trustees, The Homestead, 40 Water End, York, North Yorkshire YO30 6WP (tel: 01904 629241; email: info@jrf.org.uk)

 www.jrf.org.uk

 facebook.com/JosephRowntreeFoundation

 @jrf_uk

General information

The Joseph Rowntree Foundation's website states that it 'is an independent social organisation which through research, policy, collaboration and practical solutions, aims to inspire action and change that will create a prosperous UK without poverty'.

The website further states:

> The Joseph Rowntree Foundation funds and works in partnership with other organisations to unlock the UK from poverty.
>
> JRF works to a social change model where we develop and deliver long-term plans aimed at tackling the root causes of UK poverty, in pursuit of the following outcomes:
>
> - More people want to solve poverty, understand it and take action.
> - More people find a route out of poverty through work.
> - More people find a route out of poverty through a better system of social security.
> - More people live in a decent, affordable home.

Funding

The foundation advertises calls for proposals on its website. At the time of writing (May 2022), the foundation's website stated that it was currently in a transition period regarding its strategy and funding opportunities. Check the website for up-to-date information.

Financial information

Year end	31/12/2020
Income	£29,240,000
Assets	£446,320,000
Grants to organisations	£4,820,000

Further financial information

Only beneficiaries and projects that received grants of £25,000 and above were listed in the accounts. Grants of under £25,000 totalled £435,000.

Beneficiaries included: Centre for Progressive Policy (£675,000); Crisis (£250,000); Resolution Foundation (£150,000); Citizens UK (£82,000); Poverty and Inequality Commission (£45,000); Design Council (£30,000); Faith in the Community Scotland (£25,000).

Exclusions

The foundation's website states:

> We do not generally support:
>
> - Unsolicited proposals
> - Educational bursaries or sponsorship for individual research or further education and training courses
> - Proposals that do not have the potential to make a difference to policy or practice in the UK
> - Projects outside the topics within our current priorities
> - Development projects that are not innovative
> - Development projects from which no general lessons can be drawn
> - General appeals, for example, from national charities
> - Core or revenue funding, including grants for buildings or equipment
> - Conferences, events, websites or publications unless they are linked with work that we are already supporting
> - Grants to replace withdrawn or expired statutory funding, or to make up deficits already incurred
> - Grants or sponsorship for individuals in need

Applications

Apply for funding by responding to a call for proposals. Applicants should submit a completed budget form (available to download from the foundation's website) and a proposal for the project. Unsolicited proposals outside open calls are not accepted.

Sources of information

Accounts; annual report; Charity Commission record; funder's website.

The Royal British Legion

Armed forces

UK

£5.96 million (2019/20)

CC number: 219279

Correspondent: The Trustees, 199 Borough High Street, London SE1 1AA (tel: 0808 802 8080; email: info@britishlegion.org.uk)

 www.britishlegion.org.uk

 facebook.com/OfficialPoppyLegion

 @PoppyLegion

 @royalbritishlegion

General information

The country's largest armed forces charity with 235,000 members and 110,000 volunteers, The Royal British Legion was formed in 1921 as a caring organisation for people in need from the Service and ex-Service community. It aims to safeguard the welfare, interests and memory of those who have served in the armed forces.

Grant-making

The charity's external grants programme provides support for not-for-profit organisations planning projects for the benefit of the armed forces community.

At the time of writing (March 2022) the charity was not accepting external grant applications. The website stated:

> During this current climate of change and uncertainty related to the COVID-19 pandemic, we are not accepting external grant applications from organisations.
>
> This difficult decision has been taken in response to the unprecedented challenges our country, organisations and communities are facing at this time. Our focus is and must continue to be on meeting the need of individuals and families at their time of need through our local caseworking, care services, advice services and individual grants capability. We will of course review the situation and hope that, once life in the UK returns to its pre-March 2020 state – or an approximation thereof – we will reopen our External Grants programme.

Financial information

Year end	30/09/2020
Income	£143,110,000
Assets	£309,590,000
Grants to organisations	£5,960,000
No. of grants	23

Further financial information

In 2020, grants were awarded to 23 organisations, totalling £5.96 million (2019: 53 organisations, £12.21 million). The 2019/20 accounts state that the reduced number of grants to organisations in the year 'reflects the decision to temporarily pause the external grants programme due to uncertainty about the impact of COVID-19 on the RBL's finances'.

Beneficiaries included: Combat Stress (£2.95 million); National Memorial Arboretum (£2.3 million); Poppyscotland (£356,000).

Exclusions

See the website for up-to-date information on exclusions.

Applications

At the time of writing (March 2022), the External Grants programme was not accepting new applications due to the COVID-19 pandemic. See the charity's website for the latest information.

Sources of information

Accounts; annual report; Charity Commission record; funder's website.

The Royal Foundation of the Duke and Duchess of Cambridge

Conservation; children (early years); mental health; emergency response; COVID-19 relief

UK and overseas

£3.73 million (2020)

CC number: 1132048

Correspondent: The Trustees, c/o Kensington Palace, Palace Green, London W8 4PU (tel: 020 7101 2963; email: reception@royalfoundation.com)

 www.royalfoundation.com

 @kensingtonroyal

General information

Registered in late 2009 with broad, general charitable purposes, the foundation became fully operational in 2011. It is the primary philanthropic and charitable vehicle for The Duke and Duchess of Cambridge.

Areas of work

Following a period of review and restructure in 2019, the work of the foundation is now focused on the following themes.

Conservation

Addressing pressing environmental and conservation crises by bringing together environmentalists, businesses, global leaders and NGOs to find solutions.

The Earthshot Prize, launched in 2020, will be awarded to five winners each year between 2021 and 2030. As stated on its website, the foundation's 'nominators' seek out evidence-based solutions to the biggest environmental problems the planet faces, including:

- Protecting and restoring
- Cleaning
- Reviving
- Building
- Fixing

Early years

In 2021 the Duchess launched the Centre for Early Childhood, to drive awareness of the impact early childhood has on later life experiences. The centre will focus on the following three activities:

- Promoting and commissioning research
- Collaborating with the private, public and voluntary sectors to work on new solutions
- Developing creative campaigns

Mental health

Tackling stigma and encouraging more people to talk openly about mental health, as well as supporting new mental health services.

The foundation's 2020 annual report states: 'Looking ahead, The Royal Foundation's mental health activities will also be focused on the emergency responder community. This work draws on The Duke of Cambridge's own experiences as a search and rescue helicopter pilot.'

See the foundation's website for current initiatives and campaigns operating within these themes.

Financial information

Year end	31/12/2020
Income	£11,820,000
Assets	£8,210,000
Grants to organisations	£3,730,000
No. of grants	29

Further financial information

Grants were broken down as follows:

COVID-19 response fund	£1.12 million
Young people	£758,900
Emergency services	£623,200
Mental health	£357,300
Conservation	£340,900
United for Wildlife Taskforces	£300,000
Empowering communities	£230,700
Other	£4,400

Beneficiaries included: Invictus Games Foundation (£561,000); Mind (£250,000); The Ambulance Staff Charity (£134,200); Young Minds (£99,900); Hospice UK (£50,500); Wildlife Conservation Society (£20,000); Middlesbrough FC Foundation (£6,500).

Applications

Contact the foundation for further information.

Sources of information

Accounts; annual report; Charity Commission record; funder's website.

The Royal Masonic Trust for Girls and Boys

Children and young people; older people; social welfare; education and training; children of Freemasons

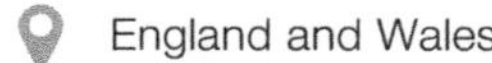

England and Wales

£3.53 million to non-Masonic charities (2020/21)

CC number: 1170336

Correspondent: The Trustees, Freemasons' Hall, 60 Great Queen Street, London WC2B 5AZ (tel: 020 3146 3333; email: info@mcf.org.uk)

Trustees: Paul Williams; Masonic Charitable Foundation.

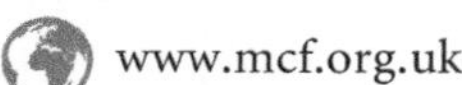

www.mcf.org.uk

facebook.com/themcf

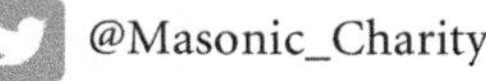

@Masonic_Charity

General information

The Royal Masonic Trust for Girls and Boys was originally established in 1982. In 2016 the charity was incorporated and is now run as part of the Masonic Charitable Foundation (Charity Commission no. 1164703). The trust is largely focused on making grants to individual children of Freemasons who are in need.

Grants are also made to non-Masonic registered charities based in England and Wales in the following categories:

- Children and young people – the trust's website states that this grant 'is open to national and local charities helping disadvantaged children and young people to overcome the challenges they face.'
- Later life – the trust's website states that this grant 'is open to local and national charities that are working to reduce loneliness and isolation in later life.'

Depending on the applicant organisation's size, the trust awards small grants typically of between £1,000 and £5,000, which are unrestricted, and large grants typically of between £10,000 and £60,000.

Additionally, the trust makes a number of grants each year to hospices across England and Wales. Its core funding grants are available to contribute to the operating costs of hospices that receive 60% or less of their funding from the NHS. The trust also has a partnership with Hospice UK.

Financial information

Year end	31/03/2021
Income	£4,370,000
Assets	£154,670,000
Grants to organisations	£3,530,000
No. of grants	432

Beneficiaries included: Over The Wall (£70,000); SHAID Ltd Single Homeless Action Initiative in Durham (£43,000); Gloucestershire Night Stop (£30,000); TRACKS Autism (£15,000); Herefordshire RDA (£1,000); Portland Drop-In Centre (£750); Revive Healthy Living (£250).

Exclusions

See the 'Grants to charities' section of the Masonic Charitable Foundation's helpful website for full details of eligibility requirements and exclusions with respect to activities and types of organisation.

Applications

Applications are made online through the Masonic Charitable Foundation's website. Application guidelines and eligibility criteria are available for each grants programme.

Sources of information

Accounts; annual report; annual review; Charity Commission record; funder's website.

The Royal National Institute for Deaf People (RNID)

Research into hearing loss and tinnitus

UK

£1.28 million (2020/21)

CC number: 207720

Correspondent: The Trustees, Brightfield Business Hub, Bakewell Road, Orton Southgate, Peterborough PE2 6XU (tel: 0808 808 0123; email: research@rnid.org.uk)

Trustees: John Morgan; Dr Brian Caul; Claire Bailey; Gideon Hoffman; Lindsay Foster; Sally Harris; Ita Murphy; Nicholas Waring.

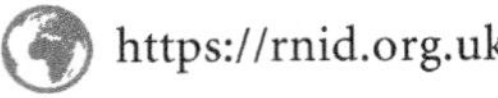

https://rnid.org.uk

facebook.com/rnid

@rnid

@rnid_uk

General information

This charity was established in 1911 by Leo Bonn, a successful banker with hearing loss who dedicated a large portion of his wealth to helping those who are deaf/have hearing loss.

According to its website, the charity is passionate about 'making life fully inclusive for deaf people and those with hearing loss or tinnitus' by funding research, campaigning for policy reform and by providing information and support.

Research funding

The charity awards biomedical research grants for projects that seek to find a cure for hearing loss and drive the development of new technologies.

According to the charity's research strategy, its areas of focus are:

- Preventing hearing loss
- Restoring hearing
- Silencing tinnitus

Details of current grant programmes can be seen on the charity's website.

Financial information

Year end	31/03/2021
Income	£34,510,000
Assets	£7,350,000
Grants to organisations	£1,280,000
No. of grants	22

Further financial information

In 2020/21, the charity awarded 39 research grants to 22 organisations totalling £1.28 million.

Beneficiaries included: University College London (£261,000 in eight grants); King's College London (£150,000 in four grants); University of Sheffield (£91,000 in four grants); Bionics Institute (£55,000); Newcastle University (£25,000 in two grants); University of Zurich (£10,000).

Applications

Details of all open grant programmes can be found on the charity's website. If you would like to be notified of new grant opportunities, email research@hearingloss.org.uk and request to be added to the research mailing list.

Sources of information

Accounts; annual report; Charity Commission record; funder's website.

The Royal Navy and Royal Marines Charity

 Organisations supporting current or former Service personnel from the Royal Navy and the Royal Marines, and their dependants

UK

£11.42 million (2020)

CC number: 1117794

Correspondent: The Trustees, Building 37, HMS Excellent, Whale Island, Portsmouth, Hampshire PO2 8ER (tel: 023 9387 1520; email: theteam@rnrmc.org.uk)

 www.rnrmc.org.uk

 facebook.com/RNRMC

 @RNRMC

 @rnrmcharity

General information

The Royal Navy and Royal Marines Charity makes grants to charities supporting current and former members of the Naval Service, and their families and dependants.

According to its 2020 annual accounts, the objects of the charity are:

> To focus on the relief in need, hardship or distress of disadvantaged persons, provide education and to improve the efficiency of the Naval Service. The range of the benefits deriving from benevolence activities includes the relief of poverty and improving the efficiency of other charities through the grants made. The RNRMC also provides its beneficiaries with facilities for sport and recreation.

Support for individuals

The charity supports serving members of the armed forces, veterans and their families by providing large block grants to military welfare organisations. A list of these organisations can be found in the charity's Impact Report 2021, available on its website.

Financial information

Year end	31/12/2020
Income	£6,460,000
Assets	£53,600,000
Grants to organisations	£11,420,000

Beneficiaries included: MOD – Gordon Messenger Centre (£2.76 million); Sailors' Children's Society (£278,000); Veterans Outreach Support (£90,000); Age UK (£45,300); Poppyscotland (£25,000).

Exclusions

According to the Funding Framework guidelines (see the website), the charity will not normally fund the following:

- Organisational fundraising activities
- Retrospective costs
- Trading ventures
- Research
- Projects that could be funded by the Service, the state or other public bodies

Applications

Apply via the charity's online application portal available on its website.

Sources of information

Accounts; annual report; Charity Commission record; funder's website; guidelines for applicants.

The Associated Board of the Royal Schools of Music

 Music education

 UK and overseas

£1.87 million (2020/21)

CC number: 292182

Correspondent: The Trustees, Associated Board of The Royal Schools of Music, 4 London Wall Place, London EC2Y 5AU (tel: 020 7467 8223; email: abrsm@abrsm.ac.uk)

www.abrsm.org

 facebook.com/abrsm

General information

Founded in 1889, The Associated Board of the Royal Schools of Music (ABRSM) is the largest music education body in the UK, providing music examinations to 650,000 candidates in over 90 countries annually. The activities carried out by ABRSM are described on the Charity Commission website, which states that it:

> Motivates musical achievement through internationally recognised examination and assessment of students, professional development of teachers and provision of published resources and online learning via its websites, apps and audio and video resources. ABRSM makes significant donations towards music education each year including the four Royal Schools of Music.

Global support for music education

The charity reinvests in music education through a number of different initiatives. It provides scholarships and supports national organisations and community projects both in the UK and internationally. It also contributes to the body of research that provides insight into music teaching and learning.

Scholarships

The charity also provides funding to particular institutions for student scholarships. These currently include:

- The four associated Royal Schools of Music
- Royal Welsh College of Music and Drama
- London Music Fund – providing scholarships to 12 young musicians in London
- Hong Kong Academy for Performing Arts

International Sponsorship Fund

The International Sponsorship Fund is open to organisations outside the UK and Ireland 'that provide musical training, performance opportunities and teacher development, particularly where there are barriers to accessing these opportunities'.

Financial information

Year end	31/01/2021
Income	£23,400,000
Assets	£13,200,000
Grants to organisations	£1,870,000

Beneficiaries included: National Youth Jazz Orchestra (£30,000); National Youth Orchestra (£26,000); The Mayor of London Fund for Young Musicians (£20,000); Dhow Countries (£6,000).

Applications

Details of scholarships and an enquiry form are available on the charity's website. (See 'About us' – 'Our reinvestment in music education' – 'Scholarships'.)

Sources of information

Accounts; annual report; Charity Commission record; funder's website.

Royal Society of Wildlife Trusts

Conservation, heritage and the environment

UK

£13.36 million (2020/21)

CC number: 207238

Correspondent: The Trustees, The Kiln, Waterside, Mather Road, Newark, Nottinghamshire NG24 1WT (tel: 01636 677711; email: info@wildlifetrusts.org)

 www.wildlifetrusts.org

 facebook.com/wildlifetrusts

 @WildlifeTrusts

 @thewildlifetrusts

General information

Royal Society of Wildlife Trusts (RSWT) was registered with the Charity Commission in 1962. It comprises 46 local Wildlife Trusts that are individual registered charities but are corporate members of the RSWT.

According to its Charity Commission record, RSWT aims to 'promote the conservation and study of nature, the promotion of research into such conservation and to educate the public in understanding and appreciating nature, in the awareness of its value and in the need for conservation'. RSWT primarily does this by supporting the work of the Wildlife Trusts, but grants are also made to other organisations.

Grants are made through several different grant programmes:

- **Biffa Award:** this grants programme comprises the Main Grants programme, which helps provide or improve local amenities and the environment in local communities within a close proximity to Biffa landfill sites, and the Partnership Grants programme, which aims to create or improve built and natural environments that are considered to be of regional or national significance
- **Our Bright Future**: this project, funded by £33 million from the National Lottery Community Fund, is led by young people and funds projects including environmental action, environmental campaigning, vocational training, sustainable enterprises, youth leadership and influencing opportunities
- **TWT Grants:** this funding stream distributes grants from the central charity to the regional Wildlife Trusts

For up-to-date information on funding opportunities see the charity's website.

Financial information

Year end	31/03/2021
Income	£18,060,000
Assets	£9,990,000
Grants to organisations	£13,360,000

Further financial information

In 2020/21, grants awarded to Wildlife Trusts totalled £8.31 million, and grants to other organisations totalled £5.05 million. The grant total includes Biffa Awards totalling £3.6 million.

Beneficiaries included: Scottish Wildlife Trust (£544,000); Northumberland Wildlife Trust (£229,000); Falkland Stewardship Trust (£136,000); Belfast Hills Partnership Trust (£92,000); Field Studies Council (£46,000); Belbroughton Recreation Centre (£33,000); Colliers End Village Hall (£15,000).

Exclusions

The charity does not make grants to individuals.

Applications

Contact the correspondent for more information regarding the application process. For the Biffa Award scheme, visit www.biffa-award.org for full details of how to apply.

Sources of information

Accounts; annual report; Charity Commission record; funder's website.

RSM UK Foundation

The environment; citizenship and community development; the advancement of education and relief of poverty in the context of access to employment

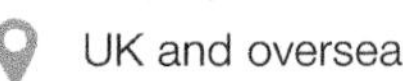

UK and overseas

£536,300 (2020/21)

CC number: 1179349

Correspondent: The Trustees, 6th Floor, 25 Farringdon Street, London EC4A 4AB (tel: 020 3201 8313; email: info@rsmukfoundation.com)

 www.rsmukfoundation.com

General information

The foundation was registered with the Charity Commission in July 2018 and is the corporate charity of RSM UK, a global provider of audit, tax and consulting services. The foundation supports four core charities (The Duke of Edinburgh's Award, Anthony Nolan Trust, Trees for Cities and Leadership Through Sport and Business) but also makes grants to other organisations in accordance to the trustees' current funding priorities, which are:

- Environmental protection or improvement
- Advancement of citizenship or community development
- Advancement of education and relief of poverty in the context of access to employment

Financial information

Year end	31/03/2021
Income	£774,800
Assets	£407,700
Grants to organisations	£536,300

Further financial information

Grants were awarded to 56 organisations during the year.

Beneficiaries included: Anthony Nolan (222,000); The Duke of Edinburgh's Award (£200,000); Air Ambulance (£40,000); Leadership Through Sport and Business (£20,000); Trees for Cities (£15,000).

Exclusions

Grants are not normally made to individuals or for projects in countries in which another RSM group corporate foundation is based.

Applications

Apply by email to the correspondent. Applications must be received by the trustees between January and March for a decision in April, or between July and September for a decision in October.

Sources of information

Accounts; annual report; Charity Commission record.

The Rubin Foundation Charitable Trust

General charitable purposes

UK

£790,600 (2020/21)

CC number: 327062

Correspondent: The Trustees, The Pentland Centre, Lakeside House, Squires Lane, Finchley, London N3 2QL (tel: 020 8346 2600; email: amcmillan@pentland.com)

General information

This charity was registered with the Charity Commission in 1986 and is closely connected with Pentland Group plc, a global brand management company.

Grants are made to organisations to support general charitable purposes in the UK. Some preference is given to Jewish organisations and causes relating to health and culture.

Financial information

Year end	05/04/2021
Income	£1,080,000
Assets	£7,460,000
Grants to organisations	£790,600

Beneficiaries included: Lancaster University (£125,000); UJIA and The Prince's Trust (£100,000 each); UCL Development Fund (£52,000); Chai Lifeline Cancer Care (£50,000).

Applications

Contact the correspondent for more information. The charity's previous annual reports suggest that it awards grants to charities known to members of the Rubin family and those associated with Pentland Group Ltd. Therefore, unsolicited applications are unlikely to succeed.

Sources of information

Accounts; annual report; Charity Commission record.

The Ruddock Foundation for the Arts

Art conservation; medieval art; theatre and playwriting

 UK

£632,900 (2020/21)

CC number: 1134994

Correspondent: Sir Paul Ruddock, Trustee, 10 Colville Mews, London W11 2DA (tel: 020 7313 9350; email: nikita@ruddockfamily.com)

Trustees: Sir Paul Ruddock; Lady Jill Ruddock; Michael Fullerlove; Sophie Ruddock; Isabella Ruddock.

General information

The foundation was established in 2010 by businessman and philanthropist Sir Paul Ruddock. He is a former chair of the Victoria and Albert Museum and chair of the University of Oxford Endowment.

According to its 2020/21 annual report, the objects of the foundation are:

- To advance, promote and educate for the benefit of the public generally all branches of the arts with particular, but not exclusive reference to the performing, literary and decorative arts.
- To advance the preservation, protection and improvement of pictures, historic records, books, manuscripts, monuments, armour, porcelain, silver and gold objects d' art and other chattels or items of artistic, historic, or national interest.
- To establish and maintain a museum and/or art gallery for the display and promotion of the arts with particular, but not exclusive, reference to the decorative and medieval arts for the benefit of the public.
- Notwithstanding the above, to support or carry out such other objects or purposes as are exclusively charitable in accordance with the laws of England and Wales.

Currently, the foundation has three focus areas:

- Institutions which look after and conserve paintings and works of art
- Research projects with a focus on medieval art
- Theatre and playwriting

Grants can be made towards exhibition costs, acquiring particular pieces of art, or research and curatorial support costs. The foundation also supports independent theatre groups.

Financial information

Year end	05/04/2021
Income	£1,580,000
Assets	£26,640,000
Grants to organisations	£632,900

Beneficiaries included: Metropolitan Museum – New York (£260,000); British Museum (£85,000); Courtauld Institute (£50,000); Afrikids and the Victoria and Albert Museum (£25,000 each).

Applications

Apply in writing to the correspondent. The trustees meet twice a year to discuss applications.

Sources of information

Accounts; annual report; Charity Commission record.

The Rugby Group Benevolent Fund Ltd

Community projects

Barrington (Cambridgeshire); Chinnor (Oxfordshire); Kensworth (Bedfordshire); Lewes (Sussex); Rochester (Kent); Rugby and Southam (Warwickshire); South Ferriby (North Lincolnshire); Tilbury (Essex)

£263,800 (2020)

CC number: 265669

Correspondent: The Trustees, Cemex UK, Cemex House, Evreux Way, Rugby, Warwickshire CV21 2DT (tel: 01788 517000; email: info@rugbygroupbenevolentfund.org.uk)

Trustees: Nigel Appleyard; Graeme Fuller; Norman Jones; Ian Southcott; Geoff Thomas; John Brooks; David Holton; Kevin Murch.

www.rugbygroupbenevolentfund.org.uk

General information

This fund was originally established in 1955 to support employees and former employees of Rugby Cement Group Ltd, and their dependants. Today, the Rugby Group is part of CEMEX UK; however, the fund remains independent. The fund has retained its original objectives but has widened its scope to support other charitable causes within the same area of benefit.

Eligibility

The fund provides support for projects in communities where former Rugby Cement plants were once located. These include:

- Barrington, Cambridgeshire
- Chinnor, Oxfordshire
- Kensworth, Bedfordshire
- Lewes, Sussex
- Rochester, Kent
- Rugby, Warwickshire
- Southam, Warwickshire
- South Ferriby, North Lincolnshire
- Tilbury, Essex

Prospective projects must be able to demonstrate benefits to the community as a whole, including past employees of the Rugby Group and their families.

Eligible organisations do not have to be registered charities but must have charitable objectives.

Grants are made towards project-related capital costs.

Financial information

Year end	31/12/2020
Grants to organisations	£263,800
No. of grants	44

Further financial information

During the year, grants paid to organisations totalled £263,800. In previous years the fund has typically given grants totalling £300,000 and above; therefore, we have included the fund in this edition of the guide.

Only beneficiaries of grants of £1,000 and above were listed in the accounts. Grants of under £1,000 (six grants) totalled £2,900.

Beneficiaries included: The Bradby Club (£34,500); Benn Partnership Centre (£25,000); British Red Cross and Rugby Credit Union (£10,000 each); Home-Start Medway and Kent Air Ambulance (£5,000 each); Muscular Dystrophy Support Centre (£3,000); The Rotary Club of Rugby Benevolent Fund (£1,000).

Exclusions

The fund does not normally provide funding to meet day-to-day revenue costs.

Applications

Potential applicants must first complete an expression of interest form, available to download from the fund's website. Applicants must be able to demonstrate that the project has been properly costed and that any other support funding is in place or in prospect. Evidence of self-help is important. The trustees meet several times a year to consider applications, meaning that applications are considered on a rolling basis.

Sources of information

Accounts; annual report; Charity Commission record; funder's website.

S. F. Foundation

Jewish religion, education and welfare

UK and overseas

£1.88 million (2020/21)

CC number: 1105843

Correspondent: Rifka Niederman, Company Secretary and Trustee, 143 Upper Clapton Road, London E5 9DB (tel: 020 8802 5492; email: sffoundation143@gmail.com)

Trustees: Hannah Lipschitz; Rifka Niederman; Miriam Schreiber.

General information

Set up in 2004, this foundation gives grants towards the advancement of the Jewish religion and Jewish religious education, as well as the alleviation of poverty among the Jewish community throughout the world.

The foundation's annual report for 2020/21 states:

> The charity was set up to support the activities of religious Jewish organisations especially in the field of education. The trustees identify institutions and organisations which meet its criteria and regularly support a number of these institutions and organisations, both in England and abroad.
>
> The charity is also supportive of organisations which are solely committed to the relief of poverty. Such organisations assist needy Jewish families financially and through the distribution of basic necessities.

Financial information

Year end	31/01/2021
Income	£4,560,000
Assets	£45,090,000
Grants to organisations	£1,880,000

Further financial information

Grants awarded in 2020/21 were broken down as follows:

Jewish religion and education	£1.51 million
The relief of poverty	£190,500
Grants to other grant-making charities	£140,800
General charitable purposes	£31,300

Only beneficiaries of grants of £90,000 and above were listed in the foundation's accounts. Grants of under £90,000 totalled £1.06 million.

Beneficiaries included: Rentrust Foundation Ltd (£366,200); Toldos Aharon Trust Ltd (£215,300); Taharat Aharon (£137,700); Zichron Ahron Trust Ltd (£100,000).

Applications

Apply in writing to the correspondent. The foundation's annual report for 2020/21 states: 'The Trustees are approached for donations by a wide variety of charitable institutions operating in the United Kingdom and abroad. The Trustees consider all requests which they receive and make donations based on the level of funds available.'

Sources of information

Accounts; annual report; Charity Commission record.

The Saddlers' Company Charitable Fund

General charitable purposes; education; equestrian charities; disadvantaged young people; social welfare; disability; churches; armed forces; saddlery and leathercraft

UK, with a preference for the City of London

£314,800 (2020/21)

CC number: 261962

Correspondent: Charities Administrator, Saddlers' Company, Saddlers' Hall, 40 Gutter Lane, London EC2V 6BR (tel: 020 7726 8661; email: clerk@saddlersco.co.uk)

Trustee: Saddlers' Company.

www.saddlersco.co.uk

facebook.com/SaddlersHall

@saddlerscompany

General information

The Saddlers' Company has a long tradition of charitable activity. Since the earliest days of the company, quarterly membership subscriptions have been used to support members' widows and children. The company also still continues the ancient tradition of Bounty Day each December, when the Court of Assistants can nominate a charity to receive a Christmas grant from the company's charitable fund.

The Saddlers' Company Charitable Fund was formed in 1970. Over time, the objects of the charity have been refined to provide support for education, young people, the British saddlery trade, the equestrian world, the City of London and general charitable activities.

The R. M. Sturdy Charitable Trust and the Mollie Priestly Fund are both part of the Saddlers' Company Charitable Fund. The Kaye's and Labourne's Charity is a linked charity that has been incorporated into the Saddlers' Company Charitable Fund's accounts since 2018/19.

R. M. Sturdy Charitable Trust

A past Master of the Worshipful Company of Saddlers and former trustee of the fund, Mr R. M. Sturdy, died in 2006. By a letter of wishes, he expressed the desire that the R. M. Sturdy Charitable Trust, of which he was the benefactor, be administered by the Worshipful Company of Saddlers after his death.

According to the 2020/21 annual accounts, this trust supports 'projects related to education and music associated with the Church of England and those pertaining to the restoration, repair and renovation of Church of England places of worship (particularly smaller churches) and the making of general charitable grants with particular preference being given to those charities associated with the Church of England'.

The Mollie Priestly Fund

This fund is directed towards helping members of the armed services as well as members of the cadet forces.

Kaye's and Labourne's Charity

According to the charity's website: 'The objectives of the Kaye's and Labourne's Charity are to relieve persons who are in need, hardship or distress, either generally or individually. In priority these would be Freemen of the Saddlers' Company, their widows and other dependants; those who are or have been employed in the trade of saddler or harness maker, their widows and other dependants who are in need, hardship or distress; and such other persons as the Trustee decides.'

Kitchin's Charity

This charity was set up by Robert Kitchin, who left a property to the company. Funding is focused on the training and education of young people under 25, and the priorities for discretionary funding are three organisations in London.

Diamond Jubilee Fund

This fund was established to mark the diamond jubilee of Queen Elizabeth II in 2012. It supports the British Equestrian Paralympic teams taking part in the Paralympic Games.

As of 2017 the trustees have decided to work in partnership with organisations that closely align to the charity's charitable purposes including the Society of Master Saddlers, the British

Equestrian Trade Association, Capel Manor College and the Saddlery Training Centre. Equestrian partnerships will focus on the British Equestrian Federation, the British Horse Society and World Horse Welfare. The charity will also make grants to organisations that work with disadvantaged young people and those with disabilities, with a preference for supporting organisations that members of the livery company have fundraised or volunteered for. Some support will be given to armed forces charities and charities in the City of London as per the charity's historic links.

Financial information

Year end	31/03/2021
Income	£389,700
Assets	£14,100,000
Grants to organisations	£314,800

Beneficiaries included: A list of beneficiaries was not available.

Applications

Potential applicants should register their interest by way of an introductory email to the Charities Administrator at tc@saddlersco.co.uk, who will advise whether the bid will be taken forward.

Sources of information

Accounts; annual report; Charity Commission record; funder's website.

The Jean Sainsbury Animal Welfare Trust

Animal welfare

UK and overseas

£395,000 (2020)

CC number: 326358

Correspondent: Barbara Georgiou, Administrator, PO Box 469, London W14 8PJ (tel: 020 7602 7948; email: jsawt7@gmail.com)

Trustees: Mrs Allen; Mr Spurdens; Valerie Pike; Mr Keliher; Jacqui Sharp; Jill Inglis; Madeleine Orchard.

http://jeansainsburyanimalwelfare.org.uk

General information

The trust was established in 1982 by Jean Beryl Lilian Sainsbury, with the objective of benefitting and protecting animals from suffering. The trust's objectives are to support smaller UK-registered charities that embrace one or more of the following:

- Benefitting or protecting animals
- Relieving animals from suffering
- Conserving wildlife
- Encouraging the understanding of animals

The trust's website states that it gives some preference to applications from smaller UK-registered animal welfare charities working in the UK or overseas:

- Which have independently examined up to date annual accounts
- Which demonstrate an active re-homing and rehabilitation policy for animals taken into their care
- Involved with conservation of wildlife, when the rescue, rehabilitation and (where possible) the release of animals is their main aim.

The trust expects all applicants to be charities registered with the Charity Commission unless their annual income is under £5,000.

The website also notes that the trust aims to make donations towards the following:

- General running costs associated with the rescue, rehabilitation and re-homing or release of domestic, wild and exotic animals.
- Costs associated with the direct protection of endangered species.
- Feeding, capture, neutering and release of feral cats.
- Assistance with vets' fees and neutering costs of animals owned by those on low incomes.
- Donations towards capital purchases involving land, buildings, vehicles, equipment and educational material. The Trustees may pledge funds towards large capital building projects, which will only be released when all other funding is in place and the work is ready to commence. The maximum pledge we will give is £35k.

According to its website, the trust will only consider funding the purchase or improvement of property or fixed buildings if:

- the property is clearly in the ownership of the charity, or
- at least 10 years is left to run on the charity's lease, or
- a letter from the landowner states that the charity will be reimbursed for the improvements on sale of the property or at the end of the lease. Otherwise, support for improvements can only be considered when they do not increase the saleable value of the property.

The trust also administers a subsidiary fund, The Joyce Evelyn Shuman Bequest, which supports animal charities involved with animal rescue work overseas (including rehoming and the neutering of feral cats and dogs), working equines, and endangered species where the rehabilitation and release of the animals is the main aim.

Financial information

Year end	31/12/2020
Income	£416,000
Assets	£29,710,000
Grants to organisations	£395,000

Beneficiaries included: Dog's Friends (£10,000); Hugs Foundation (£8,000); Bristol and Wales Cat Rescue and Care4Cats (£5,000 each); Pet Care Network (£2,000).

Exclusions

The trust will not normally support the following:

- Applications from individuals
- Charities registered outside the UK
- Charities offering sanctuary to animals, with no effort to re-home, foster or rehabilitate, unless the animals belong to an endangered species
- Charities that do not have a realistic destruction policy for animals that cannot be given a reasonable quality of life
- Charities with available reserves equal to more than one year's expenditure, unless it can be demonstrated that reserves are being held for a designated project
- Charities that spend more than a reasonable proportion of their annual income on administration or that cannot justify their costs per animal helped
- Veterinary schools, unless the money can be seen to be directly benefitting the type of animals the trust would want to support (e.g. welfare-related or low-cost first opinion vet treatment projects)
- Overseas charities for funds for capital expenditure

Applications

Application forms can be downloaded from the trust's website. Completed applications should be emailed along with the most recent audited or independently examined accounts and an information newsletter or similar. Trustees meet three times a year in the spring, summer and winter. Further application information, policy guidelines and application deadlines are available on the trust's website.

Sources of information

Accounts; annual report; Charity Commission record; funder's website.

The Alan and Babette Sainsbury Charitable Fund

General charitable purposes; civil liberties; community development; Jewish and Israeli causes; overseas causes; scientific and medical research; youth work

UK, with some preference for Southwark, and Africa

£336,000 (2020/21)

CC number: 292930

Correspondent: Robert Bell, Director, The Peak, 5 Wilton Road, London SW1V 1AP (tel: 020 7410 0330; email: proposals@sfct.org.uk)

Trustees: Jessica Sainsbury; John Sainsbury; Lindsey Anderson.

 www.sfct.org.uk

General information

The Alan and Babette Sainsbury Charitable Fund is one of the Sainsbury Family Charitable Trusts, which share a joint administration and approach to grant-making but work autonomously as independent legal entities.

The settlor of the fund, Alan Sainsbury, was the grandson of the founders of J Sainsbury plc and former chair of the company. He established the trust in 1953, became Baron Sainsbury in 1962 and died in 1998.

According to the Sainsbury Family Charitable Trusts' website, The Alan and Babette Sainsbury Charitable Fund considers applications for funding in the following specific areas:

- Arts and education projects. This category funds exclusively in the London Borough of Southwark and encourages organisations working there to apply
- Support for UK charities which defend civil liberties and human rights
- Projects in the developing world, primarily Sub-Saharan Africa, which maximise educational and employment opportunities for young people
- Scientific and medical research on Type 1 Diabetes

However, the trust's website and 2020/21 annual report and accounts caution that unsolicited applications for funds are unlikely to be successful, in part due to applications greatly exceeding available funds.

Financial information

Year end	05/04/2021
Income	£464,100
Assets	£17,350,000
Grants to organisations	£336,000

Beneficiaries included: Youth Futures (£32,500); Ashden Sustainable Solutions (£27,500); United St Saviour's (£20,000); The Sainsbury Archive (£10,000); Refugees for Justice (£5,000); Ashden Sustainable Solutions (£3,000).

Exclusions

None of the Sainsbury Family Charitable Trusts directly supports individuals, education fees or expeditions.

Applications

Applications should be submitted using the Sainsbury Family Charitable Trusts' online form, or in writing (maximum two sides of A4) to the correspondent using the online application form as a template. Funding enquiries via email are not considered.

The website stresses that most applications are unsuccessful and that all applicants receive a standard acknowledgement letter.

Sources of information

Accounts; annual report; Charity Commission record; funder's website.

The Saintbury Trust

Social welfare; education; health; citizenship and community development; arts, culture and science; sport; the environment; children and young people; homelessness; older people; palliative care

West Midlands; Warwickshire; Worcestershire; North Gloucestershire; see the website for eligible postcodes

£260,000 (2020)

CC number: 326790

Correspondent: The Trustees, PO Box 464, Dorking, Surrey RH4 9AF (email: saintburytrust@btinternet.com)

Trustees: Mrs A. E. Atkinson-Willes; Harry Forrester; Mrs V. K. Houghton; Mrs A. R. Thomas; Mrs C. E. Brogan; Anita Bhalla; Mrs J. P. Lewis; Benjamin Atkinson-Willes; Dr Sarah Wareing; Jake Houghton.

 www.thesaintburytrust.co.uk

General information

The Saintbury Trust was established by Chris and Jean Bryant in 1985. It supports charities located in the West Midlands, Warwickshire, Worcestershire and North Gloucestershire but has a particular interest in the following:

- The arts
- Heritage
- The environment
- Helping people with disabilities

Grants are made for a wide range of other purposes including social welfare, education, health, citizenship and community development, sport, children and young people, homelessness, older people and palliative care.

Most grants are of between £1,000 and £5,000.

Financial information

Year end	31/12/2020
Income	£654,500
Assets	£13,350,000
Grants to organisations	£260,000

Further financial information

In previous years grants have totalled between £400,000 and £500,000.

Beneficiaries included: Midlands Arts Centre (£30,000); St Richard's Hospice Foundation (£10,000); St Anne's Hostel (£4,000); Ackers Adventure (£2,000); Moseley Road Baths CIO and Where Next Association (£1,000 each).

Exclusions

Grants cannot be made to/for the following:

- Individuals
- Animal charities
- Charities whose purpose is the advancement of religion
- Organisations other than registered charities
- National charities
- Local branches of national charities
- Scouts, Guides and Sea Cadets
- Village halls
- Repair, maintenance and improvement of local churches

Applications

Applications can be made through the trust's website.

Sources of information

Accounts; annual report; Charity Commission record; funder's website.

Samjo Ltd

Jewish causes, including religion, health and disability, education and social welfare

Greater Manchester

£552,500 (2020/21)

CC number: 1094397

Correspondent: The Trustees, c/o Lopian Gross Barnett and Co., 1st Floor, Cloister House, New Bailey Street, Manchester M3 5FS (tel: 0161 832 8721; email: D.Stewart@prestburymanagement.co.uk)

Trustees: Rabbi Yisroel Friedman; Joshua Halpern; Samuel Halpern.

General information

Samjo Ltd was established in 2002 to make grants to charitable causes in the Jewish community. According to the charity's 2020/21 annual report, this includes 'the advancement of religion, the advancement and support of education and the relief of the elderly, vulnerable (such as young children or anyone with special needs) or those suffering poverty or hardship and other charitable purposes for the public benefit'.

The charity focusses its support on Orthodox Jewish charities. It appears to fund the same core group of beneficiaries each year, although grants are also made to other organisations.

The 2020/21 annual report states:

> The trustees have identified a number of Orthodox Jewish charities which profess and teach the principles of traditional Judaism or which carry out activities which advance religion in accordance with the Orthodox Jewish faith. Grants are given on application to the trustees by these or similar charities.

According to the charity's record on the Charity Commission's website, individuals with a disability or who are experiencing poverty may also be supported. Medical institutions and health charities are eligible for support.

Financial information

Year end	31/03/2021
Income	£2,570,000
Assets	£18,150,000
Grants to organisations	£552,500
No. of grants	12

Beneficiaries included: Teshivoh Tefilloh Tzedokoh (£106,100); Oizer Charitable Trust and Shemtov Charitable Trust (£100,000 each); Friends of Boyan Trust (£71,800); Kolyom Trust Ltd (£55,000); Gateshead Kehilla Building Foundation (£15,000); Jewish Teachers' Training College (£600).

Applications

Apply in writing to the correspondent.

Sources of information

Accounts; annual report; Charity Commission record.

The Basil Samuel Charitable Trust

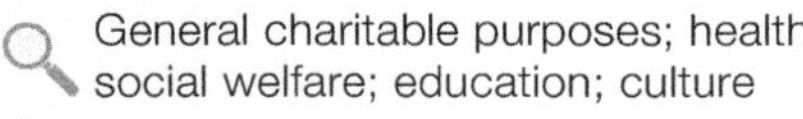

General charitable purposes; health; social welfare; education; culture

UK

£540,000 (2020/21)

CC number: 206579

Correspondent: The Trustees, c/o Smith and Williamson, 25 Moorgate, London EC2R 6AY (tel: 020 7131 4376)

Trustees: Richard Peskin; William Furber.

General information

This trust was established in 1959 for such charitable purposes as the trustees decide, either in the UK or elsewhere. The trustees describe its activities as making grants to medical, socially supportive, educational and cultural charities plus a number of other charities.

Financial information

Year end	05/04/2021
Income	£22,800
Grants to organisations	£540,000

Further financial information

Full accounts were not available to view on the Charity Commission website due to the trust's low income. We have therefore estimated the trust's grant total based on its total expenditure.

Beneficiaries included: A list of beneficiaries was not available.

Applications

Apply in writing to the correspondent.

Sources of information

Accounts; annual report; Charity Commission record.

The M. J. Samuel Charitable Trust

General charitable purposes with a preference for health, environmental causes, the arts and overseas aid

UK and overseas

£149,400 (2020/21)

CC number: 327013

Correspondent: The Trustees, Mells Park, Mells, Frome, Somerset BA11 3QB (tel: 020 7402 0602; email: claire@mellspark.com)

Trustees: The Hon. Michael Samuel; The Hon. Julia Samuel; Lord Bearsted.

General information

The trust was registered with the Charity Commission in 1986. According to its Charity Commission record, it supports a wide range of charitable causes in the UK and overseas.

Financial information

Year end	05/06/2021
Income	£65,600
Assets	£917,300
Grants to organisations	£149,400
No. of grants	8

Further financial information

The trust awarded grants totalling £149,400 during the year; however, in previous years its expenditure has exceeded £300,000.

Beneficiaries included: Full Fact (£17,500); Somerset Community Foundation (£6,000); Game and Wildlife Conservation Trust (£5,100); Tutor a Nation (£3,000); The Legatum Institute (£2,000); The Good Exchange (£1,000).

Applications

Apply in writing to the correspondent.

Sources of information

Accounts; annual report; Charity Commission record.

The Samworth Foundation

Sexual exploitation and the environment

Worldwide. In the UK, there is a preference for the East Midlands

£3.57 million (2020/21)

CC number: 265647

Correspondent: The Trustees, Chetwode House, 1 Samworth Way, Melton Mowbray, Leicestershire LE13 1GA (tel: 01664 414500; email: admin@samworthfoundation.org.uk)

Trustees: Prof. Neil Gorman; Mark Samworth; Susan Ralphs; Dr Daniela Lloyd-Williams.

https://samworthfoundation.org.uk

General information

The Samworth Foundation, formerly known as the Samworth Cadell Trust, was established in 1973. The foundation has grown over the years with annual donations from Samworth Brothers Ltd and the Samworth family.

Grants are made in the UK and abroad to organisations that address issues related to the environment/climate change and sexual exploitation. The foundation supports organisations tackling the root causes of these issues. In the UK, preference is given to work based in the East Midlands.

The foundation offers multi-year grants for core costs and projects. Its website states: 'We look to invest in organisations and their people rather than just the specific projects they deliver.'

Occasionally, the foundation operates specific special interest grant programmes. More information on the foundation's grant-making strategy can be found on its website.

Financial information

Year end	05/04/2021
Income	£2,260,000
Assets	£70,910,000
Grants to organisations	£3,570,000
No. of grants	76

Further financial information

Grants were made in three categories: core grants (£1.9 million); COVID-19 emergency response grants (£1.29 million); and transformation and innovation grants (also set up in response to COVID-19) (£373,700).

Beneficiaries included: Leicester Cathedral Charitable Trust (£500,000); The Green Alliance Trust (two grants totalling £328,000); The Stephen Lewis Foundation (two grants totalling £150,000); International Justice Mission UK (£50,000); Tearfund (£20,000); New Futures Project (£7,800); The BACA Charity (£1,700).

Applications

The foundation does not accept unsolicited applications. Causes are researched and identified by the trustees and organisations that meet the foundation's criteria are invited to apply.

Sources of information

Accounts; annual report; Charity Commission record; funder's website.

The Sanderson Foundation

General charitable purposes, including education

England and Wales

£351,000 (2020/21)

CC number: 1155744

Correspondent: Jonathan Azis, Trustee, Westwood Manor, Lower Westwood, Bradford-on-Avon, Wiltshire BA15 2AF (tel: 01225 863374; email: jonathanazis@parkepartnership.com)

Trustees: Jonathan Azis; Timothy Sanderson; Damaris Sanderson.

General information

This foundation was established in February 2014 and shares the name of Timothy and Damaris Sanderson, who are also trustees. The foundation makes grants for general charitable purposes and to promote education.

Financial information

Year end	31/03/2021
Income	£703,300
Assets	£420,600
Grants to organisations	£351,000
No. of grants	31

Further financial information

During 2020/21, the trustees considered 50 applications and awarded 31 grants totalling £351,000.

Beneficiaries included: University of Oxford (£80,000); Erasmus Forum (£40,000); Chalke Valley History Festival (£25,000); Somerset Wildlife Trust (£10,000); National Opera Studio (£5,000); Westminster City Council (£3,000); Leading The Way (£1,000).

Applications

Apply in writing to the correspondent.

Sources of information

Accounts; annual report; Charity Commission record.

The Sandhu Charitable Foundation

General charitable purposes, with a preference for education, health and children and young people

Worldwide

£322,500 (2020/21)

CC number: 1114236

Correspondent: N. Steele, Administrator and Secretary to the Trustees, c/o The Santon Group, 1st Floor, Santon House, 53–55 Uxbridge Road, Ealing, London W5 5SA (tel: 020 3478 3900; email: nsteele@thesantongroup.com)

Trustees: Bimaljit Sandhu; Pardeep Sandhu.

 www.thesantongroup.com/charity/the-sandhu-charitable-foundation

General information

The Sandhu Charitable Foundation was established in 2006. Bim Sandhu, a trustee of the foundation, is the CEO and owner of The Santon Group. The foundation was established as the long-term focus for the philanthropic activities of Bim and Pardeep Sandhu and their family.

The foundation makes grants to registered charities with general charitable purposes, although there is a preference for education, children and young people, and health. The trustees are willing to provide unrestricted funding. The trustees also support UK charities that work overseas.

Financial information

Year end	31/03/2021
Income	£292,100
Assets	£4,230,000
Grants to organisations	£322,500
No. of grants	34

Further financial information

In 2020/21, grants paid to 34 organisations totalled £322,500. An additional £125,000 in grants was committed during the year.

Beneficiaries included: Anne Frank Trust UK (£31,000); The Latymer Foundation (£22,000); Carers UK (£12,500); Lullaby Trust and Warwick University (£10,000 each); Lochaber Foodbank (£6,000); Community Radio Ltd (£3,000); Stroke Association (£2,500); Mayor's Music Fund (£1,000).

Applications

The foundation supports individual charities or charitable causes, often on a single-donation basis, which the trustees identify.

Sources of information

Accounts; annual report; Charity Commission record; funder's website.

Sandra Charitable Trust

Animal welfare and research; environmental protection; social welfare; health; development of young people

UK, with a slight preference for the South East

£649,500 (2019/20)

CC number: 327492

Correspondent: Lynne Webster, c/o Moore Family Office Ltd, 42 Berkeley Square, London W1J 5AW (tel: 020 7318 0845; email: Lynne.Webster@moorefamilyofficegroup.com)

Trustees: Michael MacFadyen; Richard Moore; Francis Moore; Lucy Forsyth.

General information

The trust was established in 1987 to support a wide variety of beneficiaries including charities involved in animal welfare and research, environmental protection, relief of poverty and youth development. Assistance is also given to nurses and those studying to become nurses.

Financial information

Year end	30/06/2020
Income	£822,200
Assets	£23,790,000
Grants to organisations	£649,500

Beneficiaries included: Barnardo's (£55,000); British Heart Foundation (£20,000); Leander Club (£15,000); Leonard Cheshire (£5,000); MS Society (£1,000).

Applications

The trust's 2019/20 annual report states:

> Unsolicited applications are not requested as the trustees prefer to support charities whose work they have researched and which is in accordance with the wishes of the settlor. The trustees receive a very high number of grant applications which are mostly unsuccessful.

Sources of information

Accounts; annual report; Charity Commission record.

Santander UK Foundation Ltd

Financial and digital empowerment

UK, including Guernsey, Jersey and the Isle of Man

£3.31 million (2020)

CC number: 803655

Correspondent: The Trustees, Santander UK plc, Santander House, 201 Grafton Gate East, Milton Keynes, Buckinghamshire MK9 1AN (email: grants@santander.co.uk)

Trustees: Sue Willis; Christopher Fallis; John Collins; Danny Jones; Judith Moran; Christopher Anderson.

 www.santanderfoundation.org.uk

General information

The Santander Foundation was established by Santander bank and supports disadvantaged people throughout the UK.

The foundation's Financial and Digital Empowerment Fund aims to help disadvantaged people become more digitally and financially empowered. The foundation's website states:

There are millions of people in our society that are already at a disadvantage – through age, education, income, disability, or unemployment. Without the right support for them, the social inequality gap will only widen.

Many charitable and community interest organisations work with such groups; with people that feel the impacts of financial or digital exclusion the most.

We want to reach lone parents, single pensioners, migrants and refugees, those with long term illnesses and disabilities, those struggling to find sustained employment and households headed by students or part-time workers. These are among the groups most commonly excluded from financial services.

People with low or unstable incomes, or those who have experienced a significant life shock, are particularly affected by financial exclusion. The pandemic will only have made this situation worse, as more and more basic services have moved to the web. We want to help charities build their capacity to help people to become digitally and financially empowered.

Financial information

Year end	31/12/2020
Income	£4,390,000
Assets	£19,540,000
Grants to organisations	£3,310,000
No. of grants	581

Further financial information

Grants were broken down as follows:

COVID-19 grants	4	£3 million
Health	241	£165,000
Social inclusion	331	£144,500
Other	5	£2,500

Only grants of over £10,000 were listed in the accounts. The Alzheimer's Society and Age UK were both charity partners of Santander UK plc.

Beneficiaries included: Alzheimer's Society (£1.65 million); Age UK (£1.5 million).

Applications

Visit the foundation's website for up-to-date information regarding open grant programmes.

The foundation's website states:

We have some important requirements that you must be able to meet to apply for a Santander Foundation Grant.

If your organisation chooses to apply you must:

- be based in the UK and working within one of the nations or regions.
- be a UK registered charity or Community Interest Company.
- have at least three unconnected Trustees, Directors or Management Committee members. By unconnected we mean not related by blood, marriage, in a long-term relationship or living together at the same address.
- have an annual income above È75,000. We anticipate most of the organisations we'll support will be small and medium-sized organisations.
- have a bank account in the organisation's name with at least two unconnected signatories.
- have been operating for at least 18 months and have at least one set of annual accounts.

Sources of information

Accounts; annual report; Charity Commission record; funder's website.

Savannah Wisdom

Social inequality; corruption; healthcare; gender rights; community work

 UK and India

 £453,000 (2020/21)

CC number: 1141619

Correspondent: The Trustees, Suite 2, Ground Floor, Torr Vale Mills, Tore Vale Road, New Mills, High Peak, Derbyshire SK22 3HS (tel: 0151 728 5997; email: admin@savannahwisdom.org)

Trustees: Simon Arora; Shalni Arora; Bobby Arora.

 https://savannahwisdom.org

General information

Savannah Wisdom was established in 2011. According to the charity's website, its projects are: 'based around social inequality, tackling issues such as corruption in the delivery of healthcare and gender rights by investing in women and girls at local community level in India and the UK. The foundation does this by partnering with a number of charities and not for profit organisations with innovative and radical ideas that try to disrupt the traditional model for delivering change.'

The charity makes grants to individuals, projects and organisations, and the trustees will consider funding projects that are seen as risky, that take a radical approach or address new, untested concerns.

Financial information

Year end	30/04/2021
Income	£8,700
Grants to organisations	£453,000

Further financial information

Full accounts were not available to view on the Charity Commission's website due to the charity's low income. We have therefore estimated the charity's grant total based on its total expenditure.

Beneficiaries included: A list of beneficiaries was not available. Previous beneficiaries include: Transparency International (£24,000); British Asia Trust; Karuna Trust; Network for Social Change; The Edelgive Foundation.

Applications

The charity does not consider unsolicited applications.

Sources of information

Accounts; annual report; Charity Commission record.

The Savoy Educational Trust

Hospitality-related projects and education

UK

£2.74 million (2020/21)

CC number: 1161014

Correspondent: Margaret Georgiou, Administrator and Secretary to the Trustees, Office 5.23, 60 Cannon Street, London EC4N 6NP (tel: 020 4509 7445; email: info@savoyeducationaltrust.org.uk)

Trustees: Ramon Pajares; Robert Davis; Howard Field; Dr Sally Messenger; David Taylor.

 www.savoyeducationaltrust.org.uk

 facebook.com/pages/Savoy-Educational-Trust/712427868829909

General information

The Savoy Educational Trust was registered with the Charity Commission in 2015. The trust's main aim is to advance and develop education, training and qualifications within the hospitality industry.

The trust awards grants for a wide variety of hospitality-related projects to:

- Educational establishments to enhance training and education facilities for their hospitality departments
- Associations to support those initiatives that will make a real difference to the hospitality industry
- Charitable organisations/social enterprises with specific hospitality-related projects
- Individuals studying hospitality

Financial information

Year end	31/03/2021
Income	£1,310,000
Assets	£63,030,000
Grants to organisations	£2,740,000

Beneficiaries included: The Springboard Charity (£1.1 million); Hospitality Action (£50,000); University of Surrey (£41,200); West College Scotland (£25,400); University of West London (£10,000); University of Essex (£9,000); Prisoners' Education Trust (£3,800).

Applications

An application form is available on the trust's website.

Sources of information

Accounts; annual report; Charity Commission record; funder's website.

Schroder Charity Trust

Education; health; arts, culture and heritage; community work; armed forces; the environment; international development

UK and overseas

£515,900 (2020/21)

CC number: 214050

Correspondent: The Trustees, 81 Rivington Street, London EC2A 3AY (tel: 020 3170 5793; email: info@schrodercharitytrust.org)

 www.schrodercharitytrust.org

General information

The trust was established in 1946 by the Schröder family. Members of the family continue to make up a large portion of the trustee board. Today the trust supports a wide range of charitable causes, including:

- Education and young people
- Communities
- The environment and conservation
- Health
- Arts, culture, and heritage
- Support for the armed forces
- International development

Registered charities can apply for grants of up to £5,000. The trust's website states that in 2020/21 the average grant was £4,000.

Financial information

Year end	31/03/2021
Income	£525,400
Assets	£15,580,000
Grants to organisations	£515,900

Beneficiaries included: National Emergencies Trust (£75,000); Refuge (£10,000); Helen Bamber Foundation, FareShare and Durham Wildlife Trust Ltd (£5,000 each); Bridge (£4,000); Green Team (£3,000); ICUSteps (£2,000); Chelsea Old Church (£1,000).

Exclusions

The trust does not support:

- Individuals
- Animal welfare organisations
- Political organisations
- Major capital appeals

Applications

Applications should be made online using the form on the trust's website. There is a short eligibility quiz that must be completed before applying for a grant. Applications can be made at any time, as decisions are generally made bi-annually, around June and November. Applicants will be notified of the decision within nine months of submitting an application.

Sources of information

Accounts; annual report; Charity Commission record; funder's website.

The Schroder Foundation

Education; the environment; arts, culture and heritage; social welfare; community; medical relief and research; international relief and development

Worldwide; in practice, mainly UK

£1.31 million (2020/21)

CC number: 1107479

Correspondent: The Trustees, 81 Rivington Street, London EC2A 3AY (tel: 020 3170 5793)

General information

Established in 2005, the Schroder Foundation shares a common administration with the Schroder Charity Trust (Charity Commission no. 214050). The foundation supports a wide range of activities in the following areas:

- Education and young people
- Environment and conservation
- Arts, culture and heritage
- Health and medicine
- Social welfare and community

Grants are also made specifically for causes and to organisations in the Islay and Jura islands.

Financial information

Year end	05/04/2021
Income	£485,000
Assets	£11,600,000
Grants to organisations	£1,310,000
No. of grants	58

Beneficiaries included: Cancer Research UK (£100,000); The Royal Horticultural Society (£50,000); University of Exeter (£30,000); British German Association and The Scouts Association (£20,000 each); OCD Action (£15,000); Human Rights Watch (£3,000)

Applications

The foundation's 2020/21 annual report states:

> The Trustees identify projects and organisations they wish to support and the Foundation does not make grants to people or organisations who apply on an unsolicited basis.

Sources of information

Accounts; annual report; Charity Commission record.

Scott (Eredine) Charitable Trust

General charitable purposes; armed forces and emergency services charities; people with disabilities

England and Wales

£371,500 (2020)

CC number: 1002267

Correspondent: The Trustees, c/o Sinclair Gibson, 3 Lincoln's Inn Fields, London WC2A 3AA

General information

The Scott (Eredine) Charitable Trust was established in 1990, with the aim of providing support for general charitable purposes across England and Wales. In particular, the trust makes grants to organisations working for the benefit of the armed forces, the emergency services and people with disabilities.

Financial information

Year end	31/12/2020
Income	£460,000
Assets	£7,000,000
Grants to organisations	£371,500

Beneficiaries included: A list of beneficiaries was not available. Previous beneficiaries include: Alzheimer's Research UK (£40,000); Mental Health Research UK (£20,000); Combined Services Disabled Ski Team (£10,000); ABF The Soldiers' Charity (£6,000); The Gurkha Welfare Trust (£5,000); RNLI (£3,500); Send a Cow (£3,000); IT Schools Africa (£2,800); Woodworks Project (£1,000).

Applications

Apply in writing to the correspondent.

Sources of information

Accounts; annual report; Charity Commission record.

Francis C. Scott Charitable Trust

Disadvantaged young people

Cumbria and North Lancashire (the Lancaster District to the west of the M6 and North of Galgate)

£1.06 million (2020)

CC number: 232131

Correspondent: Helen Carter, Director, Stricklandgate House, 92 Stricklandgate, Kendal, Cumbria LA9 4PU (tel: 01539 742608; email: info@fcsct.org.uk)

 www.fcsct.org.uk

 @fcsct63

General information

The trust was created in 1963 by Peter F Scott CBE, then chair of the Provincial Insurance Company. Peter Scott and his sister Dr Joan Trevelyan, endowed the trust with a significant holding of Provincial Insurance Company shares.

The trust's main aim is to support charitable organisations that enable young people from the most deprived areas of Cumbria/North Lancashire to achieve their full potential in life.

Area of benefit

The trust's website states:

> We consider applications from charitable organisations primarily benefiting young people living in **Cumbria** and the **North of Lancashire**.
>
> For the sake of clarity, we define North Lancashire as that part of Lancaster District to the west of the M6 and North of Galgate (near Jct 33).

Focus of work

The trust's website states:

> We are particularly interested in effective approaches to addressing the needs of children, young people and young adults (up to 24 years old) by:
>
> - raising aspirations and supporting personal development
> - inclusive practice
> - improving wellbeing and mental health
> - improving sector effectiveness
>
> The majority of our grants are multi-year revenue grants for project or core costs. We encourage including full costs in your application (including a percentage contribution to indirect costs) if applying for project costs. Trustees will also fund capital projects that make a tangible difference to a local community.
>
> **Please note** that Trustees prefer to fund small to medium-sized organisations and it is therefore unlikely they will support applications from charities with a turnover in excess of £1m. We would encourage you to seek guidance from the staff if you are unsure.

Financial information

Year end	31/12/2020
Income	£577,400
Assets	£37,570,000
Grants to organisations	£1,060,000

Further financial information

Grants were broken down as follows:

Youth work	£425,000
Mental health	£257,300
Other	£238,600
Homelessness	£118,000
Abuse survivors	£35,000
Job support	£27,400

Beneficiaries included: Carlisle Key and Families Matter (£60,000 each); West Cumbria Domestic Violence Support (£35,000); The Happy Mums Foundation (£14,700); The Growing Club CIC (£9,700); Barrow Association Football Club (£4,000).

Exclusions

According to its website, the trust does not generally consider appeals:

- from individuals
- from statutory organisations
- from national charities without a local base/project
- from charities with substantial unrestricted reserves
- from medical/health establishments
- from schools/educational establishments
- for projects principally benefiting people outside Cumbria/North Lancashire
- for retrospective funding
- for expeditions or overseas travel
- for the promotion of religion
- for animal welfare

Applications

Application forms are available to download from the trust's website or can be requested by phone, email or post. Applications for over £4,000 should be submitted at least five weeks before the trustees' meetings in March, July and November (contact the trust for exact dates). Applications for grants of less than £4,000 will be considered at small grants meetings every 3–4 weeks. Applicants are advised to contact the director for an informal discussion before submitting an application for funding.

Sources of information

Accounts; annual report; Charity Commission record; funder's website.

The Frieda Scott Charitable Trust

Social welfare; people with disabilities; community services; sport and recreation; art and music in the community

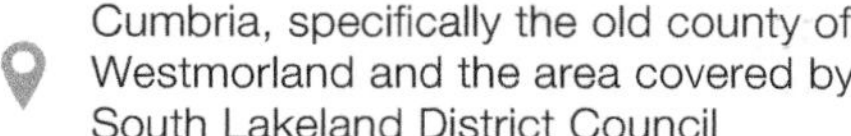

Cumbria, specifically the old county of Westmorland and the area covered by South Lakeland District Council

£264,700 (2020/21)

CC number: 221593

Correspondent: Celia Forsyth, Trust Secretary, Stricklandgate House, 92 Stricklandgate, Kendal, Cumbria LA9 4PU (tel: 01539 742608; email: info@fcsct.org.uk)

 www.friedascott.org.uk

General information

The trust was established in 1974 and makes grants to registered charities involved in a wide range of activities that meet the needs of local communities and vulnerable and disadvantaged people. Grants are provided to charities and community groups in the South Lakeland district of Cumbria, as well as the area covered by the old county of Westmorland.

The trust's priorities are listed on its website as follows:

- Older people (particularly the vulnerable and isolated)
- People with disabilities, mental health needs and/or learning difficulties
- Children and young people (particularly the most disadvantaged)
- Family support work
- Victims/survivors of domestic and sexual abuse
- Those recovering from substance misuse
- Prevention and rehabilitation of offenders
- Carers
- Village halls and community centres
- Improving access to services for rural communities
- Voluntary sector infrastructure and support
- Arts and sports projects where the primary objective is community benefit or the support of vulnerable groups
- Young people's uniformed groups

The trust has two strands of funding – small grants under £3,500 and larger grants over £3,500. The trust awards around 50 grants each year, mostly ranging from £3,500 to £20,000, although the average main grant size is around £15,000. The trustees will consider funding projects requiring capital or revenue support, and charities may apply for multi-year revenue funding where there is an ongoing or longer-term need.

Financial information

Year end	31/03/2021
Income	£197,700
Assets	£10,950,000
Grants to organisations	£264,700

Beneficiaries included: Blackwell Sailing (£37,500); The Birchall Trust (£20,000); Keppleway Trust (£7,500); Kendal Lads and Girls Club (£1,200); Diabetes UK (£1,000).

Exclusions

According to its website, the trust will not support the following:

- Retrospective funding
- Statutory bodies (including education/health
- Places of worship/promoting religion
- Individuals or expeditions
- Animal/wildlife/heritage/environmental causes
- Museums and art galleries
- National charities (with exceptions made for projects involving local volunteers/staff)

Applications

Application forms can be requested from the correspondent either by post, email or phone.

Sources of information

Accounts; annual report; Charity Commission record; funder's website.

The Finnis Scott Foundation

Horticulture; fine art; art history

UK

£212,400 (2020)

CC number: 1121475

Correspondent: Angela Moon, Grant Administrator, c/o HCR Hewitsons, Elgin House, Billing Road, Northampton, Northamptonshire NN1 5AU (email: angelamoon@hewitsons.com)

Trustees: Ian Barnett; Dr William Elliott; David Laing; Lady Kathryn Robinson; The Hon. Ursula Wide; James Miller; Dr Patricia Morison; Lord Charles Scott.

 www.finnis-scott-foundation.org.uk

General information

The Finnis Scott Foundation was established under the will of Lady Montagu Douglas Scott (Valerie Finnis) in 2006. The foundation can make grants for any purpose but is presently focused on the areas of horticulture, plant sciences, fine art and art history. Art collecting and gardening were the main preoccupations of Lady Montagu Douglas Scott and her husband, Sir David.

According to the foundation's 2020 accounts, during the year grants were awarded according to the following framework:

- The training of gardeners
- The restoration of gardens
- Scientific plant projects
- Permanent art projects, including the
- framing of pictures and the development of galleries
- The production of exhibition catalogues
- The support of the disadvantaged within horticulture

The foundation's website states:

> In general the Trustees only consider grants for up to £10,000. Exceptionally, larger grants may be considered at the Trustees' discretion. Preference is given to smaller charities where a grant would have a significant impact. The Foundation funds both capital and revenue projects.

The foundation has recently introduced The Botanical Art Award – a £10,000 award dedicated to UK- and Ireland-based botanical art groups and organisations, in recognition of previous achievements and for the promotion of innovative ideas and projects. Regional and national botanical art societies, florilegium groups, independent courses, affiliated groups and other community organisations associated with teaching or promoting botanical art may apply.

Financial information

Year end	31/12/2020
Income	£306,900
Assets	£10,850,000
Grants to organisations	£212,400

Further financial information

In previous years grants have usually totalled between £300,000 and £400,000.

Beneficiaries included: Royal Collection Trust (£50,000); Professional Gardeners Trust (£30,000); Castle Bromwich Hall Gardens (£6,000); Avon Wildlife (£4,000); Cheviot Youth (£1,500).

Exclusions

Grants are not awarded for the following:

- Expenditure which has already been incurred
- Salaries, except in the case of educational support (bursaries and apprenticeships)
- Site-specific art installations
- Conceptual or performance art

Applications

Applications can be made via the foundation's website, where application deadlines can also be found.

For further information regarding applications for The Botanical Art Award, see the foundation's website.

Sources of information

Accounts; annual report; Charity Commission record; funder's website.

The John Scott Trust Fund

General charitable purposes; health; social welfare; disability; children and young people

Scotland

£369,500 (2020/21)

OSCR number: SC003297

Correspondent: The Trustees, Kilpatrick and Walker Solicitors, 4 Wellington Square, Ayr, Ayrshire KA7 1EN

General information

This charity was established to contribute to societies, trusts and bodies established for charitable purposes. Funding is provided to organisations favoured by the charity's namesake, the late John Scott, to local charities in Scotland and also organisations nationwide. The trustees maintain the right to consider supporting other charities and organisations not favoured by Mr Scott but which have similar values.

Financial information

Year end	30/04/2021
Income	£51,000
Assets	£2,290,000
Grants to organisations	£369,500

Beneficiaries included: Ayrshire Hospice (£60,000); National Trust Scotland (£30,000); Hansel Foundation (£20,000); CHAS (£15,000); Combat Stress (£10,000); Boswell Book Foundation (£5,000); Vics in the Community (£500).

Exclusions

No grants are awarded to individuals.

Applications

Apply in writing to the correspondent.

Sources of information

Accounts; annual report; OSCR record.

The Scottish Power Foundation

General charitable purposes; education; the environment; the arts, heritage and culture; science; social welfare; citizenship and community development

UK

£1.18 million (2020)

OSCR number: SC043862

Correspondent: Rebecca Fairley, Secretary, 320 St Vincent Street, Glasgow G2 5AD (email: scottishpowerfoundation@scottishpower.com)

Trustees: Mike Thornton; Melanie Hill; Sarah Mistry; Keith Anderson; Anita Longley.

www.scottishpower.com/pages/the_scottishpower_foundation.aspx

General information

This foundation was established in 2013. It is the corporate charity of Scottish Power, the UK-wide gas and electricity supplier based in Glasgow.

According to its website, the foundation awards funding to registered charities for the following causes:

- The advancement of education
- The advancement of environmental protection
- The advancement of the arts, heritage, culture or science
- The prevention or the relief of poverty and the relief of those in need by reason of disability or other disadvantage
- The advancement of citizenship and community development

Awards

Each year, the foundation also delivers the Scottish Power Foundation Awards. A pot of £30,000 is shared between charities that are shortlisted by the trustees. A number of different awards are available, including the Education Award, the Community Engagement Award, the Innovation Award and the Charity Champion Award, details of which can be found on the foundation's website.

Financial information

Year end	31/12/2020
Income	£1,350,000
Assets	£325,800
Grants to organisations	£1,210,000
No. of grants	21

Further financial information

Grants were awarded to 21 organisations during the year totalling £1.18 million. In addition, Scottish Power Foundation Awards totalled £30,000.

Beneficiaries included: The Literacy Pirates (£100,000); Bendrigg Trust (£96,100); Bangor University (£79,000); Size of Wales (£60,000); National Theatre of Scotland (£50,000); Nightingale House Hospice (£30,000); Starcatchers Productions Ltd (£25,000).

Applications

Check the foundation's website for updates on opening dates for grant programmes.

Sources of information

Accounts; annual report; OSCR record; funder's website.

Scottish Property Industry Festival of Christmas (SPIFOX)

Financial assistance to charitable organisations providing relief to children and young people in need

Scotland

£450,400 (2019/20)

OSCR number: SC020660

Correspondent: Alasdair Carlyle, Chair of Beneficiaries Committee, c/o Saffrey Champness LLP, Edinburgh Quay, 133 Fountainbridge, Edinburgh EH3 9BA (email: alasdair@spifox.co.uk)

Trustees: Christian Bruce; Alasdair Carlyle; Andy Clark; Ross Clephane; Bill Colville; Tom Cromar; Penny Hearn; Alasdair MacConnel; David MacKenzie; Danny O'Neill; Frances Sim; Ronnie Urquhart; Craig Munro.

www.spifox.co.uk

@Spifox1

General information

The charity was founded in 1983 by a group of property and construction professionals. The main objective of the charity is to provide funding for Scottish children's charities to enable the purchase of equipment and the provision of facilities.

The following information has been taken from the charity's website:

> Our principal purpose is the donation of cash sums to specific capital projects, these projects being undertaken by Registered Charities (ideally in Scotland) specifically for the benefit of kids in Scotland. We also seek our contribution to be 'identifiable'; by that we mean if our donation is to be part of a general appeal then our funding should be used for a specific purpose therein. For example, this could be for fitting out works, equipment provision, relevant IT or specific elements within a larger project.

Financial information

Year end	30/06/2020
Income	£445,400
Assets	£58,800
Grants to organisations	£450,400
No. of grants	31

Beneficiaries included: Friends of Kilpatrick School (£38,300); Plus Forth Valley (£21,700); Scottish Ballet (£17,000); Tweed Togs (£13,000); Adoption Scotland (£10,000); Jeely Piece Club (£5,400); YMCA Bellshill and Mossend (£2,300); Borders Youth Theatre (£600).

Exclusions

The charity states on its website: 'It is not generally our policy to contribute to revenue or administrative needs, this having become our established practice from when our Charity was set up in 1983.'

Applications

Contact the correspondent, or any of the trustees known to you, for an initial discussion. Alternatively, use the contact form available on the charity's website. After this, the charity will seek further information on the project/cause to be supported, which will then be considered at the next Beneficiaries Sub-Committee meeting. The charity responds to initial applications within a few weeks.

Sources of information

Accounts; annual report; OSCR record; funder's website.

The Screwfix Foundation

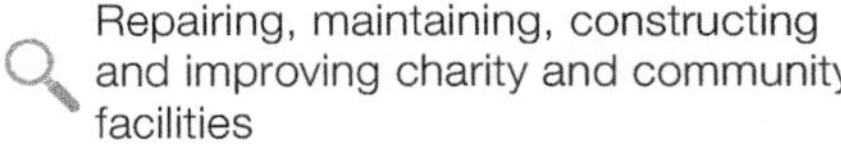
Repairing, maintaining, constructing and improving charity and community facilities

UK

£1.08 million (2020/21)

CC number: 1151375

Correspondent: The Trustees, Trade House, Mead Avenue, Houndstone Business Park, Yeovil, Somerset BA22 8RT (tel: 01935 414100; email: foundation@screwfix.com)

Trustees: Jonathan Mewett; Claire Flory; Lindsay Haselhurst; Kim McDonald; Elizabeth Bell; Stephen Dunston; Caroline Welsh; Darren Worth.

www.screwfix.com/help/screwfixfoundation

General information

The foundation was established in 2013 and supports projects that will fix, repair, maintain and improve properties and community facilities for those in need throughout the UK. The foundation's website explains:

We work with both national and local charities, donating much needed funds to help all sorts of projects, from repairing buildings and **improving facilities in deprived areas, to decorating the homes of people living with sickness and disabilities.**

Grants of up to £5,000 are made to registered charities and not-for-profit organisations.

Eligibility

To be eligible to apply, organisations must be:

- A registered charity or not-for-profit organisation
- Helping those in need by reason of financial hardship, sickness, disability, distress or other disadvantage in the UK
- Looking for funding to support projects that relate to the repair, maintenance, improvement or construction of homes, community buildings and other buildings

Financial information

Year end	31/01/2021
Income	£2,030,000
Assets	£490,000
Grants to organisations	£1,080,000

Beneficiaries included: A list of beneficiaries was not available.

Applications

Applications can be made via the foundation's website. Applications are reviewed quarterly, usually in March, June, September and December. All successful applicants will be contacted by post, email or phone to arrange the next step. Unsuccessful applicants will be contacted within one month of the review meeting.

Sources of information

Accounts; annual report; Charity Commission record; funder's website.

Seafarers UK (King George's Fund for Sailors)

The welfare of seafarers and their families and dependants; education and training of people for service at sea; prevention and relief of poverty; health; relief of those in need; armed forces

UK and Commonwealth

£3.66 million (2020)

CC number: 226446

Correspondent: Grants Team, 8 Hatherley Street, London SW1P 2QT (tel: 020 7932 0000; email: A contact form is available on the charity's website.)

Trustees: Mark Dickinson; Surgeon Cdre Peter Buxton; Mark Carden; Jeremy Monroe; Duncan Bain; Natalie Shaw; Paul Butterworth; William Lawes; Gerald Kidd; Robert Greenwood; Peter French; William Reid; Rear Admiral Iain Lower; Nusrat Ghani.

 www.seafarers.uk

 facebook.com/SeafarersUK

 @Seafarers_UK

 @seafarers_uk

General information

This charity supports people who have served at sea in the Royal Navy, Royal Marines or Merchant Navy, or who have worked on a sea-going ship (e.g. in fishing fleets), and their dependants.

Grant programmes

Main Grants Programme – funding for charities and not-for-profit organisations, delivering safety initiatives and welfare services to seafarers and fishers.

Merchant Navy Fund – funding for welfare services which support the UK's merchant seafarers.

The charity's COVID-19 Emergency Fund provided additional support to maritime welfare charities during the pandemic. The Seafarers International Relief Fund also supported seafarers in India during the pandemic.

Financial information

Year end	31/12/2020
Income	£1,550,000
Assets	£41,540,000
Grants to organisations	£3,660,000

Beneficiaries included: Fishermen's Mission (£195,000); Nautilus Welfare Fund (£118,400); Mission to Seafarers Africa (£60,000); Hull 4 Heroes (£10,000); Manx Marine Society (£1,500); Lord Kitchener Memorial Holiday Centre (£750).

Applications

Applications can be made through the charity's website.

Sources of information

Accounts; annual report; Charity Commission record; funder's website; guidelines for applicants.

The Sam and Bella Sebba Charitable Foundation

 Palliative and end-of-life care; refugees; homelessness; human rights; assistive technology

 UK; Israel; USA

£3.38 million (2020/21)

CC number: 1191713

Correspondent: Amy Horne, UK Grants Manager, PO Box 864, Gillingham, Kent ME8 1FE (tel: 07809 702920; email: admin@sebbafoundation.org)

Trustees: Judy Sebba; Tamsin Doyle; Tali Emodi; Yoav Tangir; Brian Parkinson; Odelia Sebba; Ronit Armoni; Ray Shostak.

 https://sebbafoundation.org

General information

The Sam and Bella Sebba Charitable Trust (Charity Commission no. 253351) was established in 1967 by the late Samuel Sebba for general charitable purposes. In October 2020, the original trust re-registered as a CIO with the new name, The Sam and Bella Sebba Charitable Foundation.

The trustees seek to promote a more humane society by supporting vulnerable people and protecting their rights. They do this by funding grants for social innovation capable of effecting transformative change.

Grant-making policies

The foundation's 2020/21 annual report explains that the foundation 'established its grant-making policy to achieve its objects for the public benefit by making grants to charities whose objectives are clear, that can demonstrate best practice and sustainability, whose operations are transparent and whose commitment to the public benefit is demonstrable'. According to the foundation's website, the trustees prioritise making grants 'where others are less active' and they also favour 'adventurous grants for social innovation capable of effecting transformative change'.

Current focus areas

The foundation's website states that in the UK, it currently makes grants in the areas of palliative and end-of-life care, refugees, homelessness, social respect and assistive technology. Grant areas for the USA and Israel are detailed on the website.

Financial information

Year end	31/03/2021
Income	£1,030,000
Assets	£60,080,000
Grants to organisations	£3,380,000

Further financial information

The latest accounts available were for the Sam and Bella Sebba Charitable Trust for the period January 2020 to March 2021. The trust's net assets of £60.08 million were transferred to The Sam and Bella Sebba Charitable Foundation in January 2021. A full breakdown of grants can be found in the trust's 2020/21 accounts. Only beneficiaries of grants of £10,000 and above were listed.

Beneficiaries included: Together for Short Lives (£100,000); New Horizon Youth Centre (£50,000); Greater Manchester Immigration Aid Unit (£35,000); Hospice UK (£20,000); South London Refugee Association (£16,400); St Mungo's (£12,500); Designability (£10,000).

Applications

The foundation's website states: 'Please note the Foundation undertakes its own research, in line with its current priorities, and does not accept unsolicited applications and will not acknowledge them.'

Sources of information

Accounts; annual report; Charity Commission record; funder's website.

The Segelman Trust

Disadvantaged and vulnerable children and families

UK and, occasionally, overseas

£760,300 (2020)

CC number: 1188686

Correspondent: Grants Administrator, c/o White and Co., 190 Clarence Gate Gardens, Glentworth Street, London NW1 6AD (tel: 020 7759 1129)

Trustees: Wilson Cotton; Timothy White; Rebecca Eastmond; Christopher Graves.

General information

The trust was established in 1992 by the will of Gerald Segelman (Charity Commission no. 1079151). In 2020 the trust re-registered as a CIO (Charity Commission no. 1188686). It supports UK-registered charities working with marginalised and disadvantaged people. Particular focus is given to children and young people in and leaving care and to young or otherwise vulnerable parents whose children are at risk.

The trust's primary area of focus is the UK. However, grants may also be made to support organisations achieving outstanding work elsewhere in the world.

Previous grants have been made towards core costs, project costs, start-up costs and development costs.

Financial information

Year end	31/12/2020
Income	£1,130,000
Grants to organisations	£760,300
No. of grants	21

Further financial information

A figure for assets was not available in the 2020 accounts, as the trust transferred all its funds during its re-registration as a CIO.

Grants paid to 21 organisations during the year totalled £760,300. As well as its usual grants, the trust funded three place-based collective impact initiatives whereby communities work together to identify and support unmet needs of children.

Beneficiaries included: West London Zone (£150,000); Refugee Action (£100,000); Action for Happiness (£60,000); Blue Cabin (£32,000); Care Leaders Fellowship (£12,000); Resurgo Clean Start (£5,000); Street Life Trust (£1,000).

Exclusions

The trust does not provide grants to individuals.

Applications

The trustees do not consider unsolicited applications. Instead, they identify projects and organisations they wish to support. The trust's 2020 accounts state the following:

> We look for a set of key characteristics in the organisations we fund. The Trust seeks to partner with charities that are rooted in the communities they serve, that listen and co-create with young people and families, which focus on well-being and positive relationships and which provide consistent, long-term support. We look for charity partners who can articulate clear objectives, have a framework for understanding their effectiveness and adapting in line with their learning, demonstrate well-targeted use of their resources, act with openness and transparency and are committed to sharing their learning with others.

Sources of information

Accounts; annual report; Charity Commission record.

Sellata Ltd

Advancement of the Orthodox Jewish faith and the relief of poverty

UK and Israel

£230,500 (2020/21)

CC number: 285429

Correspondent: The Trustees, 29 Fountayne Road, London N16 7EA (tel: 020 8809 5051; email: management@abarisltd.co.uk)

Trustees: Joseph Stern; Eliezer Benedikt; Aron Oberlander.

General information

The charity was established in 1980 to support the advancement of the Orthodox Jewish religion, the relief of poverty and Jewish causes.

Financial information

Year end	31/03/2021
Income	£73,400
Assets	£3,600,000
Grants to organisations	£230,500

Further financial information

During 2020/21 grants totalled £230,500; however, in previous years the charity has made grants totalling over £300,000.

Beneficiaries included: A list of beneficiaries was not available.

Applications

Apply in writing to the correspondent.

Sources of information

Accounts; annual report; Charity Commission record.

The Jean Shanks Foundation

Medical research and education and pathology

UK

£773,900 (2020/21)

CC number: 293108

Correspondent: Eric Rothbarth, Chair, Peppard Cottage, Peppard Common, Henley-on-Thames, Oxfordshire RG9 5LB (tel: 01491 628232; email: administrator@jeanshanksfoundation.org)

Trustees: Eric Rothbarth; Alistair Jones; Dr Julian Axe; Prof. Adrienne Flanagan; Prof. James Underwood; Prof. Nicholas Wright; Prof. Mark Arends.

www.jeanshanksfoundation.org

General information

Registered with the Charity Commission in November 1985, the foundation supports medical research and education, particularly in the area of pathology. According to its website:

> The Foundation was set up to fund medical research and education, primarily to fund medical students wishing to have an extra research year at medical school – this research must have a pathology focus. Grants continue to be made to medical students but are also available for other projects that the trustees consider to be worthwhile. The Foundation has grown considerably since its original inception and is now worth approximately £20m. Grants totalling in the region of £400,000 are given away annually.

Financial information

Year end	31/03/2021
Income	£357,100
Assets	£26,670,000
Grants to organisations	£773,900
No. of grants	17

Further financial information

The charity awarded 17 grants during the year.

Beneficiaries included: University College London (£206,300); University of Cambridge (£104,400); University of Leeds (£74,900); University of Edinburgh (£68,800); University of Southampton (£43,800); Academy of Medical Science (£25,000).

Exclusions

Grants are not made for financial hardship or any project without significant pathology research content.

Applications

Apply in writing to the correspondent. Full grant guidelines are available on the foundation's website.

Sources of information

Accounts; annual report; Charity Commission record; funder's website.

The Shanly Foundation

General charitable purposes; local community benefit; children and young people; homelessness; health and disability; the environment

Buckinghamshire; Berkshire; Hertfordshire; Oxfordshire; West Sussex; parts of Surrey and Hampshire

£943,200 (2020)

CC number: 1182155

Correspondent: Clare Junak, Shanly Awards Officer, Sorbon, Aylesbury End, Beaconsfield, Buckinghamshire HP9 1LW (tel: 01494 671331; email: info@shanlyfoundation.com)

Trustees: Michael Shanly; Tamra Booth; Timothy Potter; Donald Tucker; Nicholas Young.

www.shanlyfoundation.com

facebook.com/ShanlyFoundation

@ShanlyFnd

@shanly.foundation

General information

The Shanly Foundation was established in 1997 for general charitable purposes. The foundation receives its income from the profits of Shanly Homes Ltd and Sorbon Homes Ltd, and functions as the charitable arm of the Shanly Group of companies established by the foundation's founder, Michael Shanly.

The foundation aims to support causes that 'help individuals and benefit the local community, including support for young people from disadvantaged backgrounds, the homeless, those with mental health issues and people with physical disabilities, injury or life limiting illness'.

The foundation's website gives the following examples of the causes that it will consider supporting:

- Registered charities, particularly those that assist people with physical and mental disabilities
- Older people and other members of the local communities that may be disadvantaged through no fault of their own
- Organisations that help rehabilitate citizens back into local communities
- Local sports and social clubs
- Local Rotary clubs and similar community organisations
- Local Scouts and Guides groups
- Outdoor activity centres for young people
- Woodland and environmental conservation organisations
- Social and community events, festivals, exhibitions, displays, fêtes, galas and concerts that help raise funds to support local good causes

Financial information

Year end	31/12/2020
Income	£1,580,000
Assets	£3,550,000
Grants to organisations	£943,200

Further financial information

Grants were broken down as follows:

Community	£357,500
Health and welfare	£347,500
Education	£124,100
Disability	£97,800
Wildlife and conservation	£8,900
Religion	£7,500

Beneficiaries included: Thames Hospice (£82,300); Adoption UK Charity (£50,000); Marlow Opportunity Playgroup (£10,000); Jumbulance Trust (£260).

Exclusions

The foundation does not fund the following:

- Individuals
- Research
- Core costs
- Military charities
- Single-faith charities
- Animal welfare charities
- Organisations that have not been in existence for at least 12 months
- Organisations delivering services outside the area of benefit

Applications

Applications should be made through the online portal on the foundation's website. The questions can be previewed before registration. General enquiries can be submitted via the online contact form.

Sources of information

Accounts; annual report; Charity Commission record; funder's website.

ShareGift (The Orr Mackintosh Foundation)

General charitable purposes

UK

£2.32 million (2020/21)

CC number: 1052686

Correspondent: The Trustees, 4th Floor, 67–68 Jermyn Street, London SW1Y 6NY (tel: 020 7930 3737; email: help@sharegift.org)

Trustees: Paul Killik; John Roundhill; Susan Swabey; Alan Scott; Gillian Budd.

www.sharegift.org

General information

Launched in 1996, this charity was developed by the Viscountess Mackintosh of Halifax and Matthew Orr, a stockbroker whose firm, Killik and Co., provides many of the technical support services required to operate ShareGift.

The charity specialises in accepting donations of shares, which it then distributes to a broad range of UK-registered charities. The charity makes donations at its own discretion but is guided by donor suggestions. ShareGift is cause neutral and there are no restrictions on the kind of charitable work it can support.

Financial information

Year end	31/03/2021
Income	£2,920,000
Assets	£2,740,000
Grants to organisations	£2,320,000
No. of grants	367

Further financial information

In 2020/21, 407 grants were awarded to 367 charities. Grants were made to a wide range of new and existing beneficiaries, with the largest grant being of £150,000. Grant sizes were broken down as follows:

Amount donated	No. of charities	No. of grants	Total amount
£10,000 and above	73	93	£1.56 million
£5,000 – £9,999	90	102	£484,800
£2,500 – £4,999	43	49	£116,000
Up to £2,499	161	163	£161,000

Only beneficiaries of grants of £10,000 and above were listed in the charity's accounts.

Beneficiaries included: Tonbridge School Foundation (£150,000); Cambridge University (£86,000); Parkinson's UK (£65,000); ADHD Foundation (£30,000); Transform Drug Policy Foundation (£25,000); ManKind Initiative (£15,000); Leeds Community Foundation and Wakefield Hospice (£10,000 each).

Exclusions

Grants are not given to charities that are not registered in the UK.

Applications

Unsolicited applications are not accepted. See the charity's website for further information.

Sources of information

Accounts; annual report; Charity Commission record; funder's website.

The Shears Foundation

Sustainable community development; education; the environment; health and medicine (including education and research); culture and the arts

Worldwide, with a preference for the north east of England (in particular, Tyne and Wear, Northumberland, North and West Yorkshire and Greater Manchester)

£465,000 (2020/21)

CC number: 1049907

Correspondent: Bruce Warnes, Trustee, c/o The Community Foundation, Philanthropy House, Woodbine Road, Gosforth, Newcastle upon Tyne, Tyne and Wear NE3 1DD (tel: 07544 380316; email: bruce@shearsfoundation.org)

Trustees: Mr G. Lyall; Mr P. J. Shears; Mrs L. G. Shears; Bruce Warnes; Mark Horner; Richard Shears; Louise Warnes; Georgie Shears.

www.shearsfoundation.org

General information

The foundation was established in 1994 by Trevor and Lyn Shears following the sale of their transport company.

Grants are made to registered charities whose work falls into one of five core priorities:

- The development of arts and culture
- The development and provision of education for adults and children
- The protection, preservation or enhancement of the natural environment
- The promotion of health and medicine, particularly within the fields of research or education
- The creation of stronger and more sustainable communities

The trustees give priority to charities working in the Tyne and Wear and Northumberland regions. They will also consider applications from charities in North Yorkshire (specifically Harrogate and York), West Yorkshire and Greater Manchester. National charities undertaking specific work or projects in the above geographical areas are also eligible to apply.

Grants of £5,000 can be made for core costs, including salaries. The trustees look more favourably on applications where the project is being funded from a range of sources.

The foundation makes an annual contribution to the Linden Fund, held by the Community Foundation for Tyne and Wear, and an annual donation to the Bradford Grammar School bursary scheme.

Financial information

Year end	31/03/2021
Income	£544,500
Assets	£17,420,000
Grants to organisations	£465,000
No. of grants	32

Further financial information

Only six beneficiaries of grants of £25,000 and above were listed in the foundation's 2020/21 accounts. Grants of under £25,000 totalled £180,000 (26 grants).

Beneficiaries included: Community Foundation Linden Fund (£80,000); Bradford Grammar School and St Oswald's Hospice Children's Service (£50,000 each); Samling Foundation (£45,000).

Exclusions

The foundation will not normally support the following:

- Capital projects
- Individuals
- Religious causes or groups
- Political causes, groups or fundraising for lobbying
- Single-identity groups where there is no evidence of integration
- Preschool groups and playgroups
- Domestic pets – but the foundation may support charities involved in using animals for medical/care support purposes

Applications

An eligibility quiz is available on the foundation's website, along with an application form and full guidelines. Applications are considered at quarterly trustee meetings (see the foundation's website for deadlines). At the time of writing (April 2022) the foundation's website stated: 'Please make sure you've given us a call before you make an application.'

Sources of information

Accounts; annual report; Charity Commission record; funder's website; guidelines for applicants.

The Sheepdrove Trust

General charitable purposes (particularly sustainability and biodiversity); organic farming and nutrition, education and research; spiritual care; arts and culture

UK, there may be some preference for north Lambeth, London

£378,100 (2020)

CC number: 328369

Correspondent: The Trustees, Drove Farm, Sheepdrove, Lambourn, Hungerford, Berkshire RG17 7UN (tel: 01488 674726; email: helen.cravenjones@sheepdrove.com)

Trustees: Barnabas Kindersley; Juliet Kindersley; Peter Kindersley; Harriet Treuille; Anabel Kindersley.

General information

The trust was endowed with money made by the Dorling Kindersley publishing enterprise, but the trust's holding of shares in the company was sold in 2000, when the endowment was valued at £18 million. The trust has general charitable purposes but there is a particular interest in supporting initiatives involved in sustainability, biodiversity and organic farming.

In previous years the trust has made grants in the following areas of work: education; farming and wildlife preservation; medicine and health (including spiritual care); arts and culture.

Financial information

Year end	31/12/2020
Income	£210
Grants to organisations	£378,100

Beneficiaries included: A list of beneficiaries was not available. Previous beneficiaries include: Soil Association

(£27,300); Coastal Grains (£30,000); GM Watch (£25,000); University of Arts London (£23,800); The Prison Phoenix Trust (£20,000); Newcastle University (£16,700).

Applications

Apply in writing to the correspondent.

Sources of information

Accounts; annual report; Charity Commission record.

The Sheffield Town Trust

General charitable purposes

Sheffield

£312,200 (2020)

CC number: 223760

Correspondent: The Law Clerk, Commercial House, 14 Commercial Street, Sheffield, South Yorkshire S1 2AT (tel: 0114 276 5555; email: sheffieldtowntrust@keebles.com)

Trustees: Jonathan Brayshaw; Jane Ferretti; James Fulton; Nicholas Hutton; Penelope Jewitt; Marian Rae; Adrian Staniforth; Oliver Stephenson; Prof. Sarah Thomas; Mark Swales; Zahid Hamid; Dr Julie MacDonald; Jason Heath.

www.sheffieldtowntrust.org

General information

Established in 1297 by Thomas de Furnival, the Sheffield Town Trust is one of the oldest charities in England.

Grant-making policy

The average award made by the trust is between £500 and £3,000. The trust makes grants to other charities and organisations working to support Sheffield and its residents. This includes national charities, provided the grant is used exclusively in Sheffield or exclusively for the benefit of residents in Sheffield. Causes and beneficiaries typically funded by the trust include:

- Older people
- Children and young people
- People with disabilities
- The arts
- Sports
- Community events

The trust also supports projects relating specifically to buildings, heritage and the rural environment.

Financial information

Year end	31/12/2020
Income	£722,100
Assets	£9,700,000
Grants to organisations	£312,200

Beneficiaries included: Sheffield Foodbank Network (£10,000); Sheffield Theatres Trust (£5,000); Action Tutoring (£3,000); Whizz-Kidz (£1,000).

Exclusions

The trust's website states:

> The Town Trustees do not award grants to
>
> - Individuals
> - Organisations who are not working for the benefit of Sheffield and its inhabitants
> - Organisations based outside Sheffield unless the purpose of the charity is to help those in Sheffield.
> - Animal charities
> - Political organisations
> - Religious groups
> - Churches. However, the Town Trustees will consider support for church buildings as long as those buildings are to be used by the local community

Applications

Application forms can be completed on the trust's website and need to be submitted with any supporting documents.

Sources of information

Accounts; annual report; Charity Commission record; funder's website.

The Patricia and Donald Shepherd Charitable Trust

General charitable purposes and young people

York

£320,000 (2020/21)

CC number: 272948

Correspondent: The Trustees, West Mount, 129 The Mount, York, North Yorkshire YO24 1DU

Trustees: Christine Shepherd; Iain Robertson; Jane Robertson; Michael Shepherd; Patrick Shepherd; Joseph Shepherd; Rory Robertson; Annabel Robertson; Carly Robertson.

General information

The trust was established in 1973 and aims to provide assistance to organisations that are deemed by the trustees 'to be of benefit to those less fortunate in society or to society in general'. Preference is given to organisations supporting young people. Priority is given to organisations/causes in York.

Financial information

Year end	05/04/2021
Income	£313,800
Assets	£19,190,000
Grants to organisations	£320,000
No. of grants	10

Beneficiaries included: Special Boat Service Association and York Against Cancer (£50,000 each); York Museums Trust (£45,000); Antibiotic Research UK (£25,000); Shepherd Group Brass Band (£12,000).

Exclusions

Grants are not made to individuals (unless they are part of a charitable group) or local authorities.

Applications

Local charities should apply in writing to the correspondent. The trust's 2020/21 annual report states:

> The policy of the trustees is to donate only to local charities or charities of which the trustees have close personal knowledge, interest or association and particularly those involving young people.

Sources of information

Accounts; annual report; Charity Commission record.

The Archie Sherman Charitable Trust

General charitable purposes; education and training; Jewish causes; overseas aid; the arts and culture; health

UK and overseas

£393,600 (2020/21)

CC number: 256893

Correspondent: The Trustees, 274A Kentish Town Road, London NW5 2AA (tel: 020 7493 1904; email: trust@sherman.co.uk)

Trustees: Michael Gee; Allan Morgenthau; Rhona Freedman.

General information

This trust makes grants to charitable organisations in the UK and overseas to support education and training, overseas aid, the arts and culture, health and general charitable purposes. Funding is awarded predominantly, but not exclusively, to Jewish organisations.

The trust's annual report for 2020/21 states that the trustees review all commitments on a forward five-year basis so that a few new projects can be undertaken and income is made available.

Financial information

Year end	05/04/2021
Income	£1,160,000
Assets	£18,410,000
Grants to organisations	£393,600
No. of grants	21

Further financial information

Grants were broken down as follows in 2020/21:

The arts and culture and general charitable purposes	£237,100
Health	£97,900
Education and training	£38,600
Overseas aid	£20,000

Beneficiaries included: The Jacqueline and Michael Gee Charitable Trust (£60,000); Jewish Care (£37,500); The Royal National Theatre (£25,000); The Central British Fund for World Jewish Relief (£10,000); Tel Aviv University Trust (£6,900); Yad Vashem UK Foundation (£1,900).

Applications

Apply in writing to the correspondent.

Sources of information

Accounts; annual report; Charity Commission record.

Shetland Charitable Trust

 General charitable purposes; social welfare; community development; the arts

 Shetland

£8.33 million (2020/21)

OSCR number: SC027025

Correspondent: Dr Ann Black, Chief Executive, 22–24 North Road, Lerwick, Shetland ZE1 0NQ (tel: 01595 744990; email: mail@shetlandcharitabletrust.co.uk)

Trustees: Andrew Cooper; Margaret Roberts; Jolene Garriock; Ken Harrison; Yvette Hopkins; Robert Leask; Ryan Leith; Emma Miller; Ian Napier.

 www.shetlandcharitabletrust.co.uk

 facebook.com/shetlandcharitabletrust

General information

Shetland Charitable Trust started life as Shetland Islands Council Charitable Trust (SICCT) in 1976 when Sullom Voe Terminal began operating. Money was paid by the oil industry to Shetland as a way of compensating the people for the inconvenience of having the terminal based there. It was decided to establish a charitable trust to receive and disburse this money.

The trust has several grant schemes to support the arts, community development and welfare throughout Shetland. See the trust's website for details.

Financial information

Year end	31/03/2021
Assets	£456,800
Grants to organisations	£8,330,000

Beneficiaries included: Shetland Recreational Trust (£2.97 million); Shetland Link Up (£48,000); Advocacy Shetland (£35,000); Shetland Link Up (£7,600); Shetland Befriending Scheme (£7,000).

Exclusions

Exclusions can be found in the guidance notes on the trust's website.

Applications

Application forms are available to download from the trust's website.

Sources of information

Accounts; annual report; OSCR record; funder's website.

SHINE: Support and Help in Education

 Support for educational projects for disadvantaged young people

 Northern England

£1.74 million (2019/20)

CC number: 1082777

Correspondent: The Trustees, SHINE Trust, Princes Exchange, 2 Princes Square, Leeds, West Yorkshire LS1 4HY (tel: 0113 280 5872; email: info@shinetrust.org.uk)

Trustees: Cameron Ogden; Ann Mroz; Lord Jim O'Neill; Samantha Twiselton; Sarah Loftus; Mark Heffernan; Lorna Fitzsimons; Raksha Pattni; Kavita Gupta.

 www.shinetrust.org.uk

General information

SHINE is a specialist education grant-maker, established by a group of philanthropists in 1999, that works to address educational inequalities and support educational attainment in young people from disadvantaged areas in England. To achieve this goal, the charity helps to co-design and fund educational programmes that raise the attainment and aspirations of children from economically deprived areas in the north of England. To date the charity has invested over £29 million benefitting almost around 1.3 million children from 20,000 schools.

On its website, the charity states that its mission is 'to raise the attainment of children from low income homes across the Northern Powerhouse, so that they can turn their potential into success at school and beyond'.

According to its website, SHINE has the following strategic priorities for all its funding programmes until 2025:

- **Ready for School**: improving the school readiness of children during the reception year, with a priority focus on language and communication skills (age 4–5)
- **Bridging the Gap:** supporting vulnerable children who may not meet 'age related expectations' at primary school to make better academic progress during Key Stage 3 (age 9–14)
- **Flying High**: supporting high-attaining students to build on their achievements at primary school and stay on a high-attaining trajectory during the first few years at secondary school (age 9–14)

The charity provides grants to charities, schools and educational establishments for project ideas that will help disadvantaged children succeed at school. Visit the charity's very informative website for full information.

SHINE also runs an annual national funding competition called Let Teachers SHINE. According to the charity's website, the competition aims to 'provide funding to any qualified, practising teacher in England who has a great idea to raise attainment in English, maths and science. We support them to trial their project, and if their idea has an impact on attainment, to scale the project up so that it can benefit children most in need.'

Financial information

Year end	31/08/2020
Income	£4,750,000
Assets	£6,460,000
Grants to organisations	£1,740,000

Further financial information

Grants paid in 2019/20 totalled £1.74 million. The list of beneficiaries includes grants paid and approved during the year.

Beneficiaries included: Right to Succeed (£266,800); Spelling Beats CIC (£132,000); St Edmund's Nursery (£96,000); York City Council (£56,500); Wyvern College (£30,400); Watercliffe Meadow Primary School (£15,000); Character Counts Easy Peasy (£5,000); Centre for Effective Philanthropy (£1,400).

Exclusions

The charity will not fund any of the following:

- Programmes that take place outside the north of England
- Short-term or one-off projects
- Bursaries or any kind of student fees
- Direct replacement of statutory funding
- Capital build programmes for schools or other education institutions

- Projects that are not linked to attainment and cannot be measured for impact

Applications

Applicants should use the enquiry form, available on the charity's website, outlining the following points in no more than three to four paragraphs:

- An overview of the project and its aims, specifically related to academic attainment in maths, literacy or science
- How it would meet SHINE's core priorities
- The number of beneficiaries and schools it would reach
- The overall project budget and size of the request to SHINE

Sources of information

Accounts; annual report; Charity Commission record; funder's website; guidelines for applicants.

Shlomo Memorial Fund Ltd

Education; Jewish causes; relief of poverty; general charitable purposes

Worldwide, with preference for UK, Israel and USA

£2.76 million (2019/20)

CC number: 278973

Correspondent: Channe Lopian, Secretary, c/o Cohen Arnold, New Burlington House, 1075 Finchley Road, London NW11 0PU (tel: 0161 772 0444; email: info@olnato.com)

Trustees: Chaim Kaufman; Eliyah Kleinerman; Channe Lopian; Amichai Toporowitz; Hezkel Toporowitz; Meir Sulam; Esther Hoffner.

General information

This charity was established in 1978 to advance the Orthodox Jewish religion, to relieve poverty and for general charitable purposes. According to the charity's 2019/20 accounts:

> The trustees are approached for donations by a wide variety of charitable institutions operating in the United Kingdom and abroad. The trustees consider all requests which they receive and make donations based on the level of funds available. In making grants and donations, the trustees use their personal knowledge of the relevant institutions, their representatives, operational efficiency and reputation. The trustees monitor the application of the grants and donations by meeting with representatives of the institutions and obtaining information as to the utilisation of funds.

In practice, grants are made to charitable Jewish organisations and can be for up to £200,000.

Financial information

Year end	30/09/2020
Income	£10,090,000
Assets	£69,020,000
Grants to organisations	£2,760,000
No. of grants	52+

Further financial information

Only beneficiaries of grants of over £10,000 were listed in the charity's 2019/20 accounts. Grants of under £10,000 totalled £29,300.

Beneficiaries included: Layesharim Tehilla (£192,000); Yad Tomechet LeNizkak Batzafon (£181,000); Yad Latzafon (£75,500); Shaarei Tehilla (£52,000); Kollel Yeshivas Yosef Chaim (£39,000); Friends of Mosdos Torah (£21,000); Shlavim Betaasuka (£10,000).

Applications

Apply in writing to the correspondent.

Sources of information

Accounts; annual report; Charity Commission record.

Shulem B. Association Ltd

Jewish causes; relief of poverty; religious education; general charitable purposes

UK and overseas

£3.5 million (2019/20)

CC number: 313654

Correspondent: The Trustees, New Burlington House, 1075 Finchley Road, London NW11 0PU (tel: 020 8731 0777)

Trustees: Samuel Berger; Zelda Sternlicht; Sarah Klein.

General information

The charity was registered with the Charity Commission in August 1962. According to the charity's annual report for 2019/20:

> This charity was established for general charitable purposes and in particular to support the activities of Jewish religious organisations, especially in the field of education. Donations are made to organisations providing a sound religious education in accordance with the doctrines and principles of traditional Judaism [...] Shulem B. Association Limited regularly supports charitable organisations and institutions both in respect of revenue expenditure and capital projects.

Financial information

Year end	30/09/2020
Income	£3,900,000
Assets	£52,480,000
Grants to organisations	£3,500,000

Further financial information

The charity's 2019/20 accounts were the latest available at the time of writing (May 2022). Grants were broken down as follows: general charitable purposes (£1,48 million); the advancement of the Jewish religion (£1.38 million); the advancement of Jewish education (£631,500).

Only beneficiaries of grants of £50,000 and above were listed in the accounts. Grants of under £50,000 totalled £903,300.

Beneficiaries included: United Talmudical Associates Ltd (£1.8 million); Tehilois Yoel (£285,000); Yetev Lev London Jerusalem Trust (£100,000); Chevras Mo'oz Ladol (£72,000); Palmcourt Ltd (£50,000).

Applications

Applications should be made in writing to the trustees.

Sources of information

Accounts; annual report; Charity Commission record.

Sirius Minerals Foundation

Community services and development; education and training; the environment; social welfare; recreation facilities

North York Moors National Park; Scarborough; Redcar and Cleveland

£396,700 (2020/21)

CC number: 1163127

Correspondent: The Trustees, Resolution House, Lake View, Scarborough, YO11 3ZB (email: info@siriusmineralsfoundation.co.uk)

Trustees: Neil Irving; Ian Swales; Jacqueline Flynn; Jonathan Samuel; Dr Elizabeth Walmsley; Sir Martin Narey; William Woods.

www.siriusmineralsfoundation.co.uk

General information

The foundation was established in 2013 by Sirius Minerals plc, a fertiliser development company. Today, Sirius Minerals is owned by Anglo American plc and the group has committed to provide an additional £4 million to the foundation, in advance of future revenues.

According to its website, the foundation's primary aim is to 'leave a positive legacy from the Woodsmith Mine to the boroughs of Scarborough, Redcar and the North York Moors National Park'. The foundation's current charitable objectives are to:

- Advance education, including supporting projects and training that benefit people by enhancing their skills

- Promote the general health of the community
- Advance environmental protection and improvement including the enhancing of the local landscape
- Provide and improve facilities in the interests of social welfare and leisure time with the aim to improve residents' well-being
- Help gain skills to those in need, because of financial hardship by being out of work, particularly the long-term unemployed.

Financial information

Year end	31/05/2021
Income	£1,000,000
Assets	£2,660,000
Grants to organisations	£396,700

Beneficiaries included: A list of beneficiaries was not available.

Applications

For up-to-date information on open grant schemes, see the website.

Sources of information

Accounts; annual report; Charity Commission record; funder's website.

The Charles Skey Charitable Trust

The arts, culture, science and heritage; sport; social welfare; health; armed forces; community development; religion; education

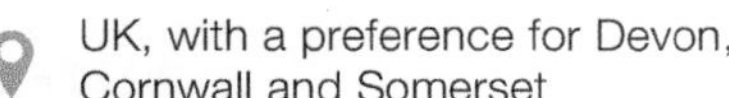

UK, with a preference for Devon, Cornwall and Somerset

£582,000 (2020/21)

CC number: 277697

Correspondent: The Trustees, Flint House, Park Homer Road, Colehill, Wimborne, Dorset BH21 2SP (tel: 01202 883778)

Trustees: Christopher Berkeley; John Leggett; The Revd James Leggett; David Berkeley; Edward Berkeley.

General information

The trust was established in 1979 for general charitable purposes. Most grants are awarded to registered charities and other non-profit organisations for specific projects. Preference is given to organisations based in Devon, Cornwall and Somerset, or national charities working within those areas.

Financial information

Year end	05/04/2021
Income	£371,400
Assets	£16,850,000
Grants to organisations	£582,000

Beneficiaries included: Centre for Enterprise Markets and Ethics (£110,000); Brasenose College – Oxford (£85,000); Polka Theatre (£60,000); Dementia UK (£10,000); Fusiliers London Fund (£7,500); Thrive Northox (£2,000).

Applications

Apply in writing to the correspondent.

Sources of information

Accounts; annual report; Charity Commission record.

The Slaughter and May Charitable Trust

General charitable purposes, particularly causes relating to children and young people

UK and, occasionally, other parts of the world

£526,900 (2020/21)

CC number: 1082765

Correspondent: The Trustees, Slaughter and May (Trust Ltd), 1 Bunhill Row, London EC1Y 8YY (tel: 020 7090 3433; email: corporateresponsibility@slaughterandmay.com)

Trustee: Slaughter and May Trust Ltd

www.slaughterandmay.com

General information

This trust was registered with the Charity Commission in 2000. It is the corporate charity of Slaughter and May, a law firm.

According to its 2020/21 annual report:

> the trust makes grants for general charitable purposes in the UK, particularly for causes relating to children and young people. Occasionally, grants are awarded in other parts of the world at the discretion of the trustees. Grants are also made to incentivise Slaughter and May employees in charitable deeds.

The trust also offers gifts in kind, usually in the form of pro bono work.

Financial information

Year end	05/04/2021
Income	£412,100
Assets	£120,000
Grants to organisations	£526,900

Beneficiaries included: The Access Project (£60,000); National Literacy Trust (£51,000); Islington Law Centre (£35,000); St Luke's Community Centre (£25,000); Legal Advice Centre (£15,000); The BIG Alliance (£12,000); St Luke's Primary School (£10,000); Mencap (£5,000).

Applications

The trust does not generally accept unsolicited applications.

Sources of information

Accounts; annual report; Charity Commission record.

Kathleen Beryl Sleigh Charitable Trust

Older people; children and young people; people with disabilities (particularly sight loss); music and culture

UK and overseas

£386,000 (2020/21)

CC number: 1082136

Correspondent: Jonathan Picken, Trustee, c/o William Sturges Solicitors, 14–16 Caxton Street, London SW1H 0QY (tel: 020 7873 1000; email: jonathan.picken@williamsturges.co.uk)

Trustees: Hazel French; Jonathan Picken.

General information

The trust was established in 2000 and is derived from the estate of Kathleen Beryl Sleigh. Miss Sleigh owned the mineral rights in part of the Cauldon Low limestone quarry in Staffordshire and these are the main source of income and funds for the trust.

Areas of work

The trust's 2020/21 accounts state:

> The Trustees consider applications from grant making charities and voluntary bodies. They also aim to assist the elderly, children and young people, people with disabilities (particularly loss of sight) and musical/cultural organisations.

Financial information

Year end	05/04/2021
Income	£203,600
Assets	£1,610,000
Grants to organisations	£386,000

Beneficiaries included: Royal College of Music (£20,000); Age UK and Refuge (£15,000 each); Earth Trust and Sight for Surrey (£5,000 each); Vision North Somerset (£2,000).

Applications

Apply in writing to the correspondent.

Sources of information

Accounts; annual report; Charity Commission record.

Smallwood Trust

Helping women to overcome financial adversity and to improve their social and emotional well-being

UK

£3.79 million (2020)

CC number: 205798

Correspondent: Grants Manager, Lancaster House, 25 Hornyold Road, Malvern, Worcestershire WR14 1QQ (tel: 01684 574645; email: info@smallwoodtrust.org.uk)

Trustees: Maureen Margie; D'Arcy Myers; Maria Toman; Catherine Hine; Rachael Bailey.

 www.smallwoodtrust.org.uk

General information

The Smallwood Trust has been helping women on low incomes since 1886. Her Majesty The Queen has been a patron of the charity since 1953. Its mission is to enable women to become financially resilient by equipping them with the skills they need to secure a confident financial future. It provides grants to organisations and individuals and works with selected partners to help women overcome financial adversity and to improve their social and emotional well-being.

Financial information

Year end	31/12/2020
Income	£3,730,000
Assets	£34,480,000
Grants to organisations	£3,790,000

Further financial information

The average grant size in 2020 was £20,000.

Beneficiaries included: New Economics Foundation (£101,900); Women's Budget Group (£89,700); Surviving Economic Abuse (£60,000); Venus (£50,000); Timewise (£30,900); The Motherhood Plan Trading As 'Pregnant then Screwed' (£25,300); Somali Welfare Trust (£15,900); Water Lily Project (£7,200).

Exclusions

Financial support is not given for the payment of white goods, tuition fees, or bankruptcy fees. The trust is also unable to offer support to those entered into an insolvency agreement such as Debt Relief Order (DRO) or Individual Voluntary Agreement (IVA).

Applications

Applicants can either call the trust on 0300 365 1886 to make an application or complete the online grant enquiry form on the trust's website. Application forms are sent out by the grants manager once the applicant has passed the initial eligibility checks.

Sources of information

Accounts; annual report; Charity Commission record; funder's website.

The SMB Trust

Christianity; social and medical welfare; education and medical research; famine relief and emergency aid; the environment

UK and overseas

£347,200 (2020/21)

CC number: 263814

Correspondent: The Trustees, 15 Wilman Road, Tunbridge Wells, Kent TN4 9AJ (tel: 01892 537301; email: smbcharitabletrust@googlemail.com)

Trustees: Jeremy Anstead; Barbara O'Driscoll; Ian Wilson.

General information

The trust awards grants to UK-registered charities that meet one of the following criteria:

- Support of the Christian faith
- Provision of social care in the UK and abroad
- Provision of famine or emergency aid
- Protection of the environment and wildlife
- Support of education or medical research

Grants are usually for between £1,000 and £4,000, but this can vary. According to its 2020/21 accounts, the trust makes regular grants to a large number of core charities, so while new applications are considered, only a small minority are likely to be successful. The founder's preferences are taken into account when deciding which of the applicants will be supported.

Financial information

Year end	31/03/2021
Income	£502,300
Assets	£12,180,000
Grants to organisations	£347,200
No. of grants	183

Beneficiaries included: Hospice of Hope (£4,000); All Nations Christian College (£3,500); Salvation Army and Speakers for Schools (£3,000 each); YMCA National Council (£2,500); London School of Theology (£2,000); Fisherman's Mission (£1,500); WaterAid and Young Minds (£1,000 each).

Exclusions

The trust does not make grants to individuals directly. If an individual applies through a charity, then the charity will receive the grant.

Applications

Apply in writing to the correspondent. The trustees normally meet four times a year to consider applications.

Sources of information

Accounts; annual report; Charity Commission record.

The Mrs Smith and Mount Trust

Mental health; disability; homelessness; community and economic development; care leavers; domestic abuse; food poverty; relief for individuals in need

Norfolk; Suffolk; Cambridgeshire; Hertfordshire; Essex; Kent; Surrey; London

£287,000 (2020/21)

CC number: 1009718

Correspondent: The Trustees, 6 Trull Farm Buildings, Tetbury, Gloucestershire GL8 8SQ (tel: 01285 841900; email: admin@mrssmithandmounttrust.org)

Trustees: Timothy Warren; Sean Shepley; Gill Gorell Barnes; Alexander Winter; Hannah Whitehead; Christine McKenzie.

 http://mrssmithandmounttrust.org

General information

The Mrs Smith and Mount Trust aims to assist disadvantaged people towards greater independence or a better quality of life.

The trust was founded by a wealthy American, who chose to make her home in the UK. According to the website, 'she stated, and her subsequent actions made clear, that she wished to remain as an anonymous philanthropist even after her death.' The original amount donated was increased by a large capital sum following the end of the Second World War, and the sale of works of art, ceramics and other items increased the trust's capital. The website describes how, 'as the founder grew older she showed that she wished to dispossess herself of all personal wealth and to have the money used for the benefit of those in poverty and need' in England.

The Mount Fund

The Mount Fund has the following priority areas, details of which have been taken from the trust's website:

Mental Health – for registered charities with an annual income of up to £1 million working with people with mental health problems. Smaller charities with an income of up to £500,000, particularly those working in rural communities, could be considered for larger grants of up to £20,000 paid over two or more years.

Homelessness – for registered charities with income of up to £1 million (if your charity also provides accommodation, your annual income must be less than £1 million after the deduction of rental income/housing benefit). In this category the trustees will support:

- Church and community shelters
- Advice and support services – the trustees encourage applicants to fund caseworkers providing direct support
- Training and employment opportunities

Health in the Community – charities working to improve health in the community. This could include groups working with young people leaving care, people recovering from domestic violence or people in food poverty. This category is for smaller registered charities (with an income of less than £500,000) for services provided primarily to rural communities. The trustees wish to provide fewer larger grants towards core funding under this category and are inviting applicants to provide details of what they most need funding for and how this will ultimately benefit the health of people in their community. Grants of up to £20,000 will be paid in two annual instalments of up to £10,000 each.

Grant types

Grants are given for projects, general running/core costs (including salaries), advice services, furnishings/equipment and organisational development.

The trustees do not normally consider building costs. Only refurbishment or alterations necessary to bring a building up to standards to meet legislative requirements will be funded.

The Mrs Smith Fund

The Mrs Smith Fund provides block grants to charities that provide small grants to disadvantaged individuals such as:

- Young people leaving state care
- Individuals leaving community, residential or long-term hospital care
- Individuals who have lost their possessions through theft, fire, flood, vandalism, etc.
- Individuals who are being rehoused after living in a refuge and who cannot collect their belongings from previous accommodation
- Individuals in rehabilitation
- Individuals who have to be rehoused due to circumstances beyond their control (e.g. harassment, disability or deterioration of property)

The funding should be used towards the purchase of household furnishings and equipment, baby equipment and, clothing. Grants under this programme are only made once a year.

Financial information

Year end	31/01/2021
Income	£225,600
Assets	£111,300
Grants to organisations	£287,000

Beneficiaries included: Domestic Abuse Volunteer Support Service (£10,000); Braintree Area Foodbank Ltd (£8,000); Home-Start South West Kent (£6,000); Support 4 Sight (£3,000); Our Special Friends (£1,800).

Exclusions

The following will not be supported:

- Individuals
- General counselling
- Charities with an income of over £1 million (or over £500,000 for the Health in the Community category)
- Non-registered charities

Applications

The Mount Fund

All applications must be submitted using the online application form on the trust's website. This can only be accessed by successfully completing the eligibility quiz.

The trustees meet three times per year, in March, July and November, and application forms and supporting documentation must be submitted at least six weeks in advance of a meeting or by the date specified on the website. Unsuccessful applicants can reapply after two years.

The Mrs Smith Fund

If you think your registered charity could be eligible, email a one-page document providing initial details about your work. An application form will then be sent to you if there is an opportunity for funding. The Mount Fund online application form cannot be used to apply to this fund.

Sources of information

Accounts; annual report; Charity Commission record; funder's website.

The DS Smith Charitable Foundation

Education and training and environmental conservation

England and Wales

£280,900 (2019/20)

CC number: 1142817

Correspondent: The Trustees, 7th Floor, 350 Euston Road, London NW1 3AX (tel: 020 7756 1823; email: charitablefoundation@dssmith.com)

Trustees: Emma Ciechan; Mark Reeve; Catriona O'Grady; Wouter van Tol.

www.dssmith.com/sustainability/building-strong-foundations/looking-after-people-and-our-communities/responsible-neighbour/charitable-foundation

General information

The DS Smith Charitable Foundation is the charity of the British-based international packaging business DS Smith plc. Registered in 2011, the foundation supports charities engaged in conservation of the environment and training or education.

The following information was taken from the foundation's website:

> Please note that only charities in the fields of environmental improvement and of education and training, will be considered, so please ensure that any application fulfils this criteria. The charity aims to make a combination of small donations (£1,000 or less) and larger donations each year. We particularly welcome opportunities to develop multi-year partnerships with key selected charities.

Financial information

Year end	30/04/2020
Income	£34,800
Assets	£1,290,000
Grants to organisations	£280,900

Beneficiaries included: Ellen MacArthur Foundation (£150,000); UNICEF (£42,600); The Royal Institute (£10,000); Litter Angels (£6,000); Earth Restoration (£2,000).

Applications

Application forms are available on the foundation's website.

Sources of information

Accounts; annual report; Charity Commission record; funder's website.

The Henry Smith Charity

Social welfare; community services and development; Christian projects; holiday grants for children

UK

£38.38 million (2020)

CC number: 230102

Correspondent: The Trustees, 6th Floor, 65–68 Leadenhall Street, London EC3A 2AD (email: Call back form on website)

Trustees: James Hordern; Piers Feilden; Emir Feisal; Vivienne Dews; Canon Paul Hackwood; Lady Bella Colgrain; Mark Granger; Ben Kernighan; Emma Davies; Heider Ridha; Jonathan Asquith; Faisel Rahman; George Roberts; Andrew Beeforth.

www.henrysmithcharity.org.uk

General information

The charity was founded in 1628 by Henry Smith, a businessman working in the City of London. Today, the charity is among the largest grant-makers in the UK. The charity remains true to the spirit of Henry Smith's will, continuing to combat disadvantage and address the challenges faced by people in need.

Grant programmes

Details of the charity's grant programmes have been taken from its website.

Improving Lives

This programme awards grants to small and medium-sized UK organisations towards project and running costs.

According to the website, the programme's six priority areas are:

- Help at a critical moment – Helping people to rebuild their lives following a crisis, critical moment, trauma or abuse.
- Positive choices – Helping people, whose actions or behaviours have led to negative consequences for themselves and others, to make positive choices.
- Accommodation/housing support – Enabling people to work towards or maintain accommodation.
- Employment and training – Sorting people to move towards or gain employment.
- Financial inclusion, rights and entitlements – Supporting people to overcome their financial problems and ensure that they are able to claim their rights and entitlements.
- Support networks and family – Working with people to develop improved support networks and family relationships.

Strengthening Communities

Running costs grants for small, grass roots, community based organisations working in the most deprived areas of the UK. We fund established organisations with a track record of delivering services directly to beneficiaries and want to fund work that enables:

- People from across the community to participate in activities which improve connectedness, opportunities and wellbeing
- People who are excluded, vulnerable or facing other forms of hardship to have access to community-based services that support positive lasting change
- A stronger, active, more engaged community

Strategic Grants – Advocacy for People with Learning Disabilities and/or Autistic People Programme

Grants to support small to medium sized organisations providing independent advocacy services for People with Learning Disabilities and/or Autistic People.

County Grants

Small grants for small organisations working with disadvantaged people and communities in three English counties.

Holiday Grants

Grants towards recreational trips and holidays for groups of children aged 13 and under who are disabled or disadvantaged.

Christian Projects

Grants to support projects that explicitly promote the Christian faith, helping to grow faith communities and churches.

Kindred

Grants, help and support for individuals descended from the family of our founder, Henry Smith.

Financial information

Year end	31/12/2020
Income	£12,070,000
Assets	£1,202,140,000
Grants to organisations	£38,380,000

Further financial information

Grants were distributed as follows:

Main grants	£27.19 million
Community Match Challenge/COVID-19 grants	£4.47 million
Strategic grants	£3.96 million
Clergy and Christian projects	£1.67 million
County grants	£1.18 million
Kindred grants	£762,000
Holiday grants	£120,000

Beneficiaries included: Action Homeless (Leicester) Ltd (£310,000); Abigail Housing (£153,800); Auckland Youth and Community Centre (£68,200); Listening Post (£20,000); Acheinu Cancer Support (£750).

Exclusions

See the grant-maker's website for a full list of exclusions regarding each grants programme.

Applications

Application processes vary between grant programmes. For application details for a specific grants scheme, along with guidance, see the website.

Sources of information

Accounts; annual report; Charity Commission record; funder's website.

The Sobell Foundation

Jewish charities; disability; care and support for children and older people; relief of poverty

Unrestricted; in practice, England, Wales, Israel and the Commonwealth of Independent States

£5.24 million (2020/21)

CC number: 274369

Correspondent: Penny Newton, Administrator, PO Box 5402, Wincanton, Somerset BA9 0BH (tel: 020 8922 9097; email: pennynewton@sobellfoundation.org.uk)

 www.sobellfoundation.org.uk

General information

The Sobell Foundation was established by the late Sir Michael Sobell in 1977 for general charitable purposes. The settlor was actively involved with the charity until shortly before his death in 1993. Grants tend to be made in line with the founder's interests, which are principally causes benefitting children, older people, people who are in need and people who have an illness or a disability. The website states: 'The trustees aim to achieve a reasonable spread between Jewish charities (operating principally in the UK and Israel) and non-Jewish charities operating in the UK.'

The foundation's website states that to be eligible, applicants must meet the following criteria:

> We consider applications from charities registered with the Charity Commission, or charities that hold a Certificate of Exemption from HMRC. Israeli applicants must supply the details of a UK registered charity through which grants can be channelled on their behalf. We prefer to focus our funding on small national and local charities. We do not accept applications from individuals.
>
> **Which countries do we support?**
>
> We restrict our funding on a geographical basis to England, Wales and Israel and we accept applications from charities based in these countries only.
>
> **What type of work do we support?**
>
> We are happy to consider applications for core funding and projects, and on occasion for capital projects, and we focus our grant-making activity on charities working in the following areas:
>
> England and Wales
>
> - Care, education and training for adults and children with special needs
> - Care and support for the elderly
> - Care and support for vulnerable children and adults
> - Support for carers, respite and palliative care
> - Access to the arts for adults and children with impairments and special needs
>
> Israel
>
> - Co-existence projects
> - Care, education and training for adults and children with special needs
> - Care and support for the elderly

Financial information

Year end	05/04/2021
Income	£1,890,000
Assets	£63,490,000
Grants to organisations	£5,240,000
No. of grants	84

Further financial information

During 2020/21 grants were distributed as follows:

In the UK:

Medical care/treatment	£1.8 million
Community	£778,600
Hardship alleviation	£679,400
Education	£320,500
Cultural and environmental causes	£79,000

In Israel:

Education	£515,500
Medical care/treatment	£464,300

Community	£295,000
Hardship alleviation	£270,000
Cultural and environmental causes	£27,000

Only beneficiaries that received grants of £50,000 and above were listed in the accounts.

Beneficiaries included: The Michael Sobell Hospice (£300,000); Jewish Care (£200,000); Desert Stars (£100,000); Royal Brompton and Harefield NHS Trust (£77,000); World Jewish Relief (£70,000).

Exclusions

Support is not given to/for the following:

- Individuals
- Charities that have never received a grant from the foundation
- Medical research, general medical care and hospital equipment
- Hospices
- Animal welfare
- Mainstream education or sport
- The environment
- Politics and campaigning
- Criminal justice

Applications

Potential applicants should first read the guidelines to determine if they are eligible to apply. If eligible, applicants can apply online through the foundation's website. Applicants, successful or otherwise, may only reapply to the foundation after one year. It is likely to be at least three months before the applicant is informed of the outcome due to the volume of appeals. At the time of writing (April 2022), the foundation was only accepting applications from charities that had received a grant from the foundation in the last five years; however, the website states that this policy is frequently reviewed.

Sources of information

Accounts; annual report; Charity Commission record; funder's website.

Social Investment Business Foundation

General charitable purposes

UK

£5.24 million (2020/21)

CC number: 1117185

Correspondent: The Trustees, 2nd Floor, CAN Mezzanine, 7–14 Great Dover Street, London SE1 4YR (tel: 020 3096 7900; email: enquiries@sibgroup.org.uk)

Trustees: James Rice; Hugh Rolo; Hazel Blears; Jagjit Dosanjh-Elton; Jenny North; Sonali Siriwardena; Richard Pelly; Robert Hewitt.

www.sibgroup.org.uk

facebook.com/socialinvestmentbusiness

@thesocialinvest

General information

The foundation was registered with the Charity Commission in December 2006. It provides loans, grants and strategic support to charities and social enterprises to help them improve people's lives.

The foundation has a number of funds that provide investment readiness grants and social investment for organisations looking to grow their services. Depending on the programme, the charity also offers loans which can be up to £250,000 (or up to £1.5 million in the case of COVID-19 recovery loans). Organisations with loans from the foundation can also access mentoring, legal assistance and other forms of non-financial support.

A variety of funds are administered by the foundation at any one time. These are either on behalf of another charity, or as a partnership between several other funds. See the website for up-to-date information on currently open funds.

Financial information

Year end	31/03/2021
Income	£9,540,000
Assets	£30,200,000
Grants to organisations	£5,240,000

Further financial information

Note: the grant total includes a mix of grants and loans.

Beneficiaries included: A list of beneficiaries was not available.

Exclusions

Refer to the website for exclusions applicable to each specific fund.

Applications

Applications can be made via the foundation's website. Each fund has specific contact details in order for potential applicants to discuss the application process – full details can be found on the funder's website.

Sources of information

Accounts; annual report; Charity Commission record; funder's website.

Societe Generale UK Foundation

Education and employability

UK and overseas

£577,900 (2020)

CC number: 1039013

Correspondent: Rachel Iles, 1 Bank Street, London E14 4SG (tel: 020 7597 3065; email: rachel.iles@sghambros.com)

Trustees: Ben Higgins; Jasvant Singh; Elise Sabran; John Oberman.

General information

This foundation is the corporate charity of Societe Generale, the investment bank of the same name.

According to its 2020 annual report, the foundation's main objective is to support Societe Generale's global citizenship guidelines of inclusion through education and employability. Although, the foundation will occasionally make grants for more general charitable purposes.

Grants are made to UK-registered charities with beneficiaries either overseas or in the UK, as well as organisations with a charitable purpose such as schools and hospitals (including social enterprises).

Types of funding

The foundation's main funding streams include:

- **Matched funding:** Societe Generale staff can apply for matched funding either linked to fundraising organised by the group itself for its charity partner, or for other fundraising efforts within the foundation's criteria
- **Key projects:** one-off or rolling donations to strategic education/employability projects which link to the bank's citizenship programme
- **Specific projects:** this funding is reserved for the Shake Climate Change project, a new nine-year programme established by Rothamsted Research in conjunction with leading academic institutions, to support entrepreneurs combatting climate change in agriculture and food production
- **Ad hoc donations:** Exceptional one-off donations and matching to support emergency appeals

Financial information

Year end	31/12/2020
Income	£292,800
Assets	£6,860,000
Grants to organisations	£577,900

Beneficiaries included: Young Lives vs Cancer (£198,500); East London Business Alliance (£41,000); National Emergencies Trust (£25,000); Alzheimer's Society (£11,100); Bristol Black Carers (£2,800); The Old Church (£2,000).

Exclusions

According to its 2020 annual report, the foundation does not support:

- Organisations which are concerned solely with promoting religious beliefs,

political parties and affiliated groups, drugs or research and animals.
- Organisations with overseas beneficiaries which are registered in the UK and work outside the scope of education and employment.
- Organisations with overseas beneficiaries which are not registered in the UK whether they work within or outside the scope of education and employment.
- Organisations whose work does not fit with Societe Generale's values and who could damage the reputation of the Societe Generale Group

Applications

The foundation does not accept unsolicited applications.

Sources of information

Accounts; annual report; Charity Commission record.

Sodexo Stop Hunger Foundation

Health, hunger, nutrition and well-being; social welfare; disadvantaged communities; life skills

UK and Ireland

£288,900 (2019/20)

CC number: 1110266

Correspondent: The Trustees, Sodexo, 1 Southampton Row, London WC1B 5HA (tel: 020 7404 0110; email: stophunger@sodexo.com)

Trustees: Gareth John; David Mulcahy; Patrick Forbes; Sean Haley; Samanthan Scott; Simon McCluskey; Nicholas Byrom; Laura Brimacombe.

 http://uk.stop-hunger.org/home.html

 facebook.com/SodexoUKIreland

 @stop_hungeruk

General information

Registered with the Charity Commission in June 2005, the Sodexo Stop Hunger Foundation is the corporate charity of the food services and facilities management company, Sodexo Ltd.

According to its website, the foundation is 'a grant giving organisation, with the aim of working with the very best charities that exist to:
- Tackle hunger and malnutrition
- Promote healthy lifestyles
- Develop life skills such as cooking'

The foundation provides regular support to a number of organisations such as FareShare and The Trussell Trust, but is open to grant applications from other charities which meet the foundation's criteria. Grantees may also receive volunteer support from Sodexo employees.

Financial information

Year end	31/08/2020
Income	£617,500
Assets	£202,400
Grants to organisations	£288,900
No. of grants	15

Beneficiaries included: FareShare (£84,000); The Trussell Trust (£70,000); SSAFA Forces Help (£45,000); Oasis Community Partnerships (£10,000); Alexander Rose Charity and Volunteer Centre Tower Hamlets (£5,000 each); Berkshire Autistic Society (£2,200).

Applications

For further information on the support available, complete the contact form on the foundation's website.

Sources of information

Accounts; annual report; Charity Commission record; funder's website.

Sofronie Foundation

Education and training for disadvantaged young people; STEM education

UK; France; the Netherlands

£1.29 million (2020)

CC number: 1118621

Correspondent: The Trustees, 16 Great Queen Street, London WC2B 5DH (tel: 020 7421 3330; email: enquiries@sofronie.org)

Trustees: Harold Goddijn; Corinne Goddijn-Vigreux; Ajay Soni; Boris Walbaum.

 www.sofronie.org

General information

The Sofronie Foundation was established in 2008 and aims to help young people by offering them opportunities with which they can improve their employment chances.

The foundation's website states:

> Sofronie is dedicated to supporting projects that provide young people with skills for jobs and programmes that increase access to higher education
>
> The Foundation works with charities and not for profit organisations that focus on improving the lives of disadvantaged young people through educational or vocational programmes.
>
> We particularly encourage a close working relationship with smaller programmes that have the potential to scale up and become more established.
>
> Evaluation processes are important to gauge and review the success of programmes and are an essential component of our grant making terms.
>
> **Supporting the STEM specialists of the future**
>
> Our focus for the immediate future is improving academic performances with an emphasis on STEM (Science, Technology, Engineering and Mathematics) skills and vocational programmes.
>
> STEM skills are expected to provide many opportunities in the future, and building competencies and awareness around this sector will ensure our young people are better prepared for future employment.
>
> We are currently focusing our work in the UK, France and the Netherlands.

The foundation makes grants to organisations in each of these three countries. Grants are typically of between £10,000 and £80,000 and may be committed for several years.

Financial information

Year end	31/12/2020
Income	£1,520,000
Assets	£33,350,000
Grants to organisations	£1,290,000

Beneficiaries included: Codam (£1.69 million); IntoUniversity and the Social Mobility Foundation (£50,000 each); TechMeUP (£42,200); Stichting Move (£9,300).

Applications

Apply via the foundation's website. Applications can be made at any time but it may take up to three months to receive a decision from the trustees.

Sources of information

Accounts; annual report; Charity Commission record; funder's website.

The Souter Charitable Trust

Relief of human suffering, particularly projects promoting spiritual welfare

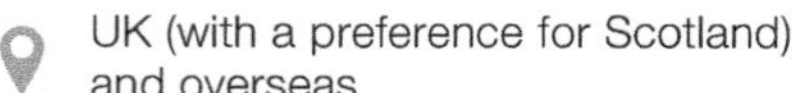

UK (with a preference for Scotland) and overseas

£9.26 million (2019/20)

OSCR number: SC029998

Correspondent: Dion Judd, Trust Administrator, PO Box 7412, Perth, Perthshire PH1 5YX (tel: 01738 450408; email: application@soutercharitabletrust.org.uk)

Trustees: Sir Brian Souter; Lady Elizabeth Souter; Ann Allen.

 www.soutercharitabletrust.org.uk

General information

This trust was established in 1992 by Scottish businessman Sir Brian Souter, one of the founders of the Stagecoach transport company, and his wife Lady Elizabeth Souter. It supports UK-registered charities carrying out projects that aid the relief of human suffering in the UK and overseas. The trust's founders are both committed Christians and are particularly interested in projects that also promote spiritual welfare.

There is no minimum or maximum grant; however, the average grant tends to be of £5,000 or less. A small number of higher value grants are also awarded annually. Small grants may be awarded for gap-year or short-term projects that last for at least one calendar year. The majority of grants are one-off, but a small number of projects receive support over a period of three years. Support is usually provided for revenue costs.

Financial information

Year end	30/06/2020
Income	£112,130,000
Assets	£90,120,000
Grants to organisations	£9,260,000

Further financial information

Only beneficiaries of grants of £15,000 and above were listed in the trust's 2019/20 accounts. Grants of under £15,000 totalled £3.84 million.

Beneficiaries included: Mail Force (£500,000); Hope for Justice (£379,200); Tearfund (£293,300); Venture Trust (£150,000); Bethany Christian Trust (£66,700); Destiny Church (£50,000); Social Bite (£20,000); Lunchbowl Network (£15,000).

Exclusions

The trust does not provide funding for capital building or renovation work. Grants will not be awarded to any organisation that is not a UK-registered charity. Individuals are generally not supported.

Applications

Apply in writing to the correspondent via post or email. The trust's website states:

> Applications should be kept short, 2 sides of A4 is sufficient. The trustees are looking for a brief outline of the project aims and what the funding is required for. A budget maybe included and a copy of your latest audited accounts should be included. The trustees generally meet once a month and all applications, whether successful or not, are acknowledged in due course.

Check the trust's website for current deadlines.

Sources of information

Accounts; annual report; OSCR record; funder's website.

W. F. Southall Trust

Quaker work and witness; peace-making and conflict resolution; environmental action and sustainability; social action

UK and overseas

£271,800 (2020/21)

CC number: 218371

Correspondent: Wil Berdinner, Trust Secretary, School House, Mytholm Bank, Hebden Bridge, West Yorkshire HX7 6DL (tel: 0300 111 1937; email: a contact form is available on the trust's website)

Trustees: Annette Wallis; Donald Southall; Joanna Engelkamp; Mark Holtom; Richard Maw; Hannah Engelkamp; Andrew Southall; Philip Coventry; Lucy Greaves; Holly Wallis.

 https://southalltrust.org

General information

This Quaker-based and family-run trust was established in 1937 by Wilfred Francis Southall, a pharmaceutical chemist from Birmingham.

The trust awards around £300,000 in grants per year to registered UK charities that are working in one or more of the following fields:

- Quaker work and witness
- Environmental action and sustainability
- Peace and reconciliation
- Social action

The trust's website states that preference is given to the following:

- Projects that encourage wider support of the categories listed above
- Projects where grants of up to £5,000 will make a quantifiable difference (we prefer to support smaller charities with 'seed corn' funding)
- Grassroots initiatives
- Charities that show creativity and innovation in their work
- Charities that promote social justice, inclusion and diversity
- Charities that challenge structural inequalities and injustice
- Charities making good use of volunteers
- Charities that are engaged with their local community and show clear evidence of support from within it (e.g. through local giving, volunteering and/or partnerships)

Applications from charities working overseas may be considered if they are registered with one of the main UK charity regulators. Grants are usually one-off but multi-year funding will be considered, typically for charities that have been supported in previous years. Funding is available for both core and capital costs.

Financial information

Year end	05/04/2021
Income	£251,500
Assets	£13,560,000
Grants to organisations	£271,800
No. of grants	83

Beneficiaries included: Britain Yearly Meeting (£50,000); Quaker Tapestry (£10,000); Rookhow, Meanwood Valley Urban Farm and Quaker Social Action (£5,000 each); Team Kenya, Five Talents UK and Faithworks Wessex (£3,000 each).

Exclusions

According to its website, the trust will not support the following:

- Emergency appeals
- Private schools
- Medical charities
- Animal welfare charities
- Individuals, groups, families or organisations that are not registered with the Charity Commission of England and Wales, the Charity Commission of Northern Ireland or OSCR (an exception is granted for Quaker Meeting Houses, so long as they hold charitable status.)
- Retrospective funding (i.e. funding for a project or work that has already taken place)
- Charities with a primary focus not fitting within one of our categories
- Charities that are national household names
- Charities with a typical annual income in excess of £1m (although, exceptions are sometimes made for charities that we have funded in the past, charities with whom our trustees have a personal connection, and charities that are a particularly strong fit in our category areas and meet most of our criteria – do get in touch before applying if your charity size is larger than £1m)
- Charities that have not complied with Charity Commission regulations (e.g. late annual returns)
- Charities that do not have at least one set of annual accounts filed with a UK charity regulator
- Charities with a high level of free reserves and/or no clear reserves policy
- Charities spending less than 80% of their annual expenditure on charitable activities
- Projects that involve counselling services are often unsuccessful

Applications

Applicants should first complete the trust's online eligibility checker; applicants that meet the criteria will then be provided with a link to the downloadable application form.

The trust aims to respond to applications for amounts of £5,000 or less within two to four months. Applications for amounts of more than £5,000 usually take longer to process as they are considered at the trustees' meetings which are held in March and November each year.

Note: the trust does not accept postal applications. Any correspondence with the trust should be by phone or email (a contact form is available on the trust's website).

Sources of information

Accounts; annual report; Charity Commission record; funder's website.

Peter Sowerby Foundation

Medical research; health and social care; education; community; the environment and conservation; the arts

UK, with some preference for North Yorkshire

£1.37 million (2019/20)

CC number: 1151978

Correspondent: David Aspinall, Chair of Trustees, 29 St John's Lane, Clerkenwell, London EC1M 4NA (tel: 0300 030 1151; email: info@petersowerbyfoundation.org.uk)

Trustees: David Aspinall; Sara Poulios; Prof. Carole Longson; Dr David Stables.

https://petersowerbyfoundation.org.uk

@petersowerbyfdn

General information

The foundation was established in 2011 with a large endowment from Dr Peter Sowerby, a former GP and medical entrepreneur.

The foundation makes grants in the following areas:

- Medical research and health, and social care
- Education
- Community
- The environment and conservation
- The arts

Grants are distributed through two main funds:

- **Good Causes Fund** – for a wide variety of projects, typically in the areas of healthcare, social care, community, the environment and conservation, education and the arts. The size of grants awarded ranges from small grants of a few thousand pounds to significant multi-year grants of over £100,000
- **Health Breakthrough Fund** – larger-scale grants for projects that are providing innovation and transformation in health and social care. From time to time, open calls are held – for updates, register your interest through the website

According to the foundation's 2019/20 accounts, 'the trustees typically favour innovative and catalytic projects, which hold the potential to influence policy and practice elsewhere'. The trustees also look for projects that use technology effectively as well as those that don't meet the criteria for mainstream funding.

Grants are awarded to charities, CICs, and registered social and healthcare providers.

The foundation does not seek unsolicited applications as it actively solicits proposals directly from relevant organisations.

Financial information

Year end	30/09/2020
Income	£596,000
Assets	£37,540,000
Grants to organisations	£1,370,000
No. of grants	21

Further financial information

Grants were awarded to 21 organisations during the year.

Beneficiaries included: The Sanata Charitable Trust (£250,000); Alzheimer's Society (£163,600); British Red Cross (£150,000); Two Ridings – Covid 19 Fund (£100,000); Guy's and St Thomas' Charity (£75,000); Orchestras Live (£25,000); Theodora Children's Charity (£7,400).

Applications

The foundation does not seek unsolicited applications. However, if you believe that your idea is closely aligned with the foundation's aims, you may fill in an online form on the charity's website, outlining your project, budget and proposed timeline. Occasionally, open calls for funding for health and social care projects are advertised on the website – sign up to the mailing list for updates.

Sources of information

Accounts; annual report; Charity Commission record; funder's website.

The Spear Charitable Trust

General charitable purposes, with some preference for animal welfare, the environment and health

Mainly UK

£783,100 (2020)

CC number: 1041568

Correspondent: Flora Gaughan, Administrator, Roughground House, Old Hall Green, Ware, Hertfordshire SG11 1HB (tel: 01920 823071)

Trustees: Nigel Gooch; Philip Harris; Hazel Spear.

General information

Established in 1994 with general charitable purposes, this trust has particular interest in helping employees and former employees of J. W. Spear and Sons plc and their families and dependants. Grants are given to UK organisations and occasionally overseas.

Financial information

Year end	31/12/2020
Income	£118,400
Assets	£9,950,000
Grants to organisations	£783,100

Beneficiaries included: Royal Philatelic Society London (£750,000); Doctor Graham's Homes (£4,500); Salvation Army (£2,500); Pekinese Rescue and Stamp Active Network (£1,000 each).

Exclusions

Appeals from individuals (other than employees or former employees of J. W. Spear and Sons plc and their dependants) are not considered.

Applications

Apply in writing to the correspondent. The trustees state in their annual report that they will make grants without a formal application but they encourage organisations to provide feedback on how grants are used. Feedback will be used for monitoring the quality of grants and will form the basis of assessment for any further applications.

Sources of information

Accounts; annual report; Charity Commission record.

Michael and Sarah Spencer Foundation

Health; social welfare; education; the environment

Worldwide, with a preference for the UK

£659,900 (2020/21)

CC number: 1184658

Correspondent: The Trustees, 3rd Floor, 39 Sloane Street, London SW1X 9LP (tel: 020 7448 0377; email: michelle.mooney@ipgl.london)

Trustees: Michael Spencer; Sarah Spencer; Marina Ritossa.

General information

This foundation was established in 2019. According its 2020/21 accounts, it has the following objects:

- The relief of sickness and preservation of health among people anywhere in the world by providing and assisting in

the provision of equipment facilities and services
- The prevention or relief of poverty anywhere in the world by providing grants, items and services to individuals in need and to charities or other organizations working to prevent or relieve poverty
- For the benefit of the public to promote the education of people anywhere in the world in such ways as the trustees think fit including by the provision of grants and financial assistance to enable individuals to study at any school college or university or other education institution and assisting any charity or other institution whose aims include advancing the education of people anywhere in the world
- The advancement of environmental protection and improvement for the benefit of the public by the protection and conservation of animals

Financial information

Year end	31/03/2021
Income	£574,000
Assets	£88,400
Grants to organisations	£659,900

Beneficiaries included: A list of beneficiaries was not available. Previous beneficiaries include: Worth Abbey School Development (£6.25 million) and Corpus Christi College (£5 million).

Applications

Apply in writing to the correspondent. The foundation's 2020/21 accounts state:

> The Trust welcomes grant applications which are discussed in the quarterly meetings attended by all Trustees.

Sources of information

Accounts; annual report; Charity Commission record.

The Spoore, Merry and Rixman Foundation

Education and training and children and young people

Maidenhead and Bray, covering the postcode area SL6 1–9 (see the map on the website)

£526,300 (2020)

CC number: 309040

Correspondent: Clerk to the Trustees, PO Box 4787, Maidenhead, Berkshire SL60 1JA (tel: 020 3286 8300; email: clerk@smrfmaidenhead.org)

Trustees: Grahame Fisher; Tony Hill; Ann Redgrave; Ian Thomas; Barbara Wielechowski; Philip Love; David Coppinger; Cllr Gerry Clark; Cllr Donna Stimson; Mayor Story.

 www.smrfmaidenhead.org.uk

General information

The origins of the foundation date back to the 17th century when Abraham Spoore, Elizabeth Merry and Mary Rixman left money derived from rents and investments to be spent for educational purposes on local children in Bray and Maidenhead. Since then, thousands of schoolchildren have benefitted from their generosity and have been helped to fulfil their educational potential.

The foundation provides grants to children and young people under the age of 25 for items such as school trips, residential courses, tuition in the arts or music, sporting equipment, musical instruments and uniforms.

Grants are also made to schools for items not funded by statutory budgets (e.g. for the development of school grounds or for specialised equipment, lighting, staging, musical instruments and so on). Other organisations for young people, such as youth clubs, are able to apply for grants to provide facilities which are educational in the wider sense.

Financial information

Year end	31/12/2020
Income	£327,300
Assets	£11,740,000
Grants to organisations	£526,300

Beneficiaries included: A list of beneficiaries was not available.

Applications

Applications can be made online or via post. See the foundation's website for details on how to apply, as application forms differ depending on the purpose of the funding. The foundation asks that applications made by post are not sent via recorded or registered post. Trustee meeting dates can be found on the website.

Sources of information

Accounts; annual report; Charity Commission record; funder's website.

The Geoff and Fiona Squire Foundation

General charitable purposes; medicine; education; disability; the welfare and healthcare of children

UK

£762,200 (2020/21)

CC number: 1085553

Correspondent: The Trustees, 18 Henry Moore Court, Manresa Road, London SW3 6AS (tel: 07759 636799; email: squirefoundation.temp@btinternet.com)

Trustees: Geoff Squire; Fiona Squire; Bartholomew Peerless.

General information

Established in 2001, the foundation has general charitable purposes, with a particular interest in medicine, education, disability and the welfare and healthcare of children. The foundation achieves its aims by making grants to registered charities in the UK. The foundation's 2020/21 annual report states it will 'work in partnership with other organisations to fund initiatives beyond the financial means of a single organisation'.

Financial information

Year end	31/03/2021
Income	£144,400
Assets	£9,130,000
Grants to organisations	£762,200
No. of grants	75

Beneficiaries included: Teenage Cancer Trust (£68,900); Wessex Children's Hospice Trust (£30,000); Support Dogs (£21,000); Leeds Cares (£13,500); Royal National College for the Blind (£8,000); Cerebral Palsy Plus (£5,000); Children's Heart Federation (£1,300); Dunedin School (£350).

Exclusions

In previous annual reports, the foundation has stated that it does not normally consider applications from large national charities (with an income of over £10 million or assets of more than £100 million), or from charities dedicated to issues that the trustees deem to be already well funded in the UK.

Applications

Apply in writing to the correspondent.

Sources of information

Accounts; annual report; Charity Commission record.

The Vichai Srivaddhanaprabha Foundation

General charitable purposes

Leicestershire and Rutland

£698,400 (2020/21)

CC number: 1144791

Correspondent: The Trustees, King Power Stadium, Filbert Way, Leicester, LE2 7FL (tel: 0116 229 4737; email: VSFoundation@lcfc.co.uk)

Trustees: Susan Whelan; Simon Capper; Tony Lander; Alan Birchenall.

 www.lcfc.com/fans-community/foundation/foundation-overview

General information

The foundation was established in 2011 as the LCFC Foxes Foundation. In November 2018 it was renamed The

Vichai Srivaddhanaprabha Foundation in honour of Leicester City's late chair, Khun Vichai, who tragically lost his life in a helicopter accident. The foundation is primarily operated by employees of Leicester City Football Club.

The foundation's website states:

> Money raised over the years has gone towards a number of important causes, including the funding of a renovation of Leicester Royal Infirmary's Children's Outpatient Ward and life-saving equipment desperately needed by the Children's Intensive Care Unit.
>
> The Vichai Srivaddhanaprabha Foundation has supported dozens of local causes throughout its seven years, including Leicester Hospitals Charity, LOROS, Rainbows Children's Hospice, Leicestershire Children's Holiday Centre and by installing life-saving defibrillators in key areas around the county.

The foundation's annual Gift of a Wish programme supports a range of community causes throughout Leicestershire and Rutland.

Financial information

Year end	31/05/2021
Income	£311,200
Assets	£147,000
Grants to organisations	£698,400

Beneficiaries included: British Legion; Hope Foundation for Cancer Research; Leicester Hospitals; OPCC For Leicestershire; Rainbows; The Adhar Project; The Laura Centre.

Applications

See the foundation's website for further information on open grant programmes.

Sources of information

Accounts; Annual Report; Charity Commission record; funder's website.

St James's Place Charitable Foundation

Disadvantaged young people; combating cancer; supporting hospices; mental health

UK and overseas

£11.06 million (2020)

CC number: 1144606

Correspondent: The Trustees, St James's Place House, 1 Tetbury Road, Cirencester, Gloucestershire GL7 1FP (tel: 01285 878037; email: sjp.foundation@sjp.co.uk)

Trustees: Malcolm Cooper-Smith; Andrew Croft; Ian Gascoigne; Sonia Gravestock; Andrew Humphries; Robert Edwards; Sir Mark Weinberg.

 www.sjpfoundation.co.uk

General information

The foundation is the corporate charity of St James's Place Wealth Management, a UK wealth management group. The foundation's grant-making in the UK is guided by four themes:

- **Supporting Young People (special needs or disadvantaged):** grants are focused on supporting children and young people under the age of 25 who are disadvantaged, who are young carers, or who have physical or mental health difficulties or life-threatening degenerative conditions. Grants are made for small capital items, support for staff working directly with beneficiaries, and support for projects of direct benefit to beneficiaries
- **Supporting People with Cancer:** grants are given for capital items of direct benefit to cancer patients, towards the salary of staff working directly with cancer patients, and for projects aimed at increasing the quality of life for cancer patients
- **Supporting Hospices:** grants are given to hospices working with all age ranges. The foundation is currently working with Hospice UK, which will distribute funds to hospices on the foundation's behalf, and, therefore, does not invite applications from hospices directly
- **Mental Health**

Funds are administered via two grant programmes:

- **Small Grants Programme:** grants of up to £10,000 are available to UK charities with an annual income of up to £1 million (this restriction does not apply to special needs schools or mainstream schools with a special needs unit)
- **Major Grants Programme:** grants for up to two or three years for capital items or revenue. This programme is by invitation only

The foundation's website states:

> Approximately 90% of the money raised goes to supporting UK charities, with the remaining 10% being allocated to charities overseas, particularly those helping children and young people to escape poverty, malnutrition and neglect. The Overseas grants programme is open via invitation only through the St. James's Place Community.

Financial information

Year end	31/12/2020
Income	£9,540,000
Assets	£4,300,000
Grants to organisations	£11,060,000
No. of grants	807

Further financial information

Grants were broken down as follows:

Disadvantaged children and young people	42%
COVID-19 emergency relief	22%
Children and young people with special needs	19%
Hospices	9%
Mental health	4%
Cancer	2%
Other	2%

A sample of recent UK beneficiaries has been taken from the foundation's website (note that these are grants awarded in 2021).

Beneficiaries included: Panathlon Foundation (£1 million); The OnSide Foundation (£500,000); School-Home Support (£120,000); Meningitis Now (£80,000); Centrestage Communities Ltd (£40,000); ThinkForward UK (£20,000); The Music Works (£5,000).

Exclusions

The foundation does not provide support to/for:

- Charities with reserves of over 50% of income
- Administrative costs
- Activities that are primarily the responsibility of statutory agencies
- NHS charities
- Pilot programmes
- Retrospective requests
- Research
- Events
- Advertising
- Holidays
- Sponsorship
- Contributions to large capital appeals
- Charities that are raising funds on behalf of another charity
- CICs

The Small Grants Programme has a policy of not granting more than £10,000 to the same charity in any two-year period.

Applications

At the time of writing (February 2022) the foundation was not accepting unsolicited applications until further notice. The foundation was inviting select charities to apply. Check the foundation's website for updates.

Sources of information

Accounts; annual report; Charity Commission record; guidelines for applicants; funder's website.

St John's Foundation Est. 1174

Health and well-being; housing; isolation; poverty; relationships; employment and skills

Bath and North East Somerset

£1.11 million (2020)

CC number: 201476

Correspondent: Louise Harvey, Director of Funding and Impact, St John's Hospital, 4–5 Chapel Court, Bath BA1 1SQ (tel: 01225 486400; email: info@stjohnsbath.org.uk)

Trustee: St John's Hospital Trustee Ltd.

 www.stjohnsbath.org.uk/funding-support

 facebook.com/stjohnsbath

 @stjohns1174

General information

St John's Foundation began life in 1174 when Bishop Reginald Fitzjocelyn established a refuge for poor and vulnerable people in his parish. Since then, the charity has continued to provide support and accommodation to the local community.

In 2021 the foundation's grants programme, called the Foundation Fund, changed its focus with an ambition to significantly reduce the educational attainment gap in Bath and North East Somerset (BaNES) by 2029. According to the foundation's website, the fund is designed to target 'children from pre-birth up until they start secondary school, providing them with the best opportunities to contribute to our communities for generations to come'.

The foundation's website states:

> This new direction will see us hone our expertise in the provision of funding and become the initiators of major social change. St John's aims to be an integral part of bringing about transformation in BaNES, acting as a focal point for diverse organisations to collaborate and support childhood development.

The fund aims to ensure every child has access to:

- Nutritious food every day
- A safe place for out of school hours
- Specialist support for behavioural and emotional needs
- Additional help with reading, writing, oracy and mathematics

The foundation also makes grants to individuals and families in need through its Crisis Programme. The programme can be accessed through a referral process.

Financial information

Year end	31/12/2020
Income	£5,200,000
Assets	£120,960,000
Grants to organisations	£1,110,000
No. of grants	76

Further financial information

Only organisations that received grants of £15,000 or more were listed in the 2020 accounts.

Beneficiaries included: Bath Mind (£40,000); We Hear You (£30,000); Make a Move and HorseWorld Trust (£25,000 each); Designability (£20,000); The Nest Project (£19,600); Read Around Bath (£15,600).

Applications

Contact the foundation for more information on the application process.

Sources of information

Accounts; annual report; Charity Commission record; funder's website.

St Monica Trust

Social welfare; older people and adults with a long-term illness or disability

Bristol and the surrounding area

£513,800 (2020)

CC number: 202151

Correspondent: Community Fund Team, Cote Lane, Westbury-on-Trym, Bristol BS9 3UN (tel: 0117 949 4003; email: community.fund@stmonicatrust.org.uk)

Trustee: St Monica Trustee Company Ltd.

 www.stmonicatrust.org.uk

 facebook.com/stmonicatrust

 @St_Monica_Trust

General information

The St Monica Trust has provided accommodation, care and support for older people, including those with disabilities, for over 90 years. The trust aims to provide sheltered accommodation, 'extra care' housing, care at home, care and support and nursing care for older people, especially those living with Alzheimer's disease and other forms of dementia.

Another branch of the trust's work, the Community Fund, offers financial help to individuals to help pay for essential items, such as wheelchairs or adaptations to an individual's home, and in the form of monthly payments.

The Community Fund also provides grants to organisations in the beneficial area which provide support and services to older people and adults with a physical disability or long-term illness.

Financial information

Year end	31/12/2020
Income	£44,110,000
Assets	£305,580,000
Grants to organisations	£513,800
No. of grants	70

Beneficiaries included: A list of beneficiaries was not available. Previous beneficiaries include: Citizens Advice (£9,800); St Peter's Hospice, Headway Bristol and Motor Neurone Disease Association (£7,500 each); IT Help@Home (£5,000); The New Place (£3,900); Bristol and Avon Chinese Women's Group (£2,000); Bath Institute of Medical Engineering (£1,500); Western Active Stroke Group (£1,000).

Exclusions

Grants are not awarded for holidays, gardening, bankruptcy fees, funeral expenses, decorating labour costs, respite care, care home fees or daily living costs.

Applications

An application form can be found on the trust's website. The correspondent can be contacted for further information.

Sources of information

Accounts; annual report; Charity Commission record; funder's website.

Stadium Charitable Trust

General charitable purposes; medical causes; health and sickness; sport and recreation

 UK

£923,600 (2020/21)

CC number: 328522

Correspondent: The Trustees, The Stadium Group, Welton Grange, Cowgate, Welton, East Yorkshire HU15 1NB (tel: 01482 667149; email: info@stadiumcity.co.uk)

Trustees: Edwin Healey; Anne Rozenbroek; Andrew Fish.

General information

The trust was established in 1989 with an initial gift from the Healey family. The trust mainly supports health and recreation and tends to support smaller charities. Its 2020/21 annual accounts state:

> The Charity accepts applicants from a wide range of parties but generally seeks to make small donations to local causes where the Trustees believe they can make the most difference.

Financial information

Year end	05/04/2021
Income	£1,000,000
Assets	£734,800
Grants to organisations	£923,600
No. of grants	27

Further financial information

During the year the trust made 27 grants to organisations.

Beneficiaries included: Dove House Hospice (£500,000); Hey Smile Foundation (£200,000); Algarve Biomedical Centre (£50,000); Sincere Support (£20,000); Sailors' Children's Society (£10,000); Asthma Relief (£3,000); Walton and Brough Sports Club (£1,000); The Children's Society (£500).

Applications

Apply in writing to the correspondent.

Sources of information

Accounts; annual report; Charity Commission record.

The Stafford Trust

General charitable purposes; animal welfare; armed forces; children; community projects; medical research; overseas appeals; sea rescue

UK, with a strong preference for Scotland

£282,300 (2020/21)

OSCR number: SC018079

Correspondent: Billy Russell, Trust Administrator, c/o Dickson Middleton CA, PO Box 14, 20 Barnton Street, Stirling, Stirlingshire FK8 1NE (tel: 01786 474718; email: staffordtrust@dicksonmiddleton.co.uk)

Trustees: Gordon Wylie; Ian Ferguson; Robert Hogg; Fiona Gillespie.

 www.staffordtrust.org.uk

General information

The Stafford Trust was established in 1991 by the late Mrs Gay Stafford of Sauchie Estate near Stirling. During her lifetime, Mrs Stafford made substantial gifts to the trust and on her death in 2005, the residue of her estate was bequeathed to the trust.

The trust makes grants to charitable organisations in the UK, with a preference towards Scotland. Support is given to a wide range of causes including:

- Child welfare
- Medical research and support
- Animal welfare
- Services personnel welfare
- Sea rescue
- Community projects
- Overseas support
- Adult welfare

Financial information

Year end	05/04/2021
Income	£479,400
Assets	£31,350,000
Grants to organisations	£282,300

Further financial information

Grants were broken down as follows:

Adult welfare	£102,500
Medical research and support	£50,800
Children and young people	£38,900
Community projects	£37,800
Service personnel welfare	£21,100
Overseas appeals and support	£15,500
Sea rescue	£10,000
Animal welfare	£6,100

Beneficiaries included: Young Lives vs Cancer (£10,000); The Hidden Gardens Trust (£5,000); Edinburgh Young Carers (£4,700); Back Up (£3,000); Any Dog'll Do Rescue (£1,100); Edinburgh Direct Aid (£1,000).

Exclusions

According to its website, the trust does not normally support:

- Religious and political organisations
- Retrospective requests
- Student travel or expeditions
- General or mailshot appeals

Applications

An application form can be downloaded from the trust's website. The trustees usually meet twice a year, in spring and autumn, to review applications. Deadlines are posted on the website.

Sources of information

Accounts; annual report; OSCR record; funder's website.

Standard Chartered Foundation

Social welfare; education; physical disabilities (visual impairments); young people

 UK and overseas

 £8.48 million (2020)

CC number: 1184946

Correspondent: The Trustees, Standard Chartered Bank, 1 Basinghall Avenue, London EC2V 5DD (tel: 020 7885 6701; email: Marina.Azdejkovic@sc.com)

Trustees: Andrew Halford; David Fein; Elizabeth Lloyd; Iraj Ispahani; Simon Cooper; Tracey McDermott.

 www.sc.com/en/sustainability/investing-in-communities/scfoundation

General information

This foundation was registered with the Charity Commission in August 2019. The foundation is the corporate charity of Standard Chartered Bank, an international bank present in 60 markets across the world. The bank is among the top 100 largest companies listed on the London Stock Exchange.

Standard Chartered has been Liverpool Football Club's main sponsor since 2010. Through this partnership, Standard Chartered and the club have engaged in many philanthropic pursuits. The Goal Programme is one of these initiatives, which aims to empower young girls through sport. Players from the Liverpool FC Women visited Zambia and South Africa to coach soccer clinics as part of the programme.

The foundation will award grants to other organisations and charities working with young people from low-income families, particularly girls and people with visual impairments. The foundation's website states that it will fund programmes in the areas of education, employability, entrepreneurship and eye health.

The foundation has been chosen as Standard Charter's lead partner in delivering the Futuremakers initiative, which aims to raise US$50 million between 2019 and 2023 to empower the next generation to 'learn, earn and grow'.

Financial information

Year end	31/12/2020
Income	£25,230,000
Assets	£27,910,000
Grants to organisations	£8,480,000

Further financial information

Grants were broken down as follows: employability (£3.78 million); entrepreneurship (£2.85 million); education (£1.83 million).

Beneficiaries included: Youth Business International (£1.08 million); St James Settlement (£641,000); St John Ambulance (£395,000); British Asian Trust (£300,000); The Garden of Hope Foundation (£152,500); Skills Builder (£31,800).

Applications

Contact the foundation for more information. Note: the foundation does not consider unsolicited grant applications.

Sources of information

Charity Commission record; funder's website.

Staples Trust

Gender issues (domestic violence, women's rights and gender studies); indigenous people's rights; human rights; civil liberties

UK and overseas; Oxfordshire

£370,100 (2020/21)

CC number: 1010656

Correspondent: The Trustees, The Peak, 5 Wilton Road, London SW1V 1AP (tel: 020 7410 0330; email: info@sfct.org.uk)

Trustees: Judith Portrait; Timothy Sainsbury; Jessica Sainsbury; Prof. Peter Frankopan.

 www.sfct.org.uk

General information

The Staples Trust is one of the Sainsbury Family Charitable Trusts, which share a joint administration but work autonomously as independent legal entities. They have a common approach to grant-making and generally discourage applications from organisations not already in contact with the trust concerned, but some are open to unsolicited approaches.

The trust's main areas of interest are:

- Gender issues – domestic violence, women's rights and gender studies
- Overseas projects which support the rights of indigenous peoples
- Charities which defend human rights and civil liberties

In addition to these areas, the trust manages The Frankopan Fund, which provides small grants to exceptionally talented students from Croatia to further their studies. Further information on the fund's eligibility criteria and application process can be found on the Staples Trust's website.

Financial information

Year end	05/04/2021
Income	£322,800
Assets	£15,380,000
Grants to organisations	£370,100

Beneficiaries included: University of Cambridge (£250,000); The Prince's Trust (£25,000); InsightShare (£20,000); Oxford Foodbank and Swindon Women's Aid (£5,000 each).

Exclusions

Grants are not normally made to individuals.

Applications

According to the trust's website, the trustees 'initiate most of the proposals they wish to consider and tend not to accept unsolicited applications'.

Sources of information

Accounts; annual report; Charity Commission record; funder's website.

Starlow Charities Ltd

Causes affecting the Orthodox Jewish community, including the relief of poverty, religion and religious education, and other charitable purposes

UK and overseas

£1.21 million (2019/20)

CC number: 1081386

Correspondent: The Trustees, 9 Craven Walk, London N16 6BS (tel: 020 8802 9517; email: mail@cohenarnold.com)

Trustees: Eve Low; Abraham Low; Avraham Shwarts; Isaac Hochhauser; Benzion Rudzinski.

General information

Starlow Charities Ltd was established in 2000 to support the activities of Jewish religious organisations. According to its 2019/20 accounts, the objects of the charity are:

- the relief of poverty amongst persons in conditions of need, hardship, and distress in the Orthodox Jewish community
- the advancement of the Orthodox Jewish religion
- the advancement of education in accordance with the tenets of the Orthodox Jewish religion
- to promote any charitable purposes for the benefit of the Orthodox Jewish community.

Financial information

Year end	31/07/2020
Income	£1,080,000
Assets	£8,850,000
Grants to organisations	£1,210,000

Further financial information

Only seven beneficiaries of grants of £40,000 and above were listed in the charity's accounts. Grants of under £40,000 totalled £487,700.

Beneficiaries included: Keren Ezra Mimeitzar (£209,000); Chevras Mo'oz Ladol (£208,900); Ezer Bekovoid Ltd (£101,000); Ezer V'hatzala Ltd (£66,700); Trenhill Ltd (£50,700); Chesed Shel Emes (£40,900).

Applications

Apply in writing to the correspondent.

Sources of information

Accounts; annual report; Charity Commission record.

The Peter Stebbings Memorial Charity

General charitable purposes; medical research; education; social welfare; community regeneration; mental health

UK (particularly London) and sub-Saharan Africa

£550,600 (2020/21)

CC number: 274862

Correspondent: Marie-Louise O'Connor, Grants Administrator (Cripps Pemberton Greenish LLP), 45 Cadogan Gardens, London SW3 2AQ (tel: 07368 652694; email: info@peterstebbingsmemorialcharity.org)

Trustees: Jennifer Clifford; Nicholas Cosin; Andrew Stebbings.

http://peterstebbingsmemorialcharity.org

General information

The Peter Stebbings Memorial Charity was registered with the Charity Commission in 1978, and was established in memory of Hedley Peter Stebbings, who was killed in active service during the Second World War. The charity funds projects in the UK, mainly London, and in sub-Saharan Africa. Funding is for UK-registered charities only.

In the UK, the charity funds:

- Medical research and care
- Social welfare
- Homelessness
- Hospices
- Mental health/counselling
- Drug and alcohol therapeutic services
- Community regeneration
- Vulnerable families, women and children
- Support for people with experience of the criminal justice system

In sub-Saharan Africa the charity funds:

- Education
- Basic skills and tools
- Health
- Sanitation, irrigation, hygiene and access to clean water
- Women
- Help for marginalised communities

According to the website, the charity prefers to assist small to medium-sized charities with annual incomes of up to £5 million. The trustees fund projects but will also consider core funding for organisations they are familiar with. Grants are generally awarded for one year but larger grants may be spread over as long as three years.

Financial information

Year end	31/03/2021
Income	£108,500
Assets	£8,370,000
Grants to organisations	£550,600

Beneficiaries included: Royal Marsden Hospital Charity (£50,000); Moorfields Eye Charity (£25,000); Savannah Education Trust (£10,000); Brain Tumour Charity (£7,500); Breaking Barriers (£5,000); Richard House Hospice (£2,500); Zambia Orphans Aid UK (£2,000); League of Remembrance (£1,000).

Exclusions

The charity will not assist:

- Individuals
- Large national/international charities
- Animal welfare
- Publications and journals (unless part of a supported project)
- General appeals
- Religious organisations or educational institutions (unless for a particular project the trustees wish to support)
- Arts organisations (unless there is a strong social welfare focus)

Applications

Application forms can be completed on the charity's website. The trustees meet twice a year to allocate grants. Upcoming meeting dates and deadlines can be found on the charity's website.

Sources of information

Accounts; annual report; Charity Commission record; funder's website.

The Steel Charitable Trust

The arts and heritage; education; the environment; health; social or economic disadvantage

UK; Luton; Bedfordshire

£1.19 million (2020/21)

CC number: 272384

Correspondent: Trust Manager, Suite 411, Jansel House, Hitchin Road, Stopsley, Luton, Bedfordshire LU2 7XH (email: info@steelcharitabletrust.org.uk)

Trustees: Peter Day; Philip Lawford; Wendy Bailey; Vanessa Fox; Nicholas Wright; Dr Mary Briggs.

 www.steelcharitabletrust.org.uk

General information

The trust was established in 1976 for general charitable purposes.

Grant-making policy

Grants of up to £25,000 are generally made on a one-off basis, but in some cases, can be awarded in instalments over a period of years. A follow-up report is expected within ten months of payment from any organisation in receipt of an award of £20,000 or more.

According to the website, the trustees' current areas of interest are:

- Arts and heritage
- Education
- Environment
- Health
- Social or economic disadvantage

Funding is typically awarded towards the following:

- Capital projects
- Specific projects
- Research programmes
- Core costs

Eligibility

Applications will be considered from:

- UK-registered charities
- Organisations that have recently applied for charitable status in the UK
- Exempt charities
- CICs
- CIOs

Applications are particularly welcomed from the founders' native Luton and the wider Bedfordshire area.

Financial information

Year end	31/01/2021
Income	£1,200,000
Assets	£50,980,000
Grants to organisations	£1,190,000

Beneficiaries included: A list of beneficiaries was not available. Previous beneficiaries include: Two Moors Festival Ltd (£50,000); Prostate Cancer UK (£25,000); Cheltenham Festivals and International Centre for Eye Health (£20,000 each); Birmingham Opera Company, Lutonian Cricket Club and The Royal Society for Blind Children (£10,000 each); Art Against Knives (£5,000).

Exclusions

Applications will not be considered from:

- Individuals
- Charities not registered in the UK
- Political parties

Applications

Applications must be made online using the form on the trust's website. The trustees meet quarterly (in March, June, September and December) to consider grant applications. See the trust's website for application deadlines.

Sources of information

Accounts; annual report; Charity Commission record; funder's website.

The Steinberg Family Charitable Trust

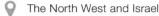

Jewish causes; medical care and treatment, including respite care and hospices; education and care of people with disabilities; older people; children and young people

The North West and Israel

£1 million (2020/21)

CC number: 1045231

Correspondent: The Trust Secretary, Lime Tree Cottage, 16 Bollinway, Hale, Altrincham, Cheshire WA15 0NZ (tel: 0161 903 8854; email: admin@sfct.co.uk)

Trustees: Lady Beryl Steinberg; Jonathan Steinberg; Lynne Steinberg.

 www.sfct.co.uk

General information

The trust was established by an initial loan from the late Lord Steinberg and has since received further donations and legacies from him.

The following information has been taken from the trust's website:

> **Which countries do we support?**
> Our main areas of support on a geographical basis are North West England and Israel. We will accept applications from charities based in other areas however chances of approval are less.
>
> **What type of work do we support?**
> We fund charities working in the following areas:Torah Institutions, including Kollelim and Yeshivot
>
> Medical care and treatment, including respite care and hospices
>
> Education and care of physically and mentally disabled adults and children
>
> Education and training for adults and children to achieve psycho-spiritual health
>
> Care and support of the elderly
>
> Care and support for children

Financial information

Year end	05/04/2021
Income	£2,040,000
Assets	£29,580,000
Grants to organisations	£1,000,000

Beneficiaries included: A list of beneficiaries was not available. Previous beneficiaries include: Aish (£75,000); Fed, Hathaway Trust, UJIA and World Jewish Relief (£50,000 each) Integrated Education Fund (£25,000); SEED (£22,000); Hale Adult Hebrew Education Trust (£20,000); Centre for Social Justice and Policy Exchange (£15,000); Ascent, Ezer Layeled, Imperial War Museum; MDA Israel, Menachim Begin Heritage Foundation and Yeshiva Bais Yisroel (£10,000 each); Chai Cancer Care and Holocaust Centre (£7,500 each); Hamayon and Hazon Yeshaya (£5,000 each); Henshaw's Society, Jewish Education in Manchester, NATA and Rainbow Trust (£2,500 each); Prostate Cancer Charity (£1,000).

Exclusions

The trust does not accept applications from individuals.

Applications

Applications can be made via the trust's website.

Sources of information

Accounts; annual report; Charity Commission record; funder's website.

The Sir Sigmund Sternberg Charitable Foundation

Interfaith activities

Worldwide

£220,500 (2020/21)

CC number: 257950

Correspondent: The Trustees, c/o HW Fisher LLP, Acre House, 11–15 William Road, London NW1 3ER (tel: 020 7388 7000)

Trustees: The Revd Dr Marcus Braybrooke; Martin Paisner; Martin Slowe; Michael Sternberg; Noam Tamir.

General information

The foundation supports the furtherance of interfaith activities to promote racial and religious harmony, in particular between the Christian, Jewish and Muslim faiths, and the education in, and understanding of, their fundamental tenets and beliefs. Most grants are made to Jewish and Israeli charities.

Financial information

Year end	05/04/2021
Income	£240,700
Assets	£3,620,000
Grants to organisations	£220,500

Further financial information

In 2020/21 the foundation awarded grants totalling £220,500. In previous years the foundation has awarded grants totalling over £300,000.

Beneficiaries included: The Faith and Belief Forum (formerly The Three Faiths Forum) (£165,300); Faith and Belief Forum – donation towards office costs (£20,300); Woolf Institute (£10,000); Queens College Cambridge (£6,500); New Israel Fund (£5,000); World Congress of Faiths (£3,500); Liberal Jewish Synagogue and Royal College of Speech and Language Therapists (£2,000 each).

Applications

Apply in writing to the correspondent.

Sources of information

Accounts; annual report; Charity Commission record.

Stevenson Family's Charitable Trust

General charitable purposes, in particular: education and training; health and medicine; arts and culture; overseas aid; heritage and conservation; the environment

UK

£228,400 (2020/21)

CC number: 327148

Correspondent: Sir Hugh Stevenson, Chair, Old Waterfield, Winkfield Road, Ascot, Berkshire SL5 7LJ (tel: 01344 620170; email: hugh.stevenson@oldwaterfield.com)

Trustees: Sir Hugh Stevenson; Lady Stevenson; Joseph Stevenson.

General information

The Stevenson Family's Charitable Trust was established in 1986 by Hugh and Catherine Stevenson. The trust makes grants for a range of purposes including:

- Education and training
- Health and medicine
- Arts and culture
- Overseas aid
- Heritage and conservation

The trust's 2020/21 annual report and accounts note that the recent emphasis on culture and the arts is set to be maintained over the foreseeable future.

Financial information

Year end	05/04/2021
Income	£878,900
Assets	£2,720,000
Grants to organisations	£228,400

Further financial information

During 2020/21 grants totalled £228,400; however, in previous years the trust has awarded grants totalling over £300,000. Grants were distributed as follows:

Purpose	Amount
Culture and the arts	£77,100
Health and medicine	£65,400
General charitable purposes	£57,900
Education and training	£16,800
Conservation and heritage	£11,300

Beneficiaries included: University of Oxford (£45,000); The Sick Children's Trust (£22,500); The National Gallery Trust (£9,100); Newbury Spring Festival (£5,000); Chelsea Physic Garden (£1,000); Newbury Cancer Care (£250); St Michael's Hospice – Basingstoke (£100).

Applications

The trust does not consider unsolicited applications.

Sources of information

Accounts; annual report; Charity Commission record.

Stewards Company Ltd

Christian evangelism and social welfare

UK and overseas

£5.79 million (2020)

CC number: 234558

Correspondent: Andrew Griffiths, Secretary and Director of Operations, 122 Wells Road, Bath, Somerset BA2 3AH (tel: 01225 427236; email: stewardsco@stewards.co.uk)

Trustees: Ian Childs; Keigh Bintley; Andrew Griffiths; Jennifer Michael; Huw Iley; Mr J. Aitken; Paul Young; Dr Joshua Fitzhugh; Simon Tomlinson; David Bingham; David Roberts; Dr John Burness; Michelangelo Leto; Philip Symons; Andrew Mayo; John Gamble; Alexander McIlhinney; Glyn Davies.

General information

The Stewards Company Ltd was registered with the Charity Commission in 1965 with the objectives of supporting Christian evangelism, the furtherance of the Christian faith, general charitable purposes and social welfare (the relief of the poor).

The charity administers a number of Christian charitable trusts and its principal activity concerns administering the J. W. Laing Trust and the J. W. Laing Biblical Scholarship Trust.

With respect to the J. W. Liang Trust, the 2020 annual report states that:

> As well as supporting individual churches, help is given to a range of evangelistic and mission organisations, movements publishing Bible resources, teaching of scripture to school children and related enterprises. Further substantial financial support is given to strategic Christian organisations in certain parts of the developing world, literature production, other evangelistic and church development programmes together with the relief of poverty in a variety of countries overseas.

Regarding the J. W. Liang Biblical Scholarship Trust, the report notes:

> The objective of the J W Laing Biblical Scholarship Trust is to encourage the study of the Holy Bible. With this as its main objective, support is given to a variety of organisations furthering this cause including a number of evangelical Christian Bible Colleges; organisations which promote Christian work among university students both in the UK and overseas; an independent Biblical studies library with a Christian foundation.

With respect to the charity's grant-making policy, the 2020 annual report and accounts state that the following are taken into account:

- the financial resources of the charities making application;
- the efforts made by members of such charities to maximise their own funding, including where appropriate sacrificial giving by themselves and their supporters; and
- the assessed value of such charities consistent with the objectives of the main grant-making trusts

Financial information

Year end	31/12/2020
Income	£3,030,000
Assets	£153,210,000
Grants to organisations	£5,790,000

Further financial information

Grants were broken down as follows:

£100,000 and above	11	£2.4 million
£25,000 to £99,000	36	£1.46 million
Under £25,000	327	£1.92 million

Only grants of over £100,000 were included in the list of beneficiaries.

Beneficiaries included: Strategic Resource Group (£409,500); Retired Missionary Aid Fund (£240,000); Tyndale (£200,000); Beatrice Lang Trust (£171,500); Gospel Literature Outreach (£115,000).

Applications

Apply in writing to the correspondent.

Sources of information

Accounts; annual report; Charity Commission record.

Sir Halley Stewart Trust

Medical, social and religious causes

UK and overseas

£1.09 million (2020/21)

CC number: 208491

Correspondent: Lorraine Faires, Grants Manager, BM Sir Halley Stewart Trust, London WC1N 3XX (tel: 020 8144 0375; email: email@sirhalleystewart.org.uk)

 www.sirhalleystewart.org.uk

General information

The trust was established in 1924 by Sir Halley Stewart, the non-conformist Christian minister, MP, pioneering industrialist and philanthropist. Sir Halley endowed the trust and established its founding principles, which are: to advance religion and education, to relieve poverty and to promote other charitable purposes beneficial to the community. A tradition of supporting medical research into the prevention of human suffering, not its relief, was established during Sir Halley's time spent as a chair for the trust. He died in 1937.

Grant programmes:

Main grants: awards of between £5,001 and £60,000 are paid in quarterly instalments over one, two or three years usually towards salary costs. Instalments cannot exceed £30,000 per annum.

Small grants: a limited number of small, one-off grants are awarded each year for projects costing up to £5,000.

The trust's website states that projects must fall into one or more of the following categories:

1) **Innovative research projects:** i.e. those which explore and test new ideas, methods, approaches, interventions and/ or devices.

2) **Pioneering/ground-breaking development projects:** i.e. those which are original and represent the first of their kind and/or lay the foundations for further developments.

The trust funds projects that focus on the prevention (rather than the alleviation) of human suffering. According to its website, the trust's three priority areas are 'medical, social and religious' with education being a central theme that runs across all three categories. Detailed criteria for each category can be seen on the trust's website.

Financial information

Year end	31/03/2021
Income	£1,320,000
Assets	£39,220,000
Grants to organisations	£1,090,000

Further financial information

Only beneficiaries of grants of £10,000 and above were listed in the trust's 2020/21 accounts. Grants of under £10,000 totalled £93,000.

Beneficiaries included: London's Air Ambulance Charity and University of Keele (£60,000 each); Islington Mind (£52,000); Migrants Organise (£44,000); National Literacy Trust (£28,000); Discovering Prayer (£16,000); The Trussell Trust (£10,000).

Exclusions

According to the trust's website, grants are never made for the following:

- Directly to individuals
- Donations to general appeals of any kind
- The purchase, erection or conversion of buildings, or other capital costs
- University overhead charges

The trust does not usually fund the following:

- Running costs of established organisations or ongoing projects
- Contributions towards the overall costs of a project (the Trust normally provides grants for salary costs, although occasionally it funds other project expenses)
- Conference attendance
- Projects proposed indirectly through other 'umbrella' organisations
- Projects from large well-funded charities
- Personal education fees or fees for taught courses -unless the proposal comes from a senior researcher who is seeking funds for research which could be undertaken by post-graduate student
- Completion of a project or PhD initiated by other bodies
- Educational or 'gap-year' projects for young people
- Projects where the Trust would not be a major supporter, with the Trust normally preferring to fund at least 50% of the total project costs.

Applications

Potential applicants are strongly encouraged to first contact the trust's grants manager by phone or email to determine the suitability of a project before applying. There is also an eligibility quiz on the trust's website.

Applications should be made online, using the form on the trust's website. Approximately one month prior to the relevant trustee meeting (dates of which can be seen on the website), applicants will receive a notification stating that their proposal will be considered at the next meeting, or that their proposal will not be given further consideration.

Proposals for small grants are considered all year round and there are no application deadlines.

Sources of information

Accounts; annual report; Charity Commission record; funder's website.

The Stewarts Law Foundation

Alleviating poverty; access to justice; supporting disability; providing educational opportunity

 UK

£633,100 (2020/21)

CC number: 1136714

Correspondent: John Cahill, Trustee, 5 New Street Square, London EC4A 3BF (tel: 020 7822 8000)

 www.stewartslaw.com/about/social-impact/the-stewarts-foundation

General information

The foundation was established in 2010 to manage the charitable giving of Stewarts Law, the UK's largest litigation-only law firm.

According to its website, the foundation's vision is to:

- Create opportunities for the disadvantaged in our society
- Treat people less fortunate than ourselves with compassion and respect
- Make a substantial social impact

It achieves this by making grants to a handful of UK registered charities, as chosen by the trustees. The foundation focuses its grant-making on four principles:

- Alleviating poverty
- Enabling access to justice
- Supporting disability
- Providing educational opportunity

The foundation has a long-term partnership with the Access to Justice Foundation.

Financial information

Year end	30/04/2021
Income	£812,400
Assets	£235,400
Grants to organisations	£633,100

Beneficiaries included: Access to Justice Foundation (£250,000); Centrepoint

(£40,000); Just for Kids Law (£39,000); Wheelpower (£30,300); Wellbeing of Women (£20,000); JUSTICE (£6,000); NHS Trusts (£5,500).

Applications

Charities are chosen by the trustees. The 2020/21 annual report states: 'It is not the policy of the Trustees to accept direct applications for funds.'

Sources of information

Accounts; annual report; Charity Commission record; funder's website.

The Stobart Newlands Charitable Trust

Christian and missionary causes

Worldwide

£1.01 million (2020)

CC number: 328464

Correspondent: The Trustees, Millcroft, Newlands, Hesket Newmarket, Wigton, Cumbria CA7 8HP (tel: 01697 478631)

Trustees: Ronnie Stobart; Linda Rigg; Peter Stobart; Richard Stobart.

General information

Established in 1989, the trust is the corporate charity of J Stobart and Sons Ltd, a manufacturer and retailer of animal feedstuffs. The trustees are directors and shareholders of J Stobart and Sons Ltd, which is the source of almost all of the trust's income. This family trust makes up to 60 grants a year, nearly all on a recurring basis to Christian religious and missionary bodies.

Financial information

Year end	31/12/2020
Income	£1,010,000
Assets	£98,700
Grants to organisations	£1,010,000

Further financial information

Only beneficiaries of grants of £10,000 and above were listed in the accounts. Grants of under £10,000 totalled £172,700.

Beneficiaries included: World Vision (£250,000); Operation Mobilisation (£157,100); Keswick Ministries (£32,500); Every Home Crusade and Tearfund (£31,500 each); City Reach (£20,000); Logos Ministries and NISCU North Cumbria (£18,000 each).

Applications

Unsolicited applications are unlikely to be successful.

Sources of information

Accounts; annual report; Charity Commission record.

Mark Stolkin Foundation

Public education in performing and visual arts; health and welfare; education; furtherance of the Christian faith; architectural heritage

England; Wales; South Africa

£568,900 (2020/21)

CC number: 1138476

Correspondent: The Trustees, 14–16 Egerton Gardens Mews, London SW3 2EH (tel: 020 7589 0899)

Trustees: Margeaux Stolkin; Mark Stolkin; Renate Lubert.

General information

The foundation was established in 2007 and makes grants throughout England, Wales and South Africa.

According to its 2020/21 annual accounts, the foundation's objects are:

- to educate the public in the art and science of music, dancing and the performing arts;
- to educate the public in the fields of painting, drawing, illustration and visual arts;
- to educate and assist young persons through their leisure time activities so as to develop their physical, mental and spiritual capacities;
- to award scholarships, exhibition, bursaries or maintenance allowances tenable at any school, university or other educational or charitable establishment approved by the Trustees to persons who are in need of financial assistance;
- to assist in relieving poverty and ill-health in all their various forms and the causes of poverty and ill-health including but not limited to victims of terrorism and other forms of trauma;
- to further education generally by the granting or giving of financial assistance to educational institutions of all kinds;
- to further the religious and charitable work for the Christian faith;
- to advance the religion(s) of Christianity;
- to protect and preserve and/or assist in the protection and preservation of buildings, monuments and sites of special historical and/or architectural interest.

Financial information

Year end	05/04/2021
Income	£96,100
Assets	£1,750,000
Grants to organisations	£568,900

Beneficiaries included: The Parochial Church Council of the Ecclesiastical Parish of Holy Trinity with Saint Paul Onslow Square and Saint Augustine South Kensington (£198,300); Church Revitalisation Trust (£100,000); Care for Children (£62,500); The Art Academy (£2,000).

Applications

Apply in writing to the correspondent.

Sources of information

Accounts; annual report; Charity Commission record.

The Stoller Charitable Trust

General charitable purposes; children and young people; healthcare

The North West, with a preference for Manchester

£1.16 million (2020/21)

CC number: 285415

Correspondent: The Trustees, 24 Low Crompton Road, Royton, Oldham, Lancashire OL2 6YR (tel: 07902 857648; email: enquiries@stollercharitabletrust.co.uk)

Trustees: Roger Gould; KSL Trustees Ltd; Sir Norman Stoller; Lady Stoller; Andrew Dixon.

General information

The trust supports a wide variety of charitable causes, but with particular emphasis on those that are based in the North West. The trustees aim to maintain a balance between regular and occasional donations and between large and smaller grants.

Financial information

Year end	05/04/2021
Income	£2,660,000
Assets	£15,920,000
Grants to organisations	£1,160,000

Beneficiaries included: Mahdlo (£442,500); Kingfisher Learning Trust (£300,000); Manchester Foundation Trust Charity (£200,000); The Duke of Edinburgh's Award (£100,000); Alzheimer's Research UK (£60,000); Royal Northern College of Music (£28,000).

Exclusions

The trust does not make grants to individuals.

Applications

Apply in writing to the correspondent. The trustees meet regularly to review applications.

Sources of information

Accounts; annual report; Charity Commission record.

The Stone Family Foundation

Mental health and disadvantaged young people in the UK; water and sanitation in financially developing countries

UK and overseas

£7.83 million (2020)

CC number: 1164682

Correspondent: The Trustees, 201 Borough High Street, London SE1 1JA (email: SFF@thinkNPC.org)

Trustees: Charles Edwards; David Steinegger; John Stone.

 www.thesff.com

 @StoneFamilyFdn

General information

The Stone Family Foundation was established in 2005 by John Stone and his wife, Vanessa, following the sale of their business. The foundation's website states that in the early years, it funded a range of projects in the UK (mental health) and overseas (education for girls, water and sanitation, and microfinance). Following a strategic review in 2010, the trustees decided to focus on:

- Water and sanitation (WASH) in the 'developing world'. Around 80% of funding is committed to this cause
- In the UK, mental health and programmes for disadvantaged young people

The foundation prefers to establish long-term partnerships with organisations aligned to its vision and focus areas. Most grants support core costs and are often multi-year commitments.

Financial information

Year end	31/12/2020
Income	£4,540,000
Assets	£44,870,000
Grants to organisations	£7,830,000
No. of grants	50

Beneficiaries included: 1001Fontaines (£572,200); Evidence Action (£396,000); IntoUniversity (£100,000); Birmingham Mind (£92,400); Samaritans (£80,000); Sport 4 Life (£65,000); Wheels Project (£25,000); Everflow Africa (£10,000).

Applications

The foundation's website states: 'We are a small, family foundation with limited resources and as a result we do not accept unsolicited proposals. If you have any questions, feel free to email: SFF@thinkNPC.org. Please note, this email inbox is only monitored periodically.'

Sources of information

Accounts; annual report; Charity Commission record; funder's website.

The Stoneygate Trust

General charitable purposes; medical research; the education of disadvantaged children and young people

 UK

£1.9 million (2020/21)

CC number: 1119976

Correspondent: The Trustees, Two Marlborough Court, Watermead Business Park, Syston, Leicestershire LE7 1AD (tel: 0116 296 2323; email: info@stoneygatetrust.org)

Trustees: Lady Nadine Adderley; Andrew Walden; Sir William Adderley; Timothy Slade.

 www.stoneygatetrust.org

General information

The trust was established in 2007 by Will and Nadine Adderley and makes grants for general charitable purposes. Its website states:

> We are a multi purpose charity with a particular focus on medical research and helping to support equal educational opportunities to economically disadvantaged children and students.

Financial information

Year end	05/04/2021
Income	£2,430,000
Assets	£11,900,000
Grants to organisations	£1,900,000

Beneficiaries included: Kidney Research UK (£206,800); University College London (£189,900); University of Sheffield (£43,500); Royal Marsden NHS Foundation (£12,900); Leicester South Foodbank (£2,500); Clifton Foodbank (£750).

Applications

Apply in writing to the correspondent. The trust's 2020/21 annual accounts state: 'The Trust is very selective in the grant-making process and applications are reviewed by the Trustees personally.'

Sources of information

Accounts; annual report; Charity Commission record.

Stratford-upon-Avon Town Trust

Reducing isolation; health and well-being; activities for young people; support during crisis; community development

Stratford-upon-Avon

£1.33 million (2020)

CC number: 1088521

Correspondent: James McHugh, Grants Manager, 14 Rother Street, Stratford-upon-Avon, Warwickshire CV32 6LU (tel: 01789 207111; email: james.mchugh@stratfordtowntrust.co.uk)

Trustees: Clive Snowdon; Quentin Willson; Tony Jackson; Matthew MacDonald; Dr Lindsay MacDonald; Timothy Bailey; David Taylor; Stephen Parker; Gillian Cleeve; Cllr Elizabeth Coles; Josephine Stevens.

 www.stratfordtowntrust.co.uk

General information

The Stratford-upon-Avon Town Trust is a grant-making charity dedicated to supporting local community projects and activities which improve the quality of life of people living in Stratford-upon-Avon. In accordance with a Charity Commission Scheme of October 2001, the trust derives its income from the properties and funds of two charities, the Guild of Holy Cross and College of Canons estates, whose origins go back to the 13th century.

According to its website, the trust awards approximately £2 million in grants per annum. The 2020 annual report states that funds were distributed to charities in accordance with the following six key priorities, identified through community consultation:

- Improve Health and Wellbeing
- Create Positive Activities for Young People
- Reduce Loneliness and Social Isolation
- Protect and Support Vulnerable Communities
- Develop Community Capacity and Resilience
- Provide Support During a Time Crisis

For organisations, the trust typically offers three different funding streams: fast-track grants (awards of up to £1,000 for urgent needs), main grants (awards of over £1,000) and multi-year funding. These streams are subject to change – visit the trust's website for the current status of each programme.

Hardship grants are also provided to individuals in need through partner organisations.

As well as its discretionary grant-giving, under the terms of its charter, the trust is also required to make grants to the following three organisations: King Edward VI School, The Vicar of Holy Trinity Church and Almshouses in Church Street.

The trust also funds Foundation House, a community hub that charitable organisations can use for a subsidised fee.

Financial information

Year end	31/12/2020
Income	£3,140,000
Assets	£60,950,000
Grants to organisations	£1,330,000
No. of grants	68

Further financial information

Grants paid during the year totalled £1.34 million, including discretionary and non-discretionary grants. Grants to organisations totalled £1.33 million and grants to individuals totalled £9,100. According to the accounts, discretionary grants were awarded to 68 organisations in the following categories:

Health and social welfare	£479,900
Facilities for education	£109,100
Facilities for recreation and leisure	£11,800
General charitable purposes	£2,200
Christianity	£1,500
Citizenship and community	£1,500
Civic pride	£1,400

Only beneficiaries of discretionary grants of over £20,000 were listed in the accounts.

Beneficiaries included: Spring Housing Association (£85,000); Citizens Advice South Warwickshire (£65,800); The Shakespeare Hospice (£50,000); Domestic Abuse Counselling Service (£33,000); Royal Shakespeare Company (£20,000).

Exclusions

Projects taking place outside, or that do not directly benefit residents of, Stratford-upon-Avon. Organisations that cannot provide evidence of a constitution (or another set of agreed rules) and a bank account (with at least two unrelated signatories) will not be considered. Additionally, CICs must be limited by guarantee.

Applications

Online application forms and full guidance for each grants programme are available on the trust's website.

The trust's website states that grants are appraised on the following criteria:

- Your application must evidence the need for the project within Stratford upon Avon.
- Your application is able to evidence genuine user involvement in its planning and ongoing delivery.
- Your proposal clearly articulates how it will lead to a demonstrable positive impact on the quality of life in Stratford upon Avon.
- Your application demonstrates a commitment to collaborative and partnership working.
- You are able to demonstrate a robust financial position (viability and sustainability), where applicable.

Should applicants have any questions regarding their application, the trust invites them to get in touch with the grants manager.

Sources of information

Accounts; annual report; Charity Commission record; funder's website.

The WO Street Charitable Foundation

Education; social and family welfare; disability; relief of poverty; children and young people; older people

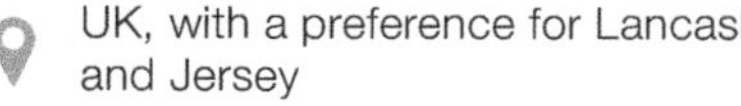

UK, with a preference for Lancashire and Jersey

£564,300 (2019/20)

CC number: 267127

Correspondent: The Trustees, c/o Zedra UK Trusts, Booths Hall, Booths Park 3, Chelford Road, Knutsford, Cheshire WA16 8GS (tel: 01565 748787; email: charities@zedra.com)

Trustees: Chris Priestley; Zedra Trust Company (UK) Ltd.

https://lancsfoundation.org.uk/funds/the-wo-street-transformation-fund

General information

The foundation was established by William Street in 1973 and the foundation continues to make grants in line with his wishes.

The priorities of the founder include education, health, the relief of poverty (particularly for children and young people), people in financial need (particularly older people, people with disabilities and those who are blind) and general social welfare.

The foundation has a particular interest in projects within Lancashire and Jersey, where Mr Street spent significant parts of his life.

In 2011 the foundation established three WO Street Transformation Funds, which are administered by Forever Manchester (Charity Commission no. 1017504) for Greater Manchester grants and by the Community Foundations for Lancashire and Merseyside (Charity Commission no. 1068887) for Lancashire and Merseyside grants. See the relevant website for eligibility criteria and grant amounts available.

According to the website, the fund 'wishes to support projects that can demonstrate engagement of the wider community with applicants identifying what they are bringing to the project such as in-kind support, skills or further funding'.

Financial information

Year end	31/01/2020
Income	£485,000
Assets	£20,270,000
Grants to organisations	£564,300
No. of grants	120+

Further financial information

During the year, the foundation increased its level of grant-making in response to the COVID-19 pandemic, awarding grants to over 120 organisations.

Beneficiaries included: WO Street Jersey Charitable Trust (£40,000); Emmott Foundation (£30,000); Age UK Lancashire (£10,000); Blind Veterans and Chailey Heritage Foundation (£5,000 each); Cancer Support UK and Child Bereavement (£3,000 each); Equal Arts (£2,000); Bradford Holy Trinity Church (£1,000).

Exclusions

According to the Community Foundation for Lancashire website, the WO Street Transformation Fund does not support the following:

- National organisations that cannot demonstrate local governance and control of local finances
- Statutory organisations or work that is their responsibility
- CICs limited by shares (unless the governing document expressly states no dividends or bonuses are issued to shareholders).
- Organisations with less than three unrelated trustees/directors/ management committee members
- Commercial ventures
- Purchase/maintenance of vehicles
- Activities that will have already taken place before we offer you a grant
- Politically connected or exclusively religious activities
- Projects for personal profit
- Organisations that are set up for the benefit of animals or plants: environmental groups that work with animals or the environment (such as city farms) are acceptable
- Debts and other liabilities
- Reclaimable VAT
- Travel outside UK

Applications made to the foundation directly from individuals are not considered.

Applications

Apply in writing to the correspondent. The foundation's 2020 annual report states: 'Applications are invited to Zedra Trust Company (UK) Ltd and an application form will be furnished for completion and subsequent consideration by the Trustees.'

Applications to the WO Street Transformation Fund can be made via the Forever Manchester website or the Community Foundations for Lancashire and Merseyside website. Attach the following to your application: a governing document; annual accounts; a safeguarding policy; your organisation's recent bank statement; a list of management committee members/ trustees/directors.

Sources of information

Accounts; annual report; Charity Commission record; funder's website; Community Foundation for Lancashire (website); Community Foundation for Merseyside (website).

The Street Foundation

Children and young people with disabilities; social welfare; education; community development; human rights; the advancement of religion

UK and overseas

£440,900 (2020/21)

CC number: 1045229

Correspondent: The Trustees, Kingsland House, Kingsland, Leominster, Herefordshire HR6 9SG (tel: 01568 708744)

Trustees: Sarah Sharp-Smith; Susan Smith; Richard Smith; Lucinda Sharp-Smith.

General information

The Street Foundation is the charity of Richard Smith, a director and shareholder of Techtest Ltd, which is part of the HR Smith Group of Companies. Techtest designs and manufactures advanced aerospace technologies.

According to the foundation's 2020/21 annual report, the foundation's objectives are the provision of grants for the relief of poverty, the advancement of education and the advancement of religion. Grants can be made to charities and other not-for-profit organisations. There is a preference for supporting organisations working with children and young people with disabilities and special needs.

Financial information

Year end	31/03/2021
Income	£850,000
Assets	£462,600
Grants to organisations	£440,900
No. of grants	13+

Further financial information

In 2020/21, grants were broken down as follows:

Education	£329,100
Human rights	£50,000
The relief of poverty	£42,500
Community	£18,300
Disability	£1,000

The foundation listed 13 beneficiaries in the accounts. Other grants totalled £33,500.

Beneficiaries included: Civitas (£73,500); Oxford University Museum of Natural History (£60,700); The Politics and Economics Research Trust (£50,000); The Centre for Social Justice (£30,000); The Maggie Oliver Foundation (£20,000); Liverpool Charity and Volunteer Services (£10,000).

Applications

Apply in writing to the correspondent.

Sources of information

Accounts; annual report; Charity Commission record.

Streetsmart – Action for the Homeless

Homelessness

UK. Grants are made to charities in the cities in which the Streetsmart campaign runs. A list is available on the charity's website

£804,100 (2019/20)

CC number: 1071657

Correspondent: Glenn Pougnet, Director, 1 St John's Lane, London EC1M 4BL (tel: 020 7292 5615; email: glenn.pougnet@streetsmart.org.uk)

Trustees: William Sieghart; Rosie Boycott; Mary Sturridge; Nick Emley.

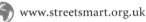

 www.streetsmart.org.uk

 facebook.com/StreetSmartUK

 @streetsmartuk

 @streetsmartuk

General information

Streetsmart has been running since 1998 and has since raised over £10.3 million for vulnerable people and those experiencing homelessness across the UK. During November and December, participating restaurants add £1 to diners' bills. The money raised is then passed on to the charity to distribute to homelessness charities. Money raised in a city is spent in that city.

The charity's website states:

> The organisations funded by StreetSmart must work progressively with their client group. Successful applications receive support for projects aimed at helping the homeless to make a better life for themselves, focussing on mental and physical health, employability and sustainable independent living. Grants are given to those who support people through the crucial stages in their progress from vagrant to valued community member.

Financial information

Year end	31/05/2020
Income	£909,900
Assets	£275,600
Grants to organisations	£804,100

Beneficiaries included: Land Aid London (£376,300); The Felix Project (£220,700); Centrepoint (£46,800); The Brick – Manchester (£6,000); Julian House – Bristol (£1,000); Homeless Oxfordshire (£700).

Applications

Apply in writing to the correspondent. The charity's website states:

> Homeless[ness] charities seeking funding from StreetSmart should submit their application in writing during December.
>
> There is no formal application process, but charities should outline the aims and achievements of the organisation, and explain in detail the specific area of their work in need of financial support, e.g.: project worker salary, educational programmes, meaningful occupation. StreetSmart does not provide funding to soup kitchens unless they form part of a drop-in centre linked into other services.
>
> If the project meets our criteria, we will then arrange for a StreetSmart representative to visit the project at some point during January and February and report back to the trustees.
>
> The trustees of StreetSmart meet in April to decide which applications have been successful.
>
> Please contact your regional campaign manager, or email glenn.pougnet@streetsmart.org.uk

Sources of information

Accounts; annual report; Charity Commission record; funder's website.

The Joseph Strong Frazer Trust

General charitable purposes; children and young people; older people; people with disabilities; medical research; maritime; armed forces; education; religion; sport and recreation; social welfare; animals and wildlife

England and Wales

£529,600 (2019/20)

CC number: 235311

Correspondent: The Trustees, c/o Joseph Miller, Floor A, Milburn House, Dean Street, Newcastle upon Tyne NE1 1LE (tel: 0191 232 8065; email: jsf@joseph-miller.co.uk)

Trustees: David Cook; Sir W. Antony Smith; Mr R. M. Read; William Smith; William Waites; Ugo Fagandini.

General information

The trust was established in 1939 and supports a wide range of causes.

The trust's 2019/20 accounts state:

> It is the aim of the trustees to support a very wide number of good causes and charitable objects and make best use of the Trust's resources. Applications for grants are considered by the trustees and distributions are made where it is thought most appropriate and effective, to organisations within England and Wales.

Financial information

Year end	30/09/2020
Income	£504,400
Assets	£14,360,000
Grants to organisations	£529,600
No. of grants	337

Further financial information

Only beneficiaries of grants of £2,000 and above were listed in the trust's 2019/20 accounts (175 grants). Grants of under £2,000 totalled £169,600 (162 grants). Grants were broken down as follows:

Medical and other research	71	£124,500
Caring organisations	52	£73,000
Children	33	£49,000
Other trusts, funds and voluntary organisations	33	£48,000
Leisure activities, animals and wildlife	24	£40,000
Hospitals	21	£39,000
Deafness and blindness	18	£33,500
Young people	27	£31,100
Disability	15	£25,500
Maritime	15	£18,500
Religious bodies	10	£16,000
Armed forces	7	£14,000
Mental health	5	£8,000
Older people	3	£6,000
Schools and colleges	3	£3,000

Beneficiaries included: Coram Family (three grants totalling £4,500); Alzheimer's Society (£3,000); Shooting Star Children's Hospices and The Parachute Regiment Charity (£2,500 each); Heart Research Wales, Royal British Legion and Support Dogs (£2,000 each).

Applications

Apply in writing to the correspondent.

Sources of information

Accounts; annual report; Charity Commission record.

The Summerfield Charitable Trust

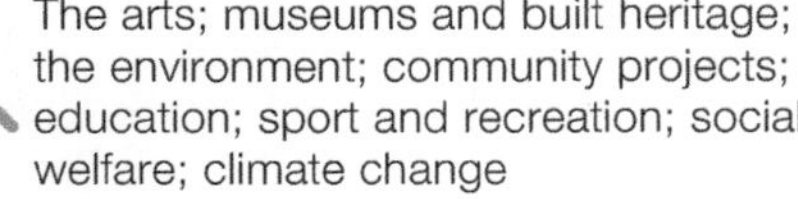

The arts; museums and built heritage; the environment; community projects; education; sport and recreation; social welfare; climate change

Gloucestershire

£305,900 (2020)

CC number: 802493

Correspondent: The Trustees, PO Box 287, Cirencester, Gloucestershire GL7 9FB (tel: 01285 721211; email: admin@summerfield.org.uk)

Trustees: Katrina Beach; Vanessa Arbuthnott; David Owen; Roger Mortlock; Antonia Shield.

www.summerfield.org.uk

General information

The trust was established by the late Ronald Summerfield, a Cheltenham antiques dealer, shortly before his death in 1989.

The following information has been taken from the trust's website:

> Charities and organisations applying to the Trust must be based in the six district councils of Gloucestershire (i.e. Cheltenham, Gloucester, Stroud, Tewkesbury, Cotswolds or Forest of Dean); or they must be engaged in a project that is of specific benefit to residents within the county.
>
> If you are applying from a charity based outside Gloucestershire, we will want to see evidence of strong engagement with people and organisations in the county.
>
> Applications are considered in the following categories;
>
> - The arts, museums and the built heritage
> - The environmental and sustainability;
> - Community work;
> - Education, sport and recreation;
> - Vulnerable and disadvantaged sectors of society.
>
> However, in 2022, the focus for our grant giving will be on:
>
> - Recovery from the impacts of the COVID-19 pandemic and support for the most vulnerable and disadvantaged communities in Gloucestershire
> - Projects that improve our environment and/or address the impacts of the climate emergency
> - At present Trustees will only award one off grants

Financial information

Year end	31/12/2020
Income	£311,700
Assets	£11,040,000
Grants to organisations	£305,900

Further financial information

Grants were broken down as follows in 2020:

Disadvantaged and vulnerable sectors	17	£203,800
Arts, museums and built heritage	8	£48,700
Community work	11	£20,400
Environment and natural heritage	5	£19,000
Education, sport and recreation	2	£14,000

Beneficiaries included: A list of beneficiaries was not available. Previous beneficiaries include: Scrubditch Care Farm (£20,000); Art Couture Festival Ltd (£10,000); Cirencester Foodbank (£8,500); Court Barn Museum, Kempsford Village Hall and Make Believe CIC (£5,000 each); Contact the Elderly (£3,000); Future Trees Trust (£2,000); Charlton Kings Cricket Club (£1,000); Birdlip School PTA (£550).

Exclusions

Grants are not made for:

- Medical research
- Private education
- Animal welfare appeals
- Trips abroad
- Retrospective projects
- Individuals

Charities which have been in receipt of a grant should not reapply for at least two years, unless they have specifically been asked to do so.

Applications

Applications should be made using the trust's online application form.

Sources of information

Accounts; annual report; Charity Commission record; funder's website; further information provided by the funder.

The Bernard Sunley Foundation

Community; education; health; social welfare

England and Wales

£3.72 million (2020/21)

CC number: 1109099

Correspondent: Sue Davies, Director, Green Park House, 15 Stratton Street, Mayfair, London W1J 8LQ (tel: 020 3036 0090; email: office@bernardsunley.org)

Trustees: Anabel Knight; Dr Brian Martin; Bella Sunley; William Tice; Inigo Paternina; Lucy Evans.

www.bernardsunley.org

General information

The Bernard Sunley Foundation was established in 1960 by Bernard and Mary Sunley and was incorporated as a charitable company in 2005.

Grant programmes

According to its 2020/21 annual report and accounts, the foundation makes grants across four categories: community, education, health and social welfare.

The community programme supports projects which:

> bring local communities together and provide greater opportunities for the young, the elderly, the disabled and the disadvantaged. Grants are made towards the building or refurbishment of scout huts, village halls, community centres, youth clubs, boxing clubs, outdoor activity centres, farm and outdoor learning centres, sports centres and pavilions, playing fields and playgrounds. The Foundation also funds the purchase of new minibuses that assist those most in need in their local communities.

The foundation's education programme:

> supports improvements and new facilities at special needs schools and the purchase of new, adapted minibuses that benefit children with special needs and disabilities. It also awards grants to educational nature centres and to new

education and learning centres at museums, galleries and other arts organisations.

The social welfare programme:

supports projects for veterans, the elderly, ex-offenders and those in prison and schemes that enable people with mental and physical disability to live fuller lives in the community.

As stated on the foundation's website, the health programme provides funding for:

building and refurbishment projects, specialist new transport and the creation of outdoor or recreational spaces for care homes, hospices, day centres and other facilities that provide relief and sanctuary for patients, their families and those with special needs. The emphasis is on helping charities that are providing an excellent standard of care and support within their communities.

Grant types

The foundation offers three levels of grants: large (over £20,000), medium (up to £20,000) and small (under £5,000). Most grants are single-year awards, but sometimes multi-year grants are made. The trustees have a strong preference for capital projects.

Eligibility

The foundation supports charities registered in England and Wales, as well as CIOs and certain organisations with exempt status, including places of worship, specialist schools, scout and guide groups, hospices, museums, galleries, heritage centres, housing associations and community benefit societies.

The foundation prefers to support smaller organisations with an income of under £10 million and does not fund projects that cost less than £5,000, to maximise impact. The foundation will fund projects that cost up to £5 million.

Financial information

Year end	31/03/2021
Income	£2,640,000
Assets	£146,340,000
Grants to organisations	£3,720,000
No. of grants	395

Further financial information

In 2020/21, the foundation received 760 grant applications, of which 98% were eligible. Of these eligible applications, 54% were awarded a grant. More than half of the charities (52%) that received a grant in 2020/21 were organisations that the foundation was funding for the first time.

Grants were broken down as follows:

Community	232	£1.73 million
Education	56	£929,000
Social welfare	67	£603,000
Health	40	£459,000

Beneficiaries included: National Gallery (£330,000); The Park Centre (£75,000); Warrington Youth Club (£50,000); Jamie's Farm (£20,000); Aspire, Stonepillow and The Forest School (£10,000 each); 3rd Brentwood Scout Group (£5,000); Cheriton Baptist Church (£3,000); Salvation Army (£1,000); Wantage Silver Band (£250).

Exclusions

According to the foundation's website, it does not support:

- Charities registered outside England or Wales
- Core costs – salaries, running costs, training programmes, rent, utility bills
- Capital fees – building surveys, planning applications or feasibility studies
- Individuals
- Second hand vehicles
- Churches or other religious bodies with no secular activity
- NHS hospitals or mainstream schools, colleges or universities
- Heritage or conservation projects with no community benefit
- Medical or research medical equipment
- Appliances, furniture, uniforms, musical instruments or any other type of equipment
- Project costs of £5 million and over
- Project costs of less than £5,000
- Charities with an annual income of £10 million and over
- Charities that have applied unsuccessfully within the previous 12 months
- Charities applying for a new grant before a successful previous application has been paid
- Newly established charities with no previous annual accounts

Applications

The foundation invites applicants to discuss their project before applying. Applicants must undertake an online eligibility quiz before completing the online application form. There are no deadlines and the application process may take up to six months.

Sources of information

Accounts; annual report; Charity Commission record; funder's website.

Sutton Coldfield Charitable Trust

Social welfare; education; arts, culture and heritage; religion; health; the environment; sport; citizenship and community development

The former borough of Sutton Coldfield, comprising four electoral wards: New Hall, Four Oaks, Trinity and almost all of Vesey ward

£1.11 million (2019/20)

CC number: 218627

Correspondent: David Cole, Grants Manager, Lingard House, Fox Hollies Road, Sutton Coldfield, West Midlands B76 2RJ (tel: 0121 794 0970; email: davidcole@suttoncharitabletrust.org)

www.suttoncoldfieldcharitabletrust.com

General information

This trust dates back to 1528 when Bishop Vesey, a native of Sutton Coldfield, persuaded Henry VIII to grant a charter establishing a Warden and Society (Corporation) to govern the town. The corporation was obliged to use rental and other income for the relief of poverty and improvement of the local area. Over the next four centuries, other bequests and endowments came within the corporation's oversight. Until 2012 the trust was known as the Sutton Coldfield Municipal Charities, but now has no direct association with the local authority.

The trust provides funding to benefit the former borough of Sutton Coldfield and its residents by making grants to organisations and individuals in the area. According to its website, the trust makes grants in the following categories:

- The relief of those in need by reason of youth, age, ill health, disability, financial hardship or other disadvantage
- Education
- Arts, culture, heritage or science
- Religion
- Health or the saving of lives
- Citizenship or community development
- Amateur sport
- Environmental protection or improvement

Organisations must be based within the former borough of Sutton Coldfield, the boundaries being those of the four wards of New Hall, Four Oaks, Trinity and almost all of Vesey Ward. Applications may occasionally be considered from organisations outside this area if their aims meet the need of a significant number of residents and there is no other similar provision.

Financial information

Year end	30/09/2020
Income	£1,913,000
Grants to organisations	£1,110,000
No. of grants	68

Further financial information

During the year, 68 grants were awarded to organisations totalling £1.11 million, of which 46 were of more than £1,000 and 22 were of £1,000 or less.

In addition, educational grants to individuals totalled £6,000 and school clothing grants to individuals totalled £42,900.

Beneficiaries included: St Chad's Church (£45,000); 4th Sutton Coldfield Scout Group (£42,000); Our Place Support CIC (£38,900); FoodCycle (£13,500); Mere Green Primary School (£12,900); Sutton Coldfield Choirs (£2,600); MeDAL (£2,800).

Applications

Contact the grants manager to make an application or to discuss further details.

Sources of information

Accounts; annual report; Charity Commission record; funder's website.

Swarovski Foundation

General charitable purposes; education and training; arts, culture, heritage and science; the environment and animals; human rights; religious and racial diversity; equality; relief of poverty; saving of lives

Worldwide

 £459,800 (2020)

CC number: 1153618

Correspondent: Nadja Swarovski, Trustee, 4th Floor, 21 Sackville Street, London W1S 3DN (tel: 020 7255 8400; email: foundationoffice@swarovskifoundation.org)

Trustees: Marisa Schiestl-Swarovski; Anouchka Rafail-Vogiatzakis; Helene Antonia vonDamm; Mag Haim-Swarovski.

 www.swarovskifoundation.org

General information

The foundation was established by Nadja Swarovski in honour of the founder of the family business, Daniel Swarovski, to further the philanthropic activities undertaken by the company. The foundation administrator is also a member of the company's executive board. The foundation was registered with the Charity Commission in September 2013. Its main aim is to assist projects in the areas of culture and creativity, social welfare and well-being, and the conservation of natural resources. Grants are awarded for the advancement of arts, culture, education, preservation of the natural and built environment, heritage, relief of poverty and sickness, and promotion of human rights and equality.

Financial information

Year end	31/12/2020
Income	£1,150,000
Assets	£138,200
Grants to organisations	£459,800

Beneficiaries included: UNFPA (£45,200); Australian Red Cross (£42,800); Room to Read (£34,900); Turquoise Mountain (£27,100); Equal Justice Initiative (£22,700); FIT Foundation (£3,900).

Applications

The Swarovski Foundation does not accept unsolicited grant requests.

Sources of information

Charity Commission record; funder's website; additional information has been obtained from press releases.

The John Swire (1989) Charitable Trust

General charitable purposes; health; older people; wildlife and conservation; education, arts and heritage; disability

 UK

£1.55 million (2020)

CC number: 802142

Correspondent: The Trustees, Swire House, 59 Buckingham Gate, London SW1E 6AJ (tel: 020 7834 7717; email: info@scts.org.uk)

Trustees: Mr B. Swire; Mr J. S. Swire; Rebecca Fitzgerald; William Leigh-Pemberton.

General information

This trust was established in 1989 by Sir John Swire and has a strong affiliation with John Swire & Sons Ltd, a diversified group of global companies. It is one of the four organisations that make up the Swire Family Charitable Trusts, a group of charities that are managed by the same team as the Swire Charitable Trust (Charity Commission no. 270726).

The trust makes grants to registered charities both in the UK and abroad for a wide range of causes. In the past, support has been given within areas such as health, older people, wildlife and conservation, education, arts and heritage, and disability.

Financial information

Year end	31/12/2020
Income	£17,340,000
Assets	£3,330,000
Grants to organisations	£1,550,000

Beneficiaries included: Kent Community Foundation (£256,000); Catching Lives (£70,000); Mind (£10,000); Pancreatic Cancer UK (£2,500); Gurkha Welfare Trust (£1,000).

Applications

Contact the trust for further information. The 2020 annual report states:

> Although the Trustees make some grants without a formal applications, they normally require organisations to submit a request explaining how the funds could be used and what would be achieved.

Sources of information

Accounts; annual report; Charity Commission record; funder's website.

The Adrian Swire Charitable Trust

General charitable purposes

 UK and overseas

 £1.27 million (2020)

CC number: 800493

Correspondent: Jo Trew, Grants and Administration Officer, Swire House, 59 Buckingham Gate, London SW1E 6AJ (tel: 020 7834 7717; email: info@scts.org.uk)

Trustees: Lady Judith Swire; Martha Allfrey; Merlin Swire; Samuel Swire; James Kidner.

 www.swirecharitabletrust.org.uk

General information

The trust, formerly known as the Sammermar Trust, was established in 1988 with general charitable purposes. It has a strong affiliation to John Swire & Sons Ltd, a diversified group of global companies. It is one of the four organisations that make up the Swire Family Charitable Trusts, a group of charities that are managed by the same team as the Swire Charitable Trust (Charity Commission no. 270726).

The trust makes grants to registered charities both in the UK and abroad for a wide range of causes. In previous years, support has been given to causes such as education, art and heritage, homelessness, young people, wildlife and conservation, and the armed forces.

Financial information

Year end	31/12/2020
Income	£1,420,000
Assets	£24,080,000
Grants to organisations	£1,270,000

Beneficiaries included: Julia's House (£30,000); Devon Wildlife Trust (£19,500); Air League Trust (£15,000); The Brain Tumour Charity and London Library (£10,000 each); Battle of Britain Memorial Trust (£5,000); Caudwell Children (£2,500).

Applications

The trust's 2020 accounts state:

> Although the Trustees make some grants with no formal applications, they normally require organisations to submit a request explaining how the funds could be used and what would be achieved.

Sources of information

Accounts; annual report; Charity Commission record; funder's website.

The Swire Charitable Trust

General charitable purposes, with a focus on creating opportunities, the environment and heritage

UK

£4.12 million (2020)

CC number: 270726

Correspondent: Sarah Irving, Grants Manager, Swire House, 59 Buckingham Gate, London SW1E 6AJ (tel: 020 7963 9423; email: info@scts.org.uk)

Trustees: Barnaby Swire; John Swire; Merlin Swire; Samuel Swire; Martha Allfrey; Rupert Hogg.

www.swirecharitabletrust.org.uk

General information

The trust was established in 1975 as an independent grant-making charity. It receives its funding from John Swire & Sons Ltd, a diversified group of global companies and parent company of the Swire Group.

Its website states that the trust makes grants to charities 'supporting some of the UK's most vulnerable people to overcome barriers and realise their potential, and to charities who are protecting our precious environment and heritage.'

Grant programmes

Grants are made through the following programmes:

Opportunity – grants are given to charities that are directly addressing challenges faced by marginalised and disadvantaged people. The programme aims to improve life chances for the following: ex-Service men and women; victims of slavery and trafficking; and children and young people who are in the care of their local authority, involved with the criminal justice system or from the most socio-economically disadvantaged backgrounds.

The environment – funding is given to charities that can connect people to the environment and that support the UK's biodiversity.

Heritage – funding is given to projects that can deliver social and economic benefits to deprived communities or disadvantaged people and charities working to safeguard endangered skills. Preference is given to grassroots organisations that engage with the local community.

COVID-19 Recovery Programme – one-year grants of £25,000 are given to charities providing a unique response to the pandemic or facing severe short-term funding pressures. The programme is a £1.5 million fund.

Eligibility

The trust's website states that across these programmes priority is given to charities that:

- Operate in some of the most economically disadvantaged parts of the UK
- Try to engage the most marginalised and vulnerable in their work
- Can clearly demonstrate the needs they are addressing
- Know what they are aiming to achieve and plan to monitor and evaluate outcomes
- Are well placed and qualified to deliver the work
- Can show a proven track record as well as solid ambitions
- Have the potential to change the way issues are tackled more widely
- Take an effective approach to using volunteers and mentors (where appropriate)
- Are seeking to make their income streams more sustainable
- Have strong and quality leadership
- Manage their finances prudently

The website also notes the following:

> We fund individual projects that are aligned with our funding priorities, though we also recognise that charities are often best placed to allocate resources within their organisations. We therefore award many grants on an unrestricted basis and are willing to support core costs, capital expenditure and salaries.

There is no maximum or minimum grant size and multi-year grants may be considered if a longer-term commitment (up to three years) can be clearly justified.

As well as the core programmes, the trust's Discretionary Fund makes donations to charities that fall outside the funding criteria, at the suggestion of the company's stakeholders.

Financial information

Year end	31/12/2020
Income	£4,440,000
Assets	£9,250,000
Grants to organisations	£4,120,000
No. of grants	197

Further financial information

During the year, grants totalled £4.12 million. Included in these grants are six overseas educational bursaries paid to universities and totalling £824,300.

Beneficiaries included: National Emergencies Trust – Coronavirus Appeal (£450,000); Ragged School Museum (£50,000); One Parent Families Scotland (£30,000); South Downs National Park Trust (£20,000); St Mungo's (£10,000); Wycombe Youth Action (£5,000); Surfers Against Sewage (£2,500); Scope (£1,000).

Exclusions

According to its website, the trust will not provide support for the following:

- Applications received by post or email, i.e. not via our online funding request form
- Organisations that are not UK registered charities
- Activities taking place outside England, Scotland, Wales or Northern Ireland
- Individual applicants or proposals that will benefit only one person
- Requests from charities that have applied to us in the last 12 months
- Work that has already taken place
- Work targeted towards people who are primarily disadvantaged due to the following:
  - physical health issues, disabilities or sensory impairments
  - learning disabilities or special educational needs
- Statutory bodies or work that is primarily the responsibility of statutory authorities (e.g. residential, respite and day care, housing)
- Activities of local organisations which are part of a wider network doing similar work (e.g. uniformed youth groups, YMCA, MIND, Mencap, Home-start, RDA, Relate, Citizens Advice Bureau, Age UK etc)
- Scholarships or bursaries

Note: the trust's Discretionary Fund is not subject to all of these exclusions.

Applications

Applicants should read the guidelines and FAQs on the website first, then complete the eligibility test. If eligible, applications can be made using the online form. Applications are considered throughout the year. Requests for less than £25,000 are considered at monthly meetings, with larger requests being considered quarterly (usually in January, April, July and October). Applications sent by post or email will not be considered.

Note: general correspondence is preferred by email rather than by post.

Sources of information

Accounts; annual report; Charity Commission record; funder's website.

The Syder Foundation

General charitable purposes

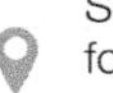
South East England, with a preference for Berkshire and the surrounding counties

£469,200 (2019/20)

CC number: 1119373

Correspondent: The Trustees, PO Box 6277, Newbury, Berkshire RG14 9PN (email: syderfoundation@gmail.com)

Trustees: Charlotte Syder; Timothy Syder.

 www.syderfoundation.org

General information

The foundation was established in 2007 and makes grants for general charitable purposes.

Large grants

The foundation aims to award around eight large grants per year, with a focus on regional charities located in Berkshire and the surrounding counties. Each grant is around £50,000. Capital projects are preferred, but programmes and other projects may be considered in exceptional cases.

Small grants

The foundation awards around £100,000 of small grants per year, with a focus on regional charities located in Berkshire, Hampshire and Wiltshire. Some Surrey, Oxfordshire and Buckinghamshire charities are also supported. National charities are unlikely to be funded.

Financial information

Year end	30/09/2020
Income	£352,600
Assets	£14,780,000
Grants to organisations	£469,200

Beneficiaries included: A list of beneficiaries was not available. Previous beneficiaries include: Hampshire Medical Fund; National Horseracing Museum; Prince's Countryside Trust; Salisbury Samaritans; The Wheelyboat Trust; Whitchurch Silk Mill.

Exclusions

The foundation does not support animal welfare, research or individuals' education.

Applications

Large grants

The trustees prefer to proactively identify projects of interest; however, you can get in touch for an initial discussion if you would like to alert the foundation to a project which fits the criteria. A formal application is not required.

Small grants

If you would like to bring a project to the foundation's attention, an application should be submitted via email or post. Requests for general running costs/core costs (including salaries) are unlikely to be funded.

Applications for small grants should be no longer than two A4 pages and should include your most recent year's income and expenditure, the cost of raising funds annually and the impact of your intended project. Applications should preferably be emailed to the correspondent, attaching your latest accounts.

Sources of information

Accounts; annual report; Charity Commission record; funder's website; further information provided by the funder.

The Charles and Elsie Sykes Trust

General charitable purposes; social welfare; medical research

UK-wide for medical grants; Yorkshire for non-medical grants

£459,700 (2020)

CC number: 206926

Correspondent: Neil Shaw, Secretary, c/o LCF Law Ltd, First Floor, The Exchange, Harrogate, North Yorkshire HG1 1TS (tel: 01423 502211; email: n.shaw@lcf.co.uk (Secretary) or helen.hawley@lcf.co.uk (Administrator))

Trustees: Martin Coultas; Mr R. Barry Kay; Dr P. Rosemary Livingstone; Dr Michael McEvoy; John Ward; Sara Buchan; Elaine Morrison; Sean Rushton; David Mead.

 www.charlesandelsiesykestrust.co.uk

General information

Charles Sykes started his career as a 12-year-old office-boy and became a successful businessman in the West Riding knitting wool trade with his own four-storey mill at Princeville, Bradford. He achieved his life ambition in his 82nd year when he launched The Charles Sykes Trust on 16 December 1954. After his death, his widow Elsie continued his charitable work.

The trust supports registered charities, education or health/medical organisations based in Yorkshire or benefitting people in Yorkshire directly, for a range of charitable purposes, but with particular interest in:

- Relief of hardship among children
- Older people
- People with disabilities
- Medical research projects

If your application relates to a medical project, then it can benefit any part of the UK and still be considered. The website states that 'applications from schools, playgroups, cadet forces, scouts, guides, and churches must be for outreach programmes, and not for maintenance projects.'

Grants are given in the following categories:

- Medical grants – supporting healthcare and medical research
- Annual grants – for ongoing programmes, with funding renewed every year
- Special grants – for one-off charitable projects
- Exceptional grants/'Super Specials' – grants made for exceptional circumstances, such as the trust's anniversary

Financial information

Year end	31/12/2020
Income	£509,400
Assets	£17,820,000
Grants to organisations	£459,700
No. of grants	126

Further financial information

During the year the trust received 402 applications and awarded 126 grants. Grants were broken down as follows:

Social and moral welfare	32	£102,400
Medical research	17	£61,500
Other	6	£61,000
Hospitals and hospices	4	£56,000
Children and young people	10	£29,700
Cultural and environmental heritage	9	£27,500
Mental health	9	£25,000
Education	7	£23,400
Disability	10	£20,300
Older people	6	£18,500
Medical welfare	9	£17,000
Blindness and partial sightedness	4	£9,500
Deafness, hardness of hearing and speech impairment	3	£8,000

Included in these grants is £60,000 of COVID-19 emergency funding given to six of the community foundations in Yorkshire.

Beneficiaries included: Bradford Hospital (£50,000); Yorkshire Cancer Research – Harrogate (£20,000); Sheffield Mencap and Gateway (£6,800); Roundabout Ltd – Sheffield (£5,000); The Brain Tumour Charity (£3,000); The British Stammering Association (£2,000); Take Heart – Leeds (£1,000); Castle Hill School – Huddersfield (£850).

Exclusions

The trust does not fund individuals, building maintenance projects, projects without either a medical link or link to Yorkshire, recently established charities or applications for overseas work.

Applications

Application forms can be downloaded from the website, along with a checklist, and should be sent by post along with a copy of the latest accounts and annual report, and any other relevant information. Further guidance is given on the website. The trustees meet in March, June, September and December, and applications should be submitted by the last Friday of January, April, July and October, respectively.

Sources of information

Accounts; annual report; Charity Commission record; funder's website.

The Hugh Symons Charitable Trust

Health; social welfare; overseas development; the environment

UK and overseas

£342,700 (2020/21)

CC number: 1137778

Correspondent: The Trustees, Stubhampton House, Stubhampton, Blandford Forum DT11 8JU (tel: 01258 830135)

Trustees: Katherine Roper; Geoffrey Roper; Lester Aldridge Trust Company; Pauline Roper.

General information

This trust was established in September 2010 and makes grants for health, social welfare, overseas development and the environment.

Hugh Symons is an information management company with offices in Bradford and Poole.

Financial information

Year end	05/04/2021
Income	£104,700
Assets	£5,780,000
Grants to organisations	£342,700

Further financial information

Grants were broken down as follows: overseas development and healthcare (£196,700); health and welfare (£96,000); environmental causes (£50,000).

Beneficiaries included: Oxfam (£77,500); British Red Cross (£55,000); Jamie's Farm (£10,000); Home-Start (£4,000); Crisis (£2,500); Sightsavers (£2,000).

Applications

Apply in writing to the correspondent.

Sources of information

Charity Commission record.

The Syncona Foundation

Medical causes, particularly oncology

UK

£442,800 (2020/21)

CC number: 1149202

Correspondent: The Trustees, 1st Floor, Shropshire House, 179 Tottenham Court Road, London W1T 7NZ (tel: 020 7387 4264; email: th@bacit.co.uk)

Trustees: James Maltin; Thomas Henderson; Rupert Adams; Nigel Keen; Lucie Kitchener.

www.synconaltd.com/about-us/charities

General information

This foundation was registered with the Charity Commission in 2012. It is funded by Syncona Ltd, a FTSE 250 life sciences investment company that is focused on founding, building and funding companies working in innovative areas of healthcare. Each year, the company donates a percentage of its net assets to charity with half of the funds going to cancer research and the other half to the Syncona Foundation.

The foundation's focus is on the prevention, treatment, cure and eradication of cancer and other diseases.

According to its 2019/20 annual report and accounts the objects of the foundation are to:

- support the prevention, treatment, cure and ultimately the eradication of cancer in all of its forms and any allied diseases;
- promote and assist
  - the study of and research into the nature, causes, diagnosis and pathology of cancer and any allied diseases
  - the development and provision of all forms of preventive, curative, management and palliative treatment of cancer and any allied diseases
  - education and training in subjects relevant to the study of cancer and any allied diseases
- co-operate with, and to promote and assist the work of, The Institute of Cancer Research ('the ICR') and, or alternatively, such other charitable organisations whose objects include any of those specified above as the Foundation may determine in addition to or in substitution for the ICR; and
- promote and assist such other charitable objects and charitable organisations as the Foundation may from time to time consider desirable.

Financial information

Year end	31/03/2021
Income	£2,820,000
Assets	£2,640,000
Grants to organisations	£442,800

Beneficiaries included: Place2Be (£60,000); The Listening Place (£33,300); Heritage of London Trust (£30,000); Matt Hampson Foundation (£30,000); Trinity College Cambridge (£10,000).

Applications

Charities are selected by Syncona shareholders from a list proposed by the trustees.

Sources of information

Accounts; annual report; Charity Commission record; funder's website.

The William Syson Foundation

Visual arts; performing arts; literature; heritage

UK, with preference for Scotland

£376,300 (2020)

OSCR number: SC049635

Correspondent: A. Syson, Foundation Manager, 5 Atholl Crescent, Edinburgh EH3 8EJ (email: hello@williamsysonfoundation.org.uk)

Trustees: H. Cockburn; J. Holloway; M. Morrison; J. Syson; R. Doyle.

www.williamsysonfoundation.org.uk

General information

The William Syson Foundation was established in 2012. The foundation's website states:

> An enthusiastic and long-time supporter of music and the visual arts, particularly in Scotland, William Syson's objective in setting up the foundation was to help provide opportunities for practice and enjoyment of the arts, and to assist and encourage the country's next generation of musical and artistic talent.

Activities that fall within its charitable purposes include:

- **Visual arts:** works of art created to be appreciated by sight, such as painting, sculpture and film-making
- **Performing arts:** creative activity performed in front of an audience, such as music, drama, theatre and dance
- **Literature**
- **Heritage:** where there is a significant element of the arts included

The foundation funds organisations and individuals, supporting core costs (including salaries), project and activity costs, and capital costs. It offers the following grant schemes:

- Small grants (up to £5,000)
- Large grants (£5,001 and over)
- Proactive grants scheme – specific sums for multi-year programmes (by invitation only)
- Scholarship or bursary funding via specific institutions – the foundation accepts applications from organisations requesting contributions to bursary funds for small-scale support (for example, for attendees of short courses)
- Award schemes for individuals – see the foundation's website for details

Eligibility

The foundation will fund: UK-registered charities, Scottish CIOs; public sector organisations and other not-for-profit organisations, including:

- Voluntary or unincorporated associations (applicants must have a written constitution and a bank account in the name of the entity)
- Companies limited by guarantee (applicants must demonstrate clear public benefit objectives)
- CICs
- Trusts
- Co-operatives

Financial information

Year end	31/12/2020
Income	£13,190,000
Assets	£13,430,000
Grants to organisations	£376,300

Further financial information

Grants to organisations were broken down as follows:

Music	£97,700
Art	£79,000
Drama, playwriting and theatre	£65,300
Combined arts	£38,900
Development	£32,300
Other	£22,000
Dance	£18,200
Writing	£13,000
Film	£10,000

In addition, grants to individuals totalled £29,500. The foundation made 87 grants in total during the year.

Beneficiaries included: Boys Brigade (£20,000); Capital Theatres (£15,000); Pier Arts Centre (£10,000); Drake Music Scotland and Firefly Arts (£5,000 each); Edinburgh Children's Hospital Charity (£4,500); East Ayrshire Pipe Band (£3,600); Scottish Documentary Institute (£3,000).

Exclusions

The foundation's website states it will not fund:

- Requests from individuals that do not relate to the awards schemes run by the foundation
- Organisations registered outside the UK
- The promotion of political or religious beliefs
- Requests for salaried posts where there is a requirement for the post holder to be of a particular faith or none
- The standalone purchase costs of buildings and/or land
- Capital work on buildings not owned by the applicant or on which the applicant does not have a long-term lease
- Any retrospective costs already incurred by the applicant
- Applications from organisations that have received funding from the foundation over a sustained period of three consecutive years. Such organisations are requested to take a break of at least one year before re-applying

Applications

Application forms are available on the foundation's website. There are no deadlines for submissions. Decisions for funding can take up to four months. Tips on what to include in the application can be found on the foundation's website.

Sources of information

Accounts; annual report; OSCR record; funder's website.

The T.K. Maxx and Homesense Foundation

Children, young people and families

UK and overseas

£1.94 million (2020/21)

CC number: 1162073

Correspondent: The Trustees, 50 Clarendon Road, Watford, WD17 1TX (tel: 01923 47300; email: TJX_Foundation@tjxeurope.com)

www.tkmaxx.com/uk/en/tkmaxx-and-homesense-foundation

General information

Established in 2015, this foundation is the corporate charity of TJX, the parent company of T.K. Maxx and Homesense, and is funded through donations from the company. It makes grants to organisations supporting vulnerable children and young people in the UK and Ireland, Germany and Poland. Grants are made to national and local charities.

Community Fund

The foundation funds and administers the Community Fund, which enables TJX, T.K. Maxx and Homesense staff to nominate charities they are passionate about, to receive a donation of £500 to make a difference in their local communities. A proportion of these grants is dedicated to charities supporting racial justice, mental health, disability and the LGBTQ+ community.

According to the website, the Community Fund delivered £1 million of COVID-19 emergency grants. This was in addition to a Tackle COVID-19 Fund that delivered £700,000 to frontline mental health and medical charities.

Financial information

Year end	30/01/2021
Income	£3,850,000
Assets	£6,880,000
Grants to organisations	£1,940,000
No. of grants	1,468

Further financial information

Donations to national charities totalled £1.2 million and donations to local charities totalled £731,000. In total 1,468 donations were made during the year, compared to 444 in 2019/20. Only a small list of large donations was detailed in the accounts.

Beneficiaries included: British Red Cross (£180,000); The Prince's Trust (£175,000); Retail Trust (£100,000); Stephen Lawrence Trust (£75,000); Mind (£50,000); School Without Racism (£40,000); Access UK (£35,000).

Applications

Contact the correspondent for further information.

Sources of information

Accounts; annual report; Charity Commission record; funder's website.

The Ashley Tabor-King Foundation

The welfare of first responders and children and young people's education

England and Wales

£400,000 (2020/21)

CC number: 1178634

Correspondent: The Trustees, c/o Global Media and Entertainment Ltd, 29–30 Leicester Square, London WC2H 7LA (tel: 020 7766 6000)

General information

The Ashley Tabor-King Foundation was registered with the Charity Commission in June 2018. Ashley Tabor, a trustee of the foundation, is the founder and president of Global, the Media and Entertainment Group.

According to its Charity Commission record, the foundation operates throughout England and Wales and focusses on first responders who suffer from post-traumatic stress disorder or physical harm associated with their employment. First responders may include paramedic staff, medical staff, call centre handlers, mountain rescuers, RNLI lifeboat rescuers, police officers, firefighters and the bereaved families of first responders who have died in service. The foundation will also support activities which develop young people's skills and enable them to participate in society as mature and responsible individuals.

Financial information

Year end	05/04/2021
Income	£400,500
Assets	£153,800
Grants to organisations	£400,000

Beneficiaries included: The Police Arboretum Memorial Trust (£300,000); [The Royal Foundation of The Duke and] Duchess of Cambridge (£100,000).

Applications

Apply in writing to the correspondent.

Sources of information

Accounts; annual report; Charity Commission record.

The Tajtelbaum Charitable Trust

Jewish causes; religious education; social welfare; health

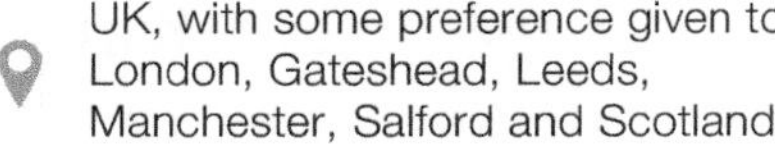

UK, with some preference given to London, Gateshead, Leeds, Manchester, Salford and Scotland

£381,800 (2020/21)

CC number: 273184

Correspondent: The Trustees, PO Box 33911, London NW9 7ZX (tel: 020 8202 3464)

General information

The trust was established in 1974 by the Tajtelbaum family. The trust's objects, outlined in the trustees' annual report for 2020/21, are 'to foster education and moral and religious training in accordance with the doctrines and principles of the Orthodox Jewish faith. Also the relief of poverty, sickness and infirmity.'

Grants are made to charities with similar objects to those above. Preference may be given to organisations/causes in London, Gateshead, Leeds, Manchester, Salford and Scotland.

Financial information

Year end	05/04/2021
Income	£490,700
Assets	£5,870,000
Grants to organisations	£381,800

Beneficiaries included: A list of beneficiaries was not available.

Applications

Apply in writing to the correspondent.

Sources of information

Accounts; annual report; Charity Commission record.

Talbot Village Trust

General charitable purposes; churches; community; education and employment; young people; older people; social welfare

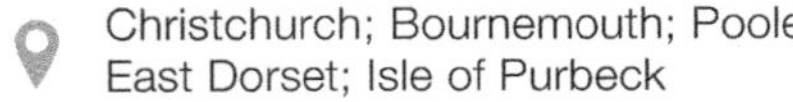

Christchurch; Bournemouth; Poole; East Dorset; Isle of Purbeck

£2.17 million (2020)

CC number: 249349

Correspondent: The Trustees, c/o Savills (UK) Ltd, Wessex House, Priors Walk, Wimbourne, Dorset BH21 1PB (email: info@talbotvillagetrust.org)

General information

The trust supports a wide range of causes in Christchurch, Bournemouth, Poole, East Dorset and the Isle of Purbeck. According to the trust's 2020 annual report, the trustees have a wide remit but focus their support on 'disadvantaged and vulnerable people, across disability issues, educational and employment opportunities and societal challenges'.

Grants are only made for capital projects promoted by a charity, church, school, college or university. According to the website, 'no scheme is too big or too small for consideration and recent grants have ranged in size from £900 to £150,000.'

Financial information

Year end	31/12/2020
Income	£3,020,000
Assets	£67,460,000
Grants to organisations	£2,170,000

Beneficiaries included: Lewis Manning Trust (£150,000); Recreate Dorset (£20,000); Healthbus and Love Church (£10,000 each); St Clement's Church – Poole (£3,000); Headway (£1,000).

Applications

Applications can be made using the online application form, or by post, including the information specified in the guidelines on the website. The trustees meet twice a year to consider applications and applicants are notified of the outcome within a couple of weeks of a meeting.

Sources of information

Accounts; annual report; Charity Commission record; funder's website.

Tallow Chandlers Benevolent Fund No. 2

Children and young people; education; health and medical research; people with disabilities; social welfare

London, mainly the City of London

£328,800 (2020/21)

CC number: 246255

Correspondent: Education and Charity Manager, Tallow Chandlers Hall, 4 Dowgate Hill, London EC4R 2SH (tel: 020 7248 4726; email: Jenna@tallowchandlers.org)

www.tallowchandlers.org

General information

The fund is a charity of the Worshipful Company of Tallow Chandlers. The current priority for the fund is to support young, disadvantaged people with education and skills, primarily in London, to enable them to succeed in life. The charity also supports some other charities with one-off donations. These are mostly small to medium-sized charities operating in London. Its one-off donations range from around £250 to £2,000.

An application may merit consideration for a larger, three-year donation if it is closely related to the fund's priority objective of supporting young people or education and skills, particularly in STEM subjects.

Financial information

Year end	05/04/2021
Income	£704,200
Grants to organisations	£328,800

Further financial information

During the year, the charity awarded 48 grants to 43 organisations.

Beneficiaries included: Cubitt Town Junior School (£57,800); Greig City Academy (£50,000); The Halley Academy (£30,000); Treloar Trust (£15,000); Into University (£10,000); London Youth Choir (£3,000); Innovations for Learning (£2,000); The Sheriffs' and Recorders' Fund (£1,500).

Exclusions

According to its website, the charity does not generally support large or national charities, charities that do not have a connection to London, charities operating overseas or individuals who apply to it directly.

Applications

Apply in writing to the correspondent. Applications are considered by the correspondent. Details of what to include in an application are available on the charity's website.

Sources of information

Accounts, annual report, Charity Commission record and funder's website.

The Talmud Torah Machzikei Hadass Trust

 Jewish causes

 UK and overseas; in practice, the London Borough of Hackney

 £280,100 (2020/21)

CC number: 270693

Correspondent: The Trustees, 34 Heathland Road, London N16 5LZ (tel: 020 8800 6599)

Trustees: Jehudah Baumgarten; Yitzchok Sternlicht; Mordechaj Wind.

General information

This trust was founded in 1975 to further the Orthodox Jewish religion in any part of the world. However, in practice, the trust appears to concentrate its activity in Hackney.

Financial information

Year end	31/03/2021
Income	£688,100
Assets	£15,090,000
Grants to organisations	£280,100

Further financial information

In 2020/21 the trust made grants totalling £280,100. In previous years, the grant total has been over £1 million.

Beneficiaries included: Moreshet Hatorah Ltd (£142,700); Dover Sholem Community Trust (£84,000); Clapton Common Boys Club (£26,300); Belz Foundation Ltd (£20,000).

Applications

Apply in writing to the correspondent.

Sources of information

Accounts; annual report; Charity Commission record.

The Tanlaw Foundation

Health and disability; medical research; overseas aid; the promotion of religion; education; wildlife and the environment; social welfare

UK and overseas

 £551,200 (2019/20)

CC number: 1094181

Correspondent: The Trustees, Rathbone Investment Management Ltd, 8 Finsbury Circus, London EC2M 7AZ (tel: 020 7399 0134; email: Neil.Warman@rathbones.com)

Trustees: Lady Tanlaw; The Hon. Asia Trotter; The Hon. Brooke Mackay; Lord Tanlaw.

General information

The foundation was established in 1996 by The Right Honourable the Lord Tanlaw and The Right Honourable the Lady Tanlaw. Grants are made in the UK and overseas for the following purposes:

- Health and disability
- Overseas aid
- Religion
- Education
- Wildlife and environment
- Relief of poverty

Financial information

Year end	31/10/2020
Income	£1,230,000
Assets	£4,680,000
Grants to organisations	£551,200

Beneficiaries included: Great Ormond Street Hospital (£255,000); United World Schools (£100,000); The Trussell Trust (£40,000); Rainbow Trust (£30,000); Borneo Rescue Centre (£10,000); Rokpa Trust (£5,000).

Applications

Apply in writing to the correspondent.

Sources of information

Accounts; annual report; Charity Commission record.

The David Tannen Charitable Trust

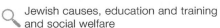

Jewish causes, education and training and social welfare

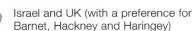

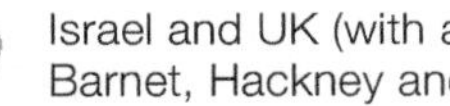 Israel and UK (with a preference for Barnet, Hackney and Haringey)

£123,400 (2019/20)

CC number: 280392

Correspondent: The Trustees, c/o Sutherland House, 70–78 West Hendon Broadway, London NW9 7BT (tel: 020 8202 1066)

Trustees: David Tannen; Jonathan Miller; Martin Irving Tannen; Daniel Asher Tannen

General information

The trust was established in 1974 and registered with the Charity Commission in 1981. The aims of the trust are to relieve poverty, distress, and suffering in any part of the world, and also to promote and advance Jewish religion and education through charitable means.

Financial information

Year end	30/06/2020
Income	£3,150,000
Assets	£20,870,000
Grants to organisations	£123,400

Further financial information

In previous years grants have totalled around £300,000.

Beneficiaries included: The ABC Trust (£30,000); The Telz Talmudical Academy (£15,000); Halacha Lemoshe Trust (£13,000); Friends of Beis Chinuch Lebanos Trust, Friends of Beis Soroh Schneirer, Mifal Hachesed Vehatzedokoh and North West London Communal Mikvah Ltd (£10,000 each).

Applications

Apply in writing to the correspondent.

Sources of information

Accounts; annual report; Charity Commission record.

Tanner Trust

 Community projects

 UK and overseas, with a preference for the south of England

£551,200 (2020/21)

CC number: 1021175

Correspondent: The Trustees, c/o Blake Morgan, New Kings Court, Tollgate, Chandler's Ford, Hampshire SO53 3LG (tel: 023 9222 1122; email: Charity.Admin@blakemorgan.co.uk)

Trustees: Alice Williams; Lucie Nottingham.

General information

The Tanner Trust was registered with the Charity Commission in 1993 and supports general charitable purposes worldwide. The trust's 2020/21 annual report states that: 'The main areas supported by the charity have been community projects in the widest sense of the word, both at home and abroad. Grants have been made to the Community Foundations of Cornwall and Oxfordshire for general community support, as well as numerous grants to local and national charities.' Over the past five years, the trust has provided grants in the following areas:

- Gardening and gardens, farming
- Conservation and the countryside
- Youth projects
- Health, and help for older people and people with disabilities
- Culture and preservation of buildings
- Foreign aid

Financial information

Year end	31/03/2021
Income	£405,700
Assets	£10,890,000
Grants to organisations	£551,200

Beneficiaries included: Garden Museum (£60,000); Aberglasney Gardens (£50,000); Cornwall Wildlife Trust (£10,000); Deafblind UK (£4,000); Azook CIC (£1,300).

Applications

The trust does not accept unsolicited applications. The trust's 2020/21 annual report states that 'the trustees decide jointly which charitable institutions are to receive donations from the Trust. No invitations are sought from eligible institutions.'

Sources of information

Accounts; annual report; Charity Commission record.

The Taurus Foundation

General charitable purposes

UK

£630,000 (2020)

CC number: 1128441

Correspondent: The Trustees, c/o Forsters LLP, 31 Hill Street, London W1J 5LS (tel: 020 7863 8580; email: cosmo.peach@taurus-foundation.org.uk)

Trustees: Carole Cook; Alan Fenton; Denis Felsenstein; Priscilla Fenton; Antony Forwood; Wendy Pollecoff; Dominic Fenton; Anthony Felsenstein; Katherine Ekers; James Goodman; Charles Vermont.

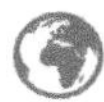
http://taurus-foundation.org.uk

General information

The foundation was established in 2009 and makes grants for general charitable purposes to organisations selected by the trustees. According to the foundation's website:

> The trustees have identified a number of overarching themes or areas of interest
> - biodiversity, embracing the environment and species conservation
> - the arts
> - disadvantaged and marginalised members of society
> - mental health
> - domestic animal welfare
> - Jewish connections
>
> Grants are usually made on an unrestricted basis and, subject to certain conditions, may be renewed.

Financial information

Year end	31/12/2020
Income	£1,300,000
Assets	£1,750,000
Grants to organisations	£630,000

Beneficiaries included: A list of beneficiaries was not available.

Applications

The foundation does not accept unsolicited applications. The trustees research and identify suitable charitable organisations prior to the annual board meeting.

Sources of information

Accounts; annual report; Charity Commission record; funder's website.

C. B. and H. H. Taylor 1984 Trust

Work of the Religious Society of Friends; social welfare; education; penal affairs

Birmingham and the West Midlands; Ireland; UK-based organisations working overseas. Quaker work is supported regardless of location

£539,900 (2020/21)

CC number: 291363

Correspondent: The Trustees, PO Box 236, Penmaenmawr LL30 9HA (tel: 07934 338005; email: cbandhhtaylortrust.info@gmail.com)

Trustees: Constance Penny; Elizabeth Birmingham; Clare Norton; John Taylor; Thomas Penny; Robert Birmingham; Simon Taylor; Camilla Middleton; Lucy Taylor.

www.cbandhhtaylortrust.com

General information

The trust was established by Christopher and Hannah Taylor in 1964. It has three main areas of work, details of which have been taken from its website:

> **1. Religious Society of Friends (Quakers)**
>
> A substantial proportion of the grants awarded by The Trust are given for the work and concerns of the Religious Society of Friends. Projects with a defined link to Quaker work or supported by Friends will be considered regardless of location.
>
> **2. Birmingham and the West Midlands**
>
> The Trust provides support to charitable organisations serving Birmingham and the West Midlands. Attention is given to applications from small locally-based charities and schemes intended to solve local problems and improve the quality of life within communities.
>
> *Social welfare*
> - Children and young people
> - Older people
> - People with disabilities
> - Homelessness
> - Women-led initiatives
> - Counselling and mediation
> - Hospice and bereavement services
>
> *Education*
> - Adult literacy schemes
> - Employment training
> - Youth work
> - Mental health education
>
> *Penal Affairs*
> - Work with offenders and ex-offenders to reduce re-offending and help reintegration
> - Support for families of offenders
> - Police backed initiatives
> - Youth projects
>
> **3. Additional Areas**
> - Aid for humanitarian emergencies is always considered
> - Other international support is given through a separate strategic fundraising agreement and unsolicited applications are unlikely to be successful
> - Donations may be made to charities which do not fall into the above categories but which are known particularly to a trustee

Financial information

Year end	05/04/2021
Income	£458,100
Assets	£16,430,000
Grants to organisations	£539,900

Beneficiaries included: Britain Yearly Meeting of the Religious Society of Friends (£190,000); Quaker Social Action (£25,000); Money for Madagascar (£11,000); Birmingham Settlement (£10,000); Samaritans Birmingham (£6,000); Medical Aid for Palestinians (£5,000); Quaker Homeless Action (£4,500); Young Women's Trust (£1,000); Young People First (£500).

Exclusions

The trust does not support the following:

- Individuals
- Projects or groups outside the trust's geographical focus
- Annual grants for revenue costs
- Repeat applications within a two-year period

Applications

Applications can be made by post or online via the trust's website.

According to the website, international support is given through a separate strategic fundraising agreement and unsolicited applications are unlikely to be successful.

Sources of information

Accounts; annual report; Charity Commission record; funder's website.

Humphrey Richardson Taylor Charitable Trust

Music

Surrey

£288,700 (2020)

CC number: 1062836

Correspondent: Kate Perry, Administrator, 32 Chipstead Station Parade, Chipstead, Coulsdon, Surrey CR5 3TF (tel: 01737 557680; email: hrtaylortrust@btconnect.com)

Trustees: Ian Catling; Rowena Cox; Colin Edgerton; William Malings;

 www.hrtaylortrust.org.uk

General information

The trust was established in 1997 for the advancement of public education in, and the appreciation of, the art and science of music and allied performing arts. It is named after its late benefactor, Mr H. R. Taylor, who lived in Surrey and was devoted to music and wished to encourage the advancement of music-making and live performance by people of every age.

Areas of support

The trust supports musical activities in Surrey and its adjacent areas. Through national bodies such as the Royal College of Music and the University of Surrey, it also supports 'musically gifted British residents' outside its primary area of benefit, as stated on the website.

Help is given to schools, musical societies and organisations, and individuals, typically for the following:

- **Schools:** music-related capital projects, purchase of instruments, music computers and software, scores and sheet music, funding of concerts for special occasions and part-funding of instrumental tuition
- **Musical societies and organisations:** annual grants towards the costs of funding live concerts (choral societies, orchestras, opera and light operatic societies, etc.)
- **Individuals:** scholarship funding for music-related undergraduate and postgraduate studies, grants towards fees and purchase of instruments

For full details see the website.

Financial information

Year end	31/12/2020
Income	£455,800
Assets	£15,520,000
Grants to organisations	£288,700

Further financial information

According to the 2020 annual report and accounts, the trust's grant expenditure was impacted by the COVID-19 pandemic. The trust typically makes grants in excess of £300,000 to organisations.

During the year, grants made to schools for musical instruments and tuition totalled £161,100. Grants to partner organisations totalled £76,700. Grants to choirs, orchestras and other music societies in support of amateur productions totalled £60,000, and grants to individual young musicians in Surrey totalled £29,100.

Beneficiaries included: Royal College of Music (£36,500); Glenthorne High School (£25,000); Overton Grange School (£10,600); Banstead Arts Festival (£6,500); Surrey Opera (£3,000); National Youth Choirs of Great Britain (£2,300); Twickenham Choral (£1,000); Overton Grange School (£400).

Exclusions

It is rare for the trust to provide funding to schools for transport costs, concert tickets or accommodation.

Applications

Applications should be made by email to the correspondent. The trustees meet five times a year to consider applications (see the website for deadlines). Applications should be no longer than four to six pages of A4 when printed. Specific application criteria and guidelines for schools, musical societies and individuals are available to view on the website.

Sources of information

Accounts; annual report; Charity Commission record; funder's website.

The Taylor Family Foundation

Disadvantaged children and young people aged 11–25; the arts; social inclusion

 UK (for smaller projects there is a particular focus on Merton)

 £2.13 million (2020/21)

CC number: 1118032

Correspondent: The Trustees, Hill Place House, 55A High Street, Wimbledon, London SW19 5BA (tel: 020 8605 2629; email: info@thetaylorfamilyfoundation.co.uk)

 www.thetaylorfamilyfoundation.co.uk

 @TTFF_uk

General information

The foundation was set up by Ian and Cristina Taylor in 2007 and has since given over £24 million to charitable causes in the UK. The main focus of the foundation is supporting charities that give opportunities to children and young people from disadvantaged backgrounds to improve their chances of attaining success and to leading fulfilling lives.

Areas of focus

The following information has been taken from the foundation's website:

- **Children and young people:** supporting charitable organisations that provide opportunities for children and young people from disadvantaged backgrounds, to improve their chances of attaining success and to leading fulfilling lives.
- **The arts:** improving access and engagement from young people and those from deprived backgrounds.
- **Social inclusion:** helping the homeless and supporting deprived and struggling families.
- **Age group:** the majority of our future grants will be used to fund projects which focus on young people 11–25 years old.
- **Geographical focus:** we fund charitable organisations based in the UK. For smaller projects we have a particular focus on the London Borough of Merton in which we are based.

Financial information

Year end	31/03/2021
Income	£2,710,000
Assets	£3,490,000
Grants to organisations	£2,130,000
No. of grants	28

Further financial information

In 2020/21, the foundation awarded 33 grants to 28 organisations.

Beneficiaries included: The Institute of Cancer Research (£1 million); Royal Opera House Covent Garden Foundation (£500,000); King's College School (£200,000); Centrepoint (£50,000); Jigsaw4u (£20,000); Power to Connect CIC (£13,000); Wimbledon Arts (£8,000); REACT (£5,000).

Exclusions

The foundation does not make grants to individuals.

Applications

Applicants should complete the contact form on the foundation's website with a summary of the project aims, beneficiaries and location. The foundation will then arrange to discuss eligibility and whether the project is something it may fund. The applicant may then be asked to complete a full application form.

Sources of information

Accounts; annual report; Charity Commission website; funder's website.

Stephen Taylor Foundation

Education; improving life chances in urban areas; reducing inequality; improving the environment; young people; community

Worldwide, but mostly England

£1.55 million (2019/20)

CC number: 1168032

Correspondent: The Trustees, c/o Farrer and Co., 65–66 Lincoln's Inn Fields, London WC2A 3LH (tel: 020 3375 7000; email: contact@stf.london)

Trustees: Lisa Taylor; Richard Walker; Martin Taylor.

 http://stf.london

General information

The foundation was registered with the Charity Commission in July 2016. The foundation was established in memory of Stephen Taylor and is funded solely by Stephen's brother, Martin Taylor. Martin founded and ran the successful London-based asset management business Nevsky Capital LLP between 2000 and 2016, and their father was a Labour councillor in Lewisham, South East London.

The foundation awards grants to charitable organisations across four overlapping themes, namely: education, improving life chances in the inner city, reducing inequality and improving the environment. Community and young people are also favoured.

Financial information

Year end	31/07/2020
Income	£269,300
Assets	£22,270,000
Grants to organisations	£1,550,000
No. of grants	10

Further financial information

In 2019/20 the foundation made a final payment of £578,500 to King's College, Cambridge for the completion of a halls of residence building. It also awarded a grant of £608,100 to the Deptford Ragged Trust to purchase the freehold of a building in Deptford which, according to the annual report, 'will then unlock public body grants to convert this building into both a community space and low cost rental housing for the disadvantaged'. The remaining grants awarded during the year were for between £10,000 and £150,000.

Beneficiaries included: Deptford Ragged Trust (£608,100); King's College Cambridge (£578,500); Age UK (£150,000); Institute for Public Policy Research (£50,000); Stephen Lawrence Day Foundation (£35,000); Youth First Ltd (£15,600); Montessori Education for Autism (£10,000).

Applications

Contact the correspondent via email for information regarding the application process. Note that the foundation will not reply to any queries received by post.

Sources of information

Accounts; annual report; Charity Commission record; funder's website.

Khoo Teck Puat UK Foundation

Social welfare; arts and culture; education; health; science

UK

£2,000,000 (2019/20)

CC number: 1142788

Correspondent: The Trustees, 2–24 Kensington High Street, London W8 4PT (tel: 020 7937 8000)

Trustees: Elizabeth Khoo; Mavis Khoo Bee Geok; Eric Hai.

General information

The foundation is the UK subsidiary of Khoo Teck Puat Foundation, a charitable organisation founded by Khoo Teck Puat, which is incorporated in Singapore. Khoo Teck Puat was a banker and hotelier who owned the Goodwood Group of boutique hotels in London and Singapore and was the largest single shareholder of the British bank Standard Chartered.

According to its 2019/20 annual report, the objects of the foundation are:

- the prevention or relief of poverty or financial hardship of the public
- the advancement of the education of the public
- the relief of sickness and the preservation and advancement of the health of the public
- the promotion and advancement of the arts, culture or science.

The report states that:

> the Foundation has two high-value income producing assets allowing it to forecast with almost certainty in excess of £5.7 million of revenues being received annually. This allows the Foundation to plan with security for the future. The Foundation will continue to contribute towards large scale medical projects which it can fund over a number of years and a small number of ancillary medical charity donations which are made on an annual basis.

Financial information

Year end	30/06/2020
Income	£5,200,000
Assets	£65,160,000
Grants to organisations	£2,000,000

Beneficiaries included: Previous beneficiaries include: Chelsea and Westminster Hospital and Great Ormond Street Hospital (£1 million each); British Red Cross (£100,000); Guy's and St Thomas' Hospital (£500,000); Norton Rose Charitable Foundation (£10,000).

Applications

Apply in writing to the correspondent.

Sources of information

Accounts; annual report; Charity Commission record.

The Tedworth Charitable Trust

Parenting; child development; family welfare; the arts; rural arts; the environment; organic gardening; sustainable living; general charitable purposes

UK and overseas

£270,700 (2020/21)

CC number: 328524

Correspondent: Robert Bell, Director, The Peak, 5 Wilton Road, London SW1V 1AP (tel: 020 7410 0330; email: info@sfct.org.uk)

Trustees: Judith Portrait; Timothy Sainsbury; Jessica Sainsbury; Margaret Sainsbury.

 www.sfct.org.uk

General information

This is one of the Sainsbury Family Charitable Trusts, which share a joint administration but work autonomously as independent legal entities.

The Tedworth Charitable Trust does not accept unsolicited applications. Established in 1990, the trust makes grants, mostly to registered charities, for the following purposes: parenting, family welfare and children's development; the arts; and the environment, including the themes of sustainable living, organic gardening and rural arts.

The trust also makes grants for general charitable purposes.

Financial information

Year end	05/04/2021
Assets	£11,340,000
Grants to organisations	£270,700

Further financial information

Grants to organisations were distributed as follows: arts and the environment (£137,300); parenting, family welfare, and children's development (£83,000); general (£50,400).

Beneficiaries included: Resurgence Trust (£58,300); Ashden Climate Solutions (£20,000); Home-Start Hellas (£13,400); Best Beginnings (£10,000); 361 Community Energy (£5,000); Two Moors Festival (£2,500); Frontline Immune Support (£1,000).

Exclusions

The trust does not make grants to individuals.

Applications

Unsolicited applications are not accepted.

Sources of information

Accounts; annual report; Charity Commission record; funder's website.

Tegham Ltd

Jewish causes; relief of poverty; religious education; general charitable purposes

UK, with a preference for Barnet

£325,900 (2020/21)

CC number: 283066

Correspondent: The Trustees, 13 Garrick Avenue, London NW11 9AR (tel: 020 8209 1535; email: admin@geraldkreditor.co.uk)

General information

This charity supports the promotion of the Jewish Orthodox faith and the relief of poverty.

Financial information

Year end	31/03/2021
Income	£245,800
Assets	£2,710,000
Grants to organisations	£325,900

Further financial information

Note that the grant total may include grants to individuals.

Beneficiaries included: A list of beneficiaries was not available.

Applications

The trustees have previously stated that the charity has enough causes to support and they do not welcome new applications.

Sources of information

Accounts; annual report; Charity Commission record.

Tenovus Scotland

Medical research

Scotland

£910,600 (2020/21)

OSCR number: SC009675

Correspondent: The Trustees, The Royal College of Physicians and Surgeons of Glasgow, 232–242 St Vincent Street, Glasgow G2 5RJ (tel: 0141 221 6268; email: general.secy@tenovus-scotland.org.uk)

 www.tenovus-scotland.org.uk

General information

The charity was established in 1967 and provides early pilot funds for initial research in medicine and healthcare. It has regional committees in Edinburgh, Grampian, Strathclyde and Tayside.

The following information on the charity's grant programmes has been taken from its website:

> *Small Pilot grants of up to £20,000*
> Our main focus is on awarding small grants to allow researchers, usually at the start of their research career, to produce preliminary data in a new area of scientific research. This then allows them to apply for funding from larger research funding organisations, further developing exciting medical possibilities.
>
> Each of the four regions (Edinburgh, Grampian, Strathclyde and Tayside) raises its own funds to support research within its region.
>
> Recent projects funded have included: research into the development of novel approaches to reduce vascular diseases, a potential new drug target for resolving sepsis and investigating new therapies for osteoarthritis.
>
> *Large grants of up to £100,000*
> A small number of larger awards (between £50,000 and £100,000) are available only in the Tayside region. This level of support is aimed at more ambitious research projects than the small research grants as they require a higher level of funding and a project duration of two to three years. These awards, however, are still primarily aimed at early career researchers or pilot projects that have potential to lead to more ambitious programmes of research than can be supported by major Research Councils or Charities.
>
> Recent projects funded have included: research into enzyme inhibitors in asthma, investigation into the causes of kidney cancer and research into the inflammation effect on heart and blood vessel disease.
>
> *Medical research PhD scholarships*
> The Princess Royal Tenovus Scotland Medical Research Scholarship Scheme gives scholarships to support young researchers through a three-year programme of training and research activity towards a PhD degree. We aim to offer at least one scholarship a year.
>
> The Moulton-Barrett Research Scholarship is a Grampian region initiative to fund talented PhD medical students for four years of full-time study
>
> Recent scholarship holders include: Anna Muriano, studying the debilitating condition of Huntingdon's Disease at the University of Dundee; Angela Ianniciello at the University of Glasgow studying Chronic Myeloid Leukaemia; and Vasiliki Mallikourti, researching non-invasive mapping of lipid and metabolite profiles in breast cancer, involving MRI methods, at the University of Aberdeen.
>
> *Researcher awards*
> We make one-off awards to researchers in recognition of the quality and importance of their work and to support further research, including awards for:
> - Most outstanding final research report
> - Best research in Scotland in a nominated field
> - Pathology intercalated degree students at the University of Glasgow
> - Contribution to the understanding of the disabilities affecting elderly people

Financial information

Year end	31/03/2021
Income	£770,800
Assets	£2,490,000
Grants to organisations	£910,600

Beneficiaries included: A list of beneficiaries was not available.

Exclusions

See the charity's helpful website for a full list of exclusions.

Applications

An application form can be requested from the relevant regional correspondent – refer to the website for contact details. Application deadlines are also posted on the website.

Sources of information

Accounts; annual report; OSCR record; funder's website.

The Theatres Trust Charitable Fund

Capital improvements for theatres

UK

£492,600 (2020/21)

CC number: 274697

Correspondent: Tom Stickland, Theatres Advisor, 22 Charing Cross Road, London WC2H 0QL (tel: 020 7836 8591; email: info@theatrestrust.org.uk or tom.stickland@theatrestrust.org.uk)

 www.theatrestrust.org.uk

 facebook.com/theatres.trust

 @TheatresTrust

General information

The Theatres Trust was established in 1976 and is the national advisory public body for theatres. According to the website, it works to promote the better protection of theatres for the benefit of the nation by 'providing advice on the design, planning, development and sustainability of theatres, campaigning on behalf of theatres old and new and offering financial assistance through grants'.

Grant schemes

The charity has three grant schemes, details of which have been taken from its website:

Small grants programme – grants of up to £5,000 for essential works to enable not-for-profit theatres across the UK to be viable and thrive in the future. This could include small capital works, the installation of key plant and machinery and works which make theatre buildings digital-ready.

Theatre Improvement Scheme – grants of up to £20,000 towards building and equipment. The current funding theme is 'Improving Environmental Sustainability'.

Theatres at Risk Capacity Building Programme – this programme is only open to theatres on the charity's 'Theatres at Risk Register' and the community and campaign groups that support them. Up to £25,000 is available to support the groups working with the buildings to commission expert support and acquire the skills and knowledge to push the project forward.

Each grants scheme has its own eligibility and application process, visit the website for more information.

Financial information

Year end	31/03/2021
Income	£1,010,000
Assets	£1,100,000
Grants to organisations	£492,600
No. of grants	92

Beneficiaries included: Northern Stage Theatrical Productions Ltd (£20,000); Derby Hippodrome Restoration Trust (£15,000); Teddington Theatre Club (£5,000); Marina Theatre Trust (£4,800); Wiltons Music Hall (£3,700); Stamford Shakespeare Company (£2,400); Tynemouth Priory Theatre (£1,500); Oldbury Repertory Players (£910).

Applications

Application forms and eligibility guidelines for each scheme can be found on the charity's website.

Sources of information

Accounts; annual report; Charity Commission record; funder's website.

The Thirty Percy Foundation

Sustainable development; environmental conservation and research; community development

England and Wales

£4.8 million (2020/21)

CC number: 1177514

Correspondent: Nikki Clegg, Director of Operations and Grants, 30 Percy Street, London W1T 2DB (tel: 020 7514 3052; email: hello@thirtypercy.org)

Trustees: Anne Mann; Mark Philip-Sorensen; Katharine Hill; Derek Bardowell.

 https://thirtypercy.org

 @thirtypercy

General information

The foundation was established in March 2018. It is the corporate charity of Skagen Conscience Capital Ltd, a global fund that specialises in sustainable businesses and owns companies such as Ecover and Method Products, which make ecologically sound cleaning products, and Aquaver, which makes clean technology. According to the foundation's 2020/21 annual report, its objectives are:

- To promote sustainable development for the benefit of the public by: The preservation, conservation and the protection of the environment and the prudent use of resources; The relief of poverty and the improvement of the conditions of life in socially and economically disadvantaged communities; The promotion of sustainable means of achieving economic growth and regeneration.
- To advance the education of the public in subjects relating to sustainable development and the protection, enhancement and rehabilitation of the environment and to promote study and research in such subjects provided that the useful results of each study are disseminated to the public at large.
- To advance such exclusively charitable purposes for the public benefit in any part of the world as the charity Trustees from time to time in their absolute discretion think fit.

Grants are awarded through the following funding programmes, details of which have been taken from the foundation's annual report:

Place-based Fund – flexible one- to three-year grants for innovative, collaborative, low-resource solutions in Gloucestershire.

Systems Fund – 'Focusing on different leverage points, where small shifts can produce big change. We provide a mix of longer term core funding and rapid response funding in relation to specific opportunities'

Leaders Fund – 'Resourcing visionary people with disruptive ideas. We provide funding to leaders for two years to amplify their work.'

Discretionary Fund – Creating space for individual visions, and resourcing organisations that build towards them. Deliberately flexible, based on individual (trustee/team) discretion.

Financial information

Year end	31/03/2021
Income	£5,300,000
Assets	£8,370,000
Grants to organisations	£4,800,000

Beneficiaries included: The Maggie Keswick Jencks Cancer Caring Centres Trust (£550,000); The A Team Foundation (£200,000); Agro-Ecology Fund (£100,000); The Friendship Cafe (£74,000); Creative Sustainability CIC (£35,000); Climate Alliance CIC (£21,000); B Lab Europe (£5,000).

Applications

Contact the correspondent for further information. There is also an option to subscribe to updates through the website.

Sources of information

Accounts; annual report; Charity Commission record; funder's website.

The Thompson Family Charitable Trust

 General charitable purposes

UK

£18.09 million (2020/21)

CC number: 326801

Correspondent: The Trustees, 15 Totteridge Common, London N20 8LR (tel: 01608 676789; email: roycopus@btconnect.com)

Trustees: Patricia Thompson; Katharine Woodward; Roy Copus.

General information

The trust was established in 1985. It makes grants throughout the UK for general charitable purposes. The trust's 2020/21 annual report states that 'applications for donations are invited from all categories of registered charity.'

The trust holds reserves which enable it to make major donations for capital projects, such as the construction and endowment of new medical or educational facilities. In 2020/21, the trust made a large capital grant of £12 million to King Edward VII Hospital.

Financial information

Year end	31/01/2021
Income	£7,340,000
Assets	£113,780,000
Grants to organisations	£18,090,000
No. of grants	64

Beneficiaries included: King Edward VII Hospital (£12 million); East Anglia's Children's Hospices (£300,000); Royal Ballet School (£250,000); Racing Welfare and Sports Aid Trust (£100,000 each); Scene and Heard (£50,000); Beyond Autism (£35,000); Newmarket Day

Centre (£10,000); Institute of Cancer Research (£5,000).

Applications

Apply in writing to the correspondent. The trust's 2020/21 accounts state: 'The Trustees meet as regularly as is necessary to assess grant applications. [...] Applications should be in writing in the first instance, and sent to the Trustees at the Charity's address.'

Sources of information

Accounts; annual report; Charity Commission record.

Sir Jules Thorn Charitable Trust

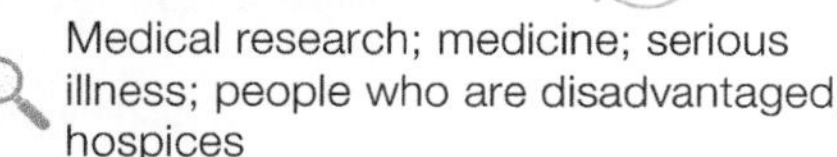

Medical research; medicine; serious illness; people who are disadvantaged; hospices

UK

£1.92 million (2020)

CC number: 233838

Correspondent: The Director, 24 Manchester Square, London W1U 3TH (tel: 020 7487 5851; email: donations@julesthorntrust.org.uk)

Trustees: Keith Bintley; Ian Childs; Jennifer Michael; Andrew Griffiths; Huw Iley; Mr J. Aitken; Paul Young; Dr Joshua Fitzhugh; Simon Tomlinson; David Bingham; David Roberts; Michelangelo Leto; Dr John Burness; Andrew Mayo; Philip Symons; John Gamble; Alexander McIlhinney; Glyn Davies.

www.julesthorntrust.org.uk

General information

The trust was established in 1964 for general charitable purposes and its primary interest is in the field of medicine. The founder of the trust, Sir Jules Thorn, made his fortune through his company Thorn Electrical Industries. Grants are awarded to universities and hospitals in the UK to support medical research, with modest donations provided also for medically related purposes. It is a member of the Association of Medical Research Charities. Outside medicine, small grants are also made for more general causes.

Grant programmes

Resources for grant-making are allocated each year and distributed competitively. The trust has four core areas of grant-making:

- **Medical research grants** – the trust offers grants to support translational biomedical research at UK medical schools or NHS organisations. There is also funding available for two four-year scholarships embedded within the doctoral training programmes of UK universities
- **Medicine-related grants** – appeals from universities, hospitals and other charitable organisations to assist with capital projects to support innovation in medical science or the care and treatment of people with severe disabilities
- **Ann Rylands Small Donations** – allocated to charities in response to appeals of a humanitarian nature. Grants of up to £5,000 are made for core costs. Grants are made to charities providing practical and emotional support for: older people; people with disabilities or severe illnesses; people in need of palliative care; and people facing challenges with mental health, social exclusion or homelessness
- **Hospice Fund** – grants of up to £5,000 for core funding are available to hospices

Financial information

Year end	31/12/2020
Income	£972,300
Assets	£128,460,000
Grants to organisations	£1,920,000

Beneficiaries included: University of Strathclyde (£450,000); The Children's Trust (£160,000); Bury Hospice and Wakefield Hospice (£5,000 each); Mobility Trust (£1,500); Open Minds (£750).

Exclusions

Refer to the website for exclusions from each specific grants scheme.

Applications

Apply via the trust's website.

Sources of information

Accounts; annual report; Charity Commission record; funder's website; further information provided by funder.

The Three Guineas Trust

People with autistic spectrum disorder

UK

£4.24 million (2020/21)

CC number: 1059652

Correspondent: The Trustees, The Sainsbury Family Charitable Trusts, The Peak, 5 Wilton Road, London SW1V 1AP (tel: 020 7410 0330; email: info@sfct.org.uk)

Trustees: Clare Sainsbury; David Wood; Dominic Flynn.

www.sfct.org.uk

General information

This is one of the Sainsbury Family Charitable Trusts, which share a joint administration but work autonomously as independent legal entities. They have a common approach to grant-making and generally discourage applications from organisations not already in contact with the trust concerned, but some are open to unsolicited approaches.

The trust accepts applications for any practical projects in the field of autism spectrum disorder (ASD). The trustees have begun to consider supporting organisations working in the fields of disability, violence and access to justice; however, they do not accept unsolicited applications under this theme.

The trust also runs an annual small grants programme for play schemes run in the summer school holidays which support children with ASD.

On the trust's website, the trustees advise that they are particularly keen to support projects which include service users in decision-making.

Financial information

Year end	05/04/2021
Income	£1,870,000
Assets	£26,440,000
Grants to organisations	£4,240,400

Beneficiaries included: The Trussell Trust (£1 million); Respond (£300,000); London Community Foundation (£250,000); Stay Safe East (£196,300); Sunbeams Play (£100,000); Project Artworks (£68,000); Resources for Autism (£20,000); University of Bath (£10,000).

Exclusions

The trust does not provide grants for:

- Individuals
- Research
- Capital projects

Applications

The trustees will only consider applications for proposals in the field of ASD. Application forms can be completed on The Sainsbury Family Charitable Trusts' website.

Sources of information

Accounts; annual report; Charity Commission record; funder's website.

Three Monkies Trust

Music and performing arts education; disadvantaged children; affordable housing for key workers in London

UK

£280,000 (2020/21)

CC number: 1164342

Correspondent: The Trustees, c/o Belsize Court Garages, Belsize Lane, Hampstead, London NW3 5AJ (tel: 07928 746013; email: info@threemonkiestrust.org)

Trustees: Anna Higgins; Nigel Higgins; Sanya Polescuk.

 www.threemonkiestrust.org

General information

The trust was established in 2015 and provides small grants to organisations operating within the UK. The trust welcomes applications from small to medium-sized charities with an annual income of less than £500,000, or for specific activities within programmes of this size in larger charities.

Areas of work

The following information has been taken from the trust's website:

> The Trustees are committed to enhancing life chances and alleviating disadvantage and distress through a focus on three key areas:
> - Promoting the advancement and accessibility of music and the arts, and in particular to support organisations helping young musicians, singers and dancers from disadvantaged backgrounds;
> - Helping children and young people under 25 years and in the greatest need to achieve well and enjoy fulfilling lives;
> - Supporting London-based charities and other non-profit organisations to campaign for and provide affordable accommodation for key workers.

Financial information

Year end	31/03/2021
Income	£2,400,000
Assets	£11,250,000
Grants to organisations	£280,000

Beneficiaries included: A list of beneficiaries was not available.

Applications

Application forms are available on the trust's website. Applications can be made in writing by email. Full details of what should be included in the application can be found on the trust's website. Applications are considered twice a year:
- Applications received by 31 May – reviewed in June/July and answered by the end of September
- Applications received 30 November – reviewed in December/January and answered by the end of February

Sources of information

Annual report and accounts; Charity Commission record; funder's website.

The TJH Foundation

General charitable purposes, particularly social welfare, medical causes and racing welfare

UK, especially the North West

£465,000 (2020/21)

CC number: 1077311

Correspondent: The Trustees, Dower House, Dawbers Lane, Euxton, Chorley PR7 6ED (tel: 01257 244720)

Trustees: Kathryn Revitt; Patrick Hemmings; Craig Hemmings; Mark Widders; Mark Tootell.

General information

The TJH Foundation was established in 1999. It makes grants to both national and North West-based charities for general charitable purposes.

Financial information

Year end	31/03/2021
Income	£953,400
Assets	£465,000
Grants to organisations	£465,000
No. of grants	52

Beneficiaries included: The Injured Jockeys Fund in four grants (£85,000); Alder Hey Children's Charity – two grants (£50,000); Manx Kidney Patients Association (£20,000); Shire Horse Society (£15,000); Juvenile Diabetes Research Foundation Ltd (£10,000); The Mental Health Foundation (£5,200); Euxton Parish Church (£2,000); National Hospital for Neurology and Neurosurgery Development Foundation (£1,000).

Applications

Apply in writing to the correspondent.

Sources of information

Accounts; annual report; Charity Commission record.

The Tolkien Trust

The arts; the environment; education; homelessness; international development; international relations and peace-building; migration; prison reform; health and medical research

UK and overseas, including Malawi, Rwanda, Democratic Republic of Congo, Haiti, the Middle East and Europe

£3.53 million (2020)

CC number: 1150801

Correspondent: Nerissa Martin, Prama House, 267 Banbury Road, Oxford, Oxfordshire OX2 7HT (tel: 01865 339330; email: nerissa.martin@outlook.com)

Trustees: Priscilla Tolkien; Michael Tolkien; Baillie Tolkien.

 www.tolkientrust.org

General information

The trust was established in 1977 by the four children of the author J. R. R. Tolkien to enable the family to give to its chosen causes on a regular basis.

The following information is taken from the trust's website:

> The trust is wholly discretionary, which means that its constitution does not impose any limitations on the charities it may benefit; the trustees are therefore free to select those causes of interest to them.
>
> The Trust does not publish any guidelines concerning the charities of interest to them but the accounts filed by the Trust with the Charity Commission give an indication of the nature and number of causes benefited in recent years. Many of the chosen charities are benefited on an annual basis, and a large number have received support from the Trust for many years.
>
> The Trust has traditionally supported a wide spectrum of charitable causes throughout the world including:
> - Arts
> - Education
> - Environment
> - Homelessness
> - International development
> - International relations and peace-building
> - Migration
> - Prison reform
> - UK and international health, and medical research

Financial information

Year end	31/12/2020
Income	£5,970,000
Assets	£36,090,000
Grants to organisations	£3,530,000
No. of grants	67

Beneficiaries included: Client Earth (£200,000); Bodleian Library (£150,000); Asylum Welcome (£40,000); Humanity and Inclusion UK (£10,000); Bloemfontein (£5,000).

Applications

Unsolicited applications are not accepted. The trust's website states:

> Please note that the Tolkien Trust does not accept uninvited applications as it does not have the capacity to assess them.
>
> Please only send an application if you have been invited to do so by the Trust.
>
> If you have been invited to apply, please refer to the instructions and advice given.

Sources of information

Accounts; annual report; Charity Commission record; funder's website.

The Tompkins Foundation

General charitable purposes; education and training; recreation; religious causes; the promotion of health

UK, with a preference for the parishes of Hampstead Norreys in Berkshire and West Grinstead in West Sussex

£296,000 (2020/21)

CC number: 281405

Correspondent: The Administrator, 7 Belgrave Square, London SW1X 8PH (tel: 020 7235 9322)

General information

The foundation was established in 1980 by Granville Tompkins, founder of Green Shield Stamps and the Argos retail chain. It was created primarily to support the advancement of education, learning and religion, and the provision of facilities for recreation and other purposes beneficial to the community. Grants are made to UK-based organisations, with a preference for those working in Hampstead Norreys in Berkshire and West Grinstead in West Sussex.

Financial information

Year end	05/04/2021
Income	£248,200
Assets	£13,760,000
Grants to organisations	£340,000

Beneficiaries included: City of London School (£75,000); Childhood First and The Police Foundation (£25,000 each); The Foundation of Nursing Studies and Guide Dogs for the Blind (£20,000 each); Maggie's (£10,000); Douglas Macmillan Hospice (£5,000).

Applications

Apply in writing to the correspondent.

Sources of information

Accounts; annual report; Charity Commission record.

The Tottenham Grammar School Foundation

Education and children and young people

Haringey

£439,800 (2020/21)

CC number: 312634

Correspondent: The Trustees, PO Box 34098, London N13 5XU (tel: 020 8882 2999; email: info@tgsf.info)

 www.tgsf.info

General information

In 1686 Sarah, Duchess of Somerset left money in her will to permanently endow a school in Tottenham by purchasing land and covering the headmaster's salary. The school closed in 1988 after more than 300 years but many of the school governors became the trustees of this foundation and continue to act within the spirit of the duchess's will by making grants for the education of young people from Tottenham.

Grants are made to schools (including special schools), charities and voluntary organisations in the London Borough of Haringey for equipment and activities not provided by local authorities. Children's centres and nurseries can also apply. The foundation prefers to contribute towards specific events, projects or purchases. Grants are also made to individuals under 25 who, or whose parents, live in the borough or who have attended school in the borough.

Financial information

Year end	31/08/2021
Income	£400,100
Assets	£28,550,000
Grants to organisations	£439,800
No. of grants	106

Further financial information

During 2020/21, 106 grants of £1,000 or more were paid to schools and other organisations. In addition, Special Somerset Awards and scholarships worth £1,000 or more were paid to, or on behalf of, 12 individuals.

Beneficiaries included: Haringey Sports Development Trust (£57,300); Harington Scheme (£42,000); Riverside Secondary Special School (£20,400); Kids Care London (£7,500); Kid City Plus (£5,200); Fortismere School (£3,300); Coleridge Primary School (£2,000).

Exclusions

According to its guidelines, the foundation cannot support:

- The employment or training of staff
- The construction, adaptation, repair and maintenance of school buildings
- The repair and maintenance of school equipment
- The direct delivery of the national curriculum
- The purchase of vehicles
- The cost of adults attending trips
- Resources exclusively for parents
- Young people aged 25 years or over

Applications

Application packs can be requested by email from grantsform@tgsf.info. Guidelines and upcoming deadlines can be found on the foundation's website.

Sources of information

Accounts; annual report; Charity Commission record; funder's website.

The Constance Travis Charitable Trust

General charitable purposes

UK and overseas, with a preference for Northamptonshire

£3.27 million (2020)

CC number: 294540

Correspondent: The Chair of Trustees, 86 Drayton Gardens, London SW10 9SB (email: travistrust86@yahoo.co.uk)

General information

Established in 1986, the trust has general charitable purposes, supporting local organisations in Northamptonshire as well as organisations working across the UK and internationally. Some of the causes regularly supported include: social welfare; medical causes and health; the environment, conservation and heritage; economic and community development; the arts and culture; disability; animals; education and training; overseas aid; religious activities; accommodation and housing; and sport and recreation.

Financial information

Year end	31/12/2020
Income	£1,800,000
Assets	£166,400,000
Grants to organisations	£3,270,000

Further financial information

In 2020 grants totalled £3.27 million. Grants were distributed as follows:

Economic/community development and employment	£1 million
Medical causes/health	£675,000
The environment/heritage/conservation	£376,000
The arts/culture	£285,000
Overseas aid/famine relief	£263,000
Education/training	£142,000
Animals	£133,000
Relief of poverty	£117,000
Accommodation/housing	£109,000
Sport/recreation	£75,000
Religious activities	£52,000
Disability	£31,000
Other	£5,000

Only beneficiaries of grants of £20,000 and above were listed in the accounts.

Beneficiaries included: Northamptonshire Community Foundation (£876,600); Unicef (£100,000); Alzheimer's Society, Prisoners' Education Trust and Woodland Trust (£50,000 each); Broadmead Baptist Church (£30,000); Royal Albert Hall Trust (£20,000).

Exclusions

The trustees only consider applications from registered or exempt charities or registered community amateur sports clubs. They do not consider applications from individuals.

Applications

Apply in writing to the correspondent. The 2020 accounts state: 'Though the Trustees may make grants with no formal application they may, if considered appropriate, invite organisations to submit a formal application.'

The trustees meet on a regular basis, normally nine times a year, to consider applications. Note: the trust does not welcome contact prior to application.

Sources of information

Accounts; annual report; Charity Commission record.

The Triangle Trust (1949) Fund

Carers; rehabilitation of people who have offended; young people

UK, with some preference for Northern Ireland, Scotland and Wales

£792,800 (2020/21)

CC number: 222860

Correspondent: Annie Corpe, Grants Assistant, Brighton Junction, 1A Isetta Square, 35 New England Street, Brighton BN1 4GQ (tel: 01273 810263 (Monday to Thursday); email: info@triangletrust.org.uk)

Trustees: Julian Weinberg; Karen Drury; Doreen Foster; Dr James Anderson; Alison Hope; James Marshall; David Loudon; Sarah Cutler.

 www.triangletrust.org.uk

General information

Established in 1949 by Sir Harry Jephcott, the charity's primary purpose is to provide grants to community organisations supporting those in need. Grants are also made to individuals, particularly carers and people who have offended.

Areas of work

According to the charity's website, its 2022 grants programme will focus on two focus areas. The charity explains:

> We have been funding the criminal justice and unpaid carers sectors for a number of years through our Development Grants programme. We have now decided to focus our grant making in these two sectors on young people as we recognise that they will experience particular challenges as a result of the COVID-19 pandemic.

Grants

According to the website, grants of up to £60,000 over two years are available. Grants are capped at a maximum of £30,000 per year.

Eligibility

The charity wants to fund organisations that have existing projects.

Applications are encouraged from organisations working in Scotland, Northern Ireland and Wales, although applications are welcomed from all non-profit organisations (within the sectors supported by the charity) with a UK-registered office. CICs and social enterprises are eligible to apply. All applicants' annual income should be between £100,000 and £1 million. However, priority is given to smaller organisations.

Faith-based organisations will need to demonstrate in their application that their services are accessible to those of no or differing faiths.

Full eligibility criteria can be seen on the website.

Financial information

Year end	31/03/2021
Income	£740,700
Assets	£23,660,000
Grants to organisations	£792,800

Beneficiaries included: Women in Prison (£50,000); Blackburn with Darwen Carers Service (£37,300); Cranfield Trust (£25,000); Newcastle Carers (£10,000); North Argyll Carers Centre (£7,700); Southend Carers Forum (£5,900); Caring Breaks (£2,600).

Exclusions

According to its website, the charity will not award funding for the following:

- Restorative justice initiatives
- Crime prevention initiatives
- Non-project specific core costs
- Organisations that are not registered in the UK
- Organisations working entirely outside the UK
- Individuals
- General appeals
- Emergency funding – unless an advertised opportunity
- Capital projects
- Academic research
- Promotion of religion
- International development work
- Disaster relief
- Organisations which have more than one year's worth of unrestricted reserves
- Organisations that have made an unsuccessful application to the trust in the last two years

The charity wants to fund organisations with existing projects.

Applications

There are two rounds of funding each year: one for organisations working with young carers and another for organisations working with young people who have offended. Opening and closing dates for each round of funding are published on the website. There is also a mailing list that organisations can sign up for, to be notified when applications open.

The application process has two stages. Following the submission of an initial online application, shortlisted applicants will be asked to host a visit from the Triangle Trust, during which they will be required to present their strategic plan for the next few years.

Sources of information

Accounts; annual report; Charity Commission record; funder's website.

The True Colours Trust

Children and young people with disabilities and life-limiting conditions; palliative care

UK and Africa

£3.14 million (2020/21)

CC number: 1089893

Correspondent: The Trustees, The Peak, 5 Wilton Road, London SW1V 1AP (tel: 020 7410 0330; email: info@truecolourstrust.org.uk)

Trustees: Lucy Sainsbury; Tim Price; Dominic Flynn; David Wood.

 www.truecolourstrust.org.uk

General information

This is one of the Sainsbury Family Charitable Trusts, which share a joint administration but work autonomously as independent legal entities. They have a common approach to grant-making and generally discourage applications from organisations not already in contact with the trust concerned, but some are open to unsolicited approaches.

Established in 2001, this is one of the newest of the Sainsbury family charitable trusts. According to its website, the trust's focus areas are:

- improving access to palliative care for babies, children and young people in the UK

- enabling disabled children and young people to live their lives to the full
- improving access to pain relief and palliative care in Africa.

UK Small Grants

This programme is designed to support local organisations and projects that work with:

- Children and young people with disabilities and their families
- Children and young people with life-limiting conditions and their families

It provides grants of up to £10,000, although many grants are smaller than this.

Financial information

Year end	05/04/2021
Income	£1,880,000
Assets	£11,590,000
Grants to organisations	£3,140,000

Further financial information

Only beneficiaries that received grants of £50,000 and above were listed in the accounts. Grants of under £50,000 totalled £527,600. Within this, small grants of under £10,000 totalled £398,600.

Beneficiaries included: Palliative Care Association of Malawi (£497,100); Rainbow Trust Children's Charity and WellChild (£100,000 each); Muscular Dystrophy UK (£98,700); Contact a Family (£86,400); Medical Mediation Foundation (£61,700); Sibs (£57,800).

Applications

The trustees only consider unsolicited applications for the Small Grants programme. Applications can be made via the trust's website.

Sources of information

Accounts; annual report; Charity Commission record; funder's website.

Truedene Co. Ltd

Jewish causes

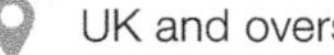

UK and overseas

£462,400 (2020/21)

CC number: 248268

Correspondent: The Trustees, Cohen Arnold, New Burlington House, 1075 Finchley Road, London NW11 0PU (tel: 020 8731 0777)

Trustees: Sije Berger; Samuel Berger; Sarah Klein; Solomon Laufer; Zelda Sternlicht.

General information

This charity was established in 1966 and receives income from its subsidiary, Jaxel Co. Ltd. The charity aims to support organisations providing religious education in accordance with traditional Jewish doctrines and principles. It also gives grants to organisations that provide aid to Jewish people facing disadvantage or hardship. Grants are awarded for revenue expenditure and capital projects.

Financial information

Year end	31/03/2021
Income	£45,000
Assets	£11,340,000
Grants to organisations	£462,400
No. of grants	30+

Further financial information

Only 30 beneficiaries of grants of £10,000 and above were listed in the charity's accounts. Grants of under £10,000 totalled £82,400.

Beneficiaries included: Yetev Lev London Jerusalem Trust (£25,000); Chevras Mo'oz Ladol (£16,000); Jcoci Educational Foundation Ltd and Kolel Shomrei Hachomoth (£15,000 each); Beis Ahron Trust, The ABC Trust and Toldos Aharon Trust Ltd (£10,000 each).

Applications

Apply in writing to the correspondent.

Sources of information

Accounts; annual report; Charity Commission record.

The Truemark Trust

Social welfare and disadvantage

UK

£324,000 (2020/21)

CC number: 265855

Correspondent: The Trustees, PO Box 2, Liss, Hampshire GU33 6YP (tel: 07970 540015; email: truemark.trust01@ntlworld.com)

Trustees: Sharon Knight; Judy Hayward; Jane Dunham; Shirley Vening; Paul Summerfield; Stephen Collins.

General information

The trust's annual report for 2020/21 states that its purpose is to make grants to other charitable organisations 'for the relief of all kinds of social distress and disadvantage' and that grants are made to 'mostly small local Charities dealing with all kinds of disadvantage, with preferences to neighbourhood-based community projects and for innovatory work with less popular groups'.

Financial information

Year end	05/04/2021
Income	£674,000
Assets	£18,350,000
Grants to organisations	£324,000
No. of grants	98

Beneficiaries included: British Library (£8,000); Make them Smile (£7,000); Off the Record (£5,000); Rocking Horse (£4,000); Dementia Forward (£2,000); Hot House Theatre (£1,000).

Applications

Apply in writing to the correspondent.

Sources of information

Accounts; annual report; Charity Commission record.

Trust for London

Relief and prevention of poverty; social welfare; human rights; religious or racial harmony

London

£21.09 million (2020)

CC number: 205629

Correspondent: The Trustees, Fourth Floor, 4 Chiswell Street, London EC1Y 4UP (tel: 020 7606 6145; email: info@trustforlondon.org.uk)

Trustee: Trust for London Trustee.

www.trustforlondon.org.uk

facebook.com/trustforlondon

@trustforlondon

General information

Trust for London funds work that tackles poverty and inequality in London. It does this by making grants to other charities and organisations, funding independent research and providing information and expertise on London's social issues to policymakers and the media. The trust was established in 1891 and was formerly known as City Parochial Foundation.

According to its website, the trust plans to spend over £10 million in grants each year and can support up to 300 organisations at any one point. This includes any organisation that is undertaking charitable activities.

The website states that the trust awards grants across six programmes:

- **Good homes and neighbourhoods:** funding for advocacy work on housing issues and housing legal advice at a specialist level
- **Better work:** progression routes out of low-paid work; specialist employment legal advice; advocacy on employment issues and capacity-building
- **Decent living standards:** advocacy on welfare reform, the cost of living, and public attitudes to poverty; representation and strategic legal action in social welfare law
- **Shared wealth:** advocacy work on issues such as understanding and reducing income and wealth inequality in London

- **Pathways to settlement:** specialist immigration legal advice and advocacy work on the immigration system and pathways to citizenship
- **Grassroots London:** support Londoners working on the ground to bring communities together, increase their collective voice, and inspire collective action

Occasionally, the trust will fund activities that fall outside these six programmes if the organisation can demonstrate why the need is exceptional. Only a small number of these 'exceptional grants' are awarded per year.

Average grants awarded from the fund are of around £80,000; however, grants can be less or more and may be spread over one, two or three years

Visit the trust's website for further information regarding each funding programme.

Financial information

Year end	31/12/2020
Income	£10,280,000
Assets	£368,470,000
Grants to organisations	£21,090,000
No. of grants	227

Beneficiaries included: Previous beneficiaries include: Child Poverty Action Group (£179,000); Solace Women's Aid (£160,000); Global Action Plan (£147,000); On Road Ltd (£100,000); Flat Justice CIC (£80,000); Interlink Foundation (£60,000); Resolution Foundation (£40,000); Police Foundation (£32,000); Centre for London (£25,000); Citizens UK (£12,800); Emmaus Greenwich (£7,500).

Exclusions

The following information is taken from the trust's application guidelines:

We will not support applications:

- Which do not benefit Londoners.
- For work relating to deaf and disabled people that are not run by deaf and disabled people themselves. This means we will only fund organisations which have a majority of deaf and disabled people on their governing body (ideally 75%) and with at least half their staff members being deaf and/or disabled.
- That directly replaces funding for services which are the primary responsibility of statutory funders, such as local and central government and health authorities or subsidises services delivered through statutory contracts.
- For mainstream public services including schools and hospitals.
- From individuals.
- From organisations which have fewer than three people on their governing body e.g. trustee board/management committee. We would normally expect more than three on a governing body.
- For the promotion of religion.
- From organisations seeking to distribute grants on our behalf.
- For work that has already taken place.
- For general appeals.
- For large capital appeals (including buildings and minibuses).
- From applicants who have been rejected by us in the last 12 months.

We are unlikely to support applications:

- Where organisations have significant unrestricted reserves (including those that are designated). Generally up to nine months' expenditure is normally acceptable.
- Where organisations are in serious financial deficit.
- From large national organisations which enjoy widespread support.
- For work that takes place in schools during school hours.
- We will not, in general, contribute to the costs of campaigns associated with individual community-led housing development proposals. We may consider making a repayable investment in such developments.

Applications

Full funding guidelines and closing dates are available on the trust's website. Applications should be made using the online portal. All shortlisted applicants will be visited by one of the grants staff. Prospective applicants can book an appointment to speak with a grant manager to discuss their application if desired – the eligibility quiz must be completed first.

Sources of information

Accounts; annual report; Charity Commission record; funder's website; guidelines for applicants.

The Trusthouse Charitable Foundation

Rural issues and urban deprivation

UK

£2.17 million (2020/21)

CC number: 1063945

Correspondent: Jessica Brown, Grants Director, Kings Buildings, 16 Smith Square, London SW1P 3HQ (tel: 020 3150 4517; email: grants@trusthousecharitablefoundation.org.uk)

Trustees: The Revd Rose Hudson-Wilkin; Sir John Nutting; The Hon. Olga Polizzi; Philippa Hamilton; Crispian Collins; Nicholas Melhuish; Carole Milner; Charlie Peyton; Patrick Reeve; The Revd Paul Gismondi; Nicholas Acland.

www.trusthousecharitablefoundation.org.uk

General information

The Trusthouse Charitable Foundation was formed out of a trust operated by the Council of Forte plc in 1997, which inherited investments in the Granada Group. The foundation is administered on a day-to-day basis on behalf of the trustees by Smith Square Trading Ltd (a subsidiary of the Centre for Social Justice), although the foundation is entirely independent.

Areas of support

According to its website, the foundation makes grants to small and medium-sized charitable organisations in the UK which have 'a demonstrable track record of success working to address local problems in communities in areas of extreme urban deprivation or remote and deprived rural districts'. The foundation has two focus areas:

- Rural issues – organisations working in areas with 10,000 or fewer inhabitants, and which are in the bottom 50% most deprived areas according to the latest indices of multiple deprivation
- Urban deprivation – organisations working in urban areas with 10,000 or more inhabitants, and which are in bottom 15% most deprived areas according to the latest indices of multiple deprivation

Applicants must clearly show in their application how their project fits into one or both of these categories.

In both categories, Northern Ireland organisations must be working in the most deprived 50% of the Northern Ireland index of multiple deprivation, with the exception of organisations in Belfast, Derry/Londonderry, Portadown and Lurgan, where the postcode of the organisation must be in the bottom 15% most deprived areas.

Grant programmes

The foundation has two grant programmes, which support charitable organisations, including CICs, social enterprises, not-for-profit registered companies and voluntary organisations.

Major Grants programme

Open to eligible organisations with an annual turnover of up to £1 million. Currently, projects must have a focus on family support (e.g. early intervention, support for families coping with addiction or support for prisoners' families).

Grants can be awarded in one of the following two ways:

- Single-year grants of between £10,000 and £100,000 for core costs, salaries, running and project costs
- Multi-year grants for a maximum of three years, not to exceed £100,000 in total over this period, for core costs, salaries, running or project costs

Small Grants programme

Open to any eligible organisation with a total annual income of under £250,000. This programme offers single-year grants of between £2,000 and £10,000 for core costs, salaries, running and project costs. Currently, projects must have a focus on community support, for example:

- **Community services:** such as information, advice, transport schemes, foodbanks, healthy eating projects, intergenerational projects, befriending, community cohesion and recovery projects for substance misuse
- **Community centres:** salary or running costs for community centres or village halls which offer a range of activities for all ages
- **Alternative education:** support schemes, homework clubs and supplementary classes
- **Counselling:** for any age in areas where statutory services are unable to cope with demand
- **Family support services:** early intervention, families coping with addiction and prisoners' families
- **Young people:** youth clubs and detached youth work, after school and holiday clubs, education and employment opportunities

Refer to the foundation's detailed funding guidelines available on its website for more comprehensive information regarding eligibility and examples of previously supported projects.

Financial information

Year end	30/06/2021
Income	£1,490,000
Assets	£91,480,000
Grants to organisations	£2,170,000
No. of grants	108

Further financial information

In 2020/21, the foundation awarded major grants totalling £2.15 million, small grants totalling £341,300 and trustee-nominated grants totalling £118,000.

Beneficiaries included: Fegans (£100,000); Ykids Ltd (£81,000); Derry Well Women (£60,000); Family Support Work (£45,000); Baltic Street Adventure Playground (£26,500); Gateway Collective CIC (£10,000); Bournemouth FoodBank (£5,000); Highland Hospice (£3,000); British Wireless for the Blind Fund (£1,000).

Exclusions

The foundation will not fund the following:

- Individuals, whether directly or through a third party
- Charities or non-governmental organisations registered outside the UK
- Statutory services including state schools, local or national authorities, prisons, NHS hospitals or services
- Universities, further education colleges and independent schools
- Hospices
- Grant-making or umbrella organisations
- Organisations whose postcode is not within the Index of Multiple Deprivation limits set out in the funding guidelines

Furthermore, according to its guidelines, the foundation does not currently fund:

- Capital projects
- Set-up costs for new organisations
- Projects outside the UK
- Animal welfare
- The environment and conservation
- Medical research
- Feasibility studies
- One-off events (except under the Small Grants programme)
- Public relations and awareness raising, fundraising salaries, events, initiatives or websites
- Projects primarily concerned with the productions of films, podcasts or other media
- For Small Grants: urban projects not delivered in the same city/town (or London borough) in which the applying organisation is based

Applications

Applications can be made through the foundation's website, following the completion of a brief eligibility questionnaire, which also identifies which type of grant may be most suitable. Eligible organisations will be directed to an online application portal. Applications are accepted throughout the year.

Sources of information

Accounts; annual report; Charity Commission record; funder's website; guidelines for applicants.

The James Tudor Foundation

Relief of sickness; medical research; health education; palliative care; overseas health projects

UK and overseas

£711,100 (2019/20)

CC number: 1105916

Correspondent: Sarah Stewart, Foundation Director, Suite 8 Clifton Business Centre, Somerset House, 18 Canynge Road, Bristol BS8 3JX (tel: 0117 440 7340; email: admin@jamestudor.org.uk)

 www.jamestudor.org.uk

General information

The James Tudor Foundation was established in 2004. It makes grants for charitable purposes, with the principal objective being the relief of human sickness.

The foundation supports small to medium-sized charities and has a preference for organisations that have been established for at least two years. Preference is also given to UK-registered charities or CIOs.

Grant programmes

The foundation awards grants across five programme areas:

Relief of human sickness – this tends to be the foundation's most popular category. In the past, grants have been made to support people with disabilities, therapy centres and salaries.

Palliative care – support is provided to adult and children's hospices in the UK. At the time of writing (March 2022), the foundation's priority was hospices in the south-west of England and south-east of Wales. Check its website for any updates.

Medical research – support is given towards medical research that has a high probability of a positive clinical outcome.

Health education – support is available towards the provision and improvement of medical education, knowledge and research.

Overseas projects – the foundation supports overseas projects for the relief of sickness that are run by UK-registered charities.

Examples of the types of organisations and projects funded can be found on the foundation's website. The foundation usually supports project costs; core costs are generally only considered for organisations with which the foundation has had a long relationship. The majority of grants are for one year. Occasionally multi-year grants are awarded, but these are never for longer than three years. Grants generally range from £30 to £30,000.

The foundation also offers non-financial support such as the provision of pro bono workshops and advice to small charitable organisations seeking funding.

Financial information

Year end	30/09/2020
Income	£817,200
Assets	£29,610,000
Grants to organisations	£711,100
No. of grants	99

Further financial information

During 2019/20 the foundation received 316 applications and awarded 99 grants. Grants were broken down as follows:

Relief of sickness	50	£300,700
Medical research	12	£163,100
Health education	12	£96,700
Palliative care	9	£89,900
Overseas projects	16	£60,700

A full list of beneficiaries can be downloaded from the foundation's website.

Beneficiaries included: University of Bristol (£39,700 in two grants); St Peter's Hospice (£22,100); Target Ovarian Cancer (£15,000); Care for Veterans (£10,600); Weston Hospice Care (£7,800); Haemochromatosis UK (£5,000); The Sequal Trust (£2,800); Brain Tumour Research (£40).

Exclusions

The foundation is unlikely to fund the following:

- Large national charities
- Local organisations which are part of a wider national network
- Projects in India
- Capital and refurbishment projects (although funding for equipment may be considered)
- Art and music therapies
- Complementary therapies
- Funding that replaces or negatively affects statutory funding
- Retrospective appeals
- Endowments
- Community development
- Sport or recreation use
- Adventure or residential courses, respite holidays or excursions, expeditions and overseas travel
- Environmental, conservation or heritage causes
- Animal welfare

Applications

In the first instance, applicants should use the eligibility checker on the foundation's website. If eligible, applicants should then download and complete an application coversheet from the foundation's website, which should be submitted by email with a one-page proposal summary. The foundation will then ask successful applicants to complete a full application. Further information and guidelines on the application process are available from the foundation's website.

Sources of information

Accounts; annual report; Charity Commission record; funder's website; guidelines for applicants.

The Tudor Trust

 Social welfare, specifically focusing on marginalised people

UK and Africa

£21.45 million (2020/21)

CC number: 1105580

Correspondent: The Grants Team, 7 Ladbroke Grove, London W11 3BD (tel: 020 7727 8522; email: There is no email address for general enquiries as the trust prefers contact via telephone; however, if you have communication difficulties, email access@tudortrust.org.uk.)

Trustees: Shilpa Shah; Francis Runacres; Elizabeth Crawshaw; Rosalind Dunwell; Carey Weeks; Ben Dunwell; Nell Bucker; Louise Collins; Monica Barlow; Jonathan Bell; James Long; Holly Baxter Baine; Catherine Antcliff; Christopher Graves; Matt Dunwell.

 www.tudortrust.org.uk

 @thetudortrust

General information

The trust was founded in 1955 by Sir Godfrey Mitchell, who endowed it with shares in the Wimpey construction company for general charitable purposes. Today, the trust makes grants, and provides other types of support, to voluntary and community groups working in any part of the UK. The trust is particularly keen to help smaller, community-led organisations that work directly with people who are at the margins of society.

Grant-making policy

The trust tends to support smaller and under-resourced organisations with an annual income of less than £1 million. On the trust's website, the trustees state that 'in our experience, smaller organisations are particularly well-placed to deliver positive change because they know their communities and can be highly responsive to need, providing an individualised and holistic response to the people they support'.

As well as registered charities, the trust supports charitable work by any organisation with a constitution and a bank account, including CICs, social enterprises, and unincorporated associations.

The trust believes that the organisations it supports are best placed to identify challenges and develop solutions. As such, it does not have specific funding programmes and most of the trust's grants take the form of core funding, which goes towards the core costs of running an organisation, including salaries, overheads, and day-to-day running costs. In 2020/21, 88% of grants made were for core costs. The website states that the trust is increasingly looking to make unrestricted grants, and it will also consider capital grants for building improvements or purchase and strengthening organisations. On the other hand, projects grants, are 'increasingly unusual'.

There is no maximum or minimum grant, although in practice it is unusual for the trust to make a grant of less than £10,000. Usually, grants are made over one, two or three years.

According to its website, the trust wants to support organisations that meet the following criteria:

Display positive organisational characteristics

- Encourage and develop positive social connections and relationships
- Are embedded in their community and can identify and channel the potential within that community
- Offer longer-term engagement and support
- Listen to and are responsive to their users and give users a voice
- Have vision, energy, and commitment and are reflective and open to change
- Want to make a step change in the way they work, but need support to do this
- Make good use of the resources they have

Address marginalisation

- Engage with a marginalised community or engage with a particularly marginalised 'community of interest' – a group of people with a particular shared need, experience or identity
- Provide direct support to individuals who are in real need and/or work with individuals and communities to challenge injustice and inequality
- Are rooted in overlooked and neglected areas where funding is hard to come by
- Affect the lives of marginalised people and communities in a positive way

Make a difference

- Generate a ripple effect – a wider impact beyond the immediate beneficiaries of the work
- Display new thinking or demonstrate best practice: offer an exemplar others can learn from
- Are interested in reflecting on their work and are generous in sharing their findings with others

The trust publishes a grant review each year to report on its grant-making strategy and to detail what grants were made and how much was given. A key feature of the trust's grant-making is that it aims to make grants which respond directly to the priorities identified by applicants.

Even though, the trust's primary focus is grant-making, it also engages with the organisations it supports in other ways, offering advice and developmental support where this is needed.

Although the trust is primarily a UK funder, it also makes a number of grants in Africa each year through a programme promoting ecological agriculture in Zimbabwe, Kenya and Uganda.

For more detailed information, consult the trust's detailed and helpful website.

Financial information

Year end	31/03/2021
Income	£4,860,000
Assets	£272,900.00
Grants to organisations	£21,450,000
No. of grants	1,052

Further financial information

Grants were broken down as follows:

Community	545	£10.77 million
Young people	139	£3.41 million
Relationships	117	£2.46 million
Mental health	72	£1.16 million
Housing	64	£902,000
Criminal justice	39	£564,000
Overseas	12	£513,000
Substance abuse	18	£469,000
Financial security	16	£420,000
Older people	18	£331,000
Learning	12	£287,000

Beneficiaries included: Previous beneficiaries include: Corra Foundation (£200,000); Barrow Cadbury Trust (£150,000); Asylum Justice (£130,000); Growing Sudley CIC (£88,000); London Renters Union (£60,000); Road to Recovery Trust (£50,000); Voice of Domestic Workers (£40,000); Sustainable Living Initiative (£30,000); Hope House Church (£25,000); Local Trust (£15,000); The School and Family Works (£3,000).

Exclusions

The trust does not make grants to/for:

- Individuals, or organisations applying on behalf of individuals
- Larger charities (both national and local) with an income of more than £1 million
- Statutory bodies
- Hospitals, health authorities or hospices
- Medical care, medical equipment or medical research
- Universities, colleges or schools
- Academic research, scholarships or bursaries
- Nurseries, playgroups or crèches
- Uniformed youth groups
- One-off holidays, residential, trips, exhibitions, conferences, events, etc.
- Animal charities
- The promotion of religion
- Routine repairs and minor improvements to community buildings (community centres, church halls, village halls, etc.)
- The restoration or conservation of buildings or habitats
- Landscaping or equipment for playgrounds, parks or recreation areas
- The promotion of religion
- The promotion of philanthropy and endowment appeals
- Retrospective appeals for costs that have already been incurred
- Work outside the UK (the trust runs a targeted grants programme promoting ecological agriculture in Zimbabwe, Kenya and Uganda; however, it does not consider unsolicited proposals from groups working overseas)

Applicants are encouraged to call the information team for advice concerning applications.

Applications

At the time of writing (May 2022), the trust was closed to applications. The trust's website stated:

> - From 1st April 2022 to 31stMarch 2023 we will be closed to 'new' applications: that is applications from groups we are not already funding.
> - Over this period we will still consider applications for continuation funding from groups we are currently supporting.
> - We are reducing our direct grant making in this way to create time and space for Tudor's staff and trustees to re-think how the Trust operates.
> - Over the year we will also be looking for opportunities to 'devolve' some of our grant making by providing funds to a number of partner or intermediary organisations for distribution.
> - We will continue to assess applications under our current guidelines throughout February and March 2022. However we will not be taking any more applications through to second stage than usual – so competition is likely to be strong.

Sources of information

Accounts; annual report; Charity Commission record; funder's website; guidance for applicants.

The Tufton Charitable Trust

Christian causes

UK

£794,100 (2020)

CC number: 801479

Correspondent: The Trustees, Tufton Place, Tufton Lane, Northiam, Rye TN31 6HL (tel: 01797 253311)

Trustee: Wates Charitable Trustees Ltd.

General information

The trust supports Christian organisations by providing grants as well as allowing them to use premises leased by the trust for retreats, known as the Oast Houses. The trust also supports a number of health-related organisations each year.

Financial information

Year end	31/12/2020
Income	£147,120
Assets	£966,000
Grants to organisations	£794,100

Beneficiaries included: The Royal Free Charity (£270,000); Church Revitalisation Trust (£150,000); Off The Fence (£30,000); ReSource (£7,500); Demelza Hospice Care for Children (£5,000).

Applications

Apply in writing to the correspondent.

Sources of information

Accounts; annual report; Charity Commission record.

The Tuixen Foundation

General charitable purposes, particularly: children and young people; education; disabilities; mental health; hospices; homelessness; relief of poverty

UK

£924,500 (2020/21)

CC number: 1081124

Correspondent: Paul Clements, Trustee, 440 Strand, London WC2R 0QS (tel: 020 7649 2903; email: Jandoole@tuixen.org.uk)

Trustees: Peter Englander; Dr Leanda Kroll; Stephen Rosefield; Paul Clements; Simon Englander; William Englander; Thomas Englander.

http://tuixen.org.uk

General information

Set up in 2000, The Tuixen Foundation makes grants to registered charities, hospitals, schools, and other charitable organisations. The foundation's website states:

> **Vision:** A world in which people have the opportunity to achieve their potential
>
> **Mission:** To provide opportunities for disadvantaged individuals to fulfil their potential
>
> **Unrestricted Funds:** Core support grants allow organisations to concentrate on how to be effective and accomplish their goals in the best possible way.

The foundation's areas of interest include children and young people, education, people with disabilities or learning disabilities, mental health, hospices, homelessness and the relief of poverty.

According to the website, approximately 20 charities are selected to receive a donation each year and some donations will be ongoing. Charities receiving donations will usually have a turnover in the range of £500,000 to £5 million and be located in the UK.

Financial information

Year end	05/04/2021
Income	£654,400
Assets	£63,450,000
Grants to organisations	£924,500

Beneficiaries included: Impetus Trust (£100,000); Winston's Wish (£50,000); City United (£30,000); Company Three (£22,000); MIT (£17,500); Storybook Dads (£10,000); Learn to Love to Read (£7,500).

Exclusions

The foundation does not give grants to individuals.

Applications

The foundation's website states that 'unsolicited applications are not sought and correspondence will not be replied to'.

Sources of information

Accounts; annual report; Charity Commission record; funder's website.

The Roger and Douglas Turner Charitable Trust

Children and young people; disability; health; the environment and heritage; the arts; community projects; social welfare; hospices

Birmingham; Dudley; Sandwell; Walsall; Wolverhampton; Worcestershire

£515,000 (2020)

CC number: 1154467

Correspondent: Jenny Harris, Grants and Compliance Officer, Arley House, Lion Lane, Upper Arley, Bewdley, Worcestershire DY12 1SQ (tel: 01299 861368; email: jenny@turnertrust.co.uk)

Trustees: Ronald Middleton; Geoffrey Thomas; Peter Millward; Dawn Long; Amanda McGeever; Sharon Stotts.

 www.turnertrust.co.uk

General information

The trust was established in 2013 following a merger between The Douglas Turner Trust (established 1964) and The RD Turner Charitable Trust (established 1971). Its aim is to provide grants to registered charities, particularly those based in Birmingham, the Black Country, (Dudley, Sandwell, Walsall and Wolverhampton) and Worcestershire. Support is given for the following causes:

- Children and young people
- Disability and health
- Environment and heritage
- The arts
- Work in the community
- Social support
- Hospices

Grants can be made for project funding, capital expenditure and core costs but not salaries.

Financial information

Year end	31/12/2020
Income	£1,550,000
Assets	£61,100,000
Grants to organisations	£515,000

Further financial information

Grants were broken down as follows:

Impaired health	49	£154,000
Hospices	9	£138,000
Community work	21	£89,000
Young people	21	£76,000
Social support	10	£31,000
The arts	6	£14,000
The environment and heritage	3	£13,000

Beneficiaries included: Birmingham St Mary's Hospice (£30,000); Acorns Children's Hospice Trust (£25,000); Compton Care (£20,000); Stonehouse Gang (£15,000); National Churches Trust (£10,000); St Anne's Hostel (£6,000); Listening Books and Sport 4 Life UK (£5,000 each).

Exclusions

According to its application guidelines, the trust will not support the following:

- Individuals and non-charities
- Grant giving Charities
- Community Interest Companies
- Social Enterprise and other not-for-profit organisations
- Charities which are principally funded by the public sector
- Charities with large investment portfolios or excessive reserves
- Charities with a large defined-benefit pension fund deficit

Applications

Application forms and guidelines can be downloaded from the trust's website.

Sources of information

Accounts; annual report; Charity Commission record; funder's website.

G. J. W. Turner Trust

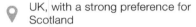

General charitable purposes

Birmingham

£309,500 (2020/21)

CC number: 258615

Correspondent: Chrissy Norgrove, Clerk to the Trustees, The Estate Office, Wharf Cottage, Broombank, Tenbury Wells, Worcestershire WR15 8NY (tel: 07799 784019)

Trustees: Lesley Davis; Kate Honeyborne; Hugh Carslake.

General information

The trust was established in 1969. According to its Charity Commission record, it makes grants to 'worthy organisations within the Birmingham area' for general charitable purposes.

Financial information

Year end	05/04/2021
Income	£314,100
Assets	13,360,000
Grants to organisations	£309,500
No. of grants	106

Beneficiaries included: A list of beneficiaries was not available.

Applications

Apply in writing to the correspondent.

Sources of information

Accounts; annual report; Charity Commission record.

The Turtleton Charitable Trust

Arts, culture and heritage; social welfare; education

UK, with a strong preference for Scotland

£260,000 (2020/21)

OSCR number: SC038018

Correspondent: The Trustees, c/o Turcan Connell, Princes Exchange, 1 Earl Grey Street, Edinburgh EH3 9EE (tel: 0131 228 8111; email: enquiries@turcanconnell.com)

 www.turcanconnell.com/the-turtleton-charitable-trust

General information

Established in 2007, the trust makes grants in the fields of heritage and the arts, principally in Scotland. According to the trust's website, grants are made to charities in support of the following causes:

- The advancement of the arts, culture and heritage – the Trustees particularly favour heritage and the visual arts, but other aspects of the arts and culture will be considered. The vast majority of grants are made in this field.
- Support of the disadvantaged and the advancement of education – the Trustees consider only a small number of grants in this field in any one year.

There is a preference for causes in Scotland.

Grants typically range between £5,000 and £25,000; larger or multi-year grants are made occasionally.

Financial information

Year end	30/06/2021
Income	£215,900
Assets	£6,610,000
Grants to organisations	£260,000
No. of grants	24

Further financial information

Grants were broken down as follows: the advancement of the arts and heritage (£205,000) and support for the disadvantaged (£55,000).

Beneficiaries included: Optimistic Sound (£30,000); Dundee Heritage Trust and Playlist for Life (£20,000 each); The Little Sparta Trust (£15,000); Children's Classic Concerts, Edinburgh International Book Festival and The Prince's Foundation (£10,000 each); Garvald Edinburgh (£5,000).

Exclusions

Grants are not made to individuals.

Applications

Apply using the online application form on the trust's website. If your charity does not have access to email, a hard-copy application can be sent to Hilary Sharkey at the above address. There is no need to send a copy of your annual accounts unless they are not available online. Applications should reach the trust by email or in hard copy no later than 31 December. The trustees meet once a year, in spring, to decide on grants for the following 12 months and normally pay grants before 30 June each year. Note that applications are not acknowledged on receipt.

Sources of information

Accounts; annual report; OSCR record; funder's website.

Two Magpies Fund

Women who have been abused and disadvantaged children

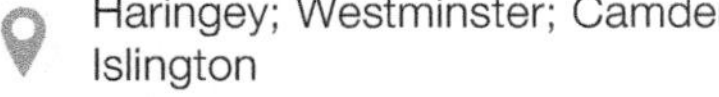

Haringey; Westminster; Camden; Islington

£402,900 (2020/21)

CC number: 1189451

Correspondent: The Trustees, 35 Stormont Road, London N6 4NR (email: info@twomagpiesfund.co.uk)

Trustees: Stian Westlake; Kirsten Westlake.

www.twomagpiesfund.co.uk

General information

The charity was registered with the Charity Commission in May 2020.

The following information has been taken from its website:

> Two Magpies Fund awards small grants to local charities and non-profit organisations working with women who have experienced abuse, as well as those organisations helping primary school aged children who are growing up in poverty or facing particularly challenging circumstances. Our focus is local and the majority of the charity's beneficiaries must live in Camden, Haringey, Islington and Westminster.
>
> For example, we fund counselling, education and support services for organisations working in the fields of domestic abuse, human trafficking, sexual abuse, forced marriage, FGM or modern slavery, as well as the activities of hostels, community groups, homework clubs, food banks, beauty banks and baby banks. We welcome applications for projects, one-off costs (equipment) and running costs. We do not fund individuals, faith-based organisations or research grants.
>
> We aim to get vital funds straight to where they are needed most, as quickly and simply as possible.

Financial information

Year end	31/03/2021
Income	£404,900
Grants to organisations	£402,900

Beneficiaries included: A list of beneficiaries was not available. Previous beneficiaries include: South Camden Community Trust; Euston Foodbank; The Avenues Youth Project; Little Village.

Exclusions

The charity does not fund individuals, faith-based organisations or research grants.

Applications

Unsolicited applications are not accepted. The charity's website states:

> We no longer accept unsolicited applications.
>
> If you would like to introduce yourself to us, please use the form below and we will invite you to apply, if your project aligns with our focus.

Sources of information

Accounts; annual report; Charity Commission record; funder's website.

Tzedakah

Jewish causes; education and training; social welfare; children and young people

Worldwide, although in practice mainly UK and Israel

£353,700 (2019/20)

CC number: 251897

Correspondent: The Trustees, Brentmead House, Britannia Road, London N12 9RU (tel: 020 8446 6767; email: lfinnco@aol.com)

Trustees: Leonard Finn; Michael Lebrett.

General information

Tzedakah was registered with the Charity Commission in 1967. According to its Charity Commission record, its main objectives are the relief of poverty, advancement of education, advancement of religion, and general charitable purposes. It typically makes over 300 grants to organisations in a year. The 2019/20 annual report states that the beneficiaries 'are chosen by the individual members'. It is not clear who the members are or if this precludes general applications to the charity.

Financial information

Year end	31/03/2020
Income	£465,200
Assets	£713,900
Grants to organisations	£353,700

Beneficiaries included: Previous beneficiaries include: Hasmonean High School Charitable Trust; Gertner Charitable Trust; Society of Friends of the Torah; Hendon Adath Yisroel Synagogue; Medrash Shmuel Theological College; Torah Temimoh; Willow Foundation; Tifferes Girls School; Sage Home for the Aged; Wizo; and Torah Movement of Great Britain.

Exclusions

Individuals are not awarded grants.

Applications

Apply in writing to the correspondent.

Sources of information

Accounts; annual report; Charity Commission record.

UBS Optimus Foundation UK

Children's health, early education and protection

UK and overseas

£25.7 million (2020)

CC number: 1153537

Correspondent: Thomas Hall, The Trustees, UBS AG London Branch, 5 Broadgate, London EC2M 2QS (tel: 020 7567 8000; email: a contact form is available on the foundation's website)

Trustees: Vineet Bewtra; Paul Dominic Vail; Edoardo Rulli; Eva-Kristiina Ispahani; Phyllis Costanza.

www.ubs.com

General information

The foundation is the corporate charity of UBS Group AG, a Swiss multinational investment bank and financial services company. The foundation receives funding from UBS AG London branch and clients of UBS AG, who can make donations to programmes that have been selected and assessed by the foundation.

According to its 2020 annual report, the foundation's objects are:

> to promote the health of children by (without limitation) preventing abuse and

> supporting the delivery of medical and other essential services to them; the prevention and relief of poverty by (without limitation) the provision of education to support the healthy development of children; to relieve the needs of children who are in need due to their youth, sickness or financial hardship; and any other purposes as are regarded as exclusively charitable under the law of England and Wales as the trustees may from time to time see fit

The foundation supports high-quality, innovative, impactful projects around the world focusing on the following themes: education, public health, nutrition and the reduction of violence against children. Grants may also be made for child-specific responses to emergencies.

Financial information

Year end	31/12/2020
Income	£26,640,000
Assets	£8,170,000
Grants to organisations	£25,700,000

Beneficiaries included: Kids Operating Room (£5.89 million); Canopy Planet Society (£1.1 million); The Prince's Trust (£660,000); Justice and Care (£440,300); One to One Children's Fund (£397,200); Skills Partnership (£45,400); Care for Children (£11,000).

Applications

The foundation's 2020 annual report states that it works to 'source and assess effective and appropriate programmes for direct funding which further the Foundation's aims'. Contact the foundation for further information.

Sources of information

Accounts; annual report; Charity Commission record; funder's website.

Ufi VocTech Trust

Vocational education

UK

£4.59 million (2020)

CC number: 1081028

Correspondent: The Trustees, First Floor, 10 Queen Street Place, London EC4R 1BE (tel: 020 7969 5500; email: info@ufi.co.uk)

Trustees: Dominic Gill; Julia Lambdon; David Ryder; Charlotte Kirby; Jonathan Scott; Anthony Bravo; Alexandra Cullen; Paolo Fresia; Jeffrey Greenidge.

 www.ufi.co.uk

 facebook.com/UfiTrust

 @ufitrust

 @ufitrust

General information

The Ufi VocTech Trust (formerly the UFI Charitable Trust) is a UK-based charity, which, as described on the website, 'aims to improve UK productivity by making innovative use of digital technology to increase the skills of the UK workforce. Its projects are all intended to demonstrate how digital approaches can bring more learning to more people, more of the time in order to improve the workforce skills available to UK businesses and organisations, and improve outcomes for individuals by enhancing their workplace skills.'

Funding 2020–25

The website states:

> Through grant funding, venture investment and advocacy we champion the power of vocational technology to improve skills for work... Our long term goal is to support a portfolio of projects that deliver positive change for learners across a wide range of sectors, job roles, geographies and access points.

The trust operates single-grant funding calls for a specific type of project as well as 'Challenge' calls where it combines funding types to test out different approaches.

Current grant programmes include:

- **VocTech Ignite** – by invitation only, for projects with potential but which are not ready for full funding
- **VocTech Seed** – grants of £15,000 to £50,000 for projects lasting 3–12 months to support the development of new ideas.
- **VocTech Impact** – grants of £150,000 to £300,000 for larger projects lasting 18–24 months. These grants are for well-developed ideas which can be delivered to a large number of learners and have clear routes to market

Eligibility

The specific criteria for projects varies between funding calls and is set out in the guidelines for each call. However, there are general criteria which apply to all projects:

- All projects must support the digital delivery of adult vocational learning, meaning learning associated with the skills and knowledge that people need for work. Adult learners are defined as people over the age of 16 years
- Projects must have the potential to reach large numbers of learners and demonstrate that there is the potential for scale
- The trust is interested in projects aimed at any and every aspect of vocational learning, including (but not limited to) the design and development of learning tools, new delivery models, evaluation and assessment, accreditation and recording evidence of achievement

Funding is open to all organisations, including charities, trade bodies, learning providers, employers, private companies, CICs and other not-for-profit organisations.

Financial information

Year end	31/12/2020
Income	£909,000
Assets	£52,810,000
Grants to organisations	£4,590,000
No. of grants	101

Further financial information

Grants were awarded to 101 projects in 2020. During the year the trust did not run the VocTech Impact Grant but instead launched a COVID-19 response fund called VocTech Now. This fund awarded 33 grants of £25,000 each.

A directory of beneficiaries can be found on the trust's website.

Beneficiaries included: Bodyswaps; Bridgend College; Game Academy; Into Games CIC; NIACRO; Renaissance Management; Sempai; University of Sheffield; Whiley and Co.

Exclusions

The website states that the trust does not fund the following:

- Projects which address generic 'access to work' skills, such as time management, CV building or interview skills training
- Basic digital skills training aimed at enabling generic digital capability and overcoming digital exclusion
- Projects that do not represent a step change in how vocational learning happens
- Standard content development work that aims to simply digitise existing content or add further content to an existing platform
- Research projects
- Projects in higher education, but higher education institutions can be involved in project delivery where the project beneficiaries are adult workplace learners
- Projects in schools, unless these can demonstrate that they are addressing specific workplace skills provision to those aged over 16, where there is an identifiable employer need
- Funding for generic enterprise or entrepreneurship skills to support people to set up or run a business

Applications

Grant funding calls are advertised on the website and are explained in detail in the trust's Delivery Plan. Applications can be made via an online portal on the trust's website. The trust usually uses a two-stage application process, where you first give a summary of your idea (stage 1) and then, if suitable, you will be invited to submit a more detailed, full application (stage 2).

Sources of information

Accounts; annual report; Charity Commission record; funder's website.

Ulster Garden Villages Ltd

Health; social welfare; young people; culture and heritage; the environment; education and training; medical research; community development

Northern Ireland

£1.04 million (2020)

CCNI number: NIC101248

Correspondent: The Trustees, Forestview, Purdy's Lane, Newtownbreda, Belfast BT8 7AR (tel: 028 9049 1111; email: admin@ulstergardenvillages.co.uk)

Trustees: Martie Boyd; Erskine Holmes; Kevin Baird; Dr Anthony Hopkins; Susan Crowe; Brian Garrett; William Webb; Dame Rotha Johnston; Colin Walsh.

 www.ulstergardenvillages.co.uk

General information

The charity was established in 1946 and funds projects that will have a positive impact in Northern Ireland.

The charity's website states:

> National Charities making an approach to the Society should relate their appeal to specific needs or projects within Northern Ireland.
>
> Funds are not given retrospectively and it is not usual to give grants for office expenses or administrative staff salaries.
>
> In addition to outright grants, assistance may be given by way of loans which may carry certain conditions at the discretion of the Committee.
>
> Preferred projects will be those demonstrating active participation and self-help. They should be innovative and developmental with an achievable, practical and sustainable objective.
>
> We will not fund activities which are the responsibility of any statutory agency, neither will we fund the direct replacement of statutory funding.
>
> The Committee will only make donations toward specific projects under the control of a responsible organisation and when large capital projects are involved, only when satisfied that the sponsoring organisation has raised or is capable of raising the remainder of the finance required.
>
> **The main objectives to which funds may be allocated are:**
>
> - Health
> - Disadvantaged sections of our society
> - Young people
> - Culture and heritage
> - Environment

According to the charity's 2020 accounts, the main funding objectives during the year were:

- **Disability** – carers, sheltered accommodation, mental and physical disabilities, transport and advice
- **Health** – hospices and hospitals, home nursing, mental health, substance abuse and prevention of disease
- **Community** – young people at risk, rehabilitation, older people, victim support, crime prevention and regeneration
- **Scientific and medical research** – fields of research which are not eligible for full government support, particularly involving older people, specific diseases such as cancer and cardiac conditions
- **Culture and heritage** – underfunded activities involving the arts, in all its forms, and the preservation of natural heritage, the restoration of buildings of historic or architectural interest and conserving artefacts
- **Education and training skills** – promotion of life skills and independent living skills, employment and training for people with disabilities and disadvantaged people, education and literacy skills for young people with disabilities

Financial information

Year end	31/12/2020
Income	£1,780,000
Assets	£50,060,000
Grants to organisations	£1,040,000

Further financial information

Grants were broken down as follows:

Community	14	£458,000
Health	15	£389,000
Education and training	7	£125,000
People with disabilities	5	£40,000
Culture and heritage	4	£30,000

Beneficiaries included: Northern Ireland Children's Hospice (£100,000); Cancer Fund for Children (£70,000); Action Cancer and Greenhill YMCA (£50,000 each).

Applications

Applications can be made via the charity's website. Applicants should first complete a short eligibility quiz in order to access the application form.

Sources of information

Accounts; annual report; Charity Commission for Northern Ireland; funder's website; guidelines for applicants.

The Ulverscroft Foundation

Opthalmic research; community projects that help visually impaired people; medical facilities and equipment; overseas projects

UK and overseas

£670,000 (2019/20)

CC number: 264873

Correspondent: Joyce Sumner, Secretary, The Green, Bradgate Road, Anstey, Leicester, Leicestershire LE7 7FU (tel: 0116 236 1595; email: foundation@ulverscroft.co.uk)

Trustees: Roger Crooks; Debra Hicks; John Sanford-Smith; Ian Moon; Robert Gent; Geoffrey Woodruff.

 www.ulverscroft-foundation.org.uk

General information

The foundation was established in 1972 with the following objectives:

- To relieve and assist, and to provide treatment and education for, people with disabilities, particularly those with visual impairments
- To support medical research and to provide and assist in the provision of facilities for the treatment or alleviation of people who have a disability or visual impairment

Grant programmes

The foundation awards grants to charities, CICs, social groups, hospitals, schools, libraries and other organisations involved in improving the lives of those who are visually impaired. Funding is divided into three categories: public library appeals, charity-to-charity donations and research projects.

The foundation does not generally fund staff salaries or ongoing running costs for an organisation. Staffing costs for specific, time-limited projects may be considered at the trustees' discretion. Research projects which involve salary costs may also be considered.

Financial information

Year end	31/10/2020
Income	£676,000
Assets	£17,480,000
Grants to organisations	£670,000

Beneficiaries included: University of Leicester (£247,000); Ruharo Eye Centre (£50,000); Second Sight (£30,000); John Fawcett Foundation (£5,000); Sense International (£2,000).

Exclusions

The foundation does not fund staff salaries or ongoing running costs for an organisation.

Applications

Applications can be made online using a form on the foundation's website. Alternatively, applicants may wish to download a copy of the form and, once completed, return it by post. The trustees meet quarterly (in January, April, July and October) to consider grant applications. Application deadlines, along with guidance notes, can be seen on the website.

Sources of information

Accounts; annual report; Charity Commission record; funder's website.

The Underwood Trust

Medicine and health; social welfare; education; the arts; the environment and wildlife

UK

£638,600 (2020/21)

CC number: 266164

Correspondent: Michele Judge, Manager, Ground Floor, 20 York Street, London W1U 6PU (tel: 020 7486 0100; email: michelej@taylorclark.co.uk)

Trustees: Robin Clark; Richard Bennison; Briony Wilson.

 www.theunderwoodtrust.org.uk

General information

The trust was established in 1973. Its name derives from Underwood Lane, Paisley, Scotland, which was the childhood home of one of the founders.

According to its website, the trust aims to 'fund a wide range of activities that will positively impact individuals and the environment'.

The trust achieves this by making long-term/annual grants mainly to UK-registered charities, and occasionally to non-registered charitable organisations.

Areas of work

The trust's grant-making covers four broad areas:

- Medicine and health
- Social welfare
- Education and the arts
- The environment and wildlife

Financial information

Year end	05/04/2021
Income	£963,000
Assets	£17,750,000
Grants to organisations	£638,600
No. of grants	24

Further financial information

Grants were made in the following categories:

Medicine and health	£281,000
Social welfare	£175,000
Education and the arts	£102,600
The environment and wildlife	£80,000

During the year, five COVID-19 grants were made totalling £100,000.

Beneficiaries included: Bristol Speech and Language Therapy Research Unit (£106,000); Farms for City Children and Living Paintings Trust (£40,000 each); Friends of the Earth and NSPCC (£20,000 each); Pimlico Opera (£10,000).

Exclusions

The trust does not fund:

- Individuals
- Political activities
- Commercial ventures or publications
- The purchase of vehicles including minibuses
- Overseas travel, holidays or expeditions

Applications

The trust's website states:

> The trustees have decided to give annual support to a number of charities and proactively seek out certain projects. This restricts the funds available for general applications and as such the Trust **is closed to unsolicited applications**.
>
> Please only make an application if you have been invited to do so. [...] Applicants must complete an application form and send it by post or email to the Trust's office. The trustees meet on a regular basis to consider applications during the year.

Sources of information

Accounts; annual report; Charity Commission record; funder's website.

The Union of Orthodox Hebrew Congregations

The advancement of the Orthodox Jewish faith

UK

£1.29 million (2020)

CC number: 1158987

Correspondent: The Trustees, 140 Stamford Hill, London N16 6QT (tel: 020 8800 6833)

Trustees: Benzion Freshwater; Sydney Sinitsky; Moses Bibelman; Jacob Goldman; Michael Lobenstein; Benjamin Roth; Myer Rothfeld; Nathan Bindinger; Victor Brinner; Aron Goldman; Chaim Goldman; Benzion Goldstein; Robert Grussgott; Michael Just; Joshua Muller; Daniel Ost; Ahron Rand; Schloime Rand; Zalman Roth; Abraham Schreiber; Shalom Seidenfeld; Mordechai Steren; Benjamin Stern; Chaim Pinter; Jehudah Baumgarten.

General information

The main objects of this charity are to advance the Orthodox Jewish faith and to establish and support institutions which will help to achieve this. Support is also given to individuals who are in need to help with expenditure at Jewish festivals.

The charity also provides a wide range of facilities for the Orthodox Jewish community in London and the UK, including advice on housing, education, religion and welfare.

Financial information

Year end	31/12/2020
Income	£1,450,000
Assets	£2,080,000
Grants to organisations	£1,290,000

Further financial information

Only beneficiaries of grants of over £7,000 were listed in the accounts.

Beneficiaries included: UOHC Foundation Ltd (£300,000); Support The Charity Worker (£87,000); Vishnitz Girls School Ltd (£63,000); Rise and Shine (£36,500); Kids Care London (£15,000); The Woodstock Mikva (£10,000); Trenhill Ltd (£7,000).

Applications

Apply in writing to the correspondent. The trustees meet regularly to review applications.

Sources of information

Accounts; annual report; Charity Commission record.

United Jewish Israel Appeal

Jewish causes, particularly engagement of young people, education and welfare

Israel and UK

£4.53 million (2019/20)

CC number: 1060078

Correspondent: The Trustees, 1 Torriano Mews, London NW5 2RZ (tel: 020 7424 6400; email: info@ujia.org)

Trustees: Marc Lester; Melvin Berwald; Louise Jacobs; Karen Goodkind; Brian May; Hilton Nathanson; Steven Kaye; Nicola Wertheim; Miles Webber; Raphael Addlestone; David Pliener.

www.ujia.org

 facebook.com/UJIAcharity

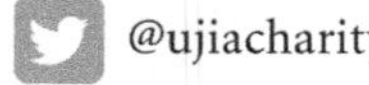 @ujiacharity

 @ujiacharity

General information

This charity supports Jewish causes in Israel (mainly the northern region of Galil) and the UK.

The charity's 2019/20 annual report states:

> Funds are allocated towards a range of educational and welfare projects in Israel that serve the needs of all Israelis, especially those from disadvantaged communities. Funds are also allocated towards the renewal of Jewish life in the United Kingdom, through support of a variety of innovative educational programmes and projects, particularly those oriented towards young people.

During 2019/20 the charity supported synagogues, primary and secondary schools, charities, community centres, community volunteering organisations and youth movements.

Financial information

Year end	30/09/2020
Income	£8,210,000
Assets	£6,010,000
Grants to organisations	£4,530,000
No. of grants	113

Further financial information

Grants made for UK programmes totalled £1.36 million, and these grants were broken down as follows:

Educational programmes	£1.03 million
Community education and awareness	£227,000
Israel experience	£72,000
Welfare	£26,000

The remaining grants were made towards programmes in Israel. A full list of grants of £1,000 and above can be requested from the charity.

Beneficiaries included: UJIA Israel (£1.05 million); Jewish Agency for Israel (£787,000); Federation of Zionist Youth (£105,000); Maccabi GB (£67,000); Danciger High School (£47,000); Atidim (£30,000); Equaliser (£7,000).

Applications

For further information, email the correspondent.

Sources of information

Accounts; annual report; Charity Commission record; funder's website.

United St Saviour's Charity

Social welfare; community development; social justice; older people

North Southwark and Bermondsey

£1.13 million (2020/21)

CC number: 1103731

Correspondent: Matthew Allgood, Grants Manager, 16 Crucifix Lane, London SE1 3JW (tel: 020 7089 9014; email: Matthew.Allgood@ustsc.org.uk or info@ustsc.org.uk)

Trustees: Shane Holland; Stephen Burns; Lord Roy Kennedy; Nicola Steuer; Claire Treanor; Dr Ben Johnson; Lucinda Glover; Kathryn Ogunbona; Izabela Szmidt; Dwight Pile-Gray.

 www.ustsc.org.uk

 facebook.com/unitedstsaviourscharity

 @UnitedStSaviour

General information

United St Saviour's is a charity that supports the people and communities of north Southwark. As stated on the website, through its grant-making programmes, the charity aims to help communities tackle social need by investing in projects that offer 'both proven and innovative ways of solving problems'. In addition to its grant-making activities the charity also administers several almshouses in Southwark.

According to its website, the charity's work is guided by the following themes:

- **Strong, resilient communities:** connecting, enabling and strengthening communities within north Southwark
- **Positive ageing:** reducing isolation and increasing well-being among older residents (in north Southwark)
- **Levelling the playing field:** targeted and life-changing support for population groups disproportionately experiencing social and economic disadvantage (in the north of Southwark)

Grant programmes

Currently the charity operates two open grant programmes:

- **Large Grants Programme:** grants of more than £5,000. This programme normally opens for applications twice a year
- **Small Grants Programme:** grants of up to the value of £5,000. This programme normally opens for applications twice a year

The charity also has a Strategic Grants Programme, which is by invitation only and has partnerships with numerous other charitable schemes – see the website for details.

Financial information

Year end	31/03/2021
Income	£1,990,000
Assets	£50,640,000
Grants to organisations	£1,130,000

Beneficiaries included: South London Cares (£80,000); Salmon Youth Centre (£21,500); Bermondsey Community Kitchen, Dad's House and Southwark Day Centre for Asylum Seekers (£10,000 each).

Exclusions

The charity does not fund any of the following:

- Projects where the main beneficiaries are living or working outside its area of benefit
- Individuals (including sole traders)
- For-profit private companies
- Local authorities
- Purely religious activity
- Political or animal welfare activity

Applications

Apply via the link on the charity's helpful website to the 'Flexigrant' online portal.

Sources of information

Accounts; annual report; Charity Commission record; funder's website; guidelines for applicants.

UnLtd (Foundation for Social Entrepreneurs)

Funding and support for social entrepreneurs

 UK

£12.86 million (2020/21)

CC number: 1090393

Correspondent: The Trustees, 123 Whitecross Street, Islington, London EC1Y 8JJ (tel: 020 7566 1100; email: info@unltd.org.uk)

Trustees: Nicolas Farhi; Susan Charteris; Nicholas Petford; Rachel Barton; Krishna Vishnubhotla; Lynne Berry; Elizabeth Sideris; James Lawson; Stephen Bediako; Tim Davies-Pugh; Anne Glover; Amma Mensah.

 www.unltd.org.uk

 facebook.com/UnLtd

 @UnLtd

General information

UnLtd was established in 2002 by seven organisations to fund and support social entrepreneurs. According to its 2020/21 annual report, the charity's objects are 'to relieve poverty, promote education and training, and advance other charitable purposes beneficial to the community'. The charity provides awards to both social entrepreneurs and social businesses in the UK.

Awards

- Starting up – funding of between £500 and £5,000 is available for social businesses that have not been established or that have been running for under a year
- Scaling up – funding of between £5,000 and £15,000 is available for social businesses that have been

running for over a year and under four years

As well as funding, the charity also offers up to 12 months of support including mentoring, workshops, a support manager and more.

Further information on eligibility and support available can be found on the charity's website.

Financial information

Year end	31/03/2021
Income	£21,780,000
Assets	£7,580,000
Grants to organisations	£12,860,000

Beneficiaries included: A list of beneficiaries was not available.

Exclusions

Support will not be given to:

- Organisations whose work is predominantly focused on having an impact on people or places outside the UK
- Organisations that have been legally established for over four years at the time of application (Companies House or Charity Commission registration)
- Organisations that had a turnover of over £250,000 in their last financial year
- Work that is political or involves religious campaigning
- Work that involves activities outside the law, against public policy or anything which encourages ethnic, religious or commercial disharmony

Applications

Applications can be made via the application portal on the charity's website.

Sources of information

Accounts; annual report; Charity Commission record; funder's website.

The Michael Uren Foundation

Armed forces; medical research and facilities; animal welfare; education (with a focus on the sciences, engineering and technology); historic buildings

UK and overseas

£3.47 million (2020/21)

CC number: 1094102

Correspondent: The Trustees, c/o Haysmacintyre, Thames Exchange, 10 Queen Street Place, London EC4R 1AG (tel: 020 7969 5500; email: mpattenden@haysmacintyre.com)

Trustees: Anne Gregory-Jones; Roger Gould; Janis Bennett; Robert Uren.

General information

The foundation was established in 2002 with general charitable purposes following an initial gift from Michael Uren. The foundation supports charities working in the following priority areas:

- **Armed forces** – support of charities relating to the armed forces, and the support of ex-Service personnel
- **Medical causes** – support of advanced medical research, and expansion and modernisation of medical facilities
- **Animal welfare** – support of endangered species, regardless of location
- **Education** – supporting the furtherance of education, with a specific focus on the sciences, engineering and technology
- **Historic buildings** – the restoration and continued maintenance of historic buildings

Financial information

Year end	05/04/2021
Income	£137,440,000
Assets	£201,890,000
Grants to organisations	£3,470,000
No. of grants	13

Beneficiaries included: Moorfields Eye Hospital (£1.8 million); Imperial College (£500,000); Combat Stress (£200,000); Royal Naval Benevolent Trust (£150,000); Marine Society and Sea Cadets and Kent Wildlife Trust (£50,000 each); Salvation Army (£25,000).

Applications

The foundation does not consider unsolicited applications.

Sources of information

Accounts; annual report; Charity Commission record.

The Utley Family Charitable Trust

General charitable purposes; music and dementia; veterans; children and young people; international aid

UK and overseas

£724,300 (2020/21)

CC number: 1157399

Correspondent: Lizzie Cody, Foundation Manager, Larkins Farm, 199 Nine Ashes Road, Ingatestone, Essex CM4 0JY (tel: 01277 821338; email: lizzie@utleyfoundation.org.uk)

Trustees: Melvyn Sims; Nicky Utley; Neil Utley; Raja Balasuriya.

http://utleyfoundation.org.uk/index.html

General information

This trust, registered in June 2014, was established by Neil and Nicky Utley. Neil Utley is an entrepreneur who made his career in the insurance industry and currently sits as a non-executive director on the board of Hastings Insurance Services Ltd. Together with Nicky Utley, his wife, he founded the record label NUA Entertainment.

The Utley Family Charitable Trust's Charity Commission record states that it awards grants for general charitable purposes. The trust supports causes at home and abroad. The record also states that, initially, the trustees have focused on causes related to children, education and health, as well as helping those with dementia through the power of music.

Financial information

Year end	31/03/2021
Income	£1,560,000
Assets	£25,060,000
Grants to organisations	£724,300

Further financial information

Grants were broken down as follows:

Music and dementia	£401,700
Children	£197,800
Other	£92,900
International aid	£32,000

Beneficiaries included: A list of beneficiaries was not available.

Applications

Apply in writing to the correspondent.

Sources of information

Accounts; annual report; Charity Commission record.

The Valentine Charitable Trust

General charitable purposes; local projects in Dorset; some preference for the environment

UK and overseas, with a preference for Dorset

£1.13 million (2019/20)

CC number: 1001782

Correspondent: The Trustees, Hinton House, Hinton Road, Bournemouth, Dorset BH1 2EN (tel: 01202 292424)

Trustees: Roger Gregory; Peter Leatherdale; Douglas Neville-Jones; Susan Patterson; Wing Cdr Donald Jack; Susan Ridley; Fiona Normington-Smith.

General information

The Valentine Charitable Trust was founded by the late Ann Cotton in 1990. It supports general charitable purposes with a particular focus on the provision of amenities and facilities for the benefit of the public, the protection and safeguarding of the countryside and wildlife and the control and reduction of pollution. Ann Cotton lived most of her life in Dorset; as such the trust particularly welcomes local projects in Dorset. The trustees will also consider making grants to charities which, while not based in the local area, operate there.

In addition to its local grants, the charity also supports a small number of initiatives in financially developing countries. The trustees are particularly interested in projects which offer sustainability to local communities.

The trust regularly makes one-off grants to specific projects but will also consider making donations towards core funding on a repeat basis. Recurring donations require a report from the applicant charity and a new application so that the position can be reviewed. If a particular charity has been supported once, then the trust takes the stance that it may be supported again, unless there have been substantial changes that do not fit in with the trust's objectives since the last grant.

The trust regularly donates to hospitals, but has a policy of requiring that any grants awarded to organisations related to the NHS are for projects or equipment which have no likelihood of being provided out of central funds in the foreseeable future.

Lastly, the trust offers social investment funding, whereby the trust will purchase premises which are then leased to a charity.

Offers of funding for projects are regularly conditional upon the applicant raising other funds. Similarly, offers of donations are sometimes made on the basis that they will only be made once the project actually proceeds.

Financial information

Year end	30/09/2020
Income	£909,500
Assets	£33,850,000
Grants to organisations	£1,130,000
No. of grants	135

Further financial information

The trust made grants to 135 charities totalling £1.13 million.

Beneficiaries included: Lewis-Manning Hospice (£30,000); MacDougall Trust (£20,000); International Care Network (£15,000); Families for Children and Poole Museum Foundation (£10,000 each); Asthma Relief (£5,000); Citizens Advice Central Dorset (£2,000); Butterfly Conservation (£1,000).

Exclusions

The trustees prefer not to fund village halls or the fabric of church buildings.

Applications

Contact the correspondent for further information. The trust's 2019/20 annual report notes that in recent years, the trust has operated a policy of not considering applications unless it has an established relationship with the applicant. However, there have been exceptions, particularly in the case of local applicants.

Sources of information

Accounts; annual report; Charity Commission record.

The Valiant Charitable Trust

General charitable purposes

Hitchin and surrounding areas

£335,000 (2020/21)

CC number: 1135810

Correspondent: Jonathon Goldstone, c/o Collyer Bristow LLP, 140 Brompton Road, London SW3 1HY (tel: 020 7242 7363; email: jonathon.goldstone@collyerbristow.com)

Trustees: Lady Valerie Dixon; Roger Woolfe; Paul Brenham.

General information

The trust was established in 2010 with general charitable purposes. The settlor of the trust is Lady Valerie Dixon, widow of the late Sir Ian Dixon, former chair of the Willmott Dixon construction group.

Financial information

Year end	05/04/2021
Income	£483,000
Assets	£5,400,000
Grants to organisations	£335,000
No. of grants	16

Beneficiaries included: Keech Hospice (£200,000); Herts Homeless (£25,000); Norman Hyde Scout Trust and PHASE Hitchin (£10,000 each).

Applications

Apply in writing to the correspondent.

Sources of information

Accounts; annual report; Charity Commission record.

The Van Neste Foundation

Social change; social welfare; the environment; children and young people; community services

UK and financially developing countries

£258,800 (2020/21)

CC number: 201951

Correspondent: The Trustees, 15 Alexandra Road, Clifton, Bristol BS8 2DD (tel: 07711 186057; email: secretary@vanneste.org.uk)

Trustees: Benedict Appleby; Tom Appleby; Jeremy Lyons; Joanna Dickens; Michael Delaney; Lucy Appleby; Jessica Lyons.

 http://vanneste.org.uk

General information

The foundation was established in 1959 and makes grants for social change and children and young people in the UK and financially developing countries.

Applications are assessed on how well they reach one or all of the three areas outlined below, details of which have been taken from the foundation's website:

> **Social Change**
> We want to encourage organisations that seek to change society in a positive way. We want to support community organisations trying include those who have become marginalised, either as a group or as individuals. We want to give to those who want to promote a sense of place and environmental improvement whether that be urban or rural.
>
> Finally we want to back those whose work encourages the systemic change necessary to alleviate poverty and make us a more just and less unequal society.
>
> **Children and Young People**
> Children and young people are the future of our society. We want to encourage those who will shape our future and help ensure that they reflect the whole of our society. We also want to support those whose work ensures that young people feel that society does offer them something. We also recognize the need for all types of activities for young people including Sport, Drama, Music, Food, Travel.
>
> **Developing World**
> We expect the majority of our grants to be within the UK but we also want to support Charities working in the developing world where their objectives coincide with our focus on Social Change and Children and Young People.

Financial information

Year end	05/04/2021
Income	£216,000
Assets	£10,360,000
Grants to organisations	£258,800

Beneficiaries included: Villiers Park Educational Trust (£25,000); Clifton Children's Society (£10,000); Amber Foundation (£5,000); Paradance (£2,000).

Applications

Application forms can be downloaded from the foundation's website. Grant applications are assessed three times a year, usually in January, June and October.

Sources of information

Accounts; annual report; Charity Commission record; funder's website.

The Vandervell Foundation

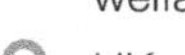

General charitable purposes, particularly education, medical care and research, the performing arts, environmental regeneration and social welfare

UK

£352,000 (2020)

CC number: 255651

Correspondent: Valerie Kaye, Administrator, Hampstead Town Hall Centre, 213 Haverstock Hill, London NW3 4QP (tel: 020 7435 7546; email: vandervell@btconnect.com)

Trustee: The Vandervell Foundation Ltd.

General information

Established in 1968, this foundation makes grants to organisations for a wide range of charitable purposes. There is a preference for supporting the following causes: education, medical care and research, the performing arts, social welfare and environmental regeneration. Various organisations have been supported, including schools, educational establishments, hospices and other health organisations.

Financial information

Year end	31/12/2020
Income	£232,900
Assets	£7,680,000
Grants to organisations	£352,000

Further financial information

Grants were broken down as follows:

Social welfare	£167,000
Medical care and research	£88,000
Advancement of education	£57,000
Performing arts	£35,000
Environmental regeneration	£5,000

Beneficiaries included: Arts Education School Tring Park, Barts and The London and British Exploring Society (£15,000 each); University of Exeter (£7,500); London's Air Ambulance (£7,000); English National Ballet and Prisoners' Education Trust (£5,000 each).

Applications

Apply in writing to the correspondent. Grants are reviewed by the trustees who meet every other month.

Sources of information

Accounts; annual report; Charity Commission record.

The Vardy Foundation

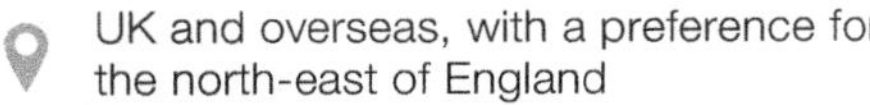

Education; religion; social welfare; arts; social care; rehabilitation of people who have offended; families; relief of poverty

UK and overseas, with a preference for the north-east of England

£5.4 million (2020/21)

CC number: 328415

Correspondent: The Trustees, 110 George Street, Edinburgh EH2 4LH (tel: 0131 374 7144)

Trustees: Richard Vardy; Lady Margaret Vardy; Peter Vardy; Sir Peter Vardy; Victoria Vardy.

General information

The foundation was set up in 1989 with general charitable objectives by Sir Peter Vardy. Sir Peter Vardy made his fortune in the motor retail business through his company, Reg Vardy plc, founded by his father.

The foundation's 2020/21 annual report states:

> The objectives of the Vardy Foundation are to support initiatives and programmes in social action and faith-based projects, predominantly focused on early intervention programmes committed to strengthening families and the relief of poverty. The Charity also seeks to support ex-offenders and those in prisons, addiction, rehabilitation, the homeless and the unemployed.

The foundation supports organisations working in the north-east of England as well as other parts of the UK.

Financial information

Year end	05/04/2021
Income	£3,100,000
Assets	£37,350,000
Grants to organisations	£5,400,000

Beneficiaries included: Peter Vardy Foundation (£1.88 million); Changing Lives (£250,000); Caring for Life (£100,000); Outward Bound Trust and St Luke's Church (£50,000 each); Northpoint Care (£30,000); The Moses Project (£20,000).

Applications

Apply in writing to the correspondent. The trustees meet every three months to review grants.

Sources of information

Accounts; annual report; Charity Commission record.

Variety, the Children's Charity

Children and young people who are sick, disadvantaged or have a disability

UK

£1.45 million (2020)

CC number: 209259

Correspondent: Grants Programme Manager, Variety Club House, 93 Bayham Street, London NW1 0AG (tel: 020 7428 8100; email: info@variety.org.uk or grants@variety.org.uk)

Trustees: Malcolm Brenner; Anthony Harris; Jason Lewis; Stanley Salter; Prof. Jonathan Shalit; Ronald Sinclair; Pamela Sinclair; Ronald Nathan; Tushar Prabhu; Dilaram Kitchlew-Williamson; Tesula Mohindra; Guy Remond.

 www.variety.org.uk

 facebook.com/VarietyGB

 @VarietyGB

 @VarietyGB

General information

Variety, the Children's Charity aims to improve the lives of children and young people throughout the UK who are sick or disadvantaged, or who have a disability. The charity's website provides the following information on how it supports schools and organisations:

> We support SEND schools and units, mainstream schools and PRU's, youth clubs, sports clubs, hospitals, hospices and other non-profit organisations that work with children and young people aged 18 and under.
>
> We provide specially adapted accessible transport in the form of our Sunshine Coaches, memorable and life-enhancing experiences through our Great Days Out Programme and grant funding for wheelchairs and specialist equipment. We typically fund sensory rooms, interactive IT and accessible playground equipment and classroom hoists but consider applications for all forms of specialist equipment.

Equipment and wheelchair grants

Special educational needs schools, mainstream schools and non-profit organisations that work with young people (under the age of 18) with disabilities or long-term health conditions can apply for an equipment grant. Examples of equipment that is eligible for funding can be found on the website.

Applications for wheelchairs can also be made by organisations on behalf of an individual. Non-profit sports clubs working with children and young people are also eligible to apply for sports wheelchairs for use at the club. The average wheelchair grant is for £5,000.

Youth Club Grants

The charity's Youth Club Grants offer part-funding for equipment required by youth clubs that are affiliated with national youth organisations such as Ambition, UK Youth or Association of Boys and Girls Clubs. Examples of resources that are eligible include:

- Sports, gym and games equipment
- Computers, printers and IT equipment
- Photography and film equipment
- Consoles, accessories and games
- Arts and crafts materials
- Musical instruments and recording equipment

Financial information

Year end	31/12/2020
Income	£3,670,000
Assets	£3,700,000
Grants to organisations	£1,450,000
No. of grants	54

Further financial information

Grants to organisations were distributed as follows: Sunshine coaches (41 grants totalling £1.38 million); equipment grants (12 grants totalling £45,600); wheelchairs (a grant of £23,900). Only beneficiaries of grants of £5,000 and above were listed in the accounts. Grants of under £5,000 totalled £14,000.

Beneficiaries included: Shenstone School – Crayford (£72,500); Claremont School – Bristol (£41,300); Cramlington Voluntary Youth Project (£34,400); Football Beyond Borders – Manchester (£28,400); Maddison Springwell School – Hartlepool (£9,900); The Golf Trust (£5,300).

Exclusions

The charity does not fund:

- Standard household equipment or furnishings
- Repayment of loans
- Garden adaptations
- Garden sheds or summerhouses
- The cost of a family/wheelchair-adapted vehicle
- Computer hardware
- Maintenance or ongoing costs
- Travel costs
- Therapy sessions
- Reimbursement of funds already paid out
- Hire/rental costs or down payments
- Trikes/bikes or buggies
- Trips abroad or holiday costs
- Trampolines
- Medical treatment
- Education or tuition fees

Applications

Download the relevant application form from the charity's website, where guidelines for each type of grant are also available. Applications should be returned to the correspondent by post or email to grants@variety.org.uk. There are no deadlines.

Sources of information

Accounts; annual report; Charity commission record; funder's website; guidelines for applicants.

The Velvet Foundation

General charitable purposes; social welfare; health; education; Jewish causes

England; Wales; Israel

£480,800 (2019/20)

CC number: 1169789

Correspondent: David Rodney, Trustee, First Floor Winston House, 349 Regents Park Road, London N3 1DH (tel: 020 8458 9223; email: davidrodney@velvetfoundation.org.uk)

Trustees: Chee Choong Cheah; David Rodney; Michael Aaronson.

General information

This foundation was registered in October 2016. Its objects, as stated in the annual report and accounts for 2020/21, can be summarised as follows:

- General charitable purposes
- Prevention or relief of poverty (through 'grants, items, facilities and services to individuals in need and to charities, or other organisations working to prevent or relieve poverty' and also through 'education, training, healthcare projects and all the necessary support designed to enable individuals to generate a sustainable income and be self-sufficient')
- Health, rehabilitation and relief of illness, including support for medical research
- Promotion of knowledge and education of the Jewish religion

Grants can be made to individuals and organisations throughout England and Wales and also Israel.

Financial information

Year end	30/09/2020
Income	£574,200
Assets	£225,000
Grants to organisations	£480,800

Beneficiaries included: Netivei Itzak (£211,000); Ahavot Shalom (£38,200); King's College London (£20,000); Pninim Seminary (£6,300).

Applications

Apply in writing to the correspondent.

Sources of information

Accounts; annual report; Charity Commission record.

The Veolia Environmental Trust

Community and environmental projects

UK. Projects should be near a Veolia site. Postcode checker is available on the charity's website

£4.27 million (2020/21)

CC number: 1064144

Correspondent: The Trustees, Ruthdene, Station Road, Four Ashes, Wolverhampton, West Midlands WV10 7DG (tel: 020 3567 6820; email: UK.EnvironmentalTrustInfo@veolia.com)

Trustees: Oswald Dodds; Caroline Schwaller; Derek Goodenough; Malcolm Marshall; Mike Smith; John Brown; Donald Macphail; Joanne Demetrius; Kevin Hurst.

 www.veoliatrust.org

 @veoliaenvtrust

General information

The Veolia Environmental Trust was established in 1997. The trust supports community and environmental projects that fulfil the following objective: the reclamation and reduction of polluted land; the protection, preservation and improvement of the environment for the benefit of the public; and the delivery of biodiversity conservation for UK species.

According to its website, the trust will consider applications for capital improvement projects at a single site with discrete start and end dates, and which fall into the one of the following categories:

- **Community buildings and rooms:** e.g. community centres; village halls; community spaces within religious buildings, Scout or Girlguiding buildings
- **Outdoor spaces:** e.g. public parks, nature reserves, community gardens, footpaths, bridleways or cycle-paths
- **Play and recreation:** e.g. play areas, skateparks, Multi Use Games Areas (MUGAs), sports grounds, pavilions or changing rooms
- **Biodiversity**

The website states that competition for funding is considerable and therefore applicants need to submit an application that does justice to their project and highlights how it is going to make a real difference to people's lives or the environment. Grants provided by the trust are usually of between £10,000 and £75,000.

Financial information

Year end	31/03/2021
Income	£4,780,000
Grants to organisations	£4,270,000

Beneficiaries included: The Lancashire Wildlife Trust (£80,000); St George the Martyr Church – Brentwood (£75,000); Friends of Stretford Public Hall (£69,000); The Pakistan Muslim Centre (£57,000).

Exclusions

Regulatory bodies; zoos, museums, theatres or arts organisations; schools or other educational institutions; works that improve the fabric of a building or amenity; staff and core costs.

Applications

Full details of the eligibility criteria, application process and deadlines are provided on the trust's helpful website. Information on the website is divided into three sections:

- Information: gives details about the trust's criteria and when to apply, and offers a postcode checker
- Guidance: guides applicants through the application process and how to manage their grant if successful
- Apply: a list of six questions that allows applicants to check if they are ready. After answering the questions, applicants are automatically directed to create a Veolia Environmental Trust User Account, which will give them access to the trust's online application form

Applicants are encouraged to make contact if they want to discuss their project. Applications are considered quarterly by the trustees.

Sources of information

Accounts; annual report; Charity Commission record; funder's website.

Versus Arthritis

 Research into the all types of arthritis and musculoskeletal conditions

UK

£53.98 million (2020/21)

CC number: 207711

Correspondent: Research Department, Copeman House, St Mary's Court, St Mary's Gate, Chesterfield S41 7TD (tel: 0300 790 0400; email: research@versusarthritis.org)

Trustees: Prof. Jonathan Cohen; Dr Rodger Macmillan; Karin Hogsander; Juliette Scott; Phillip Gray; Prof. Sarah Lamb; Prof. Martijn Steultjens; Dr Andrew Holford; Vincent Noinville; John Isaacs; Jonathan Rodgers; Iain McInnes.

 www.versusarthritis.org

 facebook.com/VersusArthritis

 @VersusArthritis

 @VersusArthritis

General information

In 2017, Arthritis Research UK and Arthritis Care joined forces to create Versus Arthritis. According to its website, the charity aims to 'develop breakthrough treatments, campaign relentlessly for arthritis to be seen as a priority and support each other'.

Research funding

The charity's 2020–26 research strategy is focused on accelerating the pace and precision of musculoskeletal research. Research funding aims to improve the understanding of arthritis and improve detection, treatment, interventions and support. Decisions on research funding are guided by the perspective of people living with arthritis, who can apply to be part of the Patient Insight Partner (PIP) group.

Financial information

Year end	31/03/2021
Income	£25,440,000
Assets	£185,510,000
Grants to organisations	£53,980,000

Further financial information

Only beneficiaries of grants of £10,000 and above were listed in the charity's 2020/21 accounts. Grants of under £10,000 totalled £147,000.

Beneficiaries included: University of Liverpool (£600,000); University of Nottingham (£300,000); The Royal Veterinary College (£139,000); Ulster University (£96,000); Keele University (£42,000); Arthur's Place (£30,000); Medical Research Council (£12,000).

Applications

Details of all open grant programmes can be found on the 'types of grants' section of the charity's website. All applications should be made via the charity's online application portal, Grant Tracker.

Sources of information

Accounts; annual report; Charity Commission record; funder's website.

The Veterans' Foundation

The armed forces community

UK

£3.3 million (2020/21)

CC number: 1166953

Correspondent: The Trustees, Thistle Court (Room 5), Thistle Street, Edinburgh EH2 1DD (tel: 0333 999 3899; email: enquiries@veteransfoundation.org.uk)

Trustees: Peter Mountford; Eline Lofgren; Bruce Walker; Mungo Tulloch; Richard Farndale.

 www.veteransfoundation.org.uk

 facebook.com/veteransfoundation

 @VeteransFdn

 @veteransfoundationuk

General information

The foundation was established in 2016 and generates income through its Veterans' Lottery and donations. It makes grants to organisations supporting the armed forces community throughout the UK.

Eligibility

The following eligibility information has been taken from the foundation's application guidelines:

> All registered charities and other organizations that support the armed forces community (veterans, serving service people and immediate dependants) may apply. The broad range of charities and organizations supported by the Veterans' Foundation is extensive and covers every aspect of social care including: homelessness, employability, poverty, disability, welfare issues, mental health, marriage guidance, care during old age and confidence building.
> Organizations are likely to be:
> - Charities
> - Not-for-profit organizations
> - Community projects Housing associations and corporations

Grants of up to £30,000 are available, which can be spread over three years. According to the website, priority is given to 'low and medium-wealth charities that need funds to continue their good work'.

Financial information

Year end	30/06/2021
Income	£6,660,000
Assets	£192,300
Grants to organisations	£3,300,000

Beneficiaries included: AFC Fylde Community Foundation; Care After Combat, EVA Women's Aid, Everton in the Community, FirstLight Trust, Flying For Freedom Ltd, Pain Association Scotland, RMA – The Royal Marines Charity, Rock2Recovery and Salford Red Devils Foundation.

Exclusions

The foundation does not normally support:

- Organisations that do not assist the armed forces or merchant navy communities
- Gap years, study trips, fundraising expeditions and sponsorship

- Housing associations and corporations (unless activities and costs are clear and charitable)
- Activities that result in a profit
- Organisations requiring payments to be sent to bank accounts outside the UK

Applications

Applications can be made online after creating an account on the foundation's website. Completed applications should be submitted by the end of the month preceding the grants committee meetings. Meetings are usually held in December, May, September and March. However, check the website for current deadlines. Full guidelines are also available to download from the foundation's website.

Sources of information

Accounts; annual report; Charity Commission record; funder's website.

Vhlt Ltd

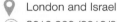

Orthodox Jewish causes and social welfare

London and Israel

£619,800 (2019/20)

CC number: 1101241

Correspondent: The Trustees, 61 Fairholt Road, London N16 5EW (tel: 020 8809 5700)

Trustees: Yehiel Frand; Yoel Marmorstein; Avrohom Streicher; Raymond Frand.

General information

The objectives of the charity are to advance religion in accordance with the Orthodox Jewish faith and the relief of poverty. For example, by assisting individuals in need of food, clothing, shelter or medical services who are unable to afford these from their own means. The charity also supports educational and religious institutions and awards grants and scholarships to suitably qualified students.

Financial information

Year end	31/08/2020
Income	£709,100
Assets	£124,200
Grants to organisations	£619,800

Further financial information

Grants were broken down as follows in the charity's 2019/20 accounts: relief of poverty (£572,700); education (£41,400); the advancement of religion (£5,600). Only beneficiaries of grants of £12,000 and above were listed in the accounts. Grants of under £12,000 totalled £19,500.

Beneficiaries included: Vaad Harabonim Israel (£572,600); Olam Chesed Yiboneh (£19,500); Keren Metzuda (£12,000).

Applications

Apply in writing to the correspondent.

Sources of information

Accounts; annual report; Charity Commission record.

Nigel Vinson Charitable Trust

Education; citizenship and community development; religion; arts, culture, heritage and science

UK

£294,900 (2020/21)

CC number: 265077

Correspondent: Hoare Trustees, c/o C. Hoare and Co., 37 Fleet Street, London EC4Y 1BT (tel: 020 7353 4522)

Trustees: The Hon. Antonia Bennett; Hoare Trustees; Lord Nigel Vinson; Bettina Witheridge; Thomas Harris; The Hon. Rowena Cowen.

General information

The trust was established in 1972 by Nigel Vinson, a British entrepreneur, inventor, philanthropist and member of the House of Lords.

In the trust's 2020/21 annual accounts, grants were made for the advancement of:

- Education
- Citizenship or community development
- Religion
- Arts, culture, heritage or science

The trustees regularly review their donations and their main criterion is to support the work of charities that appear to be underfunded.

Financial information

Year end	30/06/2021
Income	£217,100
Assets	£4,350,000
Grants to organisations	£294,900

Beneficiaries included: Buckingham University (£90,000); Institute of Economic Affairs (£25,000); Adam Smith Research Trust (£19,000); Faith, Truth and Hope (£3,000).

Applications

Apply in writing to the correspondent. The trustees meet periodically to consider applications for grants.

Sources of information

Accounts; annual report; Charity Commission record.

The Vintners' Foundation

Social welfare; homelessness; alleviation of the social effects of alcohol abuse/misuse; children and young people

Greater London with a preference for inner London

£465,100 (2020/21)

CC number: 1015212

Correspondent: Charity Secretary, The Vintners' Company, Vintners' Hall, Upper Thames Street, London EC4V 3BG (tel: 020 7651 0753; email: charity@vintnershall.co.uk)

Trustees: Sophia Bergqvist; Ann Hill; Anthony Fairbank; Edward Berry.

www.vintnershall.co.uk

General information

This foundation is the principal charitable vehicle of The Vintners' Company, one of the 12 Livery Companies of the City of London.

According to its website, the foundation's current policy on charitable giving is to provide grants to charities in Greater London, particularly inner London, that provide:

- Assistance to charities concerned with the relief of the poor, destitute and homeless in Greater London who are disadvantaged by reasons of health, education or poverty
- Assistance to charities concerned with treating the social effects of alcohol abuse or misuse
- Support to young people, youth projects and designated educational establishments in London
- Support to certain other charities, as put forward by members of the Company

It also makes a number of fixed grants each year to causes close to its heart. Preference is given to smaller, local charities. Grants are normally made in the range of £3,000 to £5,000.

Financial information

Year end	31/03/2021
Income	£475,200
Assets	£3,720,000
Grants to organisations	£465,100

Beneficiaries included: The Drinks Trust (£100,000); City Harvest (£33,200); Spitalfields Trust (£17,500); School Home Support (£15,000); New Regent's College (£10,000); Future Frontiers (£9,000); ABF The Soldiers' Charity (£6,500); St James Garlickhythe (£5,500).

Exclusions

Grants are not given to individuals or towards medical research or the maintenance/restoration of buildings.

Applications

Applications must be made via the foundation's website. The grants committee meets four times a year, usually in March, June, September and December.

Sources of information

Accounts; annual report; Charity Commission record; funder's website.

The Virgin Money Foundation

Community development and regeneration; social enterprise; children and young people

UK, with a preference for Glasgow, Sheffield, Edinburgh, Norwich, Manchester, Cardiff, London, Leeds and the north-east of England

£1.46 million (2020/21)

CC number: 1161290

Correspondent: Richard Walton, Programme Manager, Jubilee House, Gosforth, Newcastle upon Tyne, Tyne and Wear NE3 4PL (tel: 0330 123 3624; email: info@virginmoneyfoundation.org.uk)

Trustees: Joanne Curry; Lorna Bennie; Keith Burge; Hannah Underwood; Edward Younger; Keith Merrin; Amanda Jordan; Alison Kidd.

https://virginmoneyfoundation.org.uk

@VMFoundation

General information

The foundation was registered with the Charity Commission in April 2015. It was established following the demise of the Northern Rock Foundation (established by the Northern Rock Bank which was purchased by the Virgin Money bank) to work 'in partnership with organisations who are committed to regenerating their area by investing in community activities that have a meaningful impact', as stated on the foundation's website.

Grant programmes

The foundation has a range of grant programmes, at the time of writing (March 2022) these included:

- **The Community Anchors' Fund** – on its website, the foundation defines Community Anchor organisations as 'vital, independent, locally-led organisations, committed to driving positive economic, social or environmental change within a community. [...] They provide local people with support, services, activities, and volunteering opportunities. Local people shape their work and inform their activities. Typically we expect community anchors to work with a broad cross section of the community.' The fund offers grants of up to £30,000 to organisations from the north-east of England. Grants can be used to cover core costs, to continue to pay for existing work or to design and launch a new project. The award can be spent over one, two or three years
- **The Community Anchors' Fund Glasgow** – in 2020, the Community Anchors' Fund was expanded to support independent, community-led organisations in Glasgow. As the fund first opened during the COVID-19 pandemic, grants have initially focused on activity in response to COVID-19. Check the foundation's website for the latest information. At the time of writing (March 2022), the fund was only accepting applications by invitation
- **The #iwill Take Action Fund** – this fund supports youth-led social action projects that create positive change in local communities. The fund offers grants of up to £50,000 to organisations from the north-east of England

For more open funds, see the foundation's website.

Financial information

Year end	30/09/2021
Income	£2,050,000
Assets	£2,050,000
Grants to organisations	£1,460,000
No. of grants	140+

Further financial information

Grants were broken down as follows:

Community Anchors' Fund – North East	21	£585,300
Community Anchors' Fund – Glasgow	19	£389,100
National Lottery Community Fund #iwill Fund Grant	9	£317,000
National Lottery Community Fund Partnerships England Wide	9	£100,800
Colleagues in the Community Fund	82	£40,700
Community Resilience Fund	-	£20,000
Social and Sustainable Capital Fund	-	£2,900

Beneficiaries included: Community Foundation for Tyne and Wear and Northumberland (£100,000); West End Women and Girls Centre (£50,000); Rosemount Lifelong Learning (£27,500); Cranhill Development Trust (£20,000); Jack Drum Arts (£10,000); The Avenues Youth Project (£1,200); Yorkshire Imperial Band (£500).

Exclusions

See the individual grant programmes on the foundation's website for specific exclusions.

Applications

Some grant programmes are open to applications and others are by invitation only. For those open to applications, an online form can be accessed through the foundation's application portal on its website. The foundation's website provides further information on each fund, including application deadlines and detailed eligibility criteria.

Sources of information

Accounts; annual report; Charity Commission record; funder's website.

Viridor Credits Environmental Company

Community; heritage; biodiversity

England and Scotland, specifically areas near Viridor landfill sites

£4.17 million (2020/21)

CC number: 1096538

Correspondent: Grants Officer, PO Box 977, Taunton, Somerset TA1 9PQ (tel: 01823 476476; email: enquiries@viridor-credits.co.uk)

Trustees: Peter Renshaw; Simon Catford; David Robertson; Mary Prior; Dan Cooke.

www.viridor-credits.co.uk

@viridorcredits

General information

Viridor Credits Environmental Company is a registered charity that provides funding for community development, heritage and biodiversity projects through the Landfill Communities Fund and the Scottish Landfill Communities Fund.

Grant schemes

The charity has the following grants schemes in England:

Main Grants Scheme: the scheme is for community, heritage or biodiversity projects that require up to £50,000.

Large Grants Scheme: the scheme is Viridor Credits' biggest funding band and the most competitive. This scheme is for the community, heritage or biodiversity projects that require between £50,001 and £100,000.

Funding in Taunton: applications for up to £20,000 for community, heritage or biodiversity projects are accepted from properly constituted non-profit organisations in Taunton.

The charity has the following grant schemes in Scotland:

Scottish Landfill Communities Fund: funding is available in Scotland for applications up to £25,000. This scheme supports community, heritage and biodiversity projects located within ten miles of any active landfill site or transfer station accepting 2,500 tonnes of waste, under the following conditions:

- The total project cost cannot exceed £100,000
- The Viridor Credits grant cannot exceed 50% of the total project cost
- Applicants may not be considered for another grant within 12 months of a successful award

For further information on each of the above priorities, as well as deadlines and application guidance, refer to the charity's website.

Note: although the charity used to offer to fund projects in Wales, this is now administered by the Wales Council for Voluntary Action.

Financial information

Year end	31/03/2021
Income	£4,270,000
Assets	£1,590,000
Grants to organisations	£4,170,000
No. of grants	149

Further financial information

Grants awarded in England totalled £3.86 million and grants awarded in Scotland totalled £307,600. Only beneficiaries of grants of £50,000 and above were listed in the 2020/21 accounts.

Beneficiaries included: St Peter's Church – Bolton (£100,000); Mark Cricket Club (£99,100); Staveley Miners Welfare FC (£87,200); 1st Somerton Scout Group (£71,600); Chilton Polden Playing Field (£55,000); The Ipswich Unitarian Meeting House (£50,000).

Exclusions

According to the charity's guidance documents, it is unable to consider funding for the following:

- Aspects of a project that have already started
- Works to public highways; anything that may be the statutory or discretionary responsibility of the local authority
- Projects located on/in:
  - Allotments
  - Educational facilities
  - Facilities primarily used for service provision or not considered a general public amenity, such as hospitals, day centres, hospices or accommodation.
- Proportional projects – where public access is restricted at certain times
- Salaried posts or revenue funding
- Contingencies, fees and preliminaries
- Core costs of an organisation e.g. rent, energy bills, supplies
- Purchase or lease of vehicles
- Purchase of land or buildings that are not at risk of closure or loss to the community
- Multimedia or CCTV equipment, events, CDs, website or marketing materials.
- New Builds

Applications

Applicants should check the availability of funding in their area using the postcode checker on the charity's website, before submitting a stage-one application form (this can be done at any time). Applicants will receive a response from the grants officer and, if successful, may complete stage two of the online application form. There are four deadlines each year and stage-two applications must be received well in advance of the closing date. More information on the application process can be found on the charity's website.

Sources of information

Accounts; annual report; Charity Commission record; funder's website; guidelines for applicants.

Vision Foundation

Blind and partially sighted people

London

£296,200 (2020/21)

CC number: 1074958

Correspondent: Lin Richardson, Director of Grants and Impact, Sir John Mills House, 12 Whitehorse Mews, 37 Westminster Bridge Road, London SE1 7QD (tel: 020 7620 2066; email: hello@visionfoundation.org.uk)

Trustees: Keith Felton; Sharon Petrie; Robert Hughes; Heather Goodhew; Elizabeth Honer; Susanette Mansour; Ly Lam; Victoria Currey; Darren Barker; Dr Amit Patel.

 www.visionfoundation.org.uk

 facebook.com/Vision-Foundation-102194794530448

 @Vision_Fdn

 @vision_fdn/?hl=en

General information

Formerly known as the Greater London Fund for the Blind, the foundation aims to improve opportunities, well-being and inclusion for blind and partially sighted people across London.

Grant funding

Eligibility

The foundation delivers grants through The Vision Fund, which is open to the following organisations:

- UK-registered charities
- CIOs
- Charitable companies, limited by guarantee
- CICs limited by guarantee
- Exempt charities

Grant size

The foundation typically makes grants for project funding of up to £20,000, but each annual round of funding can be different, so check the foundation's website for up-to-date information. Core costs can be included in applications for project funding to ensure full cost recovery.

Focus areas

The foundation makes grants in three priority areas, details of which have been taken from its website:

> *Opening London up*
>
> Everyone living, working, or visiting London should have access to the rich cultural, economic, and social opportunities of our city. In reality, only a quarter of blind and partially sighted working-age Londoners are working. Alongside poor employment, blind and partially sighted people tell us that they face barriers in taking part in physical activity, navigating city streets, and engaging in social activities – many things sighted people take for granted.
>
> To ensure we have the biggest impact, we are interested in projects which:
>
> - Educate and influence employers.
> - Empower individuals through education and building confidence, networks, and skills.
> - Ensure sports, arts, social and cultural spaces are accessible.
> - Improve public transport and public safety.
>
> *Empowering those at-risk*
>
> Within the visually impaired community, there are certain groups who can face a "double disadvantage". When facing sight loss, those from the BAME community, older people, women, those living on a low income, and those with other disabilities are at risk of experiencing poorer outcomes. In addition, there are some consequences of sight loss that are not supported well or at all, such as the heightened risk of domestic violence, poverty, or poor mental health.
>
> To ensure we have the biggest impact, we are interested in projects which:
>
> - Identify and advocate with those particularly marginalised.
> - Identify the moments when people face the greatest risk of spiralling outcomes, including bereavement, the point of diagnosis or upon losing a job.
> - Sight loss services focused on at-risk communities.
> - Ensuring that specialist services for the general population are fully accessible and are reaching blind and partially sighted people.
>
> *Preventing avoidable blindness*
>
> 200,000 people are living with sight loss in the capital and just under 700,000 (1 in 12 adults) are living with a sight-threatening condition. Unless there are bold interventions, these figures are set to increase significantly by 2030. An estimated 50% of sight loss could be prevented if detected and treated in time.

To ensure we have the biggest impact, we are interested in projects which:

- Raise public awareness about the importance of sight tests, particularly among at-risk communities.
- Improve access to sight tests including adapted tests and community-based testing.

Financial information

Year end	31/03/2021
Income	£1,580,000
Assets	£2,230,000
Grants to organisations	£296,200
No. of grants	14

Beneficiaries included: Blind Veterans UK and SeeAbility (£50,000 each); Metro Sports and Social Club (£43,900); University of Birmingham (£17,500); Blind in Business (£10,000); London Vision (£8,900); The Photographers' Gallery (£5,800).

Exclusions

No grants are awarded directly to individuals. Projects that are delivered outside London cannot be supported.

Applications

The foundation has an online grant application platform, where proposals should be submitted. Deadlines and full details of what should be included in the proposal are outlined in the foundation's guidance notes. Registered companies are asked to contact the foundation before making an application.

Sources of information

Accounts; annual report; Charity Commission record; funder's website; guidance for applications.

The Vodafone Foundation

Projects which use mobile connectivity and technology to promote a healthier, safer and more sustainable society; digital education; humanitarian work; gender equality

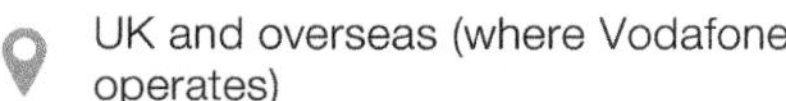

UK and overseas (where Vodafone operates)

£12.63 million (2020/21)

CC number: 1089625

Correspondent: The Trustees, 1 Kingdom Street, Paddington Central, London W2 6BY (email: groupfoundation@vodafone.com)

Trustees: Nick Land; Elizabeth Filkin; Patricia Ithau; Amparo Moraleda; Rosemary Martin; Joakim Reiter; John Otty; Leanne Wood.

 www.vodafonefoundation.org

 facebook.com/VodafoneFdn

 @vodafonefdn

 @vodafonefoundation

General information

The Vodafone Foundation was established in 2001 and receives the majority of its funding from Vodafone plc. The foundation's website states that its aim is:

> connecting communities around the world to improve lives. There is a unique network of 27 local foundations and social investment programmes that Vodafone Foundation works through.
>
> The underlying belief of this network of foundations is that connectivity drives change. By using this network Vodafone Foundation aims to connect people with the necessary tools to make a difference in the world.

The foundation currently provides funding and other support under the following headings:

- **Connected learning** – programmes and partnerships that enable some of the most vulnerable communities living in the areas in which Vodafone operates to access quality learning
- **Connected health** – programmes that use technology to connect some of the people in greatest need to health and well-being information and services
- **Connected living** – a programme that uses technology to improve the lives of people with a learning disability, their families and carers
- **Apps** – a range of apps that address some of the world's most pressing problems, from domestic violence and abuse to cancer and COVID-19
- **Take action** – employee fundraising and volunteering

Grant-making approach

The foundation's 2020/21 annual report states:

> The Vodafone Foundation directs its grants to projects and partners that align with our strategic objectives with a main focus on programmes in countries where Vodafone Group companies operate. We prioritise programmes that leverage technology for public benefit, based on the social benefits offered by digital and communications technology and their potential to deliver public benefit through innovation, scale and sustainability.

Financial information

Year end	31/03/2021
Income	£15,990,000
Assets	£5,560,000
Grants to organisations	£12,630,000

Further financial information

The financial information has been converted from Euros using the exchange rate at the time of writing (May 2022). During 2020/21, grants were distributed as follows:

Vodafone/Vodacom local foundations	£7.75 million
Digital health	£2.08 million
Humanitarian fund	£785,100
Digital education	£726,200
Gender equality	£680,700
Other activities	£439,900
UK employee matched funding	£169,800

Beneficiaries included: Vodafone Germany Foundation (£1.61 million); Vodafone UK Foundation (£431,800); TecSOS – Thames Valley Partnership (£421,200); National Emergencies Trust (£228,900); Code Like a Girl (£14,600).

Applications

The foundation usually approaches charitable organisations which it believes can help with the delivery of its charitable aims.

Sources of information

Accounts; annual report; Charity Commission record; funder's website.

Volant Charitable Trust

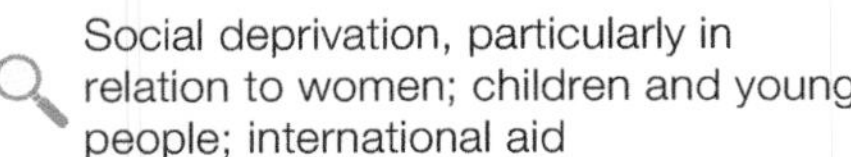

Social deprivation, particularly in relation to women; children and young people; international aid

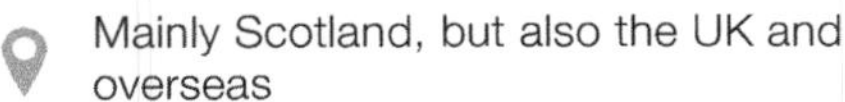

Mainly Scotland, but also the UK and overseas

£6.6 million (2020/21)

OSCR number: SC030790

Correspondent: Jennifer McPhail, Fund Advisor, c/o Turcan Connell, Princes Exchange, 1 Earl Grey Street, Edinburgh EH3 9EE (tel: 0141 341 4964; email: jennifer@foundationscotland.org.uk)

 www.volanttrust.org

General information

This trust was established in 2000 by the author J. K. Rowling. It supports Scottish charities that address social deprivation, particularly when concerned with women, children and young people at risk.

Grant-making

Open Grants programme – this programme supports Scottish charities and projects, whether national or community-based that alleviate social deprivation, particularly supporting women, children and young people at risk. It is the trust's only programme open to applications, other than the COVID-19 response fund. The programme will consider one-off projects or multi-year applications, but only in exceptional circumstances will grants exceed three years. Grants are typically of up to £15,000 per year.

The trust's website states the following:

> Specific programme areas that we cover include support for:
>
> Women – Victims of sexual abuse, rape, domestic violence and those working in the sex industry; care for young mothers and those affected by postnatal

depression, isolated and lone parents; community support for black and minority ethnic women and asylum seekers; support services for women prisoners and their families.

Children and young people – Counselling, support services and outreach projects for those who are disadvantaged or deemed to be at risk through neglect, emotional and physical abuse, alcohol or drug misuse.

Poverty and deprivation – Mental health projects for women and children; support for vulnerable families; promotion of healthy eating for families in areas of extreme deprivation.

International support – support is given to major disaster appeals from UK-registered charities.

UK and international COVID-19 response fund – support is provided to UK and international charities that demonstrate a strong focus on alleviating social deprivation and helping vulnerable groups who have been particularly impacted by the COVID-19 pandemic in the UK and internationally.

The trust provides funding towards project and administrative core costs. However, applications can be submitted for projects which include personal protection equipment (PPE) or other essential medical equipment through the COVID-19 response fund.

Financial information

Year end	05/04/2021
Income	£10,220,000
Assets	£75,830,000
Grants to organisations	£6,600,000

Further financial information

Grants were broken down as follows in 2020/21:

COVID-19 response fund	£3.81 million
Social deprivation	£2.34 million
International aid relief	£450,000

Beneficiaries included: Disasters Emergency Committee (£2 million); Foundation Scotland (£800,000); Home-Start UK (£250,000); UK Welcomes Refugees (£187,500); North Yorkshire Hospice Care (£10,200).

Exclusions

The Volant Trust will not support:

- Individuals
- Major capital projects
- Projects which do not benefit people in Scotland
- General fundraising appeals or activities
- Groups who will then distribute the funds as grants or bursaries
- The repayment of loans or payment of debts
- Retrospective appeals (i.e. for costs already incurred or completed projects)
- Trips abroad
- Purchase of second-hand vehicles

A full list of exclusions can be found on Foundation Scotland's website (www.foundationscotland.org.uk).

Applications

Applications can be made online via the Foundation Scotland website (www.foundationscotland.org.uk).

Sources of information

Accounts; annual report; OSCR record; funder's website.

The Georg and Emily Von Opel Foundation

Social welfare; health; education; nature and the environment; the advancement of the Roman Catholic faith

UK and overseas

£784,600 (2020)

CC number: 1172977

Correspondent: The Trustees, GVO Asset Management AG, Bundesplatz 14, 6300 Zug, Switzerland (tel: +415 264 70219)

Trustees: Georg Opel; Emily Opel; Rt Hon. Candida Petersham.

General information

The foundation was registered with the Charity Commission in 2017. Georg Von Opel is a German-born Swiss billionaire and great-grandson of Adam Opel, founder of the German car manufacturer.

The following information has been taken from the foundation's 2020 annual accounts:

> The Charity's objects are all purposes which are exclusively charitable for the public benefit under the law of England and Wales and in particular without prejudice to the generality of the foregoing:
>
> 1 the relief of poverty, suffering, sickness and distress;
> 2 the advancement of education;
> 3 the advancement of health;
> 4 the protection of nature and environment;
> 5 the support of the gifted;
> 6 the advancement of the Roman Catholic faith.
>
> The grant making policy identifies that the Charity will look to support exclusively charitable projects that aim to improve the circumstances and future opportunities of the young, the poor and the vulnerable. The policy also confirms that all grant recipients will either be UK registered charities; organisations that carry out activities that are charitable under UK law; or individual charitable beneficiaries.

Financial information

Year end	31/12/2020
Income	£1,210,000
Assets	£659,000
Grants to organisations	£784,600
No. of grants	11

Beneficiaries included: WaterAid (£200,000); Child's Dream Association (£150,000); University of Oxford Development Trust Fund (£100,000); Magic Bus UK (£50,000); Collateral Global (£30,000); The Latymer Foundation (£20,000); Westminster Roman Catholic Diocese Trustee (£5,000).

Applications

Apply in writing to the correspondent.

Sources of information

Accounts; annual report; Charity Commission record.

The VTCT Foundation

Medical research in the field of disfigurement

UK

£769,500 (2020/21)

CC number: 1155360

Correspondent: Amanda Shepard, Grant Manager, Aspire House, Annealing Close, Eastleigh, Hampshire SO50 9PX (tel: 07968 130339; email: amanda.shepard@vtctfoundation.org.uk)

Trustees: Rosanna Preston; Anthony Walker; Prof. Nichola Rumsey; Prof. Naiem Moiemen; Dr Wendy Edwards.

 www.vtctfoundation.org.uk

General information

The VTCT Foundation was established in 2013 to continue the charitable giving of the Vocational Training Charitable Trust (VTCT). The VTCT Foundation is focused on making grants for medical research in the field of disfigurement and providing support to organisations helping those living with visible difference.

Grant programmes

The foundation invites applications for funding in the following categories, as stated on its website:

Main grants: this programme offers grants of £25,000 and above with a focus on funding the creation, development and evaluation of digital solutions to the to the psychological and physical health needs in the community of people with visible differences.

Small grants: this programme offers grants of between £1,000 and £25,000 for organisations in the visible difference field – whether research or service delivery – to develop their capacity and sustainability. Examples of funding include:

- Employment of staff
- Training of trustees, staff or volunteers
- Regional and/or group activities
- Piloting of a new project or service
- Improving publicity materials
- Updating IT equipment
- Core costs on a short-term basis that allows the organisation to invest in both fundraising and services that underpin future viability and impact
- Improving monitoring, evaluation and impact reporting

Fellowships: the foundation funds clinical fellowships in the field of visible difference at selected universities and trusts.

Financial information

Year end	31/07/2021
Income	£90,200
Assets	£5,580,000
Grants to organisations	£769,500
No. of grants	18

Beneficiaries included: Changing Faces (£123,000); Cleft Collective (£100,000); North Bristol NHS Cleft Research (£50,000); Caring Matters Now (£25,000); British Burn Association (£20,000); The Appearance Collective (£2,600).

Exclusions

The foundation does not support projects where commercial interests are involved. It does not fund statutory or public bodies or for-profit organisations, and it will not fund any contributions towards the purchase of property or the maintenance of buildings or land the organisations do not own.

Applications

For main grants, an expression of interest should be submitted to the correspondent. For small grants, apply in writing (details of what to include can be found in the foundation's guidelines on its website). Application forms for fellowships can be downloaded from the foundation's website.

Sources of information

Accounts; annual report; Charity Commission record; funder's website; guidelines for applicants.

The Bruce Wake Charitable Trust

Disability and recreation

UK

£551,400 (2020/21)

CC number: 1018190

Correspondent: The Trustees, Oakview House, Wakerley Road, Rutland LE15 8EP (tel: 0344 879 3349; email: info@brucewaketrust.co.uk)

 www.brucewaketrust.co.uk

General information

The Bruce Wake Charitable Trust was established in 1993 to encourage and assist the provision of leisure activities for people with disabilities.

According to the trust's website, the trustees will consider a broad range of grant applications, but particularly favour applications which support the following:

- Wheelchair users with a physical disability
- Improved access for wheelchair users
- A sporting or leisure activity involving wheelchair users with a disability

The trust supports both individuals and organisations, but applications on behalf of individuals will only be accepted through a charitable organisation or equivalent recognised body.

Financial information

Year end	05/04/2021
Income	£129,800
Assets	£7,670,000
Grants to organisations	£551,400
No. of grants	176

Further financial information

Only beneficiaries of grants of over £5,000 were listed in the accounts. Grants of under £5,000 totalled £461,400.

Beneficiaries included: Wheelpower (£25,000); Charity Link Leicester (£14,000); Disability Snowsport UK (£10,000); Revitalise Respite Holidays (£6,000).

Exclusions

The website states that for-profit companies will not be considered.

Applications

Apply via the trust's website using the online application form. Charitable organisations should include a copy of their latest financial statements in their application. The trustees meet quarterly to consider applications.

Sources of information

Accounts; annual report; Charity Commission website; funder's website.

The Walcot Foundation

Relieving poverty and promoting education to young people who live in the London Borough of Lambeth

The London Borough of Lambeth

£1.88 million (2020/21)

CC number: 312800

Correspondent: Daniel Chapman, Grants Manager, 127 Kennington Road, London SE11 6SF (tel: 020 7735 1925; email: grants@walcotfoundation.org.uk)

 www.walcotfoundation.org.uk

 @walcotlambeth

General information

The Walcot Foundation (formerly the Lambeth Endowed Charities), with roots dating back to the 17th century, is an 'umbrella' title for what are now four charities: the Walcot Educational Foundation, Hayle's Charity, The Cynthia Moseley Memorial Fund and the Walcot Non-Educational Charity. The Walcott trusts sprang from the generosity of Edmund Walcot, a citizen of London and a haberdasher by trade, who in his will of 1667 left provision for people in Lambeth who are in need.

The following information has been taken from the foundation's website:

Who can apply?

> Applicants must be not-for-profit organisations. This includes properly constituted voluntary or community groups, registered charities, or social enterprises.

Grant size

> We offer revenue grants up to £25,000 per year for up to three years. The Foundation will consider providing up to 100% of reasonable project costs. A project is considered more favourably if the applicant organisation can make a contribution, either from its own resources or from funds raised elsewhere.

Types of projects

> We exist exclusively for the benefit of Lambeth individuals from low-income households. Our grants to organisations and schools are solely a means of reaching those individuals. Our grants are targeted at specific individuals or groups of individuals that meet our criteria as opposed to, for example, whole-school or whole-community projects.
>
> The strategy underpinning all our grant making is to help individuals move along these key paths:
>
> - from academic underachievement to achievement
> - from unemployable to employable
> - from unemployed to employed
> - from financially disadvantaged to financially self-sufficient

Financial information

Year end	31/03/2021
Income	£3,130,000
Assets	£128,010,000
Grants to organisations	£1,880,000
No. of grants	120

Beneficiaries included: Brixton Advice Centre (£74,200); Home-Start Lambeth (£26,600); High Trees (£24,400); Lilian Baylis Technology School (£21,000); Norwood School (£19,700); Henry Fawcett Primary School (£11,000).

Exclusions

Grants are not given for:

- Anything the foundation views as the responsibility of central or local government or the schools themselves
- Projects that do not actually benefit Lambeth residents who are in financial need
- Capital projects
- Debt repayments
- Fixing an organisation's finances

Applications

Refer to the foundation's website to check if the organisations grants scheme is currently open. Potential applicants should initially contact a member of the grants team to discuss whether their proposal is eligible and obtain an application form. Deadlines are posted on the website.

Sources of information

Accounts; annual report; Charity Commission record; funder's website.

Walton-on-Thames Charity

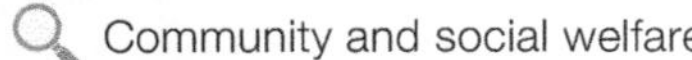

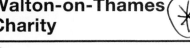

Community and social welfare

The borough of Elmbridge, Surrey

£501,900 (2020/21)

CC number: 1185959

Correspondent: Caroline Davies, Community Grants and Projects, Walton on Thames Charity, Charities House, 2 The Quintet, Churchfield Road, Walton on Thames, Surrey KT12 2TZ (tel: 01932 220242; email: admin@waltoncharity.org.uk)

Trustees: Nick Stuart; Juliet Hobbs; David Easson; Elizabeth Kennedy; Graham Mann; Paul Tajasque; James Vizzini; Robert Mills; Alexandra Fitzpatrick; Andrew Button-Stephens; Sarah Tomkins; Dennis Pillay; Kellie Scott.

 www.waltoncharity.org.uk

 @WaltonCharity

General information

The charity is an amalgamation of several other charities established in the Walton-on-Thames area in the 20th century. These charities were officially merged in 1963. The charity states that it is 'committed to ensuring that the charity is rooted in its past, while at the same time modernising and responding to the ever changing nature of poverty and need'. The charity's primary aim is to improve the lives of people living in the borough of Elmbridge.

Areas of work

The charity's 2020/21 accounts state that its six priority areas are:

- Alleviation of financial poverty/hardship
- Promote personal health and well-being
- Alleviate isolation and loneliness
- Promote affordable housing for all ages
- Work to improve educational attainment
- Improve access to affordable transport

Grant programmes

The charity awards community grants to other organisations.

Grants are also made to individuals in the area of benefit. Aside from grant-making, the charity offers sheltered housing for older people, allotments to rent and the use of properties owned by the charity for the benefit of the wider community.

Financial information

Year end	31/03/2021
Income	£2,170,000
Assets	£35,980,000
Grants to organisations	£501,900

Further financial information

Grants were broken down as follows:

Community grants	£304,800
COVID-19 grants	£105,400
School Opportunities Fund	£57,700
Delegated Fund	£34,000

Beneficiaries included: A list of beneficiaries was not available. Previous beneficiaries include: Burwood Preschool, Citizens Advice Elmbridge West, Elmbridge Borough Council, Elmbridge Youth Support Services, Surrey Fire and Rescue Service, Surrey SATRO, Thames Riverboat Project, The Delight Charity, Walton Oak School.

Applications

Application forms are available on the charity website.

Sources of information

Accounts; annual report; Charity Commission record; funder's website.

The Barbara Ward Children's Foundation

Children and young people and adults with disabilities

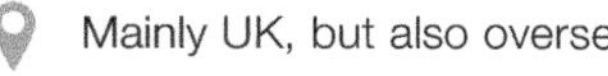

Mainly UK, but also overseas

£463,500 (2020)

CC number: 1089783

Correspondent: The Trustees, 85 Fleet Street, London EC4 1AE (tel: 020 7222 7040; email: info@bwcf.org.uk)

Trustees: David Bailey; Chris Banks; Kenneth Parker; Brian Walters; Barbara Ward; Christopher Brown; Mark Waight.

 www.bwcf.org.uk

General information

Established in 2001, this foundation makes grants to organisations working with children who are disadvantaged both in the UK and overseas. Grants may also be given to organisations supporting adults who have learning disabilities. Funding can range from one-off grants to project-related grants that run for two or more years.

According to the website, the foundation prefers to support 'financially healthy children's charities where funding is not forthcoming from statutory bodies, where incomes and fund balances are constantly put to good use and where administration overheads are kept to a minimum'.

In previous years, grants have been given for purposes including:

- Educational projects
- Support, care and respite
- Holidays
- Sport, play and leisure
- Health and well-being

Financial information

Year end	31/12/2020
Income	£539,100
Assets	£12,890,000
Grants to organisations	£463,500
No. of grants	64

Further financial information

During the year, the foundation reviewed 401 applications and made 64 grants, of which 15 were one-off grants and the rest were multi-year grants. The accounts state that all grants 'were for the benefit of children who were serious or terminally ill, disadvantaged, underprivileged or had special needs'.

Beneficiaries included: Sebastian's Action Trust (£15,000); Daisy Garland Trust (£13,800); Mudlarks Community (£10,000); Let Us Play (£7,500); Peter Pan Centre (£6,000); Hayle Youth Project (£5,000); Haworth RDA (£2,000); Leeds Community Trust (£500).

Exclusions

Grants are not made to religious charities.

Applications

Apply in writing to the correspondent by post detailing the purpose for which the grant is requested and including the latest annual report and accounts. Beneficiaries or applicants may be visited by trustees, who usually meet on a quarterly basis to review and award grants (although subgroups may meet more frequently to assess applications).

Sources of information

Accounts; annual report; Charity Commission record; funder's website.

The Warwickshire Masonic Charitable Association Ltd

Masonic organisations and general charitable purposes

Warwickshire

£300,300 (2020)

CC number: 211588

Correspondent: John Harris, Provincial Grand Almoner, Yenton Assembly Rooms, 73–75 Gravelly Hill North, Erdington, Birmingham, West Midlands B23 6BJ (tel: 0121 454 0554; email: dalec@warwickshirepgl.org)

Trustees: Peter Britton; Stanley Butterworth; Christopher Grove; Gordon Law; Michael Morris; Eric Rymer; Nigel Burton; John Hayward; William Clark; Richard Barker; Philip Hall; David Greenwood; Mervyn Kimberley; Peter Manning; John Harris; Geoffrey Walker; Stephen Tranter; Nigel Hawkins; Howard Smith; David Butcher.

www.warwickshirefreemasons.org.uk/charity

General information

The charity was established to promote the cause of Masonic charities in the province of Warwickshire. It also makes donations to non-Masonic charities.

Financial information

Year end	31/12/2020
Grants to organisations	£300,300

Further financial information

Grants were broken down as follows: non-Masonic grants (£203,500) and Masonic grants (£106,800).

Beneficiaries included: Birmingham University Hospitals Trust (£30,000); Acorns Children's Hospice (£5,200); Shakespeare Hospice (£4,000); Birmingham Crisis Centre (£3,000); Streetleague (£1,000); Focus Birmingham (£500).

Applications

Applications can be made through the Provincial Grand Lodge of Warwickshire website.

Sources of information

Accounts; annual report; Charity Commission record; funder's website.

Mrs Waterhouse Charitable Trust

Medical causes; health; welfare; the environment; wildlife; churches; heritage

UK, with an interest in the North West and particularly the Lancashire area

£321,000 (2020/21)

CC number: 261685

Correspondent: The Trustees, 2nd Floor, Parkgates, Bury New Road, Prestwich, Manchester M25 0TL (tel: 0161 904 9942; email: houghtondunnct@gmail.com)

Trustees: Alistair Dunn; Helen Dunn.

General information

The trust's annual report for 2020/21 states that:

> The trust makes donations to bodies embracing a wide range of charities, the main fields supported being medical and health, welfare in the community, environment and wildlife, and church and heritage with special reference to charities in, or with branches in the North West of England.

The trust's Charity Commission record states a preference for the Lancashire area.

Financial information

Year end	05/04/2021
Income	£325,500
Assets	£9,940,000
Grants to organisations	£321,000
No. of grants	33

Further financial information

During 2020/21, 84% of the grants were distributed to charities based in the North West or the North West operations of national charities.

Beneficiaries included: Amend (£30,000); The Children's Adventure Farm Trust (£20,000); Macmillan Cancer Support (£15,000); British Forces Foundation, Christie Hospital and National Youth Orchestra (£10,000 each); Survivors of Bereavement by Suicide (£5,000); Lancashire Cricket Foundation (£3,000).

Applications

Contact the correspondent for further information.

Sources of information

Accounts; annual report; Charity Commission record.

The Waterloo Foundation

Child development; the environment; financially developing countries; projects in Wales

UK and overseas, with a preference for Wales

£13.35 million (2020)

CC number: 1117535

Correspondent: The Trustees, c/o 46–48 Cardiff Road, Llandaff, Cardiff CF5 2DT (tel: 029 2083 8980; email: info@waterloofoundation.org.uk)

Trustees: Caroline Oakes; David Stevens; Heather Stevens.

www.waterloofoundation.org.uk

General information

The Waterloo Foundation (TWF) is an independent grant-making foundation based in Wales that was established in 2007. It makes grants to organisations in the UK and worldwide, and, according to its website, it is 'most interested in projects that help globally particularly in the areas of the disparity of opportunities and wealth and the unsustainable use of the world's natural resources'.

Grants

The foundation aims to donate £6 million annually in four core areas, each with specific sub-themes:

- World development
  - Sexual and reproductive health
  - Nutrition
  - Education
  - Water, sanitation and hygiene
- The environment
  - Marine projects working to stop the decline of fish stocks
  - Protecting tropical rainforests
- Child development
  - Research and practical projects
- Projects in Wales
  - Unpaid carers
  - Education
  - Enterprise and employment

Eligibility

Generally, the following organisations are eligible to apply:

- Registered charities
- Charities with a formal constitution and an income of less that £5,000
- Social enterprises and not-for-profit organisations
- CICs and CIOs
- Non-governmental organisations based outside the UK

- Universities and academic organisations

See the foundation's website for more programme-specific criteria.

Financial information

Year end	31/12/2020
Income	£17,780,000
Assets	£216,970,000
Grants to organisations	£13,350,000
No. of grants	440

Further financial information

Grants, including around £5 million of COVID-19 grants, were distributed as follows:

World development	45%
The environment	24%
Wales	14%
Child development	11%
Other	6%

We were unable to determine the proportion of grants given in the UK. During the year the foundation received 727 applications and made 440 grants.

Beneficiaries included: A list of beneficiaries was not available.

Exclusions

Each grants programme has specific criteria and exclusions, which are detailed on the foundation's website. In general, the foundation will not support applications from individuals or for the promotion of religious or political causes, general appeals or circulars.

Applications

Application guidelines and deadlines for each of the grant programmes are available on the foundation's website. There is no application form and all applications should be submitted via email to applications@waterloofoundation.org.uk. Details of what should be included in the application are specific to each grants programme and can be found on the foundation's website.

Sources of information

Accounts; annual report; Charity Commission record; funder's website.

Wates Family Enterprise Trust

Life opportunities for young people; community projects; sustainability and climate change; housing and homelessness

UK

£486,100 (2020)

CC number: 1126007

Correspondent: Felicity Mallam, Director, Wates House, Station Approach, Leatherhead, Surrey KT22 7SW (tel: 01372 861250; email: director@watesfoundation.org.uk)

Trustees: Andrew Wates; Andy Wates; Tim Wates; Charles Wates; Jonathan Wates; Sir James Wates; Paul Wates; Michael Wates.

www.wfet.org.uk

General information

Registered in 2008, the trust is the vehicle for the philanthropic and charitable activities of the Wates family, owners of the Wates Group.

The trust has three main themes:

- **Life opportunities for young people** – improving the life chances of disadvantaged young people through training and education
- **Housing** – exploring the housing sector to consider issues around housing and homelessness
- **Sustainability** – supporting programmes that promote public engagement with the issue of climate change

According to the trust's 2020 annual report, there are three types of grant which may be made by the trust:

- **Major/group awards** – in support of bids originating from initiatives of the Wates Group and its business units
- **Family awards** – in support of bids which are the initiative of the Wates family
- **Employee awards** – in support of initiatives of employees of the Wates businesses including staff fundraising efforts, Give As You Earn donations through payroll and volunteering, among other things

The trust matches funds raised by Wates Group employees up to £500 per individual each year. One-off Community Awards of between £500 and £1,500 are also made to charitable organisations that employees volunteer for in their own time.

Financial information

Year end	31/12/2020
Income	£832,400
Assets	£336,400
Grants to organisations	£486,100
No. of grants	185

Further financial information

Grants paid during the year totalled £486,100.

Beneficiaries included: Centre for Social Justice and Hubbub (£120,000 each); Family Business Network (£15,000); Royal Engineers Museum (£7,000); Royal British Legion (£4,000); Young Women's Trust (£2,200); The Kidney Fund (£500); Open Garage Films (£200).

Applications

All proposals come from Wates employees or the Wates family – unsolicited applications are not considered.

Sources of information

Accounts; annual report; Charity Commission record; funder's website.

The Wates Foundation

Building social values; education and employment; community health; life transitions; safer communities; strengthening the charitable and voluntary sector; the environment

Southern England

£358,600 (2020)

CC number: 247941

Correspondent: Felicity Mallam, Director, Wates House, Station Approach, Leatherhead, Surrey KT22 7SW (email: director@watesfoundation.org.uk)

Trustees: Christian Brodie; Victoria Tanner; Luke Wates; Jonathan Wates; Nichola Adams; Jonathan Heynes.

www.watesfoundation.org.uk

General information

In 1966, three brothers Norman, Sir Ronald and Allan Wates of the Wates building firm (now the Wates Construction Group) amalgamated their personal charitable trusts into the single entity of The Wates Foundation. The foundation supports issues that reflect the family's broad range of interests. These are categorised into six themes:

- Building social values
- Education and employment
- Community health
- Life transitions
- Safer communities
- Strengthening the charitable and voluntary sector
- The environment

Financial information

Year end	31/12/2020
Income	£209,400
Assets	£21,530,000
Grants to organisations	£358,600

Further financial information

Grants were broken down as follows:

Community health	£130,100
Education and employment	£97,900
Life transitions	£53,200
Building family values	£52,200
Strengthening the charitable sector	£26,200

Beneficiaries included: A list of beneficiaries was not available. Previous beneficiaries include: National Cancer Research Institute (£30,000); INQUEST and Life 2009 (£20,000 each); Imagine If Theatre Company, Oxfordshire Association for the Blind and Reach Learning Disability (£15,000 each); First Steps ED, Startuponline and West London Action for Children (£10,000 each); Ride High Ltd and The Children's Literacy Charity (£5,000).

Applications

Unsolicited applications are not accepted. The foundation is a proactive grant-maker.

Sources of information

Accounts; annual report; Charity Commission record; funder's website.

The William Wates Memorial Trust

Disadvantaged children and young people

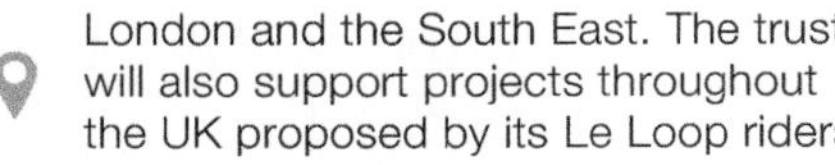

London and the South East. The trust will also support projects throughout the UK proposed by its Le Loop riders

£398,200 (2019/20)

CC number: 1011213

Correspondent: Felicity Mallam, Director, Wates House, Station Approach, Leatherhead, Surrey KT22 7SW (tel: 01372 861051; email: wwmt@wates.co.uk)

Trustees: Andrew Wates; Sarah Wates; Jonathon Wates; Richard Wates; Monty Wates; Timothy Wates; Susan Laing.

 https://wwmt.rideleloop.org

 facebook.com/williamwatesmemorialtrust

General information

The trust was established in 1998 and exists to celebrate the life of William Wates, who was killed while travelling through Central America.

The aim of the trust is to help disadvantaged young people stay away from crime and fulfil their potential. The trust achieves this by supporting charities that engage young people through the mediums of sports, arts and education.

Projects should help the most disadvantaged 5- to 19-year-olds. Support is primarily given to projects in London and the South East; however, nationwide projects proposed by the trust's Le Loop riders will be considered. Grants are typically of £30,000 over three years.

Financial information

Year end	31/08/2020
Income	£352,000
Assets	£10,000
Grants to organisations	£398,200

Further financial information

Donations of £296,200 were committed during 2019/20; however, grants actually paid out during the year totalled £398,200.

Grants made can be categorised as follows:

Mentoring	£123,600
Personal development	£94,100
Arts	£59,500
Educational support	£12,000
Sports	£7,000

Beneficiaries included: Community Foundation Surrey (£50,000); Abram Wilson Foundation (£35,000); Hackney Quest (£30,000); Our Time (£27,000); School Ground Sounds (£19,500); SIH Equine Therapy (£10,000); Manchester Youth Zone (£1,000).

Applications

Applications can be made through the trust's website. Check the website for current submission dates. Applications made before submission dates are announced will not be processed. The trustees meet three times per year.

Sources of information

Accounts; annual report; Charity Commission record; funder's website.

The Geoffrey Watling Charity

General charitable purposes, including: social welfare; churches and historic buildings; education; the arts; medical causes; sport; the environment

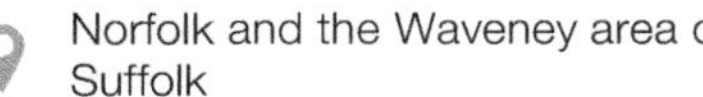

Norfolk and the Waveney area of Suffolk

£466,200 (2019/20)

CC number: 1025258

Correspondent: The Trustees, 8A Ber Street, Norwich, Norfolk NR1 3EJ (email: enquiries@geoffreywatling.org.uk)

Trustees: Alan Watling; Susan Watling; Richard Marks; David Lundean.

 www.geoffreywatling.org.uk

General information

The Geoffrey Watling Charity was established in 1993 to support general charitable purposes in Norfolk and the Waveney area of Suffolk. Its founder, Geoffrey Watling, was a local entrepreneur and former chair and president of Norwich City FC who bequeathed much of his estate to the charity so that it could continue to work with and support local charitable organisations.

The charity awards funding to organisations for general charitable purposes, with grants awarded in the following categories:

- Social welfare
- Churches and historic buildings
- Education and the arts
- The environment
- Medical causes
- Sport
- Infrastructure

Grants range up to £30,000. Applications for specific projects are favoured over applications for core costs and salaries. All charitable organisations operating in the area of benefit can apply.

Financial information

Year end	30/09/2020
Income	£726,400
Assets	£15,870,000
Grants to organisations	£466,200
No. of grants	124

Further financial information

Grants were broken down as follows:

Social welfare	60	£280,200
Education and the arts	22	£52,500
Medical causes	6	£51,500
Churches and historical buildings	22	£43,000
The environment	7	£25,500
Sport	5	£17,500
Infrastructure	2	£9,000

Only beneficiaries of grants of over £10,000 were listed in the accounts.

Beneficiaries included: Centre 81 Ltd (£50,000); University of East Anglia (£30,000); Norfolk Community Sports Foundation, Ted Ellis Trust and St Martins (£10,000 each).

Exclusions

The charity will not consider grant applications from organisations which have not submitted their annual accounts/annual return to the Charity Commission or to Companies House. Grants are not available to individuals.

Applications

Applications can be made at any time via the charity's website, where there are detailed guidelines. The trustees meet quarterly to consider applications.

Sources of information

Accounts; annual report; Charity Commission record; funder's website; guidelines for applicants.

The Weavers' Company Benevolent Fund

Disadvantaged young people and people who have offended

 UK

£370,400 (2020)

CC number: 266189

Correspondent: Anne Howe, Charities Officer, Saddlers House, 40 Gutter Lane, London EC2V 6BR (tel: 020 7606 1155; email: charity@weavers.org.uk)

Trustee: Bailiffs, wardens and assistants of the Worshipful Company of Weavers.

 https://weavers.org.uk/charity/charitable-grants

General information

The charity was established in 1973 with funds from the Worshipful Company of Weavers, which is the oldest City of London livery company, with a history dating back to before 1130 CE.

Areas of work

According to its website, the charity wishes to support work in the following areas of interest:

- Young offenders (under the age of 30) – supporting projects that involve rehabilitation
- Ex-offenders – supporting projects that help ex-offenders of all ages
- Young disadvantaged people (aged 5 to 30), especially those at risk of criminal involvement

Grant-making policy

Grants of up to £15,000 per annum are awarded for projects and associated costs, such as office/secretarial support. According to the website, the charity also makes grants for core funding for new projects, such as general administration and training 'to enable a given organisation to develop and maintain expertise'. If a project is successful and has 'proven worth', the charity will consider providing ongoing funding.

The charity particularly welcomes applications for pump-priming grants from small community-based organisations where the grant would form a major element of the funding.

In exceptional circumstances, the charity will provide grants for emergency/deficit funding for an established organisation. Those most likely to be granted emergency funding are charities which the company knows or has previously supported.

The charity provides annual support to three London primary schools in Tower Hamlets, Southwark and Stockwell. This grants programme is not open to applications. Support is also awarded to weaving departments at universities and other educational establishments to upgrade or renew existing equipment, purchase new equipment or enable their students to visit mills and factories. Grants are made by recommendation to the committee.

Eligibility

The charity is especially interested in helping smaller organisations which offer direct services. Local organisations working in a village, estate or small town should normally have an income of less than £100,000. Organisations working in larger cities and/or across the UK should have an income of less than £250,000. Under the theme of helping disadvantaged young people, applications from CICs may be considered.

Financial information

Year end	31/01/2020
Income	£595,100
Assets	£198,300
Grants to organisations	£370,400

Beneficiaries included: London Funders (£30,000); C2C Social Action (£15,000); London Village Network (£8,000); Reasons Why Foundation (£7,500); Innercity Films (£5,000); Koestler Award Trust (£1,000); Alzheimer's Society (£500); Prison Phoenix Trust (£300); City of London Police Widows' and Orphans' Fund (£150).

Exclusions

According to the website, the charity will not fund:

- Long-term support
- General appeals (sponsorship, marketing or other fundraising activities)
- Endowment funds
- Grant-giving charities
- Retrospective costs
- Replacement funding
- Building projects
- Capital projects to provide access in compliance with the Disability Discrimination Act
- Personal appeals
- Umbrella bodies or large established organisations
- Overseas organisations/projects

The charity does not *usually* fund:

- Work with children under the age of five years
- Universities or colleges
- Medical charities or those involved in medical care
- Organisations of and for people with disabilities, including learning or physical disabilities
- Environmental projects
- Work in promotion of religious or political causes

Applications

Applications should be completed online on the charity's website. While the form should be completed online, it should be returned by post only. Email applications will not be considered. The trustees meet three times a year to consider grant applications. The deadlines for applications are available to view on the application form.

Applications must arrive by midday on the closing date. Any late applications will be held over for consideration at the next closing date.

If your application is shortlisted, the charity will arrange an assessment visit.

Sources of information

Accounts; annual report; Charity Commission record; funder's website.

The Weinstock Fund

Medical care; care and education for people with disabilities; care and support of children and older people; social welfare; music and the arts

UK

£261,800 (2020/21)

CC number: 1150031

Correspondent: The Trustees, PO Box 5369, Wincanton, Somerset BA9 0BG (email: enquiries@weinstockfund.org.uk)

Trustees: Susan Lacroix; The Hon. Laura Weinstock; The Hon. Clare Renton.

www.weinstockfund.org.uk

General information

The Weinstock Fund was originally established by the late Lord Weinstock in 1962 for general charitable purposes. Lord Weinstock was actively involved in the running of the charity until his death in 2002. The charity was dissolved in December 2012, and this successor charity, with similar aims and objectives, was then created.

Areas of work

According to its website, the charity will support work in the following areas:

- Medical care and treatment, including respite care
- Education, training and care for adults and children with impairments and special needs
- Care and support of the elderly
- Care and support for children
- Hardship alleviation
- Community
- Culture and environment
- Health and welfare
- Music and the arts

Financial information

Year end	05/04/2021
Income	£2,460,000
Assets	£19,050,000
Grants to organisations	£261,800

Beneficiaries included: A list of beneficiaries was not available.

Applications

Applications can be made via the charity's website.

Sources of information

Accounts; annual report; Charity Commission record; funder's website.

The Weir Charitable Trust

Sport and recreational activities; animal welfare; health; Scottish culture

Scotland

£381,000 (2020)

OSCR number: SC043187

Correspondent: Trust Manager, Unit 201, Ettrick Riverside, Dunsdale Road, Selkirk, Scottish Borders TD7 5EB (email: enquiries@weircharitabletrust.com)

 www.weircharitabletrust.com

General information

The trust supports smaller charities and community groups with annual incomes of under £125,000 that provide services to help communities across Scotland.

The following information was taken from the trust's website:

> We support services/projects, run by Scottish-based community groups and small charities, in the following qualifying categories that address any aspect of the following purposes:
>
> - **Sport:** encouraging and increasing public participation in sport (activities which involve physical skill and exertion)
> - **Recreational facilities:** the provision or organisation of recreational facilities (buildings, pitches or similar) with the aim of improving the conditions of life for the people for whom the facilities are primarily intended. This is only in relation to facilities which are primarily intended for people who need them due to age, ill-health, disability, financial hardship or other disadvantage.
> - **Animal welfare:** for the advancement of animal welfare
> - **Health:** the advancement of health, including prevention or relief of sickness, disease or human suffering
> - **Culture:** supporting the heritage – tangible or otherwise – of Scotland, through projects that encourage participation in and preservation of Scotland's distinctive culture.

The trust offers grants up to a maximum of £25,000. All awards are for one year or less. Funding can be used for capital projects (such as equipment, fixtures, fittings and refurbishments), running costs, one-off projects, core costs and salaries. The trust's website states: 'In summary, anything you need [funding] for as long as it contributes to providing a benefit to your community.'

Financial information

Year end	31/12/2020
Income	£414,400
Assets	£4,930,000
Grants to organisations	£381,000
No. of grants	58

Further financial information

Grants were broken down as follows:

The Robert Hartness Discretionary Award	33	£178,300
Health	11	£109,900
Animal welfare	3	£29,000
Sport	6	£37,000
Recreational facilities	3	£15,700
Culture	2	£11,100

Beneficiaries included: Larger awards included: Y Suffer in Silence (£25,000); Arthurshiel Rescue Centre (£20,000); The Brunswick Community Centre (£18,400); Kids in the Street (£10,000); Nurture Scotland (£8,000); Caldwell Halls Trust (£5,000).

Exclusions

The trust will not support requests from or for the following:

- Organisations with an annual income of over £125,000
- Individuals
- Commercial activities, including start-ups
- Social enterprises
- Requests for amounts over £25,000
- Sponsorship
- Retrospective costs
- One-off events
- Large capital projects
- Community councils, PTAs or Active Schools activities
- Debts, redundancy payments or fees
- Research
- Projects or organisations outside Scotland
- Governing bodies
- Pilot projects
- Educational establishments
- Public sector bodies

Applications

An online application form is available on the trust's website. Alternatively a paper copy can be downloaded from the website and returned by post. There are two deadlines each year, at the end of February and August. Applications are accepted at any time but they will only be considered at those times. Guidelines and details of exact deadlines are also available on the trust's website.

Sources of information

Accounts; annual report; OSCR record; funder's website.

The Welland Trust

People who have experienced care

England and Wales

£607,700 (2020)

CC number: 1181775

Correspondent: The Trustees, Craftsman House, De Salis Drive, Hampton Lovett, Droitwich, Worcestershire WR9 0QE (email: enquiries@thewellandtrust.org)

Trustees: Sarah Saunders; Polly Jones; Janet Rees; Isabelle Murphy.

 www.thewellandtrust.org

General information

The trust was established in 2019 by Jan Rees and supports people who have experienced care.

The trust's website states:

> The Welland Trust focus their efforts on the sponsorship and support of projects and initiatives that benefit adults who have experienced care. We are particularly keen to support the creation of opportunities to help reduce homelessness, reduce re-offending and support that will enhance the physical and mental well being of adults who've been in care. We also have a passion for projects that support opportunities for training, employment and further education for care leavers in particular those who are older (post 25) where there is no statutory support available.

Financial information

Year end	31/12/2020
Income	£117,400
Assets	£11,380,000
Grants to organisations	£607,700

Beneficiaries included: A list of beneficiaries was not available.

Applications

Contact the charity via email or the form on its website. Applicants will need to provide a full project plan indicating how the grant will be used and the expected outcomes and benefits for care-experienced adults.

Sources of information

Accounts; annual report; Charity Commission record; funder's website.

Wellbeing of Women

Research into women's reproductive and gynaecological health

UK and Ireland

£880,000 (2020)

CC number: 239281

Correspondent: The Trustees, 10–18 Union Street, London SE1 1SZ (tel: 020 3697 7000; email: hello@wellbeingofwomen.org.uk)

Trustees: Lynn Hiestand; Eve Pollard; Philip Jansen; Prof. Mary Lumsden; Debra White; Sir Ian Powell; Margaret Horvath; Lady Helen Ward; Dame Prof. Lesley Regan; Ranee Thakar; Sacha Nathan; Gill Walton.

 www.wellbeingofwomen.org.uk

General information

Wellbeing of Women is Britain's leading charity funding research into women's health issues since 1964. The charity's mission is to improve diagnosis and treatments, find cures and preventions, and to ultimately transform the lives of women and their babies.

Research project grants

Grants of up to £200,000, for up to three years, are awarded to organisations for projects in laboratory, clinical and translational research in the following areas:

- Fertility, pregnancy and birth complications
- Gynaecological cancers
- Well-being issues

The charity also funds various grant programmes for individuals. These are:

- Research training fellowships – grants of up to £250,000 for up to three years
- Entry-level research scholarships – a single maximum payment of £20,000
- Postdoc research fellowships – a maximum of £30,000 awarded for up to three years

Visit the charity's website for full details regarding each programme.

Financial information

Year end	31/12/2020
Income	£1,340,000
Assets	£1,570,000
Grants to organisations	£888,800

Beneficiaries included: University College London (£255,300); University of Sheffield (£19,500); University of Birmingham (£8,500); University of Oxford (£6,200); Glasgow Caledonian University (£1,000).

Exclusions

See the website for a full list of exclusions for each scheme.

Applications

Application forms, along with guidelines, are available to download from the charity's website. Closing and opening dates for each call can also be seen on the website.

Sources of information

Accounts; annual report; Charity Commission record; funder's website.

The Wellcome Trust

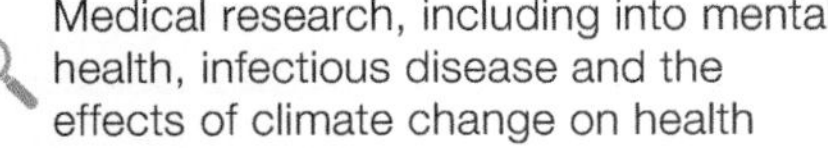

Medical research, including into mental health, infectious disease and the effects of climate change on health

UK and overseas

£759.5 million (2019/20)

CC number: 210183

Correspondent: The Grants Team, Gibbs Building, 215 Euston Road, London NW1 2BE (tel: 020 7611 8888; email: a contact form is available on the trust's website)

Trustee: The Wellcome Trust Ltd.

 www.wellcome.ac.uk

 facebook.com/wellcometrust

 @wellcometrust

General information

The pharmacist, entrepreneur, philanthropist and collector Sir Henry Wellcome died in 1936. On his death, his will established a charity for 'the advancement of medical and scientific research to improve mankind's well-being'. The Wellcome Trust is now one of the world's leading biomedical research charities, supporting scientists and researchers, and is the UK's largest non-governmental source of funds for biomedical research.

The trust's website summarises its approach as follows: 'We support researchers, we take on big health challenges, we campaign for better science, and we help everyone get involved with science and health research.'

Areas of work

The trust's website provides the following information on its vision and strategy:

> Wellcome supports science to solve the urgent health challenges facing everyone.
>
> We will achieve this vision in different ways, giving researchers the freedom to make discoveries that change the way we see the world, and using science to find solutions for three of the world's most urgent health challenges.
>
> We'll support a broad programme of discovery research across a wide range of disciplines with the potential to make important and unanticipated discoveries about life, health and wellbeing – both to help us tackle these great challenges, and to inspire further improvements in human health.
>
> And we're developing programmes of work that draw on Wellcome's expertise across science, innovation and society to deliver ambitious goals:
>
> - **Mental health:** Working with people who have lived experience of mental health issues to improve research, understanding and treatment of mental health.
> - **Infectious disease:** Working with communities affected by escalating infectious diseases to bring those diseases under control and stop epidemics.
> - **Climate and health:** Working with the communities most affected by climate change to explore the harmful effects of climate change on health, and to use research to develop new ways of protecting people's health.

Financial information

Year end	30/09/2020
Income	£743,700,000
Assets	£27,403,800,000
Grants to organisations	£759,500,000

Beneficiaries included: University of Oxford (£128.1 million); University of Cambridge (£70.9 million); Rosalind Franklin Institute (£20.2 million); Novartis AG – Switzerland (£15.2 million); Liverpool School of Tropical Medicine (£10 million); European Bioinformatics Institute (£8.1 million); Cardiff University (£7.1 million).

Exclusions

Specific criteria and exclusions for each funding programme are detailed on the trust's website.

Applications

See the trust's website for the latest information on open grant funding opportunities.

Sources of information

Accounts; annual report; Charity Commission record; funder's website.

Wellington Management UK Foundation

Improving academic performance and behaviour, reducing absenteeism and developing life skills for economically disadvantaged young people (up to the age of 26)

UK; Germany; Luxembourg; Switzerland

£963,800 (2020)

CC number: 1167369

Correspondent: The Trustees, c/o Wellington Management International Ltd, 80 Victoria Street, London SW1E 5JL (tel: 020 7126 6000; email: wmukf@wellington.com)

Trustees: John Dickson; Nicola Staunton; Damian Bloom; Joanne Carey; Richard Lienden; Anna Lunden; James Stoll; Thomas Horsey.

 www.wellington.com/en-gb/community-engagement

General information

The Wellington Management UK Foundation is the UK corporate charity of Wellington Management, one of the world's largest independent investment management firms. Established in 2016, the foundation supports programmes and organisations that improve the education of, and educational opportunities for, economically disadvantaged young people up to 26 years old. The foundation prefers to support organisations in London, where the company has a presence. It will also support organisations in Germany, Luxembourg and Switzerland.

According to its website, the foundation seeks to achieve this mission by providing grants to charities and not-for-profit organisations of various sizes that work to 'improve academic performance, improve behaviour, reduce absenteeism and develop life skills for economically disadvantaged youth up to 26 years'. Preference is given to organisations with an annual income of under £2 million.

The foundation's website states that 'Grantee organisations may use [the] funding as they see fit, either for programmatic or operating expenses.' Grants are awarded on annual basis, although multi-year grants will be considered once a relationship has been established. The foundation will consider applications from newer as well as more-established organisations. Furthermore, the foundation notes that it prefers to fund organisations that can demonstrate 'the strength of their management and that have a measurable track record of success'.

Financial information

Year end	31/12/2020
Income	£972,600
Assets	£61,900
Grants to organisations	£963,800
No. of grants	24

Further financial information

During the year, the foundation awarded 24 grants to organisations, of which 21 were based in the UK.

Beneficiaries included: Action Tutoring and London Music Masters (£60,000 each); Westminster City School (£46,300); ReachOut (£35,000); Debate Mate, Kiln Theatre and The Children's Literacy Charity (£30,000 each); London Youth Rowing (£27,500).

Exclusions

Scholarship programmes are not eligible for funding.

Applications

For current information on the foundation's application process, see its website. Note that in 2021, the foundation did not accept new applications from charities that were not already being funded.

Sources of information

Accounts; annual report; Charity Commission record; funder's website.

The Welsh Church Act Fund

General charitable purposes; education; social welfare; health; arts, culture and heritage; social and recreational; medical and social research; probation; older people; blind people; places of worship; emergency and disaster relief

Rhondda Cynon Taff, Bridgend and Merthyr Tydfil county borough councils

£341,500 (2020/21)

CC number: 506658

Correspondent: Chris Bradshaw, Chief Executive, c/o Rhondda Cynon Taff County Borough Council, Council Offices, Bronwydd, Porth, Rhondda Cynon Taf CF39 9DL (tel: 01443 680734; email: treasurymanagement@rctcbc.gov.uk)

Trustees: Christopher Lee; Rhondda Cynon Taff County Borough Council.

General information

The history of the fund is described in its 2020/21 annual report and accounts as follows:

> Lloyd George, under the provisions of the 1914 and 1919 Welsh Churches Acts, established the Welsh Church Act Fund. These two acts transferred certain categories of secularised property to a Welsh Church Act Fund to be administered by the County Councils. However, these funds were not activated until 1942–47, when property to the value of almost £2.5m was handed over to the County Councils. The Welsh Churches Acts state that income of the funds should be devoted to charitable or alms giving purposes and that each Council is required to prepare a scheme for the use of the fund.

This fund was established in 1976 to make grants for projects in the areas of Bridgend, Merthyr Tydfil and Rhondda Cynon Taff. Applications may be considered from organisations based outside the beneficial area providing the work has a local significance (to the beneficial area).

As stated in the 2020/21 annual report and accounts, the charitable purposes to which the fund may be applied are:

- Education
- Social welfare
- Libraries, museums, art galleries
- Social and recreation projects
- Protection of historical buildings and heritage
- Medical and social research and treatment
- Probation
- Blind people
- Older people
- Places of worship and burial grounds
- Emergencies or disasters
- Other general charitable purposes

According to the 2020/21 annual report, grant limits during the year were as follows:

> Grants under £2,000 did not require match funding, grants exceeding £2,000 required a minimum of 10% match funding and grants exceeding £10,000 required a minimum of 20% match funding from non-Welsh Church Fund sources. Maximum grant available was £50,000.

Financial information

Year end	31/03/2021
Income	£408,000
Assets	£13,530,000
Grants to organisations	£341,500
No. of grants	23

Beneficiaries included: Cynon Valle Museum Trust and Pontypridd YMCA (£50,000 each); Cory Band (£35,500); Pete's Shop Ltd (£8,100); Ramoth Christian Centre (£3,200).

Exclusions

The following are not supported:

- Students
- Individuals
- Clubs with a liquor licence
- Projects operating outside the area of benefit
- Structural work without a professional assessment
- Day-to-day running expenses

Applications

Apply in writing to the correspondent, submitting your application together with estimates, accounts and constitutions. The 2020/21 annual report states:

> When projects are fully developed and ready for a decision, recommendations are made by officers via a Grant Assessment Report. Decisions to accept or reject these recommendations are made by the Regeneration Manager in consultation with the Cabinet Member and following consultation with Bridgend and Merthyr Tydfil County Borough Councils.

Sources of information

Accounts; annual report; Charity Commission record.

West Herts Charity Trust Ltd

Donations of vehicles and minibuses

Hertfordshire

£391,300 (2020/21)

CC number: 278891

Correspondent: Mike Humphreys, Ver House, Park Industrial Estate, Frogmore, St Albans, Hertfordshire AL2 2WH (email: info@whct.org.uk)

Trustees: Paul Miller; Michael Humphreys; Peter Miller; Mr R. D. Minashi; Matthew Humphreys.

 www.whct.org.uk

 facebook.com/West-Herts-Charity-Trust-155771234929924

 @whctrust

General information

The trust was originally called The West Herts Transport Training Ltd and provided management and driving training in South East England. In 2006 the training side of the business was sold but the offices were kept and leased out to companies. The name was changed to West Herts Charity Trust Ltd and its aim became to provide vehicles and minibuses to schools, uniformed groups, hospices, charities and other local organisations in need.

The trust's website states:

> To date, we have provided more than one hundred vehicles and minibuses – many of which with wheelchair access – to local charities and organisations [...] The value of our contributions over the last ten years has been well over £2 million.

Financial information

Year end	31/07/2021
Income	£281,400
Assets	£3,510,000
Grants to organisations	£391,300

Further financial information

Expenditure on the purchase and modification of vehicles during the year totalled £391,300.

Beneficiaries included: A list of beneficiaries was not available. Previous beneficiaries include: Abbotts Langley Primary School; Batchworth Sea Scouts; Brockswood Primary and Nursery School.

Applications

Application forms can be downloaded from the charity's website. Completed forms should be returned by email.

Sources of information

Accounts; annual report; Charity Commission record; funder's website.

The Westfield Health Charitable Trust

Health

 UK

£124,100 (2020/21)

CC number: 246057

Correspondent: The Trustees, Westfield House, 60 Charter Row, Sheffield, South Yorkshire S1 3FZ (tel: 0114 250 2079; email: charity@westfieldhealth.com)

Trustees: Graham Moore; David Whitney; Lynn Clarke.

 www.westfieldhealth.com/charitable-trust

General information

This trust was previously known as The Sheffield and District Hospital Services Charitable Fund. The trust receives its income from Westfield Health, a not-for-profit organisation providing well-being and healthcare services.

The following was taken from the trust's website:

> As a not for profit company, we've always believed in giving something back to the communities we work in. And with the NHS facing increasing pressures and charitable donations more essential than ever, our support can be invaluable.
>
> Since 1996, we've donated more than £15 million to the NHS and health and wellbeing related charities, helping to keep thousands of people at their healthy best.
>
> We donate to both large national and smaller, local charities, helping out wherever we can and working harder to nurture the health and wellbeing of communities across the UK.
>
> **Application criteria**
>
> As long as your charity meets our criteria (A medical, NHS related or health and wellbeing focussed charity registered with the charities commission for England and Wales, the Charity Commission for Northern Ireland, the OSCR in Scotland or the Association of Jersey Charities) then you would be eligible for consideration.

Financial information

Year end	05/04/2021
Income	£450,500
Assets	£512,000
Grants to organisations	£124,100

Further financial information

The trust awarded grants totalling £124,100 during the year; however, in previous years its expenditure exceeded £300,000.

Beneficiaries included: The Children's Hospital Charity (£50,000); High Peak Hospice Care (£32,300); Wellness Medical (£3,700); Care in Crosspool (£1,000); Ruby's Fund (£500); Sheffield Churches Council (£100).

Applications

Apply in writing to charity@westfieldhealth.com. Applications should include a covering letter detailing the specifics of what you are applying for, any supporting information and a breakdown of costs. There are no deadlines – applications are considered throughout the year.

Sources of information

Accounts; annual report; Charity Commission record; funder's website.

The Mohn Westlake Foundation

Young people; education; recreation and leisure; the arts and science; research; general charitable purposes

 England and Wales

£18.33 million (2020)

CC number: 1170045

Correspondent: Chris Thurlow, c/o Ludlow Trust Co. Ltd, Centric House, 390–391 Strand, London WC2R 0LT (tel: 020 4534 2750; email: chris.thurlow@ludlowtrust.com)

Trustees: Marit Mohn; Robert Westlake; Stian Westlake; Diana Tresurer.

 www.themohnwestlakefoundation.co.uk

General information

The foundation was established in 2016 by Marit Mohn and her son Stian Westlake following the sale of their share in the family company. The foundation aims to make a difference in young people's lives by giving them opportunities they would not otherwise have had, through education, performing arts or other activities. It also wishes to advance data transparency, increase access to impartial information and promote the public good through the collection and analysis of useful data by working with charities or approved agencies pioneering in this space.

The foundation supports the development of young people by providing resources and facilities to charities which are not normally provided by statutory bodies, including facilities for recreation and leisure activities, particularly in the fields of the arts and science.

Financial information

Year end	31/12/2020
Income	£10,320,000
Assets	£10,830,000
Grants to organisations	£18,330,000
No. of grants	18

Further financial information

During the year, 18 grants were awarded to 16 organisations.

Beneficiaries included: Reach Foundation (two grants totalling £5.16 million); Royal National Theatre (two grants totalling £2.5 million); Kingston University (£1.03 million); Open Data Institute Leeds (£423,600); Community Foundation for Surrey (£200,000); Murston All Saints Trust (£100,000); The Young Foundation (£45,000).

Exclusions

The foundation does not support:

- Individuals
- Charities or projects based outside the UK
- Animal welfare charities
- Faith charities and places of worship
- Campaigning and lobbying work

Applications

Registered charities should send a written application to the correspondent by email or post, clearly marked 'The Mohn Westlake Foundation'.

Applications should include:

- Purpose of the funding
- Evidence of need
- Outcomes
- Amount of grant sought
- Set of latest accounts

The foundation's website states:

> Please note that although unsolicited applications will be accepted, our intention is that most funding will be allocated through specific call-outs. Where appropriate, this site will carry details of this.

Sources of information

Accounts; annual report; Charity Commission record; funder's website.

Westminster Amalgamated Charity

The prevention and relief of poverty

City of Westminster

£7.2 million (2020)

CC number: 207964

Correspondent: Julia Moorcroft, School House, Drury Lane, London WC2B 5SU (tel: 020 7395 9460; email: wac@3chars.org.uk)

Trustees: Jenny Bianco; Paul Gardner; Jean Rymer; Linda McHugh; Graham Mordue; Simon Carruth; David Cavaye; Kate Bowyer; Matthew Keane; Toby Jameson-Till; Geraldine Elliott.

 www.w-a-c.org.uk

General information

The Westminster Amalgamated Charity was registered with the Charity Commission in 1961. According to its website:

> The aim of the Charity today is to continue the activity common to all the predecessor charities, namely the relief of need in Westminster by way of Grants, both for individuals and for organisations.
>
> The Charity tries to help all those in need in Westminster, providing the eligibility criteria have been met. Grants are awarded on a one-off basis at Trustees' discretion and beneficiaries should not expect to receive continuous or year-on-year funding.
>
> The Trustees are keen that organisations should, where relevant, demonstrate the active promotion of the learning of English and integration into British culture.

Financial information

Year end	31/12/2020
Income	£0
Grants to organisations	£7,200,000

Further financial information

Full accounts were not available to view on the Charity Commission's website due to the charity's low income. We have therefore estimated the charity's grant total based on its total expenditure.

Beneficiaries included: A list of beneficiaries was not available.

Exclusions

According to the charity's website, the following exclusions apply:

> Applications from organisations that are running a commercial business as their primary objective, but also have charitable status, will not be considered. Such organisations are likely to include theatres, art galleries and museums aimed at the paying public. In addition, applications from institutions of higher education will not be considered.

If in doubt, contact the grants administrator before making an application. A contact form is available on the website.

Applications

Application forms can be completed on the charity's website. Applications received by email or post will not be considered.

The charity's website explains:

> The application form should be completed by the referring agency. This must be a recognised agency such as Social Services, Citizens Advice Bureau, Housing Association, Hostel, or any registered charity working in Westminster.

See the charity's website for up-to-date details of application deadlines.

Sources of information

Accounts; Charity Commission record; funder's website.

Westminster Foundation

General charitable purposes, with a focus on children, young people and families

Westminster (parts of the old metropolitan borough of Westminster); Cheshire West and Cheshire; the north-west of rural Lancashire (near the Forest of Bowland); the north-west of Sutherland

£13.27 million (2020)

CC number: 267618

Correspondent: Oliver Woodford, Grants Manager, The Grosvenor Office, 70 Grosvenor Street, London W1K 3JP (tel: 020 7408 0988; email: westminster.foundation@grosvenor.com)

Trustees: James Hanbury; Mark Preston; Victoria Hornby; The Duke of Westminster.

 www.westminsterfoundation.org.uk

 @WestminsterFdn

General information

The foundation was established in 1974 for general charitable purposes by the fifth Duke of Westminster. In 1987 the Grosvenor Foundation, a separately registered charity, transferred all its assets to the Westminster Foundation. The foundation continues to receive regular donations from Grosvenor Group Ltd and supports a wide range of charities through its grant-making, with a focus on young people in the areas in which the group operates.

The following information is taken from the foundation's website:

> **What we fund**
>
> The Westminster Foundation works with local organisations who create opportunities for young people up to the age of 25, so that they and their families have the resilience, skills and capacity to lead happy and healthy lives. Our priority is to award grants that benefit young people facing deprivation or intergenerational equality.
>
> - Charities registered with the Charity Commission or organisations with exclusively charitable objectives
> - Community organisations (e.g. schools, colleges and youth hubs) who understand the local need and have the capacity to support their young people over time
> - Charities based in Westminster, Chester, Rural Cheshire, Rural Lancashire or Rural Sutherland
> - Initiatives making early positive interventional change
> - Both core cost and project specific
>
> **Funding**
>
> We have three grant giving programmes:
>
> **Small Grant Programme**
>
> One-off Small Grants are available up to the value of £10,000, for registered charities (or organisations with exclusively charitable objectives) working in Chester, Westminster, and rural communities within Lancashire and Sutherland, where the Grosvenor Estate operates.
>
> **Charity Office Space**
>
> We offer subsidised charity office accommodation in central London. The offices are provided by the Grosvenor Group for around 20 charities.
>
> **Partnership Grant Programme**
>
> The Westminster Foundation's primary grant giving programme awards grants on

a proactive basis. Proposals are invited by the Trustees where they feel our funding can make the most impact. Partnership Grants are typically awarded for five years at £100,000 per annum.

Financial information

Year end	31/12/2020
Income	£13,420,000
Assets	£121,800,000
Grants to organisations	£13,270,000
No. of grants	249

Further financial information

Grants paid during the year totalled £13.27 million. The grant total was higher than usual as £9.4 million was awarded from a COVID-19 response fund, set up in March 2020. Over 150 short-term grants were awarded through this fund. COVID-19 response grants of £50,000 and above are listed in the 2020 accounts.

During the year, the foundation's small grants criteria were adapted in response to the COVID-19 pandemic – the upper grant limit was increased from £10,000 to £20,000 per year. Small grants totalled £373,200 during the year (45 grants).

Beneficiaries included: NHS Charities Together (£5 million); One Small Thing (£500,000); The Country Trust (£200,000); Young Minds (£160,000); Future Men (£100,000); Veterans Aid (£68,800); Turn2Us (£50,000); Cheshire Community Foundation (£20,000).

Exclusions

The following information has been taken from the foundation's website:

Unfortunately we don't fund:

- Requests for individuals or projects benefiting only one school; including student fees and bursaries
- Holidays or trips including respite programmes
- Projects that are overtly political or religious
- Gifts and prizes for events and auctions
- Organisations that have applied to us unsuccessfully within the previous 12 months
- Capital costs in isolation
- Specific medical conditions and medical research

Applications

Applications for small grants can be made online and there are no deadlines. Charities can also join the waiting list for office space online. Partnership grants are by invitation only.

Sources of information

Accounts; annual report; Charity Commission record; funder's website.

The Galen and Hilary Weston Foundation

Medical research, specifically research into treatment for neurodegenerative diseases

UK; Netherlands; Republic of Ireland

£1.87 million (2020)

CC number: 1167260

Correspondent: The Trustees, Selfridges Group, Nations House, 103 Wigmore Street, London W1U 1QS (tel: 020 7318 2318)

Trustees: Anthony Edwards; Alannah Cochrane; Paul Kelly; Adam Batty; Alexandria Forbes.

General information

The Galen and Hilary Weston Foundation (previously known as The Selfridges Group Foundation) was created to support research into treatment for neurodegenerative diseases such as Alzheimer's and Parkinson's. The foundation works with the Weston Brain Institute and its scientific advisory board to select research projects in the UK, the Netherlands and the Republic of Ireland, and specifically focusses on discovering new biomarkers that will help to diagnose neurodegenerative diseases in their early stages.

In 2020, additional grants were awarded to charities in the areas of benefit in support of COVID-19 response and recovery. These grants were aimed at charities working with older people, people experiencing homelessness and people with mental health issues.

Financial information

Year end	31/12/2020
Income	£2,020,000
Assets	£895,800
Grants to organisations	£1,870,000
No. of grants	21

Further financial information

During the year, grants made to 9 registered charities totalled £1.37 million, and grants to 12 other organisations (mainly universities) for medical research totalled £504,600.

Beneficiaries included: Centrepoint and Mental Health Innovations (£300,000 each); The Alzheimer Society of Ireland (£100,000); Age Action Ireland (£75,000); University of Oxford (£73,900); Rare Dementia Support Centre (£50,000); Swansea University (£10,000).

Exclusions

The foundation does not support the promotion of any religion.

Applications

Applications for research project funding can be made via the Weston Brain Institute: https://westonfoundation.ca/weston-brain-institute. Open funding calls are advertised here.

Sources of information

Accounts; annual report; Charity Commission record; Weston Family Foundation (website).

The Garfield Weston Foundation

Social welfare; young people; community; the arts; faith; the environment; education; health; museums and heritage

UK

£98.3 million (2020/21)

CC number: 230260

Correspondent: The Trustees, Weston Centre, 10 Grosvenor Street, London W1K 4QY (tel: 020 7399 6565; email: admin@garfieldweston.org)

Trustees: Kate Hobhouse; Sophia Weston; George Weston; Eliza Mitchell; Guy Weston; Jana Khayat; Melissa Murdoch; Georgie Dalglish; Alannah Weston.

www.garfieldweston.org

@GarfieldWFdn

General information

The Garfield Weston Foundation was established in 1958 by Willard Garfield Weston, a Canadian businessman who moved to the UK with his family in 1932. He was the creator of Associated British Foods and the foundation was endowed with the donation of family-owned company shares.

The foundation provides support in the following areas:

- The arts
- Community
- Education
- The environment
- Faith
- Health
- Museums and heritage
- Welfare
- Youth

There are two types of grant administered by the foundation: regular grants (up to £100,000) and major grants (over £100,000). Grants are made in one of three areas: capital projects, revenue/core costs and project costs/specific activities. Specific details can be found in the foundation's application guidelines, available from its website.

The Weston Culture Fund was increased to over £30 million due to the level of need caused by COVID-19. Grants ranging from £100,000 to £1.5 million (based on the size of the organisation) have been awarded to over 100 cultural organisations across the UK. This fund supports a diverse range of organisations from national touring ballet companies to museums and regional theatres.

Financial information

Year end	05/04/2021
Income	£83,960,000
Assets	£97,970,000
Grants to organisations	£98,320,000

Further financial information

During the year, 2,129 grants were awarded as follows:

Arts	254	£32 million
Welfare	420	£19 million
Health	164	£8 million
Youth	264	£7.3 million
Museums and heritage	68	£7.1 million
Environment	116	£7 million
Education	123	£6.5 million
Community	355	£6.4 million
Faith	367	£3 million
Other	7	£400,000

Beneficiaries included: SASC Trust (£5 million); National Theatre (£1.5 million); Industry, Manchester (£1 million); Philharmonic Society (£750,000); Birmingham Royal Ballet (£600,000); The Young Vic (£200,000); NK Theatre Arts (£25,000); The Hepworth Brass Band (£3,000).

Exclusions

The regular and major grant programmes are unable to support:

- Individuals
- CICs
- Social enterprises without UK Charity Commission registration
- Sporting associations that are not registered charities
- Work that does not deliver a direct benefit in the UK, even if the organisation is a UK-registered charity
- Animal welfare charities
- Charities that spend the majority of their income outside the UK
- Local authorities and councils

See the foundation's website for a list of activities that will not be supported.

Applications

Apply via the foundation's website.

Sources of information

Accounts; annual report; Charity Commission record; funder's website.

Westway Trust

Community development and enterprise; young people; arts, culture and heritage; the environment; well-being; sport

The Royal Borough of Kensington and Chelsea, with a particular focus on North Kensington, in and around the Westway

£502,100 (2020/21)

CC number: 1123127

Correspondent: The Trustees, 1 Thorpe Close, London W10 5XL (tel: 020 8962 5720; email: info@westway.org)

Trustees: Dr Marwan Elnaghi; Thomas Fitch; Tobias Belson; Huey Walker; Eve Wedderburn; Sheraine Williams; Marie-Therese Rossi; Alexander Korda; Jonathan Kelly; Minal Patel.

 www.westway.org

 facebook.com/WestwayTrust

 @WestwayTrust

 @westway_trust

General information

The trust (previously known as Westway Development Trust) was established in 1971 when the A40 Westway Flyover was built, leaving 23 acres of derelict land. The trust manages and regenerates the land on behalf of the local community. According to its website, 'funding local residents, groups and projects through grants or investments is how Westway Trust makes a big difference to North Kensington'.

At the time of writing (May 2022), the trust had six priority areas:

1 Isolation
2 Spaces for young people
3 Recreation and exercise
4 Economic participation
5 Arts and culture
6 The environment

At the time of writing, the trust was reviewing its grant-making process; check the trust's website for updated information on its grant programmes.

Community investments and grants

The only funding available at the time of writing (May 2022) was the Emergency Response Fund, which offers emergency grants to organisations and individuals with a clear need, on a discretionary basis.

Financial information

Year end	31/03/2021
Income	£5,980,000
Assets	£62,720,000
Grants to organisations	£502,100

Further financial information

In 2020/21, grants were broken down as follows:

Small grants to local charities and community groups	£259,300
Adult and community learning	£71,200
Festival funds	£52,900
Artists' professional development, training and commissions	£49,200
COVID-19 support	£37,000
Capacity strengthening	£22,500
Rent subsidies to charity tenants	£6,900
Grenfell response	£3,100

Beneficiaries included: Migrants Organise (£31,100); An Nisa Empowerment Response (£25,500); Bike Works CIC (£10,300); Baraka Youth Association (£7,700); Dadihiye Somali Organisation (£6,600); The Bevington Trust (£5,000); Notting Hill Therapy Clinic (£2,500); Tendercare Nurseries Ltd (£160); Tudor Environmental (UK) Ltd (£30).

Exclusions

Refer to the trust's website for exclusions of specific grant programmes.

Applications

When grant programmes open, a link to an online application portal is made available on the trust's website. Applicants will need to create an account and log in to make an application. Guidelines are also made available for each open funding programme.

Sources of information

Accounts; annual report; Charity Commission record; funder's website.

The Melanie White Foundation Ltd

Areas of interest to the trustees (including health, medicine and social welfare)

 Mainly UK

£305,300 (2020/21)

CC number: 1077150

Correspondent: The Trustees, 61 Grosvenor Street, London W1K 3JE (tel: 020 3011 1100; email: melaniewhitefoundation@gmail.com)

Trustees: Melanie White; Andrew White; Adrian de la Touche.

General information

The Melanie White Foundation Ltd was registered with the Charity Commission in 1999. According to its Charity Commission record, the principal activity of the foundation is its grant-making programme, through which the trustees support charitable causes in areas of particular interest to them. These areas include health, medicine and social welfare.

Financial information

Year end	05/04/2021
Income	£2,660,000
Assets	£13,150,000
Grants to organisations	£305,300

Beneficiaries included: Dr Meyer Rassin Foundation (£205,000); Waves for Inclusion (£26,500); Alfred Dunhill Foundation (£20,000); Lend a Hand Bahamas (£15,700); Saints Foundation (£12,500); Windsor Academy – Nassau (£6,300).

Applications

The foundation do not accept unsolicited donations as the trustees proactively identify beneficiaries themselves.

Sources of information

Accounts; annual report; Charity Commission record.

Charity of Sir Richard Whittington

General charitable purposes; young people and education; older people and housing; churches and communities

UK, particularly London and disadvantaged areas of the east and north-east of England

£3.61 million (2020/21)

CC number: 1087167

Correspondent: The Trustees, c/o The Mercers' Company, 6 Frederick's Place, London EC2R 8AB (tel: 020 7776 7250; email: grants@mercers.co.uk)

Trustee: The Mercers' Company.

www.mercers.co.uk/philanthropy

General information

The Charity of Sir Richard Whittington was founded in 1424 under the will of Richard Whittington, who was Mayor of London four times and Master of the Mercers' Company three times. The Charity is the amalgamation of both The Charity of Sir Richard Whittington and Lady Mico's Almshouse Charity and is regulated by a Scheme of the Charity Commission dated April 2001.

The charity makes grants through three programmes (the following information has been taken from the charity's website).

Older people and housing

This programme funds not-for-profit community-led organisations operating in London and Norfolk that:

- Combat loneliness in older people
  - Working in areas with a high risk of chronic loneliness
  - Providing opportunities for older adults to foster new connections
  - Providing opportunities to support and maintain existing relationships
- Provide housing solutions
  - Providing innovative ideas for older people's future housing
  - Tackling the issues faced by older private renters
  - Enabling older people to live well in their own home

Preference is given to organisations working with older people who are at high risk of chronic loneliness, defined by the charity as 'black or ethnic minoritised communities, LGBTQ+ communities, people living with long-term conditions, and informal carers', as stated on its website.

Grants range from £50,000 to £100,000 for up to three years. At the time of writing (May 2022) this programme was paused for applications and aimed to reopen in autumn 2022.

Church and communities

This programme funds churches, as well as other faith and secular community-based organisations that strengthen communities and families. It focuses on organisations that build better outcomes for families, particularly those facing poverty or hardship, or which support carers or people who are experiencing homelessness, including refugees. Grants range from £10,000 to £100,000 for up to three years.

The charity will consider applications for funding in the areas where The Mercers' Company has links through its patronage of Church Livings and other historic associations. These areas are:

- London
- The North East (County Durham, Tyne and Wear, Northumberland and Tees Valley)
- Norfolk
- Lincolnshire

Young people and education

This programme aims to support the education and progress of children up to the age of 18 in London to help them:

- Get a good start in life
- Feel supported through challenging transitions in their lives
- Work towards good mental health

This programme is not open to general applications. The charity works with selected partners to help deliver mental health, well-being and leadership schemes in schools, as well as special initiatives that support disadvantaged children with literacy, early years education and successful transition from secondary school to work, training or further education. The charity also works closely with its associated schools to improve the quality of teaching and implement the schemes described above.

Financial information

Year end	31/03/2021
Income	£3,880,000
Assets	£123,490,000
Grants to organisations	£3,610,000

Further financial information

In 2020/21, grants awarded to organisations were broken down as follows:

Older people and housing	£1.12 million
Young people and education	£919,500
Church and communities	£907,600
COVID-19 Rapid Response Fund	£258,700

In addition, under the young people and education programme, the charity made 162 donations to individuals totalling £196,500.

Beneficiaries included: Thomas Telford School (£160,000); National Children's Bureau (£112,500); The Scout Association (£80,800); Redbridge Carers Support Service (£48,700); West Ham United Foundation (£25,000); Manna Society (£10,000); Doorstep Library Network (£5,000); Southwark Pensioners Centres (£1,700).

Applications

All information (including guidelines and notes on exclusions) is available on the charity's website. Note that only applications using the application form on the charity's website are accepted.

Sources of information

Accounts; annual review; Charity Commission record; funder's website; further information provided by the funder.

The Wigoder Family Foundation

General charitable purposes and Jewish causes

England and Wales

£490,500 (2019/20)

CC number: 1086806

Correspondent: The Trustees, c/o Network HQ, 508 Edgware Road, The Hyde, Colindale, London NW9 5AB (tel: 020 8955 5000)

Trustees: Elizabeth Wigoder; Charles Wigoder; Martin Rose.

General information

The Wigoder Family Foundation was established in 2000 by Charles Wigoder, a telecommunications entrepreneur, and his wife Elizabeth to support general charitable purposes throughout England and Wales.

The foundation does not specify any particular aims or objectives in its Charity Commission record or annual report but its beneficiaries have included charities that support Jewish causes.

Financial information

Year end	30/11/2020
Income	£7,280,000
Assets	£63,080,000
Grants to organisations	£490,500

Further financial information

Only beneficiaries of grants of £5,000 and above were listed in the accounts. Grants of under £5,000 totalled £84,800.

Beneficiaries included: Kitov (£75,000); Jewish Learning Exchange (£30,000); Prince's Trust Fellowship Institute (£25,000); Jewish Care (£15,000); Henry Jackson Society and The Chicken Soup Shelter (£10,000 each); Chai Cancer Care (£6,000); Noah's Ark – The Children's Hospice (£5,000).

Applications

Apply in writing to the correspondent. According to the foundation's 2019/20 annual report, 'The Trustees meet as many times as deemed appropriate but not less than twice a year to discuss grants, based on applications received throughout the year.'

Sources of information

Accounts; annual report; Charity Commission record.

The Will Charitable Trust

Blindness; cancer; learning disabilities

UK

£921,000 (2020/21)

CC number: 801682

Correspondent: The Grants Administrator, Bridge House, 11 Creek Road, East Molesey KT8 9BE (tel: 020 8941 0450; email: admin@willcharitabletrust.org.uk)

Trustees: Rodney Luff; Alastair McDonald; Vanessa Reburn; Joanna Dyson.

 http://willcharitabletrust.org.uk

General information

Established in 1990, the trust supports UK registered or exempt charities whose activities fall within the following three categories:

- **People who are blind** – the care of and services for people who are blind and the prevention and/or cure of blindness
- **People with learning disabilities** – the long-term care of people with learning disabilities either in a residential care or supported living environment, especially those that provide a family environment and a wide choice of activities and lifestyle or by providing long-term day/employment activities
- **People with cancer** – care of and services for people with cancer and their families

Other categories may be supported but this is rare and reserved for causes that have come to the attention of individual trustees. Unsolicited applications for causes outside the three areas listed above are unlikely to be considered.

Larger exceptional grants are occasionally considered but this is unusual and generally confined to charities that are well known by the trustees. There is no separate application process for this and applicants will be identified from the normal grant round.

Grants are exclusive to UK registered or exempt charities. They must have proven track records of successful work in their field of operation or, in the case of newer charities, convincing evidence of ability. Charities of all sizes are considered and grants vary in amount accordingly. Grants generally fall within the range of £3,000 to £30,000 and are typically made on a one-off annual basis, although successful grantees are encouraged to apply in the next and subsequent years.

Financial information

Year end	05/04/2021
Income	£559,100
Assets	£21,157,856
Grants to organisations	£921,000
No. of grants	98

Further financial information

During 2020/21, grants were distributed as follows:

Cancer	40	£380,000
Learning disabilities	29	£281,000
Blindness	28	£255,000
Disability	1	£5,000

Beneficiaries included: Minstead Trust (£25,000); Deafblind Scotland and Wessex Cancer Trust (£20,000 each); British Blind Sport, Prince of Wales Hospice and Watford Mencap (£10,000 each); Ayrshire Cancer Support (£5,000).

Exclusions

The trust's website states that support will not be given for:

- Organisations that are not registered charities (or properly exempt)
- General appeals or letters/mail-shots requesting donations (you must follow our guidelines)
- Individuals, or charities applying on their behalf
- Grant-making organisations seeking funding for the purpose of awarding grants to others
- Applications for less than £3,000
- Charities with a turnover of less than £50,000
- Charities with liquid (free) reserves covering more than 18 months' expenditure unless they can clearly demonstrate that they are in financial need
- Charities that do not yet have a track record of service delivery (or other convincing evidence of ability)
- Ongoing running (including salaries) and core costs, ongoing projects or services (although they will support an extension to existing provision if additional cost is incurred), unless there is an exceptional reason to do so and if you think this is the case you should telephone the Grants Office to discuss before applying
- Projects which benefit people outside the UK, *except* in the blind field
- Projects which are complete (i.e. retrospective funding)
- Minibuses
- Academic research projects
- Campaigning or lobbying projects
- Work usually considered a statutory responsibility
- Items of equipment intended for use by the NHS

Applications

Applications should be made in writing to the correspondent and sent by post – emailed applications will not be accepted. Guidance on what to include in the application is given on the website, along with more detailed eligibility criteria. There are separate deadlines for each area of focus. Visit the website for current deadlines.

Sources of information

Accounts; annual report; Charity Commission record; funder's website.

The HDH Wills 1965 Charitable Trust

General charitable purposes, particularly wildlife conservation and the environment

UK (predominantly) and overseas

£1.17 million (2020/21)

CC number: 1117747

Correspondent: Sue Trafford, Trust Administrator, Henley Knapp Barn, Fulwell, Chipping Norton, Oxfordshire OX7 4EN (tel: 01608 678051; email: suetrafford@hdhwills.org or trust@hdhwills.org)

Trustees: John Carson; Charles Francklin; Martin Fiennes; Thomas Nelson; Dr Catherine Wills; Richard Tulloch.

 www.hdhwills.org

General information

The trust has been endowed by the family of Sir David Wills, from a fortune derived largely from the tobacco company of that name. The trust's website states that it makes grants to general, environmental and wildlife charities, so long as they are registered with the Charity Commission of England and Wales, OSCR or they are exempt or excepted charities.

The trust has two main grant schemes: monthly grants and large grants.

Monthly grants

The monthly grants programme has two strands, as explained on the trust's website:

> **General fund:** We seek to make donations to general charities which are small enough in size or are applying for support for a modest project such that the charity will benefit substantially from a donation of between £250 and £500. We also make grants to charities, which focus on the conservation of wildlife and the environment which are typically between £1,000 to £2,000.
>
> **The Martin Wills Wildlife Maintenance Trust:** The focus of our support is the conservation and maintenance for the benefit of the public of the natural environment and its indigenous woodland flora and fauna with particular reference to the conservation and maintenance of the character and amenity of rural areas. Grants are typically in the £1,000 to £2,000 range, though sometimes up to £5,000. Grants are made only to charities, which focus on the conservation of wildlife and the environment.

In both cases, grants are made towards revenue, capital or project expenditure and funding decisions are made on a monthly basis.

Large grants

According to the trust's website:

> These are made by the trust in a fixed seven-year cycle. In only two years of that cycle are grants made in response to applications from external charities, and then only to charities for wildlife and environmental causes, typically in the £5,000 to £50,000 range. The most recent open years were 2016 and 2017. The next time applications for Large Grants for wildlife and the environment will be accepted are from January 2023 through to December 2024.

The trust also administers the Knockando Church Fund for the upkeep of Knockando Church in Morayshire.

Financial information

Year end	31/03/2021
Income	£3,130,000
Assets	£95,250,000
Grants to organisations	£1,170,000
No. of grants	118

Further financial information

In 2020/21, grants were distributed in the following categories: The Martin Wills Fund (£1.03 million); General Fund (£125,200); Knockando Church Fund (£7,500). Only beneficiaries of grants of £1,000 and above were listed in the trust's accounts. Grants of under £1,000 totalled £47,000 (95 grants).

Beneficiaries included: Magdalen College, Oxford (£1.03 million); 21st Century Trust (£17,500); Suffolk Horse Society (£2,500); St Luke's Hospital and Wigmore Hall Trust (£2,000 each); Oxfordshire Youth and The Garden Museum (£1,000 each).

Exclusions

Grants are not made to organisations that have been supported in the previous 24 months or to individuals.

Applications

Monthly grants can be applied for using an online form on the trust's website. Alternatively, applications can be made in writing and returned by post or email, attaching supporting documents. Details on what should be included are given on the trust's website. There is no deadline for applications.

When the large grants programme opens (January 2023 through to December 2024), applications can be made in the same way.

Sources of information

Accounts; annual report; Charity Commission record; funder's website.

Sumner Wilson Charitable Trust

General charitable purposes

UK

£206,100 (2020/21)

CC number: 1018852

Correspondent: The Trustees, Mercer and Hole, 72 London Road, St Albans AL1 1NS (tel: 01727 869141; email: sumnerwilsoncharity@gmail.com)

Trustees: Amanda Christie; Anne-Marie Challen; Davina Longsdon.

www.sumnerwilson.uk

General information

Sumner Wilson Charitable Trust was established by Mike Wilson in 1992. This trust has general charitable purposes and supports charities working in a wide range of areas. It supports UK-based charities working across the country and abroad. The trustees favour causes supported by the settlor.

Financial information

Year end	05/04/2021
Income	£98,700
Assets	£6,600,000
Grants to organisations	£206,100

Further financial information

During 2020/21 grants totalled £206,100; however, in previous years the trust has awarded grants totalling over £300,000.

Beneficiaries included: Macmillan Cancer Support (£55,000); Wheelpower and Young Gloucestershire (£10,000 each); Royal Academy Dramatic Art (£5,000); British Pilgrimage Trust (£3,000); Hands Up Foundation (£2,000); St James's Place Foundation (£250).

Applications

The trust does not accept unsolicited applications.

Sources of information

Accounts; annual report; Charity Commission record; funder's website.

The Wimbledon Foundation

Children and young people; sport; tennis; well-being; education; relief in need, including emergency relief; community development; overseas development

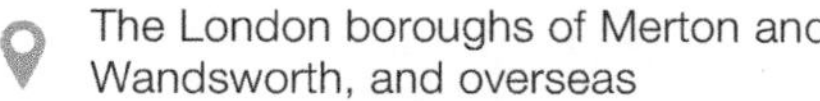

The London boroughs of Merton and Wandsworth, and overseas

£1.82 million (2019/20)

CC number: 1156996

Correspondent: Lauren Palmer, Grants and Community Officer, Church Road, Wimbledon, London SW19 5AE (tel: 020 8971 2702; email: foundation@aeltc.com)

Trustees: Ian Hewitt; Sir Nicholas Young; Sir Keith Ajegbo; Henry Weatherill; Nicholas Bitel; Kevin Havelock; Anne Bretherton.

www.wimbledon.com/en_GB/foundation/index.html

General information

The Wimbledon Foundation was established in 2013 and is the charity of The All England Lawn Tennis Club and The Championships. The aim of the Wimbledon Foundation is to help change people's lives using the resources and heritage of Wimbledon.

The foundation achieves its goals by delivering programmes and projects, providing grants and financial support, donating in-kind gifts, providing use of its facilities and working collaboratively with its partners. It has a particular focus on supporting: organisations in the London boroughs of Merton and Wandsworth; charities associated with or promoted by key groups involved in The Championships; and projects that use the power of sport (and particularly tennis) to provide opportunities to assist people, especially young people, with education and personal development.

As stated on its website, the main aims of the foundation are to:

- **Strengthen [the] local community** by tackling social disadvantage in Merton and Wandsworth
- **Promote healthy and active lives** by advancing good mental and physical health for all
- **Inspire the next generation** by creating opportunities for young people to learn valuable skills for life
- **Respond in times of need** by making a difference to those facing adversity.

According to its annual report for 2019/20, the foundation has a number of funds through which it distributes grants. For example:

The Wimbledon Foundation Community Fund: administered in conjunction with the London Community Foundation, the fund awards grants to projects helping to meet social needs and reduce inequalities in Merton and Wandsworth.

The Health and Well-being Fund: grants for up to three years for projects aimed at improving mental and physical health issues across Merton and Wandsworth.

The Get Set, Get Active Fund: grants of up to £2,500 for community groups and sports clubs working to encourage physical activity in Merton and Wandsworth.

The Roof for All Homelessness Fund: strengthening the organisational capacity of homelessness charities through investment in strategic personnel and digital systems.

Arts and Community Engagement Fund: designed to support creative projects that engage the local community, particularly disadvantaged groups that might not ordinarily access the arts.

Check the foundation's website for open funding rounds.

The foundation also commits to a small number of partnerships with charities working overseas, such as WaterAid and Magic Bus.

Financial information

Year end	31/07/2020
Income	£2,090,000
Assets	£1,770,000
Grants to organisations	£1,820,000

Further financial information

Grants were distributed through a number of funds and programmes including:

Coronavirus Fund	£495,000
The Championships and Club-related grants	£255,000
Health and Well-being Fund	£200,000
Strengthening Our Local Community	£122,000
Emergency Relief Fund	£100,000
The Roof for All Homelessness Fund	£77,000
Get Set, Get Active Fund	£63,000
Wimbledon Foundation Community Fund	£62,000
Arts and Community Engagement Fund	£15,000

The remaining grants were awarded to individual organisations.

Beneficiaries included: WaterAid (£225,000); Youth Sport Trust (£117,000); Magic Bus (£90,000); Place2Be (£77,000); The Prince's Trust (£50,000).

Applications

Details of open funding rounds and application procedures are made available on the foundation's website as they arise.

Sources of information

Accounts; annual report; Charity Commission record; funder's website.

The Wingate Foundation

Jewish life and learning; performing arts; music; education; social exclusion; medical research travel grants

UK and overseas

£442,000 (2020/21)

CC number: 264114

Correspondent: The Administrator, Somerset House, South Wing, Strand, London WC2R 1LA (tel: 020 3701 7479; email: admin@wingate.org.uk)

Trustees: Prof. Robert Cassen; Jonathan Drori; Daphne Hyman; Emily Kasriel; Dr Richard Wingate; Roger Wingate; Barbara Arnold; Melanie Morris.

 www.wingatefoundation.org.uk

General information

The foundation was established in 1960 for Jewish causes and other charitable purposes. Its objectives are to support the arts and education projects, and to establish and endow scholarships, fellowships, professional chairs, prizes and awards.

Grant programmes

Grants are made to small registered charities. To be eligible for funding, an organisation's work must fall under one of the following categories, as stated on the website:

- **Jewish life and learning:** applications are accepted from organisations that promote Jewish culture and learning, including museums, libraries, literary publications and academic institutions. According to its website, the foundation is particularly keen to support organisations 'with a demonstrable track-record in effective inter-faith engagement, in the promotion of mutual understanding and reconciliation between Jews in Israel and their Arab neighbours, and the encouragement of liberal values in both communities'
- **Performing arts:** grants are made to charities with a 'record of artistic excellence' to broaden their repertoire or help to develop work of 'potentially outstanding interest'. Applications for training and professional development for creative talent or technical professions will also be considered. Additionally, the trustees are particularly interested in funding projects that place an emphasis on addressing educational or social exclusion outcomes
- **Music:** under this grants scheme, priority is given to organisations that give opportunities to young professional musicians and to education projects for young people as well as for new adult audiences. This would include direct assistance to individuals as well as funding for organisations that promote their work or performance or provide support for master classes
- **Medical research travel grants:** individuals wanting to learn new clinical or laboratory techniques are eligible for medical research travel grants. Funding of up to £1,000 is awarded towards travel and subsistence costs

The foundation also administers a number of literary prizes – see the website for details.

Financial information

Year end	05/04/2021
Income	£44,900
Assets	£6,330,000
Grants to organisations	£442,000

Further financial information

During 2020/21, grants were distributed as follows:

Performing arts	38%
Jewish life and learning	27%
Music	21%
Education and social exclusion	6%
Literary prizes	5%
Development projects	2%
Medical research including travel grants	1%

Beneficiaries included: The Karuna Trust (£20,000); World ORT Trust (£17,0000); Cardboard Citizens (£10,000); Music in Detention (£5,000); Finding Rhythms (£3,000); Little Angel Theatre (£2,500); Llandudno Museum (£1,500); Cardiff University (£1,000).

Exclusions

The foundation will not award funding for gap years, the Duke of Edinburgh Award or Operation Raleigh. Grants for stage productions are not available under performing arts funding. Travel to congresses and symposia are not supported under medical research funding. Large charities who are well represented, or local branches of large organisations, are not eligible.

Applications

Application forms are available to download on the foundation's website. Once completed, forms should be returned to the correspondent by email only. Applications should include supporting documentation and the applicant's most recent accounts. The trustees usually meet quarterly to consider grant applications. Details of upcoming meetings can be found on the website.

Sources of information

Accounts; annual report; Charity Commission record; funder's website.

The Francis Winham Foundation

 Welfare of older people

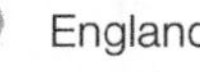 England

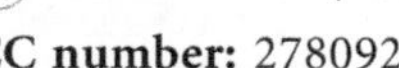 £3.96 million (2020/21)

CC number: 278092

Correspondent: The Trustees, 18 Gilston Road, London SW10 9SR (tel: 020 7795 1261; email: francinetrust@outlook.com)

Trustees: Elsa Peters; Josephine Winham; Desmond Corcoran; Fuschia Peters.

General information

This foundation was established in 1979. Grants are awarded to registered and exempt charities that support older people.

Financial information

Year end	05/04/2021
Income	£362,500
Assets	£4,700,000
Grants to organisations	£3,960,000
No. of grants	172

Further financial information

Only beneficiaries that received grants of £5,000 and above were listed in the accounts. Grants of under £5,000 totalled £94,300 and were awarded to 40 organisations.

Beneficiaries included: Age UK (£97,000 in 11 grants); Centre for Sustainable Energy (£12,500); The Grateful Society (£10,000); Event Mobility (£8,000); 4Sight Vision Support and Stroke Association (£5,000 each).

Applications

Apply in writing to the correspondent.

Sources of information

Accounts; annual report; Charity Commission record.

The Wixamtree Trust

General charitable purposes; medicine and health; social welfare; education; training and employment; the arts; the environment and conservation; sport and leisure; work overseas

 Bedfordshire

£1.04 million (2020/21)

CC number: 210089

Correspondent: Mia Duddridge, Clerk to the Trustees, 6 Trull Farm Buildings, Tetbury, Gloucestershire GL8 8SQ (tel: 020 8777 4140; email: wixamtree@thetrustpartnership.com)

Trustees: Harry Whitbread; Charles Whitbread; Paul Patten; Arthur Polhill; Marion Stern.

 www.wixamtree.org

General information

This trust was established by Humphrey Whitbread in 1949 for general charitable purposes. According to the trust's website, the trustees focus most support on organisations and projects based or operating in Bedfordshire. The trustees are keen to support applications from organisations of which the late Humphrey Whitbread was a benefactor.

Grants are usually of between £1,000 and £10,000, with a small number of donations outside this range. The trust's Small Grants Programme awards grants of up to £3,000.

The trust makes an annual grant each year to Bedfordshire and Hertfordshire Historic Churches Trust, which distributes funds to churches.

Financial information

Year end	05/04/2021
Income	£693,800
Assets	£33,030,000
Grants to organisations	£1,040,000

Further financial information

Grants were distributed as follows:

Social welfare	£474,400
The environment and conservation	£152,000
International	£150,000
Medicine and health	£120,700
Education	£51,200
The arts	£45,000
Sport and leisure	£30,500
Training and employment	£12,000

Beneficiaries included: A list of beneficiaries was not available.

Applications

Applications can be made via the trust's website, where deadlines and guidance can also be found.

Sources of information

Accounts; annual report; Charity Commission record; funder's website.

The Maurice Wohl Charitable Foundation

Employment; emergency response; Jewish education; health and medical sciences; social welfare; arts and culture; Jewish life

 UK and Israel

£3.67 million (2020)

CC number: 244519

Correspondent: Joseph Houri, Secretary, Fitzrovia House, 2nd Floor, 153–157 Cleveland Street, London W1T 6QW (email: info@wohl.org.uk)

Trustees: Martin Paisner; Ella Latchman; Daniel Dover; Sir Ian Gainsford; Prof. David Latchman.

 www.wohl.org.uk

General information

The Maurice Wohl Charitable Foundation is part of The Wohl Legacy, a group of three charitable foundations established by the late Maurice and Vivienne Wohl.

The foundation mainly funds capital projects, with particular focus given to the following areas:

- Pathways to employment
- Emergency response
- Jewish education
- Medical advancement
- Care and welfare
- Arts and culture
- Jewish and communal life

Financial information

Year end	31/12/2020
Income	£1,370,000
Assets	£82,860,000
Grants to organisations	£3,670,000

Further financial information

Grants were distributed as follows:

Jewish community	£1.48 million
Care and welfare	£1.44 million
Jewish education	£482,500
Pathways to employment	£207,900
Medical advancement	£60,000

Beneficiaries included: Jerusalem Foundation (£1.21 million); Jewish Care Homes Consolidated Appeal (£333,000); Norwood (£270,800); Children Ahead (£150,000); Hasmonean MAT (£20,000).

Applications

The Wohl Legacy website states:

> The Wohl Legacy does not accept unsolicited applications for funding. The Foundations have a full-time staff working with the trustees to identify suitable projects. The trustees operate on the basis of a policy of unanimous decision-making.

Sources of information

Accounts; annual report; Charity Commission record; funder's website.

The Charles Wolfson Charitable Trust

Medicine; education; social welfare

Worldwide, mainly UK

£4.36 million (2020/21)

CC number: 238043

Correspondent: Joanne Cowan, 8/10 Hallam Street, London W1W 6NS (tel: 020 7079 2506; email: admin@cwctcharity.org.uk)

Trustees: Lord Simon Wolfson; Dr Sara Levene; The Hon. Andrew Wolfson; Deborah Edwards; Lord Jonathan Mendelsohn.

General information

The trust was established in 1960. According to its Charity Commission record, income is generated from property and other investments through its subsidiary undertakings with Benesco Charity Ltd (Charity Commission no. 269181). Aside from funding a large portion of the trust's grant-making, the Benesco Charity makes a number of direct grants for similar causes.

Grant-making policy

Grants are made to registered charities, hospitals, schools or other similar charitable institutions. Grants are typically made towards capital and project costs in the following areas:

- Medicine
- Education
- Welfare

The 2020/21 annual report states that 'particular, but not exclusive, regard is given to the needs of the Jewish community'.

Financial information

Year end	05/04/2021
Income	£5,870,000
Assets	£218,080,000
Grants to organisations	£4,360,000

Beneficiaries included: JFS (£500,000); Jewish Care (£400,000); Music in Secondary Schools Trust (£350,000); Norwood (£200,000); Chief Rabbinate Trust (£140,000); London School of Jewish Studies (£100,000); Tikun (£75,000); Jewish Leadership Council (£50,000).

Exclusions

Grants are not awarded to individuals.

Applications

Apply in writing to the correspondent.

Sources of information

Accounts; annual report; Charity Commission record.

The Wolfson Family Charitable Trust

Capital funding for projects supporting the UK Jewish community, with preference for older people, disability, education, culture and heritage; capital funding for universities and hospitals in Israel in support of science, medicine and health

UK and Israel

£2.09 million (2020/21)

CC number: 228382

Correspondent: The Trustees, 8 Queen Anne Street, London W1G 9LD (tel: 020 7323 5730; email: grants@wolfson.org.uk)

Trustees: Sir Ian Gainsford; Martin Paisner; Sir Bernard Rix; Lord Turnberg; The Hon. Laura Townsley; Dame Janet Botton; The Hon. Elizabeth Peltz; Alexandra Halamish; Sir Michael Pepper.

 www.wfct.org

General information

The trust was established in 1958 as a sister charity of the Wolfson Foundation (Charity Commission no. 1156077).

Grants in the UK

Grants of between £10,000 and £50,000 are made to UK organisations (with charitable status) for capital costs, i.e. buildings, refurbishment and equipment. Organisations should generally have an annual income of above £50,000. All applicants should have guaranteed match funding in place before making an application to the trust.

Funding is aimed at projects that support the Jewish community, with a particular focus on older people and people with disabilities, education, and culture and heritage. In the area of heritage, the trust is particularly interested in historic synagogues.

Grants in Israel

Universities and hospitals receive funding for equipment from the trust. For universities, equipment is funded in support of nationally co-ordinated programmes on research themes including attosecond science, single-cell analysis and high-intensity lasers. For hospitals, grants are awarded mainly for medical equipment with a research focus.

Cultural institutions with national importance and organisations working with people with disabilities are also in receipt of funding from the trust. Note: the Israel funding programmes do not currently accept unsolicited applications.

Financial information

Year end	31/03/2021
Income	£1,500,000
Assets	£41,560,000
Grants to organisations	£2,090,000

Further financial information

During 2020/21, grants were distributed as follows:

Science and medicine	£1.1 million
Health and disability	£885,000
Education	£107,000

Beneficiaries included: Hebrew University of Jerusalem – Israel (£220,000); Academy of Medical Sciences – London (£100,000); JW3 – London (£75,000); Manchester Jewish Community Cares (£50,000); Hospice of the Upper Galilee – Israel (£20,000); SOS Children's Villages Israel (£16,000); Prism – London (£7,100).

Exclusions

Grants in the UK

According to its website, the trust does not fund:

- The purchase of land or existing buildings
- Grants direct to individuals
- Grants through conduit organisations
- Overheads, maintenance costs, VAT and professional fees
- Non-specific appeals (including circulars) and endowment funds
- Film promotional materials
- Repayment of loans
- Projects that have already been completed or will be by the time of the award

Applications

Grants in the UK

There is a two-stage application process for grants in the UK. A stage 1 application can be submitted on the trust's website, where guidance is also provided. All requests are responded to and eligible organisations will be invited to submit a stage 2 application.

Grants in Israel

Unsolicited applications are not currently accepted. Applicants are invited by the trust's Advisory Committee based in Israel.

Sources of information

Accounts; annual report; Charity Commission record; funder's website.

The Wolfson Foundation

Education; science; medicine; the arts; humanities; health; disability

UK

£35.72 million (2020/21)

CC number: 1156077

Correspondent: Paul Ramsbottom, Chief Executive, 8 Queen Anne Street, London W1G 9LD (tel: 020 7323 5730; email: grants@wolfson.org.uk)

Trustees: Dame Janet Botton; The Hon. Laura Townsley; Sir Prof. David Cannadine; Dame Hermione Lee; Sir Michael Pepper; Dame Prof. Jean Thomas; Lord Turnberg of Cheadle Md; Sir Peter Ratcliffe; Rebecca Marks; Charles Townsley; Allegra Berman.

www.wolfson.org.uk

facebook.com/WolfsonFoundation

@wolfsonfdn

General information

The foundation was founded in 1955 by Sir Isaac Wolfson, his wife and their son.

Grant-making policy

The website states that around 85% of funding is made towards capital infrastructure, i.e. buildings (new build or refurbishments). These awards are designed to encourage excellence across the following fields:

- Education
- Science and medicine
- Heritage
- The arts and humanities
- Health and disability

Organisations typically funded by the foundation include other charities, places of worship, hospices, libraries, museums schools and universities. A detailed list of all eligible organisations, along with tailored funding criteria, can be seen on the website.

The foundation also awards research and education grants to individuals, which make up around 15% of all grant-making. Grants are made in the form of bursaries, scholarships and fellowships. These grants are generally administered by partner organisations, not paid directly to individuals. For more information, see the website.

Financial information

Year end	31/03/2021
Income	£18,800,000
Assets	£875,040,000
Grants to organisations	£35,720,000

Further financial information

During 2020/21, grants were distributed as follows:

Science	£15.05 million
Arts and humanities	£7.5 million
Health	£6.76 million
Education	£6.42 million

Beneficiaries included: Royal Marsden Cancer Charity (£2 million); University of Kent (£250,000); National Space Centre – Leicester (£235,000); Bar-Ilan University – Israel (£188,400); New Wolsey Theatre – Ipswich (£70,000); Lightburn Elderly Association Project – Glasgow (£40,000); St Michael's Church – Brent Knoll (£3,000).

Exclusions

The foundation does not fund:

- Purchase of land or existing buildings (including a building's freehold)
- Grants directly to individuals
- Grants through conduit organisations
- Overheads, maintenance costs or VAT
- Non-specific appeals (including circulars) or endowment funds
- Costs of meetings, exhibitions, concerts, expeditions, conferences, lectures, etc.
- Salary costs
- Running costs, including vehicle fuel and maintenance
- Film, websites or promotional materials
- Repayment of loans
- Projects that have already been completed or will be by the time of award
- Projects with a total cost of under £15,000
- CICs

Further exclusions differ for each grants programme – see the website for details.

Applications

There is a two-stage application process. A stage 1 application can be submitted on the foundation's website, where guidance is also provided. Eligible organisations will be invited to submit a stage 2 application. Applications can usually be submitted at two points during the year. Check the foundation's website for the latest application deadlines.

Speculative applications are not considered for research and education grants for individuals.

Sources of information

Accounts; annual report; Charity Commission record; funder's website.

The Victoria Wood Foundation

The arts

UK, with a preference for the north of England and London

£348,200 (2020/21)

CC number: 1170494

Correspondent: The Trustees, Plumpton House, Bents Drive, Sheffield, South Yorkshire S11 9RN (email: a contact form is available on the foundation's website)

Trustees: Roger Glossop; Charlotte Scott; Piers Wenger; Jane Wymark; Nigel Lilley; Lucy Ansbro; Davina Walter.

https://victoriawoodfoundation.org.uk

General information

The foundation was registered with the Charity Commission in November 2016 in memory of the late comedian Victoria Wood, who died from cancer in April 2016.

The trustees support all aspects of the arts, particularly in and around London and the north of England.

Financial information

Year end	05/04/2021
Income	£202,800
Assets	£3,950,000
Grants to organisations	£348,200

Beneficiaries included: A list of beneficiaries was not available.

Exclusions

According to its website, the foundation will not consider applications for:

- Individuals
- Courses of study
- Expeditions and foreign travel
- General appeals
- Youth and community associations
- Retrospective funding
- Statutory bodies
- Places of worship or which promote religion
- Animal, wildlife, heritage and environmental causes

Applications

Applications can be made through the foundation's website.

Sources of information

Accounts; Charity Commission record.

The Wood Foundation

Economic development and education

Scotland and sub-Saharan Africa

£35.49 million (2020/21)

OSCR number: SC037957

Correspondent: The Trustees, Blenheim House, Fountainhall Road, Aberdeen, Aberdeenshire AB15 4DT (tel: 01224 619862; email: info@thewoodfoundation.org.uk)

Trustees: Sir Ian Wood; Lady Helen Wood; Graham Good.

 www.thewoodfoundation.org.uk

 @TWF_Scotland

General information

The Wood Foundation was established in 2007 by Sir Ian Wood and his family. The foundation uses venture philanthropy, investing money and expertise into projects that it supports. Whether leading or supporting a project, the foundation prefers to take an active role, and the trustees are generally involved in developing the principles of the project, planning, training, guidance and performance evaluation.

The foundation's key themes are:

- Venture philanthropy transforming livelihoods in Africa
- Developing young people in Scotland
- Facilitating economic and education development in Scotland

More information about each key theme can be found on the foundation's website.

Financial information

Year end	31/03/2021
Income	£4,430,000
Assets	£95,630,000
Grants to organisations	£35,490,000

Further financial information

During 2020/21, grants were distributed as follows:

Miscellaneous grants/capacity support costs	£33.6 million
Developing young people in Scotland	£1 million
Venture philanthropy transforming livelihoods in Africa	£887,000

Beneficiaries included: A list of beneficiaries was not available.

Applications

Contact the foundation for more information.

Sources of information

Accounts; annual report; funder's website; OSCR record.

Wooden Spoon Society

Children and young people under the age of 25 with disabilities or other disadvantages; sports and recreation

UK and Ireland

£957,900 (2020/21)

CC number: 326691

Correspondent: Projects Team, Sentinel House, Ancells Business Park, Harvest Crescent, Fleet, Hampshire GU51 2UZ (tel: 01252 773720; email: projects@woodenspoon.org.uk)

Trustees: Christine Braithwaite; Callum Whitton; Brett Bader; Graham Allen; Jane Harwood; Joanna Coombs; John Gibson; Mark McCafferty; Quentin Smith; George Whitefoot; Adrian Alli.

 www.woodenspoon.org.uk

 facebook.com/WoodenSpoonCharity

 @charityspoon

 @charityspoon

General information

Wooden Spoon Society was established in 1983, when a defeat of the England rugby team by Ireland resulted in a wooden spoon being presented to a group of England supporters. On return to England, these supporters organised a golf competition with the wooden spoon as the trophy, while raising money for charity in the process. The Wooden Spoon Society has since donated over £29 million to a wide range of causes benefitting disadvantaged young people through rugby.

According to its website, the charity 'funds life-changing projects that support children and young people with disabilities or living in disadvantage'.

In particular, its focus is to help children and young people through projects such as sensory rooms, playground and outdoor activities, health and well-being, and specialist equipment. Projects must benefit people in the UK and Ireland.

The following information has been taken from the charity website:

> If a project is a physical, tangible asset, of a permanent nature the following must apply:
>
> - Must have a minimum predicted life-span of five years (preferably ten years), be non transferable and of a permanent nature. (Special consideration may be given to funding life enhancing/medical treatment equipment if it can be shown that the useable life of such equipment is likely to be at least five years.)
> - Grants will not be considered for salaries, administration costs, professional fees and on-going overheads related to a capital project.
>
> If a project is educational or disability sports focused the following must apply:
>
> - There must be a key rugby element to engage children and young people
> - Must have a clearly defined project brief to include detail on: description of project need and objectives, stakeholders, description of participants (age, gender, geography), recruitment of participants, project activity and budget, legacy planning, monitoring and evaluation and finally reporting to Wooden Spoon
> - Grants will be considered for kit and equipment, salaries and administration costs

Although there is no minimum or maximum grant available, it is unlikely that capital project applications for amounts under £5,000 will meet the charity's criteria.

Financial information

Year end	31/03/2021
Income	£1,450,000
Assets	£1,120,000
Grants to organisations	£957,900

Beneficiaries included: Waterside Centre Cafe (£85,000); HITZ (£80,000); The Wooden Spoon Welcome Hub (£35,000); The Forest School (£31,400); Beechbrae SCIO (£25,000).

Exclusions

See the grant-maker's website for exclusions relating to different types of project.

Applications

The charity recommends first submitting an Expression of Wish form, which can be completed on the website. Eligible organisations may then complete an application form, which can also be downloaded from the website. Applications will be sent to the regional committee for approval.

Sources of information

Accounts; annual report; Charity Commission record; funder's website.

Woodroffe Benton Foundation

Social welfare; older people; education and development of young people; the environment and conservation; physical well-being

 UK

£308,600 (2019/20)

CC number: 1075272

Correspondent: Joanna Noles, Secretary to the Trustees, PO Box 309, Cirencester, Gloucestershire GL7 9HA (email: secretary@woodroffebenton.org.uk)

Trustees: James Hope; Richard Page; Jill Wesley; Edward White; Chiyo Rimington; Edward Behrens; William White.

 www.woodroffebenton.org.uk

General information

This foundation was established in 1988 by the late Alfred Woodroffe Benton. It later amalgamated with the S. Wolfe Memorial Fund.

According to its website, the foundation makes grants to registered charities and educational organisations in the following categories:

- Relief of hardship
- Care for older people
- Education and development of young people
- The environment and conservation
- Physical well-being

All UK-based charitable organisations and educational organisations, such as schools and universities, are eligible to apply, whether or not they have charitable status. The trustees prefer to give core funding and support for specific projects, in particular for smaller charities where smaller grants are likely to be of greater benefit.

Financial information

Year end	02/12/2020
Income	£234,700
Assets	£8,390,000
Grants to organisations	£308,600
No. of grants	179

Further financial information

The foundation's annual report states that 179 grants were paid during the year in the following categories:

- Ongoing support – 32 grants to 23 charities totalling £186,300
- Small grants – 133 grants totalling £105,800 (out of 559 applications)
- Grants awarded at the discretion of individual trustees – 22 grants totalling £16,500

The accounts state that £308,600 of these grants were actually paid during the year, with a further £51,000 committed for future grants.

Beneficiaries included: A list of beneficiaries was not available.

Exclusions

The foundation has the following exclusions, as stated on its website:

- Organisations that operate primarily outside the UK or for the benefit of non-UK residents.
- Places of worship seeking funds for restoration or upgrade of facilities.
- Students requesting a grant for tertiary education or a gap year.
- Educational organisations based outside the Derbyshire region – **although the trustees may choose to do so.**
- Museums, historical or heritage organisations.
- Funding of palliative care.
- Organisations without a Charity Commission registration.
- Organisations that have not been operating for more than 12 months.
- Animal welfare organisations whose primary purpose is not conservation of the environment.
- Bodies affiliated to or a local 'branch' of a national organisation, even when registered as a separate charity

The foundation is also unlikely to provide multiple grants to the same charity within a 12-month period.

Applications

Applications must be made using an online form, which is made available on the foundation's website when funding rounds open. Check the foundation's website for the latest information and deadlines.

Sources of information

Accounts; annual report; Charity Commission record; funder's website.

Worth Waynflete Foundation

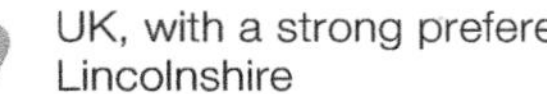

General charitable purposes, including the environment and heritage

UK, with a strong preference for Lincolnshire

£340,100 (2020)

CC number: 1068892

Correspondent: Margaret Dawson, Foundation Manager, PO Box 9986, Grantham, Lincolnshire NG31 0FJ (tel: 01400 250210; email: info@waynfletecharity.com or margaretdawson@waynfletecharity.com)

Trustees: Michael Worth; Graham Scrimshaw; Hubert Lewczuk-Tilley.

 www.waynfletecharity.com

General information

This trust was established in 1986 to support charitable organisations, particularly those in South Lincolnshire.

According to its website, the trust prefers to support:

- Lincolnshire based charities and volunteer-led organisations
- National charities and organisations that benefit and help Lincolnshire residents
- Individual projects and initiatives
- Rural projects promoting the enhancement of the Lincolnshire landscape and ecology
- Preservation of heritage assets
- Small local school initiatives, including IT equipment.

The trust also notes that it prefers to support the following activities:

- Enhancement of skills and qualifications of existing staff
- Training and proficiency of new volunteers
- Core day to day running costs and special needs
- Start-up initiatives with additional staged funding programmes
- Landscape and planning issues in particular wind turbines and affordable housing.

Financial information

Year end	31/12/2020
Income	£0
Grants to organisations	£340,100

Further financial information

Full accounts were not available to view on the Charity Commission's website due to the foundation's low income. We have therefore estimated the foundation's grant total based on its total expenditure.

Beneficiaries included: A list of beneficiaries was not available. Previous beneficiaries include: Lincolnshire Blind Society (£6,000); Canine Partners, Lincolnshire and Nottinghamshire Air Ambulance and the Order of St John (£4,000 each); Deafblind UK (£2,500); Action for Kids, Gurkha Welfare Trust and Marine Conservation Society (£1,000 each); Braille Chess Association, Children's Safety Education Foundation and Royal National Lifeboat Fund (£500 each); Mouth and Foot Painting Artists (£100).

Exclusions

The foundation does not provide grants to individuals.

Applications

Applicants should contact the foundation by email or post, providing their name, address, organisation, contact details and a brief outline of their activities and proposal. Alternatively, contact one of the foundation managers, whose details can be found on the website.

Sources of information

Charity Commission record; funder's website.

The Eric Wright Charitable Trust

Young people; older people; education and training; health; carers' support

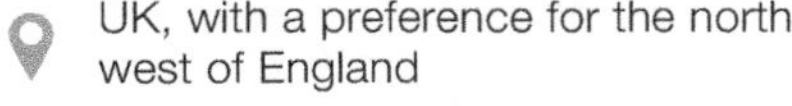

UK, with a preference for the north-west of England

£334,000 (2020)

CC number: 1002966

Correspondent: The Trustees, Sceptre House, Sceptre Way, Bamber Bridge, Preston, Lancashire PR5 6AW (tel: 01772

694613; email: rebeccam@ericwright.co.uk)

Trustees: Michael Collier; Hugh MacDonald; Alan Sturrock; Alison Wright; Janette Collier; Martin Newsholme; Catherine Wilson.

 www.ericwright.co.uk/charitable-trust

General information

The Eric Wright Charitable Trust was established in 1990 by businessman Eric Wright. According to the trust's website, the trust was formed, 'based on the belief that the role of business in society is not to create wealth for the few but instead is fundamental to the building of a strong community'. Following a gift from Mr Wright, the trust today holds 100% of shares in The Eric Wright Group Ltd, a provider of construction, civil engineering, property development and facilities management services.

The trust has a broad range of causes, primarily in the north-west of England, with a particular focus on:

- Young people's well-being
- Services for older people
- Education and training
- Health
- Carers' support
- Mental health
- Child/family support

Grant programmes

The trust has three separate grant programmes, as detailed on its website.

> - **Major grants** – Major Grants are aimed at assisting and supporting the development of well-established Borough and County-wide charitable organisations which deliver services directly to beneficiaries. While there is no minimum/maximum size requirement for the organisation, it is likely to have an income/expenditure of between £500,000–£2,000,000 per annum and have been in operation for at least 5 years.
> - **Community grants** – Community Grants are aimed at assisting and supporting the development of smaller local charitable organisations which deliver services directly to beneficiaries. While there is no minimum or maximum size requirement for the organisation, it is likely to have an income/expenditure of between £100,000–£500,000 per annum and have been in operation for at least 3 years.
> - **Minor grants** – Minor Grants are aimed at supporting small local charitable organisations which deliver services directly to beneficiaries. While there is no minimum size requirement for the organisation, it is likely to have an income/expenditure of between £50,000–£100,000 per annum and have been in operation for at least 2 years.

In addition to its grant-making activities, the trust is also directly involved in running two of its own charities: the Water Park Lakeland Adventure Centre and Eric Wright Learning Foundation.

Financial information

Year end	31/12/2020
Income	£219,530,000
Assets	£81,760,000
Grants to organisations	£334,000
No. of grants	48

Further financial information

Grants were broken down as follows:

Community voluntary services	£90,000
Education and training	£86,000
Carers	£43,000
Young people	£33,000
Health	£30,000
Older people	£25,000
Other	£12,000
Child and family support	£10,000
Mental health	£5,000

Beneficiaries included: A list of beneficiaries was not available. Previous beneficiaries include: Galloway Society for the Blind (£50,000); Age UK Lancashire, Blackburn Youth Zone, Lancashire Mind, The Children's Adventure Farm Trust and Wigan Boys and Girls Club (£25,000 each).

Applications

Major grants are by invitation only. In regard to applications for community grants and minor grants, the trust's website states:

> If you would like to apply, we would strongly advise you in the first instance to contact the Trust to discuss the nature of your application and the process involved.

Sources of information

Accounts; annual report; Charity Commission record; funder's website.

Wychville Ltd

Jewish causes; education; relief of poverty; general charitable purposes

UK and overseas

£494,300 (2020/21)

CC number: 267584

Correspondent: The Trustees, 44 Leweston Place, London N16 6RH (tel: 020 8802 3948)

Trustees: Mr E. Englander; Mrs B. R. Englander.

General information

Established in 1974, this charity supports the advancement of religion in accordance with the Orthodox Jewish faith, the relief of poverty and general charitable purposes. The charity's 2020/21 annual report states the following about its grant-making policy:

> The Trustees are approached for donations by a wide variety of charitable institutions operating in the United Kingdom and abroad. The Trustees consider all requests which they receive and make donations based on the level of funds available.

Financial information

Year end	31/03/2021
Income	£433,000
Assets	-£214,800
Grants to organisations	£494,300
No. of grants	7+

Further financial information

Seven beneficiaries were listed in the charity's 2020/21 accounts, while 'other grants' totalled £29,300.

Beneficiaries included: Friends of Mercaz Hatorah Belz Machnivka (£216,200); Mifal Hachesed Vehatzdokoh (£56,500); One Heart – Lev Echod (£50,000); Friends of Beis Chinuch Lebonos (£39,000); Beis Aharon Trust Ltd (£36,800).

Applications

Apply in writing to the correspondent.

Sources of information

Accounts; annual report; Charity Commission record.

The Wyfold Charitable Trust

General charitable purposes

England and Wales

£225,000 (2020/21)

CC number: 1157483

Correspondent: The Trustees, c/o RF Trustee Co. Ltd, 15 Suffolk Street, London SW1Y 4HG (tel: 020 3696 6721; email: charities@rftrustee.com)

Trustees: Roderick Fleming; Adam Fleming; Nicholas Powell; Angus Fleming; Hermione Fleming.

General information

This trust was established in 2014 and is administered by RF Trustee Co. Ltd, the office of the Fleming family, and four members of the Fleming family act as trustees. The Fleming family has associations with various charities, notably The Fleming-Wyfold Art Foundation (Charity Commission no. 1080197), which is responsible for The Fleming Art Collection, a gallery exhibiting a private collection of Scottish art.

Both one-off and recurrent grants are given to charitable organisations for a wide range of purposes. Particular focus is given to the following areas:

- Health
- Education
- Art, culture, heritage and science

Financial information

Year end	31/03/2021
Income	£268,000
Assets	£10,000,000
Grants to organisations	£225,000

Further financial information

During 2020/21 the trust made grants totalling £225,000. However, in previous years the trust has made grants totalling over £300,000. Only beneficiaries that received grants of over £10,000 were listed in the trust's accounts. Grants of over £10,000 totalled £85,500.

Beneficiaries included: The Fleming-Wyfold Art Foundation (£25,000); Young Epilepsy (£15,000); Bridewell Gardens, Fleetwood Museum, Haydn Festival Trust, Missing Salmon Alliance and Wordsworth Trust (£10,000 each).

Applications

Apply in writing to the correspondent. The trustees meet twice a year to consider applications.

Sources of information

Accounts; annual report; Charity Commission record.

Yorkshire Building Society Charitable Foundation

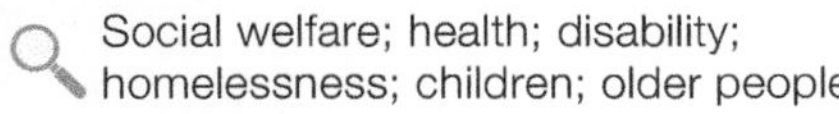
Social welfare; health; disability; homelessness; children; older people

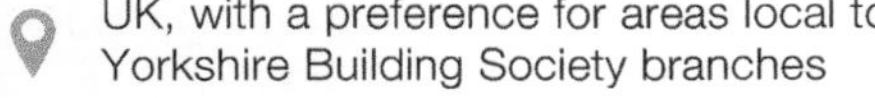
UK, with a preference for areas local to Yorkshire Building Society branches

£415,600 (2020)

CC number: 1069082

Correspondent: Ms D. Colley, Secretary, Yorkshire House, Yorkshire Drive, Bradford, West Yorkshire BD5 8LJ (tel: 0345 166 9271; email: corporateresponsibility@ybs.co.uk)

Trustees: Vanessa White; Gordon Rogers; Sarah Jackson; Lloyd Latibeaudiere; Erin Fuller.

www.ybs.co.uk/your-society/charitable-foundation/index.html

General information

Established in 1998, the foundation is the charitable arm of Yorkshire Building Society (YBS). The foundation is largely funded by YBS's Small Change Big Difference scheme, whereby members and staff donate the annual interest from their savings or mortgage accounts to the foundation.

Aims

The foundation's main aim is to alleviate poverty, improve health and save lives in the areas where YBS's members and staff live and work. It is particularly interested in supporting children, older people, people with disabilities and serious illness and people who are experiencing homelessness.

Grants

The foundation funds specific projects and/or items that will have a positive impact on the charity's beneficiaries. Although the foundation does not support core costs, the trustees are keen to support full cost recovery for projects.

Examples of project costs funded include:

- Contributions towards salaries for core staff or project workers
- Contributions towards rent or utilities
- A dedicated laptop for the project
- Staff or volunteer training

For capital costs, priority is given to applications where the donation covers the total cost of an item. Examples of previous capital donations include:

- Sensory toys for children with special needs
- Medical equipment for a hospice
- Kitchen equipment for a foodbank (e.g. an industrial freezer)

Eligibility

To be eligible charities must:

- Be a registered charity
- Use the funding to help alleviate poverty, improve health or save lives
- Be nominated by a YBS member or colleague
- Have beneficiaries in the UK
- Have not received a donation in the last two years
- Have annual returns submitted to the relevant charity regulator

Note: at the time of writing (February 2022) the foundation had relaxed its eligibility criteria in response to the COVID-19 pandemic and was considering applications for running costs. It was also accepting applications from charities that have been unable to submit their most recent accounts. Check the website for updates.

See the foundation's guidelines for full details.

Financial information

Year end	31/12/2020
Income	£437,200
Assets	£77,500
Grants to organisations	£415,600
No. of grants	299

Further financial information

In 2020, the foundation set up a COVID-19 response fund with a donation of £100,000 from YBS. This fund supported 61 smaller charities with grants ranging from £500 to £2,000. General grants were awarded to 238 other organisations.

Beneficiaries included: Be Free Young Carers, Coffee4Craig, Emmaus Sheffield, Hive Bradford, King's Lynn Debt Centre, Musical Keys, St Ann's Hospice, The Primrose Centre Ltd and Warrington Foodbank (£2,000 each).

Exclusions

The following will not be considered:

- Applications that do not fit the criteria outlined in the guidance notes
- Charities serving only a specific sector of the community selected on the basis of political or religious grounds/advancement
- Animal welfare charities
- Charities with beneficiaries not in the UK
- CICs, community or voluntary organisations that are not registered charities
- Individuals
- Applications for large capital fundraising appeals (e.g. fundraising for a minibus)
- Applications for any administration, fundraising or marketing equipment for a charity's own use

Applications

To be eligible for a grant you must be recommended by one of the building society's members or colleagues. If you are a member and would like the foundation to consider supporting a charity, an online application portal can be found on the foundation's website.

All applications are reviewed on a quarterly basis by the trustees. The application deadlines are 31 March, 30 June, 30 September and 31 December annually. You can expect to hear back within three months of submitting an application.

Sources of information

Accounts; annual report; Charity Commission record; funder's website; guidelines for applicants.

Yorkshire Cancer Research

Cancer research

Yorkshire

£5.91 million (2020/21)

CC number: 516898

Correspondent: Research Team, Jacob Smith House, 7 Grove Park Court, Harrogate, North Yorkshire HG1 4DP (tel: 01423 501269; email: hq@ycr.org.uk)

Trustees: Graham Berville; Sandra Dodson; Dr Yvette Oade; Bobby Ndawula; Elizabeth Richards; Rosemary Cook; Christopher Slater; Clare Field; Dr James Rice; Craig Bonnar.

https://yorkshirecancerresearch.org.uk

facebook.com/yorkshirecancerresearch

 @yorkshirecancer

 @yorkshirecancerresearch/?hl=en

General information

Yorkshire Cancer Research aims to 'improve cancer outcomes for people in Yorkshire by investing in research-led innovation that will help us all avoid, survive and cope with cancer'. The charity achieves its objectives by working with researchers, the NHS, public health bodies and charities – particularly universities and teaching hospitals.

According to the charity's website, it aims to:

- Become one of the leading authorities on regional cancer-related issues so that people living in Yorkshire are among the best-informed in England.
- Educate and influence better lifestyle decisions that will improve health, reduce the risk of cancer or support successful recovery from cancer.
- Encourage the earliest possible diagnosis and increase uptake rates into national screening programmes, improve services and develop more effective techniques and practices.
- Invest in research-led innovation at every stage of the cancer patient journey from first diagnosis through to treatment, clinical trials, palliative and end of life care.
- Help deliver better cancer services and significantly increase national research funding specifically to improve cancer outcomes in our region.

Cancer research funding

The charity has a range of a range of funding opportunities that researchers can apply for to help people in Yorkshire avoid cancer, get the earliest possible diagnosis and receive better treatments. Its priorities include:

- Reducing the risk of developing cancer
- Improving early diagnosis and cancer screening
- Improving treatments

For research enquiries, contact research@ycr.org.uk.

Services funding

The charity works in partnership with the NHS, Clinical Commissioning Groups, Local Authority Public Health teams, GPs, other health professionals and communities to implement initiatives and support services across Yorkshire. It provides funding and advice to help test new initiatives and improve existing services. Priorities include:

- Improving the uptake of lung, cervical, breast and bowel cancer screening
- Delivering cancer exercise rehabilitation
- Supporting patients to quit smoking

For enquiries contact services@ycr.org.uk.

Financial information

Year end	31/03/2021
Income	£20,290,000
Assets	£69,030,000
Grants to organisations	£5,910,000
No. of grants	49

Beneficiaries included: University of Leeds (£3.36 million in 17 grants); Leeds City Council (£250,800); Northumbria University (£85,900); University of Bradford (£25,800); Leeds Beckett University (£7,000).

Exclusions

Refer to the guidance notes on the charity's website for specific exclusions.

Applications

See the charity's website for information on current funding rounds, as well as deadlines, guidance and application forms.

Sources of information

Accounts; annual report; Charity Commission record; funder's website.

The Yorkshire Dales Millennium Trust

The environment; conservation; heritage; rural communities

 The Yorkshire Dales

£320,200 (2020/21)

CC number: 1061687

Correspondent: Josephine Boulter, Company Secretary, Main Street, Clapham, Lancaster, Lancashire LA2 8DP (tel: 01524 251002; email: info@ydmt.org)

Trustees: Andrew Campbell; His Honour Peter Charlesworth; Karen Cowley; Carl Lis; Stephen MacAre; Thomas Wheelwright; Jane Roberts; Prof. Christine Leigh; Eileen Spencer; Tracy Walker; Mark Cunliffe-Lister; Eloise Brown; Claire Brightley; William Downs; Conor Rushby; Kelsey Williamson; Thomas Pratt.

 www.ydmt.org

 facebook.com/ydmt.news

 @ydmt

General information

The Yorkshire Dales Millennium Trust was established to support the environmental, social and economic well-being of the Yorkshire Dales. It achieves this objective by raising and distributing funds to local projects, managing and distributing grants on behalf of external funders such as The National Lottery Heritage Fund and the Learning and Skills Council, and delivering projects directly.

The trust manages a wide variety of grant programmes. Here is a small sample of the charity's current programmes:

Green Futures: funding to help young people from all backgrounds make a positive impact on the environment and their own lives.

Stories in Stone Heritage Grants: funding for community-led heritage projects in the Ingleborough area.

Woodland Grants: advice and funding for new woodland creation.

Roger Stott Community Grants: support for community initiatives that benefit local people in the Yorkshire Dales and nearby areas.

Financial information

Year end	31/03/2021
Income	£1,730,000
Assets	£1,630,000
Grants to organisations	£320,200

Further financial information

Included in the 2020/21 grant total is £59,500 of community grants.

Beneficiaries included: Stories in Stone (£137,000); Capital Grants Woodlands (£63,100); Westmorland Dales Haytime (£25,000); Green Futures Youth Environmental Action Fund (£7,800).

Applications

Application processes may vary depending upon the specific programme. Guidance and application forms for all current grant programmes can be downloaded from the trust's website. The trustees meet at regular intervals during the financial year.

Sources of information

Accounts; annual report; Charity Commission record; funder's website.

The William Allen Young Charitable Trust

Medical causes; community; education; culture; human rights; animal welfare; social welfare

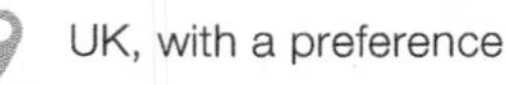

UK, with a preference for London

£45,000 (2020/21)

CC number: 283102

Correspondent: The Trustees, Young and Co. Brewery plc, 26 Osiers Road, Wandsworth, London SW18 1NH (tel: 020 8875 7000; email: claire.hill@youngs.co.uk)

Trustees: Torquil Sligo-Young; James Young; Caroline Chelton.

General information

The trust supports humanitarian causes, with a large number of health and social welfare organisations supported each year. Grants are made to local and national organisations throughout the UK, although there appears to be some preference for those based in London.

Financial information

Year end	05/04/2021
Income	£70
Grants to organisations	£45,000

Further financial information

In previous years grants have totalled between £500,000 and £800,000. Full accounts were not available to view on the Charity Commission website due to the charity's low income. We have therefore estimate the annual grant total for 2020/21 based on the charity's total expenditure.

Beneficiaries included: A list of beneficiaries was not available. Previous beneficiaries include: The Halow Project (£41,600); Anti-Slavery International and Shelter (£20,000 each); Imperial College London (£10,000); Shire Horse Society (£5,000); Alzheimer's Society (£4,000); Smallwood Primary School (£300).

Applications

The 2019/20 annual report notes that 'The trustees aim to support those organisations they have supported in the past on an ongoing basis although one-off donations are considered.'

Sources of information

Accounts; annual report; Charity Commission record.

Youth Music

Music and children and young people

England; Wales; Scotland

£11.09 million (2020/21)

CC number: 1075032

Correspondent: Angela Linton, Chief Operating Officer, Suites 3–5, Swan Court, 9 Tanner Street, London SE1 3LE (tel: 020 7902 1095; email: angela.linton@youthmusic.org.uk)

Trustees: Yolanda Brown; Chris Price; Rachel Lindley; Rachel Nelken; Samuel Ross; Tim Berg; Mirjana Buac; Robert Aitken; Samuel Denniston; Nathifa Jordan; Sophia Hall.

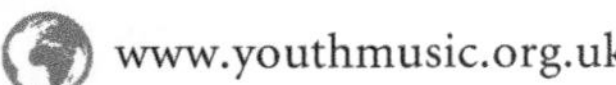
www.youthmusic.org.uk

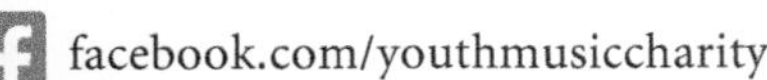
facebook.com/youthmusiccharity

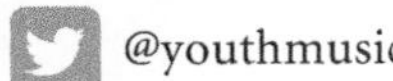
@youthmusic

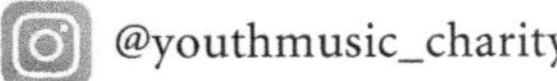
@youthmusic_charity

General information

Previously known as the National Foundation for Youth Music, the primary object of Youth Music is 'to advance the education of the public (especially young people) in the art and science of music', as stated on the website. Youth Music supports music-making activities, particularly for the country's most disadvantaged children and young people.

Youth Music is funded by Arts Council England with funds from the National Lottery. It also receives funding from the People's Postcode Lottery, meaning it now has some funds targeted at Wales and Scotland. The charity also raises funds through gifts and donations.

Aims and funding

The website states that the charity's aim is to 'equalise access to music', with a 'focus on those who would otherwise miss out because of who they are, where they live, or what they're going through'.

The charity has six priority areas:

- Early years
- Youth justice settings
- Young people facing barriers
- Young people with disabilities
- Young adults
- Organisations and the workforce

The upper age limit for participants has been extended from 18 to 25.

The charity has three main funds:

- **Fund A:** grants of £2,000 to £30,000 for high-quality projects that will help to achieve a musically inclusive England, delivered over 6–24 months
- **Fund B:** grants of £30,001 to £200,000 for music-making and music-making-related activities for children and young people (aged 0–25) facing barriers, and/or workforce and organisational development to promote a relevant, diverse, and inclusive music offer for all children and young people. Projects should last between 18 and 48 months
- **Fund C:** grants of up to £160,000 per year for programmes with a dual role of delivery and strategic work; expanding and embedding high-quality, inclusive music-making

The charity also has a number of other funds that are advertised on the website as they arise. For example:

- **Incubator Fund:** grants of £5,000 to £30,000 for businesses, collectives, and not-for-profits working in the music industries in England, Scotland and Wales. The fund is designed to help open up access to sustainable careers in music for people aged 18–25, particularly those who are underrepresented, and to support creative employers to innovate and incubate new and diverse talent

See the website for further information on open funds.

Financial information

Year end	31/03/2021
Income	£13,210,000
Assets	£4,310,000
Grants to organisations	£11,090,000

Beneficiaries included: A list of beneficiaries was not available.

Exclusions

See the grant-maker's website for a full list of fund-specific exclusions.

Applications

The three main funds from which grants are awarded each differ in their funding criteria and application process. Potential applicants are advised to refer to the Youth Music Network website for up-to-date criteria, priorities, guidelines and deadlines. Applications are made online, via the Youth Music Network website. Guidance on other current funds not mentioned here can also be found on the website.

Note: at the time of writing (May 2021) Fund C was closed for applications until further notice.

Sources of information

Accounts; annual report; Charity Commission record; funder's website.

The Elizabeth and Prince Zaiger Trust

General charitable purposes; older people; children and young people; disability; education; animal welfare

UK, with some preference for Somerset, Dorset and the South West

£653,000 (2020/21)

CC number: 282096

Correspondent: The Trustees, Gatesmoor, Hawkridge, Spaxton, Bridgwater, Somerset TA5 1AL (tel: 01278 671353)

Trustees: John Davidge; Peter Harvey; Derek Long; Edward Parry; Dr Robin Keyte.

General information

The trust was established in 1981 to support general charitable causes. As listed in the annual report for 2020/21, the trust's objects include:

- The relief of older people
- The relief of people who have mental and physical disabilities
- The advancement of education of children and young people
- The provision of care and protection for animals
- Other charitable purposes

Grants are made to organisations in the UK, although our research suggests that there is some preference for those based in Somerset, Dorset and the South West. Grants range up to £50,000. On occasions, individuals in need have also been supported.

Financial information

Year end	31/03/2021
Income	£584,400
Assets	£20,920,000
Grants to organisations	£653,000
No. of grants	96

Beneficiaries included: Variety, the Children's Charity (£25,000); Teenage Cancer Trust (£14,000); Whizz-Kidz (£10,000); Spark Somerset (£7,000); Roy Castle Lung Cancer Foundation (£6,000); Topsham Adventure Centre (£3,000); Home-Start Southwark (£2,000).

Applications

The trust's Charity Commission record states: 'This trust does not respond to unsolicited applications for funds. Don't apply – it wastes your time and money.'

Sources of information

Accounts; annual report; Charity Commission record.

The Marjorie and Arnold Ziff Charitable Foundation

Jewish causes and organisations; health; welfare; general charitable purposes

UK, with a preference for Leeds

£356,900 (2020/21)

CC number: 249368

Correspondent: The Trustees, Town Centre House, The Merrion Centre, Leeds, West Yorkshire LS2 8LY (tel: 0113 222 1234)

Trustees: Ann Manning; Michael Ziff; Edward Ziff; Dr Marjorie Ziff.

General information

The foundation was established in 1966 to support general charitable purposes, and in practice has a preference for Jewish causes and organisations. The foundation's Charity Commission record states that it has the capacity to support a limited number of projects, which the trustees are usually directly involved in. The foundation's 2020/21 annual report states:

> In particular the Trustees find that capital projects for any of the causes mentioned deserve their major support as public cash for building works is very difficult to obtain either from local or national government.

Financial information

Year end	05/04/2021
Income	£323,100
Assets	£7,020,000
Grants to organisations	£356,900
No. of grants	36

Beneficiaries included: United Jewish Israel Appeal (£85,000); Maccabi GB (£51,000); Opera North (£33,300); Chief Rabbinate Trust (£15,000); Western Marble Arch Synagogue (£7,200); Jerusalem Foundation Charity (£1,000); The Chicken Soup Shelter (£300); The Compassionate Friends (£60).

Applications

Apply in writing to the correspondent.

Sources of information

Accounts; annual report; Charity Commission record.

The Zochonis Charitable Trust

A range of charitable purposes, including: social welfare; education; children and young people; homelessness; community work; armed forces; older people; rescue services

UK (particularly Greater Manchester) and overseas (particularly Africa)

£3.42 million (2020/21)

CC number: 274769

Correspondent: The Trustees, Manchester Business Park, 3500 Aviator Way, Manchester M22 5TG (tel: 0161 435 1005; email: enquiries@zochonischaritabletrust.com)

Trustees: Christopher Green; Archibald Calder; Paul Milner.

General information

Registered in 1978, the trust was established by the late Sir John Zochonis. Sir Zochonis was a former head of PZ Cussons plc, the soap and toiletries manufacturer, and had shares in the company. The trust has general charitable objectives but tends to favour local charities with a particular emphasis on education and the welfare of children.

Financial information

Year end	05/04/2021
Income	£3,660,000
Assets	£171,330,000
Grants to organisations	£3,420,000
No. of grants	205

Further financial information

During 2020/21, grants were distributed as follows:

Education	£1.06 million
Health	£769,800
Children and young people	£343,000
Overseas	£333,000
Emergency	£310,000
Homelessness	£235,000
Social provision	£157,000
Community	£57,500
Current and former armed forces personnel	£52,500
Family	£42,500
Rescue services	£35,000
Older people	£13,800
Religious	£10,000

Beneficiaries included: A list of beneficiaries was not available.

Applications

Apply in writing to the correspondent. The trust's 2020/21 annual report states that 'grant requests are reviewed by the trustees on an individual basis'.

Sources of information

Accounts; annual report; Charity Commission record.

Zurich Community Trust (UK) Ltd

Social welfare; community and economic development; disadvantaged people

UK and overseas, with priority given to locations where Zurich Insurance UK has offices

£2.27 million (2020)

CC number: 266983

Correspondent: Steve Grimmett, Head of ZCT (UK), PO Box 1288, Swindon, Wiltshire SN1 1FL (tel: 07875 886341; email: steve.grimmett@zct.org.uk)

Trustees: Tim Culling; Ian Lovett; Wayne Myslik; Anne Torry; Andrew Jepp; Tulsi Naidu; Richard Peden; Stephen Collinson.

www.zct.org.uk

facebook.com/zurichcommunitytrust

@ZCTrust

@_zctrust

General information

The trust was established in 1973. It is the corporate charity of Zurich Insurance UK and is one of the longest-established corporate trusts in the UK. Today, the trust awards around £1.75 million in grants and support each year to improve the quality of life for more than 100,000 people experiencing hardship.

Multi-year partnerships

In recent years, the trust has funded multi-year partnerships with national charities and charities local to Zurich's offices. Partners are voted for by Zurich Insurance employees. All partners receive funding as well as donations of time, money and skills from employees, typically over a three-year period.

Local grant programmes

In addition to multi-year partnerships, certain Zurich Insurance offices have the capacity to award one-off 'Local Grants'. Under this scheme, which is part of the 'Zurich Cares' grants programme, the trust awards grants to registered charities, and organisations that 'are charitable in nature', that help people facing day-to-day challenges in their life. Grants are awarded towards core/ running costs such as salaries, purchases and project/pilot costs.

In 2020, the social issues supported included health and mental health, disability, life-limiting conditions, vulnerable young people, homelessness, older people, and young carers and bereavement.

Strategic funding

This scheme focuses on the more challenging issues of today and supports the most vulnerable people in society. The are several funding opportunities available under this scheme and programmes change periodically, so see the website for all current grant schemes. The strategic funding programmes are typically long-term. Applications for this programme are by invitation only.

Financial information

Year end	31/12/2020
Income	£3,680,000
Assets	£5,010,000
Grants to organisations	£2,270,000

Further financial information

During the year, grants made towards the trust's strategic funding programmes totalled £281,000. Grants made to long-term national partners totalled £452,000 and grants made to local partners totalled £1.47 million. The remaining £64,000 was awarded to Openwork Foundation.

The 2020 accounts state: 'During 2020, £2,273,000 was given out in grants, the vast majority of which was supporting existing partners of the Trust as part of the Trust's COVID-19 response plan.'

Beneficiaries included: The Openwork Foundation (£448,000); Aston Villa Foundation (£203,000); Greenwich Leisure Ltd (£160,000); Saints Foundation (£133,000); Dementia UK and Place2Be (£76,000 each); Mental Health Foundation (£22,000); Action for Kids (£40,000); University of Bath (£15,000); Addaction (£5,000).

Applications

Multi-year partners are nominated by Zurich Insurance employees and the strategic funding programmes are by invitation only. For more information visit the 'Meet the Team' web page for individual contact details.

Sources of information

Accounts; annual report; Charity Commission record; funder's website.

Community foundations

This section of the guide includes the details of the 47 UK community foundations, which distribute funding for a wide range of purposes.

Potential applicants are advised to visit their local community foundation's website or contact its grants team to find the most suitable funding stream.

Name	*Website*	*Phone*	*Email*
Bedfordshire and Luton Community Foundation	www.blcf.org.uk	01525 306690	administartor@blcf.org.uk
Berkshire Community Foundation	www.berkshirecf.org	0118 930 3021	info@berkshirecf.org
Buckinghamshire Community Foundation	www.heartofbucks.org	01296 330134	info@heartofbucks.org
Cambridgeshire Community Foundation	www.cambscf.org.uk	01223 410535	info@cambscf.org.uk
Cheshire Community Foundation	www.cheshirecommunityfoundation.org.uk	01606 330607	office@cheshirecommunityfoundation.org.uk
Community Foundation for Calderdale	www.cffc.co.uk	01422 349700	grants@cffc.co.uk
Community Foundation for Northern Ireland	www.communityfoundationni.org	028 9024 5927	info@communityfoundationni.org
Community Foundation for Staffordshire	www.staffsfoundation.org.uk	01785 339540	office@staffsfoundation.org.uk
Community Foundation for Surrey	www.cfsurrey.org.uk	01483 478092	info@cfsurrey.org.uk
Community Foundation for Wiltshire and Swindon	www.wiltshirecf.org.uk	01380 729284	info@wiltshirecf.org.uk
Community Foundation Wales	https://communityfoundationwales.org.uk	02920 379580	info@communityfoundationwales.org.uk
Community Foundation Tyne and Wear and Northumberland	www.communityfoundation.org.uk	0191 222 0945	general@communityfoundation.org.uk
Community Foundations for Lancashire and Merseyside	www.cfmerseyside.org.uk https://lancsfoundation.org.uk	0330 440 4900	info@cflm.email

COMMUNITY FOUNDATIONS

Name	*Website*	*Phone*	*Email*
Cornwall Community Foundation	www.cornwallcommunityfoundation.com	01566 779333	office@cornwallfoundation.com
County Durham Community Foundation	www.cdcf.org.uk	0191 378 6340	info@cdcf.org.uk
Cumbria Community Foundation	www.cumbriafoundation.org	01900 825760	enquiries@cumbriafoundation.org
Devon Community Foundation	www.devoncf.com	01884 235887	grants@devoncf.com
Dorset Community Foundation	www.dorsetcommunityfoundation.org	01202 670815	admin@dorsetcf.org
East End Community Foundation	www.eastendcf.org	020 7345 4444	info@eastendcf.org
Essex Community Foundation	www.essexcommunityfoundation.org.uk	01245 356018	grants@essexcf.org.uk
Forever Manchester	www.forevermanchester.com	0161 2140940	info@forevermanchester.com
Foundation Derbyshire	www.foundationderbyshire.org	01773 525860	hello@foundationderbyshire.org
Foundation Scotland	www.foundationscotland.org.uk	0131 524 0300	enquiries@foundationscotland.org.uk
Gloucestershire Community Foundation	www.gloucestershirecf.org.uk	01242 851357	A contact form is available on the website
Hampshire and the Isle of Wight Community Foundation	www.hiwcf.com	01962 798693	grantsadmin@hiwcf.com
Heart of England Community Foundation (serves Coventry, Warwickshire, Solihull, Birmingham and the Black Country)	www.heartofenglandcf.co.uk	024 77800 520	info@heartofenglandcf.co.uk
Herefordshire Community Foundation	www.herefordshirecf.org	01432 272550	A contact form is available on the website
Hertfordshire Community Foundation	www.hertscf.org.uk	01707 251351	grants@hertscf.org.uk
Kent Community Foundation	www.kentcf.org.uk	01303 814500	admin@kentcf.org.uk
Leeds Community Foundation (also serves Bradford)	www.leedscf.org.uk	0113 242 2426	grants@leedscf.org.uk
Leicestershire and Rutland Community Foundation	www.llrcommunityfoundation.org.uk	0116 262 4804	grants@llrcommunityfoundation.org.uk
Lincolnshire Community Foundation	www.lincolnshirecf.co.uk	01529 305825	info@lincolnshire.co.uk
London Community Foundation	www.londoncf.org.uk	020 7582 5117	info@londoncf.org.uk
Milton Keynes Community Foundation	www.mkcommunityfoundation.co.uk	01908 690276	info@mkcommunityfoundation.co.uk
Norfolk Community Foundation	www.norfolkfoundation.com	01603 623958	grants@norfolkfoundation.com
Northamptonshire Community Foundation	www.ncf.uk.com	01604 230033	enquiries@ncf.uk.com
Nottinghamshire Community Foundation	www.nottscf.org.uk	01623 620202	enquiries@nottscf.org.uk
One Community Foundation (serves Kirklees)	www.one-community.org.uk	01484 468397	info@one-community.org.uk

Name	*Website*	*Phone*	*Email*
Oxfordshire Community Foundation	www.oxfordshire.org	01865 798666	ocf@oxfordshire.org
Quartet Community Foundation (serves Bristol, Bath and North East Somerset, North Somerset and South Gloucestershire)	www.quartetcf.org.uk	0117 989 7700	applications@quartetcf.org.uk
Somerset Community Foundation	www.somersetcf.org.uk	01749 344949	info@somersetcf.org.uk
South Yorkshire's Community Foundation	www.sycf.org.uk	0114 242 4294	grants@sycf.org.uk
Suffolk Community Foundation	www.suffolkcf.org.uk	01473 602602	info@suffolkcf.org.uk
Sussex Community Foundation	www.sussexgiving.org.uk	01273 409440	info@sussexgiving.org.uk
Two Ridings Community Foundation (serves York, Hull, East Yorkshire and North Yorkshire)	www.trcf.org.uk	01904 929500	grants@tworidingscf.org.uk
Worcestershire Community Foundation	www.worcscf.org.uk	01684 312752	grants@comfirst.org.uk

Glossary of terms

This glossary has been written to clarify some of the terms you may come across when using this guide or delving deeper into your research on funders.

Assets

Money, goods and property owned or controlled by an organisation, including any legal rights it may have to receive money, goods, services and property from others.

Capacity building

Grants, loans, pro bono services or in-kind support to increase an established organisation's ability to deliver services.

Capital costs

The costs of tangible items (such as building or refurbishment costs, or the costs of purchasing equipment or vehicles).

Capital appeals

A capital appeal or campaign is a co-ordinated organisational fundraising initiative with a defined timetable and goals which has the aim of increasing an organisation's assets.

Charitable objects

Charitable objects describe and identify the legal purpose for which a charity has been set up.

Core costs

The costs of keeping an organisation going that are not directly connected to any particular project (such as administration, management, research and development, audit, head office costs, IT and finance costs or insurance). Sometimes called 'running costs' or 'central costs'.

Development funding

Grants, loans or in-kind support to extend or improve an established project or service.

Direct costs

Direct costs are costs directly related to an activity (such as the salaries of the staff who work on a specific project and their expenses or the hire of the venue for a particular event).

Indirect costs

Indirect costs are costs not directly related to an activity, but still incurred by the organisation, without which the activity would not happen (in other words, the costs of managing and administering an activity).

In-kind support

Also referred to as gifts in kind, this is the provision of goods or services to an organisation (such as office equipment, computers, software, pro bono work or administrative support).

Matched funding

Funding that depends on an organisation raising a proportion of the total funding it needs from other sources.

Permanent endowment

Assets to be held by a charity forever, which are often used to generate income for the charity (as in the case of permanently endowed investments).

Project funding

A project is an activity or a service which is separate from the organisation's primary work. Project funding covers the costs of specific projects but not the core costs of the organisation.

Seed funding/start-up funding

Seed funding assists with the start-up costs of an organisation or an organisation's new project.

SORP (Statement of Recommended Practice)

Sets out standards for accounting by charities, including what information should be included in annual accounts. It applies to almost all charitable organisations in England and Wales, Scotland and Northern Ireland. The only exceptions are charities that have their own SORP (for example, the SORP for Registered Social Landlords).

Strategic funding

Grants or loans to deliver an established organisation's strategy.

Statutory funding

Funding for activities which are the legal responsibility of the government or local authority (such as teachers' salaries).

Support costs

Additional costs incurred in the process of making a grant. DSC does not include support costs in the grant totals quoted in its funding guides.

Unsolicited applications

These are applications that have not been invited by the funder.

Unrestricted funding

Funding that can be used for any purpose to advance the objects of a charity or to support its administration or management.

Subject index

The following subject index begins with a list of categories used. The categories are very wide-ranging, in order to keep the index as simple as possible. DSC's subscription website (www.fundsonline.org.uk) has a much more detailed search facility for the categories. There may be considerable overlap between the categories – for example, children and education, or older people and social welfare.

The list of categories is followed by the index itself. Before using the index, please note the following.

How the index was compiled

1) The index aims to reflect the grant-makers' most recent grant-making practice. It is therefore based on our interpretation of what each funder has given to, rather than what its policy statement says or what its charitable objects allow it to do in principle. For example, where a grant-maker states that it has general charitable purposes, but its grants list shows a strong preference for social welfare, we index it under social welfare.
2) The index has been compiled from the latest information available to us.

Limitations

1) Grant-makers' policies may change – some more frequently than others.
2) Sometimes there will be a geographical restriction on a funder's grant-giving which is not shown in this index, or the grant-maker may not give for the specific purposes you require under that heading. It is important to read each entry carefully.

You will need to check whether:

(a) The grant-maker gives in your geographical area of operation

(b) The funder gives for the specific purposes you require

(c) There is no other reason to prevent you from making an application to the grant-maker

Under no circumstances should the index be used as a simple mailing list. Remember – each funder is different. Often the policies or interests of a particular grant-maker do not fit easily into the given categories. Each entry must be read individually before you make an application. Indiscriminate applications are usually unsuccessful and they waste funders' as well as your resources.

The categories are as follows.

Arts, culture, sport and recreation

Arts, culture and heritage

Sports and recreation

Children and young people

Community services and development

Advice and counselling services

Disability

Education and training

The environment and animals

Animals

The environment

Climate change

General charitable purposes

Health

Mental health

Housing and homelessness

Medical research

Older people

Religion

Christianity

Inter-faith activities

Islam

Judaism

Science and technology

Social justice

Human rights

Conflict resolution

Social sciences, policy and research

Social welfare

Voluntary sector

Women

Work outside the UK

Geographical index

The following index aims to highlight when a grant-maker gives preference for, or has a special interest in, a particular geographical area. Before using the index, please note the following.

1) Read the information about this index given below, as well as the introduction to the subject index on page 453. This index should not be used as a simple mailing list and it is not a substitute for detailed research.
2) When you have used this index to identify relevant grant-makers, please read each entry carefully before making an application. Simply because a funder gives grants in your geographical area, it does not mean that it gives to your type of work.
3) Most funders in this list are not restricted to one area – usually the geographical index indicates that the grant-maker gives some priority for the area(s) in question.

Each section is ordered alphabetically according to the name of the funder. The categories for indexes are as follows.

Some grant-makers may be found in more than one category due to them providing grants in more than one area (for example, those with a preference for the north of England will appear under both North East and North West).

This category includes the Middle East section. Please note that most of the funders listed under it are primarily for the benefit of Jewish people and the advancement of the Jewish religion.

United Kingdom

England

North East

North West

Yorkshire and the Humber

East Midlands

West Midlands

Eastern England

South West

South East

Greater London

Channel Islands

Wales

Scotland

Northern Ireland

Republic of Ireland

Europe

Africa

Americas and the West Indies

Asia

Oceania

Middle East

Worldwide

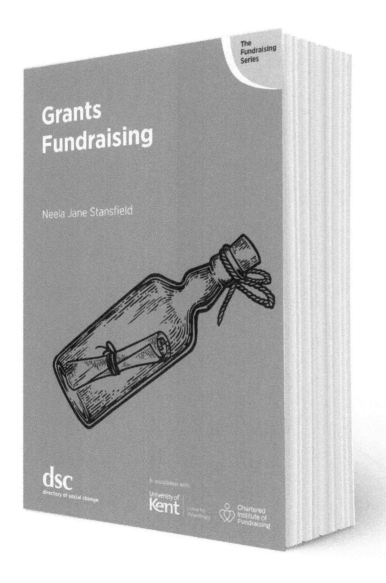

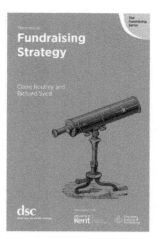

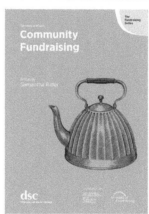